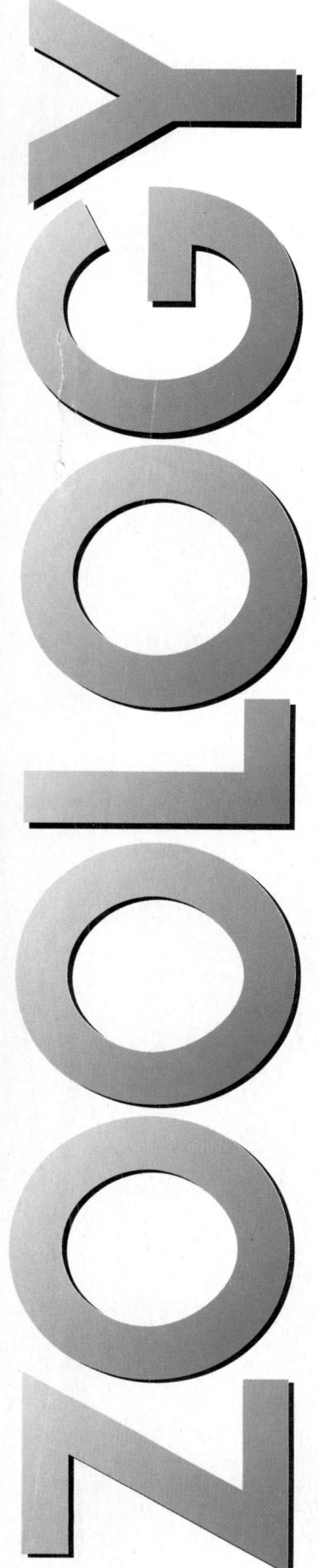

Third Edition

Stephen A. Miller
The College of the Ozarks

John P. Harley
Eastern Kentucky University

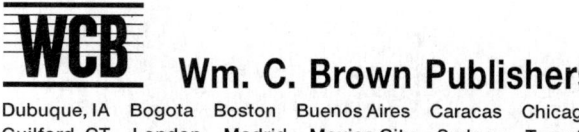

Wm. C. Brown Publishers

Dubuque, IA   Bogota   Boston   Buenos Aires   Caracas   Chicago
Guilford, CT   London   Madrid   Mexico City   Sydney   Toronto

Book Team

Editor *Margaret J. Kemp*
Developmental Editor *Kathleen R. Loewenberg*
Production Editor *Jane E. Matthews*
Designer *Kristyn A. Kalnes*
Art Editor *Kathleen M. Timp*
Photo Editor *Janice Hancock*
Permissions Coordinator *Gail I. Wheatley*

Wm. C. Brown Publishers

President and Chief Executive Officer *Beverly Kolz*
Vice President, Publisher *Kevin Kane*
Vice President, Director of Sales and Marketing *Virginia S. Moffat*
Vice President, Director of Production *Colleen A. Yonda*
National Sales Manager *Douglas J. DiNardo*
Marketing Manager *Thomas C. Lyon*
Advertising Manager *Janelle Keeffer*
Production Editorial Manager *Renée Menne*
Publishing Services Manager *Karen J. Slaght*
Royalty/Permissions Manager *Connie Allendorf*

A Times Mirror Company

Copyedited by Linda Gomall

Photo research by Connie Mueller

Cover photos © Tony Stone Images

The credits section for this book begins on page 723 and
is considered an extension of the copyright page.

PART SIX

FORM AND FUNCTION: A COMPARATIVE PERSPECTIVE 525

CONTENTS

CONTENTS

chapter four

ENERGY AND ENZYMES: LIFE'S DRIVING AND CONTROLLING FORCES 55

chapter five

HOW ANIMALS HARVEST ENERGY STORED IN NUTRIENTS 65

PART TWO 2

THE CONTINUITY OF ANIMAL LIFE 79

chapter six

CELL DIVISION 81

chapter seven

INHERITANCE PATTERNS 95

PART THREE 3

EVOLUTION 151

chapter twelve

EVOLUTION AND GENE FREQUENCIES 165

PART FOUR 4

BEHAVIOR AND ECOLOGY 179

chapter thirteen

ANIMAL BEHAVIOR 181

chapter fourteen

ECOLOGY I: INDIVIDUALS AND POPULATIONS 193

chapter fifteen

ECOLOGY II: COMMUNITIES AND ECOSYSTEMS 207

PART FIVE 5

ANIMALLIKE PROTISTS AND ANIMALIA 227

chapter sixteen

ANIMAL CLASSIFICATION, PHYLOGENY, AND ORGANIZATION 229

chapter seventeen

ANIMALLIKE PROTISTS: THE PROTOZOA 243

PART SIX

FORM AND FUNCTION: A COMPARATIVE PERSPECTIVE 525

chapter thirty-six

CIRCULATION, IMMUNITY, AND GAS EXCHANGE 597

chapter thirty-seven

NUTRITION AND DIGESTION 621

chapter thirty-eight

TEMPERATURE AND BODY FLUID REGULATION 647

chapter thirty-nine

REPRODUCTION AND DEVELOPMENT 669

Our primary goal in preparing the third edition of *Zoology* was to retain the character and integrity of the second edition. Instructors and students alike praised many features from the second edition for contributing to the understanding of zoology as an exciting and dynamic scientific field. We are grateful for their recommendations and hope that the third edition will serve the needs of students and instructors even better than the second.

Once again, the challenge was to publish a comprehensive, general zoology textbook that is manageable in size and adaptable to the variety of approaches used to teach zoology. The finished product, like the second edition, is less than 700 pages in length, and it is now full-color throughout. *Zoology* is also available in complete hardbound and paperbound versions. There is also a separate book entitled *Animal Kingdom* for adopters who wish to focus primarily on animal diversity.

Zoology is organized into six parts. As an introduction to the study of zoology, we have tried to emphasize the interrelationships of all life-forms by covering the common life processes early in the textbook. Part One includes an introduction to zoology, as well as coverage of cellular chemistry, structure, and function. Part Two covers the basic biological concepts of molecular biology, genetics, and embryology. Part Three addresses evolution, and Part Four covers behavior and ecology. Evolutionary and ecological topics precede the survey of the animal phyla and the form and function sections of the textbook to emphasize the important foundation that they provide for all aspects of zoology.

Part Five is the survey of animals, emphasizing evolutionary relationships, aspects of animal organization that unite major animal phyla, and animal adaptations. Chapter 16 covers classification, organization, and phylogeny of animals. The coverage of the principles of cladistics in chapter 16 has been expanded, and evolutionary relationships are depicted using cladograms in chapters 17–31. Cladistic analysis has become increasingly important in animal systematics. While cladistic analysis has resulted in some nontraditional taxonomic groupings, it is essential that beginning students are introduced to these methods. These chapters have also been improved with lists of phylum characteristics, cladograms, and additional full-color visuals. The lesser-known invertebrate phyla are covered in the form of Endpapers that are strategically placed between specific chapters to reflect the evolutionary relationships of the animals discussed in each chapter, and to prevent the discussions of these animals from getting lost within lengthy chapters.

Part Six covers animal form and function. The chapters in this part cover form and function using a comparative approach.

This approach includes descriptions and full-color artwork that depict the evolutionary changes in the structure and function of selected organ systems. Part Six includes an appropriate balance between invertebrate and vertebrate descriptions.

CUSTOMIZE ZOOLOGY TO YOUR COURSE

To accomodate the variety of approaches and time constraints in zoology courses today, the third edition can be customized for your course—by chapter—and in full color! Design the text that best fits your course and have an opportunity to reduce the cost to your students. For more information on customizing *Zoology* to your course, contact your local sales representative or call 1-800-228-0634.

SUPPLEMENTARY MATERIALS

Supplementary materials are available to assist instructors with their presentations and general course management.

1. An **Instructor's Manual/Test Item File** prepared by Eric Nelson, Ohio Northern University, provides examples of lecture/reading schedules for courses with various emphases. In addition, each chapter contains a detailed outline, purpose, objectives, key terms, summary, sources for audiovisual materials and computer software, and approximately 50 multiple-choice test questions.

2. A **Student Study Guide,** prepared by Jay M. Templin, contains chapter summaries, outlines, key terms with phonetics, pretest assessment questions, various learning activities, and mastery tests.

3. A set of 100 full-color acetate **transparencies** and 150 **transparency masters** are available and may be used to supplement classroom lectures.

4. **General Zoology Laboratory Manual,** third edition, by Stephen A. Miller, is an excellent corollary to the text and incorporates many of the same learning aids. This edition offers improved illustrations and laboratory exercises that emphasize animal adaptations and ecology. A **Laboratory Resource Guide** is also available and contains additional information about materials and procedures, and the answers to lab exercises.

5. The **Customized Laboratory Manual.** Each lab manual exercise is also available individually as offprints, so students need buy only those exercises used in the laboratory. Contact your local sales representative for more details.

6. **Life Science Animations** is a series of five videotapes featuring more than 50 animations of key physiological processes spanning the breadth of concepts covered in a typical life science course. Of particular interest to professors teaching zoology are tape three, *Animal Biology: Part I*, and tape four, *Animal Biology, Part II*. These full-color animations enable the student to more fully and easily grasp concepts such as the formation of the myelin sheath, saltatory nerve conduction, signal integration, reflex arcs, and the organ of static equilibrium. (ISBNs 25050 and 25071)

7. **How to Study Science** by Fred Drewes, offers students valuable tips on note-taking, how to interpret text figures, how to manage time, how to prepare for tests, and how to overcome "science anxiety." (ISBN 14474)

8. **The Life Science Living Lexicon CD-ROM,** by William Marchuk, provides comprehensive coverage of all the life science disciplines—biology, anatomy, physiology, botany, zoology, environmental science, and microbiology—by combining complete lexicon components:

   Overview of word construction and how to use the textual material

   Glossary of common biological root words, prefixes, and suffixes

   Glossary of descriptive terms

   Glossary of common biological terms, characterized by discipline

   Section describing the classification system

   in a powerful interactive CD-ROM with more than 1,000 vivid illustrations and animations of key processes and systems—including histology micrographs, and an interactive quizzing program. (ISBN 12133)

9. **Critical Thinking: A Collection of Readings,** by David J. Stroup and Robert D. Allen is available to instructors who are working to integrate critical thinking into their curricula. This inexpensive text will help in the planning and implementation of programs intended to develop students' abilities to think logically and analytically. The reader is a collection of articles that provide instruction and examples of current programs. The authors have included descriptions and evaluations of their personal experiences with incorporating critical thinking study in their coursework. (ISBN 14556)

ACKNOWLEDGMENTS

We wish to express our thanks to the reviewers who provided detailed criticism and analysis of the textbook during development. In the midst of their busy teaching and research schedules, they took time to read our manuscript and offer constructive advice that greatly improved the final text.

REVIEWERS

Rodney P. Anderson
Ohio Northern University

Thomas P. Buckelew
California University of Pennsylvania

Elizabeth A. Desy
Southwest State University

DuWayne C. Englert
Southern Illinois University at Carbondale

Mary Sue Gamroth
Joliet Junior College

Beth Gaydos
San Jose City College

Michael C. Hartman, Ph.D.

Dan F. Ippolito
Anderson University

Richard Lewis
Grant MacEwan Community College
Edmonton, Alberta, Canada

Eddie Lunsford
Tri County Community College
Murphy, North Carolina

Eric V. Nelson
Ohio Northern University

Richard E. Trout
Oklahoma City Community College

Robert W. Yost
Indiana University-Purdue University

We also remain indebted to the following individuals who reviewed previous editions and whose helpful guidance has been carried forth to this text:

Barbara J. Abraham
Hampton University

Jane Aloi
Saddleback College

C. Jane Barrett
Oklahoma City Community College

Ron Basmajian
Merced College

Bayard H. Brattstrom
California State University–Fullerton

William Brueske
Humboldt State University

Steven K. Burian
Southern Connecticut State University

James E. Cole
Bloomsburg University of Pennsylvania

Harry N. Cunningham, Jr.
Pennsylvania State University at Erie—The Behrend College

Opal H. Dakin
Hinds Community College

J. William Dapper
Troy State University at Dothan

Peggy Rae Dorris
Henderson State University

Lee C. Drickamer
Southern Illinois University

Joseph G. Engemann
Western Michigan University

DuWayne C. Englert
Southern Illinois University

Stephen Ervin
California State University—Fresno

William F. Evans
University of Arkansas

Daniel R. Formanowicz, Jr.
University of Texas—Arlington

John C. Frandsen
Tuskegee University

Mildred J. Galliher
Cochise College

Judith Goodenough
University of Massachusetts—Amherst

Ross E. Hamilton
Okaloosa-Walton Community College

Earl A. Holmes
Friends University

Ronald L. Hybertson
Mankato State University

Ronald L. Jenkins
Samford University

Thomas A. Leslie
Saddleback College

Roger M. Lloyd
Florida Community College at Jacksonville

Jacqueline Ludel
Guilford College

Steele R. Lunt
University of Nebraska at Omaha

Edward B. Lyke
California State University

Richard N. Mariscal
Florida State University

Neal F. McCord
Stephen F. Austin State University

John C. McGrew
Colorado State University

J. E. McPherson
Southern Illinois University

Alex L. A. Middleton
University of Guelph

Grover C. Miller
North Carolina State University

Thomas C. Moon
California University of Pennsylvania

Ronald L. Morris
West Valley College

Eric V. Nelson
Ohio Northern University

Larry R. Petersen
San Jacinto College-Central

Robert Powell
Avila College

James A. Raines
North Harris College

John D. Rickett
University of Arkansas—Little Rock

Richard G. Rose
West Valley College

Tim V. Roye
San Jacinto College

Joseph L. Simon
University of South Florida

Thomas P. Simon
Indiana University NW

John Snyder
Furman University

Dean Stevens
University of Vermont

J. L. Sumich
Grossmont Community College

Barbara A. Taber
Southwest Missouri State University

Jay M. Templin
Widener University

Richard E. Trout
Oklahoma City Community College

Olivia White
University of North Texas

Richard L. Whitman
Indiana University NW

Sr. Mary L. Wright
College of Our Lady of the Elms

Harold L. Zimmack
Ball State University

The production of a textbook requires the efforts of many people. We are grateful for the work of our colleagues at Wm. C. Brown Publishers, who have shown extraordinary patience, skill, and commitment to this textbook. Marge Kemp, our editor, and Kevin Kane, publisher, have helped shape *Zoology* from its earliest planning stages. Our developmental editor, Kathy Loewenberg, helped make the production of the third edition remarkably smooth. Jane Matthews, our production editor, kept us on schedule and the production moving in the plethora of directions that are nearly unimaginable to us.

Finally, but most importantly, we wish to extend appreciation to our families for their patience and encouragement. Janice A. Miller lived with this textbook through many months of planning and writing. She died suddenly two months before the first edition was released. Our wives, Carol A. Miller and Jane R. Harley, have been supportive throughout the revision process. We appreciate the sacrifices that our families have made during the writing and revision of this textbook. We dedicate this book to the memory of Jan and to our families.

Stephen A. Miller
John P. Harley

special FEATURES

Second edition adopters and reviewers made it clear that they found *Zoology* to be clear, concise, and intriguing—and we think you will find the third edition even more so. *Zoology* is unique in its emphasis on learning aids for the student. Consistent features include:

CHAPTER-OPENING OUTLINES

Chapter-opening **Outlines** present a brief structure of the chapter as a preview to the student.

CHAPTER-OPENING CONCEPTS

The chapter-opening **Concepts** help prepare the student for major concepts covered in the chapter and also serve as a study tool for review.

chapter 1

ZOOLOGY: ITS PLACE IN SCIENCE

Outline

A One-World View
  Genetic Unity
  The Fundamental Unit of Life
  Evolutionary Oneness and the
    Diversity of Life
  Animals and Their Environment
What Is Zoology?
  The Classification of Animals
The Scientific Method

Concepts

1. The field of zoology is a subdiscipline of biology, the study of life.
2. All life shares a common genetic molecule (DNA), unit of organization (the cell), evolutionary forces, and environment (the earth).
3. Zoology, the study of animals, is a very broad field with many subdisciplines.
4. The scientific method is a procedure that allows an investigator to objectively analyze biological occurrences.

Would You Like to Know:

1 what is the relationship between zoology and biology? (p. 4)

2 what fundamental molecule carries the genetic code for life? (p. 4)

3 how old the earth is? (p. 5)

4 why boa constrictors have remnants of pelvic appendages? (p. 6)

These and other useful questions will be answered in this chapter.

This chapter contains evolutionary concepts, which are set off in this font.

BOX 21.1 THE ZEBRA MUSSEL—ANOTHER BIOLOGICAL INVASION

Chapter 21 *Molluscan Success* 333

About 100 years ago, a bird fancier released a few starlings in New York City's Central Park. Today the starling is the most common bird in the United States. In 1866 the gypsy moth was transported from Europe to the New England forests. It proliferated at the expense of North American forests. Today, these European invaders are joined by another, the zebra mussel (*Dreissena polymorpha*). This invasion, like the others before it, has been very costly, both economically and ecologically for much of North America.

The zebra mussel is actually one of about 120 exotic invaders of the Great Lakes. The invasion began in 1985 or 1986 when larval mussels were picked up in freshwater ports of Europe when cargo ships filled their ballast tanks with fresh water. The larvae were released when ballast tanks were emptied into the Great Lakes. Within three or four years the mussel spread into Lakes Erie, Ontario, Huron, and southern Lake Michigan. By June 1991, records of the mussels were being made in the Illinois River and the mussel now threatens much of the Mississippi River drainage basin.

Many of the problems associated with the zebra mussels are a result of their high reproductive potential. A single female may release 40,000 eggs. Their veliger larval stages may drift in the plankton for up to five weeks and be carried long distances by water currents. When larvae settle on a hard substrate, they attach by tough byssal threads. They grow to a length of about 2 cm, and densities of 200 individuals/m² are common (figure 1).

Economic problems associated with zebra mussels result from their settling on, and clogging, water intake pipes. Detroit Edison officials reported 700,000 mussels/m² on a single water intake screen. In December 1988, mussels and ice shards blocked water intake to the Detroit Edison plant, which resulted in power outages throughout Detroit. It cost the company $250,000 to restore electricity to the city. Detroit Edison officials spent six million dollars on a new intake system that they hope will reduce the fouling problems. It is estimated that throughout the Great Lakes, two billion dollars will be spent cleaning and refitting pipes in Great Lakes port cities through the 1990s.

Zebra mussels also threaten the ecology of freshwater ecosystems. They are very efficient filter feeders and are expected to disrupt freshwater food webs. As larvae settle and encrust hard substrates, they may disrupt the spawning ground of game fish such as

FIGURE 1 The zebra mussel (*Dreissena polymorpha*) invaded U.S. fresh waters and is threatening native bivalves and other freshwater species.

walleyed pike. There is particular concern for the Mississippi River drainage basin. The Mississippi River and its tributaries contain the highest diversity of clams in the world. Some of these clams are endangered species. In other places, where native clams have been enhanced by the zebra mussel, the valves of a native clam make an excellent substrate for the attachment of the zebra mussel. The native clam can be so densely covered that feeding is impossible.

While research efforts are under way to monitor the spread of the zebra mussel and to search for its "Achilles' heel," a larger question looms in the background: "Are more invaders on the way?" One study of the ballast water of 55 cargo ships revealed that 17 species of animals were still alive in each ship by the time they arrived in fresh waters of North America. Estimates of the number of individuals alive per species ranged between 10,000 and eight billion! A relatively simple, partial solution to the problem of ballast-water invaders has been to require ships to dump ballast water from foreign, freshwater ports into the open ocean. This ballast water is then replaced with seawater. Seawater kills most freshwater organisms, and freshwater kills most marine organisms.

Some surface-dwelling bivalves are attached to the substrate either by proteinaceous strands called byssal threads, which are secreted by a gland in the foot, or by cementation to the substrate. The former method is used by the common marine mussel *Mytilus*, and the latter by oysters.

Boring bivalves live beneath the surface of limestone, clay, coral, wood, and other substrates.
(a) Boring begins

after the larvae settle to the substrate, and it occurs by mechanical abrasion of the substrate by the anterior margin of the valves. Physical abrasion is sometimes accompanied by acidic secretions from the mantle margin that dissolve limestone. As the bivalve grows, portions of the burrow recently bored are larger in diameter than other, usually external, portions of the burrow. Thus, the bivalve is often imprisoned in its rocky burrow.

21.13

PREVIEW QUESTIONS

Approximately 5–8 **"Would You Like to Know"** questions are presented at the beginning of each chapter and are intended to pique the student's interest in the topic. Answers are found within the chapter and are indicated by a number corresponding to the question.

BOXED READINGS

Nearly every chapter contains at least one boxed reading covering an interesting subject relevant to the surrounding text. For example, topics include **"The Zebra Mussel—Another Biological Invasion"**; **"Malaria Control—A Glimmer of Hope"**; **"Bright Skies and Silent Thunder,"** a discussion of the extinction of the passenger pigeon; and **"Suspension Feeding in Invertebrates and Nonvertebrate Chordates."**

Boldfaced Terms

Important **Key Terms** are emphasized in bold type and clearly defined when they are first presented.

Evolutionary Concepts

Incorporated into the design of the third edition are visual cues to let the reader know when concepts of evolution are being discussed.

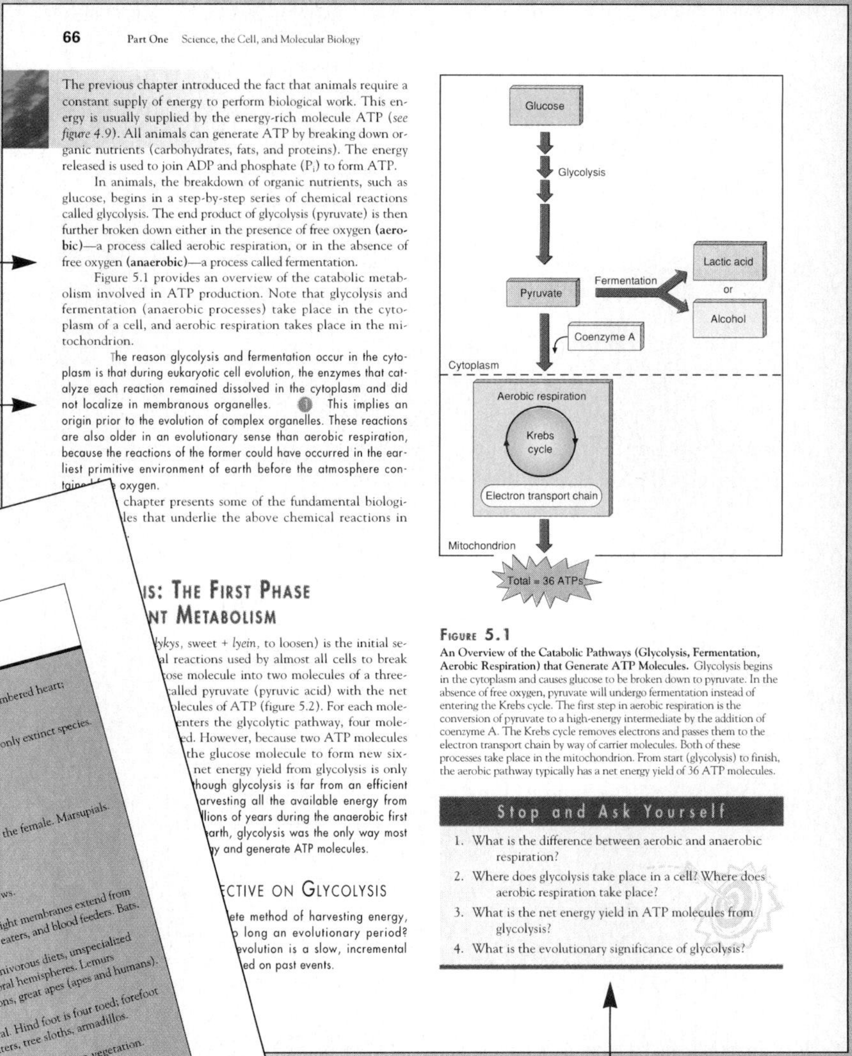
66 Part One Science, the Cell, and Molecular Biology
The previous chapter introduced the fact that animals require a constant supply of energy to perform biological work. This energy is usually supplied by the energy-rich molecule ATP (see figure 4.9). All animals can generate ATP by breaking down organic nutrients (carbohydrates, fats, and proteins). The energy released is used to join ADP and phosphate (P_i) to form ATP.
In animals, the breakdown of organic nutrients, such as glucose, begins in a step-by-step series of chemical reactions called glycolysis. The end product of glycolysis (pyruvate) is then further broken down either in the presence of free oxygen (aerobic)—a process called aerobic respiration, or in the absence of free oxygen (anaerobic)—a process called fermentation.
Figure 5.1 provides an overview of the catabolic metabolism involved in ATP production. Note that glycolysis and fermentation (anaerobic processes) take place in the cytoplasm of a cell, and aerobic respiration takes place in the mitochondrion.
The reason glycolysis and fermentation occur in the cytoplasm is that during eukaryotic cell evolution, the enzymes that catalyze each reaction remained dissolved in the cytoplasm and did not localize in membranous organelles. This implies an origin prior to the evolution of complex organelles. These reactions are also older in an evolutionary sense than aerobic respiration, because the reactions of the former could have occurred in the earliest primitive environment of earth before the atmosphere con- oxygen.
chapter presents some of the fundamental biologi- les that underlie the above chemical reactions in
IS: THE FIRST PHASE
NT METABOLISM
lykys, sweet + lyein, to loosen) is the initial se- l reactions used by almost all cells to break ose molecule into two molecules of a three- alled pyruvate (pyruvic acid) with the net lecules of ATP (figure 5.2). For each mole- enters the glycolytic pathway, four mole- d. However, because two ATP molecules the glucose molecule to form new six- net energy yield from glycolysis is only hough glycolysis is far from an efficient arvesting all the available energy from lions of years during the anaerobic first arth, glycolysis was the only way most y and generate ATP molecules.
ECTIVE ON GLYCOLYSIS
ete method of harvesting energy, o long an evolutionary period? volution is a slow, incremental ed on past events.
Glucose
Glycolysis
Pyruvate
Fermentation
Lactic acid
or
Alcohol
Coenzyme A
Cytoplasm
Aerobic respiration
Krebs cycle
Electron transport chain
Mitochondrion
Total = 36 ATPs
FIGURE 5.1
An Overview of the Catabolic Pathways (Glycolysis, Fermentation, Aerobic Respiration) that Generate ATP Molecules. Glycolysis begins in the cytoplasm and causes glucose to be broken down to pyruvate. In the absence of free oxygen, pyruvate will undergo fermentation instead of entering the Krebs cycle. The first step in aerobic respiration is the conversion of pyruvate to a high-energy intermediate by the addition of coenzyme A. The Krebs cycle removes electrons and passes them to the electron transport chain by way of carrier molecules. Both of these processes take place in the mitochondrion. From start (glycolysis) to finish, the aerobic pathway typically has a net energy yield of 36 ATP molecules.
Stop and Ask Yourself
1. What is the difference between aerobic and anaerobic respiration?
2. Where does glycolysis take place in a cell? Where does aerobic respiration take place?
3. What is the net energy yield in ATP molecules from glycolysis?
4. What is the evolutionary significance of glycolysis?

Interior Chapter Review Questions

Interspersed throughout the text are small sets of **"Stop and Ask Yourself"** questions directly correlated to material the student has just read. They allow students to test their knowledge and understanding of the section's factual material before continuing their reading. Visually highlighted, the questions are easy to find and make excellent study tools after the complete chapter has been read.

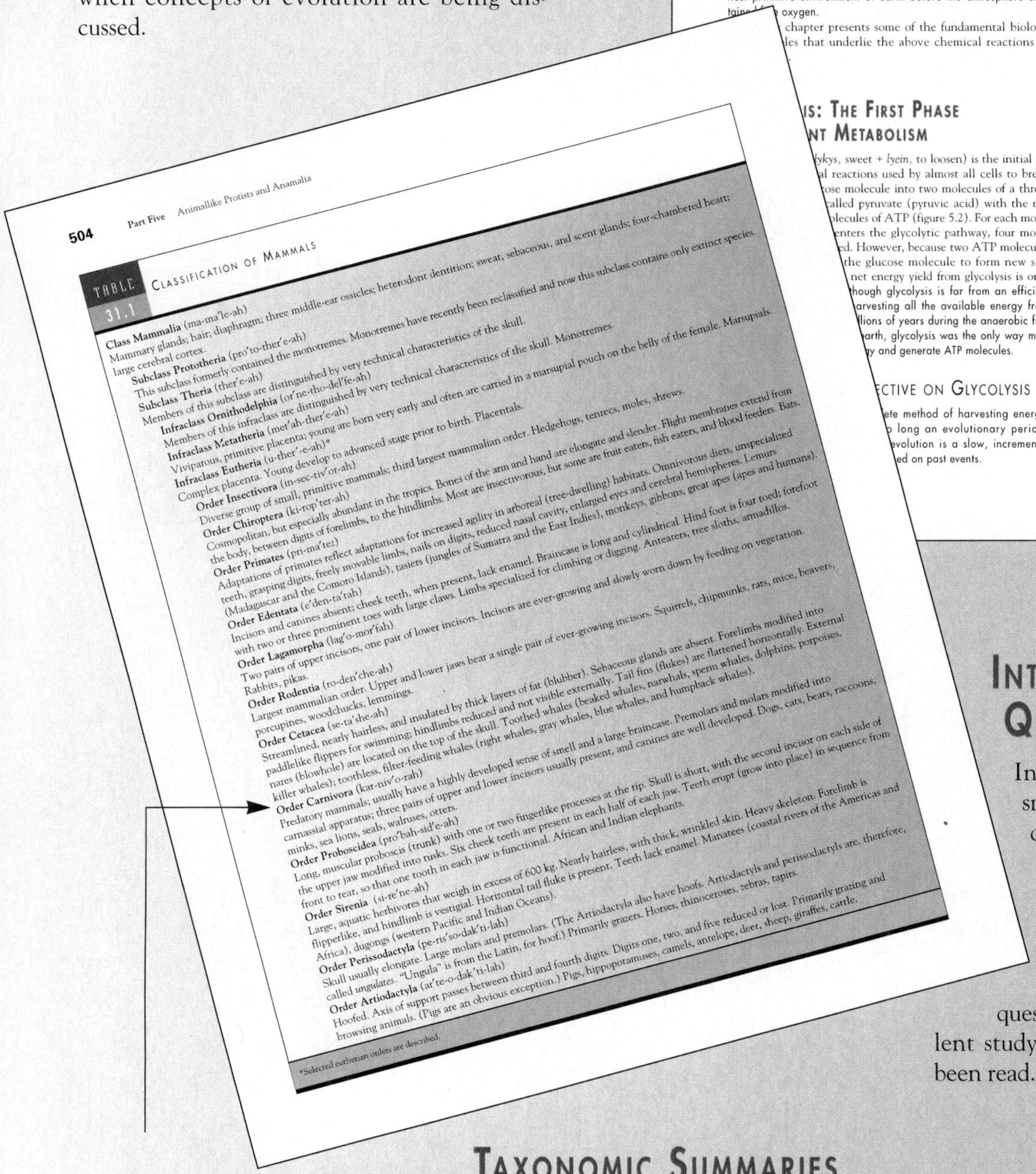
504 Part Five Animallike Protists and Anamalia
TABLE 31.1 CLASSIFICATION OF MAMMALS
Class Mammalia (ma-ma'le-ah)
Mammary glands; hair; diaphragm; three middle-ear ossicles; heterodont dentition; sweat, sebaceous, and scent glands; four-chambered heart; large cerebral cortex.
Subclass Prototheria (pro'to-ther'e-ah)
This subclass formerly contained the monotremes. Monotremes have recently been reclassified and now this subclass contains only extinct species.
Subclass Theria (ther'e-ah)
Members of this subclass are distinguished by very technical characteristics of the skull.
Infraclass Ornithodelphia (or'ne-tho-del'fe-ah)
Members of this infraclass are distinguished by very technical characteristics of the skull. Monotremes.
Infraclass Metatheria (met'ah-ther'e-ah)
Viviparous, primitive placenta; young are born very early and often are carried in a marsupial pouch on the belly of the female. Marsupials.
Infraclass Eutheria (u-ther'e-ah)*
Complex placenta. Young develop to advanced stage prior to birth. Placentals.
Order Insectivora (in-sec-tiv'or-ah)
Diverse group of small, primitive mammals; third largest mammalian order. Hedgehogs, tenrecs, moles, shrews.
Order Chiroptera (ki-rop'ter-ah)
Cosmopolitan, but especially abundant in the tropics. Bones of the arm and hand are elongate and slender. Flight membranes extend from the body, between digits of forelimbs, to the hindlimbs. Most are insectivorous, but some are fruit eaters, fish eaters, and blood feeders. Bats.
Order Primates (pri-ma'tez)
Adaptations of primates reflect adaptations for increased agility in arboreal (tree-dwelling) habitats. Omnivorous diets, unspecialized teeth, grasping digits, freely movable limbs, nails on digits, reduced nasal cavity, enlarged eyes and cerebral hemispheres. Lemurs (Madagascar and the Comoro Islands); tarsiers (jungles of Sumatra and the East Indies), monkeys, gibbons, great apes (apes and humans).
Order Edentata (e'den-ta'tah)
Incisors and canines absent; cheek teeth, when present, lack enamel. Braincase is long and cylindrical. Hind foot is four toed; forefoot with two or three prominent toes with large claws. Limbs specialized for climbing or digging. Anteaters, tree sloths, armadillos.
Order Lagamorpha (lag'o-mor'fah)
Two pairs of upper incisors, one pair of lower incisors. Incisors are ever-growing and slowly worn down by feeding on vegetation. Rabbits, pikas.
Order Rodentia (ro-den'che-ah)
Largest mammalian order. Upper and lower jaws bear a single pair of ever-growing incisors. Squirrels, chipmunks, rats, mice, beavers, porcupines, woodchucks, lemmings.
Order Cetacea (se-ta'she-ah)
Streamlined, nearly hairless, and insulated by thick layers of fat (blubber). Sebaceous glands are absent. Forelimbs modified into paddlelike flippers for swimming; hindlimbs reduced and not visible externally. Tail fins (flukes) are flattened horizontally. External nares (blowhole) are located on the top of the skull. Toothed whales (beaked whales, narwhals, sperm whales, dolphins, porpoises, killer whales); toothless, filter-feeding whales (right whales, gray whales, blue whales, and humpback whales).
Order Carnivora (kar-niv'o-rah)
Predatory mammals; usually have a highly developed sense of smell and a large braincase. Premolars and molars modified into carnassial apparatus; three pairs of upper and lower incisors usually present, and canines are well developed. Dogs, cats, bears, raccoons, minks, sea lions, seals, walruses, otters.
Order Proboscidea (pro'bah-sid'e-ah)
Long, muscular proboscis (trunk) with one or two fingerlike processes at the tip. Skull is short, with the second incisor on each side of the upper jaw modified into tusks. Six cheek teeth are present in each half of each jaw. Teeth erupt (grow into place) in sequence from front to rear, so that one tooth in each jaw is functional. African and Indian elephants.
Order Sirenia (si-re'ne-ah)
Large, aquatic herbivores that weigh in excess of 600 kg. Nearly hairless, with thick, wrinkled skin. Heavy skeleton. Forelimb is flipperlike, and hindlimb is vestigial. Horizontal tail fluke is present. Teeth lack enamel. Manatees (coastal rivers of the Americas and Africa), dugongs (western Pacific and Indian Oceans).
Order Perissodactyla (pe-ris'so-dak'ti-lah)
Skull usually elongate. Large molars and premolars. (The Artiodactyla also have hoofs. Artiodactyls and perissodactyls are, therefore, called ungulates. "Ungula" is from the Latin, for hoof.) Primarily grazers. Horses, rhinoceroses, zebras, tapirs.
Order Artiodactyla (ar'te-o-dak'ti-lah)
Hoofed. Axis of support passes between third and fourth digits. Digits one, two, and five reduced or lost. Primarily grazing and browsing animals. (Pigs are an obvious exception.) Pigs, hippopotamuses, camels, antelope, deer, sheep, giraffes, cattle.
*Selected eutherian orders are described.

Taxonomic Summaries

Tables within the text include **Taxonomic Summaries** where appropriate.
The summaries provide pronunciation guides and descriptive outlines of taxonomic sequences.

CLADOGRAMS

New to this edition are **cladograms,** which introduce the student to cladistic analysis and help them to visualize evolutionary pathways.

CHAPTER SUMMARIES

These **End-of-Chapter Summaries** reiterate important chapter concepts and are intended to serve as a guide for study.

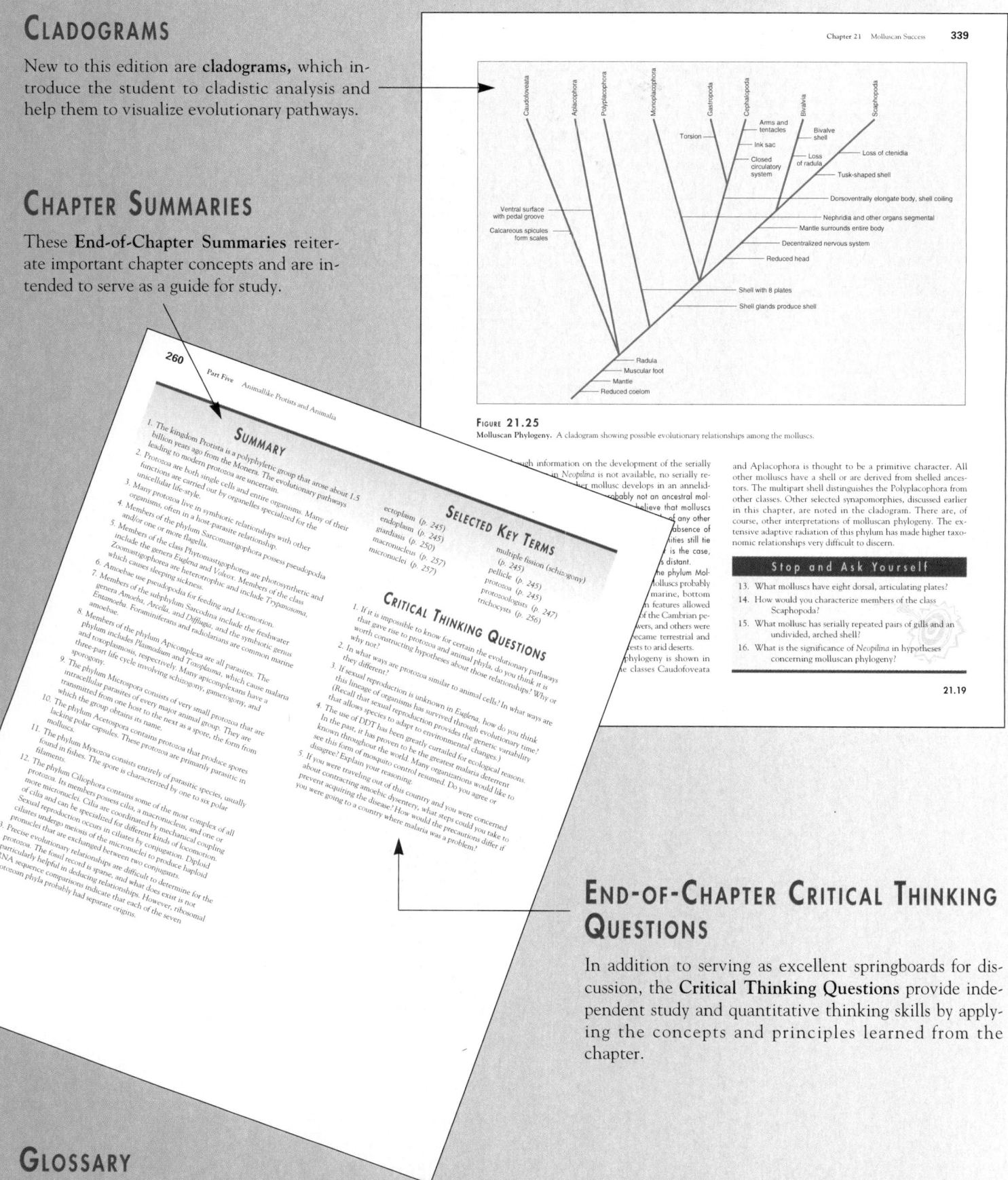

FIGURE 21.25
Molluscan Phylogeny. A cladogram showing possible evolutionary relationships among the molluscs.

ough information on the development of the serially in *Neopilina* is not available, no serially re-
...er mollusc develops in an annelid-
...obably not an ancestral mol-
...believe that molluscs
...of any other
...absence of
...ities still tie
...is the case,
...s distant.
...he phylum Mol-
...olluscs probably
...marine, bottom
...m features allowed
...of the Cambrian pe-
...wers, and others were
...ecame terrestrial and
...rests to arid deserts.
...phylogeny is shown in
...e classes Caudofoveata

and Aplacophora is thought to be a primitive character. All other molluscs have a shell or are derived from shelled ancestors. The multipart shell distinguishes the Polyplacophora from other classes. Other selected synapomorphies, discussed earlier in this chapter, are noted in the cladogram. There are, of course, other interpretations of molluscan phylogeny. The extensive adaptive radiation of this phylum has made higher taxonomic relationships very difficult to discern.

Stop and Ask Yourself

13. What molluscs have eight dorsal, articulating plates?
14. How would you characterize members of the class Scaphopoda?
15. What mollusc has serially repeated pairs of gills and an undivided, arched shell?
16. What is the significance of *Neopilina* in hypotheses concerning molluscan phylogeny?

21.19

SUMMARY

1. The kingdom Protista is a polyphyletic group that arose about 1.5 billion years ago from the Monera. The evolutionary pathways leading to modern protozoa are uncertain.
2. Protozoa are both single cells and entire organisms. Many of their functions are carried out by organelles specialized for the unicellular life-style.
3. Many protozoa live in symbiotic relationships with other organisms, often in a host-parasite relationship.
4. Members of the phylum Sarcomastigophora possess pseudopodia and/or one or more flagella.
5. Members of the class Phytomastigophorea are photosynthetic and include the genera *Euglena* and *Volvox*. Members of the class Zoomastigophorea are heterotrophic and include *Trypanosoma*, which causes sleeping sickness.
6. Amoebae use pseudopodia for feeding and locomotion. Members of the subphylum Sarcodina include the freshwater genera *Amoeba, Arcella,* and *Difflugia,* and the symbiotic marine amoebae. Foraminiferans and radiolarians are common marine amoebae.
7. Members of the phylum Apicomplexa are all parasites. The phylum includes *Plasmodium* and *Toxoplasma,* which cause malaria and toxoplasmosis, respectively. Many apicomplexans have a three-part life cycle involving schizogony, gametogony, and sporogony.
8. The phylum Microspora consists of very small protozoa that are intracellular parasites of every major animal group. They are transmitted from one host to the next as a spore, the form from which the group obtains its name.
9. The phylum Acetospora contains protozoa that produce spores lacking polar capsules. These protozoa are primarily parasitic in molluscs.
10. The phylum Myxozoa consists entirely of parasitic species, usually found in fishes. The spore is characterized by one to six polar filaments.
11. The phylum Ciliophora contains some of the most complex of all protozoa. Its members possess cilia, a macronucleus, and one or more micronuclei. Cilia are coordinated by mechanical coupling of cilia and can be specialized for different kinds of locomotion. Sexual reproduction occurs in ciliates by conjugation. Diploid ciliates undergo meiosis of the micronuclei to produce haploid pronuclei that are exchanged between two conjugants.
12. Precise evolutionary relationships are difficult to determine for the protozoa. The fossil record is sparse, and what does exist is not particularly helpful in deducing relationships. However, ribosomal RNA sequence comparisons indicate that each of the seven protozoan phyla probably had separate origins.

SELECTED KEY TERMS

ectoplasm (p. 245)
endoplasm (p. 245)
giardiasis (p. 250)
macronucleus (p. 257)
micronuclei (p. 257)

multiple fission (schizogony) (p. 245)
pellicle (p. 245)
protozoa (p. 245)
protozoologists (p. 245)
trichocysts (p. 247)

CRITICAL THINKING QUESTIONS

1. If it is impossible to know for certain the evolutionary pathways that gave rise to protozoa and animal phyla, do you think it is worth constructing hypotheses about those relationships? Why or why not?
2. In what ways are protozoa similar to animal cells? In what ways are they different?
3. If sexual reproduction is unknown in *Euglena,* how do you think this lineage of organisms has survived through evolutionary time? (Recall that sexual reproduction provides the genetic variability that allows species to adapt to environmental changes.)
4. The use of DDT has been greatly curtailed for ecological reasons. In the past, it has proven to be the greatest malaria deterrent known throughout the world. Many organizations would like to see this form of mosquito control resumed. Do you agree or disagree? Explain your reasoning.
5. If you were traveling out of this country and you were concerned about contracting amoebic dysentery, what steps could you take to prevent acquiring the disease? How would the precautions differ if you were going to a country where malaria was a problem?

7.18

END-OF-CHAPTER CRITICAL THINKING QUESTIONS

In addition to serving as excellent springboards for discussion, the **Critical Thinking Questions** provide independent study and quantitative thinking skills by applying the concepts and principles learned from the chapter.

GLOSSARY

Helping students learn the extensive vocabulary of zoology is a continuing concern, which we have addressed in this edition by reducing the number of unnecessary technical terms. We also define new terms when they are first introduced, with word derivations and a pronunciation guide. A Glossary, which has undergone careful revision and expansion for the third edition, is included at the end of the text.

part ONE

SCIENCE, THE CELL, AND MOLECULAR BIOLOGY

One of the fundamental principles of modern biology is that processes occurring in organisms obey the laws of chemistry and physics, just as processes in nonliving systems do. The special properties of life arise because of the

complex organization of organisms and the chemical processes that occur within them. Biologists must understand certain principles of chemistry in order to better analyze the organization and function of life on earth.

Another key to understanding life on our planet is recognizing the role of the cell as the fundamental organizational unit of life. As you learn more about cell function and structure, you will find that many cellular components and chemical processes are identical or very similar in cells from a variety of organisms. Recognition of these similarities at the cellular level provides an important unifying framework within which biologists approach the diversity of organisms.

All organisms require energy for maintenance, growth, and reproduction. Some organisms obtain energy by harnessing light energy from the sun (photosynthesis) and then producing materials they need. Other organisms, however, are not capable of using light energy in this way. They must use photosynthesizing organisms as sources of energy and materials.

In chapter 1, we will examine some of the underlying principles of zoology. Chapters 2 through 5 cover the biologically important concepts of chemistry, some basic characteristics of the cells that constitute organisms, and some of the energy relationships upon which animal life depends.

Male Resplendent Quetzal, *Pharomachrus mocinno*.

ZOOLOGY:
ITS PLACE IN SCIENCE

Outline

Concepts

1. The field of zoology is a subdiscipline of biology, the study of life.
2. All life shares a common genetic molecule (DNA), unit of organization (the cell), evolutionary forces, and environment (the earth).
3. Zoology, the study of animals, is a very broad field with many subdisciplines.
4. The scientific method is a procedure that allows an investigator to objectively analyze biological occurrences.

Would You Like to Know:

1 what is the relationship between zoology and biology? (p. 4)

2 what fundamental molecule carries the genetic code for life? (p. 4)

3 how old the earth is? (p. 5)

4 why boa constrictors have remnants of pelvic appendages? (p. 6)

These and other useful questions will be answered in this chapter.

This chapter contains evolutionary concepts, which are set off in this font.

What were your first experiences with **zoology** (Gr. *zoon*, animal + *logos*, to study), the study of animals? If your experiences were like those of many professional zoologists, your interests in zoology began at a very early age with a fascination for animals (figure 1.1). These early interests in zoology probably came from experiences with petting and feeding domestic animals and observing animals in zoos, pet stores, and in the wild. Your questions regarding where these animals live and what they eat reflected a natural curiosity and a desire to learn.

As you matured, your curiosity should not have lessened. Your ability to think critically and solve difficult problems, however, should have matured. ❶ The questions that you now ask about animals should reflect this maturity. They will still include questions about where an animal lives and what it eats. Other important questions will also be asked: "What are the building blocks of animals, and how do properties of these building blocks explain characteristics of the entire organism?" In asking these kinds of questions, you are beginning to learn the relationship between zoology and **biology** (Gr. *bios*, life + *logos*, to study), the study of all life. Two goals of this textbook are to continue cultivating your natural curiosity and to provide the background that helps you understand the interrelationships of all life forms. The authors hope that this textbook will help you to develop a framework for critical thinking that can be used to answer questions about life in general and animal life in particular.

A One-World View

In spite of life's diversity, there is a fundamental unity that embraces all of the biological disciplines. As modern biology probes deeper into the secrets of life, it becomes clearer that all life shares a common genetic blueprint (in DNA); a common organizational unit (the cell); common evolutionary forces that influence the form, function, and habitat of the animal; and a common environment (the earth).

Genetic Unity

❷ All life is based on the fundamental molecule, deoxyribonucleic acid (DNA). This molecule carries the genetic code and codes for all proteins that make up the structural and functional components of life (figure 1.2). Understanding the structure of the DNA molecule has led to tremendous advances in the field of biology called "molecular biology." These advances have left no area of biology untouched. The fundamental importance of the DNA molecule in all aspects of biology should become clearer as you study later chapters.

Figure 1.1

A Budding Zoologist. A part of a zoologist's training encourages the natural curiosity of youth to mature into a framework for solving zoological problems as adults.

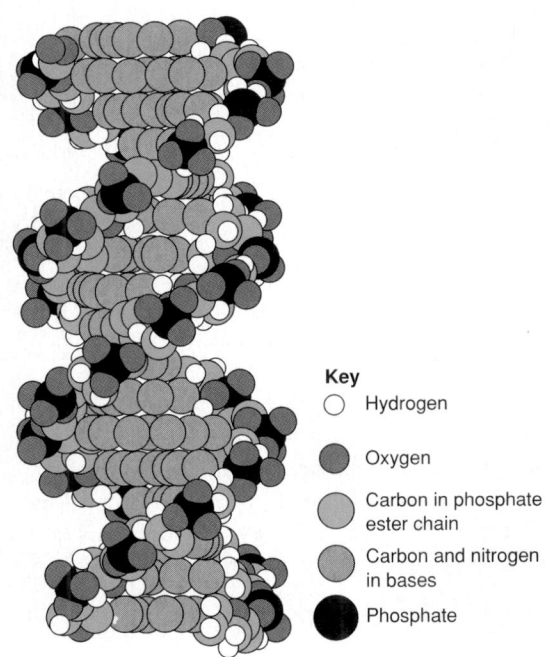

Key
○ Hydrogen
● Oxygen
● Carbon in phosphate ester chain
● Carbon and nitrogen in bases
● Phosphate

Figure 1.2

DNA, the Genetic Material of Life. This computer-generated model shows part of a DNA molecule.

THE FUNDAMENTAL UNIT OF LIFE

The cell is the fundamental unit of life. At the cellular level, biology transcends the boundaries that are sometimes constructed to organize life's diversity. A strong background in cell biology is required, regardless of whether one is studying animal biology (zoology), plant biology (botany), or any other subdiscipline of biology.

However, just as one can never view an animal apart from its cells, one fails to perceive the animal by focusing only on the cell. The interaction of cells determines what animals look like, how they live, and frequently, when they die.

EVOLUTIONARY ONENESS AND THE DIVERSITY OF LIFE

Animals are united at all levels because of their common evolutionary origin and the shared forces that influenced their history. Evolutionary processes are remarkable for their relative simplicity, yet they are awesome because of the effects they have had on life-forms. Evolutionary processes have resulted in an estimated 4 to 30 million species of organisms living today. (Only 1.4 million species have been described.) Many more existed in the past and have become extinct.

The theory of organic evolution is the concept that organisms change over time. Charles Darwin (1809–1882) published convincing evidence for his "theory of evolution by natural selection" in *On the Origin of Species by Means of Natural Selection* in 1859. By 1900, most biologists were convinced that evolution occurs, and that natural selection is a reasonable explanation of how it occurs.

Evidence of Evolution

Today, a wealth of evidence documents the basic premises of evolution. Nowhere is that evidence more convincing than in zoology.

Biogeography   **Biogeography** is the study of the geographic distribution of plants and animals. Biogeographers attempt to explain why organisms are distributed as they are. Biogeographic studies have shown that life-forms in different parts of the world have had distinctive evolutionary histories. For example, large areas of the world often have similar climatic and geographic factors. Each of these geographic regions usually has distinctive plants and animals that have particular roles in the environment. Compare the large meat-eating mountain lion (also called a cougar) of North America with the lion of Africa (figure 1.3). Their similar form suggests a distant common ancestry, and they have similar life-styles. Obvious differences, however, result from millions of years of independent evolution.

Recognizing that plants and animals in different parts of the world have distinctive evolutionary histories, biogeographers have divided the world into six major biogeographic regions (figure 1.4). Each region has a characteristic group of plants and animals, and even though one may move from one region to another and experience similar climates, the different plants and animals encountered may make it seem as if one has entered another world.

Paleontology   **Paleontology** (Gr. *palaios*, old + *on*, existing + *logos*, to study), which is based on the study of the fossil record, has provided some of the most direct evidence for evolution. **Fossils** (L. *fossilis*, to dig) are evidence of plants and animals that existed in the past and have become incorporated into the earth's crust (e.g., as rock or mineral) (figure 1.5). For fossilization to occur, an organism must be quickly covered by sediments to prevent scavenging, and in a way that seals out oxygen and slows decomposition. Fossilization is most likely to occur in aquatic or semiaquatic environments. The fossil record is, therefore, more complete for those groups of organisms living in or around water and for organisms with hard parts. This documentation provides some of the most convincing evidence for evolution. In spite of gaps in the fossil record, paleontology has resulted in nearly complete understanding of many evolutionary lineages (figure 1.6).   (3)   Paleontologists have estimated the age of earth (about 4.6 billion years old), as well as the ages of many rocks and fossils (table 1.1).

Comparative Anatomy   A structure in one animal may resemble a structure in another animal because of a common evolutionary origin. **Comparative anatomy** is the subdiscipline of zoology that is fundamentally based on this relationship. Comparative anatomists study the structure of fossilized and living animals, looking for similarities that could be indications of evolutionarily close relationships. Structures derived from common ancestry are said to be **homologous** (Gr. *homolog* + *os*, agreeing) (i.e., having the same or a similar relation). Some examples of homology are obvious. For example, the appendages of vertebrates have a common arrangement of similar bones, even though the function of the appendages may vary (figure 1.7). Along with other evidence, this similarity in appendage structure indicates that the vertebrates evolved from a common ancestor.

Not all such similarities indicate homology. **Convergent evolution** occurs when two unrelated organisms adapt to similar conditions, resulting in superficial similarities in structure. For example, the wing of a bird and the wing of an insect are both adaptations for flight, but are not homologous (figure 1.8). Any similarities are simply reflections of the fact that, to fly, an animal must have a broad, flat gliding surface. Instead of

(a)

(b)

(c)

Figure 1.3

Biogeography as Evidence of Evolutionary Change. (*a*) A mountain lion (*Felis concolor*) of North and South America has a similar ecological role as (*b*) a lion (*Panthera leo*) found in Africa. Their similar form suggests a distant common ancestry and similar life-styles. Obvious differences, however, result from millions of years of independent evolution. (*c*) The distribution of lions found in Africa and North and South America.

being homologous, these structures are said to be **analogous** (i.e., having a similar function but dissimilar origin).

   Structures are often retained in an organism, even though the structures may have lost their usefulness. They are often poorly developed, and are called **vestigial structures.**   ④   For example, boa constrictors have minute remnants of hind (pelvic) limb bones that have no function in these snakes. They are left over from appendages of their reptilian ancestors. Such remnants of once useful structures are clear indications of change, hence evolution.

Molecular Biology   Recently, **molecular biology** has yielded a wealth of information on evolutionary relationships. Just as animals can have homologous structures, animals may also have homologous processes.

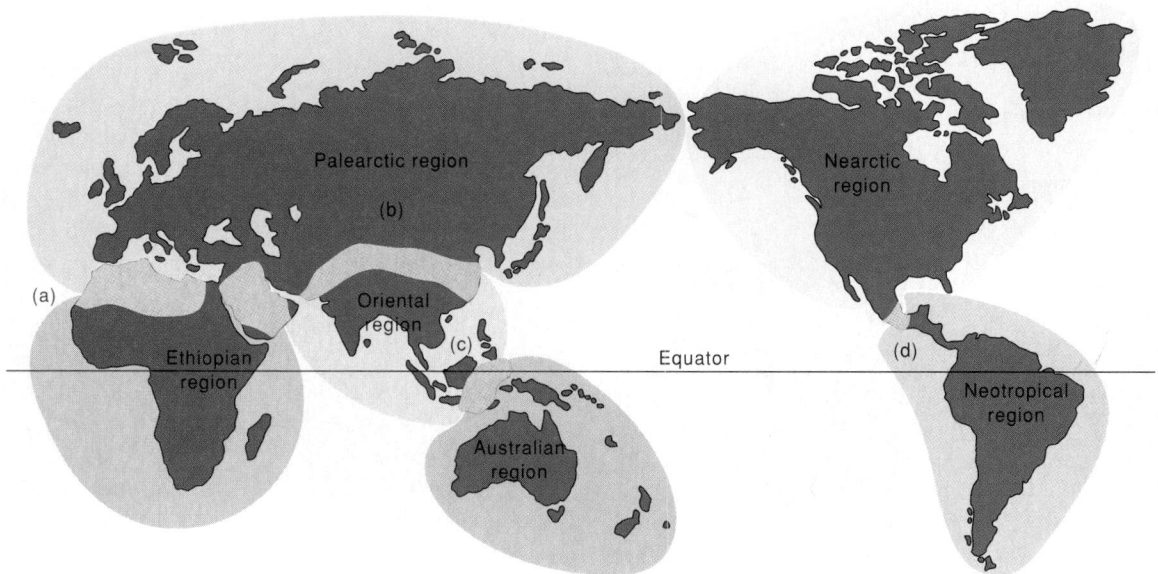

FIGURE 1.4

Biogeographic Regions of the World. Biogeographic regions of the world are separated from one another by barriers, such as oceans, mountain ranges, and deserts. The Ethiopian region is separated from the Palearctic by the Sahara and Arabian Deserts (*a*), the Palearctic region is separated from the Oriental region by the Himalayan Mountains (*b*), the Oriental and Australian regions are separated by deep ocean channels (*c*), and the Nearctic and Neotropical regions are separated by the mountains of southern Mexico and the tropical lowlands of Mexico (*d*).

FIGURE 1.5

Paleontological Evidence of Evolutionary Change. Fossils, such as this trilobite (*Phacops rana*), are direct evidence of evolutionary change. Trilobites were in existence about 500 million years ago and became extinct about 250 million years ago. Fossils form when an animal dies and is covered with sediments. Water dissolves calcium from hard body parts and replaces calcium with another mineral, forming a hard replica of the original animal. This process is called mineralization.

Ultimately, structure and function are based on the genetic blueprint found in all living animals, the DNA molecule. Related animals have DNA derived from their common ancestor. Because DNA carries the codes for proteins that make up each animal, related animals are expected to have similar proteins. With the modern laboratory technologies now available, zoologists can extract and analyze the structure of proteins from animal tissue, and compare the DNA of different animals. By looking for dissimilarities in the structure of related proteins and DNA, and by assuming relatively constant mutation rates, molecular biologists can estimate the elapsed time since divergence from a common ancestral molecule.

The above fields of study have generated impressive documentation of evolution since the initial studies of Darwin. There is no doubt in the minds of the vast majority of scientists as to the reality of evolution. Evolutionary theory has impacted biology like no other single theory. It has impressed scientists with the fundamental unity of all of biology. As you progress through this text, you will continually be reminded of the unity that exists within life because of its common origin.

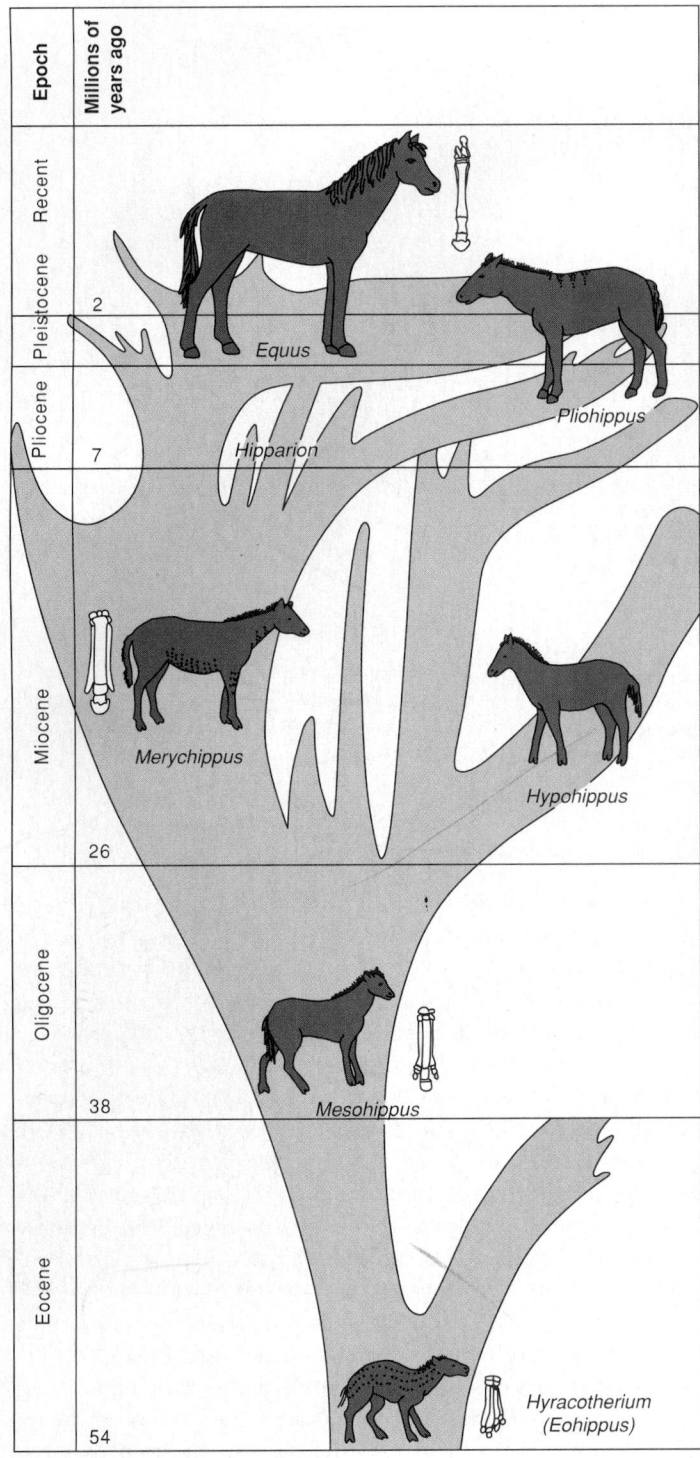

FIGURE 1.6

Reconstruction of an Evolutionary Lineage Based on Evidence in the Fossil Record. Evolution of the horse has been traced back about 60 million years using the fossil record. *Hyracotherium (Eohippus)* was a dog-sized animal with four prominent toes on each foot. A single middle digit of the toe and vestigial digits on either side of that remain in modern horses. About 17.7 million years ago there was a very rapid evolutionary diversification that resulted in the grazing life-style of modern horses. About 15 million years ago, 10–12 contemporaneous species of fossil horses occurred in North America. Note that evolutionary lineages are seldom simple ladders of change. Instead, numerous evolutionary side branches often meet with extinction.

ANIMALS AND THEIR ENVIRONMENT

Life is also united by a common environment. Unfortunately, because modern humans have been slow to realize this fact, the environment has suffered. In some parts of the world, the land is recovering from decades of abuse. One needs only to compare the polluted Lake Erie of the 1960s to the much cleaner lake of the 1990s. A lake once unfit for fishing and other recreational uses is now used extensively for these purposes. Tracts of land have been set aside for use as natural and wilderness areas. Many nonbiodegradable (not broken down by biological processes) substances have been taken out of the marketplace. These developments and others like them offer hope. Certainly, some societies are beginning to realize that all life shares a dependence on the earth's resources.

Even though there is hope, societies have not abandoned those values that treat land, water, and air as commodities that can be bought and sold, or neglected and abused. The problems are most acute in the third world countries, which look at industrialized nations of the world and do all that is in their power to gain a similar wealth. In the process, the land suffers, population growth goes unchecked, toxic wastes are dumped, plant and animal species become extinct, and deserts and famine expand.

Governmental and private agencies (e.g., Worldwatch Institute) have undertaken large-scale evaluations of the environmental health of the world. The results of such studies deserve the serious attention of every concerned citizen.

Population

Global overpopulation is at the root of virtually all other environmental problems. Human population growth is expected to continue into the next century. Through the year 2000, most growth (92%) can be expected to occur in less developed countries, where 5 billion out of a projected total of 6.35 billion humans will live. With a high proportion of the population of childbearing age, even faster growth could occur in the next century. As the human population grows, the disparity between the wealthiest and poorest nations is expected to increase.

World Resources

Stress is being placed on world resources as a result of human overpopulation. Although new technologies continue to increase food production, most food is produced in industrialized countries that already have a high per-capita food consumption. Maximum oil production is expected to continue during the 1990s. Continued use of fossil fuels adds more carbon dioxide to the atmosphere, contributing to the greenhouse effect and global warming. Deforestation of large areas of the world results from continued demand for forest products and fuel. This trend contributes to the greenhouse effect; causes severe, regional water shortages; and results in the extinction of many plant and animal species, especially tropical forests. Preservation of forests would undoubtedly result in the identification of new species of plants and animals that could serve as important human resources: new foods, drugs, building materials, and predators of pests (figure 1.9).

TABLE 1.1	THE HISTORY OF THE EARTH: GEOLOGICAL ERAS, PERIODS, AND MAJOR BIOLOGICAL EVENTS*			

ERA	PERIOD	AGE (MILLIONS OF YEARS)	MAJOR BIOLOGICAL EVENTS
CENOZOIC	Quaternary	0.01	Subtropical forests gave way to cooler forests and grassland areas.
CENOZOIC	Tertiary	65	Modern orders of mammals evolved. Evolution of humans in the last 5 million years.
MESOZOIC	Cretaceous	135	Continental seas and swamps spread. Extinction of ancient birds and reptiles.
MESOZOIC	Jurassic	195	Climate warm and stable. High reptilian diversity. Birds first appeared.
MESOZOIC	Triassic	240	Climate warm. Extensive deserts. Mammal-like reptiles replaced by dinosaurs. First true mammals.
PALEOZOIC	Permian	285	Climate cold early, but then warmed. Mammal-like reptiles common. Widespread extinction of amphibians.
PALEOZOIC	Carboniferous	375	Warm and humid with extensive coal-producing swamps. Arthropods and amphibians were very common. First reptiles appeared.
PALEOZOIC	Devonian	420	Land high and climate cool. Freshwater basins developed. Fish diversified. Early amphibians appeared.
PALEOZOIC	Silurian	450	Extensive shallow seas. Warm climate. First terrestrial arthropods. First jawed fish.
PALEOZOIC	Ordovician	520	Shallow extensive seas. Climate warmed. Many marine invertebrates. Jawless fish widespread.
PALEOZOIC	Cambrian	570	Extensive shallow seas and warm climate. Trilobites and brachiopods were common. Earliest vertebrates were found late in the Cambrian.
PROTEROZOIC		2,000	Multicellular organisms appeared and flourished. Many invertebrates. Eukaryotic organisms appeared (1,500 million years ago). Oxygen accumulated in the atmosphere.
ARCHEAN		4,600	Prokaryotic life appeared (3,500 million years ago). Origin of the earth (4,600 million years ago).

*Note that the time scale in the Proterozoic and Archean eras are greatly compressed.

Solutions

No easy solutions are available for these problems. Unless we deal with the problem of human overpopulation, however, it will be impossible to solve the other problems. The one certainty is that there is no time for delay. We must begin to work as a world community to prevent the spread of disease, famine, and other forms of suffering that accompany overpopulation. Bold and imaginative steps toward improved social and economic conditions and better resource management are needed.

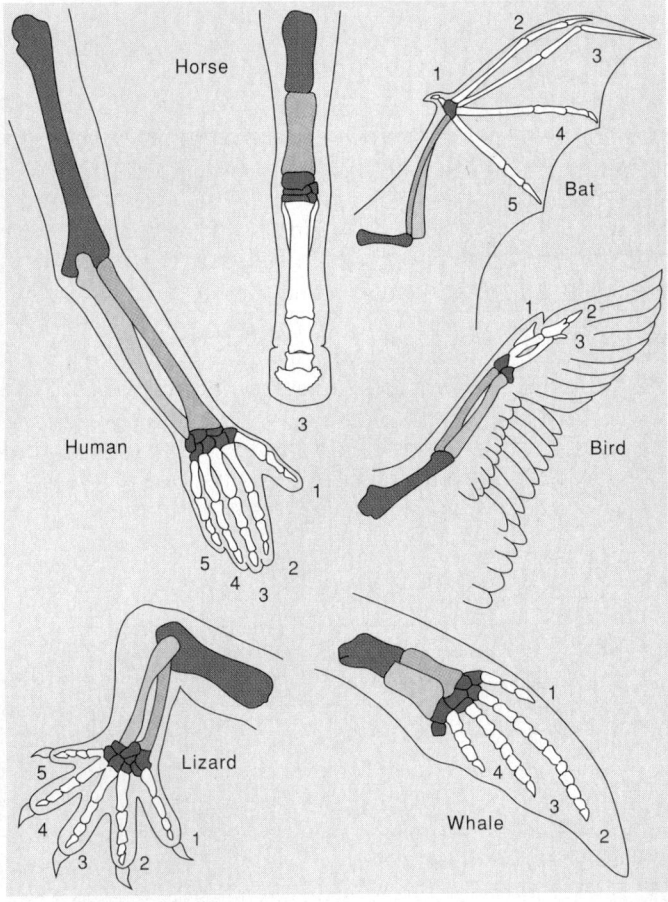

Figure 1.7

The Concept of Homology. The forelimbs of vertebrates evolved from an ancestral pattern. Even in vertebrates as dissimilar as whales and bats, the same basic arrangement of bones can be observed. The digits (fingers) are numbered 1 (thumb) to 5 (little finger). Homologous bones are indicated by color coding.

Stop and Ask Yourself

1. What are four unifying themes of biology? Why is the study of each an important part of any biologist's training?

2. What is organic evolution?

3. How do each of the following contribute to the evidence for evolution? (a) biogeography, (b) paleontology, (c) molecular biology, and (d) comparative anatomy.

4. What are the conclusions of studies on the environmental health of the world regarding (a) the earth's population in the year 2001, (b) resources for the year 2001, and (c) solutions for environmental problems?

(a)

(b)

Figure 1.8

The Concept of Analogy. The wings of a bird (a) and an insect (b) are analogous. They are specialized for similar function, and that similar function has coincidentally led to flat, planing surfaces required for flight. Both kinds of wings arose independently and, therefore, are not homologous.

(a)

(b)

Figure 1.9

Tropical Rain Forests: A Threatened World Resource. A tropical rain forest before (*a*) and after (*b*) clear-cutting and burning to make way for agriculture. These soils will quickly become depleted, and will be abandoned for richer soils of adjacent forests. Loss of tropical forests results in extinction of many valuable forest species.

What Is Zoology?

Zoology is one of the broadest fields in all of science. The diversity of the subdisciplines within zoology reflects the breadth of the field. These subdisciplines are based on particular functional, structural, or ecological interests that span many animal groups (table 1.2). It is also possible to specialize in the biology of a particular group of animals (table 1.3). When one considers the size of some animal groups, it is no wonder that further specialization is also common. For example, there are approximately 300,000 described (and many undescribed) species of beetles! One person cannot possibly be an expert in all areas of beetle biology. Therefore, one can specialize even further and become a beetle taxonomist, physiologist, or ecologist. Obviously, the subdisciplines within zoology are not separated by sharply defined boundaries, and much information is shared among them.

The Classification of Animals

Like all organisms, animals are named and classified into a hierarchy of relatedness. Although Karl von Linné (1707–1778) is primarily remembered for collecting and classifying plants, his work was also a milestone for zoology. His system of naming, **binomial nomenclature,** has been adopted for animals as well as plants. Each kind of organism is described with a two-part name. The first part indicates the genus, and the second part of the name indicates the species to which the organism belongs. Using these two-part names, each kind of organism can be recognized throughout the world. Above the species and genus level, organisms are grouped into families, orders, classes, phyla, and kingdoms, based on a hierarchy of relatedness (figure 1.10). Organisms in the same species are more closely related than organisms in the same genus, and organisms in the same genus are more closely related than organisms in the same order, and so on.

The Scientific Method

Science is knowledge obtained by observation. The usefulness of science is limited, therefore, to what we can detect with our senses or technological extensions of our senses. Science functions in the realm of matter and energy. It is a serious mistake to think that the methods of science can be applied in areas of investigation involving other aspects of human experiences (e.g., matters of the mind or spirit). Trying to use science to either support or disprove spiritual matters is a mistake (box 1.1). Scientific knowledge is neither inherently good nor bad. The same scientific knowledge that resulted in nuclear medicine (e.g., radiation therapy for cancer victims) also brought us nuclear wastes. Although scientific knowledge is used by scientists and others in making ethical decisions, science itself is ethically neutral.

TABLE 1.2	EXAMPLES OF SPECIALIZATIONS IN ZOOLOGY
SUBDISCIPLINE	**DESCRIPTION**
Anatomy	The study of the structure of entire organisms and their parts
Cytology	The study of the structure and function of cells
Ecology	The study of the interaction of organisms with their environment
Embryology	The study of the development of an animal from the fertilized egg to birth or hatching
Genetics	The study of the mechanisms of transmission of traits from parents to offspring
Histology	The study of tissues
Molecular biology	The study of subcellular details of animal structure and function
Parasitology	The study of animals that live in or on other organisms at the expense of the host
Physiology	The study of the function of organisms and their parts
Systematics	The study of the classification of, and the evolutionary interrelationships between, animal groups

TABLE 1.3	EXAMPLES OF SPECIALIZATIONS IN ZOOLOGY BY TAXONOMIC CATEGORIES
Entomology	The study of insects
Herpetology	The study of amphibians and reptiles
Ichthyology	The study of fishes
Mammology	The study of mammals
Ornithology	The study of birds
Protozoology	The study of protozoa

Science is based on observation; however, science is not without presuppositions. They are as follows: (1) Nature is real. What we sense is reality. (2) Cause-and-effect relationships are consistent in nature—that is, the processes that shaped the world in the past are the same as those operating today and in the future. Stated another way, an experiment performed yesterday and repeated today yields the same results both days. (3) Even though there is no perfect knowledge and no perfect observer, nature is understandable. These presuppositions are not provable, but past experience makes them reasonable assumptions.

Observation is the authority in science, but it is always carried out by humans. Because science is a human activity, and because one person cannot observe everything, scientists must rely on the observations of others and accept those observations as being valid or accurate. Scientists rely on observation, so the methods used in these observations must be based on a frame of mind allowing investigators to analyze an occurrence objectively. This objective process is often called **the scientific method** (figure 1.11). Traditionally, there is a series of steps used by all scientists to study natural occurrences. Some problems lend themselves to solution by designing experiments; others are solved by detailed observations of processes or structures. The scientific method is an objective process that helps ensure accurate observations. Because science is a human endeavor, human errors can occur. Further, time and space considerations may influence observations. Therefore, the scientific method depends on repeated investigations by many scientists for confirmation or rejection of experimental results.

Traditionally, the scientific method involves asking questions based on a set of observations. Being able to look at nature and ask relevant questions regarding biological (or other) processes is not as easy as it may seem. Knowing the right questions requires background in one's discipline as well as a perceptive mind. Asking the proper questions frequently determines whether the data gathered can be used to formulate reliable answers.

Following the initial questioning, scientists attempt to formulate a reasonable explanation for the question. This explanation is called a **hypothesis.** To be useful, a hypothesis must be testable. Frequently, a hypothesis is so broad that it cannot be directly tested. Rather, some predictions of the hypothesis are

FIGURE 1.10

A Hierarchy of Relatedness. The classification of a housefly, horsefly, honeybee, and human.

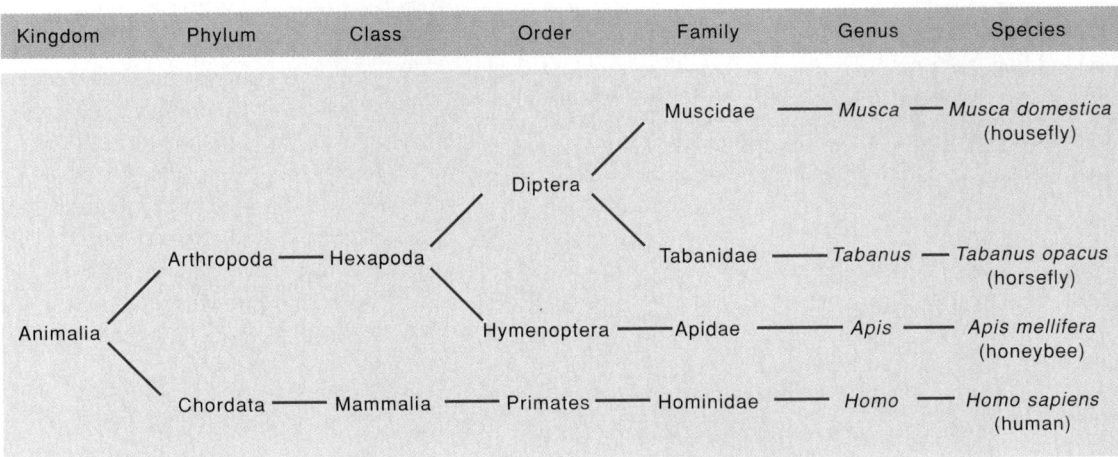

Kingdom	Phylum	Class	Order	Family	Genus	Species
				Muscidae	*Musca*	*Musca domestica* (housefly)
			Diptera	Tabanidae	*Tabanus*	*Tabanus opacus* (horsefly)
	Arthropoda	Hexapoda	Hymenoptera	Apidae	*Apis*	*Apis mellifera* (honeybee)
Animalia						
	Chordata	Mammalia	Primates	Hominidae	*Homo*	*Homo sapiens* (human)

BOX 1.1 "SCIENTIFIC" CREATIONISM

Creationism is the idea that religious accounts of creation reflect the actual sequence of events that occurred at the beginning of life on earth. Most of these religious accounts have common elements that are reflected in the biblical creation accounts found in the book of Genesis. Believers in creationism (creationists) have interpretations of creation that vary somewhat, depending on how literally they interpret scriptures, but the following are common elements of creationism. (1) There was a sudden creation of matter, energy, and life from nothing. (2) Modern ideas regarding mechanisms of changes in life-forms insufficiently explain life's diversity. Although many creationists admit that changes in species occur, most will not accept the origin of new species through evolutionary mechanisms. (3) Humans and apes have a separate ancestry. (4) The earth's geography and geology are explained by catastrophic events (e.g., a worldwide flood). (5) Life had a relatively recent inception.

In "scientific" creationism, an attempt is made to place these views into a scientific framework. The vast majority of scientists reject the validity of this effort for the following reasons. (1) Science is the study of natural occurrences based on observations of matter and energy. Scientific creationism depends on creation from nothing; therefore, the cause-and-effect relationships in creationism violate the observable natural order. This premise of creationism is not open to scientific investigation. (2) For anything to be investigated scientifically, one must be able to test its predictions against the material world. Creationism's creation event is not considered an ongoing process and, therefore, its implications cannot be tested by modern science. (3) Science depends on falsification. For any concept to be scientifically supported, it must withstand efforts by scientists to falsify the concept. Creationism is based on literal interpretations of religious writings that are supported by tradition and statements of faith. No amount of scientific evidence is permitted to falsify creation accounts in creationists' minds.

Creationism is not scientific. Creationists bring into their doctrine a set of assumptions that are not open to investigation and modification by a scientific community. Instead, creationism is a set of religious doctrines based on a particular interpretation of religious writings. Not only are these interpretations unscientific, but they are not accepted in the same literal manner by many modern religious organizations.

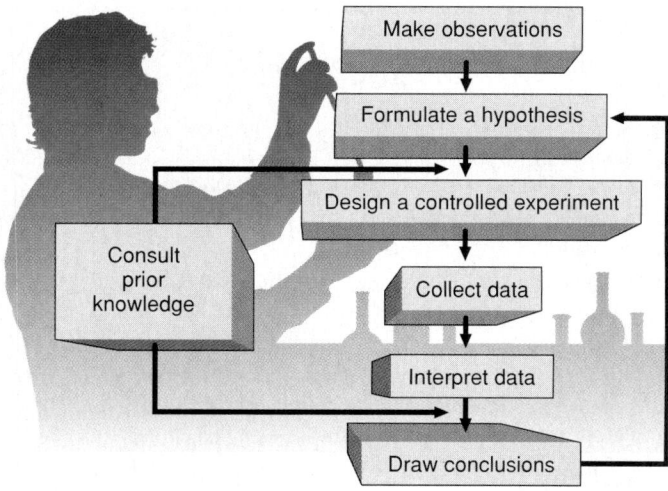

FIGURE 1.11

Steps of the Scientific Method. Application of the scientific method usually involves both sequential steps (center arrows and boxes) and repeating cycles of hypothesis formation, experimentation, and evaluation (side arrows and box).

any conclusions, and the results must be communicated to other scientists. This communication may take the form of an article published in one of the hundreds of biological journals, or a paper presented orally at one of the many gatherings of scientists throughout the world. Regardless of the vehicle chosen, these reports must include discussions of the hypothesis, the methodology, the results, and the conclusions. The results of any biologist's work are thus available for the scrutiny of others.

After repeated testing, related hypotheses that have been accepted by scientists may be assembled into a generalized statement that can be used in a predictive fashion and is called a **theory.** To a scientist, "theory" means something very different from the common use of the word as a conjecture or a guess. Scientists recognize that the details of what is known today will probably change with future research, and most realize that their knowledge is incomplete, as history has repeatedly shown. When scientists talk about the theory of evolution (or the theory of anything else), they are talking about a concept that has been supported by data from years of research. What scientists can never do, however, is claim that all of the details of evolutionary (or other) mechanisms have been worked out. Thus, scientific theories are always provisional.

tested. The simplest explanations that seem to be consistent with the evidence available are usually the ones most easily tested.

The hypothesis is tested by collecting data from further observations or from an experiment that has been designed. It is essential to include a control in any experiment. A **control group** is treated the same as an experimental group, except that the variable being tested is omitted. A control serves as a basis for comparing the data from the experiment. Any differences between the results in the control and experimental groups must be a result of the variable being tested. Regardless of the outcome of an experiment, further testing is needed to back up

Stop and Ask Yourself

5. What is zoology? Why do most zoologists choose to specialize in a field within zoology?
6. What is the scientific method?
7. What is a hypothesis?
8. What is a scientific theory? How is the word theory, used in this context, different from everyday usage?

SUMMARY

1. Biology, the study of life, has four themes that unify all of its divergent disciplines. They are (1) a common genetic molecule—DNA, (2) a common unit of organization—the cell, (3) a common evolutionary history, and (4) a common environment—the earth.

2. Evidence for evolution comes from the fields of biogeography, paleontology, comparative anatomy, and molecular biology.

3. All animals share a common environment. Excessive human population growth has placed undue pressure on all of the earth's resources. Human values must change to successfully check deterioration of the environment.

4. Zoology is the study of animals. It is a very broad field that requires zoologists to specialize.

5. Animals are classified into a hierarchical system of classification that uses a two-part name for every different kind of animal.

6. The scientific method provides a frame of mind that allows the investigator to objectively analyze an occurrence.

SELECTED KEY TERMS

binomial nomenclature (*p. 11*)	hypothesis (*p. 12*)
biology (*p. 4*)	the scientific method (*p. 12*)
convergent evolution (*p. 5*)	theory (*p. 13*)
homologous (*p. 5*)	zoology (*p. 4*)

CRITICAL THINKING QUESTIONS

1. Zoologists need to consider the broader perspective that unites zoology with biology as a whole. Could this broader perspective also include the arts and humanities? Explain.

2. What is the difference between analogy and homology? In an evolutionary context, how could analogous structures arise?

3. Why is perfect objectivity impossible to attain in science?

4. Imagine that you have just gotten into your car and turned the key but the engine did not start. Outline how you would go about solving this problem using an objective, scientific approach. (If you would rather substitute another everyday problem, go ahead.)

5. What are some current issues that involve both zoology and questions of ethics or public policy? What should be the role of zoologists in helping to resolve these issues?

6. An astronomer makes the following statement: "I have studied the universe, and I have seen no evidence of a god. Therefore, a god(s) does not exist." Which part of this statement reflects the astronomer's science? Which part of the statement reflects the astronomer's theology? Do you think that astronomers' science should be used to support their theological position?

THE CHEMICAL BASIS OF ANIMAL LIFE

Outline

Concepts

1. Animals are made up of molecules, which are collections of atoms bound to one another. The life processes within an animal are based, to a large degree, on the chemical properties of atoms, ions, and molecules.
2. Carbon is the key element of organic molecules because it has the unique physical and chemical characteristics.
3. Carbohydrates and lipids serve as the principal source of energy for most animals.
4. Proteins, nucleotides, and nucleic acids are large molecules that provide the basis for structure, function, information storage, energy transfer, and genetic regulation in animals.

Would You Like to Know:

1 what the four most common elements in most animals are? (*p. 16*)

2 what holds different water molecules together? (*p. 19*)

3 why the type of fat called an oil is liquid at room temperature? (*p. 24*)

These and other useful questions will be answered in this chapter.

Chemical processes are essential to everything that goes on within the body of an animal. Without these chemical processes, life as we know it could not exist. This chapter presents the chemistry you will need to understand the basic chemical processes that enable animals to function in the environment as living entities.

Chemistry is the branch of science dealing with the composition of substances and chemical reactions. In chemical reactions, bonds between atoms are broken or joined, and different combinations of atoms or molecules are formed. A knowledge of chemistry is essential for understanding the structure (**anatomy** [Gr. *ana*, again + *temnein*, to cut]) and function (**physiology** [Gr. *physis*, nature]) of animals, because body functions involve chemical changes that occur in structural units, such as cells. As interest in the chemistry of animals grew, and knowledge in this area expanded, a new subdivision of science called **biochemistry** ("the chemistry of life") emerged. Biochemistry is the study of the molecular basis of life.

ATOMS AND ELEMENTS: BUILDING BLOCKS OF ALL MATTER

Matter is anything that occupies space and has mass. It includes all the solids, liquids, and gases in our environment, as well as those in bodies of all forms of life. **Mass** refers to the amount of matter in an object. Matter is composed of **elements,** which are chemical substances that cannot be broken down into simpler units by ordinary chemical reactions. An element is designated by either a one- or two-letter abbreviation of its Arabic, English, German, or Latin name. For example, O is the symbol for the element oxygen, H stands for hydrogen, and Na for sodium (from the Latin, *natrium*). Currently, scientists recognize 92 elements occurring in nature. ① About 15 elements are found in most animals, and four of these (carbon, hydrogen, oxygen, and nitrogen) account for the majority (97%) of an animal's body weight (table 2.1). The remaining 3% of an animal's weight consists primarily of calcium, phosphorus, and potassium. Some elements present in trace amounts include sodium, sulfur, manganese, magnesium, copper, iodine, iron, and chlorine.

Elements are composed of units of matter called atoms. An **atom** (Gr. *atomos*, indivisible) is the smallest part of an element that can enter into a chemical reaction. Atoms vary in size, weight, and the diverse ways they interact with each other. For example, some atoms are capable of combining with atoms like themselves or with dissimilar atoms; others lack this ability.

STRUCTURE OF ATOMS

Atoms have two main parts—a central core called a nucleus and the surrounding electron cloud (figure 2.1). The nucleus contains two major particles: the positively charged **protons (p$^+$)** and the uncharged **neutrons (n^0).** Surrounding the nucleus are negatively charged particles called **electrons (e$^-$).** Any one electron moves so rapidly around the nucleus that it cannot be

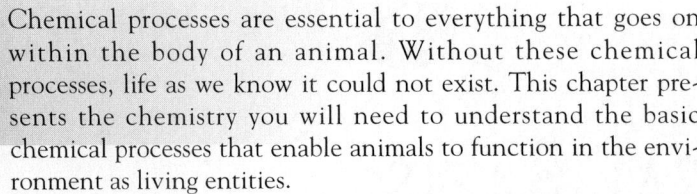

TABLE 2.1	NATURALLY OCCURRING ELEMENTS IN ANIMALS			
ELEMENT	SYMBOL	ATOMIC NUMBER	ATOMIC MASS	PERCENT WET WEIGHT OF BODY*
Oxygen	O	8	16	65 ⎫
Carbon	C	6	12	19 ⎪ 97%
Hydrogen	H	1	1	10 ⎬
Nitrogen	N	7	14	3 ⎭
Calcium	Ca	20	40	1 ⎫
Phosphorus	P	15	31	1 ⎪
Potassium	K	19	39	0.2 ⎪
Sulfur	S	16	32	0.1 ⎪
Sodium	Na	11	23	0.1 ⎬ approx. 3%
Chlorine	Cl	17	35	0.1 ⎪
Magnesium	Mg	12	24	0.1 ⎪
Manganese	Mn	25	55	0.1 ⎪
Iron	Fe	26	56	0.1 ⎪
Copper	Cu	29	64	0.1 ⎪
Iodine	I	53	127	0.1 ⎭

* Includes water.

found at any given point at any particular moment in time; therefore, its location is given as an electron cloud.

Atomic nuclei contain protons and neutrons, collectively called **nucleons.** Nucleons consist of **quarks.** Two up quarks (each with +2/3 electron charge) and a down quark (–1/3 charge) make up positively charged protons. The neutron is a neutral particle consisting of an up quark and two down quarks. **Gluons** bind quarks together. Because the number of negatively charged electrons outside the nucleus is equal to the number of charged protons, the atom is electrically uncharged or neutral.

The chemical and physical properties of an atom are determined by the number of protons and neutrons in its nucleus and by the number and arrangement of electrons in the electron cloud. The **atomic number** of an element is the number of protons in the nucleus of one of its atoms. Elements are identified by their atomic number. For example, if an atom has one proton, it is hydrogen; if it has six, it is carbon; and if an atom has eight protons, it is oxygen.

Another measure of an atom is its atomic mass. The **atomic mass** is equal to the number of neutrons and protons in its nucleus. Because carbon contains six protons and six neutrons, its atomic mass is 12 and is symbolized with a superscript preceding the element's symbol: ^{12}C (read "carbon-12"). The atomic numbers and atomic masses of the more important elements in a typical animal are given in table 2.1.

Most naturally occurring elements are actually a mixture of slightly varying forms of that element. All atoms of a given element have the same number of protons in the nucleus, but some have different numbers of neutrons, and thus different

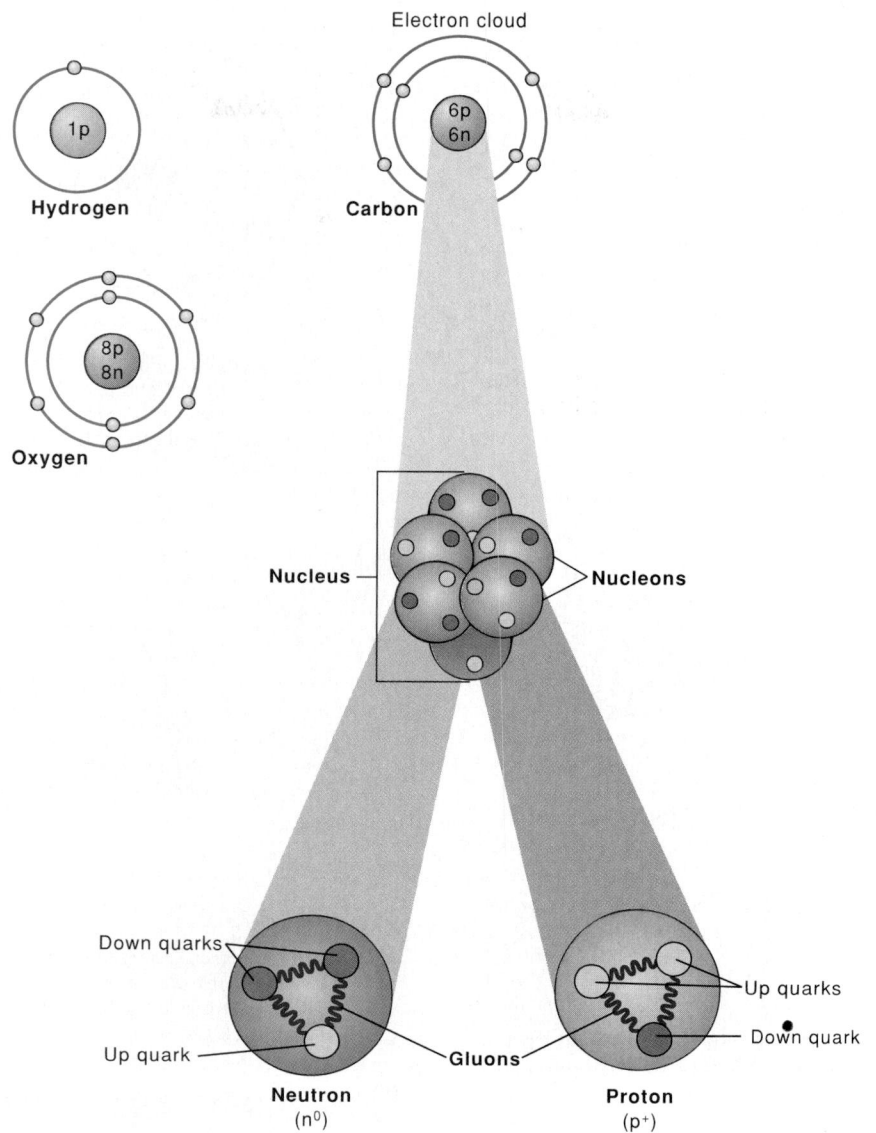

FIGURE 2.1

Structure of the Atom. See text for details.

atomic masses. These different forms with the same atomic number but different atomic masses are called **isotopes.** For example, the most common form of carbon atom has six protons and six neutrons in the nucleus and an atomic mass of 12 (^{12}C). A carbon isotope with six protons and seven neutrons has an atomic mass of 13 (^{13}C), and a carbon isotope with six protons and eight neutrons has an atomic mass of 14 (^{14}C) (figure 2.2).

Some isotopes (e.g., ^{12}C and ^{13}C) are stable and do not break down. Other isotopes (e.g., ^{14}C) are unstable and tend to break down (decay or decompose) by periodically emitting small particles and energy. These unstable isotopes are termed **radioisotopes** (radioactive isotopes). Oxygen, iron, cobalt, iodine, and phosphorus are all elements that have radioactive isotopes.

ENERGY-LEVEL SHELLS

The electrons of an atom are distributed around its nucleus in orbitals called **energy-level shells** or **clouds of electrons** (figure 2.3). The location of these electrons in relation to the nucleus greatly influences the way atoms react with each other. Seven energy-level shells are possible. Each shell can hold only a certain number of electrons. There are never more than two electrons in the shell nearest the nucleus; as many as eight electrons can be in each of the second and third shells; larger numbers fill the more distant shells. When an atom has a complete outer shell—that is, the shell holds the maximum number of electrons possible—the shell is complete and stable. An atom with an incomplete, or unstable, outer shell tends to

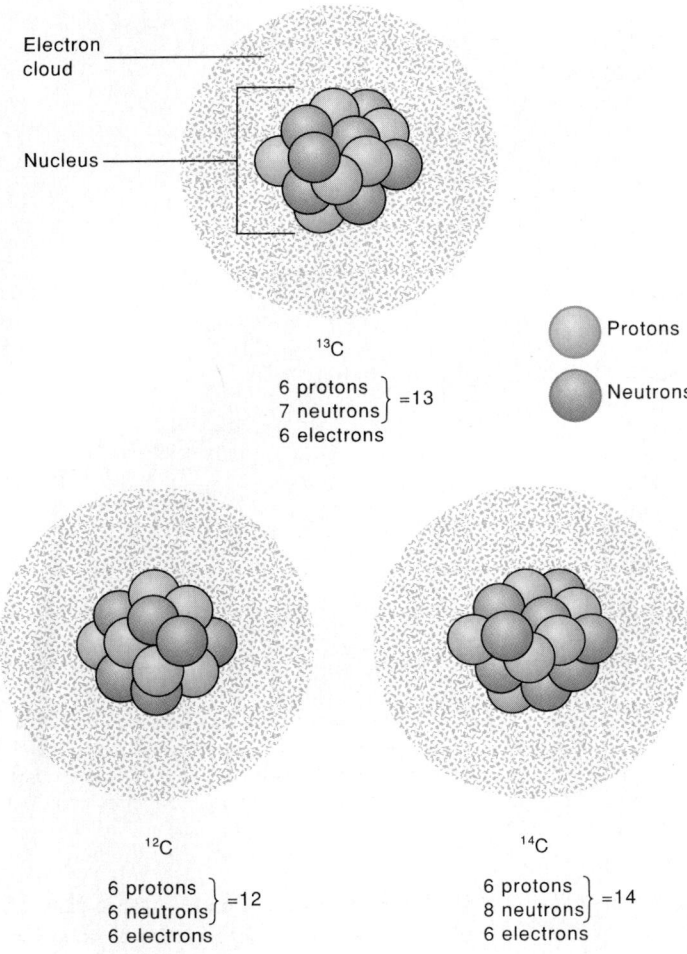

¹³C

6 protons
7 neutrons } =13
6 electrons

Protons

Neutrons

¹²C

6 protons
6 neutrons } =12
6 electrons

¹⁴C

6 protons
8 neutrons } =14
6 electrons

Figure 2.2

Isotopes—Variations on Normal Atomic Structure. The nuclei of these carbon isotopes differ in their number of neutrons, although each has six protons. ^{12}C has six neutrons, ^{13}C has seven neutrons, and ^{14}C has eight neutrons.

gain, lose, or share electrons with another atom. For example, an atom of sodium has 11 electrons arranged as illustrated in figure 2.3: two in the first shell, eight in the second shell, and one in the third shell. As a result of this arrangement, this atom will tend to form chemical bonds with other atoms where it loses the single electron from its outer shell, which leaves the second shell filled and the atom stable.

Stop and Ask Yourself

1. What is the relationship between matter and elements?

2. How are electrons, protons, and neutrons positioned within an atom?

3. What is the difference between atomic number and atomic mass?

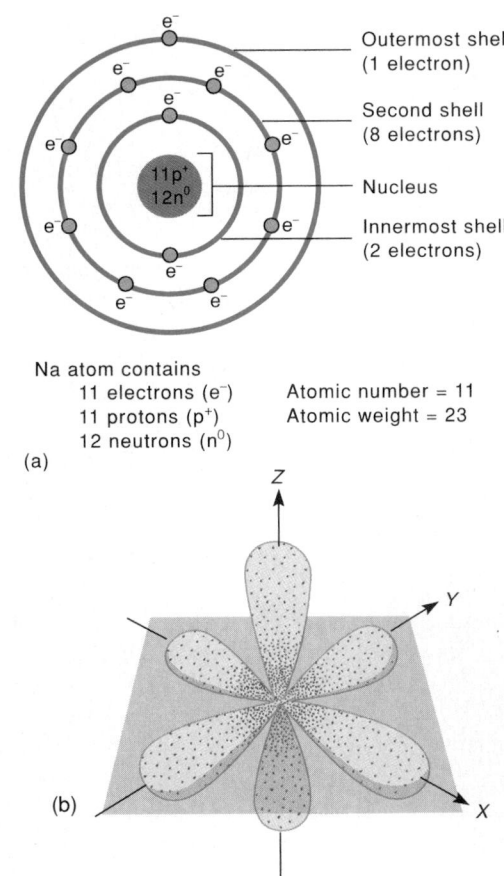

Outermost shell
(1 electron)

Second shell
(8 electrons)

Nucleus

Innermost shell
(2 electrons)

Na atom contains
    11 electrons (e⁻)
    11 protons (p⁺)
    12 neutrons (n⁰)

Atomic number = 11
Atomic weight = 23

(a)

(b)

Figure 2.3

How Electrons Are Arranged in Atoms. (*a*) A diagram of a sodium atom showing its three energy-level shells. (*b*) In reality, electrons are not found in a definite location, but travel rapidly in a three-dimensional space (X, Y, and Z planes) around the nucleus.

COMPOUNDS AND MOLECULES: AGGREGATES OF ATOMS

In addition to being an element, a substance can also be a compound. A **compound** is a substance composed of atoms of two or more elements chemically united in fixed proportions. For example, in water there are two H atoms and one O atom. This composition does not change (i.e., a compound cannot be separated into its pure components—the atoms of the elements present—except by chemical methods).

When atoms interact chemically to form **molecules,** the atoms are held together by electrical forces called chemical bonds. Three types of chemical bonds are covalent, hydrogen, and ionic.

COVALENT BONDS: SHARING ELECTRON PAIRS

When atoms share outer-shell electrons with other atoms, the chemical bond that is formed is called a **covalent bond** (the prefix *co-* indicates a shared condition) (figure 2.4). In covalent bonding, electrons are always shared in pairs. When a pair of electrons is shared (one from each molecule), a single bond is formed (e.g., the hydrogen [H — H] molecule); when two pairs

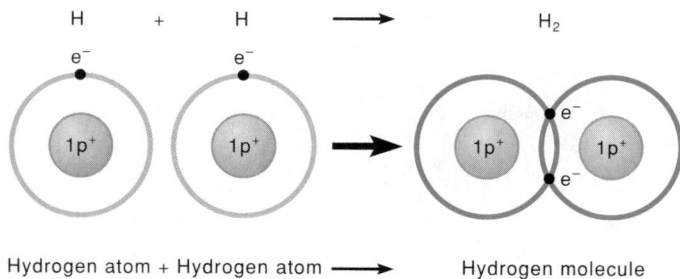

Figure 2.4

A Covalently Bonded Molecule—Hydrogen (H₂). A single covalent bond is formed when two hydrogen atoms share a pair of electrons.

are shared, a double bond is formed (e.g., the oxygen [O = O] molecule); and when three are shared, a triple bond is formed (e.g., the nitrogen [N ≡ N] molecule).

In a molecule like H_2, the electrons spend as much time orbiting one nucleus as the other. Therefore, the distribution of charges is symmetrical, and the bond is called a **nonpolar covalent bond.** Because of this equal sharing, the molecule is electrically balanced, and the molecule as a whole is neutral.

In other molecules, such as H_2O, where two hydrogen atoms combine with one oxygen atom, the electrons spend more time orbiting the oxygen nucleus than the hydrogen nuclei. The electrical charge from the cloud of moving electrons is thus asymmetrical, and the bond is called a **polar covalent bond.** Such a bond leaves the oxygen atom with a slightly negative charge and the hydrogens with a slightly positive charge even though the entire molecule is electrically neutral. The entire shape of the H_2O molecule reflects this polarity; rather than the linear arrangement H − O − H, the two hydrogens are at one end, a bit like the corners of a triangle. This shape and polarity can lead to the formation of another kind of chemical bond—the hydrogen bond.

Hydrogen Bonds

In molecules in which hydrogen is bonded to certain other atoms (e.g., O, N, or Fe), the hydrogen electron is drawn toward another atom, leaving a proton behind. As a result, the hydrogen atom gains a slight positive charge. The remaining proton is attracted to negatively charged atoms of, for example, oxygen in nearby molecules. When this happens, a weak attraction, called a **hydrogen bond,** is formed.   ❷   The hydrogen atom in one water molecule forms a hydrogen bond with the oxygen atom in another water molecule, and so forth, until many molecules are bonded together (figure 2.5).

Ionic Bonds: Opposites Attract

When an atom either gains or loses electrons, it acquires an electrical charge and is called an **ion** (Gr. *ion,* going). If an atom loses one or more electrons, it becomes positively charged, because more positively charged protons are now in the nucleus than negatively charged electrons surrounding the nucleus. This positive charge is shown as one or more "plus" signs. Conversely, if an atom gains one or more electrons, it becomes negatively charged,

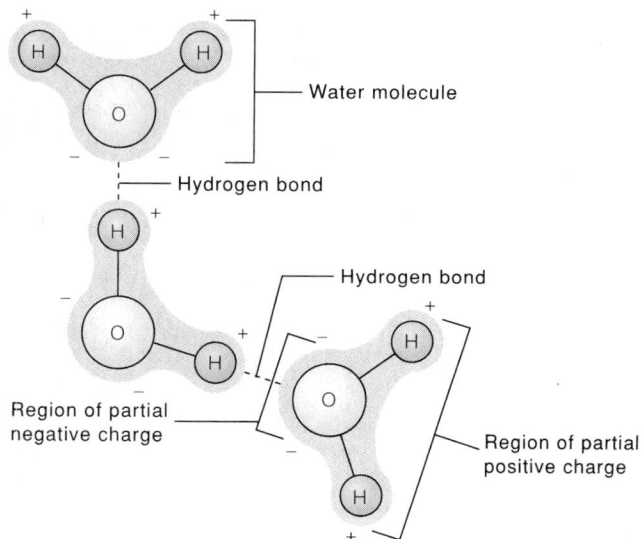

Figure 2.5

Hydrogen Bonds and Water Droplets. Hydrogen bonds are formed when oxygen atoms of different water molecules are weakly joined together by the attraction of the electronegative oxygen for the positively charged hydrogens. Because of the arrangement of electron orbitals and the bonding angles between oxygen and hydrogen, the molecule as a whole is polar (it carries a slight negative charge at one end and a slight positive charge at the other end). Many properties of water can be traced to this polarity.

and this negative charge is shown as one or more "minus" signs. A positive ion is known as a cation, and a negative ion is an anion. Examples of cations are sodium (Na^+), potassium (K^+), hydrogen (H^+), calcium (Ca^{2+}) and iron (Fe^{3+}). Some anions are chloride (Cl^-), hydroxyl (OH^-), bicarbonate (HCO_3^-), sulfate (SO_4^{2-}), phosphate (PO_4^{3-}), and carboxyl (COO^-).

Ionic bonds are formed when an atom or group of atoms develops an electrical charge and becomes attracted to an atom or group of atoms with an opposite charge. Figure 2.6 shows how an ionic bond is formed between sodium and chlorine to produce sodium chloride. When a sodium atom and chlorine atom come together, an electron is donated from the sodium atom to the chlorine atom. This electron transfer changes the balance between the protons and electrons in each of the two atoms. The sodium atom ends up with one more proton than it has electrons, and the chlorine atom with one more electron than it has protons. The sodium atom is left with a net charge of +1 (Na^+), and the net charge of the chlorine atoms is –1 (Cl^-). These unlike charges attract each other and form the ionic bond.

Stop and Ask Yourself

4. What is a chemical bond?
5. What is a double covalent bond?
6. How is a hydrogen bond formed?
7. What is an ion?

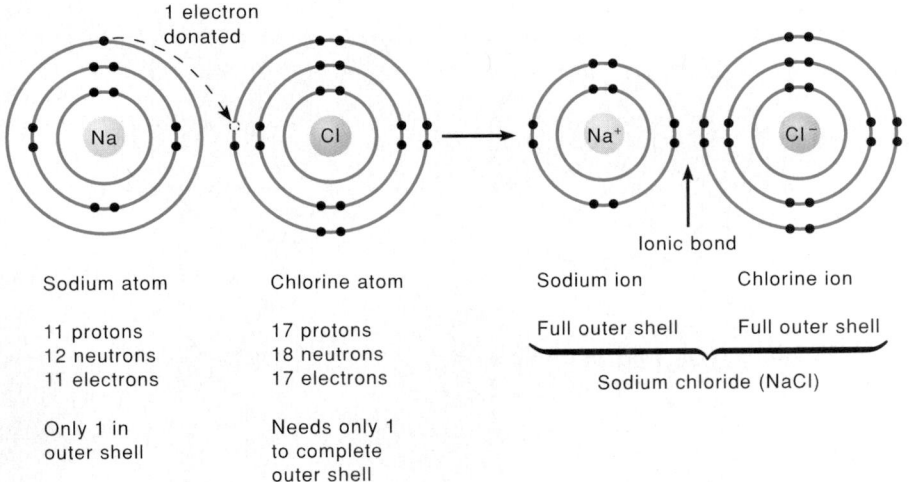

Figure 2.6

An Ionically Bonded Molecule—Table Salt (NaCl). In the formation of sodium chloride, an electron from the outermost shell is transferred from the sodium atom to the chlorine atom, giving both atoms complete outermost shells. This transfer gives the sodium atom a net charge of +1 (sodium ion) and the chlorine atom a net charge of –1 (chloride ion). An ionic bond is formed between the oppositely charged ions.

Acids, Bases, and Buffers

An **electrolyte** is any substance, such as sodium chloride (NaCl), that conducts electricity when in solution. Many fluids contain strong electrolytes that break down (ionize) into ions. Most acids and bases are electrolytes.

An **acid** is a substance that releases hydrogen ions (H^+) when dissolved in water. Because a hydrogen atom without its electron is only a proton, an acid can be described as a proton donor:

$$HCl \rightarrow H^+ + Cl^-$$

One molecule of hydrogen chloride dissolves in water to produce hydrochloric acid, which dissociates into one hydrogen ion and one chloride ion.

In contrast, a **base** is a substance that releases hydroxyl ions (OH^-) when dissolved in water:

$$NaOH \rightarrow Na^+ + OH^-$$

One molecule of sodium hydroxide dissolves in water to give one sodium ion and one hydroxyl ion.

When a base has dissolved in water, it acts to remove free protons from the water; therefore, it can be called a proton acceptor:

$$OH^- + H^+ \rightarrow H_2O$$

pH: Measuring Acidity and Alkalinity

The chemical reactions involved with life processes are often affected by the presence of hydrogen and hydroxyl ions; therefore, the concentrations of these ions in body fluids are important. The higher the concentration of hydrogen ions (H^+), the more acidic the solution, and the higher the concentration of hydroxyl (OH^-) ions, the more basic (alkaline) the solution. A solution is neutral when the number of hydrogen ions equals the number of hydroxyl ions.

The numerical scale that measures acidity and alkalinity is called the **pH scale.** The pH scale runs from 0 to 14, with neutrality at 7. Table 2.2 shows the relationship between hydrogen ion concentration and pH. Acidic solutions have a pH of less than 7, and basic (alkaline) solutions have a pH above 7. Each whole number on the pH scale represents a tenfold change (logarithmic) in acidity; therefore, a solution with a pH of 3 is 10 times more acidic than a solution with a pH of 4, and a pH of 9 is 10 times more basic than a pH of 8. Actually, the pH value is equal to the negative logarithm of the hydrogen ion concentration

$$pH = -\log [H^+]$$

or

$$pH = \log(1/[H^+])$$

pH: Control with Buffers

A stable internal environment in an animal can be maintained only if there is a relatively constant pH of the body fluids. Too much of a strong acid or base can destroy the stability of cells. Also, too sudden a change in pH may be destructive. The fluid systems of most animals contain chemical substances that help regulate the acid-base balance. These substances, called **buffers,** are substances that resist changes in pH by accepting H^+ ions when they are in excess and donating H^+ ions when they are depleted. The most important buffers are the bicarbonates, phosphates, and organic molecules, such as amino acids and proteins.

TABLE 2.2	THE RELATIONSHIP BETWEEN HYDROGEN ION (H+) CONCENTRATION, HYDROXYL ION (OH−) CONCENTRATION, AND pH		

H+ (HYDROGEN ION)		pH	OH− (HYDROXYL ION)
10^{0} = 1		0	10^{-14} = 0.00000000000001
10^{-1} = 0.1		1	10^{-13} = 0.0000000000001
10^{-2} = 0.01		2	10^{-12} = 0.000000000001
10^{-3} = 0.001	Acidic	3	10^{-11} = 0.00000000001
10^{-4} = 0.0001		4	10^{-10} = 0.0000000001
10^{-5} = 0.00001		5	10^{-9} = 0.000000001
10^{-6} = 0.000001		6	10^{-8} = 0.00000001
10^{-7} = 0.0000001	Neutral	7	10^{-7} = 0.0000001
10^{-8} = 0.00000001		8	10^{-6} = 0.000001
10^{-9} = 0.000000001		9	10^{-5} = 0.00001
10^{-10} = 0.0000000001		10	10^{-4} = 0.0001
10^{-11} = 0.00000000001	Basic	11	10^{-3} = 0.001
10^{-12} = 0.000000000001	(Alkaline)	12	10^{-2} = 0.01
10^{-13} = 0.0000000000001		13	10^{-1} = 0.1
10^{-14} = 0.00000000000001		14	10^{0} = 1

The carbonic acid-bicarbonate ion system is an important buffer system involved in the buffering of the blood of many vertebrates:

$$H_2CO_3 \rightleftharpoons H^+ + HCO_3^-$$

Carbonic acid dissociates to form hydrogen ion and bicarbonate ion.

In this example, if H^+ are added to the system, they combine with HCO_3^- to form H_2CO_3 (the reaction goes to the left). This reaction removes H^+ and keeps the pH from changing. If excess OH^- are added, they react with the H^+ to form water, and more H_2CO_3 will ionize and replace the H^+ ions that were used (the reaction goes to the right). Again, pH stability is maintained.

Stop and Ask Yourself

8. What is an electrolyte? What is an acid? What is a base?

9. With respect to pH, what is a neutral solution?

10. What is the relationship between pH and H^+ concentration?

11. How do buffers function? Why are buffers important to animals?

THE MOLECULES OF ANIMALS

The chemicals that enter into metabolic reactions or are produced by them can be divided into two large groups: (1) **organic molecules,** which contain carbon atoms, and (2) **inorganic molecules,** which lack carbon atoms. (A few simple molecules containing carbon, such as CO_2, are considered for convenience to be inorganic.)

The most important characteristics of organic molecules depend on properties of the key element, carbon—the indispensable element for all life. The carbon atom has four electrons in its outer orbital; thus, it must share four additional electrons by covalent bonding with other atoms to fill its outer orbital with eight electrons. This unique bonding requirement enables carbon to bond with other carbon atoms to form chains and rings of varying lengths and configurations, as well as to bond with hydrogen and other atoms.

With only four electrons in its outer shell, carbon atoms can form covalent bonds to fill this shell. Adjacent carbon atoms may share one or two pairs of electrons. When one pair of electrons is shared, they form a single covalent bond, leaving each carbon free to bond to as many as three other atoms (figure 2.7a). When two pair of electrons are shared, they form a double covalent bond, leaving each carbon free to bond to only two additional atoms (figure 2.7b).

Hydrocarbons are organic molecules that contain only carbon and hydrogen and most have their carbons bonded in a linear fashion. Hydrocarbons are important since they form the framework of all organic molecules.

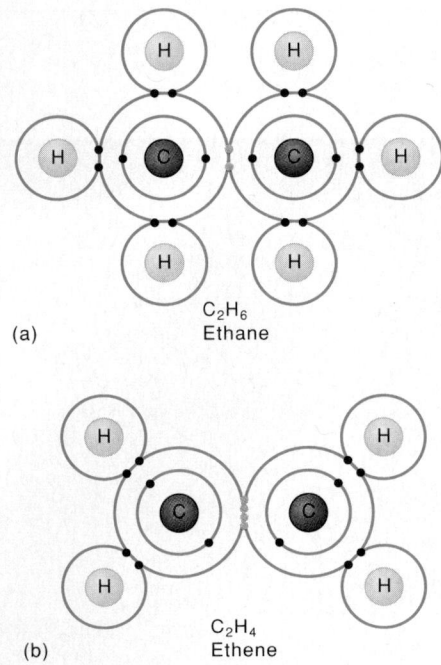

(a)
C₂H₆
Ethane

(b)
C₂H₄
Ethene

Figure 2.7

Carbon Bonding. (*a*) Two carbon atoms are joined by a single covalent bond. The remaining three pairs of electrons are shared with hydrogen atoms in this molecule. (*b*) Two carbon atoms are joined by a double covalent bond. In this case, only two pairs of electrons are shared with hydrogen atoms.

The carbon chain or ring of many organic molecules provides a relatively inactive molecular "backbone," to which reactive groups or atoms are attached. These are known as the functional groups of the molecule and are responsible for the unique chemical properties and behavior of the molecule. Some of the more important functional groups are illustrated in figure 2.8.

The important groups of organic molecules in animals include carbohydrates, lipids, proteins, nucleotides, and nucleic acids. Each of these groups is now briefly discussed.

CARBOHYDRATES: STORED ENERGY AND STRUCTURAL SUPPORT

Carbohydrates are the major source of energy for animals. Most animal cells have the chemical machinery to break down the energy-rich carbon-hydrogen (C—H) bonds found in sugars and starches. Simple carbohydrates (e.g., monosaccharides) are composed of atoms of carbon, hydrogen, and oxygen.

Carbohydrates are classified according to their molecular structure. The simplest types with short carbon chains are called **monosaccharides** (Gr. *monos*, single + *sakharon*, sugar) or sugars. As their name implies, monosaccharides taste sweet. Monosaccharides are the building blocks of more complex carbohydrate molecules. Four common monosaccharides found in animals are glucose, fructose, glyceraldehyde, and dihydroxyacetone (figure 2.9).

—OH
Hydroxyl group

—C=O with OH
Carboxyl group

—NH₂
Amino group

C=O
Carbonyl group

—C=O with H
Aldehyde group

H—C—H with H
Methyl group

—O—P—O⁻ with O⁻ and O
Phosphate group

—SH
Sulfhydryl group

—S—S—
Disulfide group

Figure 2.8

Some Functional Groups of Organic Molecules. The functional groups confer the distinctive properties on carbon compounds. The "unfilled" bond is attached to a carbon or other atom in the rest of the molecule.

Figure 2.9

Monosaccharides. Structural formulas of four simple sugars: glyceraldehyde and dihydroxyacetone have three carbons (i.e., they are trioses), and glucose and fructose have six carbons (i.e., they are hexoses). The functional groups are shaded. Notice that glyceraldehyde and dihydroxyacetone, and glucose and fructose have the same ratio and number of atoms; thus, they are structural isomers of each other.

Two monosaccharides can be combined to form a **disaccharide** (*di*, two) (figure 2.10) by removing a molecule of water (dehydration synthesis). Disaccharides all have the same molecular formula, $C_{12}H_{22}O_{11}$. Compounds with the same molecular formula but different structure are called **isomers.** Each isomer has unique properties. Examples of disaccharide isomers are sucrose, lactose, and maltose. Sucrose (table sugar) is a disaccharide formed by linking a molecule of glucose to a molecule of fructose. If a glucose molecule is bonded to another monosaccharide, galactose, the resulting disaccharide is lactose (commonly called

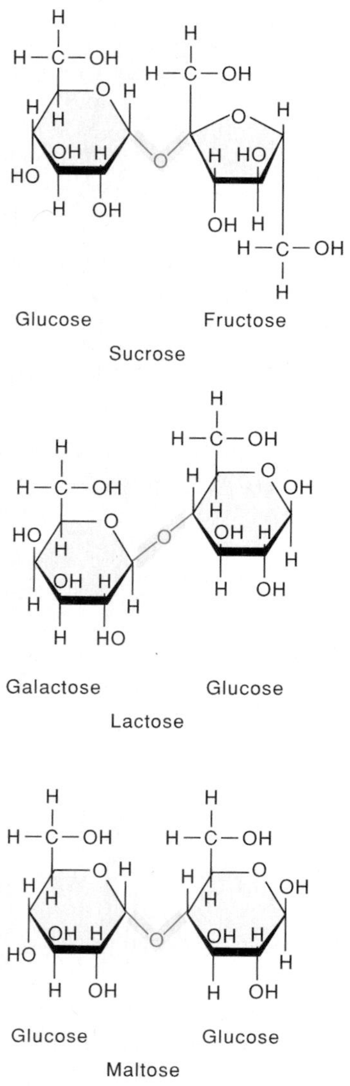

FIGURE 2.10

Disaccharides. Sucrose is ordinary table sugar and lactose is the sugar in milk. Maltose is found in malt. Glycosidic bonds are highlighted in color.

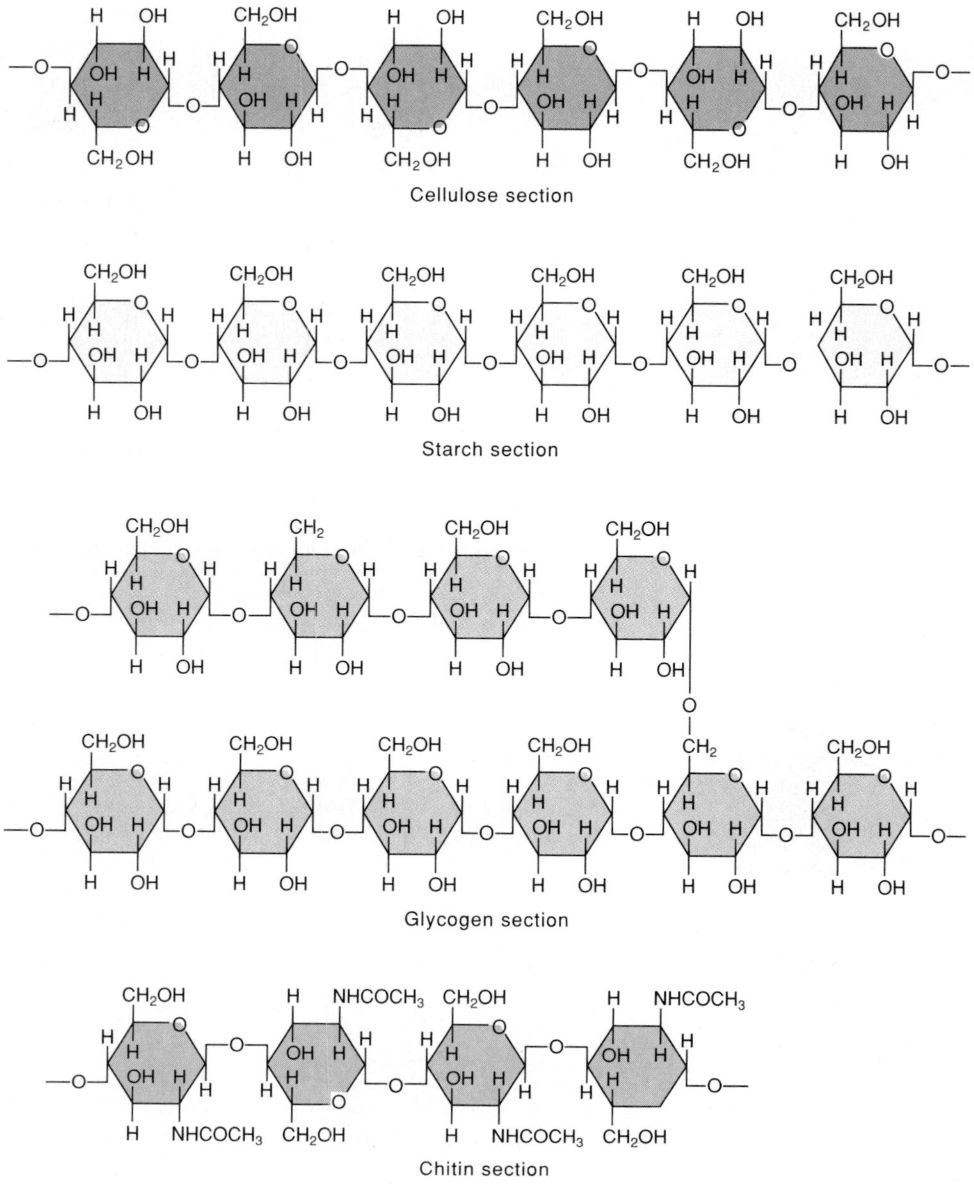

Glucose   Fructose

Sucrose

Galactose   Glucose

Lactose

Glucose   Glucose

Maltose

Cellulose section

Starch section

Glycogen section

Chitin section

FIGURE 2.11

Polysaccharides. The complex carbohydrates, cellulose, starch, and glycogen are all chains of glucose subunits, but they differ in structure. Notice that the glucose subunits of cellulose are linked together differently than the glucose subunits of starch. Glycogen is also a glucose polymer, but is more highly branched than either cellulose or starch. Chitin is a polymer of acetylglucosamine units.

milk sugar). Maltose, two joined glucose subunits, gives barley seeds a sweet taste. Beer brewers ferment barley into alcohol.

Other carbohydrates are made up of many monosaccharides joined together to form **polysaccharides** (*poly,* many) (figure 2.11). Glycogen, a major storage form for glucose in animals, is an example of a polysaccharide. Because the number of glucose units within the glycogen molecule may vary, it is symbolized by the formula $(C_6H_{10}O_5)_n$, with n equal to the number of glucose units in the molecule. Other biologically important polysaccharides include chitin (a major component of the exoskeleton of insects and of crustaceans, such as lobsters and crabs), starch (a storage form of carbohydrate in plants), and cellulose (a woody structural component of the cell wall of plants).

LIPIDS: ENERGY, INTERFACES, AND SIGNALS

Unlike the other three groups of organic molecules, **lipids** are nonpolar organic molecules that are insoluble in polar water but soluble in nonpolar organic solvents, such as ether, alcohol, and chloroform. Phospholipids and cholesterol are lipids that are important constituents of cell membranes. The most common lipids in animals, however, are fats. Fats are used to build cell parts and to supply energy for cellular activities.

Lipid molecules are composed primarily of carbon, hydrogen, and oxygen atoms, although some may contain small amounts of phosphorus and nitrogen. They contain a much smaller proportion of oxygen than do carbohydrates, as can

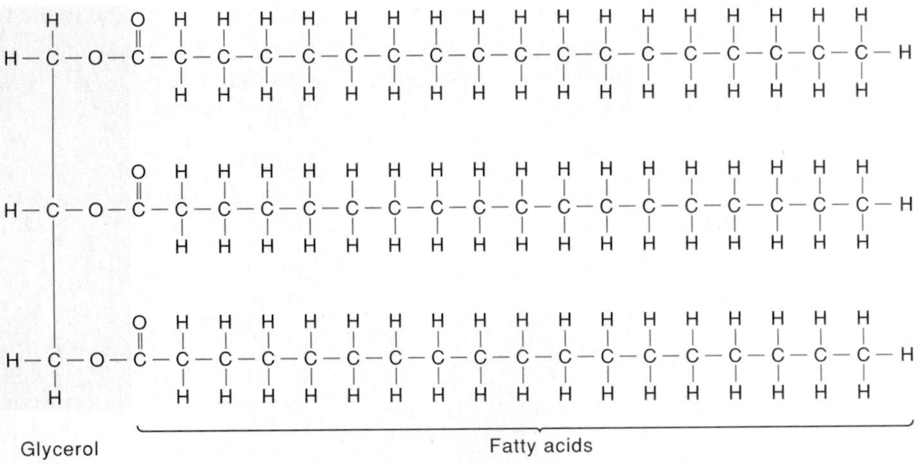

Figure 2.12

Triglycerides. A triglyceride is a fat molecule consisting of a glycerol molecule bonded to three fatty acid molecules. Beef fat, with three stearic acids, is shown.

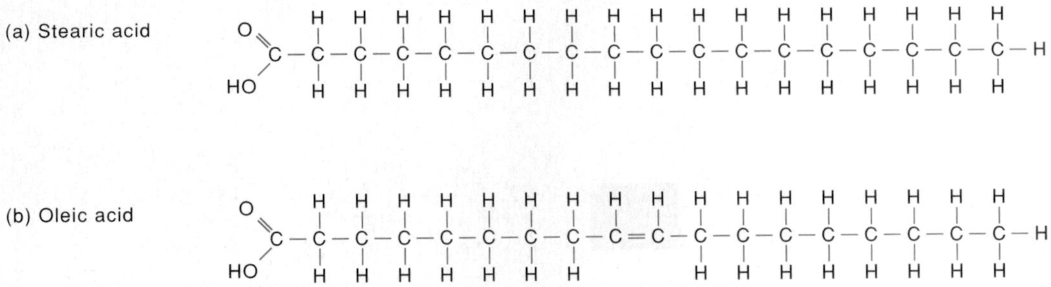

Figure 2.13

Fatty Acids. Structural formulas for (a) saturated (stearic) and (b) unsaturated (oleic) fatty acids. Notice the double bond in the carbon backbone of oleic acid.

be illustrated by the formula for the fat, tristearin, $C_{57}H_{110}O_6$. The building blocks of fat molecules are fatty acids and glycerol. Fatty acids contain long hydrocarbon chains bonded to carboxyl (—COOH) groups. Glycerol is a three-carbon alcohol with each carbon bearing a hydroxyl (—OH) group. These molecules are united so that each glycerol molecule is combined with three fatty acid molecules, each of which is joined to each of the three carbon atoms in the glycerol backbone (figure 2.12). Because there are three fatty acids, the resulting fat molecule is called a triglyceride neutral fat, or triacylglycerol.

Although the glycerol portion of every fat molecule is the same, there are many kinds of fatty acids and, therefore, many kinds of fats. Fatty acid molecules differ in the length of their carbon chains and in the ways the carbon atoms are combined. The most common are even-numbered chains of 14 to 20 carbons. In some cases, the carbon atoms are joined by single carbon-carbon bonds, and each carbon atom is bound to as many hydrogen atoms as possible. This type of fatty acid is said to be saturated (figure 2.13a). Other fatty acids have one or more double bonds between carbon atoms and are said to be unsaturated (figure 2.13b) because the double bonds replace some of the hydrogen

atoms, and therefore the fatty acids contain fewer than the maximum number of hydrogen atoms. Fatty acids with one double bond are monounsaturated, and those with numerous double bonds are said to be polyunsaturated.

Unsaturated fats have low melting points because their chains bend at the double bonds and the fat molecules cannot be aligned closely with one another, which would lead to solidification.   ③   Consequently, the fat may be fluid at room temperature. A liquid fat is called an oil. Most plant fats are unsaturated. Animal fats, in contrast, are often saturated and occur as hard or solid fats.

A phospholipid molecule is similar to a fat molecule in that it contains a glycerol portion and fatty acid chains. However, the phospholipid has only two fatty acid chains. In the place of the third chain, there are phosphate (PO_4^{3-}) and nitrogen-containing groups. The polar phosphate and nitrogen groups are soluble in water (hydrophilic) and form the "head" of the molecule; the insoluble (nonpolar, hydrophobic) fatty acid portion forms the "tail." Phospholipids are the major structural components of cell membranes because of this tendency to be soluble at one end and insoluble at the other.

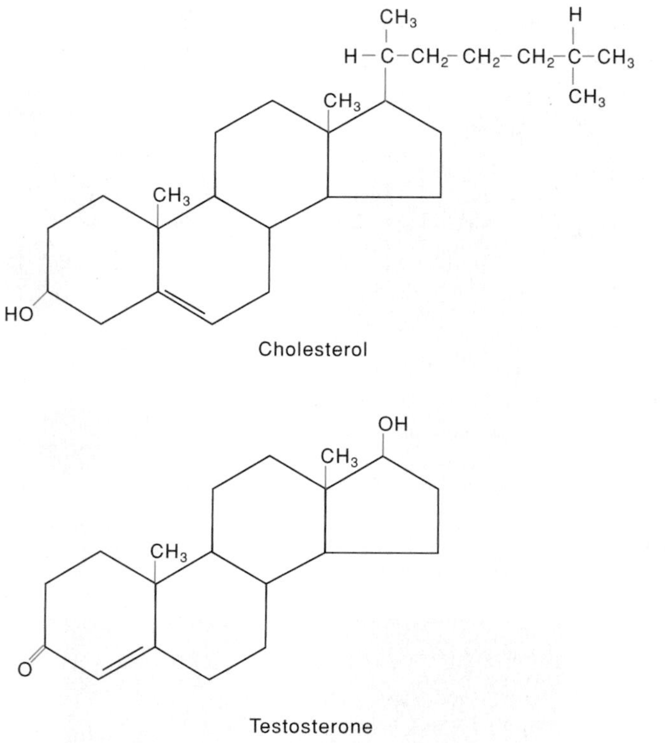

Figure 2.14

Steroids. Structures of two common steroids showing the backbone of one five-carbon ring and three six-carbon rings. Cholesterol affects the fluidity of membranes. Testosterone is a male hormone in mammals that is responsible for the development and maintenance of secondary sex characteristics, and for the maturation and functioning of sex organs.

Steroids are naturally occurring, lipid-soluble molecules composed of four carbon rings (figure 2.14). The four rings of carbon atoms are fused together, giving a somewhat rigid structure. Three of the rings are six-sided, and the fourth is five-sided. The four rings contain a total of 17 carbons. Cholesterol is an important biologically active steroid, as are vitamin D, hormones of the adrenal gland (e.g., aldosterone), the ovaries (e.g., estrogen), and the testes (e.g., testosterone).

PROTEINS: THE BASIS OF LIFE'S DIVERSITY

In animals, **proteins** serve as structural material, energy sources, protection against disease in higher animals, chemical messengers (hormones), and receptors on cell membranes. Some proteins play important roles in metabolic reactions by acting as biological catalysts called enzymes. They enter and speed up specific chemical reactions without being used up themselves. (Enzymes will be discussed in more detail in chapter 4.)

Proteins always contain atoms of carbon, hydrogen, nitrogen, and oxygen, and sometimes sulfur. The individual building blocks of proteins are called **amino acids.** Amino acids always contain an amino group ($-NH_2$), a carboxyl group ($-COOH$), a hydrogen atom, and a functional group designated R, all bonded to a central carbon atom:

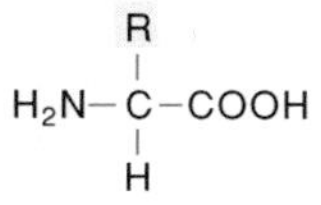

The identity and unique chemical properties of each amino acid are determined by the nature of the R group linked to the central carbon atom. Twenty different amino acids occur in animals. The individual amino acids are joined together in chains by covalent bonds called **peptide bonds.** In the formation of a peptide bond, the carboxyl group of one amino acid is bonded to the amino group of another amino acid, with the elimination of water (a dehydration synthesis reaction), as follows:

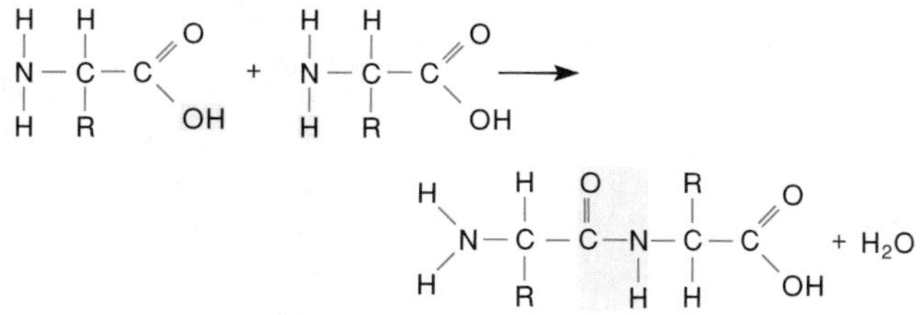

When two amino acids are bonded together, they form a unit called a dipeptide; three amino acids bonded together form a tripeptide. When many amino acids bond together, the unit they form is a chain called a polypeptide.

The length of the chain of amino acids can vary in different proteins from less than 50 to more than 2,000 amino acids. Each kind of protein contains a specific number and kind of amino acids arranged in a particular sequence, which may be coiled and folded up or interact with other protein molecules to form a unique three-dimensional structure. Different kinds of protein molecules have different shapes that are related to their particular functions in life processes.

Several different levels of structure can be distinguished in a protein molecule. The primary structure is the linear sequence of amino acids in the polypeptide chains comprising the molecule (figure 2.15a). The secondary structure of a protein is a repeating pattern of bonds (often hydrogen bonds) between amino acids, and it commonly takes the shape of an alpha helix or pleated sheet (figure 2.15b). The tertiary structure results from the folding of the helix into a three-dimensional shape (figure 2.15c). In some instances, two protein chains associate to form a larger protein, the chains are assembled into a whole, the shape of which is called the quaternary structure (figure 2.15d).

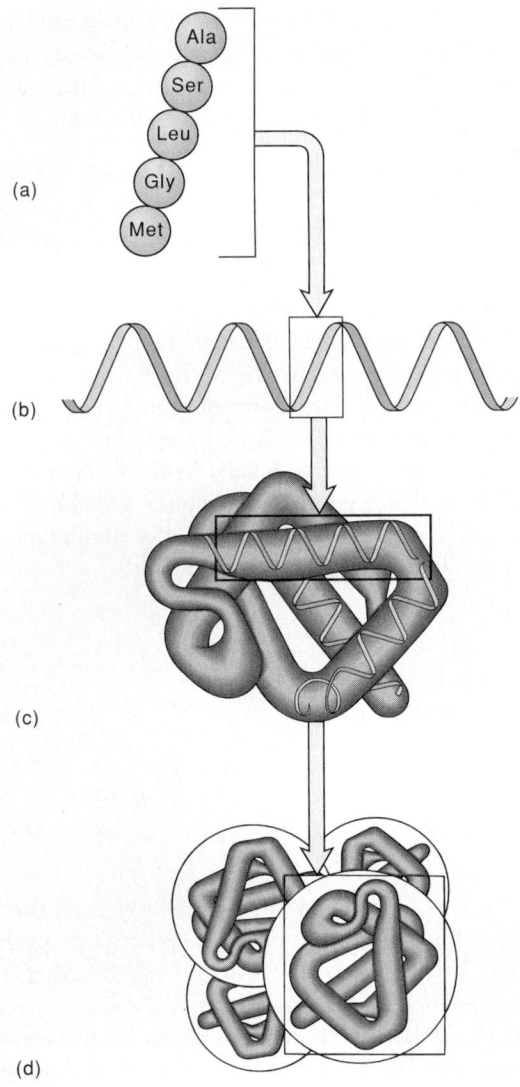

(a)

(b)

(c)

(d)

Figure 2.15

Levels of Protein Structure. (*a*) Primary structure of a protein is its linear sequence of amino acids. (*b*) Secondary structure is determined by the repeating configurations in the structure of the amino acids. (*c*) Tertiary structure is determined by the three-dimensional folding of the secondary structure. (*d*) The three-dimensional arrangement of polypeptides with tertiary structure gives a protein its quaternary structure.

Nucleotides and Nucleic Acids: Information Storage, Chemical Messengers, and Energy Transfer

Small organic compounds called nucleotides are essential to life. Each **nucleotide** is composed of three substances: (1) a nitrogen-containing organic base, (2) a five-carbon sugar (ribose or deoxyribose), and (3) phosphate (figure 2.16). Two

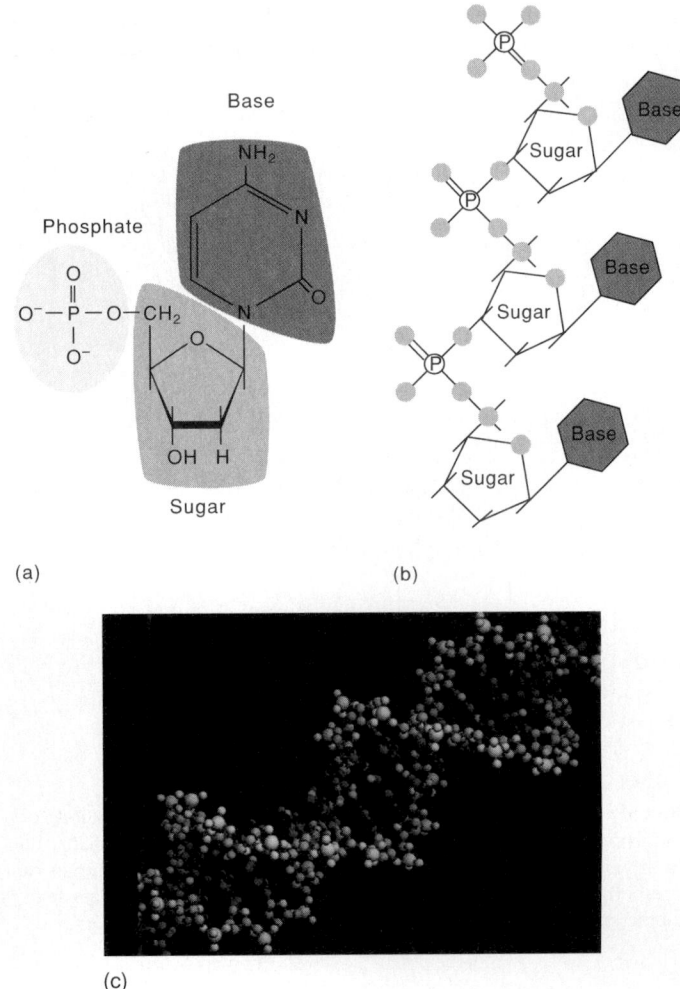

(a)   (b)

(c)

Figure 2.16

Examples of a Nucleotide. (*a*) A nucleotide has a phosphate group, a ribose or deoxyribose sugar, and a nitrogen-containing base. There are five types of bases, each with a slightly different chemical composition. DNA uses four of the five, while RNA uses a different set of four. (*b*) A single-stranded DNA molecule consists of many nucleotide monomers joined together to form a long chain. (*c*) In this computer-generated model, two single-stranded chains twist about each other to form the double-stranded (helix) DNA molecule.

examples of nucleotides are the adenosine phosphates and nucleotide coenzymes; nucleic acids are examples of nucleotide polymers.

Adenosine phosphates are small molecules that function as chemical messengers within and between cells, and as energy transfer molecules. An example of a chemical messenger is cyclic adenosine monophosphate (cAMP). Adenosine triphosphate (ATP) is a nucleotide that functions as an energy carrier, and will be discussed in detail in chapter 4.

Nucleotide coenzymes, such as NAD+ and FAD, play an important role in energy transfer within the cell, and will be discussed in detail in chapter 5.

Nucleic acids are large single- or double-stranded chains of nucleotide subunits. The two nucleic acids are **deoxyribonucleic acid (DNA)** and **ribonucleic acid (RNA).** DNA makes up the chromosomes in the cell's nucleus, is able to replicate itself, and contains the genetic (hereditary) information of the cell. RNA may be present in either the nucleus or the cytoplasm, which is the part of the cell outside the nucleus, and acts as a carrier of information between the DNA and the cellular sites of protein synthesis. Nucleic acids will be examined in more detail in chapters 8 and 9.

Stop and Ask Yourself

12. What is a typical carbohydrate? What is one function of a carbohydrate in an animal?

13. What is a lipid? Where would you find lipids in an animal?

14. What is the difference between a fat and an oil? How are fats used in animals?

15. What is a peptide bond?

16. What is a nucleotide? What are several functions of nucleotides in animals?

Summary

1. Matter is anything that has mass and occupies space. The most important particles of matter are protons, neutrons, and electrons, all of which associate to form atoms. The nucleus of an atom contains the protons and neutrons; electrons orbit around the nucleus.

2. The chemical nature of an atom is largely determined by the distribution of electrons in its outermost shell. There is a tendency for atoms to lose or gain electrons until stability in the outer shell is obtained.

3. Atoms react with other atoms to form molecules. The forces holding atoms together are called chemical bonds. A covalent bond results from the sharing of one or more pairs of electrons. A hydrogen bond is formed by the attraction of the partial positive charge of a hydrogen atom of one water molecule with the partial negative charge of the oxygen atom of another water molecule. An ionic bond results from the attraction of opposite charges.

4. An acid is a substance that releases hydrogen ions (protons) when dissolved in water. A base is a substance that releases hydroxyl ions (accepts protons) when dissolved in water.

5. The degree of alkalinity or acidity of a solution is measured by a pH scale that indicates the concentration of free hydrogen ions in water.

6. Simple carbohydrates are made of carbon, hydrogen, and oxygen, and they are important sources of energy for most animals. Carbohydrates are classified as monosaccharides, disaccharides, or polysaccharides, depending upon how many sugars they contain.

7. Lipids are molecules containing many more C—H bonds than carbohydrates. Fats and oils are familiar lipids. Lipids can store large amounts of energy in an organism's body.

8. Proteins are large, complex molecules composed of smaller structural units called amino acids. The amino acids are linked together via peptide bonds to form chains called polypeptides.

9. Nucleic acids are very large molecules composed of bonded units called nucleotides. The two nucleic acids are deoxyribonucleic acid (DNA) and ribonucleic acid (RNA). Nucleic acids carry the hereditary messages and regulate the synthesis of proteins. Two other nucleotides are the adenosine phosphates (cAMP and ATP) that function as energy transfer molecules within and between cells, and nucleotide coenzymes (NAD^+ and FAD) that play a role in energy transfer within the cell.

Selected Key Terms

atom (*p.16*)

atomic mass (*p. 16*)

atomic number (*p. 16*)

buffers (*p. 20*)

carbohydrates (*p. 22*)

disaccharide (*p. 22*)

electrons (*p. 16*)

elements (*p. 16*)

ion (*p. 19*)

isomer (*p. 22*)

mass (*p. 16*)

matter (*p. 16*)

neutrons (*p. 16*)

pH scale (*p. 20*)

proteins (*p. 25*)

protons (*p. 16*)

steroids (*p. 25*)

Critical Thinking Questions

1. Considering the major elements of which all living organisms are composed, is it likely that the earth's surface could have been the major chemical "breadbasket" for the origin of life? Explain.

2. What is meant by the statement, "evolution resulted in carbon-based life?"

3. Why should a zoologist who studies animal life also be interested in the properties of chemical bonds?

4. The major biological molecules are polymers—long chains of subunits. What are some reasons that linear polymers are so common in living animals?

5. Why are all forms of life composed of, and affected by, the same elements?

CELLS, TISSUES, ORGANS, AND ORGAN SYSTEMS OF ANIMALS

Outline

Concepts

1. Cells are the basic organizational units of life.
2. Eukaryotic cells exhibit a considerable degree of internal organization, with a dynamic system of membranes forming internal compartments termed organelles.
3. The structure and function of a typical cell usually applies to all animals.
4. Cells are organized into structural and functional units called tissues, organs, and organ systems.

Would You Like to Know:

1. what the functional unit of life is? (*p. 30*)
2. why most cells are so small? (*p. 32*)
3. why most higher animals need cholesterol? (*p. 33*)
4. what the "fingerprints" of a cell are? (*p. 36*)
5. why red blood cells can burst when placed in distilled water? (*p. 38*)
6. how cells "drink" water? (*p. 40*)
7. why the mitochondria are called the "power generators" of the cell? (*p. 45*)
8. if cells have a skeleton? (*p. 45*)

These and other useful questions will be answered in this chapter.

This chapter contains evolutionary concepts, which are set off in this font.

Because all animals are made of cells, the cell is as fundamental to an understanding of zoology as the atom is to an understanding of chemistry. In the hierarchy of biological organization (figure 3.1), the cell is the simplest organization of matter that exhibits the properties of life. Some organisms are single celled; others are multicellular. An animal has a body composed of many kinds of specialized cells. A division of labor among cells allows specialization into higher levels of organization (tissues, organs, and organ systems). Yet, everything that an animal does is ultimately happening at the cellular level.

This chapter will present an overview of the structure and function of a "generalized" animal cell. Because cells exchange and utilize matter and energy with their surroundings, this exchange and utilization will be covered in the next two chapters.

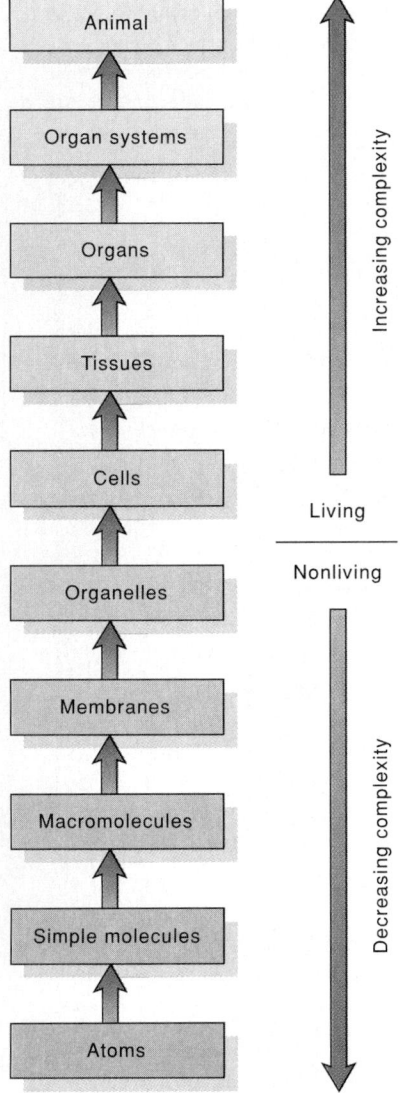

FIGURE 3.1

The Structural Hierarchy in an Animal. At each level, function depends on the structural organization of that level and those below it.

TABLE 3.1	COMPARISON OF PROKARYOTIC AND EUKARYOTIC CELLS	
COMPONENT	PROKARYOTE	EUKARYOTE
Cell wall	Present	Absent in animals (present in plants)
Centrioles	Absent	Present in animals (absent in plants)
Chloroplasts	Present in some cells	Present in some cells
Genetic material	Single circular chromosome of DNA	Arranged in multiple chromosomes; DNA associated with protein
Cilia (9 + 2)	Absent	Present in some cells
Cytoskeleton	Absent	Present
Endoplasmic reticulum	Absent	Present
Flagellum	Often present	Present in some cells
Glycocalyx	Absent	Present
Golgi apparatus	Absent	Present
Lysosomes	Absent	Present
Mitochondria	Absent	Present
Nucleus	Absent	Present
Plasma membrane	Present	Present
Ribosomes	Present	Present
Vacuoles	Present	Present
Vesicles	Present	Present

WHAT ARE CELLS?

Cells are the functional units of life, in which all of the chemical reactions necessary for the maintenance and reproduction of life take place. They are the smallest independent units of life. Structurally speaking, cells are either prokaryotic or eukaryotic. All **prokaryotes** ("before nucleus") are independent, single-celled organisms (e.g., bacteria). The word prokaryote describes cells in which DNA is localized in a region but is not bound by a membrane. Some of the more salient characteristics of a prokaryotic cell are summarized in table 3.1.

All **eukaryotes** ("true nucleus") have cells with a membrane-bound nucleus containing DNA (box 3.1). In addition, eukaryotic cells contain many other structures called organelles. An **organelle** ("little organ") is a structure in the cell that carries out specific functions. Eukaryotic cells also have a network of specialized structures called filaments and tubules organized into the cytoskeleton, which gives shape to the cell and allows intracellular movement.

All eukaryotic cells (table 3.1) have three basic parts:

1. The **plasma membrane** is the outer boundary of the cell. It separates the internal metabolic events from the environment and allows them to proceed in organized,

BOX   3.1   THE ORIGIN OF EUKARYOTIC CELLS

The first cells were most likely very simple prokaryotic forms. Radiometric dating indicates that the earth is approximately 4 to 5 billion years old, and that prokaryotes may have arisen more than 3.5 billion years ago, whereas eukaryotes are thought to have first appeared about 1.5 billion years ago.

The evolution of the eukaryotic cell might have occurred when a large anaerobic (living without oxygen) amoeboid prokaryote ingested small aerobic (living with oxygen) bacteria and stabilized them instead of digesting them. This idea is known as the **endosymbiont hypothesis** (figure 1a) and was first proposed by Lynn Margulis, a biologist at Boston University. (**Symbiosis** is an intimate association between two organisms of different species.) According to this hypothesis, the aerobic bacteria developed into mitochondria, which are the sites of aerobic respiration and most energy conversion in eukaryotic cells. The possession of these mitochondrialike endosymbionts conferred the advantage of aerobic respiration on its host.

Flagella (whiplike structures) may have arisen through the ingestion of prokaryotes similar to spiral-shaped bacteria called spirochetes. Ingestion of prokaryotes that resembled present-day cyanobacteria could have led to the endosymbiotic development of the chloroplasts in plants.

Another hypothesis for the evolution of eukaryotic cells proposes that the prokaryotic cell membrane invaginated (folded inward) to enclose copies of its genetic material (figure 1b). This invagination resulted in the formation of several double-membrane-bound entities (organelles) in a single cell. These entities could then have evolved into the eukaryotic mitochondrion, nucleus, and chloroplasts.

Although the exact mechanism for the evolution of the eukaryotic cell will never be known with certainty, the emergence of the eukaryotic cell led to a dramatic increase in the complexity and diversity of life-forms on the earth. At first, these newly formed eukaryotic cells existed only by themselves. Later, however, some probably evolved into multicellular organisms in which various cells become specialized into tissues, which in turn led to the potential for many different functions. These multicellular forms then adapted to life in a great variety of environments.

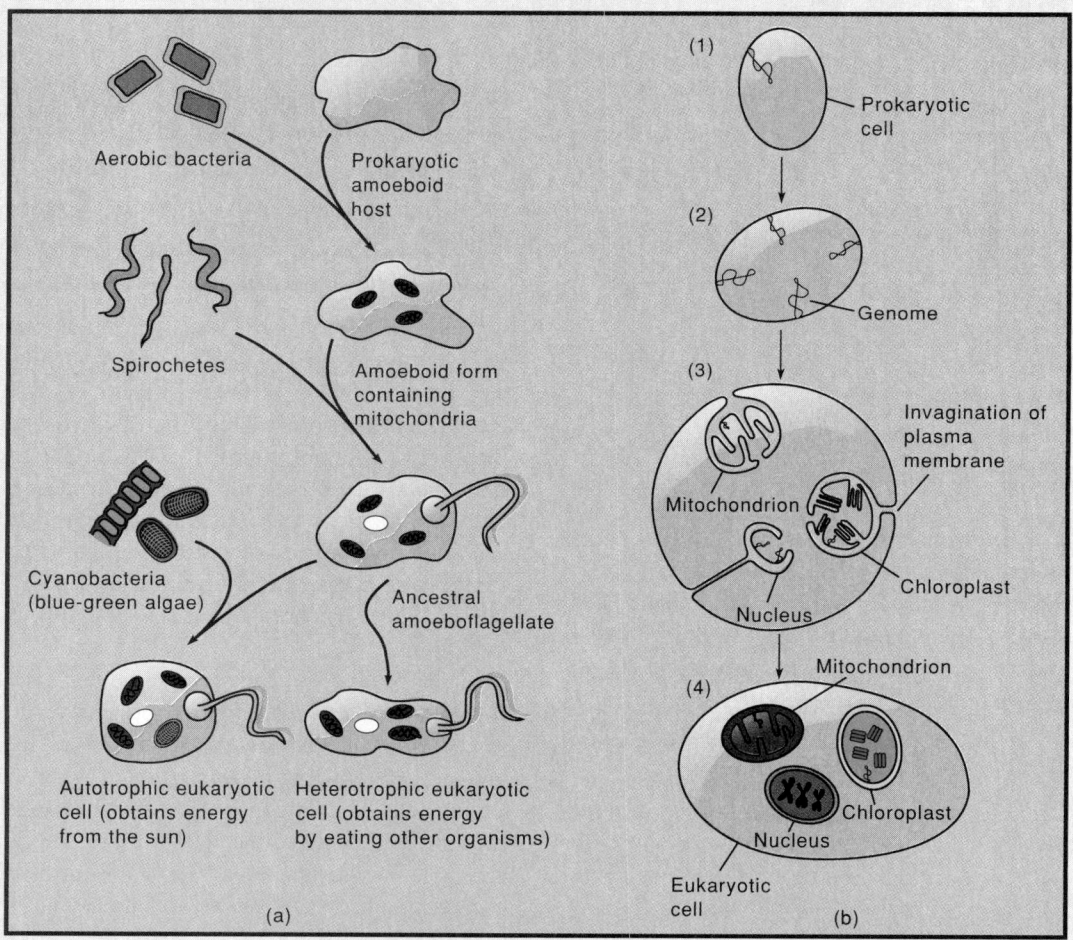

FIGURE 1   **Two Hypotheses on the Evolution of the Eukaryotic Cell.** (a) The endosymbiont hypothesis. (b) The membrane invagination hypothesis. A prokaryotic cell (1) duplicates its genetic material (genome) (2). This is followed by invagination of the plasma membrane to form double-membrane-bound organelles and the separation of the individual genomes from each other (3). The nuclear genome eventually enlarges while the other organelle genomes lose many of their genes resulting in a eukaryotic cell (4). *Redrawn from T. Uzzell and C. Spolsky, "Origin of the Eukaryotic Cell," American Scientist 62:334–343, copyright 1974 Sigma Xi, The Scientific Research Society. Used by permission.*

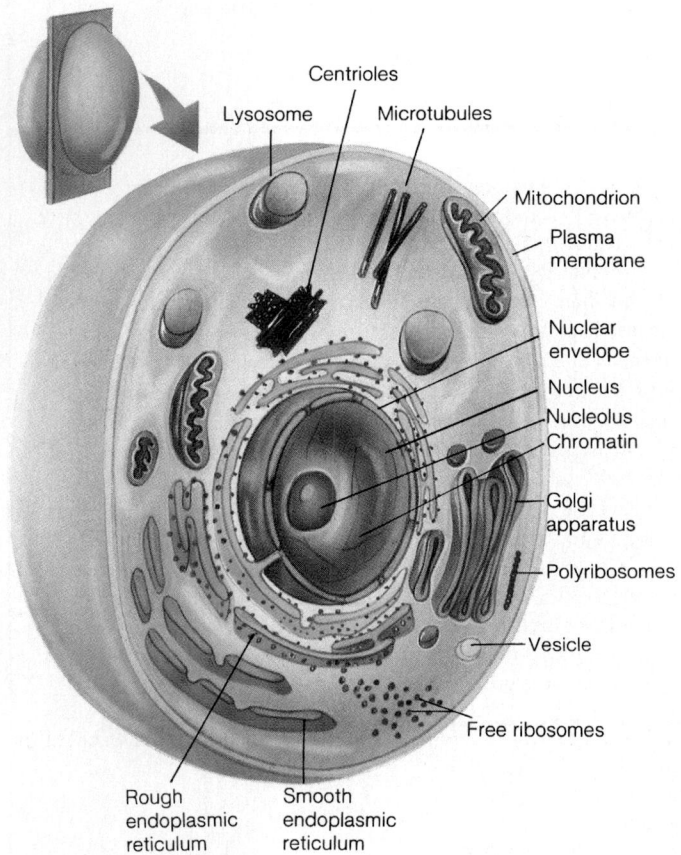

FIGURE 3.2

A Generalized Animal Cell. Our understanding of the structures in this cell is based mainly on electron microscopy. The sizes of some organelles and structures are exaggerated to show detail.

Radius (r)	1 cm	2 cm	4 cm
Surface area (SA)	12.57 cm^2	50.26 cm^2	201.06 cm^2
Volume (V)	4.19 cm^3	33.51 cm^3	268.08 cm^3
SA/V	3.0	1.50	0.75

Surface area of a sphere = $4 \pi r^2$
Volume of sphere = $4/3 \pi r^3$

FIGURE 3.3

A Portrayal of the Relationship between Surface Area and Volume. As the radius of a sphere becomes greater, its volume increases more rapidly than its surface area. SA/V = surface area to volume ratio.
Source: Leland G. Johnson, Biology, 2d ed. Copyright © 1987 Wm. C. Brown Communications, Inc., Dubuque, Iowa.

Stop and Ask Yourself

1. What are the three basic parts of the cell?
2. What is the difference between cytoplasm and cytosol?
3. How do nucleoplasm and cytoplasm differ?

controlled ways. The plasma membrane also has specific receptors for external molecules that alter the cell's function.

2. **Cytoplasm** (Gr. *kytos*, hollow vessel + *plasm*, fluid) is the portion of the cell outside the nucleus. The semifluid portion of the cytoplasm is called the cytosol. Suspended within the cytosol are the organelles.

3. The **nucleus** (pl., nuclei) is the control center of the cell. It contains the chromosomes, and is separated from the cytoplasm by its own nuclear envelope. The nucleoplasm is the semifluid material in the nucleus.

Because cells vary so much in form and function, no "typical" cell exists. However, to help you learn as much as possible about cells, figure 3.2 shows an idealized version of a eukaryotic cell and most of its component parts.

WHY ARE MOST CELLS SMALL?

Although there are exceptions (e.g., the eggs of most vertebrates [fishes, amphibians, reptiles, and birds] and some long nerve cells), most cells are small and can be seen only with the aid of a microscope (box 3.2). One reason for this smallness is that the ratio of the volume of the cell's nucleus to the volume of its cytoplasm must not be so small that the nucleus, the major control center of the cell, cannot control the cytoplasm.

Another aspect of cell volume works to limit cell size. As the radius of a cell becomes larger, its volume increases more rapidly than its surface area (figure 3.3). The need for nutrients and the rate of waste production are proportional to the volume of the cell. The cell takes up nutrients and eliminates wastes through its surface plasma membrane. If the cell volume becomes too large, the surface area to volume ratio will be too small to carry out an adequate exchange of nutrients and wastes.

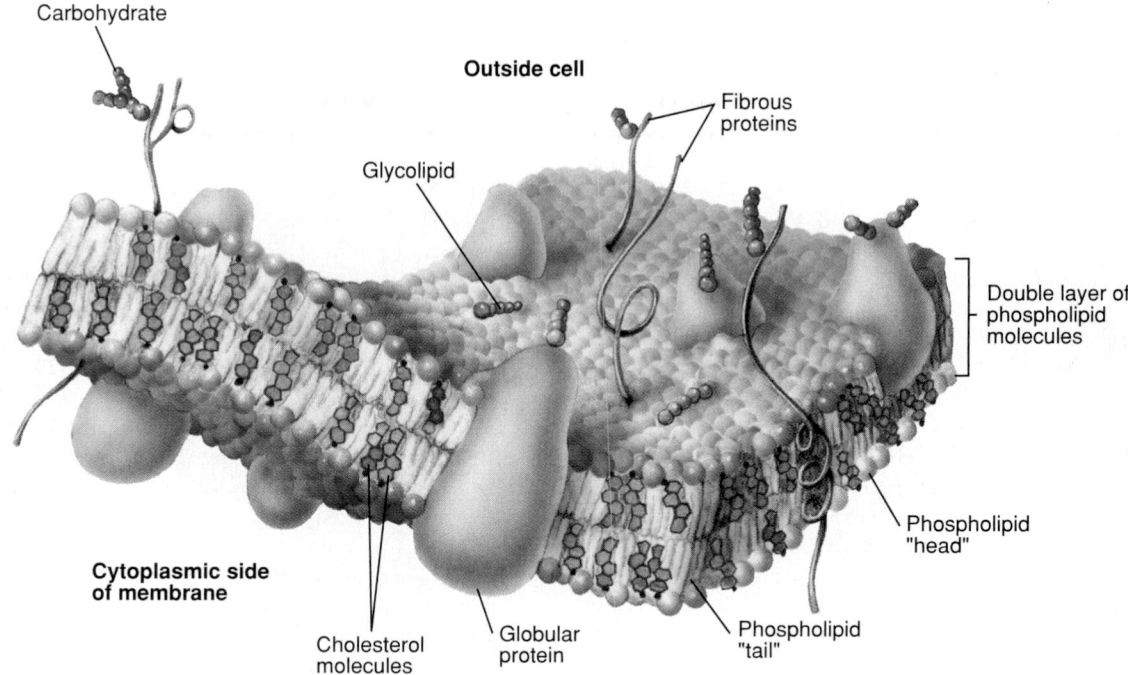

FIGURE 3.4

The Fluid-Mosaic Model of Membrane Structure. Intrinsic globular proteins may protrude above or below the lipid bilayer and may move about in the membrane. Peripheral proteins are attached to either the inner or outer surfaces.

CELL MEMBRANES

The membrane that surrounds the cell is called the **plasma membrane.** Other membranes inside the cell enclose some organelles and have properties similar to the plasma membrane.

STRUCTURE OF CELL MEMBRANES

In 1972, S. Jonathan Singer and Garth Nicolson developed the fluid-mosaic model of membrane structure. According to this model, the membrane is a double layer (bilayer) composed of proteins and phospholipids, and is fluid rather than solid. The phospholipid bilayer forms a fluid "sea" in which specific proteins float like icebergs (figure 3.4). Being fluid, the membrane is in a constant state of flux—shifting and changing, while retaining its uniform structure. The word mosaic refers to the many different kinds of proteins that are found dispersed in the phospholipid bilayer.

The following are important points of the fluid-mosaic model:

1. The phospholipids have one polar end and one nonpolar end. The polar ends are oriented on one side toward the outside of the cell and into the fluid cytoplasm on the other side, and the nonpolar ends face each other in the middle of the bilayer. The "tails" of the phospholipid molecules are attracted to each other, and are repelled by water (they are hydrophobic, "water dreading"). As a result, the polar spherical "heads" (the phosphate portion) are located over the cell surfaces (outer and inner) and are "water attracting" (they are hydrophilic).

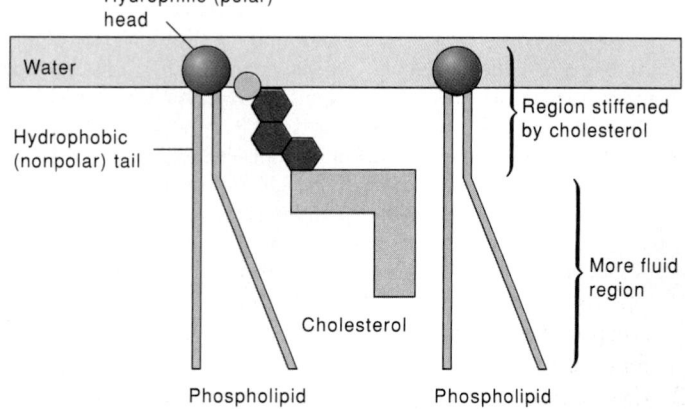

FIGURE 3.5

Drawing Showing the Arrangement of Cholesterol between Lipid Molecules of a Lipid Bilayer. Cholesterol stiffens the outer lipid bilayer and causes the inner region of the bilayer to become slightly more fluid. Only half the lipid bilayer is shown; the other half is a mirror image.

2. ③ Cholesterol is present in the plasma membrane and organelle membranes of eukaryotic cells. The cholesterol molecules are embedded in the interior of the membrane and help to make the membrane less permeable to water-soluble substances. In addition, the relatively rigid structure of the cholesterol molecules (figure 3.5) helps to make the membrane more stable than it would be otherwise.

BOX 3.2 MICROSCOPES—WINDOWS INTO THE CELL

Despite the very small size of most cells, knowledge of cell structure and function has accumulated through the use of various techniques. One technique is **microscopy**—the use of microscopes to peer into the innermost parts of a cell. Several types of microscopes are used.

The **light microscope** relies on the bending (refraction) of light rays. Light rays pass through the center of a curved lens. The farther they are from the center, the more they bend (figure 1a). The compound microscope that is used in most zoology laboratories contains at least two of these lenses (figure 1b,e). All the rays eventually converge through the lens-system onto one focal point—the eye(s). To make the different parts of the cell "stand out," specific stains are often used to highlight certain structures. Unfortunately, these staining procedures kill the cell. However, living cells can be observed through the phase contrast microscope. In this type of light microscopy, small differences in the way different parts of the cell refract light are converted to larger variations in brightness. In the dark-field microscope, living cells can be observed by making the field surrounding the specimen appear black while the specimen itself is brightly illuminated. The best light microscopes magnify images approximately 2,000 times.

In the **transmission electron microscope (TEM),** an electron beam is focused on a very thin section or slice of the cell by means of electromagnets (figure 1c,f). After passing through the cell, the electron beam travels through more magnetic lenses, which magnify the image and project it onto either a fluorescent screen or photographic film. Magnifications of several hundred thousand times are possible with the TEM.

The **scanning electron microscope (SEM)** is used to study surfaces rather than thin sections of cells (figure 1d,g). SEM photomicrographs, with their three-dimensional quality, reveal remarkable details of the surface of cells or other objects. Surfaces to be studied are first covered with a very thin layer of metal, such as

gold. In the SEM, electron beams scan the surface of the specimen, driving off electrons from the atoms of the metal surface—called secondary electrons. The pattern of these scattered secondary electrons is then detected on a cathode ray tube like that in a television set. Maximum magnifications of the SEM are usually around 20,000 times.

The **scanning tunneling microscope (STM)** was invented in the 1980s and can achieve magnifications of over 100 million. At this magnification, atoms on the surface of a solid can be viewed. The electrons surrounding the surface atoms tunnel or project a very short distance from the surface. The STM has a needle probe with a point so sharp that there is often only one atom at its tip. The probe is lowered toward the surface of the specimen until its electron cloud just touches the surface atoms. When a small voltage is applied between the tip and specimen, electrons flow through a narrow channel in the electron clouds. The arrangement of atoms on the surface of the specimen is determined by moving the probe tip back and forth over the surface. As the tip follows the surface contours, its motion is recorded and analyzed by a computer to create an accurate, three-dimensional image of the surface atoms. The surface map can be either displayed on a computer screen or plotted on paper. The microscope's inventors, Gerd Binnig and Heinrich Rohrer, shared the 1986 Nobel Prize in Physics for their work. Interestingly, another recipient of the prize was Ernst Ruska, the inventor of the first transmission electron microscope.

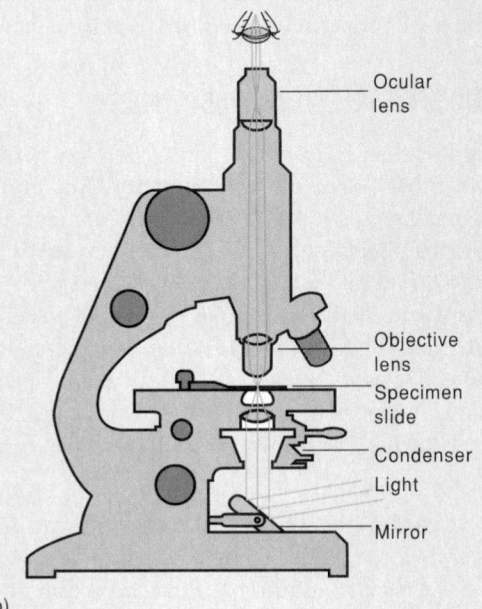

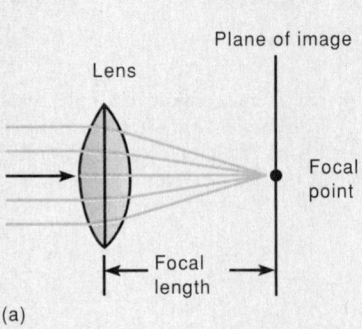

FIGURE 1   **Types of Microscopes and Their Images (Sperm Cells).** (a) Focusing of light rays. (b) Compound light microscope. (c) Transmission electron microscope. (d) Scanning electron microscope. Three images of human sperm from the three different types of microscopes. (e) The image of sperm as seen with a compound light microscope (×400), (f) a transmission electron microscope (×18,000), and (g) a scanning electron microscope (×5,000).   *Thomas D. Brock, Biology of Microorganisms, 3e., © 1979, p. 774, 775. Adapted by permission of Prentice Hall, Englewood Cliffs, New Jersey.*

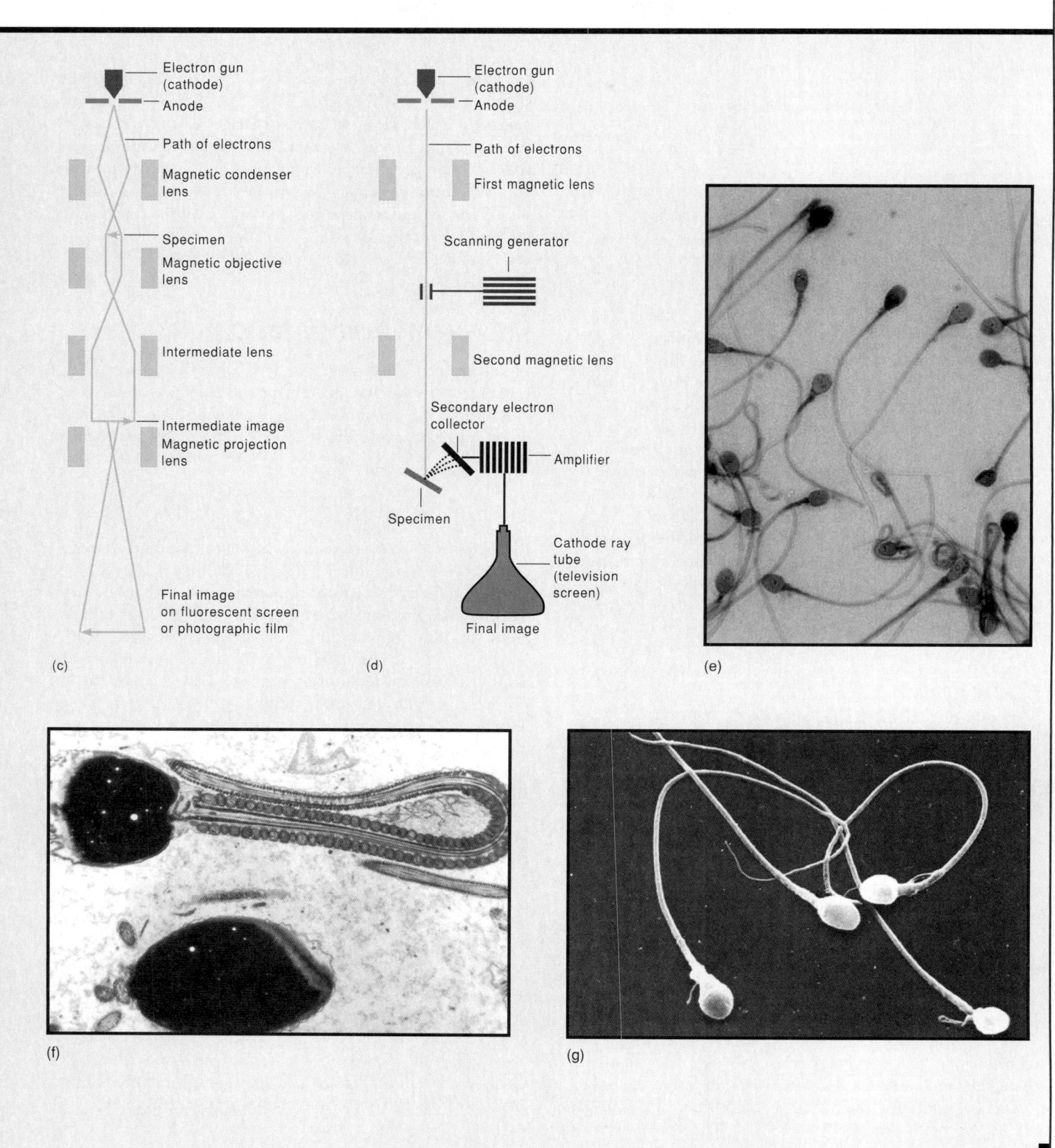

Electron gun
(cathode)
Anode

Path of electrons

Magnetic condenser
lens

Specimen
Magnetic objective
lens

Intermediate lens

Intermediate image
Magnetic projection
lens

Final image
on fluorescent screen
or photographic film

(c)

Electron gun
(cathode)
Anode

Path of electrons

First magnetic lens

Scanning generator

Second magnetic lens

Secondary electron
collector

Amplifier

Specimen

Cathode ray
tube
(television
screen)

Final image

(d)

(e)

(f)

(g)

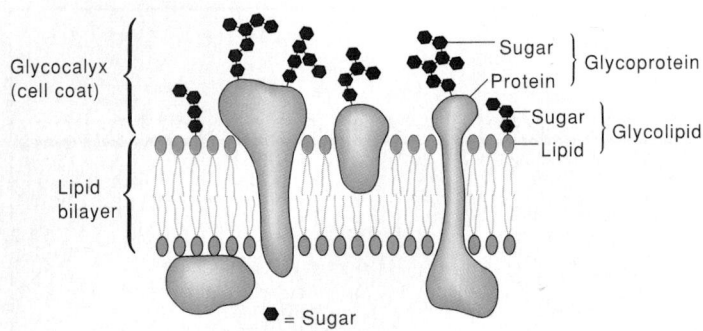

FIGURE 3.6

The Glycocalyx. An illustration of the glycocalyx showing the glycoproteins and glycolipids. Note that all of the attached carbohydrates are on the outside of the plasma membrane.

3. The membrane proteins are individual molecules attached to the inner or outer membrane surface (peripheral proteins) or embedded in it (intrinsic proteins) (*see figure 3.4*). Intrinsic proteins serve as links to sugar-protein markers on the cell surface. Some intrinsic proteins help to move ions or molecules across the membrane, and others attach the membrane to the cell's inner scaffolding (the cytoskeleton) or to various molecules outside the cell.

4. When carbohydrates unite with proteins, they form glycoproteins, and when they unite with lipids, they form glycolipids on the surface of a plasma membrane. Surface carbohydrates and portions of the proteins make up the **glycocalyx** ("cell coat") (figure 3.6). **4** The complexly arranged and distinctively shaped groups of sugar molecules of the glycocalyx act as a molecular "fingerprint" for each cell type. The glycocalyx is necessary for cell-to-cell recognition and the behavior of certain cells, and is a key component in coordinating cell behavior in animals.

Stop and Ask Yourself

4. What do the terms fluid and mosaic refer to in the fluid-mosaic model of an animal cell membrane?

5. What is the function of the glycocalyx?

6. What is the function of cholesterol in the plasma membrane? The phospholipid? The protein?

FUNCTIONS OF CELL MEMBRANES

Cell membranes play important roles in (1) regulating material moving into and out of the cell, and from one part of the cell to another; (2) separating the inside of the cell from the outside;

(3) separating various organelles within the cell; (4) providing a large surface area on which specific chemical reactions can occur; (5) separating cells from one another; and (6) serving as a site for receptors containing specific cell identification markers that differentiate one cell type from another.

The ability of the plasma membrane to let some substances in and keep others out is called **selective permeability** (L. *permeare* or *per,* through + *meare,* pass), and is essential for maintaining cellular homeostasis. **Homeostasis** (Gr. *homeo,* always the same + *stasis,* standing) is the maintenance of a relatively constant internal environment despite fluctuations in the external environment. However, before we can fully understand how substances pass into and out of cells and organelles, we must understand how the molecules of those substances are able to move from one place to another.

MOVEMENT ACROSS MEMBRANES

Molecules can cross membranes in a number of ways, both using their own energy and relying on an outside source of energy. Table 3.2 summarizes the various kinds of transmembrane movement and the following sections discuss them in more detail.

SIMPLE DIFFUSION

Molecules tend to move randomly (due to spontaneous molecular motion) from areas where they are highly concentrated to areas of lower concentration, until they are evenly distributed in a state of dynamic equilibrium. This process of molecules spreading out randomly until they are evenly distributed is called **simple diffusion** (L. *diffundre,* to spread). Simple diffusion accounts for most of the short-distance transport of substances moving into and out of cells. Figure 3.7 shows the diffusion of sugar particles away from a sugar cube placed in water.

FACILITATED DIFFUSION

For polar molecules (not soluble in lipids), diffusion may occur through protein channels (pores) in the lipid bilayer (figure 3.8). It is generally accepted that the protein channels offer a continuous pathway for specific molecules to move across the plasma membrane so that they never come into contact with the hydrophobic layer or its polar surface.

Large molecules and some of those not soluble in lipids require assistance in passing through the plasma membrane. The process used by these molecules is called **facilitated diffusion,** and like simple diffusion, requires no energy input to occur. To pass through the membrane, a molecule temporarily binds with a carrier protein in the plasma membrane and is transported from an area of higher to one of lower concentration (figure 3.9).

TABLE 3.2	DIFFERENT TYPES OF MOVEMENT ACROSS PLASMA MEMBRANES	
TYPE OF MOVEMENT	**DESCRIPTION**	**EXAMPLE IN THE BODY OF A FROG**
Simple diffusion	No cell energy is needed. Molecules move "down" a concentration gradient. Molecules spread out randomly from areas of higher concentration to areas of lower concentration until they are distributed evenly—equilibrium is reached.	A frog inhales oxygen, which moves into the lungs and then diffuses into the bloodstream.
Facilitated diffusion	Carrier proteins in a plasma membrane temporarily bind with molecules, and assist their passage through the membrane. Other proteins form channels for movement of molecules through the membrane.	Glucose in the gut of a frog combines with carrier proteins to pass through the gut cells into the bloodstream.
Osmosis	Water molecules diffuse through selectively permeable membranes from areas of higher concentration to areas of lower concentration.	Water molecules move into a frog's red blood cell when the concentration of water molecules outside the blood cell is greater than it is inside.
Filtration	Hydrostatic pressure forces small molecules through selectively permeable membranes from areas of higher pressure to areas of lower pressure.	A frog's blood pressure forces water and dissolved wastes into the kidney tubules during the process of urine formation.
Active transport	Specific carrier proteins in the plasma membrane bind with molecules or ions to help them across the membrane "up" a concentration gradient; energy is required.	Movement of sodium ions from inside the neurons of the sciatic nerve of a frog (the sodium-potassium pump) to the outside of the neurons.
Endocytosis	The bulk movement of material into a cell by formation of a vesicle.	
Pinocytosis	Plasma membrane encloses small amounts of fluid droplets (in a vesicle) and takes them into the cell.	The kidney cells of a frog take in fluid in order to maintain fluid balance.
Phagocytosis	Plasma membrane forms a vesicle around a solid particle or other cell and draws it into the phagocytic cell.	The white blood cells of a frog engulf and digest harmful bacteria.
Receptor-mediated endocytosis	Extracellular molecules bind with specific receptors on a plasma membrane, causing the membrane to invaginate and draw molecules into the cell.	The intestinal cells of a frog take up large molecules from the inside of the gut.
Exocytosis	The movement of material out of a cell. Vesicle (with particles) fuses with plasma membrane and expels particles or fluids from cell through plasma membrane.	The sciatic nerve of a frog releases a chemical (neurohumor).

OSMOSIS

The diffusion of water through a selectively permeable membrane from an area of higher concentration to an area of lower concentration is called **osmosis** (Gr. *osmos*, pushing). Osmosis is just a special type of diffusion, not a different method (figure 3.10).

The term **tonicity** (Gr. *tonus*, tension) refers to the relative concentration of solutes in the water inside and outside the cell. Using red blood cells as an example, in an **isotonic** (Gr. *isos*, equal + *tonus*, tension) solution, the solute concentration

(a)   (b)   (c)   (d)

Figure 3.7

Simple Diffusion. When a sugar cube is placed in water (*a*) it slowly dissolves (*b*) and disappears. As this happens, the sugar molecules diffuse from a region where they are more concentrated to a region (*c*) where they are less concentrated. When they are evenly distributed throughout the water, diffusion equilibrium is reached (*d*).

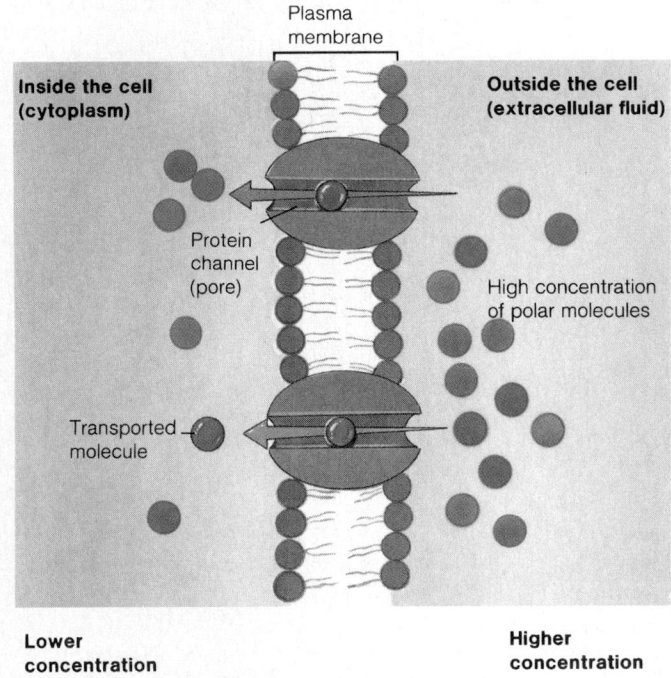

Figure 3.8

Transport Proteins. Molecules can move into and out of cells through integrated channel proteins (pores) in the plasma membrane without the use of energy.

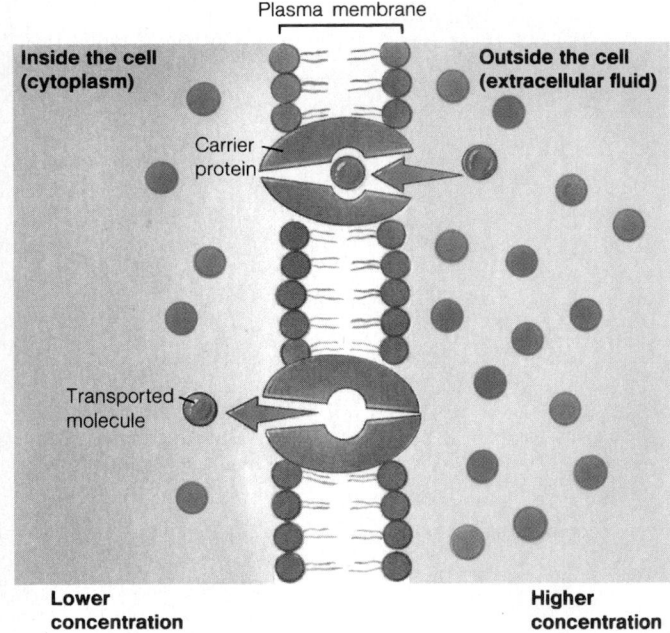

Figure 3.9

Facilitated Diffusion and Carrier Proteins. Some molecules move through the plasma membrane with the assistance of carrier proteins that transport the molecules down their concentration gradient, from a region of higher concentration to one of lower concentration. A transport protein alternates between two configurations, moving a molecule across a membrane as the shape of the protein changes. The rate of facilitated diffusion depends on how many carrier proteins are available in the membrane and how fast they can move their specific molecule.

is the same inside and outside the cell (figure 3.11*a*). The concentration of water molecules is also the same inside and outside the red blood cell; thus, water molecules move through the plasma membrane at the same rate in both directions, and there is no net movement of water in either direction.

In a **hypertonic** (Gr. *hyper,* above) solution, the solute concentration is higher outside the red blood cell than inside it. Because there is a higher concentration of water molecules inside the cell than outside, water moves out of the cell, which shrinks (figure 3.11*b*). This condition is called crenation in red blood cells.

In a **hypotonic** (Gr. *hypo,* under) solution, the solute concentration is lower outside the red blood cell than inside. Conversely, the concentration of water molecules is higher outside the cell than inside.   ⑤   As a result, water moves into the cell, which swells and may burst (figure 3.11*c*).

3.10

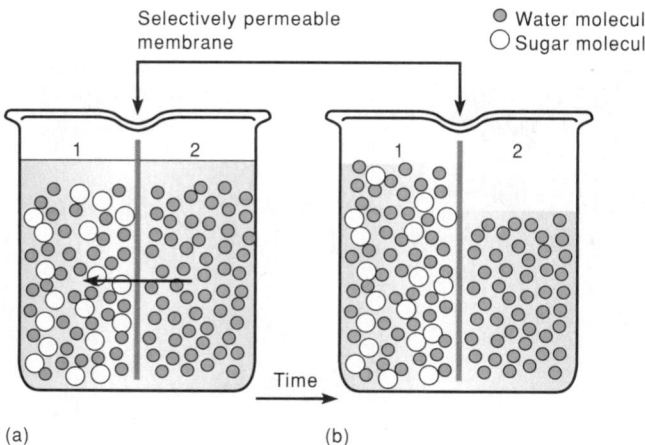

Selectively permeable membrane

● Water molecule
○ Sugar molecule

Time

(a)   (b)

FIGURE **3.10**

Osmosis. (*a*) The beaker is separated into two compartments by a selectively permeable membrane. Initially, compartment 1 contains sugar and water molecules, and compartment 2 contains only water molecules. Due to molecular motion, water will move down the concentration gradient (from 2 to 1) by osmosis. The sugar molecules remain in 1 because they are too large to pass through the membrane. (*b*) At osmotic equilibrium, there will be no further increase in water molecules in 1.

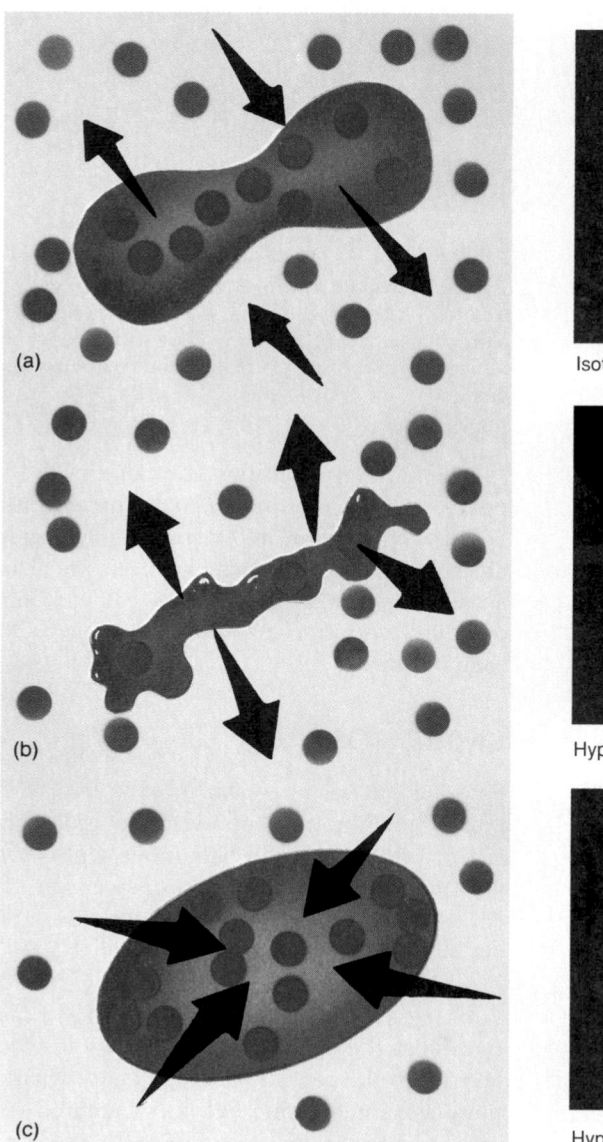

(a)

(b)

(c)

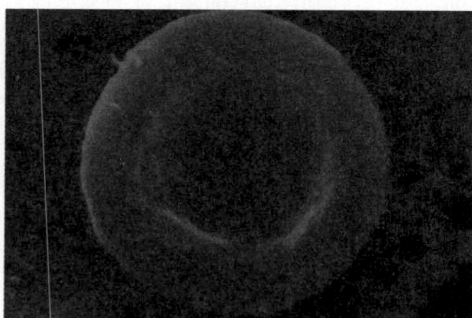

Isotonic (no net change in water movement)

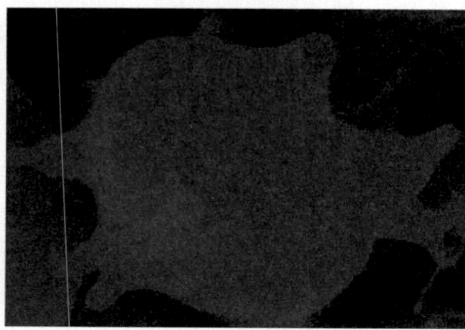

Hypertonic (water diffuses outward)

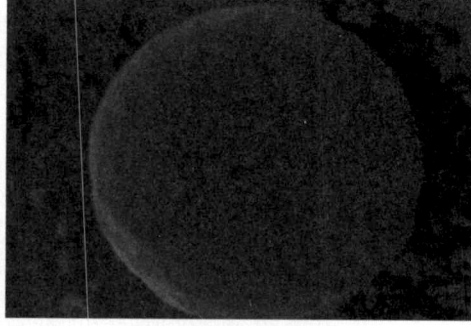

Hypotonic (water diffuses inward)

FIGURE **3.11**

The Effect of Salt Concentration on Cell Volumes. (*a*) An isotonic solution with the same salt concentration inside and outside the cell has no effect on the size of the red blood cell. (*b*) A hypertonic (high salt) solution causes water to leave the red blood cell and results in a shrunken appearance. (*c*) A hypotonic (low salt) solution results in an inflow of water, causing the red blood cell to swell. Arrows indicate direction of water movement. (Scanning electron micrographs ×18,000.)

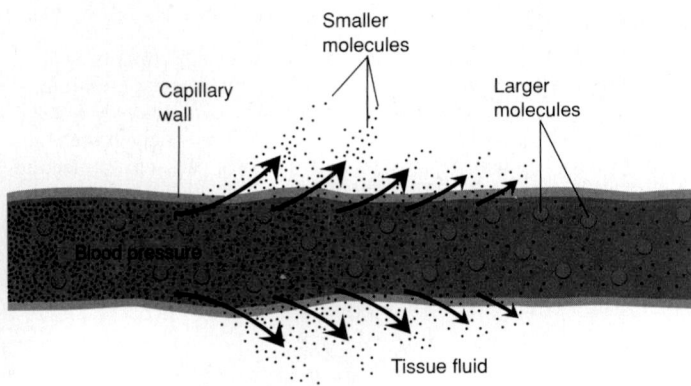

Figure 3.12

Filtration. Small molecules are forced through the wall of a capillary by the high blood pressure in the capillary. Larger molecules cannot pass through the small openings in the capillary wall and remain in the capillary. Arrows indicate the direction of small molecule movement.

FILTRATION

Filtration is a process that forces small molecules through selectively permeable membranes with the aid of hydrostatic (water) pressure (or some other externally applied force, such as blood pressure). For example, in the body of an animal such as a frog, filtration is evident when blood pressure forces water and dissolved molecules through the permeable walls of small blood vessels called capillaries (figure 3.12). In filtration, large molecules, such as proteins, do not pass through the smaller membrane pores. Filtration also takes place in the kidneys when water and dissolved wastes are forced out of the blood vessels into the kidney tubules by blood pressure, as the first step in the formation of urine.

Stop and Ask Yourself

7. How does diffusion occur in an animal cell?
8. What is osmosis? How does it differ from diffusion?
9. What is the difference between simple diffusion and facilitated diffusion?
10. What is the purpose of facilitated diffusion? Filtration?

ACTIVE TRANSPORT

Active-transport processes move molecules and other substances through a selectively permeable membrane against a concentration gradient—that is, from an area of lower to one of higher concentration. Because the movement is against the concentration gradient, ATP energy is required.

The active-transport process is similar to facilitated diffusion, except that the transport protein in the plasma membrane must use energy to move the molecules against their concentration gradient (figure 3.13).

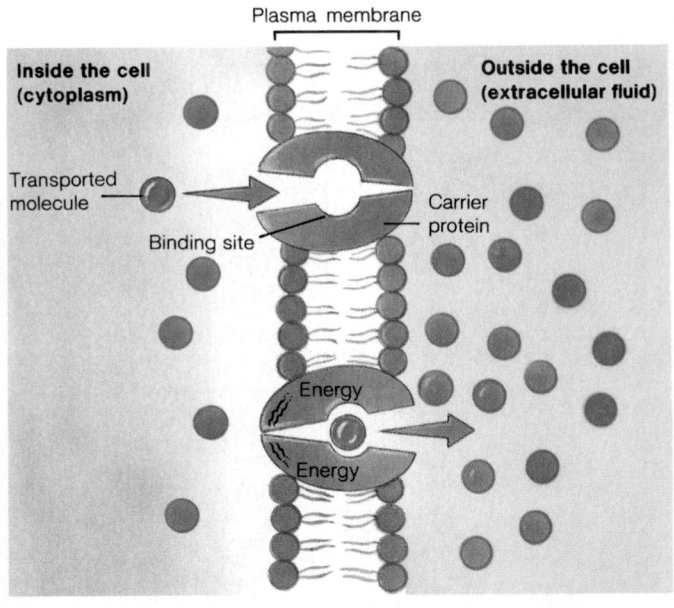

Lower concentration   Higher concentration

Figure 3.13

Active Transport. During active transport, a molecule combines with a carrier protein whose shape is altered as a result of the combination. This change in configuration, along with energy, helps move the molecule through the plasma membrane against a concentration gradient.

One active-transport mechanism, the sodium-potassium pump, helps maintain the high concentrations of potassium and low concentrations of sodium ions inside nerve cells that are necessary for transmission of electrical impulses. Another active-transport mechanism, the calcium pump, keeps the calcium concentration many hundred times lower inside the cell than outside.

ENDOCYTOSIS

Another process by which substances may move through the plasma membrane is called endocytosis. **Endocytosis** (Gr. *endon*, within) involves bulk movement of materials across the plasma membrane, rather than movement of individual molecules. There are three forms of endocytosis: pinocytosis, phagocytosis, and receptor-mediated endocytosis.

Pinocytosis ("cell drinking," from Gr. *pinein*, to drink + *cyto*, cell) is nonspecific uptake of small droplets of extracellular fluid. Any small solid dissolved in the fluid is also taken into the cell. Pinocytosis occurs when a small portion of the plasma membrane becomes indented (invaginated). The open end of the invagination seals itself off, forming a small vesicle. This tiny vesicle becomes detached from the plasma membrane and moves into the cytoplasm (figure 3.14a).

Phagocytosis ("cell eating," from Gr. *phagein*, to eat + *cyto*, cell) is similar to pinocytosis, except that the material taken into the cell is solid rather than liquid. Commonly, an organelle called

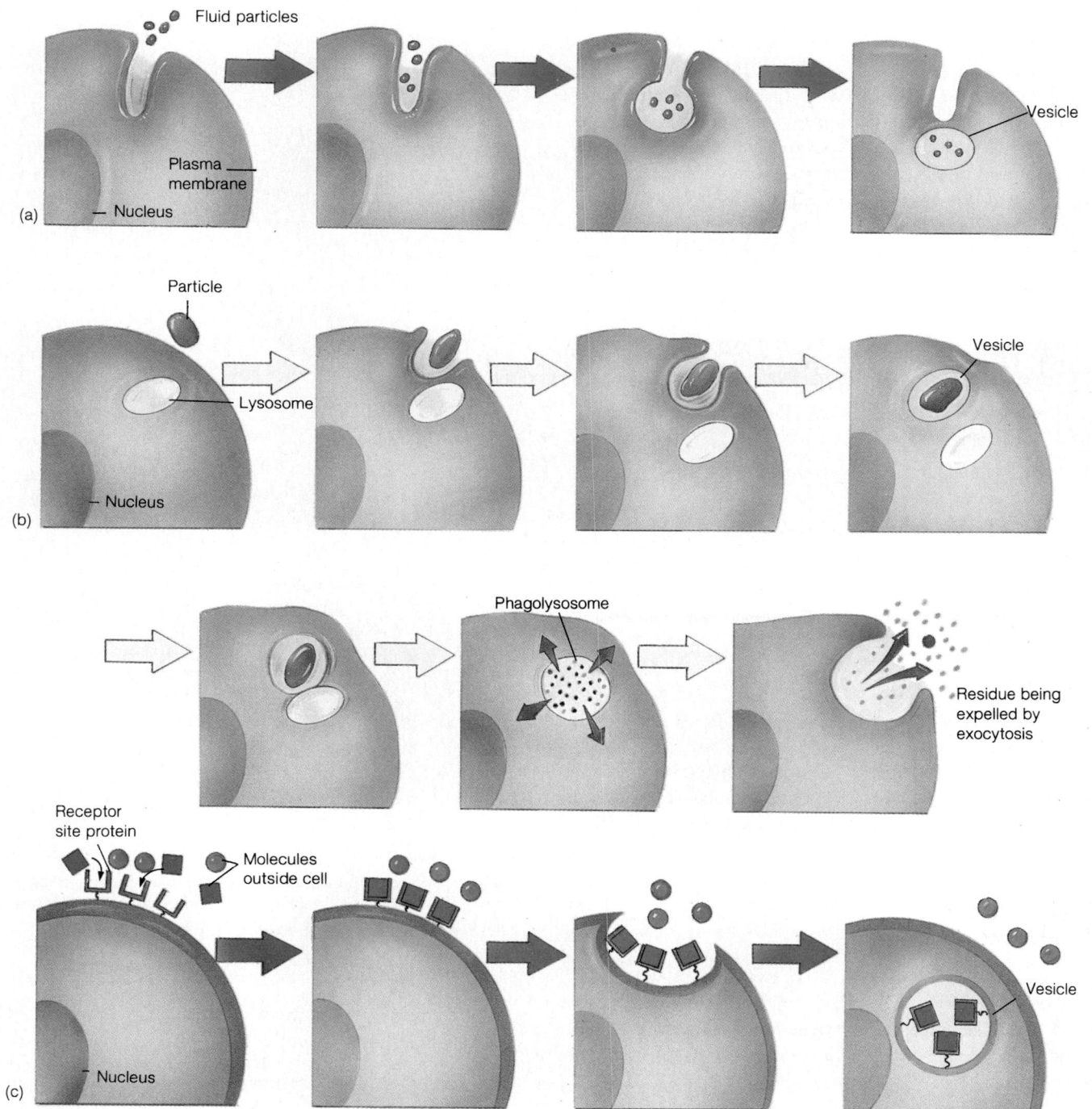

FIGURE 3.14

Endocytosis and Exocytosis. (*a*) Pinocytosis. A cell takes in small fluid particles and forms a vesicle. (*b*) Phagocytosis. A cell takes in a solid particle and forms a vesicle. A lysosome combines with a vesicle, forming a phagolysosome. Lysosomal enzymes digest the particle. The vesicle can also fuse with the plasma membrane and release its contents by exocytosis. (*c*) In receptor-mediated endocytosis, a specific molecule binds to a receptor protein, inducing the formation of a vesicle.

a lysosome (*see page* 44) combines with the vesicle to form a **phagolysosome** ("digestion vacuole"), and lysosomal digestive enzymes cause the contents to be broken down (figure 3.14*b*).

Receptor-mediated endocytosis involves a specific receptor on the plasma membrane that "recognizes" an extracellular molecule and binds with it (figure 3.14*c*). This reaction somehow stimulates the membrane to indent and create a vesicle that contains the selected molecule. A variety of important molecules (such as cholesterol) are brought into cells in this manner.

EXOCYTOSIS

Proteins and other molecules produced in the cell that are destined for export (secretion) are packaged in vesicles by an organelle known as the Golgi apparatus (described in a later section). In the process of **exocytosis** (Gr. *exo*, outside), these secretory vesicles fuse with the plasma membrane and release their contents into the extracellular environment (figure 3.14*b*). This process adds new membrane material, which replaces that which was lost from the plasma membrane during endocytosis.

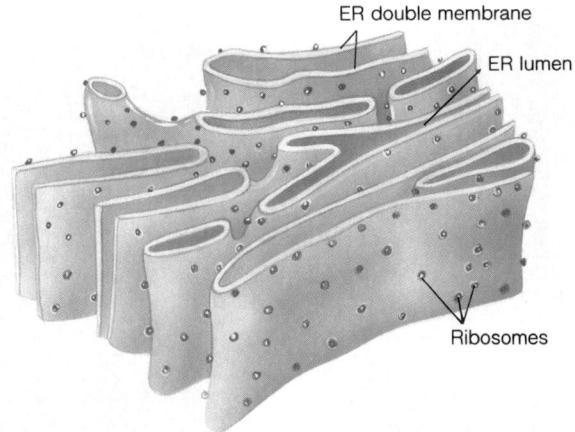

(a)   Rough endoplasmic reticulum

Stop and Ask Yourself

11. How do active transport and facilitated diffusion across plasma membranes differ?
12. What is the difference between endocytosis and exocytosis?
13. How does receptor-mediated endocytosis occur?
14. Where does an active-transport process occur in an animal?

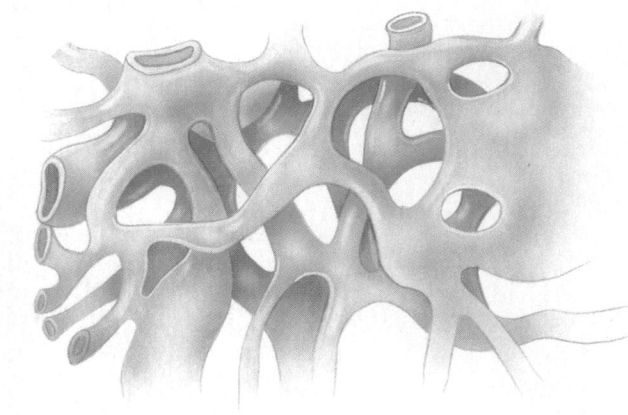

(b)   Smooth endoplasmic reticulum

CYTOPLASM, ORGANELLES, AND CELLULAR COMPONENTS

Many cell functions that are performed in the cytoplasmic compartment result from the activity of specific structures called organelles. The structure and function of these organelles are summarized in table 3.3 and discussed in the following sections.

CYTOPLASM

The cytoplasm of a cell is composed of two distinct phases. The particulate phase consists of well-defined structures, such as organelles and lipid droplets. The aqueous phase consists of the fluid **cytosol,** in which the above structures are suspended and in which are dissolved various molecules.

RIBOSOMES: PROTEIN WORKBENCHES

Ribosomes are non-membrane-bound structures that are the sites for protein synthesis. They contain almost equal amounts of protein and a special kind of ribonucleic acid called ribosomal RNA (rRNA). The role of ribosomes in protein synthesis is discussed in chapter 9. Some ribosomes are attached to the ER (see next section), and some float freely in the cytoplasm. Whether ribosomes are free or attached, they are usually grouped in clusters that are connected by a strand of another kind of ribonucleic acid called messenger RNA (mRNA). These clusters are called polyribosomes or polysomes (*see figure 3.2*).

FIGURE 3.15

Endoplasmic Reticulum. (*a*) Rough ER is coated with ribosomes. Notice the double membrane and the lumen (space) between each membrane. (*b*) Smooth ER lacks ribosomes.

ENDOPLASMIC RETICULUM: PRODUCTION AND TRANSPORT

The **endoplasmic reticulum (ER)** is a complex, membrane-bound labyrinth of flattened sheets, sacs, and tubules that branch and spread throughout the cytoplasm. The ER is continuous from the plasma membrane to the nuclear envelope (*see figure 3.2*) and functions as a series of channels that help various materials circulate throughout the cytoplasm. It also serves as a storage unit for enzymes and other proteins and serves as a point for attachment of ribosomes. ER that has ribosomes attached to it is called rough ER (figure 3.15*a*), and ER that does not have ribosomes attached is called smooth ER (figure 3.15*b*). Smooth ER is the site for the production of steroids, detoxification of a wide variety of organic molecules, and storage of calcium ions in muscle cells. Most cells contain both types of ER, although the relative proportion varies among cells.

TABLE 3.3	STRUCTURE AND FUNCTION OF CELLULAR COMPONENTS	
COMPONENT	**STRUCTURE/DESCRIPTION**	**FUNCTION**
Centriole	Located within centrosome; contains nine triple microtubules	Forms basal body of cilia and flagella; functions in mitotic spindle formation
Chloroplast	Organelle that contains chlorophyll and is involved in photosynthesis	Light energy is trapped, transformed, and used to convert carbon dioxide and water into glucose and oxygen
Chromosomes	Nucleic acid (DNA) and protein make up the different chromosomes	Control heredity and cellular activities
Cilia, flagella	Threadlike processes	Cilia move small particles past fixed cells; are a major form of locomotion in some cells; flagella propel cells
Cytoplasm	Semifluid enclosed within plasma membrane; consists of fluid cytosol, organelles, and other structures	Dissolves substances; houses organelles, vesicles, inclusions
Cytoplasmic inclusions	Temporary substances in cytoplasm	Store products of cell's metabolic activities
Cytoskeleton	Interconnecting microfilaments and microtubules; flexible cellular framework	Assists in cell movement; provides support; site for binding of specific enzymes
Cytosol	Fluid part of cytoplasm; enclosed within plasma membrane; surrounds nucleus	Houses organelles; serves as fluid medium for metabolic reactions
Endoplasmic reticulum (ER)	An extensive membrane system extending throughout the cytoplasm from the plasma membrane to the nuclear envelope	Storage and internal transport; rough ER serves as site for attachment of ribosomes; smooth ER makes steroids
Golgi apparatus	Stacks of disklike membranes	Sorts, packages, and routes cell's synthesized products
Lysosome	Membrane-bound sphere	Digests materials
Microfilaments	Rodlike structures containing the protein actin	Give structural support and assist in cell movement
Microtubules	Hollow cylindrical structures	Assist in movement of cilia, flagella, and chromosomes; transport system
Mitochondrion	Organelle with double, folded membranes	Converts energy into a form usable by the cell
Nucleolus	Rounded mass within nucleus; contains RNA and protein	Preassembly point for ribosomes
Nucleus	Spherical structure surrounded by a nuclear envelope; contains nucleolus and DNA	Contains DNA that controls cell's genetic program and metabolic activities
Peroxisome	Membrane-bound organelle containing oxidative enzymes	Carries out metabolic reactions and destroys hydrogen peroxide, which is toxic to the cell
Plasma membrane	The outer bilayered boundary of the cell; composed of protein, cholesterol, and phospholipid	Protection; regulation of material movement, cell-to-cell recognition
Ribosomes	Contain RNA and protein; some are free and some are attached to ER	Sites of protein synthesis
Vacuole	Membrane-surrounded, often large, space in the cytoplasm	Site of storage of food and other compounds; also used to pump water out of a cell (e.g., contractile vacuole)
Vesicle	A small membrane-surrounded space; contains enzymes or secretory products	Site of intracellular digestion, storage, or transport

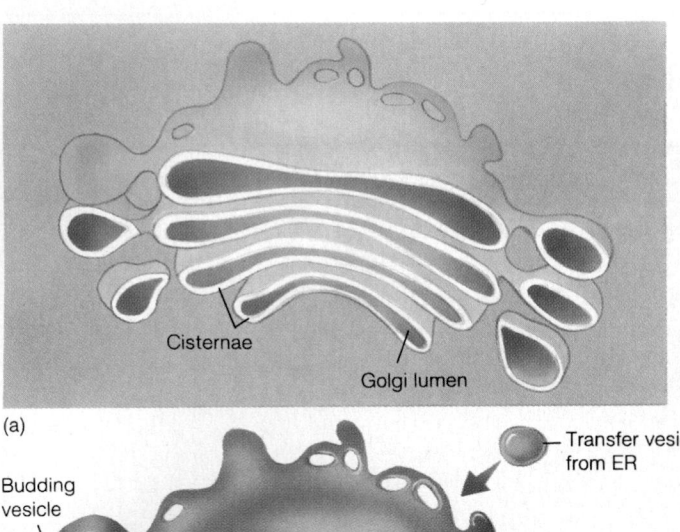

Cisternae

Golgi lumen

(a)

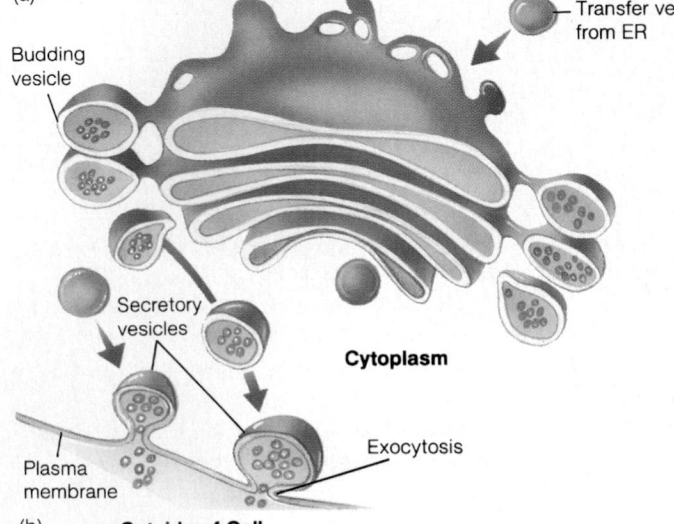

Transfer vesicle from ER

Budding vesicle

Secretory vesicles

Cytoplasm

Plasma membrane

(b) **Outside of Cell**

Exocytosis

Figure 3.16

The Golgi Apparatus. (*a*) The Golgi apparatus consists of a stack of cisternae. Notice the curved nature of the cisternae. (*b*) The Golgi apparatus functions in the storing, sorting, packaging, and secretion of cell products. Secretory vesicles move from the Golgi apparatus to the plasma membrane and fuse with it, releasing their contents to the outside of the cell via exocytosis.

Golgi Apparatus: Packaging, Sorting, and Export

The **Golgi apparatus** or **complex** (named for Camillo Golgi, who discovered it in 1898), is a collection of membranes associated physically and functionally with the ER in the cytoplasm (figure 3.16*a; see also figure 3.2*). It is composed of flattened stacks of membrane-bound cisternae (s., cisterna; closed spaces serving as fluid reservoirs). The Golgi apparatus functions in the sorting, packaging, and secretion of proteins and lipids.

Proteins that are synthesized by ribosomes attached to the rough ER are sealed off in little packets called transfer vesicles that pass from the ER to the Golgi apparatus and fuse with it (figure 3.16*b*). In the Golgi apparatus, the proteins can be con-

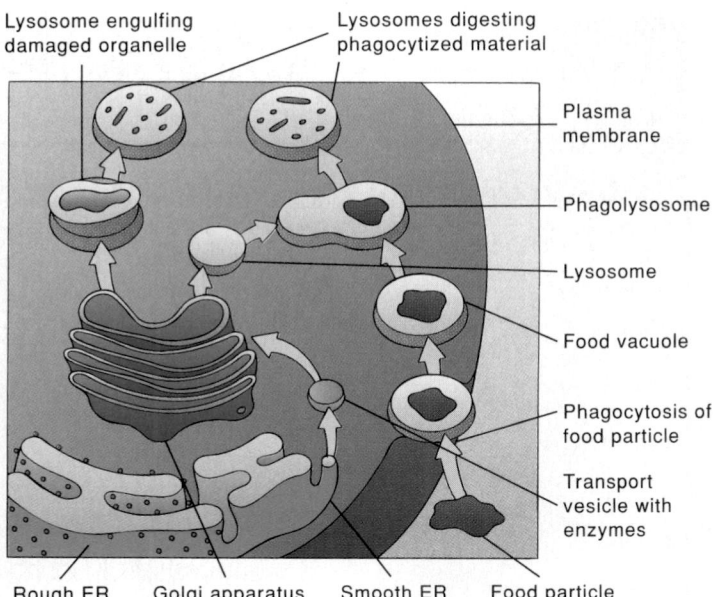

Lysosome engulfing damaged organelle

Lysosomes digesting phagocytized material

Plasma membrane

Phagolysosome

Lysosome

Food vacuole

Phagocytosis of food particle

Transport vesicle with enzymes

Rough ER   Golgi apparatus   Smooth ER   Food particle

Figure 3.17

Lysosome Formation and Function. Lysosomes arise from the Golgi apparatus and fuse with vesicles that have engulfed foreign material to form digestive vesicles (phagolysosomes). These vesicles function in the normal recycling of cell constituents.

centrated and chemically modified. One function of this chemical modification seems to be to mark and sort the proteins into different batches for different destinations. Eventually, they are packaged into secretory vesicles, which are released into the cytoplasm close to the plasma membrane. When the vesicles reach the plasma membrane, they fuse with it and release their contents to the outside of the cell by exocytosis. Golgi apparatuses are most abundant in cells that secrete chemical substances (e.g., pancreatic cells secreting digestive enzymes and nerve cells secreting transmitter substances). As noted below, the Golgi apparatus also produces lysosomes.

Lysosomes: Digestion and Degradation

Lysosomes (Gr. *lyso*, dissolving + *soma*, body) are membrane-bound spherical organelles that contain enzymes called acid hydrolases, which are capable of digesting organic molecules (lipids, proteins, nucleic acids, and polysaccharides) under acidic conditions. The enzymes are synthesized in the ER, transported to the Golgi apparatus for processing, and then secreted by the Golgi apparatus in the form of lysosomes or as vesicles that fuse with lysosomes (figure 3.17). Lysosomes fuse with phagocytic vesicles, thus exposing the vesicle's contents to the lysosome's enzymes.

Cells can also selectively digest portions of their own cytoplasm or organelles. When the digested materials are returned to the cytoplasm, they can be reused by the cell, recycling the cell constituents.

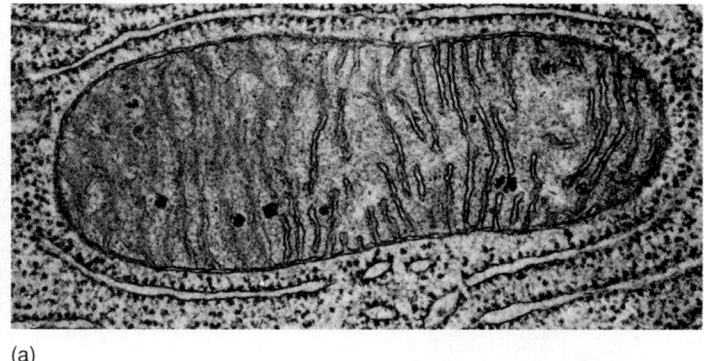

(a)

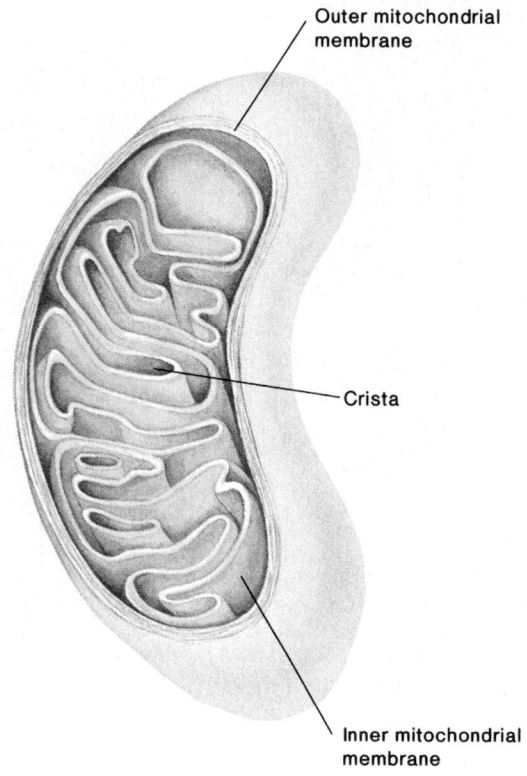

FIGURE 3.18

Mitochondrion. (*a*) An electron micrograph illustrating the mitochondrial membranes, cristae, and matrix. The matrix contains DNA, ribosomes, and enzymes ($\times$36,300). (*b*) Drawing of a "typical" mitochondrion.

MITOCHONDRIA: POWER GENERATORS

Mitochondria (s., mitochondrion) are double-membrane-bound organelles that are spherical to elongate in shape. The outer membrane is separated from the inner membrane by a small space. The inner membrane folds and doubles in on itself to form incomplete partitions called cristae (s., crista; figure 3.18). The cristae increase the surface area available for the chemical reactions that trap usable energy for the cell. The space between the cristae is the matrix. The matrix contains ri-

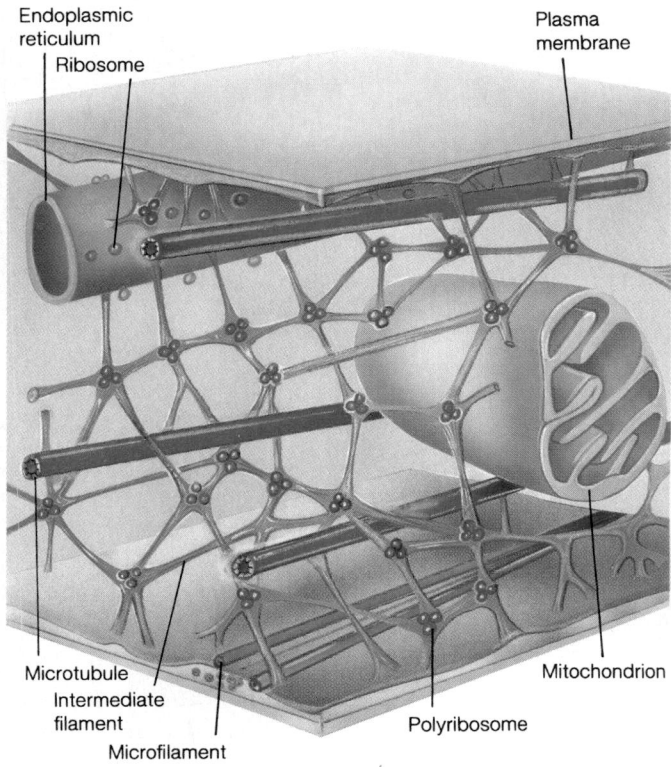

FIGURE 3.19

The Cytoskeleton. A model of the cytoskeleton showing the three-dimensional arrangement of the microtubules, intermediate filaments, and microfilaments.

bosomes, circular DNA, and other material.   ⑦   Because they convert energy to a usable form, mitochondria are frequently called the "power generators" of the cell. Mitochondria usually multiply when a cell needs to produce more energy. The production of cellular energy will be covered in more detail in chapter 5.

CYTOSKELETON: MICROTUBULES, INTERMEDIATE FILAMENTS, AND MICROFILAMENTS

⑧   In most cells, the microtubules, intermediate filaments, and microfilaments form the flexible cellular framework called the **cytoskeleton** ("cell skeleton") (figure 3.19). This latticed framework extends throughout the cytoplasm, connecting the various organelles and cellular components.

Microtubules are hollow, slender, cylindrical structures found in animal cells. Each microtubule is made of spiraling subunits of globular proteins called tubulins (figure 3.20*a*). Microtubules function in the movement of organelles, such as secretory vesicles, and in chromosome movement during division of the cell nucleus. They are also part of a transport system within the cell. For example, in nerve cells, they help move materials through the long nerve processes. Microtubules are an

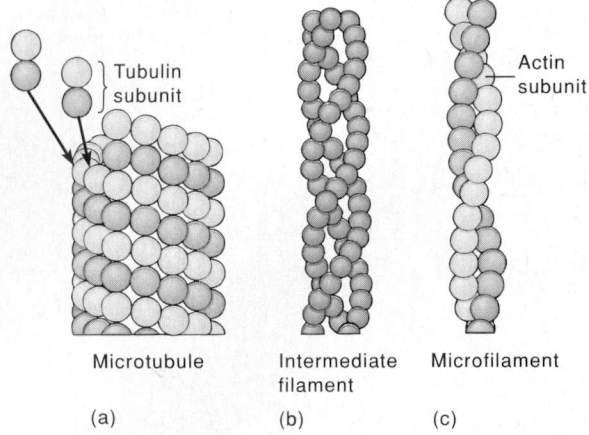

FIGURE 3.20

The Three Major Classes of Protein Fibers Making Up the Cytoskeleton of Eukaryotic Cells. (*a*) Microtubules consist of globular protein subunits (tubulins) linked in parallel rows. (*b*) Intermediate filaments in different cell types are composed of different protein subunits. (*c*) The protein actin is the key subunit in microfilaments.

important part of the cytoskeleton in the cytoplasm, and they are involved in the overall shape changes that cells undergo during periods of specialization.

Intermediate filaments are a chemically heterogeneous group of protein fibers, the specific proteins of which can vary with cell type (figure 3.20*b*). These filaments help to maintain the shape of the cell, the spatial organization of organelles, and promote mechanical activities within the cytoplasm.

Microfilaments are solid strings of protein (actin) molecules (figure 3.20*c*). They are most highly developed in muscle cells as myofibrils, which help these cells shorten or contract. Actin microfilaments in nonmuscle cells provide mechanical support for various cellular structures, and help form contractile systems responsible for some cellular movements (e.g., amoeboid movement in some protozoa).

CILIA AND FLAGELLA: MOVEMENT

Cilia (s., cilium; L. "eyelashes") and **flagella** (s., flagellum; L. "small whips") are elongated appendages on the surface of some cells. They are the means by which cells, including many unicellular organisms, propel themselves. In stationary cells, cilia or flagella move material over the cell's surface.

Although flagella are 5 to 20 times as long as cilia, and move somewhat differently, they have a similar structure. Both are membrane-bound cylinders that enclose a matrix. In this matrix is an **axoneme** or **axial filament,** which consists of nine pairs of microtubules arranged in a circle around two central tubules (figure 3.21). This is called a 9 + 2 pattern of microtubules. Each microtubule pair (a doublet) also has pairs of dynein (protein) arms projecting toward a neighboring doublet and spokes extending toward the central pair of microtubules. Cilia and flagella move as a result of the microtubule doublets sliding along one another.

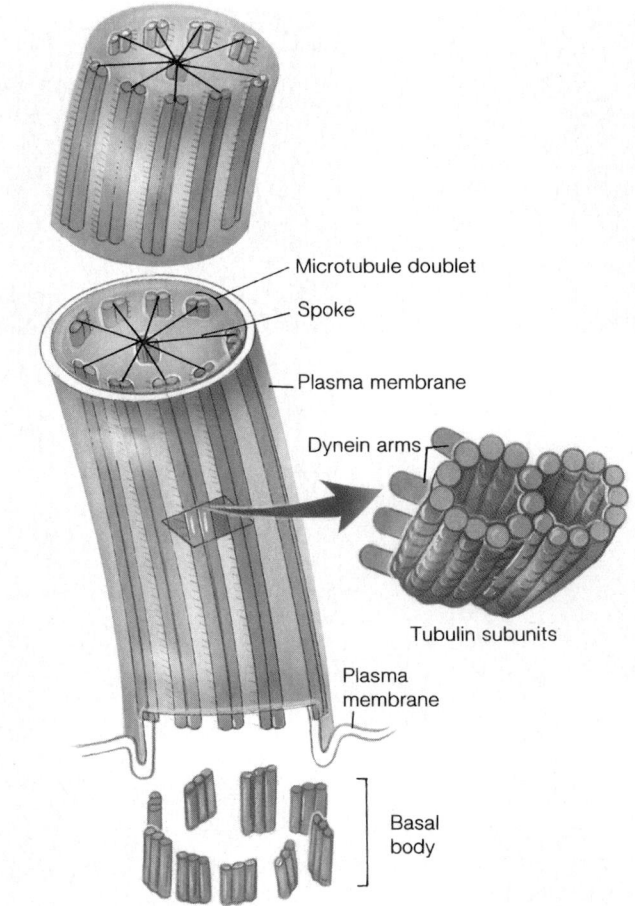

FIGURE 3.21

Drawing of the Internal Structure of Cilia and Flagella. In cross section, the arms extend from each microtubule doublet toward a neighboring doublet, and spokes extend toward the central paired microtubules. The dynein arms push against the adjacent microtubule doublet to bring about movement. *Redrawn from N.K. Wessels and J.L. Hopson, Biology, 3d ed. Copyright © 1988 McGraw-Hill, Inc. Used by permission.*

In the cytoplasm at the base of each cilium or flagellum lies a short, cylindrical **basal body,** also made up of microtubules. The basal body controls the growth of microtubules in cilia or flagella. The microtubules in the basal body form a 9 + 0 pattern; nine sets of three with none in the middle.

CENTRIOLES: SPECIALIZED MICROTUBULES

The specialized nonmembranous region of cytoplasm near the nucleus is called the **centrosome.** The centrosome contains two organelles called **centrioles** (*see figure 3.2*) that lie at right angles to each other. Each centriole is composed of nine triplet microtubules that radiate from the center like the spokes of a wheel. The centrioles are duplicated preceding cell division, are involved with the movement of the chromosomes, and help organize the cytoskeleton.

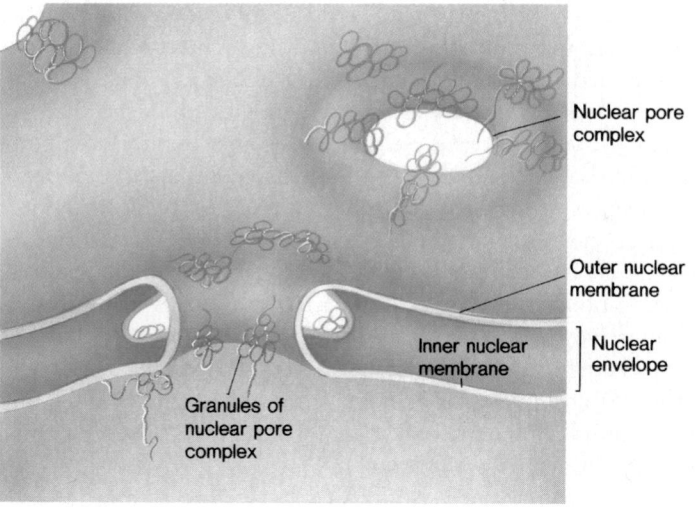

FIGURE 3.22

Nuclear Envelope. An artist's interpretation of pore structure showing how the pore spans the two-layered nuclear envelope. The protein granules around the edge and in the center govern what passes through the pores.

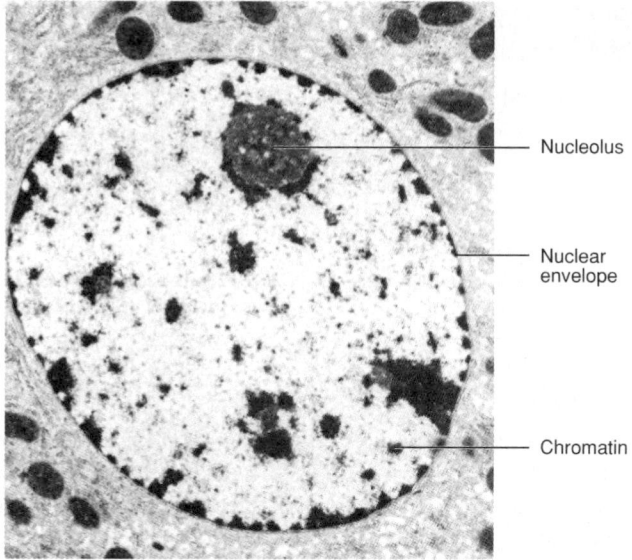

FIGURE 3.23

The Nucleus. The nucleolus, chromatin, and nuclear envelope are visible in this nucleus (×16,000).

CYTOPLASMIC INCLUSIONS: STORAGE

In addition to organelles, the cytoplasm also contains **cytoplasmic inclusions,** which are usually either basic food material or stored products of the cell's metabolic activities. These inclusions are not permanent components of a cell, and are constantly being destroyed and replaced.

THE NUCLEUS: INFORMATION CENTER

The nucleus contains the DNA and is the control and information center for the eukaryotic cell. It has two major functions. The nucleus directs the chemical reactions that occur in cells by transcribing genetic information in the DNA into RNA, which then translates this specific information into proteins (e.g., enzymes) that determine the cell's specific activities. The nucleus also stores genetic information and transfers it during cell division from one cell to the next, and from one generation of organisms to the next.

NUCLEAR ENVELOPE: GATEWAY TO THE NUCLEUS

The **nuclear envelope** is a membrane that separates the nucleus from the cytoplasm, and is continuous with the endoplasmic reticulum at a number of points. Over 3,000 nuclear pores penetrate the surface of the nuclear envelope (figure 3.22). These pores make it possible for materials to enter and leave the nucleus, and for the nucleus to be in direct contact with the endoplasmic reticulum (*see figure 3.2*). Nuclear pores are not simply holes in the nuclear envelope; each is composed of an ordered array of globular and filamentous granules, probably proteins. These granules form the nuclear pore complex, which governs the transport of molecules into and out of the nucleus. The size of the pores prevents DNA from leaving the nucleus, but permits RNA to be moved out.

CHROMOSOMES: GENETIC CONTAINERS

The nucleoplasm is the inner mass of the nucleus. In a cell that is not dividing, it contains genetic material called **chromatin.** Chromatin consists of a combination of DNA and protein and is the uncoiled, tangled mass of **chromosomes** ("colored bodies"), containing the hereditary information in segments of DNA called genes. During cell division, each chromosome becomes tightly coiled, making it visible when viewed through a light microscope.

NUCLEOLUS: PREASSEMBLY POINT FOR RIBOSOMES

The **nucleolus** (pl., nucleoli) is a non-membrane-bound structure in the nucleoplasm that is present in nondividing cells (figure 3.23). Two or three nucleoli form in most cells, but there can be thousands or more in some cells (e.g., amphibian eggs). Nucleoli function in the synthesis of ribosomes, and there are usually proteins and RNA in many stages of synthesis and assembly. The nucleolus can be described as a preassembly point for ribosomes, because their assembly is completed after leaving the nucleus through the pores of the nuclear envelope.

15. What are several functions of the nucleus?
16. Why are the pores in the nuclear envelope important?
17. What is the difference between chromatin, nucleoplasm, and chromosomes?
18. What is the function of a nucleolus?

TISSUES

In an animal, individual cells differentiate during development to perform special functions. These specialized cells carry out their functions as aggregates called tissues. A **tissue** (Fr. *tissu*, woven) is a group of similar cells specialized for the performance of a common function. Animal tissues are classified as one of four types: epithelial, connective, muscular, or nervous.

EPITHELIAL TISSUE: MANY FORMS AND FUNCTIONS

Epithelial tissue exists in many structural forms. In general, it either covers or lines something, and is typically made up of renewable flat sheets of cells that have surface specializations adapted for their specific roles. Usually, epithelial tissues are separated from underlying, adjacent tissues by a basement membrane. The typical functions of epithelial tissues are absorption (e.g., the lining of the small intestine), transport (e.g., kidney tubules), excretion (e.g., sweat glands), protection (e.g., the skin), and sensory reception (e.g., the taste buds in the tongue). The size, shape, and arrangement of epithelial cells are directly related to these specific functions.

Epithelial tissues are classified on the basis of shape and the number of layers present. Epithelium can be simple, consisting of only one layer of cells, or stratified, consisting of two or more layers stacked one on top of each other (figure 3.24*e*). The shapes of the individual epithelial cells can be flat (squamous epithelium; figure 3.24*a*), cube shaped (cuboidal epithelium; figure 3.24*b*), or columnlike (columnar epithelium; figure 3.24*c*). The cells of pseudostratified ciliated columnar epithelium possess cilia and appear stratified or layered, but they are not; hence, the prefix pseudo. The layered effect occurs because their nuclei are located at two or more levels within cells of the tissues (figure 3.24*d*).

CONNECTIVE TISSUE: CONNECTION AND SUPPORT

Connective tissues serve to support and bind tissues together. Unlike epithelial tissues, connective tissues are distributed throughout an extracellular matrix. This matrix frequently contains fibers that are embedded in a ground substance, which has a consistency anywhere from liquid to solid. To a large extent, the functional properties of the various connective tissues are determined by the nature of this extracellular material.

Connective tissues are of two general types, depending on whether the fibers are loosely or densely packed. In **loose connective tissue** (figure 3.24*g*), the matrix contains strong, flexible fibers of the protein collagen that are interwoven with fine, elastic, and reticular fibers, giving loose connective tissue its elastic consistency, and making it an excellent binding tissue (e.g., binding the skin to underlying muscle tissue). **Fibrous connective tissue** (figure 3.24*h*) is made up of fibers that are very densely packed. The collagen fibers lie parallel to one another, creating very strong cords, such as tendons (which connect muscles to bones or to other muscles), and ligaments (which connect bones to bones).

Adipose tissue is a type of loose connective tissue that consists of large cells that store lipid (figure 3.24*f*). Most often the cells accumulate in large numbers to form what we commonly call fat.

Cartilage is a hard yet flexible tissue (figure 3.24*i–k*) that supports such structures as the outer ear, and forms the entire skeleton of such animals as sharks and rays. Cells called chondrocytes lie within spaces called lacunae that are surrounded by a rubbery matrix. This matrix is secreted by chondroblasts, and with the collagen fibers, gives cartilage its strength and elasticity.

Bone cells (osteocytes, osteoblasts, or osteoclasts) also lie within lacunae (figure 3.24*l*), but the matrix around them is heavily impregnated with calcium phosphate, making this kind of tissue very hard and ideally suited for its functions of support and protection. The structure and function of bone will be considered in more detail in chapter 32.

Blood is a connective tissue in which specialized red and white blood cells plus platelets are suspended in a fluid called plasma (figure 3.24*m*). Blood transports various substances throughout the body of animals and will be covered in more detail in chapter 36.

MUSCLE TISSUE: MOVEMENT

Muscle tissue allows movement. The details of this contractile process will be discussed in chapter 32. Therefore, at this point we will only introduce the three kinds of muscle tissue: smooth muscle, skeletal muscle, and cardiac muscle (figure 3.24*o–q*).

NERVOUS TISSUE: COMMUNICATION

Nervous tissue is composed of individual cells called neurons (figure 3.24*n*). Neurons are specialized for conducting electrical impulses. Neurons receive information about changes in the external and internal environments of an animal, and stimulate other tissues or organs to respond appropriately to those changes. Neurons occur in a wide variety of shapes and sizes. Interspersed among them are glial cells that support the neurons. Nervous tissue will be covered in more detail in chapter 33.

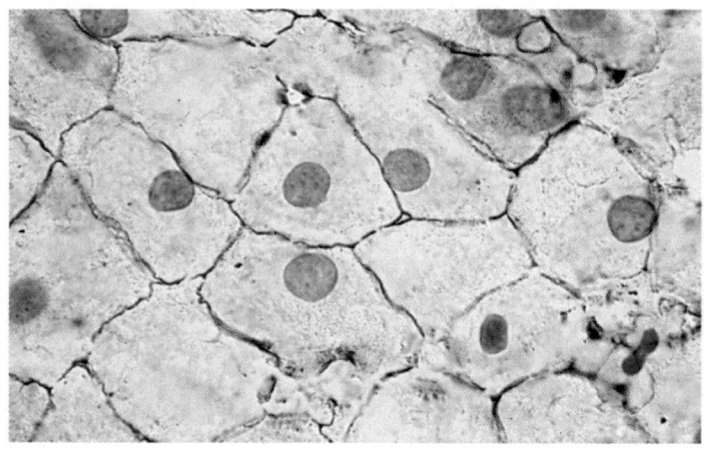

FIGURE 3.24

Tissue Types. (*a*) Simple squamous epithelium consists of a single layer of tightly packed flattened cells (×250).

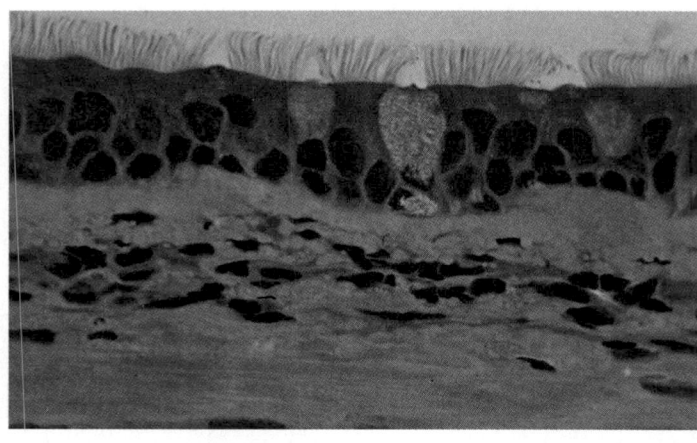

(*d*) Pseudostratified ciliated columnar epithelium. Notice the tuft of cilia at the top of each cell (×500).

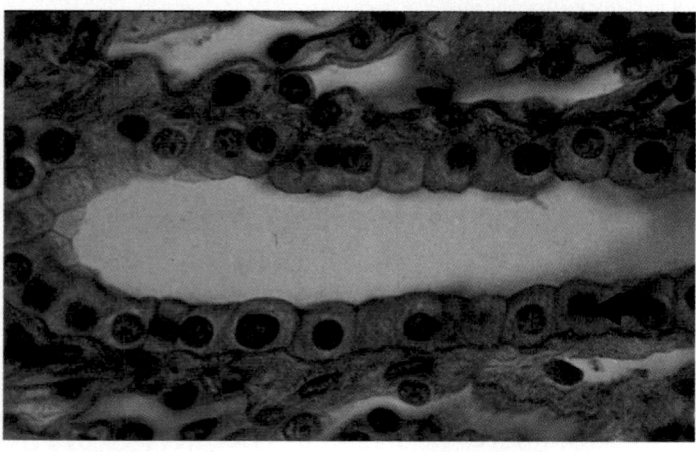

(*b*) Simple cuboidal epithelium consists of a single layer of tightly packed cube-shaped cells. Notice the single layer of cells indicated by the arrow (×250).

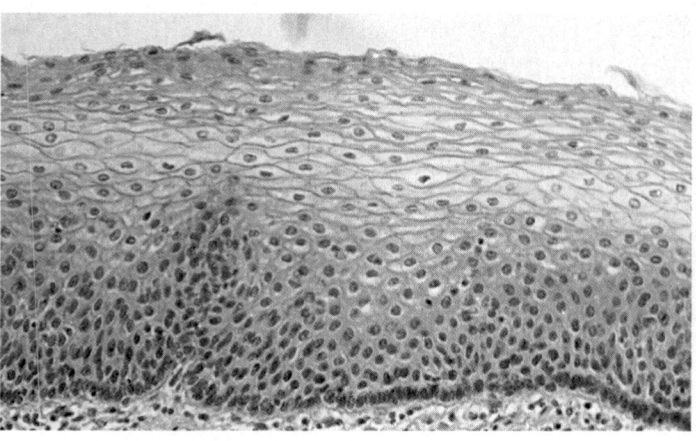

(*e*) Stratified squamous epithelium consists of many layers of cells (×67).

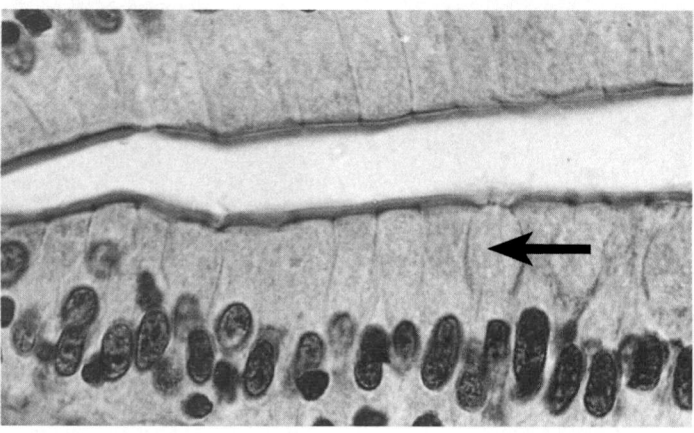

(*c*) Simple columnar epithelium consists of a single layer of elongated cells. The arrow is pointing to a specialized goblet cell that secretes mucus (×400).

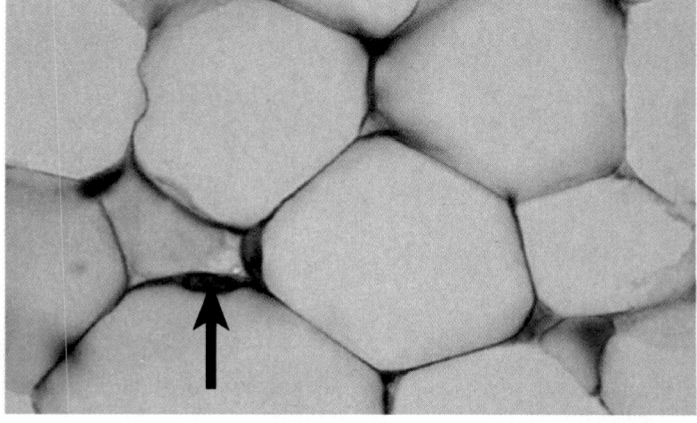

(*f*) Adipose tissue cells contain large fat droplets that cause the nuclei to be pushed close to the plasma membranes. The arrow is pointing to a nucleus (×250).

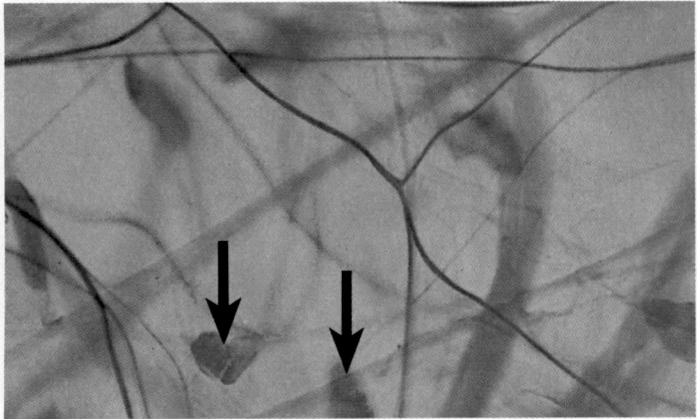

(g) Loose connective tissue contains numerous fibroblasts (arrows) that produce collagenous and elastic fibers (×250).

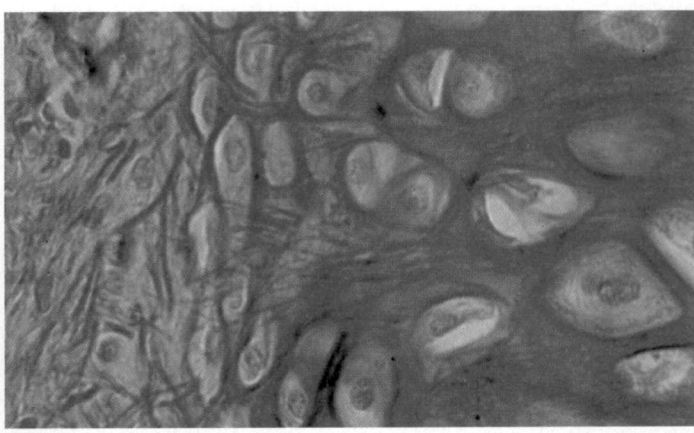

(j) Elastic cartilage contains fine collagenous fibers and many elastic fibers in its intercellular material (×100).

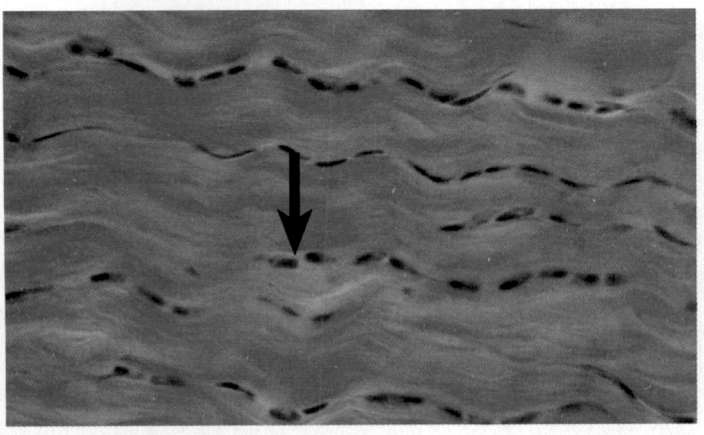

(h) Fibrous connective tissue consists largely of tightly packed collagenous fibers (×100). The arrow is pointing to a fibroblast.

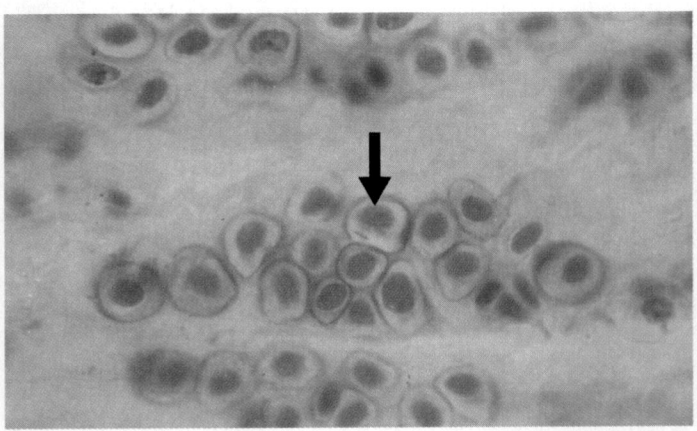

(k) Fibrocartilage contains many large collagenous fibers in its intercellular material (×195). Arrow is pointing to a fibroblast.

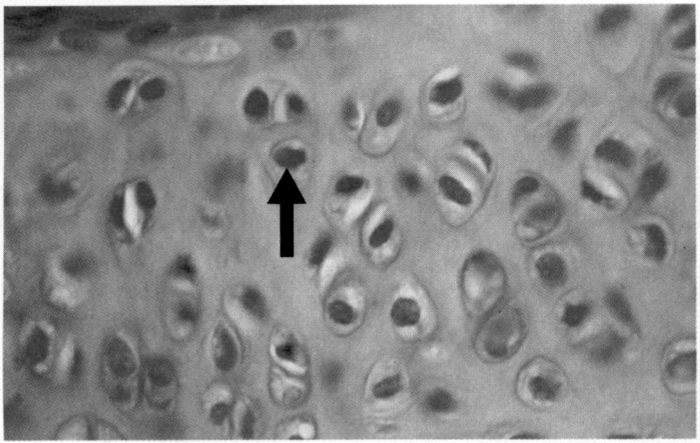

(i) Hyaline cartilage cells are located in lacunae (arrow) surrounded by intercellular material containing fine collagenous fibers (×250).

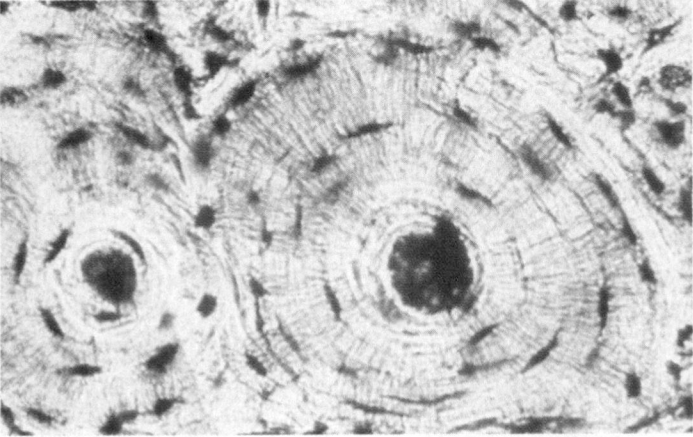

(l) Bone matrix is deposited in concentric layers around osteonic canals (×160).

3.22

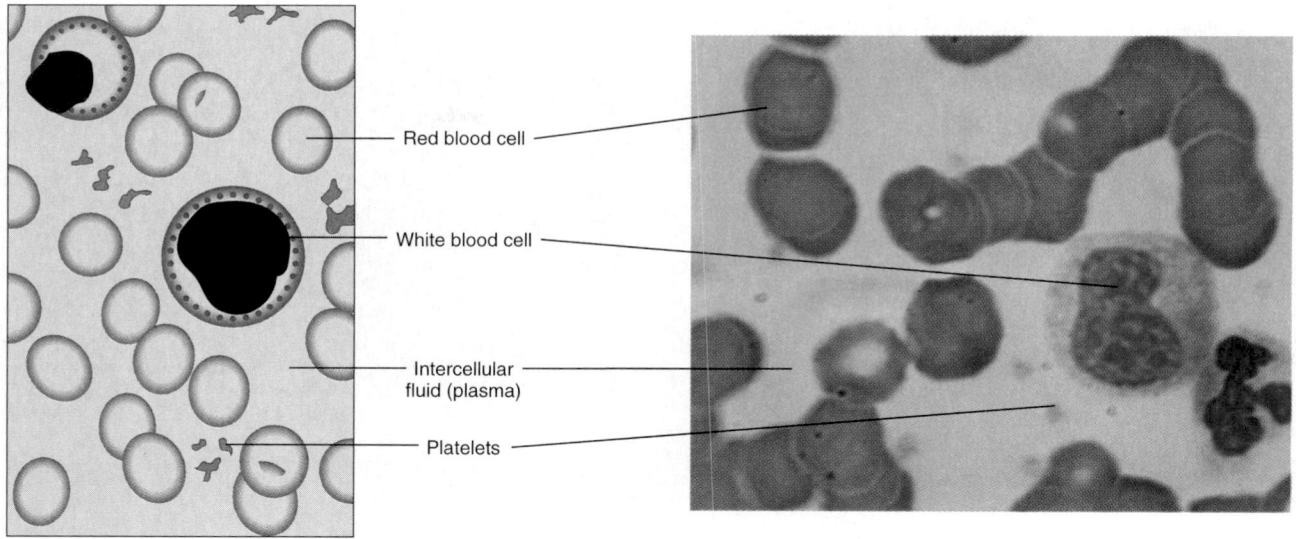

Red blood cell

White blood cell

Intercellular
fluid (plasma)

Platelets

(*m*) Blood is a type of connective tissue. It consists of an intercellular fluid (plasma) in which red blood cells, white blood cells, and platelets are suspended. (Photomicrograph at right is magnified ×640.)

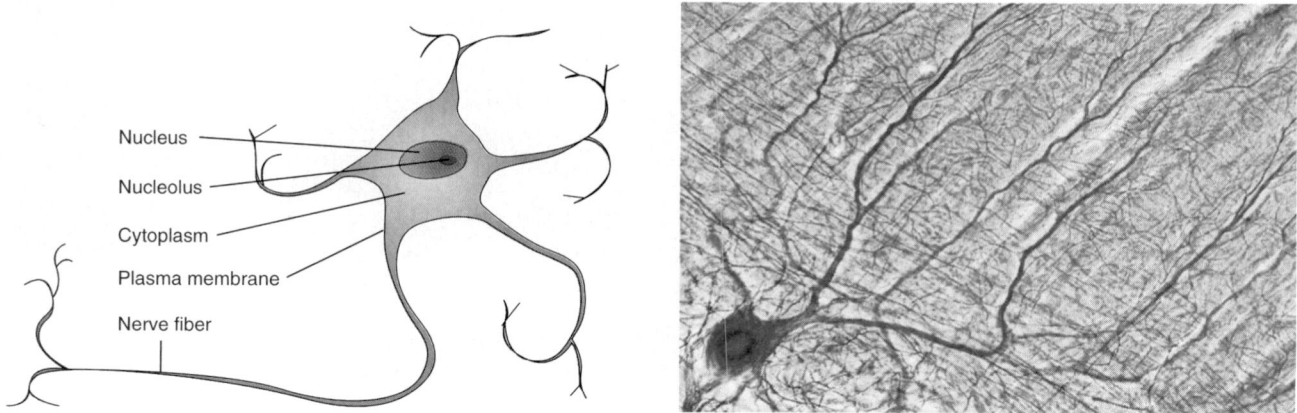

Nucleus

Nucleolus

Cytoplasm

Plasma membrane

Nerve fiber

(*n*) Nervous tissue. Neurons in nerve tissue function to transmit impulses to other neurons or to muscles or glands. (Photomicrograph at right is magnified ×450.)

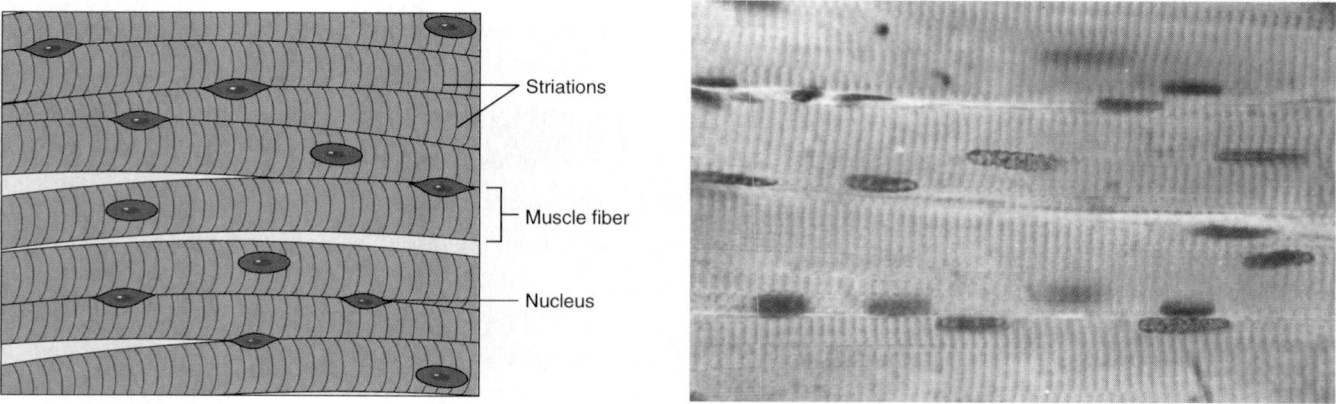

Striations

Muscle fiber

Nucleus

(*o*) Skeletal muscle tissue is composed of striated muscle fibers (cells) that contain many nuclei. (Photomicrograph at right is magnified ×250.)

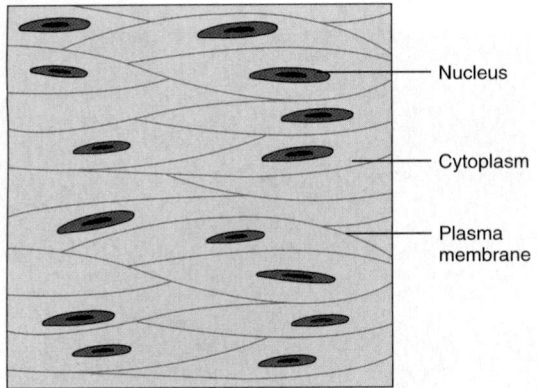
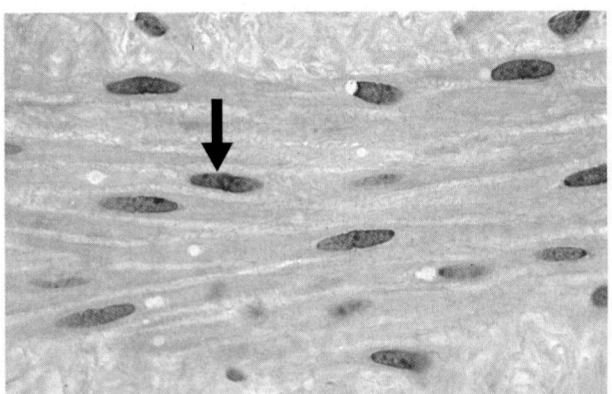

(*p*) Smooth muscle is formed of spindle-shaped cells, each containing a single nucleus (arrow). (Photomicrograph at right is magnified ×250.)

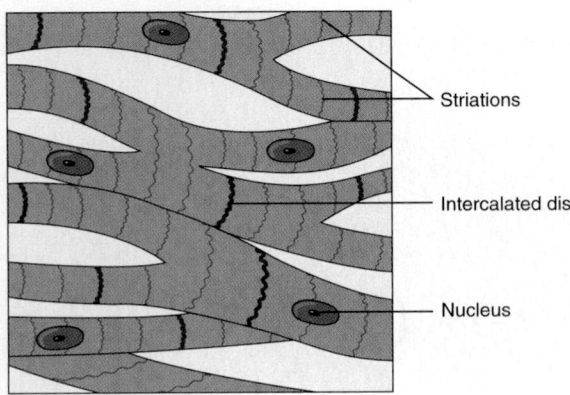
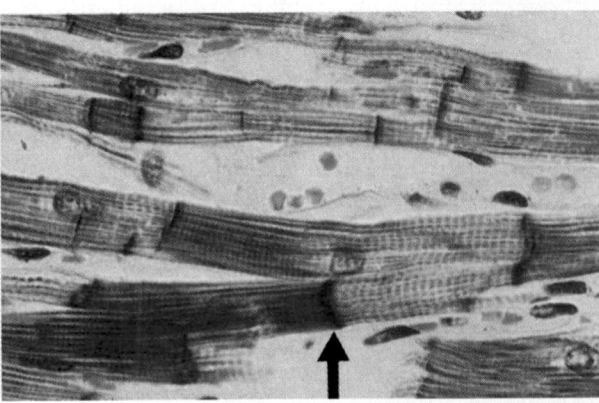

(*q*) Cardiac muscle consists of striated cells, each containing a single nucleus and specialized junctions called intercalated disks (arrow). (Photomicrograph at right is magnified ×400.)

ORGANS

Organs (Gr. *organnon,* an independent part of the body) are the functional units of an animal's body that are made up of more than one type of tissue. Examples include the heart, lungs, liver, spleen, and kidneys.

ORGAN SYSTEMS

The next higher level of structural organization in animals is the organ system. An **organ system** (Gr. *systema,* being together) is an association of organs that together perform an overall function. The systems that are found in higher vertebrate animals are the integumentary, skeletal, muscular, nervous, endocrine, circulatory, lymphatic, respiratory, digestive,

urinary, and reproductive systems. These will be discussed in detail in chapters 32 through 39.

The highest level in an animal body is the organismic level. All the parts of the animal body functioning with one another contribute to the total organism—a living entity or individual.

Stop and Ask Yourself

19. What is a tissue?
20. What are some functions of epithelial tissue? Where would these tissues be found in a higher animal?
21. How are epithelial tissues classified?
22. What are the different types of connective tissue?

SUMMARY

1. All animal cells have three basic parts: the nucleus, cytoplasm, and the plasma membrane.

2. Cell membranes are composed mainly of phospholipids and proteins and allow certain materials to move through them. This quality is called selective permeability. The fluid-mosaic model is based on our knowledge of the plasma membrane.

3. Some molecules use their own energy to pass through a cell membrane from areas of higher concentration to areas of lower concentration. Examples of these passive processes are simple diffusion, facilitated diffusion, osmosis, and filtration.

4. Active transport across cell membranes requires energy from the cell to move substances from areas of lower concentration to areas of higher concentration. Additional processes that move molecules across membranes are endocytosis and exocytosis. Three types of endocytosis are pinocytosis, phagocytosis, and receptor-mediated endocytosis.

5. The cytoplasm of a cell is composed of two phases. The particulate phase consists of organelles and various inclusions. The aqueous phase consists of the fluid cytosol.

6. Ribosomes are the sites of protein synthesis.

7. The endoplasmic reticulum (ER) is a series of channels that functions in transport, enzyme and protein storage, and provides a point of attachment for ribosomes. Two types of ER exist: smooth and rough.

8. The Golgi apparatus aids in the synthesis and secretion of glycoproteins, as well as the processing and modification of other materials (e.g., enzymes).

9. Lysosomes digest nutrients and clean away dead or damaged cell parts.

10. Mitochondria convert energy in food molecules to a form usable by the cell.

11. Microtubules, intermediate filaments, and microfilaments make up the cytoskeleton of the cell. The cytoskeleton functions in transport, support, and the movement of structures in the cell, such as organelles and chromosomes.

12. Centrioles assist in cell division and are involved with the movement of chromosomes during cell division.

13. Cytoplasmic inclusions are usually either food material that the cell needs or the stored products of the cell's metabolic activities.

14. The nucleus of a cell contains DNA, which controls the cell's genetic program and other metabolic activities.

15. The nuclear envelope contains many pores that allow material to enter and leave the nucleus.

16. The chromosomes in the nucleus have DNA organized into genes, which are specific DNA sequences that control and regulate the activities of the cell.

17. The nucleolus is a preassembly point for ribosomes.

18. Tissues are groups of cells with a common structure and function. Four types exist: epithelial, connective, muscular, and nervous.

19. An organ is composed of more than one type of tissue. An organ system consists of an association of organs.

SELECTED KEY TERMS

centrioles (*p. 46*)
cytoplasm (*p. 32*)
cytoskeleton (*p. 45*)
endoplasmic reticulum (ER) (*p. 42*)
epithelial tissue (*p. 48*)

Golgi apparatus (*p. 44*)
homeostasis (*p. 36*)
lysosomes (*p. 44*)
mitochondria (*p. 45*)
nucleolus (*p. 47*)
nucleus (*p. 32*)

CRITICAL THINKING QUESTIONS

1. Why is the mitochondrion called the "power generator" of the cell?

2. One of the larger facets of modern zoology can be described as "membrane biology." What are the common principles that unite the diverse functions of membranes?

3. Why is the current model of the plasma membrane called the "fluid-mosaic" model? What is the fluid and in what sense is it fluid? What makes up the mosaic?

4. If you could visualize osmosis, seeing the solute and solvent particles as individual entities, what would an osmotic gradient look like?

5. Why do some animal cells have the ability to transport materials against a concentration gradient? Could animals survive without this capability?

ENERGY AND ENZYMES:
LIFE'S DRIVING AND CONTROLLING FORCES

Outline

Concepts

1. All life processes in a cell are driven by energy. Energy is the capacity to do work. It can exist in two forms: kinetic energy is actively involved in doing work, and potential energy is stored for future use.
2. The cell obtains energy by utilizing chemical fuel and obeying the first and second laws of thermodynamics.
3. The speed of a chemical reaction depends on the activation energy necessary to initiate it. Catalysts reduce the amount of activation energy necessary to initiate a chemical reaction and, therefore, speed up the reaction. Cells use specialized proteins called enzymes as biological catalysts.
4. The activity of an enzyme is affected by any factor that alters its three-dimensional shape; for example, temperature, pH, and other chemicals. An enzyme can also employ metal ions or organic molecules to facilitate its activity; these are called cofactors. Specific cofactors that are nonprotein organic molecules are called coenzymes.
5. ATP is the universal energy currency of all cells.

Would You Like to Know:

1. what a food chain is? *(p. 56)*
2. what work is? *(p. 56)*
3. how an animal accomplishes biological work? *(p. 56)*
4. how the shape of an enzyme can be compared with a handshake? *(p. 59)*
5. what the energy currency of all animal life is? *(p. 61)*

These and other useful questions will be answered in this chapter.

This chapter contains evolutionary concepts, which are set off in this font.

An animal's use of the sun's radiant energy begins with the "capture" of that energy by photosynthetic plants (and certain microorganisms) that convert light energy to chemical energy in the form of carbohydrates. Because plants capture the sun's energy, they are called **primary producers** (figure 4.1). A **primary consumer** is a plant-eating animal, or herbivore (L. *herba,* grass + *vorare,* to devour), that obtains organic molecules by eating producers or their products. They use the energy in the organic molecules to carry out all of their cellular activities, including the synthesis of complex organic molecules.   ①   Primary consumers are preyed on by other animals, the **secondary consumers,** and so on, in what is termed a **food chain.** As each of these organisms dies, its constituents are broken down by digestion or by various **decomposers,** such as bacteria and fungi. This producer-consumer-decomposer sequence in a food chain represents a flow of both energy and matter.

Nutrients are continuously being broken down to provide the energy necessary for life. In fact, life can be viewed as a constant flow of energy, channeled by an animal, to do the work of living. This "living chemistry" is called metabolism. **Metabolism** (Gr. *metaballein,* to change) is the total of all the chemical reactions occurring in an animal's cells. It involves the acquisition and use of energy in stockpiling, breaking down, assembling, and eliminating substances to ensure the maintenance, growth, and reproduction of the animal. Metabolism consists of synthetic processes called **anabolism** (Gr. *anabole,* building up) and degrading processes called **catabolism** (Gr. *katabole,* breaking down). This chapter will focus on what energy is, how an animal uses it, and how metabolism is controlled via enzymes. The next chapter will present the network of chemical reactions that is the highway system for the flow of energy through an animal.

WHAT IS ENERGY?

Energy is the capacity to do work.   ②   **Work** is the transfer of energy. Energy can also be transformed. For example, solar (radiant) energy can be transformed into the chemical energy in a plant (*see figure 4.1*). The plant can then be burned in a steam generator and the energy transformed into the energy of motion (e.g., the turning of a wheel). Energy has many forms: the heat from a furnace, the sound of a jet plane, the electric current that lights a bulb, the radioactivity in a heart pacemaker, or the pull of a magnet.

Energy exists in two states: kinetic and potential. **Kinetic energy** is the energy of motion (e.g., a thundering waterfall). **Potential energy** is stored energy (e.g., a giant boulder poised on a pinnacle). In a living animal, energy in chemical bonds is a form of potential energy.   ③   The bond energy in organic molecules is used by animals to accomplish biological work. Much of the work performed by an animal involves the transformation of potential energy to kinetic energy in its cells.

The most convenient way to measure energy is in terms of heat production. This is why the study of energy is called **thermodynamics** (Gr. *therme,* heat + *dynamis,* power). The

most commonly employed unit for measuring heat in an animal is the **kilocalorie (kcal)** or nutritional Calorie (notice the large "C"). A kilocalorie is the amount of heat necessary to raise 1 kg of water 1° C and is equal to 1,000 calories. A reasonable daily intake of energy for an average person is approximately 2,000 to 2,500 kcal. A **calorie** (notice the small "c") is the amount of heat it takes to raise the temperature of 1 g (1 cc) of water 1° C (usually from 14.5 to 15.5° C).

<table>
<tr><td>

Stop and Ask Yourself

1. How would you define metabolism?
2. What is energy? What is work?
3. What is the difference between kinetic and potential energy?
4. What defines a primary producer? A secondary consumer?

</td></tr>
</table>

THE LAWS OF ENERGY TRANSFORMATIONS

Energy transformations are governed by two laws of thermodynamics. The **first law of thermodynamics,** sometimes called the law of conservation of energy, states that energy can neither be created nor destroyed, only transformed. What this means is that energy can change from one form to another (e.g., electrical energy passes through a hot plate to produce heat energy), or can be transformed from potential to kinetic energy (e.g., a squirrel eats a nut and then uses this energy to climb a tree), but it can never be lost or created. Thus, the total amount of energy in the universe must always remain constant.

The **second law of thermodynamics** states that all objects in the universe tend to become more disordered, and that the total amount of disorder in the universe is continually increasing. The measure of this degree of disorganization is called **entropy.** Consider this simple illustration. When natural gas is burned in a stove, the potential chemical energy stored in the bonds of the gas molecules is converted to light (the blue flame) and heat. Some of the heat energy can be used to boil water on the stove, and some is dissipated into the kitchen where it is no longer available to do work. This unusable energy represents increased entropy.

ACTIVATION ENERGY

Most chemical reactions require an input of energy to start (e.g., a match is lit, and the heat energy is used to start wood burning in a fireplace). At the level of chemical activity, it is necessary to break existing chemical bonds before it is possible to form new bonds and input energy is required to do so.

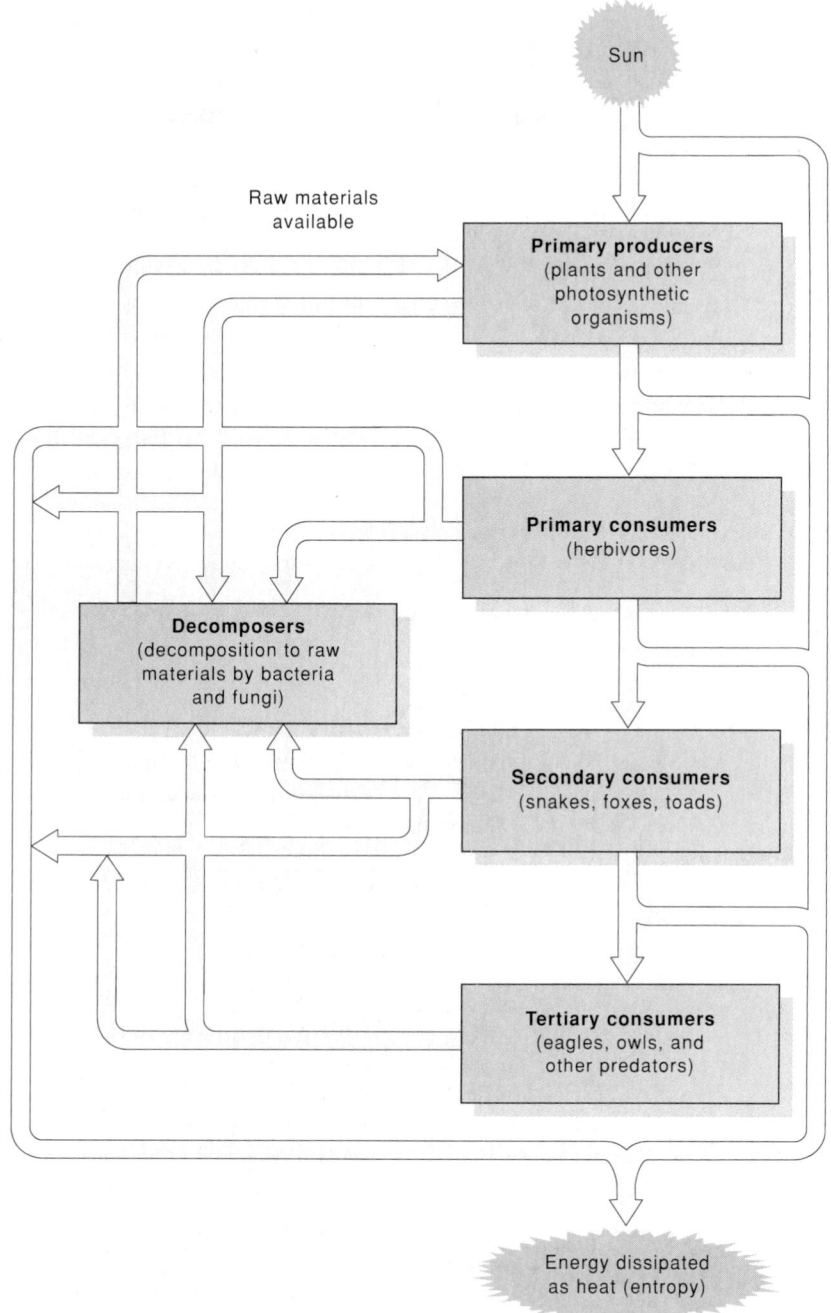

Figure 4.1

The Sun's Radiant Energy Sustains Virtually All Organisms. This figure represents a food chain and the flow of energy and materials through living systems.

In thermodynamics, this input energy is called activation energy (figure 4.2).

A reaction with a net release of energy is one in which the reactant contains more energy than the products. In other words, the amount of this excess energy (called "free energy") released into the environment is greater than the activation energy required to initiate the reaction. These reactions occur spontaneously and are called **exergonic** (L. *ex*, out + Gr. *ergon*, work)

(figure 4.3*a*). In contrast, a chemical reaction in which the product contains more energy than the reactants requires a greater input of energy from the environment than is released (figure 4.3*b*). Because these reactions do not occur spontaneously, they are called **endergonic** (Gr. *endon*, within + *ergon*, work).

The amount of reactant substance(s) converted to product substance(s) in a given period of time is called the reaction rate. The reaction rate of an exergonic reaction does not depend on

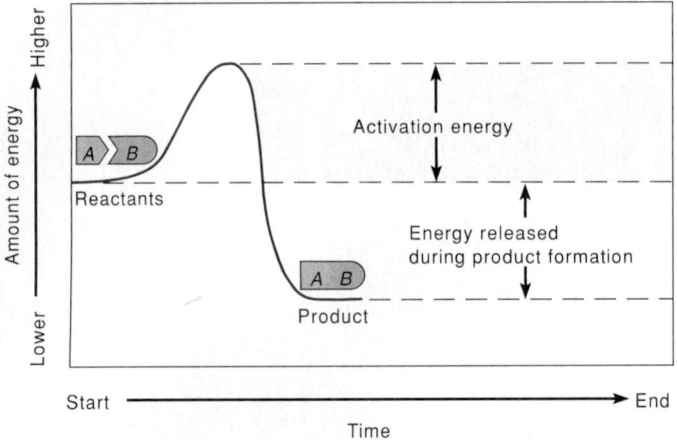

FIGURE 4.2

An Energy Diagram. Before a chemical reaction occurs, energy must be supplied to destabilize existing chemical bonds. This energy is called activation energy.

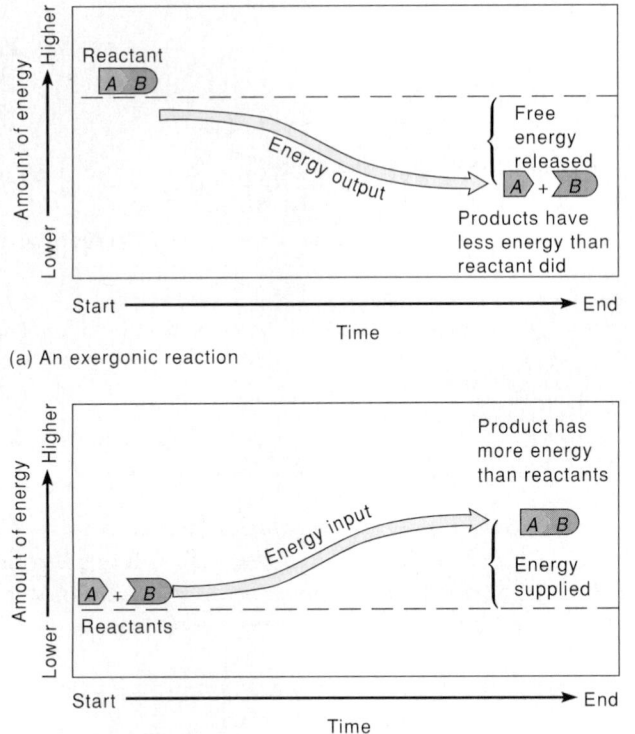

(a) An exergonic reaction

(b) An endergonic reaction

FIGURE 4.3

Exergonic and Endergonic Reactions. (*a*) In an exergonic reaction, the products have less energy than the reactant, and excess energy is released to the environment. (*b*) In an endergonic reaction, the product of the reaction contains more energy than the reactants, so energy input is needed for the reaction to occur.

how much energy the reaction releases, but instead on the amount of activation energy that is required for the reaction to begin. The larger the activation energy of a chemical reaction, the more slowly it will occur, because at a given temperature, fewer molecules succeed in overcoming the initial energy hurdle. However, activation energies are not fixed. For example, when stress is placed on certain chemical bonds, they may break more easily. Affecting a chemical bond in a way that lowers the activation energy of a reaction is an example of **catalysis.** Any substance that performs catalysis is called a catalyst. A **catalyst** (Gr. *kata*, down + *lysis*, a loosening) can be defined as a substance that accelerates the rate of a chemical reaction (or allows it to proceed at a lower environmental temperature) by decreasing the activation energy, without itself being used up in the reaction (figure 4.4). In cells, the catalysts are almost always protein enzymes.

Stop and Ask Yourself

5. What is the difference between an exergonic and endergonic chemical reaction?
6. What is meant by activation energy?
7. What are the first and second laws of thermodynamics?

ENZYMES: BIOLOGICAL CATALYSTS

Enzymes are proteins having enormous catalytic power; they greatly enhance the rate at which specific chemical reactions take place. The metabolism of an animal is organized and controlled specifically at the points where catalysis takes place. Therefore, one of the most important foundations in all of biology is that life is a series of chemical processes regulated by enzymes. An **enzyme** (Gr. *enzymos*, leavened) is a biological catalyst that is capable of accelerating a specific chemical reaction by lowering the required activation energy, but is unaltered itself in the process. In other words, the same reaction would have occurred to the same degree in the absence of the catalyst, but it would have progressed at a much slower rate. Because it is unaltered, the enzyme can be used over and over.

An enzyme is extremely selective for the reaction it will catalyze. The reactants of enzymatic reactions are called **substrates.** The precise "fit" between an enzyme and its specific substrate is crucial to the metabolism of a cell. For example, cellular concentrations of many reactants must be kept at low levels in order to avoid undesirable side reactions. At the same time, concentrations must be kept high enough for the required reactions to occur at a rate that is compatible with life. As presented in the next chapter, metabolism proceeds under these seemingly conflicting conditions because enzymes channel molecules into and through specific chemical pathways. With the exception of the several digestive enzymes that were the first to be discovered (e.g., pepsin and trypsin), all enzyme names end with the suffix *ase.*

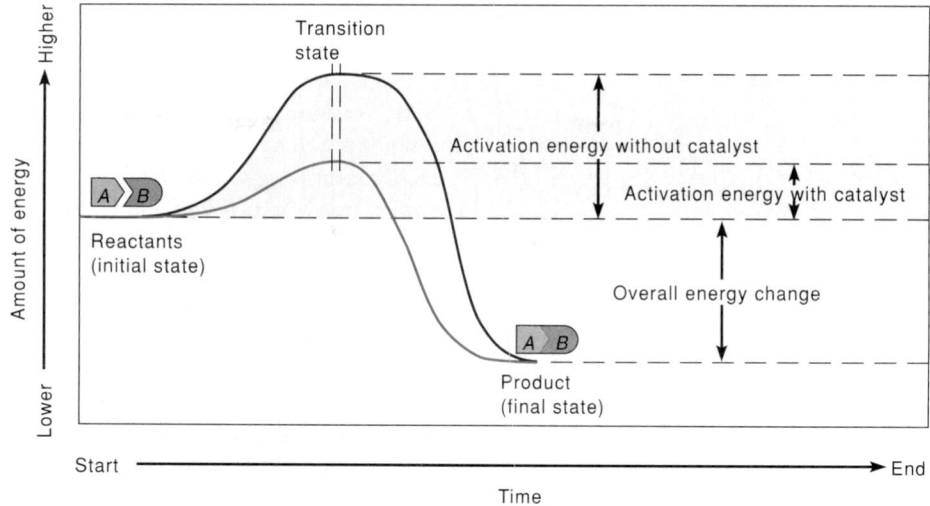

FIGURE 4.4

The Function of a Catalyst. Catalysts lower the amount of activation energy required to initiate a chemical reaction. As a result, at the same temperature, the reaction moves to completion much more quickly.

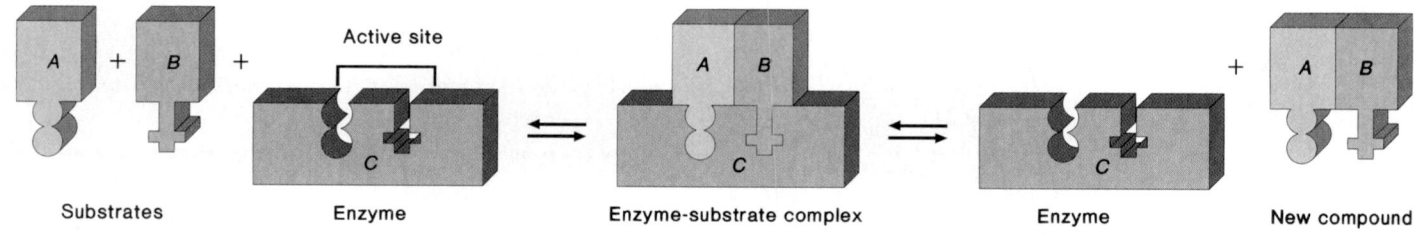

FIGURE 4.5

Enzymes. Enzyme action is like a "lock and key" fit. Substrate molecules A and B fit into the active site of enzyme C. An enzyme-substrate complex is formed, and A and B react to form the new compound AB. AB is released from the enzyme, and the enzyme is recycled.

ENZYME STRUCTURE

Enzymes are globular protein molecules that have three-dimensional shapes, with at least one surface region having an area with a crevice or pocket. This crevice occupies only a small portion of the enzyme's surface and is known as its active site (figure 4.5). This site is shaped so that a substrate molecule (or several substrate molecules, depending on the reaction), fits into it in a very specific way and is held in place by weak chemical forces, such as hydrogen bonds. Binding of the substrate to the enzyme causes a change in the enzyme's shape. This phenomenon of change in an enzyme's shape following binding of substrate is called **induced fit.** 4 The induced fit is like a clasping handshake. The embrace of the substrate by the active site brings chemical groups of the active site into positions that enhance their ability to work on the substrate and catalyze the chemical reaction. When the reaction is completed, the product (new compound) of the catalyzed reaction is released, and the enzyme resumes its initial conformation (shape), ready to catalyze another chemical reaction.

ENZYME FUNCTION

When a substrate molecule has bound to the active site of an enzyme, an **enzyme-substrate complex (ES)** is formed. Formation of an enzyme-substrate complex is the essential first step in enzyme catalysis and can be summarized as follows:

Enzyme + substrate ⇌ enzyme-substrate complex
⇌ products + enzyme

Once the unstable, high-energy ES has formed, amino acid side groups of the enzyme are placed against certain bonds of the substrate. The amino acid side groups of the enzyme react with the substrate by stressing or distorting their bonds, which lowers the activation energy needed to break the bonds. The bonds are broken, releasing the substrates, which are now free to react, producing the final products and releasing the enzyme.

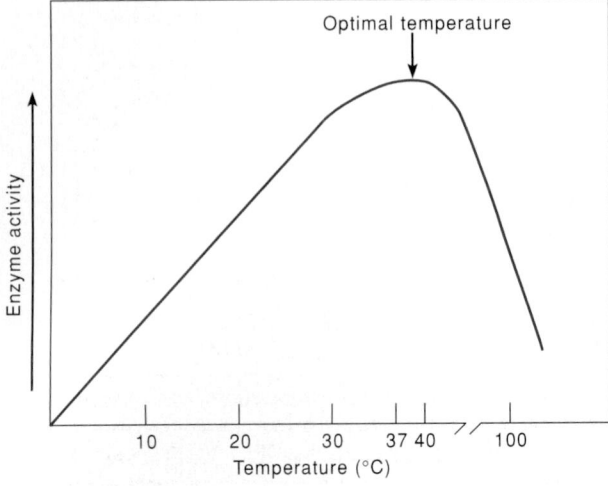

(a)

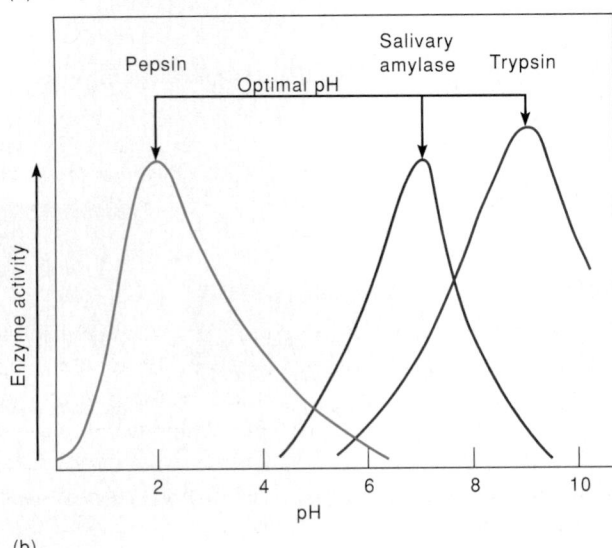

(b)

Figure 4.6

How the Environment Affects Enzymes. (*a*) Effect of temperature on enzyme activity. (*b*) The effect of pH on three different enzymes.

Factors Affecting Enzyme Activity

Any condition that alters the three-dimensional shape of an enzyme will also affect its activity. Two such factors that affect enzyme activity are temperature and pH.

As presented in chapter 2, the shape of a protein is determined largely by its hydrogen bonds (*see figure 2.15*). Hydrogen bonds are easily disrupted by temperature changes. For example, most higher animals, such as birds and mammals, have enzymes that function best within a relatively narrow temperature range between 35 and 40° C (figure 4.6*a*). Below 35° C, the bonds that determine protein shape are not flexible enough to permit the shape change necessary for substrate to fit into a reactive site. Above 40° C, the bonds are too weak to hold the protein in proper position and maintain its shape. When proper shape is lost, the enzyme is in essence destroyed; this loss of shape is called **denaturation.**

Most enzymes also have a pH optimum, usually between 6 and 8 (figure 4.6*b*). For example, when the pH is too low, the H^+ ions combine with the R groups of the enzyme's amino acids, reducing their ability to bind with substrates. Acid environments can also denature enzymes if they are not adapted to such conditions. There are, however, some enzymes that function at a low pH. For example, pepsin is the enzyme found in the stomach of mammals and has an optimal pH of approximately 2. Pepsin is able to function at such a low pH because it has an amino acid sequence that maintains its ionic and hydrogen bonds, even in the presence of large numbers of hydrogen ions (low pH). Conversely, trypsin is active in the more basic medium (pH 9) found in the small intestine of mammals. Overall, the pH optimum of an enzyme reflects the pH of the body fluid in which the enzyme is found.

8. What is an enzyme? What is a substrate?
9. How are enzymes named?
10. What is the structure of an enzyme?
11. How do enzymes function?
12. How do temperature, pH, and other factors affect enzyme function?

Cofactors and Coenzymes

Cofactors are metal ions such as Ca^{2+}, Mg^{2+}, Mn^{2+}, Cu^{2+}, and Zn^{2+}. Many enzymes must use these metal ions to change a nonfunctioning active site to a functioning one. In these enzymes, the attachment of a cofactor causes a shape change in the protein that allows it to combine with its substrate (figure 4.7*a*). The cofactors of other enzymes participate in the temporary bonds between the enzyme and its substrate when the enzyme-substrate complex is formed (figure 4.7*b*).

Coenzymes are nonprotein, organic molecules that participate in enzyme-catalyzed reactions, often by transporting electrons, in the form of hydrogen atoms, from one enzyme to another. Many vitamins function as coenzymes or are used to make coenzymes (e.g., niacin and riboflavin). Just as a taxi transports people around a city, so coenzymes transport energy, in the form of hydrogen atoms, from one enzyme to another.

One of the most important coenzymes in the cell is the hydrogen acceptor **nicotine adenine dinucleotide (NAD$^+$),** which is made from a B vitamin. When NAD$^+$ acquires a hydrogen atom from an enzyme, it becomes reduced to NADH (figure 4.8). The electron of the hydrogen atom contains energy that is then carried by the NADH molecule. For example, when various foods are oxidized in the cell, the cell strips electrons from the food molecules and transfers them to NAD$^+$, which is reduced to NADH. As more and more NADH molecules accumulate in the cell, the potential energy of the cell increases.

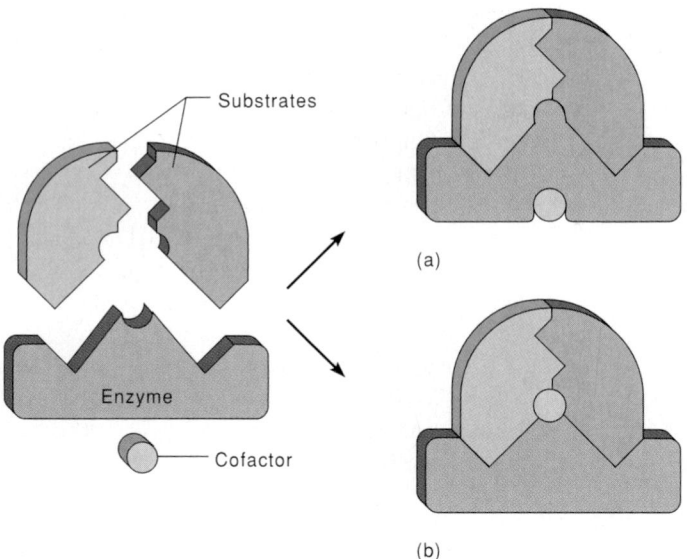

FIGURE 4.7

Cofactors. (*a*) The cofactor changes the conformation of the active site, permitting a better fit between enzyme and its substrate. (*b*) The cofactor participates in the temporary bonding between the active site of the enzyme and the substrate.

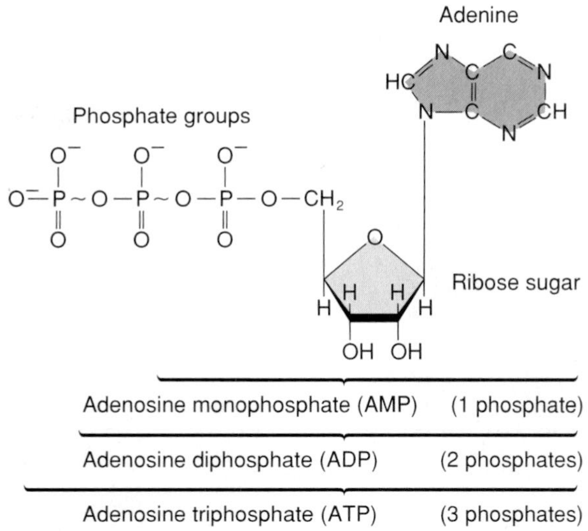

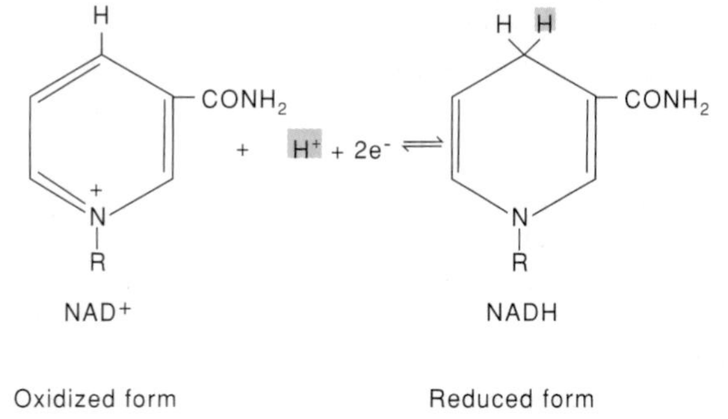

FIGURE 4.8

Nicotine Adenine Dinucleotide (NAD): Oxidized (NAD⁺) and Reduced (NADH) Forms. When the NAD is reduced, one electron is attached to the nitrogen atom at position 1. The second electron attaches to a carbon atom at position 4 and is accompanied by a hydrogen ion.

ATP: THE CELL'S ENERGY CURRENCY

⑤ The major energy currency of all cells is a nucleotide called **adenosine triphosphate (ATP).** Because ATP plays a central role as the energy currency in all organisms, it must have appeared early in the history of life.

The ability of ATP to store and release energy stems from the molecule's structure. Each ATP molecule (figure 4.9) is composed of three subunits: (1) adenine, an organic molecule composed of two carbon-nitrogen rings; (2) ribose, a five-carbon sugar; and (3) three phosphate groups linked in a

FIGURE 4.9

Structural Formula for Adenosine Triphosphate, or ATP. The ATP molecule is the primary energy currency of the cell. It consists of an adenine portion, the sugar ribose, and three phosphates. The wavy lines (tildes) connecting the last two phosphates represent high-energy chemical bonds from which energy can be quickly released.

linear chain. The covalent bond connecting these phosphates is indicated by the "tilde" symbol (~) and represents a high-energy bond. However, the energy is not localized in the bond itself; it is a property of the entire molecule and is simply released as the phosphate bond is broken. These bonds have a low activation energy (*see figure 4.4*) and are broken easily. When one bond is broken, about 7.3 kcal (7,300 calories) are released per mole of ATP as follows:

$$ATP + H_2O \rightarrow ADP + P_i + energy\ (7.3\ kcal/mole)$$

The energy from ATP is sufficient to drive most of the endergonic reactions of the cell. In a typical energy reaction, only the outermost of the two high-energy bonds is broken (hydrolyzed). When this happens, ATP becomes **ADP (adenosine diphosphate).** In some cases, ADP can be hydrolyzed to **AMP (adenosine monophosphate)** as follows:

$$ADP + H_2O \rightarrow AMP + P_i + energy\ (7.3\ kcal/mole)$$

Cells contain a reservoir of ADP and phosphate (P_i). As long as a cell is living, ATP is constantly being cleaved into ADP plus phosphate to drive the many energy-requiring processes of the cell, enabling the animal to perform biological work (figure 4.10). However, ATP cannot be stored for long. Once formed, ATP lasts only a few seconds before it is used to perform biological work. Thus, cells are constantly recycling their ADP. Using the energy derived from foodstuffs and from stored fats and starches, ADP and phosphate are recombined to form ATP, with 7.3 kcal of energy per mole contributed to each newly formed high-energy phosphate bond.

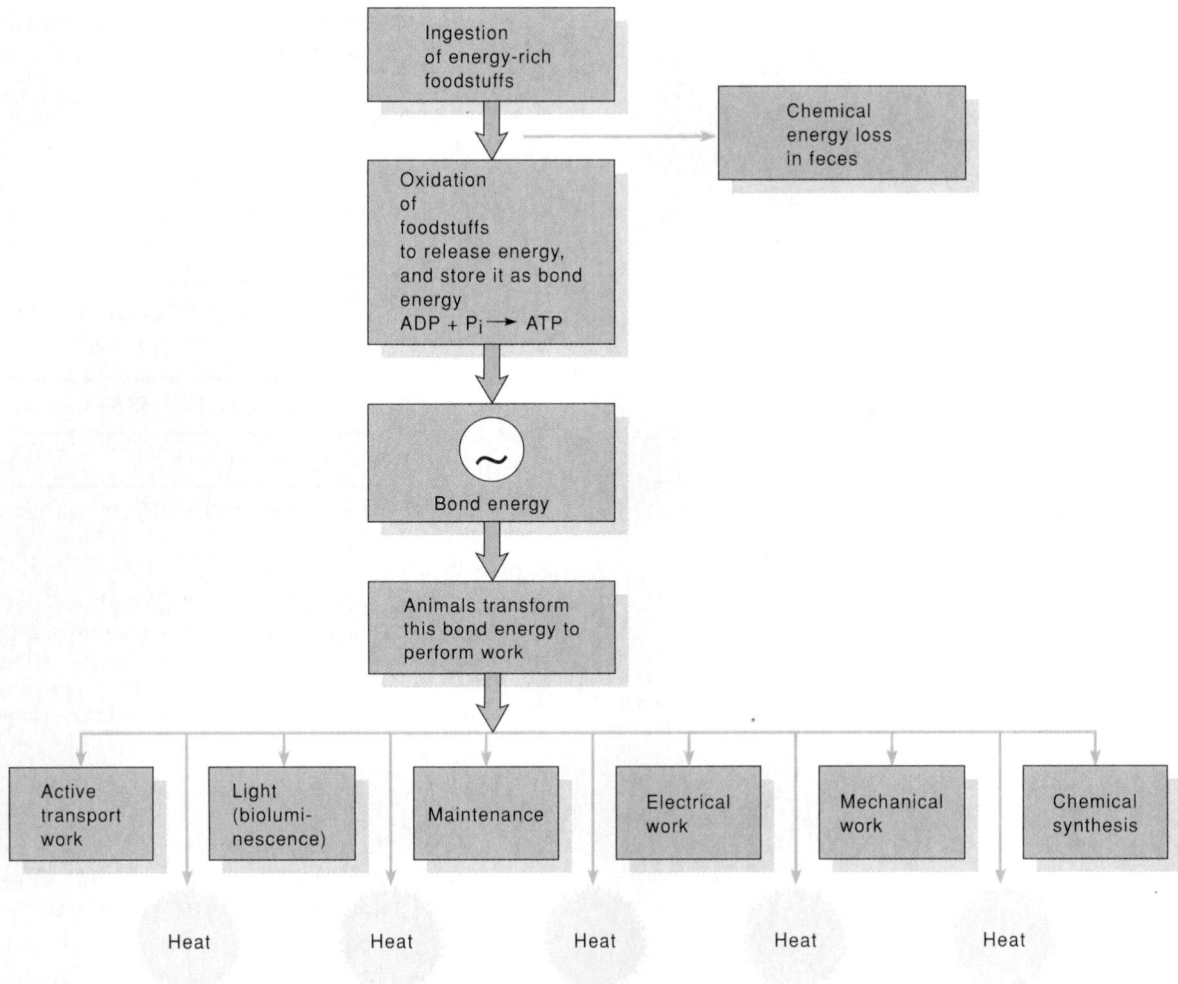

FIGURE 4.10

Some Energy Utilization Pathways in Animals. Notice that heat is lost in every transformation.

HOW CELLS TRAP ENERGY: AN OVERVIEW

Within their cells, animals make ATP in two ways: substrate-level phosphorylation and chemiosmosis. As noted above, the formation of ATP from ADP and phosphate requires the input of energy (the same 7.3 kcal that is released when ATP is hydrolyzed). Thus, to get the energy required for the synthesis of ATP from ADP and phosphate, the reaction is coupled with an exergonic reaction (figure 4.11a). A phosphate group is transferred by an enzyme to ADP from a substrate with a phosphate bond even more easily broken than that of ATP (i.e., the energy from the exergonic reaction is greater than the input of energy necessary to drive the synthesis of ATP). The generation of ATP by coupling strongly exergonic reactions with the synthesis of ATP from ADP and phosphate is called **substrate-level phosphorylation.** Substrate-level phosphorylation probably appeared very early in the history of organisms because (1) the initial use of

carbohydrates by organisms as an energy source is accomplished by substrate-level phosphorylation; (2) the mechanism for substrate-level phosphorylation is present in most living animal cells; and (3) substrate-level phosphorylation is one of the most fundamental of all ATP-generating reactions.

Although substrate-level phosphorylation may be the oldest method of generating ATP, far more ATP is generated using another process called **chemiosmosis** (figure 4.11b). Organisms possess transmembrane channels in their mitochondrial membranes that can pump protons. These proton pumps use a flow of electrons to induce a shape change in the protein, which in turn causes protons to move out of the inner compartment of a mitochondrion. As the proton (H^+) concentration in the outer compartment of the mitochondrion becomes greater than the inside, the outer protons are driven through the membrane by an electrical-chemical proton gradient. As protons move down this gradient between outer and

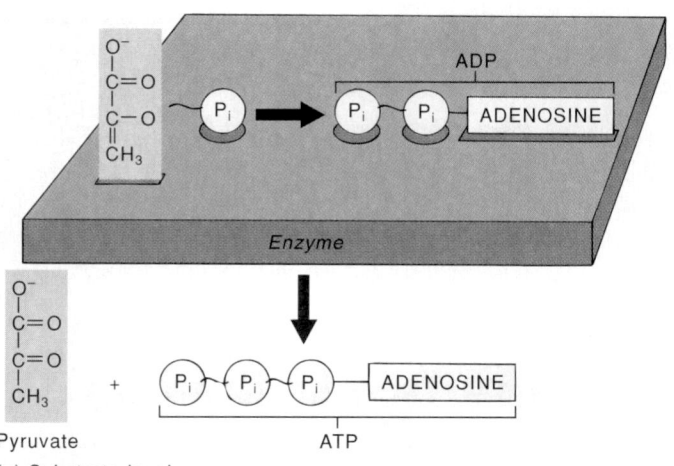

(a) Substrate-level phosphorylation

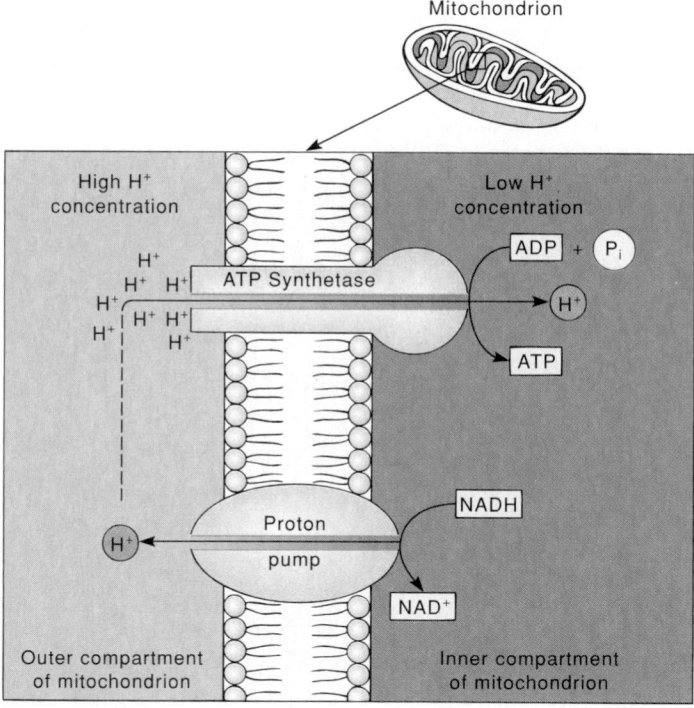

(b) Chemiosmosis

FIGURE 4.11

ATP Generation. (*a*) Substrate-level phosphorylation. In this example, a phosphate group is transferred from an enzyme-substrate complex to ADP to form ATP. This reaction takes place because the high-energy bond of the substrate has higher energy than the phosphate bonds of ADP. (*b*) Chemiosmotic synthesis occurs via hydrogen ions moved from one side of a membrane to the other, generating a proton gradient across the membrane. When protons move back across the membrane through special channels, their passage generates ATP from ADP and P_i.

inner mitochondrial compartments, they induce the formation of ATP from ADP, phosphate, and the enzyme ATP synthetase.

The electrons that drive the electron transport system involved in chemiosmosis are obtained from chemical bonds of food molecules in all organisms and from photosynthesis in plants. This electron-stripping process is called **cellular respiration,** or **aerobic respiration** because free oxygen is needed. Basically, aerobic respiration is the oxidation of food molecules to obtain energy and is the subject of the next chapter.

Biologists have been questioning what biological molecules do for approximately 100 years. This chapter presents some facts on how these molecules function via enzymes. Enzymes have evolved over 3 billion years of evolution, and they have a great deal to teach us. Happily, there is some hope that the number of lessons is merely finite, for we already see examples of enzyme molecules, unrelated by evolution, but with almost identically arranged working parts. Hopefully, the next chapter will help clarify what enzymes are "trying to tell us" about the universality of energy-harvesting pathways and animal life.

Stop and Ask Yourself

13. What three component parts make up the ATP molecule?
14. Why doesn't ATP accumulate in a cell?
15. What is substrate-level phosphorylation? Chemiosmosis?
16. How do cofactors function? Coenzymes?

SUMMARY

1. Energy is the capacity to do work. Kinetic energy is the energy that is actively engaged in doing work, whereas potential energy is stored energy. Animals convert potential energy into kinetic energy to perform biological work, which is the transfer of energy.

2. The first law of thermodynamics states that the amount of energy in the universe is fixed, and that energy cannot be created or destroyed; however, energy can be converted from one form to another.

3. The second law of thermodynamics states that the randomness or disorder in the universe is increasing. This process is called entropy.

4. The speed of a chemical reaction depends on the amount of activation energy required to break existing bonds. Catalysis is the chemical process of increasing the reaction rate by lowering the amount of activation energy required to initiate the reaction. Enzymes are the biological catalysts of cells.

5. Enzymes have a specific three-dimensional shape, with one or more reactive sites that bind substrates. Cells contain many different enzymes, each of which catalyzes a different chemical reaction.

6. Factors such as temperature, pH, substrate concentration, cofactors, and coenzymes can affect the reaction rate of an enzyme.

7. Cells focus their energy resources on the manufacture of ATP from ADP and phosphate, a process that requires the cell to supply 7.3 kcal/mole of energy, which it obtains from electrons stripped from foodstuffs. Mitochondrial membranes are the main site of ATP production. Cells use ATP to drive endergonic reactions and accomplish biological work.

8. The harvesting of chemical energy takes place via either substrate-level phosphorylation or chemiosmosis. In substrate-level phosphorylation, a phosphate group is transferred from an enzyme-substrate complex to ADP by coupling an endergonic reaction to a highly exergonic one. In chemiosmosis, there is a transport of electrons to an electron transport system in the mitochondrial membrane. In the process, a gradient of H^+ ions (protons) is established that powers the synthesis of ATP.

SELECTED KEY TERMS

anabolism (*p. 56*)

catabolism (*p. 56*)

catalysis (*p. 58*)

catalyst (*p. 58*)

endergonic (*p. 57*)

energy (*p. 56*)

entropy (*p. 56*)

enzyme (*p. 58*)

enzyme-substrate complex (ES) (*p. 59*)

exergonic (*p. 57*)

CRITICAL THINKING QUESTIONS

1. Does the living state of an animal violate the second law of thermodynamics? In other words, how does an animal maintain a high degree of organization, even though there is a universal trend toward disorganization?

2. Why are the two laws of thermodynamics called laws, whereas the central organizing concept of biology, evolution, is called a theory?

3. Living organisms are constantly transforming energy via many different mechanisms. Give several examples in animals where one form of energy is transformed into another form.

4. As you read this statement, you are losing energy. At the risk of losing even more, describe what this means with respect to entropy.

5. Why is ATP the major energy-carrying molecule in all organisms?

How Animals Harvest Energy Stored in Nutrients

Concepts

1. All animals harvest energy from nutrients to fuel their metabolism with energy from ATP. The involved catabolic processes include glycolysis, fermentation, and aerobic respiration.
2. Glycolysis is a specific metabolic pathway that does not require oxygen and involves chemical reactions that transfer chemical energy by rearranging the chemical bonds of glucose to form molecules of pyruvate and generate two usable molecules of ATP.
3. Animals that live in an anaerobic environment (low in oxygen) utilize fermentation to transfer the electrons and associated hydrogen produced in glycolysis to another atom or molecule. Molecules other than oxygen (e.g., NAD^+) serve as electron acceptors.
4. In aerobic respiration, the Krebs cycle completes the breakdown of pyruvate to carbon dioxide, water, and H^+ (protons). In the mitochondrion, electrons from hydrogen (H) atoms are channeled to the inner mitochondrial membrane to drive proton pumps and generate ATP by way of the electron transport chain and chemiosmosis.
5. Fats and proteins can also serve as nutrients for animals. These molecules are broken down to intermediates that are eventually fed into the Krebs cycle.

Would You Like to Know:

1. how the first organisms obtained energy in the absence of oxygen? (p. 66)
2. why an incomplete method of harvesting energy has persisted through eons of time? (p. 66)
3. how glycolysis is a metabolic memory of an animal's past? (p. 68)
4. why animals store excess energy in the form of fat? (p. 72)
5. how cells are thrifty, expedient, and responsive in their metabolism? (p. 74)

These and other useful questions will be answered in this chapter.

This chapter contains evolutionary concepts, which are set off in this font.

The previous chapter introduced the fact that animals require a constant supply of energy to perform biological work. This energy is usually supplied by the energy-rich molecule ATP (*see figure 4.9*). All animals can generate ATP by breaking down organic nutrients (carbohydrates, fats, and proteins). The energy released is used to join ADP and phosphate (P_i) to form ATP.

In animals, the breakdown of organic nutrients, such as glucose, begins in a step-by-step series of chemical reactions called glycolysis. The end product of glycolysis (pyruvate) is then further broken down either in the presence of free oxygen (**aerobic**)—a process called aerobic respiration, or in the absence of free oxygen (**anaerobic**)—a process called fermentation.

Figure 5.1 provides an overview of the catabolic metabolism involved in ATP production. Note that glycolysis and fermentation (anaerobic processes) take place in the cytoplasm of a cell, and aerobic respiration takes place in the mitochondrion.

The reason glycolysis and fermentation occur in the cytoplasm is that during eukaryotic cell evolution, the enzymes that catalyze each reaction remained dissolved in the cytoplasm and did not localize in membranous organelles.   **1**   This implies an origin prior to the evolution of complex organelles. These reactions are also older in an evolutionary sense than aerobic respiration, because the reactions of the former could have occurred in the earliest primitive environment of earth before the atmosphere contained free oxygen.

This chapter presents some of the fundamental biological principles that underlie the above chemical reactions in animal cells.

GLYCOLYSIS: THE FIRST PHASE OF NUTRIENT METABOLISM

Glycolysis (Gr. *glykys*, sweet + *lyein*, to loosen) is the initial sequence of chemical reactions used by almost all cells to break the six-carbon glucose molecule into two molecules of a three-carbon compound called pyruvate (pyruvic acid) with the net production of two molecules of ATP (figure 5.2). For each molecule of glucose that enters the glycolytic pathway, four molecules of ATP are formed. However, because two ATP molecules are used to rearrange the glucose molecule to form new six-carbon compounds, the net energy yield from glycolysis is only two ATP molecules. Although glycolysis is far from an efficient pathway with respect to harvesting all the available energy from glucose, for hundreds of millions of years during the anaerobic first stages of life on the planet earth, glycolysis was the only way most organisms could harvest energy and generate ATP molecules.

EVOLUTIONARY PERSPECTIVE ON GLYCOLYSIS

If glycolysis is such an incomplete method of harvesting energy, why has it persisted through so long an evolutionary period?   **2**   One reason might be that evolution is a slow, incremental process whereby change occurs based on past events.

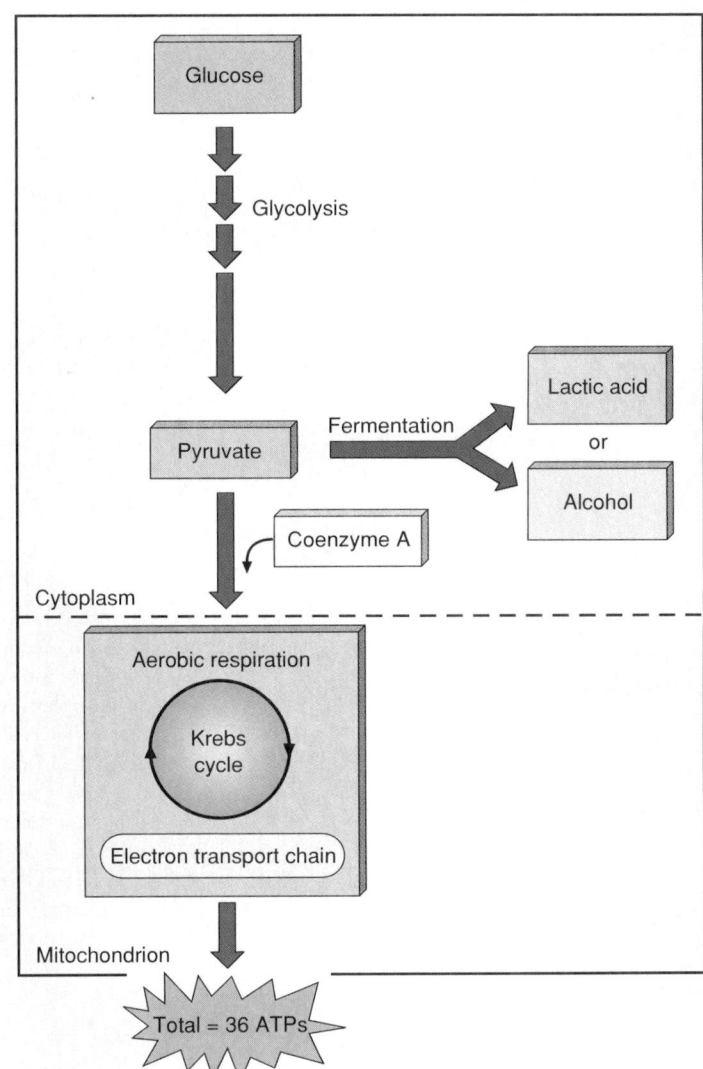

FIGURE 5.1

An Overview of the Catabolic Pathways (Glycolysis, Fermentation, Aerobic Respiration) that Generate ATP Molecules. Glycolysis begins in the cytoplasm and causes glucose to be broken down to pyruvate. In the absence of free oxygen, pyruvate will undergo fermentation instead of entering the Krebs cycle. The first step in aerobic respiration is the conversion of pyruvate to a high-energy intermediate by the addition of coenzyme A. The Krebs cycle removes electrons and passes them to the electron transport chain by way of carrier molecules. Both of these processes take place in the mitochondrion. From start (glycolysis) to finish, the aerobic pathway typically has a net energy yield of 36 ATP molecules.

Stop and Ask Yourself

1. What is the difference between aerobic and anaerobic respiration?
2. Where does glycolysis take place in a cell? Where does aerobic respiration take place?
3. What is the net energy yield in ATP molecules from glycolysis?
4. What is the evolutionary significance of glycolysis?

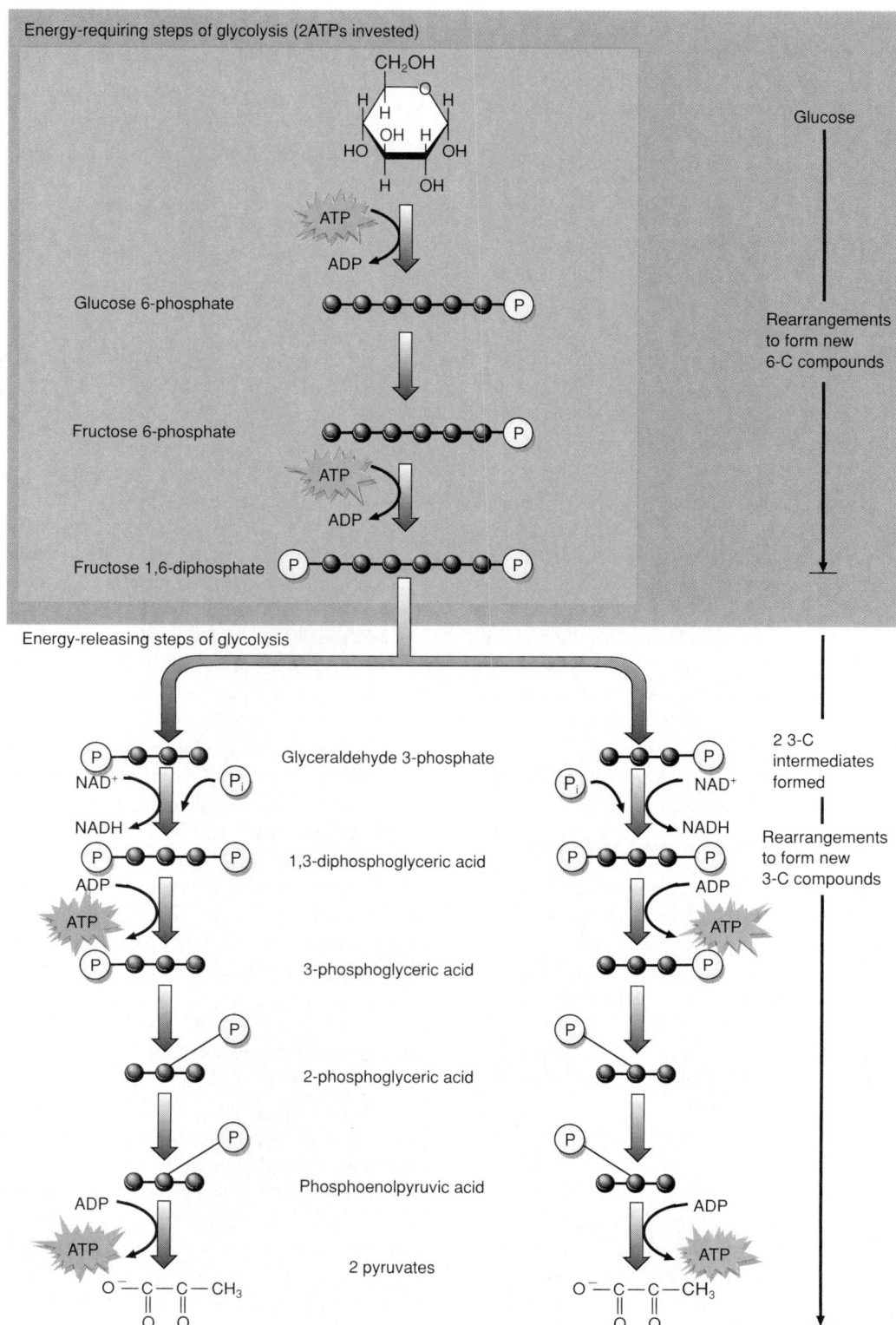

Figure 5.2

Glycolysis. In the reactions of glycolysis, glucose is rearranged, split into two three-carbon intermediates, then rearranged further to yield two molecules of pyruvate. Along the way, four ATP and two NADH molecules are produced. However, since two ATPs are used in the initial steps of glycolysis, the net yield is only two ATP molecules.

When glycolysis first occurred, it gave cells possessing it a competitive advantage over those cells that did not utilize glycolysis. The biochemistry of contemporary organisms indicates that only those organisms that were capable of glycolysis survived the early competition of life on the planet earth. Obviously, later evolutionary changes in catabolism built on this success. During this building process, glycolysis was not discarded, but instead, used as a stepping stone for the evolution of another process for the complete breakdown of glucose. Just as successive layers of paint are added by an artist to a painting in order to obtain a final product, so evolution added another layer of chemical reactions (aerobic respiration) onto the foundation layer (glycolysis) to produce a very complete method of harvesting energy.   ③   Looking at glycolysis in another way, all forms of animal life (including humans) carry on glycolysis within their cells—a metabolic memory of an animal's evolutionary past.

FERMENTATION: "LIFE WITHOUT OXYGEN"

Fermentation (L. *fermentum*, leaven) is either an evolutionary bypass that some organisms use to keep glycolysis functioning under anaerobic conditions, or more likely, a biochemical remnant that evolved very early in the history of life when the earth's atmosphere contained little or no oxygen. As with glycolysis, the ubiquity of fermentation is strong evidence for the common descent of organisms from primitive cells in which glycolysis and fermentation first appeared and still persist.

In fermentation, the hydrogen atoms generated by glycolysis are donated to organic molecules as follows:

Pyruvate + NADH → reduced compound + NAD⁺

The reduced (**reduction** is the gain of electrons) compound can be an organic acid (e.g., lactic acid), or an alcohol such as ethanol (figure 5.3).

The important point to remember about fermentation is that glucose is not completely degraded, so considerable energy still remains in the products. Beyond the two ATP molecules formed during glycolysis, no more ATP is produced. Fermentation serves only to regenerate NAD⁺ (the oxidized form of NADH; **oxidation** is the loss of electrons).

Two types of organisms can carry out fermentation: obligative anaerobic and facultatively anaerobic ones. Obligative anaerobic organisms include certain types of bacteria that survive only in the complete absence of molecular oxygen. Facultative anaerobic organisms and tissues include certain bacteria and yeasts and cells (e.g., animal muscle) that can ferment nutrients when oxygen is absent to generate some ATP by providing NAD⁺ for glycolysis. Facultatively anaerobic organisms and tissues carry out more efficient energy harvesting when oxygen is present; hence the term facultative (not obligative).

AEROBIC RESPIRATION: THE MAJOR SOURCE OF ATP

As noted above, the anaerobic generation of ATP through the reactions of glycolysis and fermentation are relatively inefficient. The end product of glycolysis (pyruvate) still contains a great deal of potential bond energy that can be harvested by further oxidation. The evolution of aerobic respiration in microorganisms and in the mitochondria of eukaryotic cells became possible only after free oxygen had accumulated in the earth's atmosphere as a result of photosynthesis. The addition of an oxygen-requiring stage to the energy-harvesting mechanisms of cells provided them with a more powerful and efficient way of extracting energy from nutrient molecules. Indeed, without the large-scale ATP production by mitochondria, life would have to be at a "snail's pace," and most animals present on earth today would never have evolved.

In aerobic respiration, the pyruvate produced by glycolysis is shunted into a metabolic pathway called the Krebs cycle or **citric acid cycle;** the NADH goes to the electron transport chain. During this aerobic metabolism, free oxygen accepts electrons and is reduced to H_2O as follows:

Pyruvate + O_2 → CO_2 + H_2O + 34ATP + heat energy

During the above reaction, 34 molecules of ATP are produced for each molecule of pyruvate consumed.

Like in glycolysis, aerobic respiration is organized into a number of reactions, each catalyzed by a specific enzyme and organized into what is called the **Krebs cycle** and the electron transport chain. The Krebs cycle, named after Hans Krebs (who began working out its details in the 1930s), is a series of reactions in which the pyruvate from glycolysis is oxidized to CO_2. Two electron carriers, nicotine adenine dinucleotide (NAD) (*see figure 4.8*) and **flavin adenine dinucleotide (FAD)** (figure 5.4) act as hydrogen acceptors and are reduced to NADH and $FADH_2$. During this phase of the cycle, three molecules of CO_2 are generated from each pyruvate molecule,

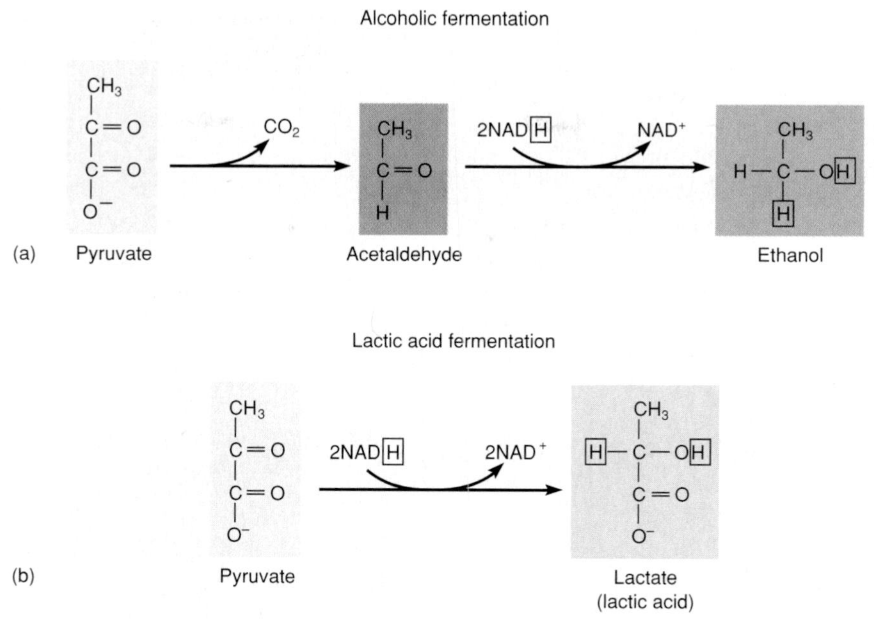

Alcoholic fermentation

(a) Pyruvate   Acetaldehyde   Ethanol

Lactic acid fermentation

(b)   Pyruvate   Lactate
                                        (lactic acid)

FIGURE 5.3

Fermentation. The purpose of fermentation is to regenerate NAD$^+$, which is needed to drive glycolysis to ultimately obtain ATP. The boxed hydrogens indicate the hydrogen ions donated by reduced NADH and the positions where the donated hydrogen ions end up after fermentation is completed. (*a*) The pathway from pyruvate to ethanol. (*b*) The pathway from pyruvate to lactate (lactic acid). Certain animal cells, deprived of oxygen, temporarily carry out lactic acid fermentation.

FAD   FADH$_2$
Oxidized form   Reduced form

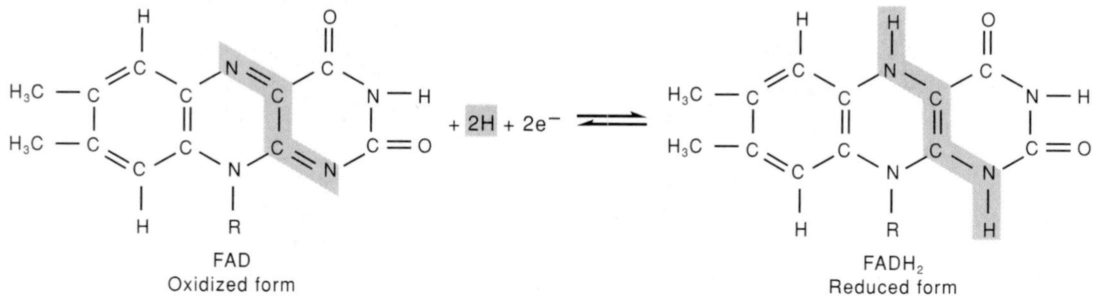

FIGURE 5.4

The Electron Carrier Flavin Adenine Dinucleotide (FAD). The equation illustrates the oxidized form of FAD going to the reduced form (FADH$_2$). The reactive sites are shaded, and the rest of the molecule is indicated by an R.

and some energy is harvested in the form of ATP (figure 5.5). Most of the remaining energy is in the form of NADH and FADH$_2$. These two molecules are shuttled into the **electron transport chain.** In this chain (figure 5.6), the reduced NADH and FADH$_2$ are oxidized, and their electrons are passed along a series of oxidation-reduction reactions to the final acceptor, oxygen.

As previously mentioned, in eukaryotic cells, aerobic respiration takes place in the mitochondria. The Krebs cycle occurs in the mitochondrial matrix (figure 5.7). The enzymes that are used to catalyze these reactions are dissolved in the fluid matrix. (In prokaryotic cells, the enzymes occur in the cytoplasm.) The proteins (cytochromes) that bring about the reactions of the electron transport chain are bound to the inner mitochondrial membrane, which is arranged in numerous folds called cristae (s., crista) (in prokaryotes, they are bound to the plasma membrane). Pyruvate, oxygen, ADP, and inorganic phosphate (P$_i$) continuously diffuse into the mitochondrial matrix. In turn, the end products of aerobic metabolism—ATP, CO$_2$, and H$_2$O— diffuse outward into the cytoplasm.

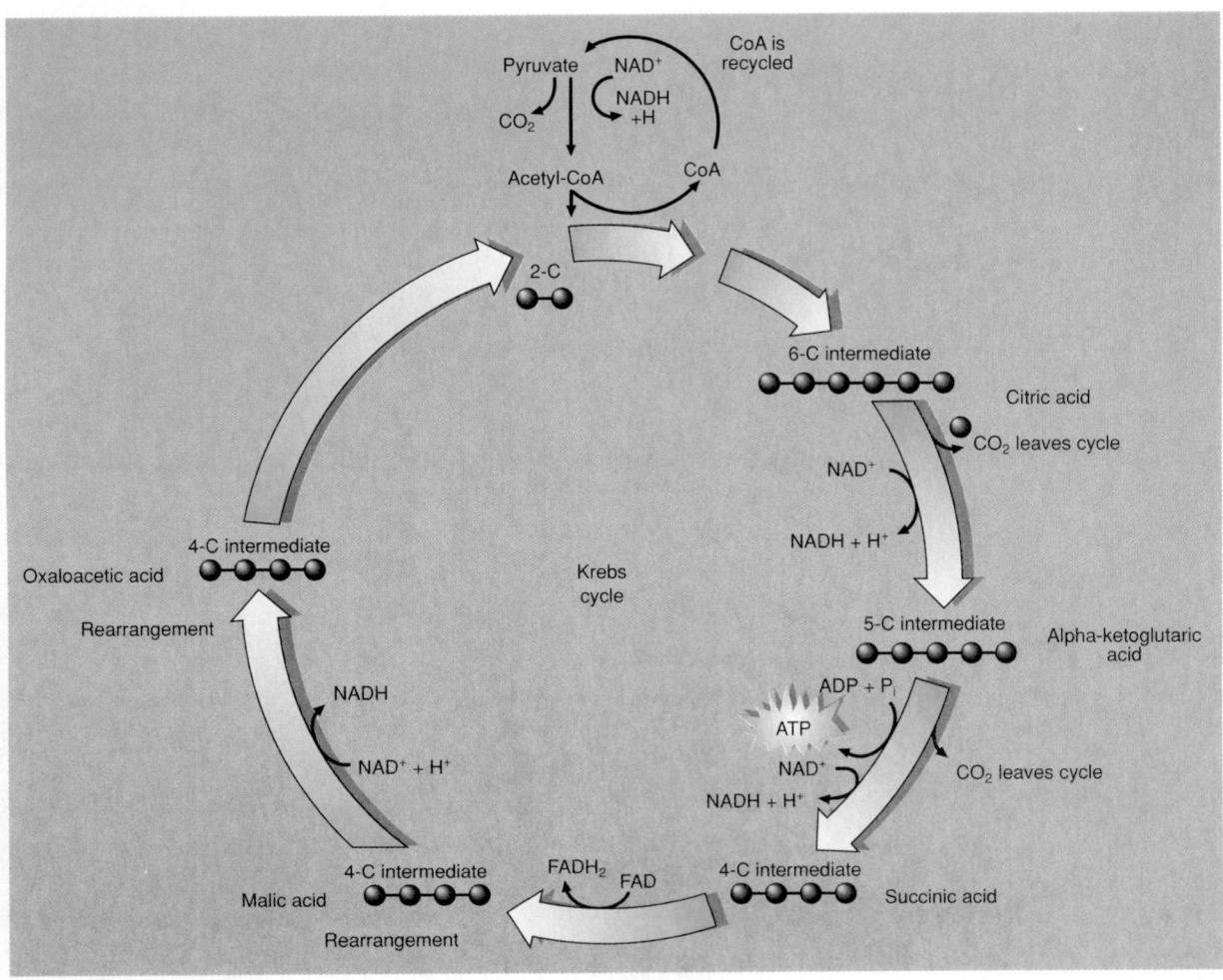

Figure 5.5

The Krebs Cycle. For each pyruvate molecule that enters the Krebs cycle by way of acetyl-CoA, two CO_2 molecules, one ATP, three NADH molecules, and one $FADH_2$ are formed. Each of these events occurs twice for each glucose molecule that is broken down into two molecules of acetyl-CoA.

THE ENERGY SCORE FOR AEROBIC RESPIRATION: A BALANCE SHEET

The eukaryotic cell obtains a net gain of 36 ATP molecules from the breakdown of each glucose molecule (table 5.1). Four ATP molecules are produced during glycolysis, but two of them are used in the glycolytic reactions. The two molecules of NADH formed during glycolysis yield six ATP molecules, but two are used in the reactions that transport the NADH electrons across the inner mitochondrial membrane into the matrix to enter the Krebs cycle. One molecule of NADH is produced as pyruvate is converted to acetyl-coenzyme A, and one molecule

of CO_2 is released as acetyl-coenzyme A enters the Krebs cycle. Two more ATP molecules are produced in the Krebs cycle, as well as six NADH and two $FADH_2$ molecules. The six NADH from the Krebs cycle and two NADH from the entry of acetyl-coenzyme A into the cycle yield 24 ATP molecules, and the oxidation of the two molecules of $FADH_2$ produced during the Krebs cycle yields four more molecules of ATP. The net gain from all these reactions is 36 molecules of ATP. As table 5.1 illustrates, the electron transport chain is more efficient at producing ATP for the cell's activities, although the importance of glycolysis for ATP production in anaerobic conditions should not be overlooked and cannot be replaced by the aerobic reactions of the Krebs cycle and electron transport chain.

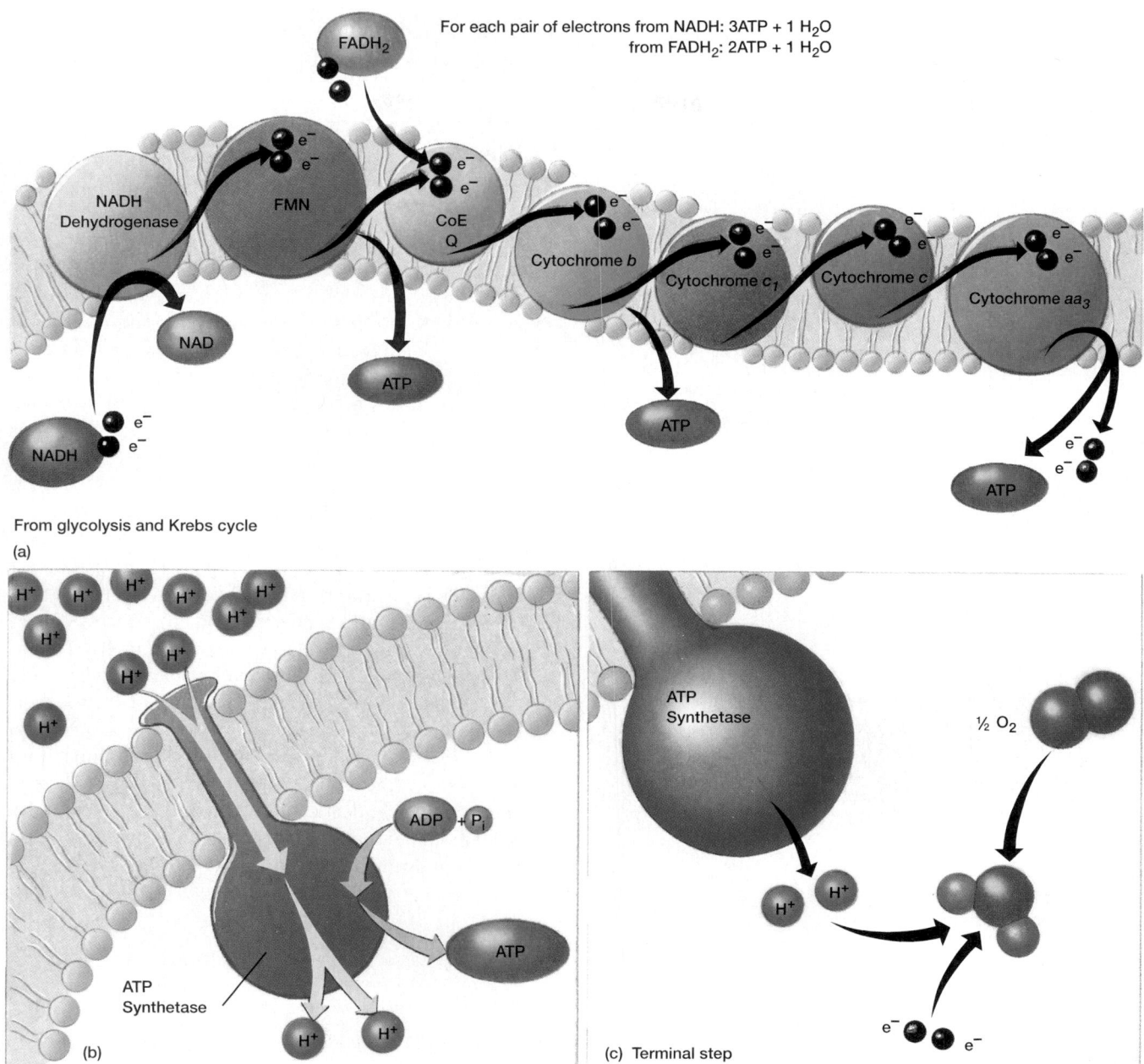

FIGURE 5.6

The Electron Transport Chain and Oxidative Phosphorylation. (*a*) Electrons from NADH and $FADH_2$ generated in glycolysis and the Krebs cycle are passed along electron-carrier molecules (colored circles) in the electron transport chain by way of oxidation-reduction reactions. (*b*) The energy released along the way is captured in the high-energy phosphate bonds of ATP by way of oxidative phosphorylation. (*c*) When the electrons reach the end of the chain, an oxygen molecule accepts the electrons and combines with hydrogen to generate a water molecule.

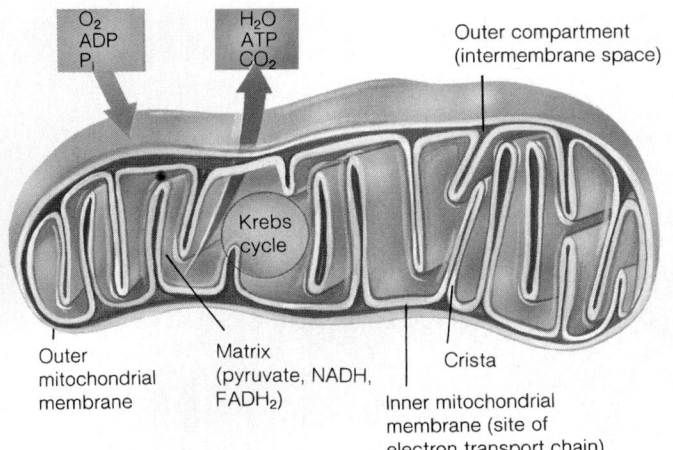

FIGURE 5.7

Mitochondrial Architecture. Aerobic respiration occurs in the mitochondrial matrix. The reactions in the electron transport chain are carried out by molecular complexes that are an integral part of the inner membrane.

TABLE 5.1	APPROXIMATE ATP YIELD FROM THE COMPLETE AEROBIC OXIDATION OF ONE MOLECULE OF GLUCOSE		
PROCESS	ATP PRODUCED	NADH, FADH$_2$ PRODUCED	ATP USED
Glycolysis	4ATP	2NADH	–2ATP
Entrance of NADH to Krebs cycle		2NADH	–2ATP
Krebs cycle	2ATP	6NADH, 2FADH$_2$	
Electron transport chain:			
3ATP for each of 2NADH generated via glycolysis	6ATP		
3ATP for each of 8NADH generated via Krebs cycle and entrance to the cycle	24ATP		
2ATP for each of 2FADH$_2$ generated via Krebs cycle	4ATP		
Total	40ATP		–4ATP
Net ATP	36ATP		

METABOLISM OF FATS AND PROTEINS: ALTERNATIVE FOOD MOLECULES

Even though the catabolism of glucose is the most common metabolic pathway in cells, animals also consume fats and proteins, which may be used to harvest energy. Recall from chapter 2 that those fats that are built from long-chain fatty acids and glycerol are called triglycerides. The initial catabolism of a fat begins with the digestion of the triglycerides (by way of an enzyme called a lipase) to glycerol and three fatty acid molecules (figure 5.8). The glycerol is phosphorylated and can enter the glycolytic pathway at the level of glyceraldehyde 3-phosphate. The free fatty acids move into the mitochondrion where their carbons are removed, two at a time, to form acetyl-coenzyme A plus additional NADH and FADH$_2$. The acetyl-coenzyme A is then oxidized by the Krebs cycle, and the NADH and FADH$_2$ that are produced are oxidized via the electron transport chain. Interestingly, 1 g of fat provides about 2.5 times more ATP energy than does either 1 g of carbohydrate or protein, because there are more hydrogen atoms per unit weight of fat than in carbohydrates or protein. This is why many animals store energy in the form of fat in adipose tissue (*see figure 3.24f*).

Proteins are initially digested by animals to yield individual amino acids. Some of these are distributed throughout the body and used for the synthesis of new proteins. Other amino acids are transported in the blood or extracellular fluid and comprise the amino acid pool. If needed for fuel, these amino acids can be further degraded by removal of the amine group to yield ammonia. This process is called a **deamination reaction** and can be illustrated as follows:

$$R-\underset{\underset{NH_2}{|}}{CH}-COOH + H_2O \longrightarrow R-\underset{\underset{\parallel}{O}}{C}-COOH + NH_3 + H_2$$

Amino acid   Water   Keto acid   Ammonia Hydrogen

In deamination, an amine group is replaced by an oxygen atom to form a keto acid. The keto acid can then be funneled into the Krebs cycle (figure 5.8). Eventually, the carbon skeleton of the amino acid is dismantled and oxidized to CO_2. On the average, 1 g of protein yields about the same amount of energy (about 4 kcal) as does 1 g of glucose. The ammonia that is produced from the complete catabolism of an amino acid is highly toxic and must be excreted. The various ways in which different animals rid their bodies of toxic wastes will be discussed in chapter 38.

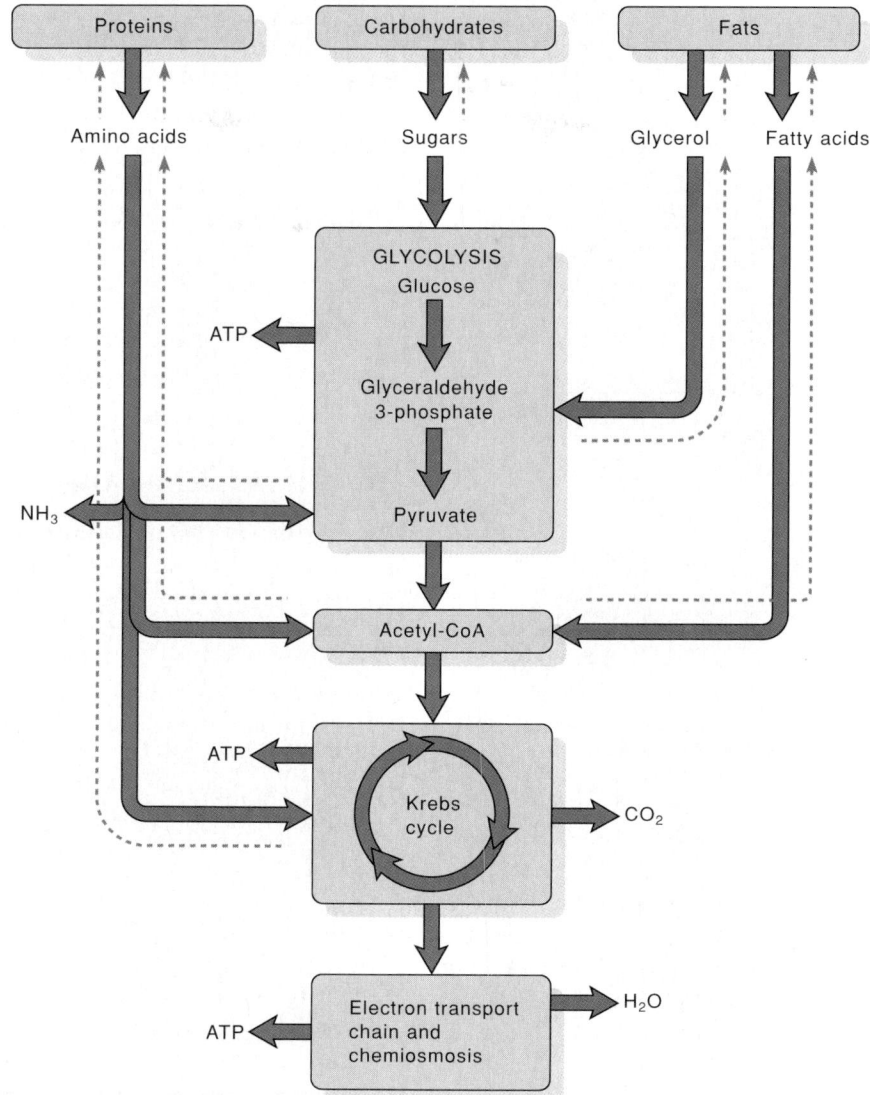

Figure 5.8

Catabolism of Various Food Molecules. While only certain molecules can feed directly into the Krebs cycle (e.g., acetyl-CoA), proteins, carbohydrates, and fats can also be broken down into constituent parts and used as fuel for respiration. The dashed arrows indicate that the system can also work in anabolic (synthetic) reactions.

CONTROL OF METABOLISM

The cell is very efficient. It does not waste energy by making more of a substance than it needs. For example, if there is an overabundance of a certain amino acid in the amino acid pool, the anabolic pathway that synthesizes that amino acid from an intermediate in the Krebs cycle is turned off. The most com-

mon mechanism for this control uses **end-product (feedback) inhibition.** In end-product inhibition, the end product of the anabolic pathway inhibits the enzyme that catalyzes a key step in the pathway.

The cell can also control its catabolism. For example, if a cell (e.g., a muscle cell) is working very hard and its ATP concentration begins to decrease, aerobic respiration increases.

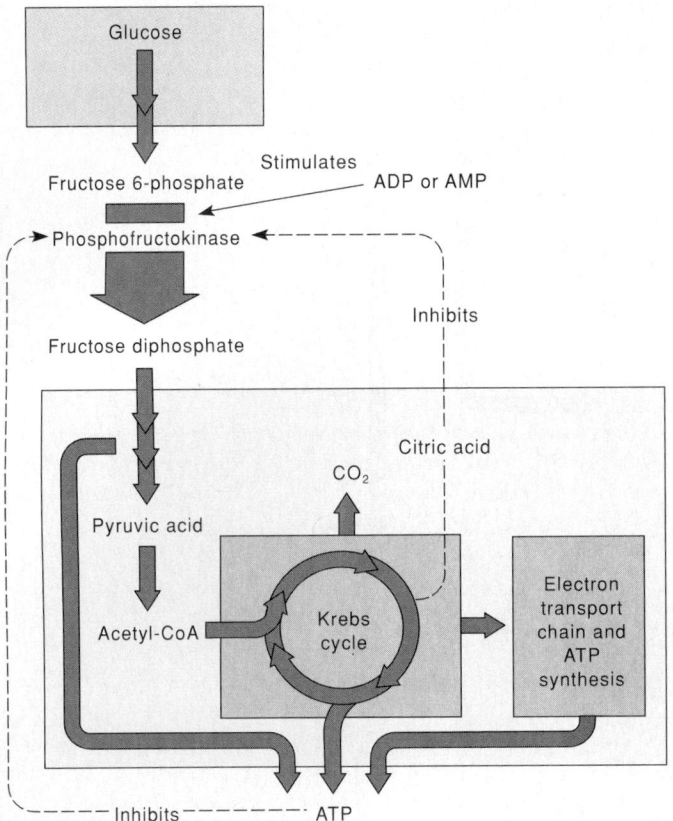

FIGURE 5.9

Control of Cellular Respiration. The enzyme, phosphofructokinase, responds to activators and inhibitors to regulate the rate of glycolysis and the Krebs cycle. It is stimulated by ADP and AMP but inhibited by ATP and citric acid.

When there is ample ATP to meet demand, aerobic respiration slows down, sparing valuable organic molecules for other necessary functions. ⑤ As is the case for anabolism, control is based on regulating the activity of enzymes at strategic points in the catabolic pathway. As a result, cells are thrifty, expedient, and responsive in their metabolism.

One of the main controlling points in aerobic respiration is the enzyme phosphofructokinase. By controlling the rate of this step, a cell can either speed up or slow down this entire metabolic process. Phosphofructokinase is an enzyme with receptor sites for specific inhibitors and activators. It is inhibited by ATP and stimulated by either ADP or AMP.

Phosphofructokinase is very sensitive to the energy needs of the cell and the ratio of ATP to ADP or AMP (figure 5.9). If ATP begins to accumulate, this enzyme shuts down glycolysis. If ADP or AMP begin to accumulate, phosphofructokinase becomes active and turns on the glycolytic pathway. Phosphofructokinase is also inhibited by citric acid in the cytoplasm. This control pathway helps synchronize the rates of glycolysis and the Krebs cycle. For example, when citric acid begins to accumulate, glycolysis slows down, and the supply of acetyl-coenzyme A to the Krebs cycle is reduced. Conversely, if citric acid consumption increases, glycolysis accelerates and meets the needed demand for more acetyl-coenzyme A.

THE METABOLIC POOL

The degradative chemical reactions (catabolism) of glycolysis and the Krebs cycle do more than just harvest energy for ATP production. They also constitute a metabolic pool that supplies materials for synthesis (anabolism) of many important cellular components (*see figure 5.8*). Overall, it is the balance between catabolism and anabolism that maintains homeostasis in the cell, and in turn, the whole animal. For example, glycolysis and the Krebs cycle are open systems. An open system is one that has a two-way flow of materials into and out of it. Various compounds enter the pathways at different points so that carbohydrates, fats, and proteins can all be oxidized. At the same time, some of the intermediates of these pathways can be withdrawn from the energy-harvesting machinery and used in synthesis reactions. Thus, the products of glycolysis and the Krebs cycle are all part of a metabolic pool whereby materials are either added or withdrawn.

Stop and Ask Yourself

9. How many ATP molecules are produced during complete aerobic metabolism of one molecule of glucose?
10. How does the flow of electrons generate ATP molecules?
11. How do fats serve as an alternative food molecule?
12. What is end-product (feedback) inhibition?

SUMMARY

1. During glycolysis, glucose is broken down anaerobically to yield two molecules of pyruvate, which is processed further in aerobic respiration. Glycolysis harvests chemical energy by rearranging the chemical bonds of glucose to form two pyruvate molecules and two molecules of ATP.

2. Organisms living in anaerobic environments require a mechanism to dispose of the hydrogen and the associated electrons produced in glycolysis. The electrons can be donated to a number of other compounds in a process called fermentation.

3. Each pyruvate formed during glycolysis loses a carbon dioxide molecule and combines with coenzyme A to form acetyl-coenzyme A. Coenzyme A transfers the acetyl group to the Krebs cycle. During one turn of the cycle, the equivalents of the acetyl group's two carbons are removed in the form of carbon dioxide. Some ATP is also produced. During the process, NAD^+ and FAD accept electrons and become NADH and $FADH_2$. They carry these electrons to the electron transport chain.

4. Most of the energy harvested during aerobic respiration is produced by the electron transport chain. In total, the oxidation of one molecule of glucose results in the net production of 36 ATP molecules.

5. Many other metabolic pathways feed into glycolysis and the Krebs cycle from the metabolic pool, enabling cells to use many organic compounds in addition to glucose as food sources to generate usable energy to perform biological work.

6. End-product inhibition helps regulate metabolism and maintain homeostasis within organisms.

SELECTED KEY TERMS

aerobic (*p. 66*)

anaerobic (*p. 66*)

deamination reaction (*p. 72*)

electron transport chain (*p. 69*)

end-product (feedback) inhibition (*p. 73*)

fermentation (*p. 68*)

flavin adenine dinucleotide (FAD) (*p. 68*)

glycolysis (*p. 66*)

CRITICAL THINKING QUESTIONS

1. The aerobic metabolism of glucose generates exactly the same chemical end products and the same amount of energy as when glucose is burned. However, when a cell "burns" glucose, it does so in many small steps. Why has evolution divided glucose catabolism into so many small steps?

2. In anaerobic catabolism of glucose, further conversions of pyruvate to lactate do not yield any more usable energy. What, then, is the advantage of these conversions?

3. Why is anaerobic respiration wasteful and potentially harmful to an animal?

4. Diverse organisms, such as dogs and yeasts, have certain enzymes in common and even share similar metabolic pathways. What are the implications of these similarities in terms of evolution?

5. When an animal cell contains more than enough ATP to carry out its functions, the excess ATP signals a slowing down of the respiratory chain by decreasing the production of acetyl-coenzyme A. When ATP levels fall below what is required for cellular functions, the increased ADP signals increased breakdown of glucose. What general metabolic phenomenon is demonstrated by these relationships?

SUGGESTED READINGS

BOOKS

Alberts, B., Bray, D., Lewis, J., Raff, M., Roberts, K., and Watson, J. 1994. *Molecular Biology of the Cell.* 3d ed. New York: Garland Publishing Co.

Atkins, P. 1984. *The Second Law.* New York: W. H. Freeman.

Atkins, P. W. 1987. *Molecules.* New York: W. H. Freeman.

Avers, C. J. 1986. *Molecular Cell Biology.* Reading, Mass.: Addison-Wesley.

Baker, J. J. W., and Allen, G. E. 1981. *Matter, Energy, and Life.* 4th ed. Reading, Mass.: Addison-Wesley.

Becker, W. M. 1977. *Energy and the Living Cell: An Introduction to Bioenergetics.* New York: Harper & Row.

Blum, H. F. 1962. *Time's Arrow and Evolution.* New York: Harper & Row.

Brown, L. R., Durning, A., Flavin, C., Heise, L., Jacobson, J., Postel, S., Renner, M., Shea, C. P., and Starke, L. 1989. *State of the World:* New York: W. W. Norton.

Calvin, M., and Pryor, W. A. 1973. *Organic Chemistry of Life: Readings from Scientific American.* New York: W. H. Freeman.

Carson, R. 1962. *Silent Spring.* Burlington: Houghton Mifflin.

Cristensen, H. N., and Cellarius, R. A. 1972. *Introduction to Bioenergetics: Thermodynamics for the Biologist.* Philadelphia: W. B. Saunders.

Danpier, W. C. 1966. *A History of Science and Its Relation to Philosophy and Religion.* New York: Cambridge University Press.

Darnell, J., Lodish, H., and Baltimore, D. 1986. *Molecular Cell Biology.* New York: Scientific American Books.

DeDuve, C. 1986. *A Guided Tour of the Living Cell,* vols. 1 and 2. New York: Scientific American Books.

Fersht, A. 1985. *Enzyme Structure and Mechanism*. 2d ed. New York: W. H. Freeman.

Gould, S. J. 1980. *The Panda's Thumb: More Reflections in Natural History*. New York: W. W. Norton.

Henderson, L. S. 1958. *The Fitness of the Environment*. Boston: Beacon Press.

Kuhn, T. S. 1970. *Structure of Scientific Revolutions*. Chicago: University of Chicago Press.

Lehninger, A. L. et al. 1993. *Principles of Biochemistry*. New York: Worth Publishers.

Rodella, T. D. et al. 1989. *Through the Molecular Maze*. Los Altos, Calif.: W. Kaufmann Press.

Sayre, A. 1975. *Rosalind Franklin and DNA*. New York: W. W. Norton.

Schrodinger, E. 1967. *What Is Life?* and *Mind and Matter*. New York: Cambridge University Press.

Stryer, L. 1988. *Biochemistry*. 3d ed. New York: W. H. Freeman.

The Global 2000 Report to the President: Entering the Twenty-First Century, vol. 1–3. 1983. Washington D.C.: U.S. Government Printing Office.

Thomas, L. 1974. *The Lives of a Cell*. New York: Viking Press.

Watson, J. D. 1968. *The Double Helix*. New York: Signet Books.

ARTICLES

Armbruster, P., and Munzenberg, G. Creating superheavy elements. *Scientific American* May, 1989.

Bingham, R. 1982. On the life of Mr. Darwin. *Science '82* 3(3):82.

Bretscher, M. S. The molecules of the cell membrane. *Scientific American* October, 1985.

Bretscher, M. S. How animal cells move. *Scientific American* December, 1987.

Capaldi, R. A. A dynamic model of cell membranes. *Scientific American* March, 1974.

DeDuve, C. Microbodies in the living cell. *Scientific American* May, 1983.

Diamond, J. The search for life on earth. *Natural History* April, 1991.

Dickerson, E. Cytochrome *c* and the evolution of energy metabolism. *Scientific American* March, 1980.

Doolittle, R. Proteins. *Scientific American* October, 1985.

Eiseley, L. C. Charles Darwin. *Scientific American* February, 1956.

———. Alfred Russel Wallace. *Scientific American* February, 1959.

Feldman, G., and Steinberger, G. The number of families of matter. *Scientific American* February, 1991.

Frieden, E. The chemical elements of life. *Scientific American* July, 1972.

Glover, D. The centrosome. *Scientific American* June, 1993.

Gould, S. J. 1980. Wallace's fatal flaw. *Natural History* 89:26.

Hinkle, P. C., and McCarthy, R. E. How cells make ATP. *Scientific American* March, 1978.

Karplus, M., and McCammon, A. The dynamics of proteins. *Scientific American* April, 1986.

Koshland, D. E. Protein shape and biological control. *Scientific American* October, 1973.

Kraut, J. 1988. How do enzymes work? *Science* 242: 533–539.

Krebs, H. A. 1970. The history of the tricarboxylic acid cycle. *Perspectives in Biology and Medicine* 14:154–170.

Leninger, A. L. How cells transform energy. *Scientific American* September, 1961.

Levine, M. H., Stammers, D., and Stuart, D. 1978. Structure of pyruvate kinase and similarities with other enzymes: Possible implications for protein taxonomy and evolution. *Nature* 271:626–630.

Luria, S. E. Colicins and the energetics of cell membranes. *Scientific American* December, 1975.

McCarty, R. E. 1980. H-ATPase in oxidative and photosynthetic phosphorylation. *BioScience* 35:27–30.

McPherson, A. Macromolecular crystals. *Scientific American* March, 1989.

Mitchell, P. 1979. Klein's respiratory chain concept and its chemiosmotic consequences. *Science* 206:1148–1159.

Nauenberg, M., Stroud, C., and Yeazell, J. The classical limit of an atom. *Scientific American* June, 1994.

Paabo, Svante. Ancient DNA. *Scientific American* November, 1993.

Phillips, D. C. The three-dimensional structure of an enzyme molecule. *Scientific American* November, 1966.

Porter, K., and Tucker, J. The ground substance of the living cell. *Scientific American* March, 1981.

Racker, E. 1980. From Pasteur to Mitchell, a hundred years of bioenergetics. *Federation Proceedings* 39:210–215.

Rebek, J. Synthetic self-replicating molecules. *Scientific American* July, 1994.

Richards, F. The protein folding problem. *Scientific American* January, 1991.

Rothman, J. E. The compartmental organization of the Golgi apparatus. *Scientific American* September, 1985.

Satir, B. The final steps in secretion. *Scientific American* October, 1975.

———. How cilia move. *Scientific American* October, 1974.

Schulman, R. G. NMR spectroscopy of living cells. *Scientific American* January, 1983.

Sharon, N. Carbohydrates. *Scientific American* November, 1980.

———. Glycoproteins. *Scientific American* May, 1974.

Singer, S. J., and Nicolson, G. 1972. The fluid-mosaic model of the structure of cell membranes. *Science* 175:720–731.

Slayman, C. 1985. Proton chemistry and the ubiquity of proton pumps. *BioScience* 35:16–17.

Staehelin, L. A., and Hull, B. E. Junctions between living cells. *Scientific American* May, 1978.

Staff writers. 1991. The 23rd environmental quality index. *National Wildlife* 29(2):33–40.

Todorov, I. How cells maintain stability. *Scientific American* December, 1990.

Upton, A. C. The biological affects of low level ionizing radiation. *Scientific American* February, 1982.

Weber, K., and Osborn, M. The molecules of the cell matrix. *Scientific American* October, 1985.

Weinberg, C., and Williams, R. Energy from the sun. *Scientific American* September, 1990.

Weinberg, R. A. The molecules of life. *Scientific American* October, 1985.

Welch, W. How cells respond to stress. *Scientific American* May, 1993.

Zewail, A. The birth of molecules. *Scientific American* December, 1990.

part TWO

THE CONTINUITY OF ANIMAL LIFE

The ability to reproduce is a fundamental property of living organisms. All organisms age and eventually die. For the species, however, reproduction provides a potential means of increasing the size of a population, and results

in continual replacement of aging individuals with young, vigorous ones. In addition, sexual reproduction produces individuals with new genetic combinations, which increases genetic diversity, and makes long-term survival of the species more likely. Sexual reproduction also leads to individual variation—and variation is the foundation for evolution.

Reproductive processes involve specific activities of individual cells. In unicellular organisms (protists), one individual divides to produce two individuals. Most animals produce individual reproductive cells, such as eggs and sperm. Characteristics are transmitted from one generation to the next by specific genetic mechanisms. Each offspring has a new set of genes that is somewhat different from each of the parent's.

An animal's genetic makeup is expressed through developmental processes and continues throughout life in the form of growth, maturation, and aging. Developmental processes are also involved in the continual replacement of body cells, in healing of injuries, and in specific responses to infection and disease. However, developmental processes gone awry, such as in abnormal growth, can be life threatening.

Chapters 6 through 10 present the cell division mechanisms involved in animal reproduction and development, and the means by which genetic information is transmitted and expressed.

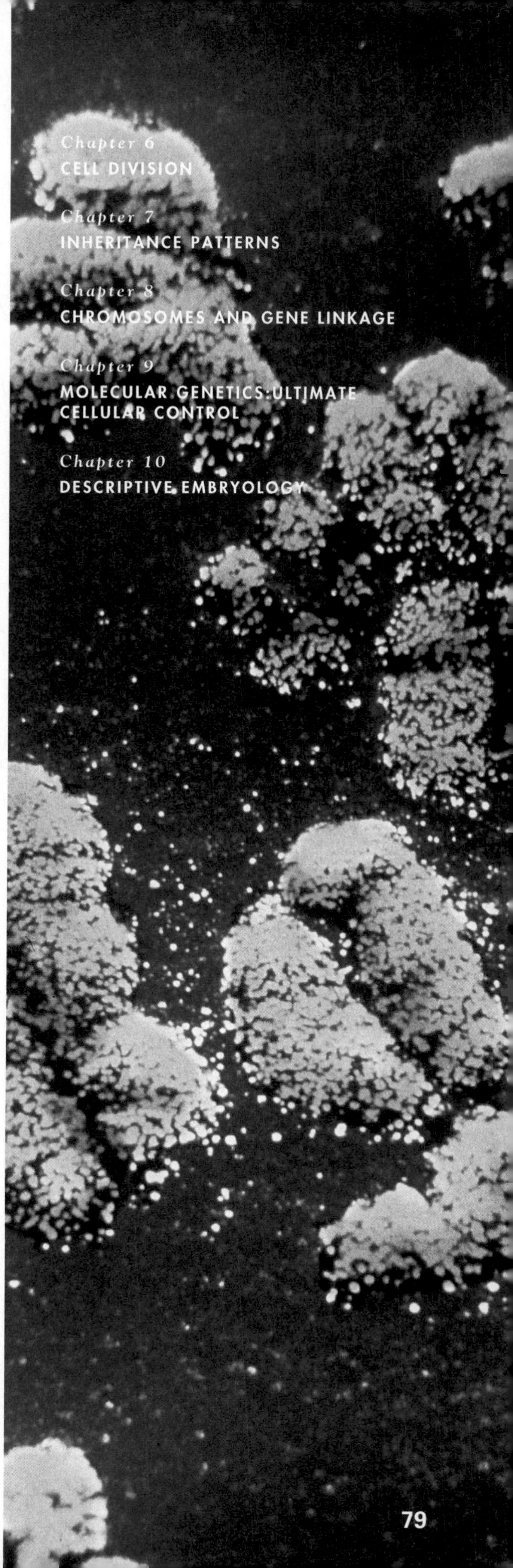

Scanning electron micrograph of human chromosomes (×2500).

CELL DIVISION

Outline

Concepts

1. The cell cycle consists of four phases: G_1, a period of normal metabolism; S, the phase of DNA replication; G_2, a brief period of structural preparation; mitosis (nuclear division) and cytokinesis (cytoplasmic division). G_1, S, and G_2 are referred to as interphase, and mitosis and cytokinesis are known as the mitotic phase (M).
2. The process that ensures an orderly and accurate distribution of chromosomes during the cell cycle is mitosis, which can be divided into four phases: prophase, metaphase, anaphase, and telophase. Cytokinesis often begins during late anaphase or early telophase, and soon after mitosis has ended, two daughter cells are evident.
3. Meiosis is a special type of cell division that reduces the chromosome number by 1/2. Meiosis allows for the random distribution of one of each pair of parental chromosomes to the offspring.
4. Gamete formation involves meiosis and the formation of specialized reproductive cells called sperm and eggs.

Would You Like to Know:

1 why in cell division, DNA undergoes untwisting, unzipping, rezipping, and retwisting? (p. 83)

2 how long a DNA molecule in a human cell is? (p. 84)

3 how cell division is related to a motion picture? (p. 84)

4 what is happening to a cell that looks like someone tied a cord around it and pulled the rope tight? (p. 86)

These and other useful questions will be answered in this chapter.

This chapter contains evolutionary concepts, which are set off in this font.

Reproduction is essential to life. Each organism exists solely because its ancestors succeeded in producing progeny that could themselves develop, survive, and reach reproductive age. Reproduction at the level of the organism ranges from the simplest fission of unicellular organisms (asexual reproduction) to the complicated processes involved in the sexual reproduction of higher animals. At the molecular level, reproduction involves the unique capacity of the cell to manipulate large amounts of DNA and of the ability of DNA to replicate itself.

The cellular capacity to manipulate large amounts of DNA (the information-carrying molecule) emerged more than a billion years ago among the ancestors of modern-day eukaryotes. This capacity was based on two occurrences: (1) the "packaging" of DNA and its associated proteins into compact structures called chromosomes, and (2) the development of an apparatus that could move the chromosomes. Eukaryotic cell division evolved as a result of these two developments.

One of the most intriguing activities of a cell is its ability to reproduce itself by a process called cell division. In some cases, an entire new organism is reproduced, as when the unicellular protozoan called *Amoeba proteus* divides to form duplicate offspring. In other cases, cell division enables a multicellular organism, such as yourself, to grow and develop from a single cell. In fact, even after you are fully grown, cell division continues to function in renewal and repair to maintain homeostasis.

DNA controls cell division. What is most remarkable about this control is the faithfulness with which genetic programs are passed from one generation to the next. A cell preparing to undergo cell division first copies all of its genes and then allocates them equally to its two daughter cells. The key to biological inheritance—the bridge to the next generation—is in this division process.

MITOSIS, CYTOKINESIS, AND THE CELL CYCLE: AN OVERVIEW

Cell division occurs in all animals. Cells divide in two basic stages: **mitosis** is division of the nucleus, and **cytokinesis** (Gr. *kytos*, hollow vessel + *kinesis*, motion) is division of the cytoplasm. However, cell division is just one phase in the life history of a cell. Between divisions (interphase), the cell must grow and carry out its various metabolic processes. The **cell cycle** is that period from the time a cell is produced until it completes mitosis (figure 6.1).

The cell cycle is a dynamic process with four consecutive phases that can be expressed as follows:

$$G_1 \rightarrow S \rightarrow G_2 \rightarrow M$$

The G_1 (first growth or gap) phase represents the early growth phase of the cell. In many organisms, this phase occupies the major portion of the cell's life span. During the S (DNA synthesis) phase, growth continues but this phase also involves DNA duplication, whereby a replica of the genome (the total genetic constitution of an organism) is synthesized. The G_2

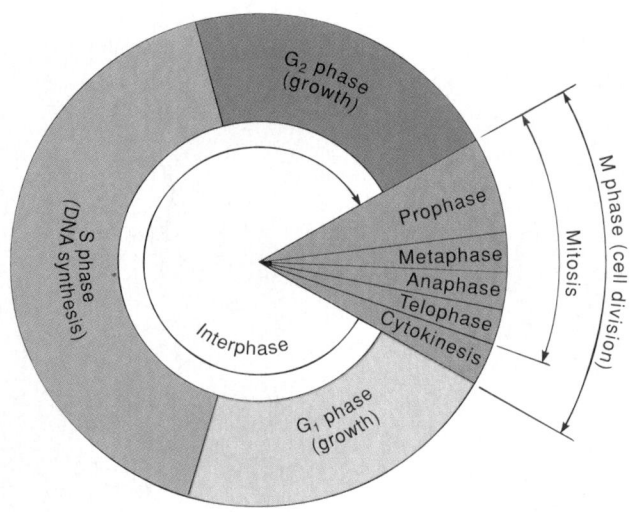

FIGURE 6.1

The Life Cycle of a Eukaryotic Cell. During G_1, components of the cell are synthesized and metabolism occurs, often resulting in cell growth. During the S (synthesis) phase, the chromosomes replicate, resulting in two identical copies called sister chromatids. During G_2, metabolism and growth continue until the mitotic phase is reached. This drawing is generalized, and there is a great deal of variation in the length of different stages from one cell to the next. *Source: Stuart Ira Fox, Human Physiology, 4th ed., copyright © 1993 Wm. C. Brown Communications, Inc., Dubuque, Iowa.*

(second growth or gap) phase prepares the cell for genomic separation. It includes replication of the mitochondria and other organelles, synthesis of microtubules and protein that will make up the mitotic spindle fibers, and chromosome condensation. The M (mitotic) phase is represented by the assembly of the microtubules, their binding to the chromosomes, the separation of the duplicated chromosomes, reformation of nuclear membranes in daughter cells, and cytokinesis. Cytokinesis usually begins late in mitosis when the cytoplasm of the cell divides, creating two daughter cells.

INTERPHASE: REPLICATING THE HEREDITARY MATERIAL

Often erroneously described as a resting period between cell divisions, **interphase** (L. *inter*, between) (includes G_1, S, and G_2 phases) is actually a period of great metabolic activity that typically occupies about 90% of the total duration of the cell cycle. It is the period during which the normal activities of the cell take place. Interphase also sets the stage for cell division, because DNA replication is completed during the S phase of interphase.

Before a cell divides, the DNA in its nucleus must produce a perfect copy of itself. This process is called replication, because the double-stranded DNA makes a replica, or duplicate, of itself. Replication is essential to ensure that each daughter cell receives the same genetic material as is present in the parent cell.

6.2

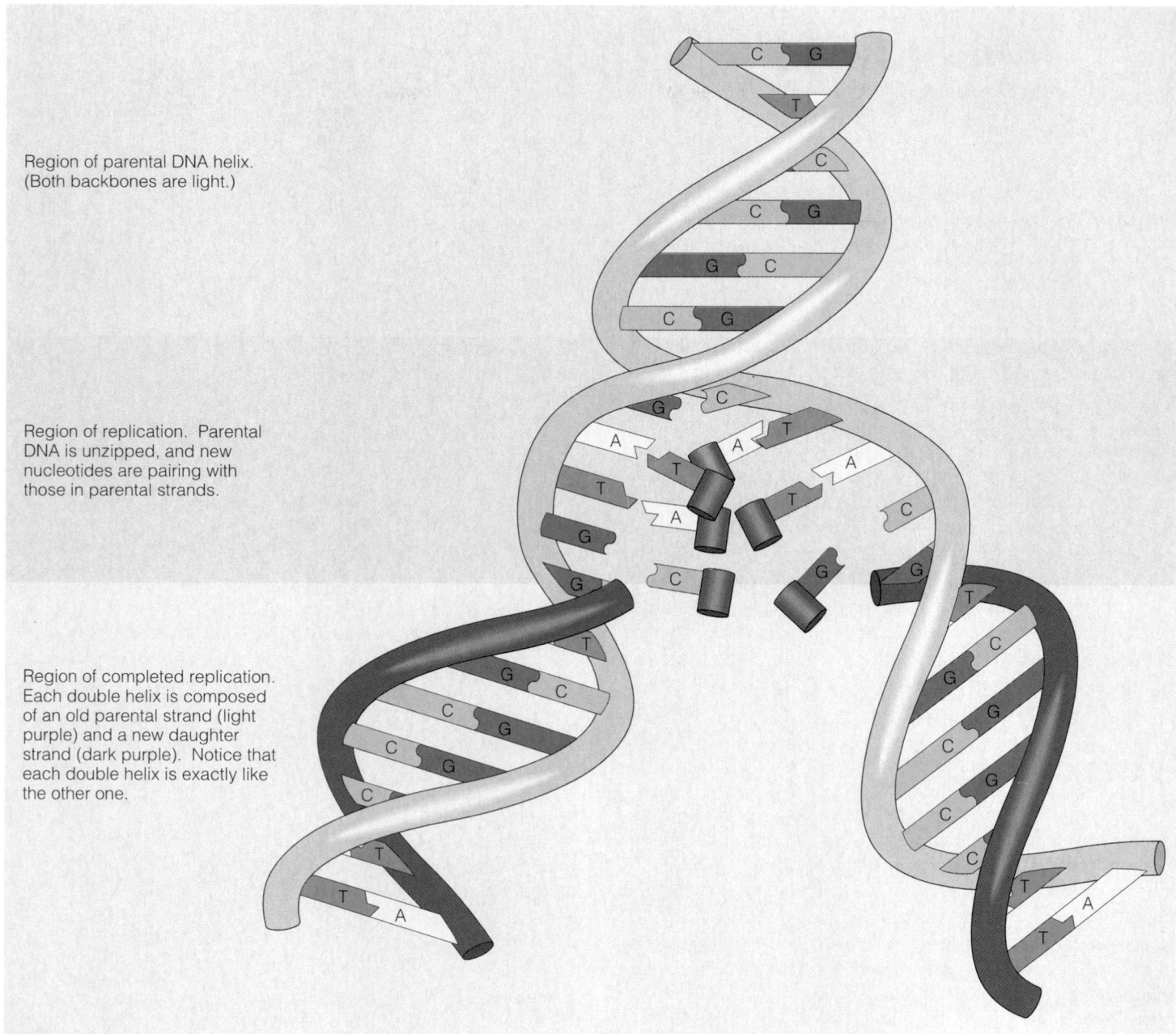

Region of parental DNA helix.
(Both backbones are light.)

Region of replication. Parental
DNA is unzipped, and new
nucleotides are pairing with
those in parental strands.

Region of completed replication.
Each double helix is composed
of an old parental strand (light
purple) and a new daughter
strand (dark purple). Notice that
each double helix is exactly like
the other one.

FIGURE 6.2

DNA Replication. When a DNA strand replicates, a group of enzymes separate the strands and previously unattached nucleotides (that have accumulated in the nucleus) diffuse and pair up with appropriate bases. The new bases are linked together by another enzyme to form new strands. The new strands that are formed are identical to the parent DNA molecule, and in each, one strand is conserved from the parent and one is formed anew.

Replication, begins with the strands of DNA untwisting (figure 6.2). The weak hydrogen bonds joining the purine and pyrimidine bases are broken by an enzyme, and the DNA molecule begins to "unzip" itself. As soon as new bonds are formed, the untwisted strands begin to twist again. ① Apparently, the activities of untwisting, unzipping, rezipping, and retwisting take place sequentially and ensure that each newly formed double helix is exactly like the other one. The final result is a pair of

sister chromatids (figure 6.3). A **chromatid** is a copy of a chromosome produced by replication. Each chromatid is attached to its other copy, or sister, at a point of constriction called a centromere. The **centromere** is a specific DNA sequence of about 220 nucleotides and has a specific location on any given chromosome. Bound to each centromere is a disk of protein called a **kinetochore,** which will eventually serve as an attachment site for the microtubules of the mitotic apparatus.

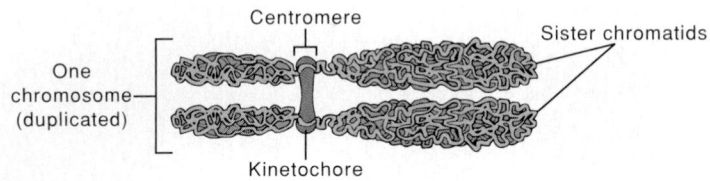

Figure 6.3

Duplicated Chromosomes. Each parent chromosome replicates to make two genetically identical sister chromatids attached at a region called the centromere.

After replication, the chromosomes are fully extended. For example, the total length of the DNA strands in the nucleus of a human cell is greater than the length of the entire human body, but the strands are too thin to be seen with the light microscope. As the cell cycle moves into the G_2 phase, however, the chromosomes begin the process called condensation. During condensation, each sister chromatid becomes coiled and supercoiled into a very tightly compacted structure, which can now be seen with the light microscope. During the G_2 phase, the cell also begins to assemble the structures that it will later use to move the chromosomes to opposite poles (ends) of the cell. For example, centrioles replicate, and there is extensive synthesis of alpha and beta tubulins, which are the proteins that make up the microtubules (*see figure 3.20*).

PHASES OF MITOSIS

Mitosis is divided into four phases: prophase, metaphase, anaphase, and telophase. In a dividing cell, however, the process is actually continuous, with each phase smoothly flowing into the next phase. There are no start and stop positions; the phases make up a continuum (figure 6.4). If you were to watch a film on mitosis, you would see that each drawing in figure 6.4 is merely a single frame of a continuous, changing drama.

PROPHASE: FORMATION OF THE MITOTIC APPARATUS

The first phase of mitosis, **prophase** (Gr. *pro*, before + phase), begins when chromosomes become visible with the light microscope as threadlike structures. (The term mitosis refers to this emergence; it comes from the Greek, *mitos*, which means thread.) By the time the cell cycle enters prophase, the chromatids are well folded, and the nucleoli and nuclear envelope begin to break up and their components are resorbed into the endoplasmic reticulum (figure 6.5a). The spindle microtubules assemble between the separating centrioles, and the two centriole pairs move apart.

By the end of prophase, the centriole pairs have moved to opposite poles of the cell. The position of the centrioles at the poles determines the direction in which the cell divides. The

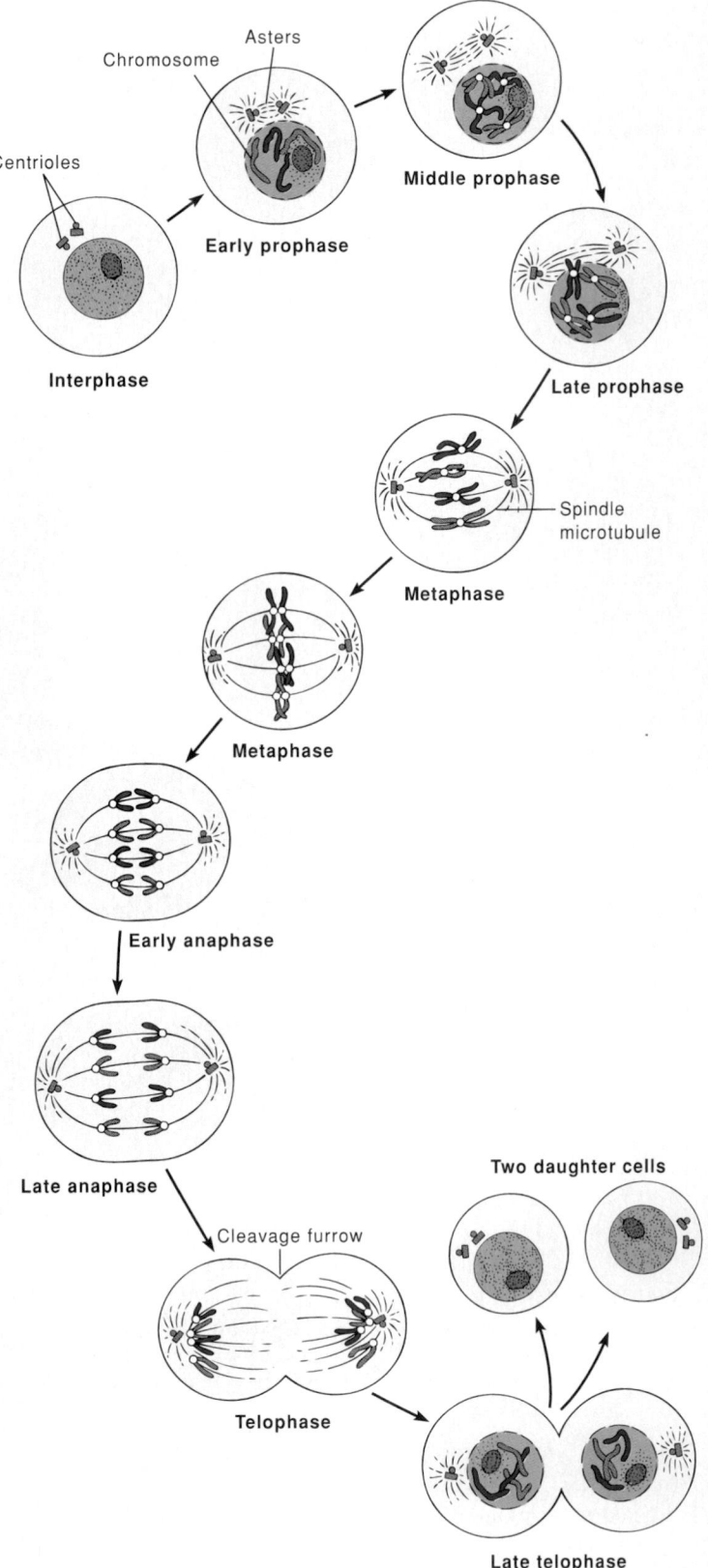

Figure 6.4

The Continuum of Mitosis and Cytokinesis. Mitosis is a continuous process during which the nuclear parts of a cell are divided into two equal portions.

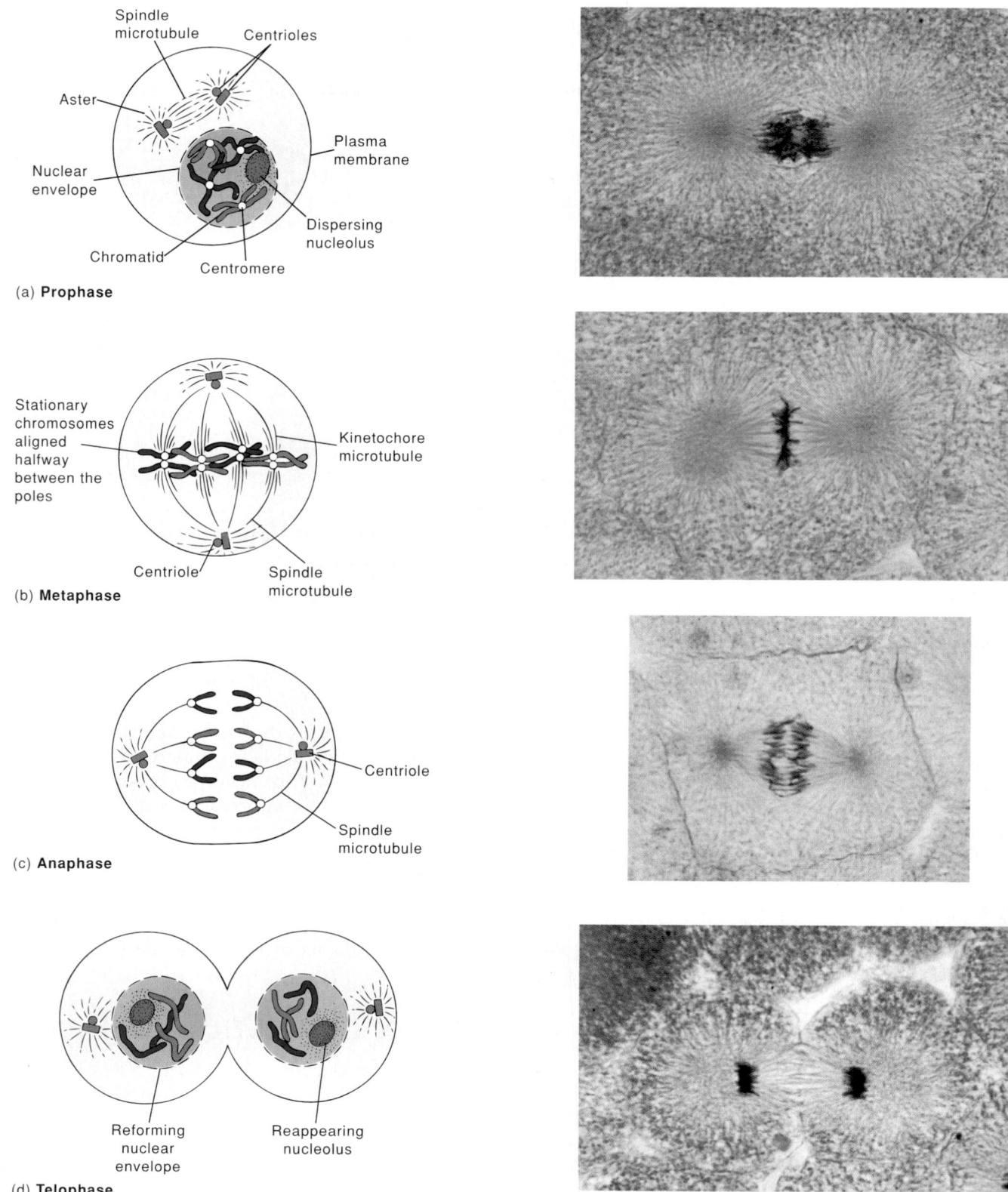

(a) **Prophase**

Spindle microtubule
Centrioles
Aster
Nuclear envelope
Plasma membrane
Dispersing nucleolus
Chromatid
Centromere

(b) **Metaphase**

Stationary chromosomes aligned halfway between the poles
Kinetochore microtubule
Centriole
Spindle microtubule

(c) **Anaphase**

Centriole
Spindle microtubule

(d) **Telophase**

Reforming nuclear envelope
Reappearing nucleolus

Figure 6.5

Stages of Mitosis. (*a*) During prophase, the nucleoli disappear, and the sister chromatids become folded into discrete chromosomes. In the cytoplasm, the centrioles move apart, and the mitotic apparatus begins to form. (*b*) At metaphase, the centriole pairs are now at opposite poles of the cell. The chromatids line up in the center of the cell, arranged so their centromeres all lie in one plane. (*c*) Anaphase begins when the paired chromatids move apart. (*d*) At telophase, daughter nuclei begin to form at the two poles of the cell where the chromosomes have gathered. (Photomicrographs at right are whitefish mitosis at ×315.)

centrioles also radiate an array of microtubules called **asters** (L. *aster*, little star), which brace each centriole against the plasma membrane, mechanically stiffening the point of microtubular attachment. Between the centrioles, the microtubules form a spindle of fibers that extends from pole to pole. The asters, spindle, centrioles, and microtubules are collectively called the **mitotic apparatus.**

As prophase continues, a second group of microtubules grows out from the kinetochore to the poles of the cell. These kinetochore microtubules connect each sister chromatid to the poles of the spindle.

METAPHASE: ALIGNMENT OF CHROMOSOMES

As the dividing cell moves into **metaphase** (Gr. *meta*, after + phase), the chromatids begin to align in the center of the cell, along the metaphase, or equatorial, plate (figure 6.5b). With the help of the microtubules attached to the individual kinetochores, the chromatids become neatly arrayed in the center of the cell, each centromere equidistant from each pole of the cell.

ANAPHASE: MOVEMENT OF THE DAUGHTER CHROMOSOMES

Toward the end of metaphase, the centromeres divide and free the two sister chromatids from their attachment to each other, although they remain aligned next to each other. After the centromeres divide, the sister chromatids are considered full-fledged chromosomes (called daughter chromosomes).

Of all the phases of mitosis, **anaphase** (Gr. *ana*, back again + phase) occupies the shortest time period (figure 6.5c). Each daughter chromosome moves apart from its copy (the sister chromatid that had been attached to it) as it is pulled toward its respective pole. When the chromosomes are being moved to the poles, they can appear straight, V-shaped, or J-shaped, depending on the location of the centromere region. Anaphase ends when all the daughter chromosomes have moved to the poles of the cell; each pole now has a complete, identical set of chromosomes.

TELOPHASE: REFORMATION OF NUCLEI

Telophase (Gr. *telos*, end + phase) begins once the daughter chromosomes arrive at the opposite poles of the cell. During telophase, the mitotic spindle is disassembled (figure 6.5d). The alpha and beta tubulin monomers from the microtubules are now used to construct the cytoskeleton of the new cells. A nuclear envelope reforms around each set of chromosomes, which begin to uncoil for gene expression to begin. One of the first genes to be expressed is the rRNA gene that results in the reappearance of the nucleolus. The cell also begins to pinch in the middle. Mitosis is over, but cell division is not.

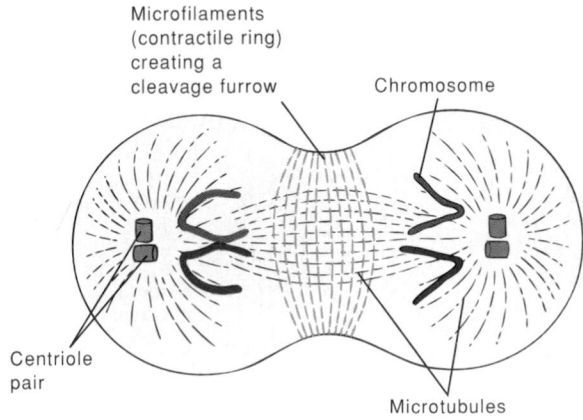

FIGURE 6.6
Cytokinesis. Diagram of the spatial relationship between the contractile ring of microfilaments and the microtubules of the mitotic spindle.

CYTOKINESIS: PARTITIONING THE CYTOPLASM

The final phase of cell division is cytokinesis, in which the cytoplasm divides (figure 6.6). Cytokinesis usually starts sometime during late anaphase or early telophase. Before cytokinesis, the two newly formed nuclei still share the same cytoplasmic compartment, but are positioned at opposite ends of the cell. Cellular separation is accomplished by a pinching of the plasma membrane by a contracting belt of microfilaments called the contractile ring. The ring lies midway between the two spindle poles and asters, and the microfilaments of the ring are linked to the inner surface of the plasma membrane so that their contractile activity pulls the cell surface inward. The cleavage furrow, located where the pinching occurs, looks as though a cord were tied around the circumference of the cell and pulled tight. Two new, genetically identical daughter cells are formed, each about half the size of the original parent cell.

CONTROL OF THE CELL CYCLE

One of the most exciting areas of cell biology is the study of how the cell cycle is controlled. Converging lines of evidence have led to a "universal model" specifying that cell division follows the same biochemical pathway in all eukaryotic cells—from yeasts to humans (figure 6.7a). Most of the details center on the enzyme cdc2 kinase, which has changed little in its structure, and none in its function, during a billion years of evolution. Cdc2 kinase is one part of a protein complex called the maturation-promoting factor (MPF). Once activated, MPF plays a role in most of the events of the cell cycle, such as (1) condensation of

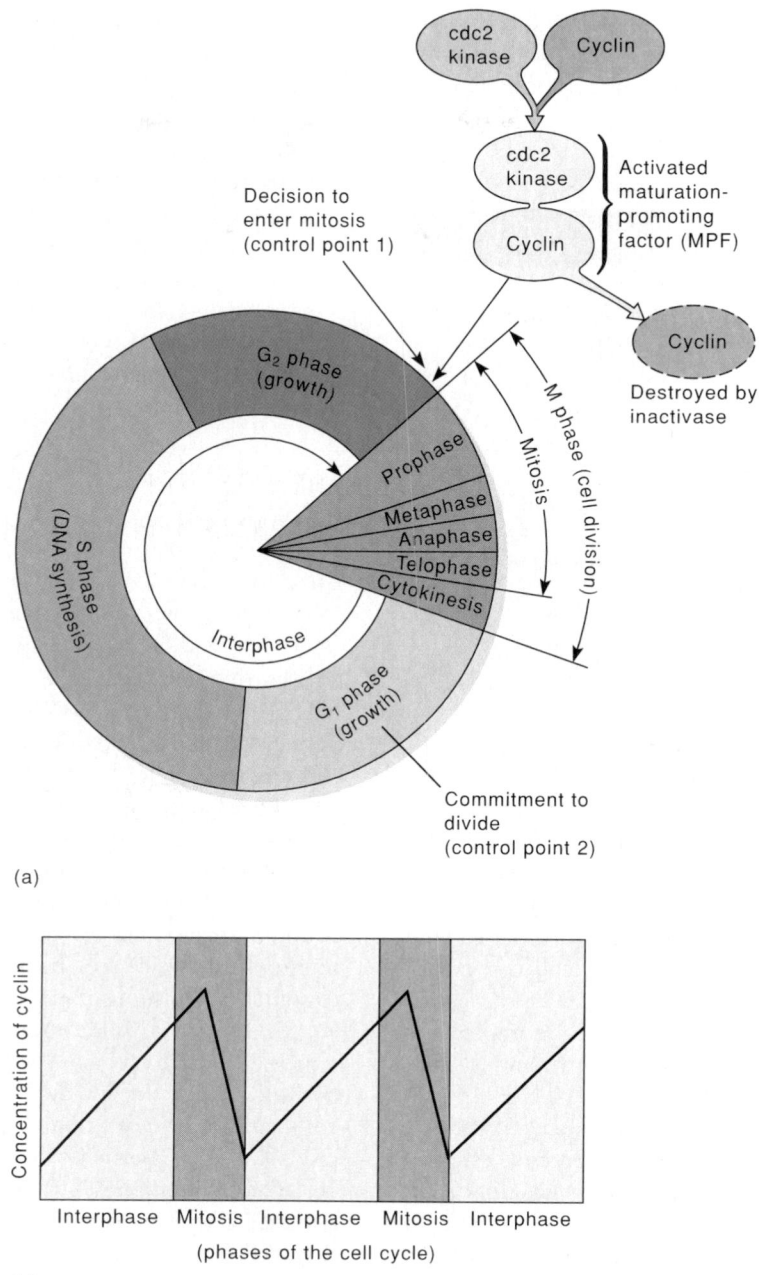

(a)

(b)

FIGURE 6.7

Control of the Cell Cycle. (*a*) This "universal model" shows how mitosis may be regulated at two control points. At control point 1, cyclin accumulates during interphase and, at a critical concentration, associates with cdc2 kinase to form a complex (maturation-promoting factor), which triggers mitosis (M) and activates enzymes (inactivases) that destroy cyclin. (*b*) As cyclin is destroyed, the cyclin-destroying enzymes become inactive. Thus, cyclin accumulates once again. Passage through control point 2, (the time when a cell becomes committed to divide) is also thought to be highly regulated by cyclin. *Source: Stuart Ira Fox, Human Physiology, 4th ed., copyright © 1993 Wm. C. Brown Communications, Inc., Dubuque, Iowa.*

chromosomes, (2) reorganization of the cell's structure, (3) breakdown of the nuclear envelope, and (4) segregation of the chromosomes into daughter cells during mitosis. In addition, MPF is an initiator of the M and S phases.

Evidence indicates that the cell cycle is not controlled by events in the nucleus. Instead, the process is driven by an autonomous oscillator: a set of chemical reactions in the cytoplasm that, with the regularity of a clock, control cell division.

The basic mechanism of this control involves the activation and inactivation of MPF by cyclin proteins. During interphase, cyclin accumulates until the rate of MPF activation by cyclin exceeds the rate of cyclin destruction by an inactivase enzyme—the concentration of which is assumed to be constant (figure 6.7*b*). As a consequence, active MPF accumulates, leading to a series of modifications of other mitotic substrates. The activity of MPF also induces the activation of cyclin destruction, and cyclin disappearance results in MPF destabilization by the inactivase. The interphase structures are then reestablished, and cyclin begins accumulating and initiates the next mitotic cycle.

Stop and Ask Yourself

1. Why is cell division referred to as a continuum?
2. What is the function of the mitotic spindle?
3. What happens during each of the following phases of mitosis: prophase, metaphase, anaphase, and telophase?
4. What is cytokinesis? How does it occur?
5. How is the cell cycle controlled?

MEIOSIS: THE BASIS OF SEXUAL REPRODUCTION

The vast majority of animals do not simply divide in half to reproduce, as do single cells, but instead undergo sexual reproduction. Sexual reproduction requires a genetic contribution from two different sex cells. Egg and sperm cells are specialized sex cells called **gametes** (Gr. *gamete*, wife; *gametes*, husband). In animals, a male gamete (sperm) unites with a female gamete (egg) during fertilization to form a single cell called a **zygote** (Gr. *zygotos*, yoked together). The fusion of gametes is called **syngamy** (Gr. *gamos*, marriage). The zygote is the first cell of the new animal. Each of the two gametes contributes 1/2 the genetic information to the zygote.

To maintain a constant and stable number of chromosomes in the next generation, animals that reproduce sexually must produce gametes with 1/2 the chromosome number of their ordinary body cells (called **somatic cells**). All of the cells in the body, except for the egg and sperm cells, have the diploid (2N) number of chromosomes. A diploid set of chromosomes contains a species-specific number of chromosome pairs. The chromosomes are in pairs because each cell contains one chromosome of each type from one parent and another chromosome of each type from the other parent. Humans have 46 total chromosomes (2N), comprising 23 pairs of chromosomes. The necessary reduction of chromosome number is accomplished by a type of cell division called **meiosis** (Gr. *meiosis*, dimunition). Meiosis occurs in specialized cells of the ovaries and testes and reduces the number of chromosomes to 1/2 the diploid (2N) number. The cells that result (eggs and sperm) are said to be haploid (N), or have the haploid number of chromosomes. Haploid cells have only one of each type of chromosome (only one member of each pair of chromosomes found in diploid cells). When the nuclei of the two gametes combine during fertilization, the diploid number is restored.

Meiosis begins after the G$_2$ phase in the cell cycle—after DNA replication has occurred (*see figure 6.2*). Two successive nuclear divisions take place, designated meiosis I and meiosis II. Each division has a prophase, metaphase, anaphase, and telophase. The microtubular spindles function in meiosis just as they do in mitosis. The result of mitosis is two identical daughter cells, each with the same number of chromosomes as the parent cell, whereas the two nuclear divisions of meiosis result in four daughter cells, each with 1/2 the number of chromosomes as the parent cell. Moreover, these daughter cells are not genetically identical. Like mitosis, meiosis is a continuous process, and only for convenience do biologists divide it into the following phases.

THE FIRST MEIOTIC DIVISION: PROPHASE I TO TELOPHASE I

During interphase, each of the chromosomes has already replicated to form two sister chromatids joined at their centromeres (*see figure 6.3*). In prophase I, DNA folds more and more tightly, and becomes visible under a light microscope (figure 6.8a). Because a cell has a copy of each type of chromosome from each original parent cell, it contains the diploid number of chromosomes. The chromosomes of each homologous pair contain the same genes in the same order along the length of the chromosome. Chromosomes that carry genes for the same traits are called **homologous chromosomes,** are the same length, and have a similar staining pattern, making them identifiable as matching pairs. During prophase I, homologous chromosomes line up side-by-side in a process called **synapsis** (Gr. *synapsis*, conjunction) forming a **tetrad** of chromatids (also called a bivalent). The tetrad thus contains the two homologous chromosomes, each with its copy, or sister chromatid (figure 6.9a–c). A network of protein and RNA is laid down between the sister chromatids of the two homologous chromosomes. This network holds the sister chromatids in a precise union so that each gene is located directly across from its sister gene on the homologous chromosome. An analogy would be zipping up a zipper. Within this complex, portions of the DNA helix of each chromatid unwinds (*see figure 6.2*), and single strands of DNA pair with their complementary member from the other homologue.

Synapsis also initiates a series of events called **crossing-over,** whereby segments of DNA are exchanged between the nonsister chromatids of the two homologous chromosomes in a tetrad (figure 6.9b,c). This process effectively redistributes genetic information among the paired homologous chromosomes, and produces new combinations of genes on the various chromatids in homologous pairs. Thus, each chromatid ends up with new combinations of instructions for a variety of traits. Crossing-over is a form of **genetic recombination** and is a major source of genetic variation in a population of a given species. It will be discussed in more detail in chapter 8.

The point of crossing-over can be seen under the light microscope as an X-shaped structure called a **chiasma** (pl., chiasmata; Gr. cross) (figure 6.9b). The presence of a chiasma

6.8

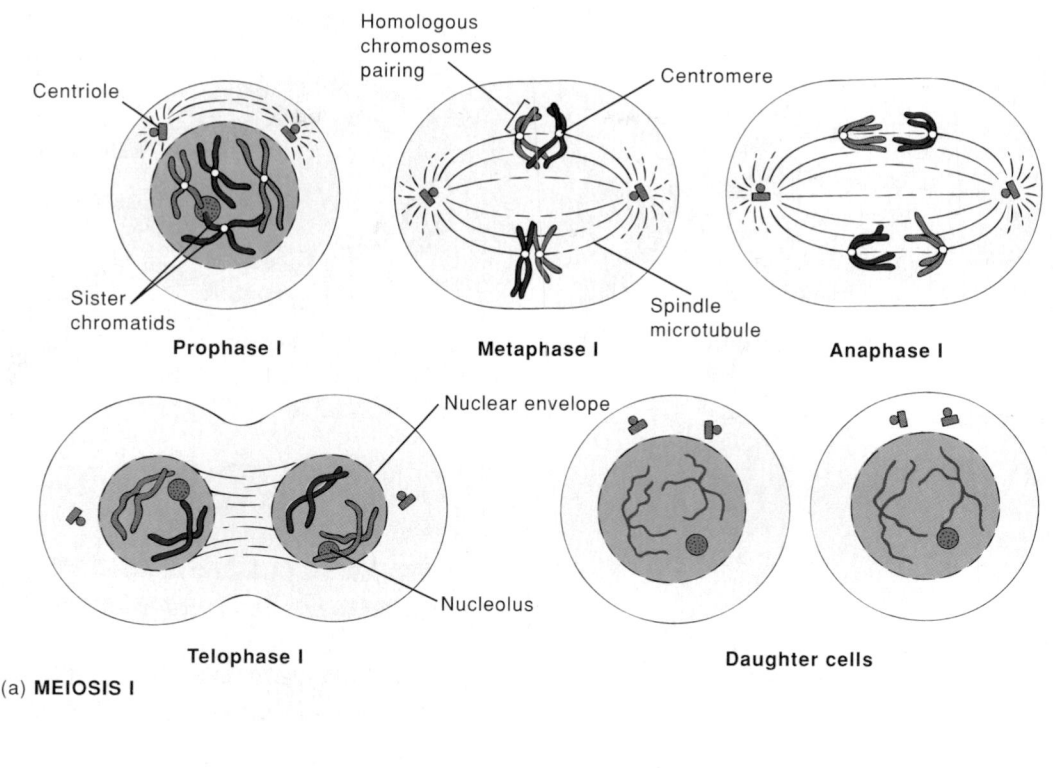

(a) MEIOSIS I

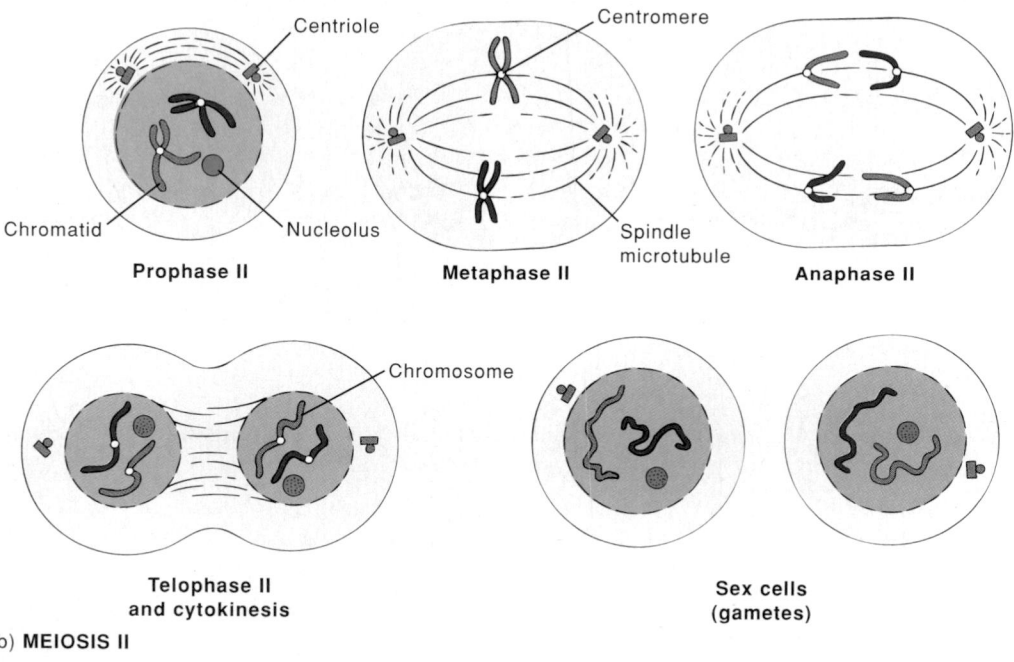

(b) MEIOSIS II

FIGURE **6.8**

Meiosis and Cytokinesis. (*a*) Stages in the first meiotic division. (*b*) Stages in the second meiotic division.

indicates that two nonsister chromatids of paired homologous chromosomes have exchanged parts. Apparently, the continued attachment of nonsister chromatids at chiasmata plays a role in aligning homologues at the equatorial plate during metaphase I.

In metaphase I, the microtubules form a spindle apparatus just as in mitosis (*see figures 6.4 and 6.5*). However, unlike mitosis where homologous chromosomes do not pair, each pair of homologues lines up in the center of the cell, with centromeres on each side of the equatorial plane.

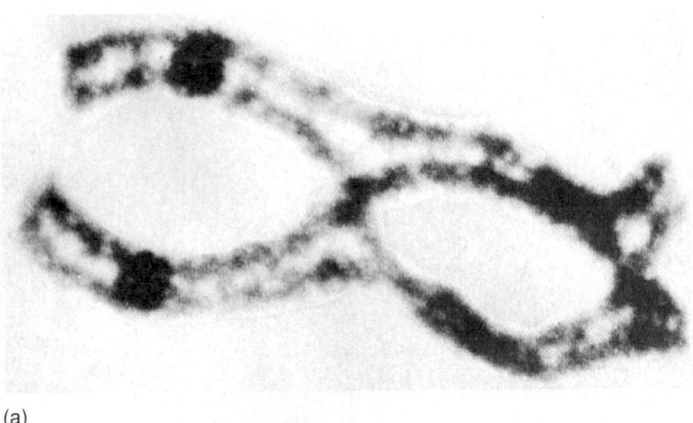

(a)

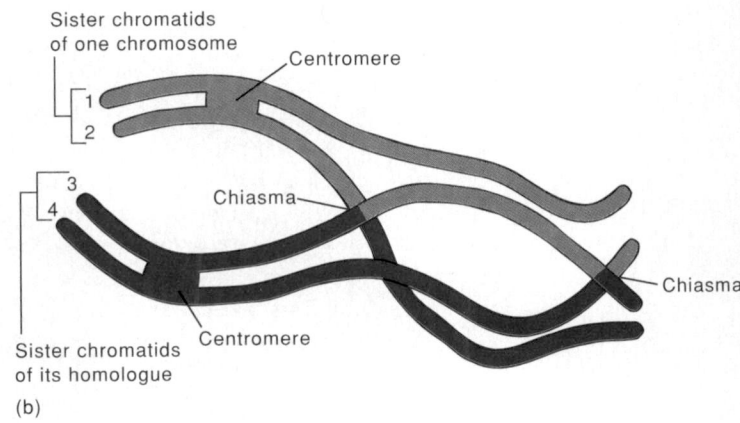

(b)

Figure **6.9**

Synapsis and Crossing-Over. (*a*) A pair of homologous chromosomes in late prophase. The sister chromatids are visible, as are the centromeres. (*b*) A diagram illustrating how crossing-over occurs, and the location of chiasmata where nonsister chromatids remain temporarily attached. (*c*) The same chromosomes diagrammatically separated to show the result of crossing-over.

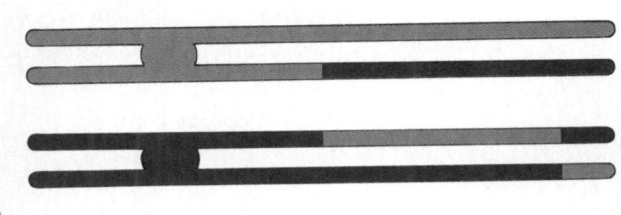

(c)

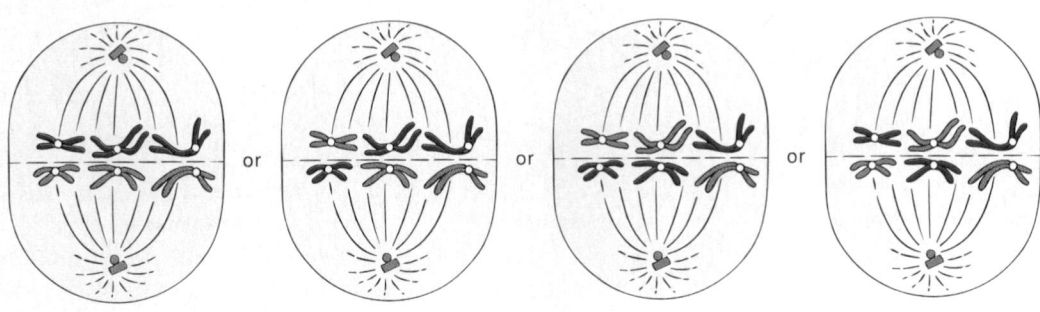

Figure **6.10**

Chance Alignment of Paired Homologous Chromosomes During Metaphase I of Meiosis. Which member of a pair of chromosomes faces which pole of the cell is random. For some pairs, the maternal (initial) chromosome may face "north," while for the other pairs, the maternal chromosome may face "south."

When all chromosome pairs are in the center of the cell, all those inherited from one parent do not necessarily line up on the same side as those inherited from the other parent. Using only three homologues as an example, any of the alignments shown in figure 6.10 are possible. Any one of these four alignments is as likely to occur as any other. As a consequence, each gamete is different regarding the combination of paternal and maternal chromosomes it receives. This random alignment of chromosomes at metaphase I is another major source of genetic variation in sexually reproducing animals.

Anaphase begins when homologous chromosomes separate and begin to move toward each pole (*see figure* 6.8a). Because the chromosomes of each homologous pair are moving in opposite directions, each daughter cell will receive one chromosome from each homologous pair. However, sister chromatids do not part at this stage because there is no centromere division in the first meiotic division. Thus, each of these chromosomes still consists of two chromatids and is called a **dyad** (Gr. *dyas*, two). Each pole of the cell now has just one complete set of chromosomes: one member of each homologous pair. Because the orientation of each pair of homologous chromosomes in the center of the cell is random (figure 6.10), the specific chromosomes that each pole receives from each pair of homologues are also random.

Meiotic telophase I is similar to mitotic telophase in that the parent cell divides into two daughter cells via cytokinesis (*see figure 6.6*). During this phase, nuclear envelopes appear around the chromosome sets, the nucleoli reappear, and the spindle fibers disappear. The transition to the second nuclear division is called interkinesis. Cells proceeding through interkinesis do not replicate their DNA. After a varying time period, meiosis II occurs.

THE SECOND MEIOTIC DIVISION: PROPHASE II TO TELOPHASE II

The second meiotic division (meiosis II) resembles an ordinary mitotic division (*see figure 6.8b*). The phases are referred to as prophase II, metaphase II, anaphase II, and telophase II. During prophase II, the spindle apparatus appears, and the chromosomes line up on the equatorial plate during metaphase II. During anaphase II, centromere division finally occurs, and the sister chromatids separate to become individual chromosomes, maintaining the haploid number that was produced at anaphase I. At the end of telophase II and cytokinesis, the final products of these two divisions of meiosis are four new "division products." In most animals, each of these "division products" is haploid and may function directly as a gamete (sex cell).

Stop and Ask Yourself

6. What are gametes?
7. What is synapsis?
8. What is the importance of crossing-over?
9. In meiosis, why don't sister chromatids part during anaphase I?
10. What happens during the second meiotic division?

GAMETE FORMATION

During the life cycle of most animals, some diploid cells undergo meiosis and haploid gametes are formed in a process called **gametogenesis.** In the testes of the male, the type of gametogenesis that produces sperm is called spermatogenesis; in the ovaries of the female, the production of ova (eggs) is called oogenesis.

SPERMATOGENESIS

Spermatogenesis produces mature sperm as follows (figure 6.11a):

1. Spermatogenesis begins in unspecialized germ cells called spermatogonia (s., spermatogonium). The spermatogonium increases in size and becomes a primary spermatocyte.
2. A primary spermatocyte undergoes meiosis (meiotic division I) and produces two smaller secondary spermatocytes.
3. Both secondary spermatocytes undergo a second meiotic division (meiotic division II) to form spermatids. (Notice that each primary spermatocyte gives rise to four spermatids, each with the haploid number of chromosomes.)
4. The spermatids develop into mature sperm (spermatozoa) without undergoing any further cell division.

OOGENESIS

Oogenesis, the maturation of ova (s., ovum) or eggs, differs from spermatogenesis in several ways and proceeds as follows (figure 6.11b):

1. Oogenesis begins in unspecialized germ cells called oogonia (s., oogonium), which undergo mitosis.
2. An oogonium develops and grows into a primary oocyte, which contains the diploid number of chromosomes. The primary oocyte undergoes a first meiotic division to produce two daughter cells of unequal size.
3. The larger of the daughter cells is the secondary oocyte. It contains almost all of the food-rich cytoplasm of the primary oocyte, which provides nourishment for the developing ovum.
4. The smaller of the two daughter cells is a first polar body, and is essentially only a nucleus. It may divide again, but eventually it degenerates.
5. In some animals, if the secondary oocyte is fertilized, it begins to go through a second meiotic division, producing a haploid ovum, and another tiny polar body is formed. This second polar body is also destined to disintegrate. When the haploid sperm and ovum nuclei merge (syngamy), the ovum becomes a zygote. Notice that in oogenesis, each primary oocyte gives rise to only one functional gamete instead of four as in spermatogenesis.

Stop and Ask Yourself

11. What are the main steps in spermatogenesis? In oogenesis?
12. How does oogenesis differ from spermatogenesis?

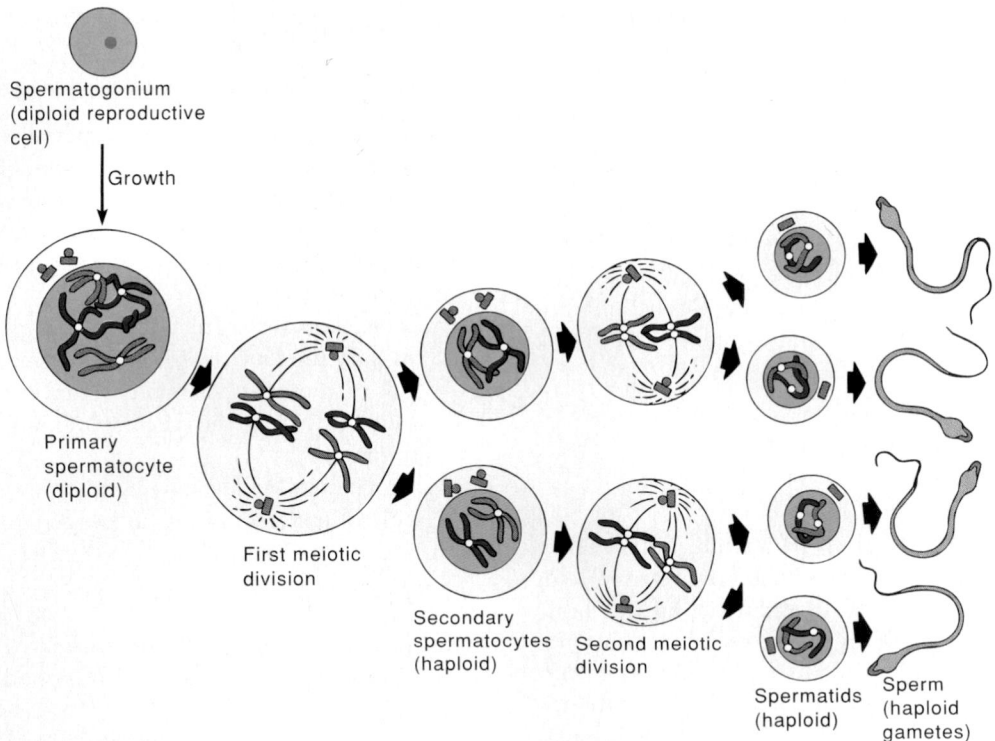

(a) **Spermatogenesis**

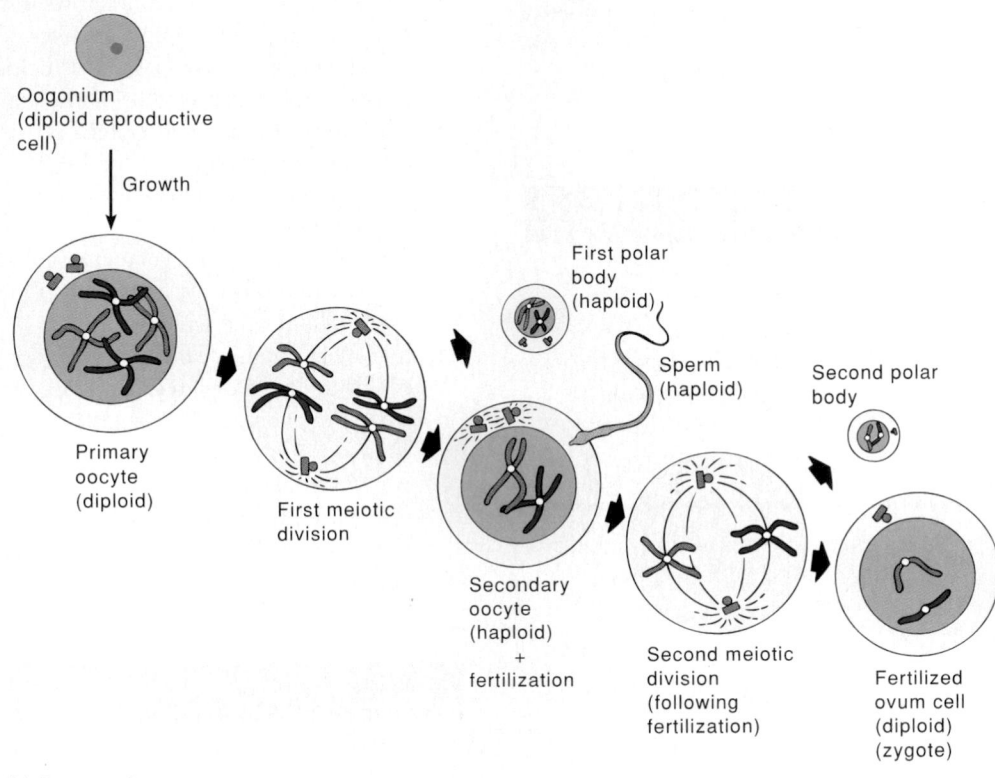

(b) **Oogenesis**

FIGURE 6.11

Gametogenesis. (*a*) Spermatogenesis is a meiotic process that involves two successive divisions. (*b*) In oogenesis, meiosis is completed following fertilization of the secondary oocyte.

SUMMARY

1. The replication of DNA and its subsequent allocation to daughter cells during mitosis involves a number of phases, collectively called the cell cycle. The cell cycle is that period from the time a cell is produced until it goes through mitosis.

2. Mitosis maintains the parental number of chromosome sets in each daughter nucleus. It separates the sister chromatids of each (duplicated) chromosome for distribution to daughter nuclei.

3. Interphase represents about 90% of the time of the eukaryotic cell cycle.

4. The first phase of mitosis is prophase, during which the mitotic apparatus forms. At the end of prophase, the nuclear envelope disintegrates, and microtubules attach each of the sister chromatids to the two poles of the cell.

5. The second phase of mitosis is metaphase. During this phase, the sister chromatids align along the metaphase plate in the center of the cell. At the end of metaphase, the centromeres joining each pair of sister chromatids split, freeing each chromatid, although the sister chromatids remain next to each other.

6. The third phase of mitosis is anaphase, during which the chromosomes and their copies (the sister chromatids that have been joined to them) are pulled to opposite poles of the cell by the microtubules.

7. The final phase of mitosis is telophase, during which the mitotic apparatus is disassembled, the nuclear envelope reforms, and the chromosomes unfold in the nucleoplasm.

8. Most cells undergo cytokinesis by being pinched in two by a belt of microfilaments and microtubules.

9. The cell cycle (mitosis) is highly regulated. During interphase, cyclin accumulates and associates with the cdc2 enzyme to form maturation-promoting factor (MPF). MPF triggers mitosis and activates enzymes that degrade cyclin. As cyclin is destroyed, MPF disappears and the cyclin-degrading enzymes become quiet. Thus, cyclin accumulates once again to start another cell division.

10. Meiosis is a special form of nuclear division that occurs during gamete formation in most eukaryotes. It consists of a single replication of the chromosomes and two nuclear divisions that result in four daughter cells, each with 1/2 the original number of chromosomes.

11. In the life cycle of most animals, certain diploid cells undergo gametogenesis to form haploid gametes (sperm in males and eggs in females). Fusion of a sperm and an egg nucleus at fertilization produces a new diploid cell (zygote), which undergoes mitosis and cytokinesis to develop into a new individual.

SELECTED KEY TERMS

anaphase (p. 86)
cell cycle (p. 82)
crossing-over (p. 88)
cytokinesis (p. 82)
interphase (p. 82)
meiosis (p. 88)
metaphase (p. 86)
mitosis (p. 82)
prophase (p. 84)
telophase (p. 86)

CRITICAL THINKING QUESTIONS

1. Humans are diploid organisms and are biased in favor of diploidy over haploidy. However, what are the biological advantages of having diploid cells? Are there advantages for some organisms being haploid?

2. If the function of meiosis were only to make haploid cells from a diploid cell, this could be accomplished in a single cell division—that is, canceling chromosome replication and separating homologous chromosomes would produce two haploid gametes from each diploid cell. If this could occur, what important aspect of meiosis would be omitted from this simple procedure?

3. Is reproduction life's death-defying escape from inevitable destruction? Explain.

4. Which do you think evolved first, meiosis or mitosis? Why? What do you think may have been some of the stages in the evolution of one from the other?

5. How do new genetic combinations arise during meiosis?

INHERITANCE PATTERNS

Outline

Concepts

1. Modern genetics began with the work of Gregor Mendel. The principles that he described explain the inheritance patterns of many animal traits. The concepts that Mendel described include the following:
   a. dominance
   b. the principle of segregation
   c. the principle of independent assortment
2. Rapid developments in twentieth-century genetics have expanded on the work of Gregor Mendel. Geneticists have discovered that
   a. many alternative forms of a gene may exist in a population.
   b. these alternative forms may interact in different ways.
   c. some traits are determined by interactions between many gene pairs.
   d. the environment influences the expression of genes.

Would You Like to Know:

1. why modern genetics is so important to zoology and our modern society? (p. 96)
2. how an Augustinian monk ever got started crossing garden peas? (p. 96)
3. why there are so many expressions of some traits? (p. 101)
4. why some traits, such as height, show a range of variation, whereas other traits show an all-or-none expression? (p. 102)
5. how the environment influences the expression of some genes? (p. 103)

These and other useful questions will be answered in this chapter.

Genetics (Gr. *gennan*, to produce) is the study of the transmission of biological information from one generation to a following generation, and of how information is expressed in an organism. Humans have been aware for centuries that certain traits are passed from parents to offspring and have used that knowledge in selective breeding of domesticated plants and animals.

The importance of genetics to modern societies, however, surpasses anything that ancient animal breeders could have imagined. Modern genetics began with the work of Gregor Mendel (1822–1884). Since then, geneticists have been performing crosses, characterizing the genetic material (DNA), and investigating the functions of DNA.

The genetics revolution has had a tremendous effect on biology. Genetics can explain why offspring are, in some ways, similar to their parents, whereas in other ways, they are very different. Genetic mechanisms also help explain how species change over evolutionary time. Genetic and evolutionary themes are interdependent in biology, and biology without either would be unrecognizable from its present form.

① Emerging genetic technologies are also forcing our society to come face-to-face with some very important decisions regarding what, if any, limits should be placed on genetic manipulations. The benefits of genetic technologies include the following: the mass production of hormones and antibodies, increased agricultural production, and the replacement of defective genes.

Even though genetic technologies hold great promise for the future, they must not be pursued without consideration of possible negative effects. Recall that science is ethically neutral (*see chapter 1*). Thus, society must deal with questions relating to the effects of genetically engineered bacteria and other organisms on the environment, the use of genetically engineered organisms for waging war, and the moral and ethical dilemma faced by anyone who tries to decide what kinds of genetic manipulations may be performed on humans.

In light of these concerns, we devote three chapters of this textbook to genetics. Many of the genetic principles that can be traced back to the beginnings of modern genetics are covered in this chapter. The chromosomal basis of inheritance is covered in chapter 8. Modern concepts of genes and gene functions, and some of the modern technologies that allow humans to manipulate genes, are covered in chapter 9.

THE BIRTH OF MODERN GENETICS

Gregor Mendel (figure 7.1) was born in 1822 in an area of Europe now known as the Czech Republic. He was the son of a farmer and grew up knowing about the cultivation and propagation of crop plants. Mendel entered an Augustinian monastery in Brunn (Brno, Czech Republic) and became a priest at the age of 25. He was then given the opportunity to study physics, mathematics, and natural sciences at the University of Vienna in Austria. Mendel's studies in Vienna were completed in 1854, and he returned to Brunn where he began teaching.

FIGURE 7.1

Gregor Mendel (1822–1884): The Father of Genetics. Gregor Mendel's work with garden peas, although unappreciated during his time, was rediscovered and confirmed in 1900. This rediscovery marks the beginning of modern genetics.

In 1857, Mendel began experiments with the garden pea, *Pisum sativum*. He was not the first scientist to study inheritance; however, his approach was unique. ② Mendel selected an experimental organism whose pollination could be easily controlled, and chose seven clearly defined traits to study. He carried his crosses through multiple generations and approached his experiments as a mathematician, as well as a biologist. Mendel published his work in 1866, but the importance of his conclusions was unrecognized by scientists of his day. Mendel died in 1884. The rediscovery and confirmation of his writings in 1900 propelled genetics into the twentieth century.

Stop and Ask Yourself

1. What is genetics?
2. Why is a basic understanding of genetics an important part of any zoologist's training?
3. In what way was Mendel's approach to the study of genetics unique?

MENDELIAN INHERITANCE PATTERNS

The fruit fly, *Drosophila melanogaster*, has become a classic tool for studying inheritance patterns. Its utility stems from its ease of handling, short life cycle, and easily recognized characteristics.

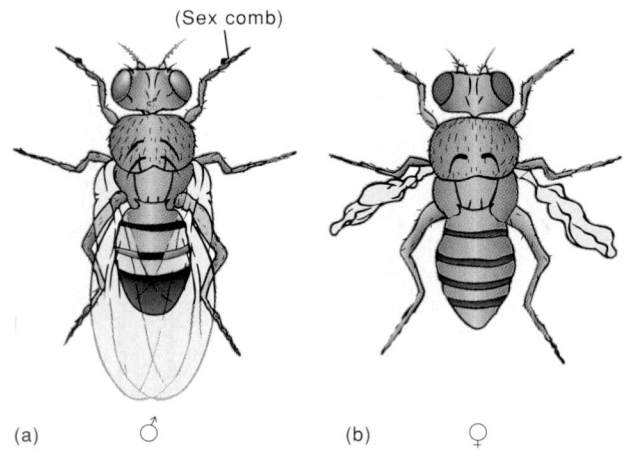

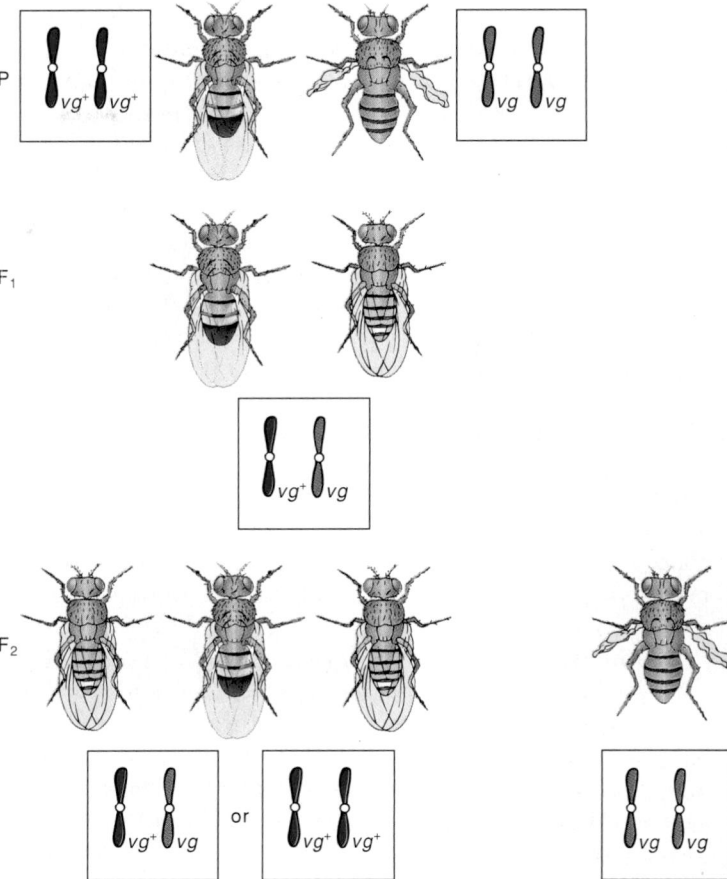

FIGURE 7.2

Distinguishing Sexes and Phenotypes of *Drosophila melanogaster.* (*a*) A male with wild-type wings and wild-type eyes. (*b*) A female with vestigial wings and sepia eyes. In contrast to the female, the posterior aspect of the male's abdomen has a wide dark bank and a rounded tip.

FIGURE 7.3

A Cross Involving a Single Trait. A cross between parental flies with wild-type wings and vestigial wings, carried through two generations.

When any fruit fly trait is studied, comparisons are always made to a wild-type fly. If a fly has a characteristic similar to that found in wild flies, it is said to have the wild-type expression of that trait. (In the examples used below, wild-type wings lay over the back at rest, and extend past the posterior tip of the body, and wild-type eyes are red.) Numerous mutations from the wild-type body form have been described, such as vestigial wings (reduced, shriveled wings) and sepia (dark brown) eyes (figure 7.2).

SEGREGATION

During the formation of gametes, units of inheritance in each parent are incorporated into separate gametes. We call these units of inheritance **genes** (Gr. *genos*, race). Recall that during anaphase I of meiosis, homologous chromosomes move toward opposite poles of the cell, and the resulting gametes have only one member of each chromosome pair. Genes carried on one member of a pair of homologous chromosomes end up in one gamete, and genes carried on the other member are segregated into a different gamete. Mendel's **principle of segregation** states that pairs of hereditary factors are distributed between gametes during gamete formation. (Mendel, of course, knew nothing of the cellular basis of gamete formation.) Fertilization results in the random combination of gametes and brings homologous chromosomes together again.

Mendel's principle of segregation can be illustrated by crossing wild-type fruit flies with flies having vestigial wings. (The flies being crossed come from stocks of flies that have been inbred for generations to be sure they bred true for wild-type wings or vestigial wings.) These flies are members of the parental generation, and one finds that all of their offspring

(progeny) have wild-type wings. The wild-type progeny are members of the first generation of offspring, or the first filial (F_1) generation (figure 7.3). If the flies are allowed to mate with each other, the progeny that result are members of the second filial (F_2) generation. Approximately 1/4 of these flies have vestigial wings and 3/4 have wild wings (figure 7.3). Note that the vestigial characteristic, although present in the parental generation, disappears in the F_1 generation and reappears in the F_2 generation. In addition, the ratio of wild-type flies to vestigial-winged flies in the F_2 generation is approximately 3:1. We would also find that reciprocal crosses would yield similar results. (Reciprocal crosses involve the same characteristics, but the investigator reverses the sexes of the individuals, introducing a particular expression of the trait into the cross.)

From similar results in his experiments, Mendel concluded that traits were determined by heritable "factors" (genes). Genes that determine the expression of a particular trait can exist in alternative forms called **alleles** (Gr. *allelos*, each other). The vestigial allele is present in the F_1 generation in our example, and even though it is masked by the wild-type allele for wing shape, it retains its uniqueness because it is expressed again in some members of the F_2 generation. Mendel defined **dominant** factors as those that can hide the expression of another factor; **recessive** factors were those whose expression could be masked. In our example, the wild-type allele is dominant because it can mask the expression of the vestigial allele, which is therefore recessive.

The occurrence of flies with masked traits brings up two more important points that Mendel noticed in his pea experiments.

The visual expression of alleles may not always indicate the underlying genetic makeup of an organism. This visual expression is called the **phenotype,** and the genetic makeup is called the **genotype.** In our example, the flies of the F_1 generation had the same phenotype as one of the parents, but they differed genotypically because they carried both a dominant and recessive allele. They are hybrids, and because this cross concerns only one pair of genes and a single trait, it is called a **monohybrid cross** (Gr. *monos*, one + L. *hybrida*, offspring of two kinds of parents).

An organism is said to be **homozygous** (L. *homo*, same + Gr. *zygon*, paired) if it carries two identical genes for a given trait, and is **heterozygous** (Gr. *heteros*, other) if the genes are different. Thus, in our example, all members of the parental generation are homozygous because we chose true-breeding flies to cross. All members of the F_1 generation are heterozygous.

Crosses are often diagrammed using symbols to represent different alleles. A letter or letters are chosen that are descriptive of the trait in question. Often, the first letter of the description of the dominant allele is used. In fruit flies, and other organisms where all mutants are compared with a wild-type, the symbol is taken from the allele that was derived by a mutation from the wild condition. A superscript "+" next to the symbol represents the wild-type allele. A capital letter means that the allele being represented is dominant, and a lowercase letter means that the allele being represented is recessive. Thus, we can represent our original cross as follows:

	Wild-type	Vestigial
P generation	$vg^+ \ vg^+$ ×	$vg \ vg$
F_1 generation		$vg^+ \ vg$

Matings of the F_1 flies resulted in a ratio of three wild-type flies to one vestigial fly in the F_2 generation. Mendel recognized that a 3:1 ratio would result when two alleles, each present in a separate gamete, combined randomly at fertilization (*see chapter* 6).

Analyzing crosses becomes easier when one approaches it in a systematic fashion. The **Punnett square** is a tool used by

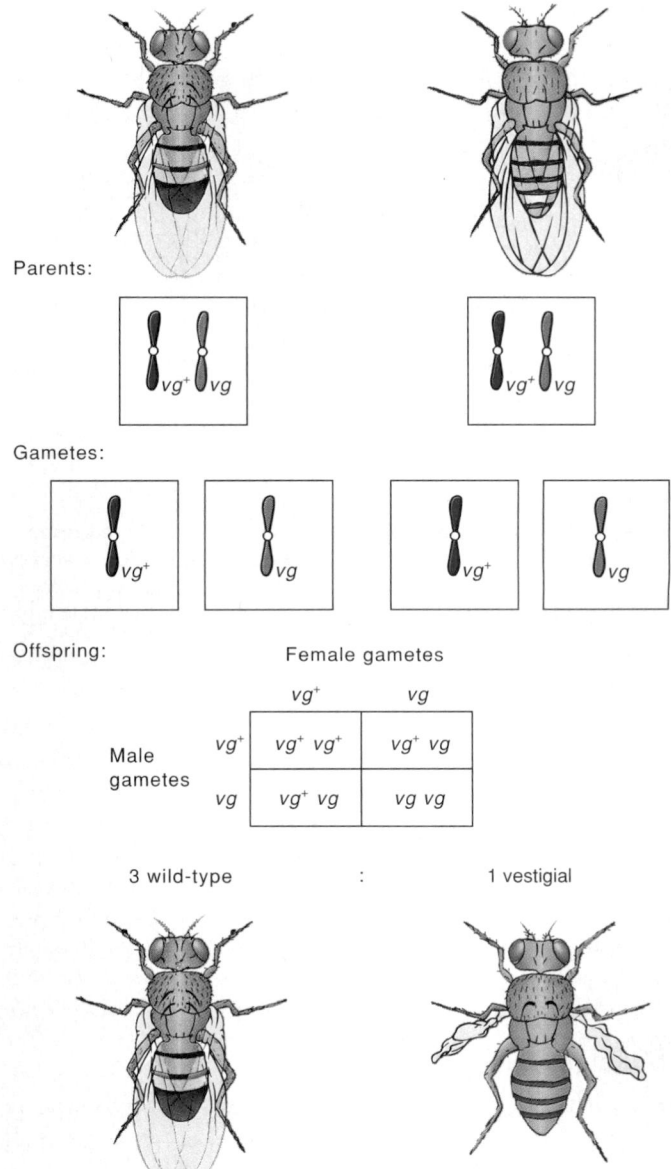

Parents:

Gametes:

Offspring:

		Female gametes	
		vg^+	vg
Male gametes	vg^+	$vg^+ \ vg^+$	$vg^+ \ vg$
	vg	$vg^+ \ vg$	$vg \ vg$

3 wild-type   :   1 vestigial

FIGURE 7.4

Use of a Punnett Square. A Punnett square can be used to help predict the results of a cross. After determining the kinds of gametes produced by each member of a cross, gametes produced by each sex are placed along the axes of a square. Results of matings are analyzed by combining gametes and counting results.

geneticists to help predict the results of crosses. A cross of two F_1 flies from our example will be used to illustrate the use of a Punnett square (figure 7.4). The first step is to determine the kinds of gametes produced by each parent. One of the two axes of a square is designated for each parent, and the different kinds of gametes produced by each parent are placed along the appropriate axis. Combining gametes in the interior of the square tells us the results of random fertilization. Figure 7.4 shows that the F_1 flies are heterozygous, with one wild-type allele and one vestigial allele. The F_2 generation is shown on the inside of the Punnett square. There are two phenotypes, in a ratio of 3:1.

The **phenotypic ratio** expresses the results of a cross according to the relative numbers of progeny in each visually distinct class (e.g., 3 wild-type : 1 vestigial). The Punnett square has thus explained in another way the F_2 results in figure 7.3. It also shows that there are three different genotypes in F_2 individuals. The **genotypic ratio** expresses the results of a cross according to the relative numbers of progeny in each genotypic category (e.g., 1 vg^+vg^+: 2 vg^+vg : 1 $vgvg$). A 3:1 phenotypic ratio and a 1:2:1 genotypic ratio are typical results of monohybrid crosses. The results of crosses rarely achieve phenotypic or genotypic ratios exactly. Instead, the results approximate these expected ratios and generally are closer to the expected values as more progeny are produced. You have now seen that Mendel's principle of segregation is an explanation of how members of a pair of genes are distributed into separate gametes. At fertilization, the paired condition is restored. When a large number of progeny from these fertilizations is counted, the predictable phenotypic and genotypic ratios are obtained.

INDEPENDENT ASSORTMENT

In his crosses, Mendel also followed two pairs of characteristics. We can make similar crosses using flies that have vestigial wings and sepia eyes and flies that are wild for these characteristics. Sepia eyes are dark brown, and wild-type eyes are red. The results of crosses carried through two generations are shown in figure 7.5.

Note that in the parental generation, the flies are homozygous for the traits in question, and each parent produces only one kind of gamete. Gametes have one allele for each trait. Because each parent produces only one kind of gamete, fertilization must result in offspring heterozygous for both traits. The F_1 flies have the wild-type phenotype; thus, we know that wild-type eyes are dominant to sepia eyes. The F_1 flies are hybrids, and because the cross involves two pairs of genes and two traits, it is called a **dihybrid cross** (Gr. *di*, two + L. *hybrida*, offspring of two kinds of parents).

Gregor Mendel recognized the 9:3:3:1 ratio as what would be expected if genes obey certain probability laws. He concluded that during gamete formation, the distribution of genes determining one trait did not influence how genes determining the other trait were distributed. In our example, this means that an F_1 gamete that ends up with a vg^+ gene for wing condition may also have either the *se* or *se*$^+$ gene for eye color, as shown in the F_1 gametes of figure 7.5. Note that all combinations of the eye color and wing condition genes are present, and all combinations are equally likely. This example illustrates Mendel's **principle of independent assortment,** which states that during gamete formation pairs of factors segregate independently of one another.

Mendel's principle of independent assortment is explained by events of meiosis (*see figure* 6.8). Cells produced during meiosis have one member of each homologous pair of chromosomes. Independent assortment simply means that when homologous chromosomes line up at metaphase I and then segregate, the behavior of one pair of chromosomes does not influence the behavior of any other pair (figure 7.6; *see also figure* 6.10). Notice that after meiosis, maternal and paternal chromosomes are distributed randomly among cells.

Accurately determining all possible gametes produced by participants in a cross is critically important when learning to work genetics problems. You must remember that (1) all gametes must have one (and only one) allele for each trait, and (2) all possible combinations of alleles for the traits being considered must be represented in the gametes.

TESTING PHENOTYPES

The wild-type flies in the F_2 generation of our monohybrid cross had two different genotypes. How could we determine the genotype of any one wild-type fly? One way is by carrying out a **testcross,** which involves crossing the phenotypically dominant fly to a fly that shows the recessive phenotype. (Remember that any organism that shows a recessive trait is homozygous for that trait.) The results of a testcross will be different depending on whether the phenotypically dominant fly is homozygous or heterozygous. A testcross with a fly homozygous for a dominant trait will always yield phenotypically dominant offspring, and a testcross with a fly heterozygous for a dominant trait will always yield a 1:1 ratio of phenotypically dominant to phenotypically recessive offspring (table 7.1).

Stop and Ask Yourself

4. What is Mendel's principle of segregation? What events of meiosis does this principle reflect?

5. What is Mendel's principle of independent assortment? What events of meiosis does it reflect?

6. How would you define the following terms: homozygous, heterozygous, phenotype, genotype, and allele?

7. What is a testcross?

OTHER INHERITANCE PATTERNS

Traits that we have considered so far have been determined by two genes, where one allele was dominant to a second. In this section, you will find that there are often many alleles in a population, not all traits are determined by an interaction between a single pair of dominant or recessive genes, and various internal and external environmental factors can affect the phenotype.

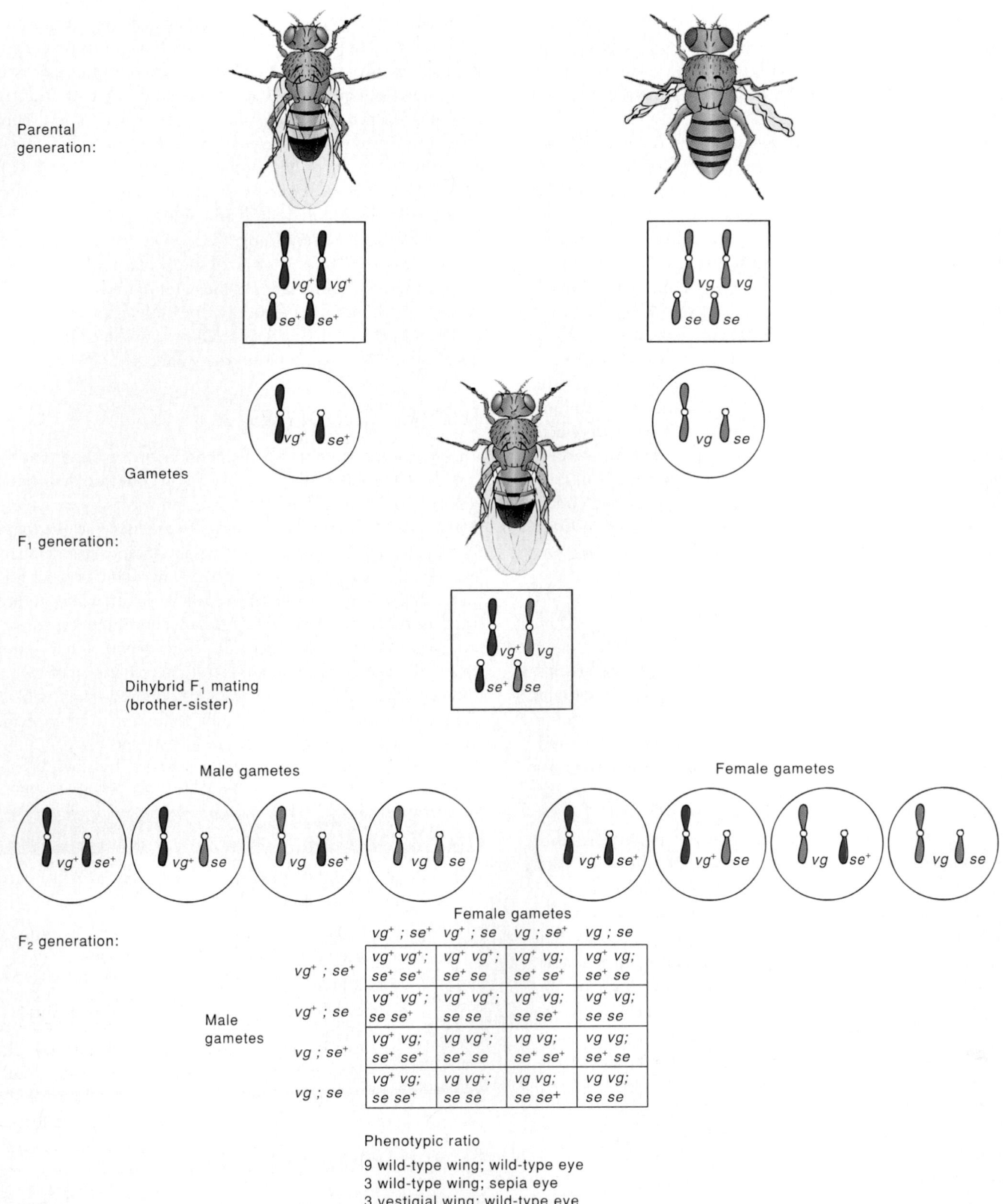

Parental generation:

Gametes

F₁ generation:

Dihybrid F₁ mating (brother-sister)

Male gametes

Female gametes

F₂ generation:

Female gametes

Phenotypic ratio

9 wild-type wing; wild-type eye
3 wild-type wing; sepia eye
3 vestigial wing; wild-type eye
1 vestigial wing; sepia eye

Figure 7.5

Constructing a Punnett Square for a Cross Involving Two Characteristics. Note that every gamete has one allele for each trait and that all combinations of alleles for each trait are represented.

7.6

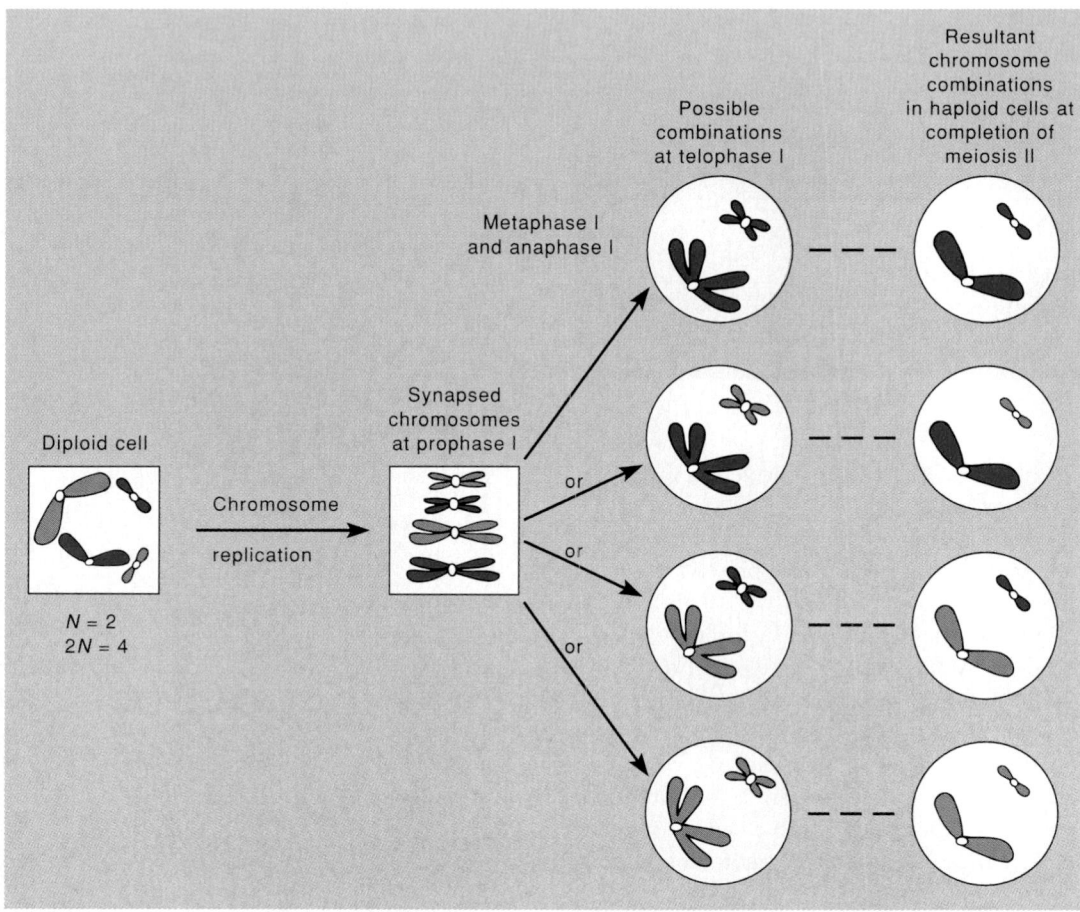

FIGURE 7.6

Independent Assortment of Chromosomes During Meiosis. Maternal and paternal chromosomes are distinguished by color. Homologous chromosomes are indicated by similar size. During the first meiotic division, one homologous pair of chromosomes (and hence the genes this pair carries) is segregated without regard to the movements of any other homologous pair. Thus there are all possible combinations of large and small chromosomes in the cells at telophase I, and in the cells at the completion of telophase II. Most organisms have more than two pairs of homologous chromosomes in each cell. As the number of homologous pairs increases, the number of different kinds of gametes also increases.

TABLE 7.1	A Comparison of the Results of a Testcross of Heterozygous and Homozygous Dominant Flies
Dominant Phenotype (wild-type wings)	

If homozygous (vg^+vg^+)	If heterozygous (vg^+vg)
Testcross: $vgvg \times vg^+vg^+$	$vgvg \times vg^+vg$
Gametes: vg vg^+	vg vg^+,vg
Offspring: vg^+vg	vg^+vg, $vgvg$
all wild-type wings.	1 wild-type wings: 1 vestigial wings.

MULTIPLE ALLELES

Traits are determined in one individual by two genes, one carried on each chromosome of a homologous pair. ❸ Unlike the situation in an individual, a population may have many different alleles with the potential to contribute to the phenotype of any member of the population. These are called **multiple alleles.** Genes for a particular trait are located at the same position on a chromosome. The gene's position on the chromosome is called its **locus** (L. *loca*, place). As will be presented in chapters 12 to 14, the diversity of alleles in a population is very important in supplying the phenotypic variation on which evolution can act.

Numerous human loci have multiple alleles. The familiar ABO blood types are determined by three alleles, symbolized

TABLE 7.2	GENOTYPES AND PHENOTYPES IN THE ABO BLOOD GROUPS	
GENOTYPE(S)	PHENOTYPE	
$I^A I^A$, $I^A i$	A	
$I^B I^B$, $I^B i$	B	
$I^A I^B$	A and B	
ii	O	

I^A, I^B, and i. The combinations of alleles that determine a person's phenotype are shown in table 7.2. Note that i is recessive to I^A and to I^B. I^A and I^B, however, are neither dominant nor recessive to each other. When I^A and I^B are present together, both are expressed.

The Rh blood type is also determined by multiple alleles. It was discovered during World War II that matching ABO blood types did not always ensure a successful transfusion. Another blood cell trait, first discovered in the rhesus monkey, was found to be responsible for transfusion rejections when the ABO blood type was matched. The Rh system is inherited as if it is determined by two alleles with Rh positive being dominant to Rh negative. In fact, the system is much more complex. It now appears that there are in excess of 30 alleles determining the Rh phenotype!

INCOMPLETE DOMINANCE AND CODOMINANCE

Incomplete dominance is an interaction between two alleles that are expressed more or less equally, and the heterozygote is different from either homozygote. For example, in cattle, the alleles for red coat color and for white coat color interact to produce an intermediate called roan. Because neither the red nor the white allele is dominant, we use uppercase letters and a prime or a superscript to represent genes. Thus red cattle would be symbolized RR, white cattle would be symbolized $R'R'$, and roan cattle would be symbolized RR'.

Codominance occurs when the heterozygote expresses the phenotypes of both homozygotes. Thus, in the ABO blood types, the $I^A I^B$ heterozygote expresses both alleles.

Another example of codominance is the inheritance of sickle cell anemia. Sickle cell anemia arose in Africa as a result of a mutation in the genes coding for one of the proteins making up the hemoglobin molecule. The normal allele is symbolized Hb^A, and the sickle allele is symbolized Hb^S. When present in the homozygous condition, the sickle cell allele results in severe sickling (having a crescent shape) of red blood cells, and the anemia that results is usually fatal. Even though the Hb^S allele is very detrimental in the homozygous state, it is much less dangerous when heterozygous. Heterozygotes have about equal numbers of Hb^A and Hb^S hemoglobin molecules in their red blood cells, and sickling only develops under oxygen stress. The

anemia is not only less severe, but heterozygotes are less susceptible to infections by the organism that causes malaria. Prior to malarial control programs in Africa, heterozygotes had a better chance of surviving than either homozygote!

Crosses involving incomplete dominance and codominance are analyzed in exactly the same manner as the previous crosses discussed. Mendelian rules are obeyed, but the results are interpreted differently. For example, a cross between a roan bull and a roan cow would be analyzed as follows:

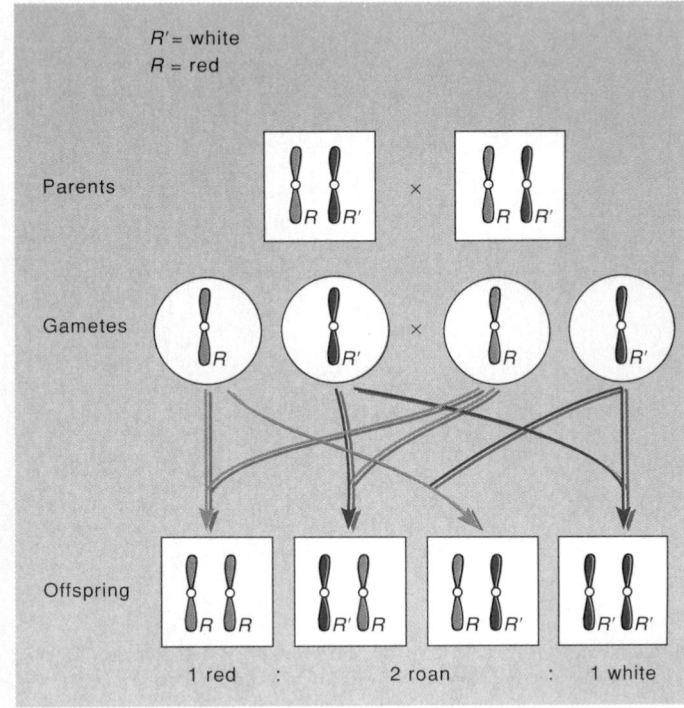

The 1:2:1 genotypic ratio is now also the phenotypic ratio.

QUANTITATIVE TRAITS: POLYGENES

In all traits considered thus far, genes produced discrete variations in phenotypes. It is easy to distinguish a vestigial-winged fruit fly from a wild-type winged fruit fly, or a person with type A blood from a person with type O blood. Such traits display discontinuous variation. Many other traits, however, vary by small increments and must be categorized by some kind of quantitative measure (e.g., weight or height must be measured). Traits such as height, skin color, weight, and intelligence display continuous variation over a range of phenotypes. ④ Traits that display continuous variation are often determined by an interaction of multiple loci, where each locus adds a small increment to a phenotype. A mating between very tall and very short individuals (figure 7.7*a*) would produce offspring intermediate in height (figure 7.7*b*). A mating between two individuals that are heterozygous at each locus produces a range of phenotypes (figure 7.7*c*). Plotting the frequency of each phenotype in the phenotypic range produces the bell-shaped distribution that is commonly seen

(a)

Grandparent 1	Grandparent 2
AABBCC	A'A'B'B'C'C'
120 cm	198 cm

(b)

F₁ offspring
AA'BB'CC'
159 cm

(c) Possible F₂ offspring

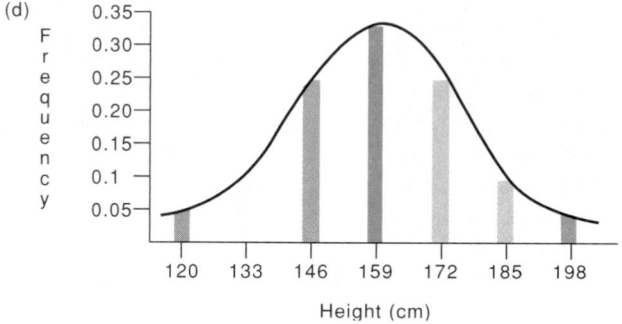

Female gametes

	A'B'C'	A'BC'	A'B'C	AB'C'	ABC'	A'BC	AB'C	ABC
A'B'C'	198	185	185	185	172	172	172	159
A'BC'	185	172	172	172	159	159	159	146
A'B'C	185	172	172	172	159	159	159	146
AB'C'	185	172	172	172	159	159	159	146
ABC'	172	159	159	159	146	146	146	133
A'BC	172	159	159	159	146	146	146	133
AB'C	172	159	159	159	146	146	146	133
ABC	159	146	146	146	133	133	133	120

(Male gametes, labeled vertically on the left)

(d) Frequency vs Height (cm) bar graph with bell curve. X-axis: 120, 133, 146, 159, 172, 185, 198. Y-axis: 0.05, 0.1, 0.15, 0.20, 0.25, 0.30, 0.35.

FIGURE 7.7

Polygenic Inheritance of Height. An example of how polygenic inheritance can produce continuous variation. Assume three loci are involved with the determination of height, and assume that each gene designated with a prime adds 13 cm to a base height of 120 cm. (*a*) Grandparents showing the two phenotypic extremes. (*b*) Offspring in the next generation are intermediate in height. (*c*) A mating between one member of that second generation and a person of similar stature could produce offspring that are very tall, very short, or anywhere between those extremes. (The numbers in the Punnett square were derived by multiplying 13 by the number of primed alleles in a cell and adding that product to 120 cm.) (*d*) Note in the bar graph that the distribution between extremes approaches a normal (bell-shaped) curve. Slight environmental variations would smooth the steplike transitions from one phenotypic class to another.

in polygenic inheritance in a population (figure 7.7*d*). Because it requires quantitative measurements to distinguish between phenotypes, traits like these are often called **quantitative traits.** Similarly, the participation of multiple loci in determining these traits prompts the use of the term **polygenes** when referring to the genes involved.

The steplike transitions between phenotypes seen in figure 7.7*d* are made smaller as more loci are added to a cross. As discussed in the next section, no genes are isolated from external and internal environments. Environmental conditions often influence the degree to which genes are expressed and, therefore, they make transitions between phenotypes of quantitative traits smoother.

ENVIRONMENTAL EFFECTS AND GENE EXPRESSION

Our genetic makeup is not necessarily a set of blueprints that dictates our final form, just like the blueprints of a building dictate the final form of a home. For most traits, the outcome of a set of genetic instructions is the product of a genotype interacting with the environment.   ⑤   We can think of the interaction as a genotype establishing a more or less fixed potential; and whether or not that potential will be realized depends on important environmental influences. For example, nutritional factors may influence whether or not animals achieve their genetic potential regarding physical or mental stature.

It is not too difficult to investigate the effects of the environment on gene expression in animals that can be manipulated experimentally. One simply maintains animals of identical genotypes in different environments and observes the effect of the environment on the phenotype. Numerous traits in the fruit fly are influenced by the environment. For example, the number of facets (lenses) in certain compound eye mutants is affected by the temperature at which cultures are maintained.

Stop and Ask Yourself

8. What are multiple alleles?
9. Define the term locus.
10. What are polygenes?
11. How do quantitative inheritance patterns explain the occurrence of continuous variation in some traits?
12. What human traits do you think are influenced by environmental factors?

SUMMARY

1. Genetics is the study of the transmission of information from one generation to a following generation. During the last 20 years, genetic research has influenced both science and society.

2. Gregor Mendel worked with garden peas and concluded that traits are determined by pairs of factors (genes), and that one gene may be dominant to another (the recessive gene). These genes are passed unaltered from parents to offspring.

3. Mendel's principle of segregation states that pairs of genes are distributed between gametes during gamete formation when homologous chromosomes are distributed to different gametes during meiosis.

4. Mendel's principle of independent assortment states that during gamete formation, pairs of genes segregate independently of one another. This is a result of meiotic processes in which members of one homologous pair of chromosomes are not influenced by the movements of any other pair of chromosomes.

5. Populations may have many alternative expressions of a gene at any locus. Human traits, like the ABO and Rh blood groups, are examples of traits determined by multiple alleles.

6. Incomplete dominance is an interaction between two alleles where the alleles contribute more or less equally to the phenotype. The heterozygote is intermediate between the parental extremes.

7. Codominance is an interaction between two alleles where both alleles are expressed in the heterozygote.

8. Quantitative traits vary by small increments, displaying continuous variation. These traits are the result of genes at many loci (polygenes) adding small increments of expression to a phenotype.

9. Most traits are not determined only by the genotype of an organism. Rather, the environment influences the degree to which a genotype will be expressed.

SELECTED KEY TERMS

alleles (p. 97)
dominant (p. 98)
genes (p. 97)
genetics (p. 96)
genotype (p. 98)
phenotype (p. 98)

principle of independent assortment (p. 99)
principle of segregation (p. 97)
quantitative traits (p. 103)
recessive (p. 98)

CRITICAL THINKING QUESTIONS

1. Supply the genotypes, as completely as possible, for the parents and progeny of the following crosses:

   a. wild-type wing; sepia eye × wild-type wing; wild-type eye =
      3 wild-type wing; sepia eye : 1 vestigial wing; sepia eye :
      3 wild-type wing; wild-type eye : 1 vestigial wing; wild-type eye

   b. wild-type wing; sepia eye × wild-type wing; wild-type eye =
      1 wild-type wing; sepia eye : 1 wild-type wing; wild-type eye

   c. vestigial wing; wild-type eye × wild-type wing; sepia eye =
      all wild-type wing; wild-type eye

   d. vestigial wing; wild-type eye × wild-type wing; sepia eye =
      1 vestigial wing; wild-type eye : 1 vestigial wing; sepia eye :
      1 wild-type wing; sepia eye : 1 wild-type wing; wild-type eye

2. The following progeny are the result of a cross between two fruit flies. Unfortunately, the phenotypes of the parental flies were not recorded. Formulate a hypothesis regarding the genotypes of the parental flies. (Hint: consider the ratio between wing phenotypes separately from eye phenotypes in formulating your hypothesis.)

   Progeny:
      293 wild-type wing; wild-type eye
      310 wild-type wing; sepia eye
      97 vestigial wing; wild-type eye
      100 vestigial wing; sepia eye

3. Indicate the ABO genotypes of the members of the following family. (You may not have enough information to fill in all genotypes completely.)

   Grandfather—Type A _____   Grandfather—Type O _____
   Grandmother—Type AB _____   Grandmother—Type B _____
                    ↓   ↓
   Father—Type A   ×   Mother—Type B
   _____   _____
                    ↓
   Son₁—Type A   Daughter—Type B   Son₂—Type AB
   _____   _____   _____

4. Do you think that Mendel's conclusions regarding assortment of genes for two traits would have been any different if he had used traits encoded by genes carried on the same chromosome? Explain.

5. Explain why the phenotypic range of polygenic traits shows a gradual transition between phenotypes rather than the stair-step transitions shown in figure 7.7d.

6. Design an experiment that could be used to determine whether or not a particular trait in fruit flies is influenced by an environmental factor, such as temperature, light, or nutritional state. Why is the investigation of environmental effects more difficult in human genetics studies than in studies of fruit flies?

7. In guinea pigs, black fur is dominant over white fur. How could an animal breeder test whether a black guinea pig is homozygous or heterozygous?

8. To observe the laws of chance, toss a dime and a quarter simultaneously 10 times and count the number of head-head, head-tail, and tail-tail combinations. How close are your results to a 1:2:1 ratio? Now toss the coins 90 times more for a total of 100 tosses. How close are your new results to a 1:2:1 ratio? Explain the difference.

CHROMOSOMES AND GENE LINKAGE

Concepts

1. The genetic material is organized into chromosomes, although during interphase only diffuse chromatin is visible. Chromosomes may be represented differently in males and females; however, the number of chromosomes is constant for a given species.
2. Genes that are on the same chromosome (linked) tend to be inherited together. Inheritance patterns differ depending on whether genes are linked on sex chromosomes or on autosomes and the distance between linked genes. Linkage relationships are used to help determine the position of loci on chromosomes.
3. Human pedigree analysis allows geneticists to determine how a trait is inherited.
4. Changes in chromosome number and structure can occur. The phenotypic consequences of such changes depend on the amount of genetic material lost or duplicated.

Would You Like to Know:

1. why there are approximately equal numbers of males and females in the world? (p. 106)
2. why some traits, such as color blindness, are more common in males than in females? (p. 110)
3. how "sex checks" of Olympic athletes are carried out? (p. 111)
4. whether or not females can express pattern baldness? (p. 111)
5. what causes genetic diseases, such as Down syndrome? (p. 112)

These and other useful questions will be answered in this chapter.

This chapter contains evolutionary concepts, which are set off in this font.

Can you imagine compacting a mass of thread into a ball that is 10,000 times smaller than the length of the original thread? Imagine unwinding the thread again, mixing it with 45 other similar lengths of thread, and repeating the process? For those of us who have problems keeping knots out of extension cords and garden hoses, the task seems Herculean! Yet, a similar feat is done every time a human cell divides. The formation of human chromosomes involves compacting 46 microscopic threads of DNA and protein, whose total length is about one meter, into a single cell. This packaging occurs in a very precise manner so that the DNA and protein can be dispersed in the nucleus of the cell after division is completed, and the genes carried by the chromosomes will continue to function normally. This chapter describes chromosomes, how genes are arranged on chromosomes, and how these arrangements influence patterns of inheritance.

EUKARYOTIC CHROMOSOMES

A few years before Mendel's death, Friedrich Schneider (1831–1890) and Walther Flemming (1843–1905) described darkly staining nuclear threads, now called chromosomes. Around the turn of the century, Edouard van Beneden (1849–1922) announced that the number of chromosomes was usually constant in each cell of an organism. The only exception occurred during gamete formation, when the number of chromosomes was reduced by ½. These discoveries were quickly followed by those of Thomas Hunt Morgan (1866–1945) and his co-workers, showing that genes occur in linear arrays on chromosomes.

Since these early studies, research has shown that metaphase chromosomes consist of two chromatids, joined at the centromere (*see figure 6.3*). Chromosomes of most animals exist in homologous pairs, which carry genes that code for the same traits and are visually similar. Chromosome size, centromere position, and staining patterns help geneticists recognize homologous pairs.

ORGANIZATION OF DNA AND PROTEIN

It has been known for many years that **chromatin** consists of DNA and histone proteins. Research over the past 15 years has begun to explain how the association of DNA and protein helps with the complex jobs of packing the DNA into chromosomes and regulating the activity of DNA.

There are five different histone proteins. Pairs of four of these proteins form a core particle. DNA wraps in a coil around the proteins, a combination called a **nucleosome** (figure 8.1*a*, *b*). A fifth histone, sometimes called the linker protein, is not needed for the formation of the nucleosome, but it is thought to help anchor the DNA to the core and promote the winding of the chain of nucleosomes into a cylinder (figure 8.1*c*). Further folding and the addition of protective proteins result in the formation of chromosomes we can recognize during mitosis and meiosis.

Many geneticists originally believed that histone proteins simply facilitated the packing of DNA into chromosomes. It was discovered, however, that histone proteins are very similar between different species. For example, histones of peas are almost identical to those of cows. Absence of change in a protein over evolutionary time is usually an indication of a function so critical to life that mutation is not tolerated. Evidence is now accumulating that histones do much more than package DNA. They are also involved with regulating gene function. When DNA is loosely associated with core histones, associated genes are active; and when DNA is tightly bound to the core histones, genes are inactive. (The 10 nm configuration seen in figure 8.1 shows the loosely associated state, and the 30 nm configuration shows the tightly bound state.)

It is important that not all chromatin is equally active. Some human genes, for example, are active only after adolescence. In other cases, entire chromosomes may not function in particular cells. Inactive portions of chromosomes produce dark banding patterns with certain staining procedures and are called **heterochromatic regions,** whereas, active portions of chromosomes are said to be **euchromatic regions.**

SEX CHROMOSOMES AND AUTOSOMES

In the early 1900s, attention turned to the cell to find a chromosomal explanation for determination of maleness or femaleness. The first evidence for a chromosomal basis for sex determination came from work with the insect *Protenor*. One darkly staining chromosome of *Protenor*, called the X chromosome, is represented differently in males and females. All somatic (body) cells of males have one X chromosome (XO), and all somatic cells of females have two X chromosomes (XX). Similarly, ½ of all sperm contain a single X and ½ contain no X. All female gametes contain a single X. This pattern suggests that fertilization of an egg by an X-bearing sperm will result in female offspring, and fertilization of an egg by sperm with no X chromosome will result in a male offspring. As illustrated in figure 8.2, this sex determination system explains the approximately 50:50 ratio of females to males in this insect species. Chromosomes that are represented differently in females than in males and function in sex determination are called **sex chromosomes.** Chromosomes that are alike and not involved in determining sex are called **autosomes** (Gr. *autus*, self + *soma*, body).

The system of sex determination described for *Protenor* is called the X-O system. It is the simplest system for determining sex because it involves only one kind of chromosome. Many other animals (e.g., humans and fruit flies) have an X-Y system of sex determination. In the X-Y system, males and females have an equal number of chromosomes, but the male is usually XY and the female is XX. (In birds, the sex chromosomes are designated Z and W, and the female is ZW.) The sex chromosomes may look quite different and carry different genes; however, they function during meiosis as a homologous pair. ❶ This mode of sex determination also results in approximately equal numbers of male and female offspring:

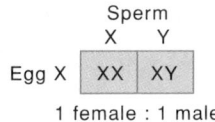

1 female : 1 male

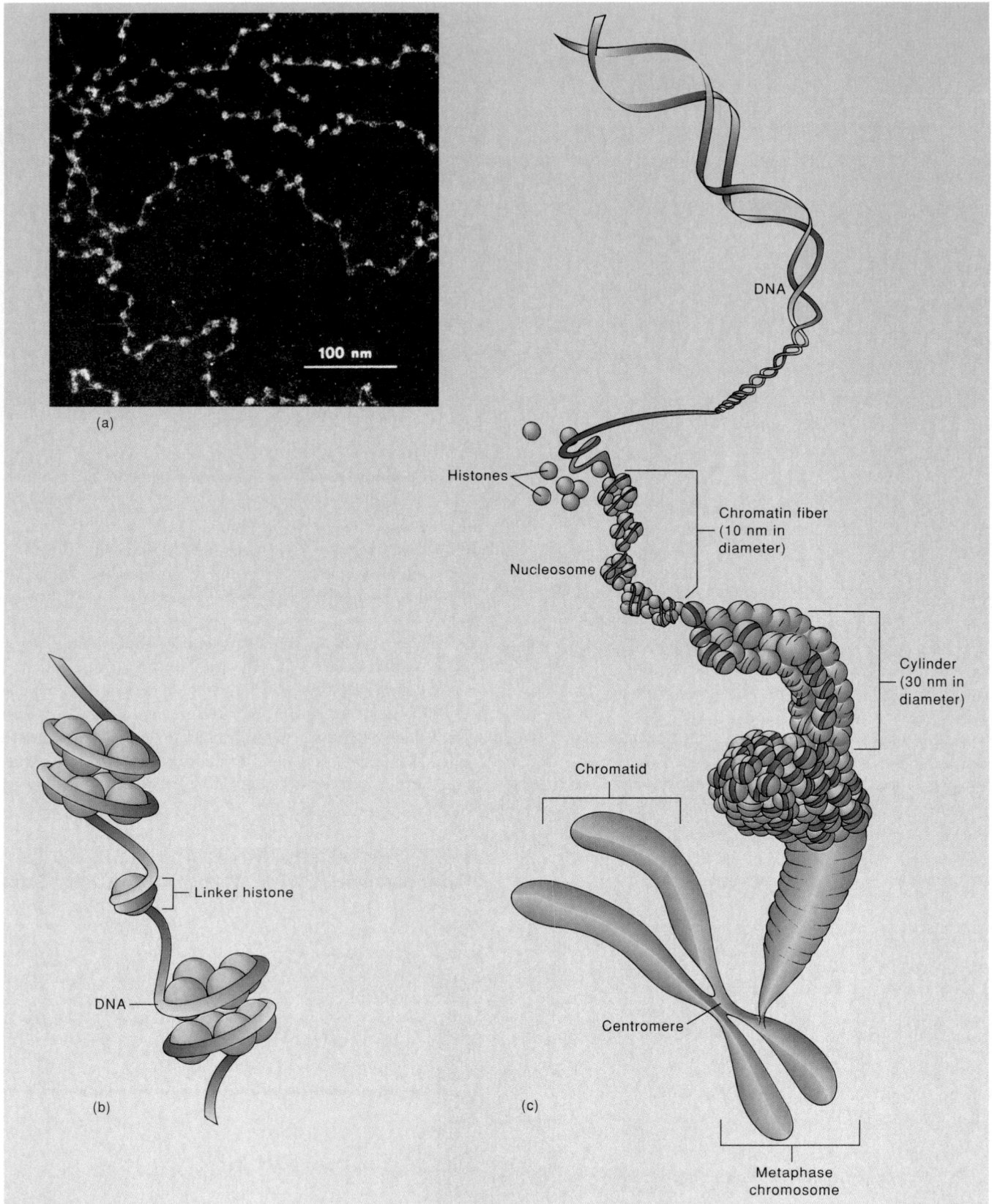

Figure 8.1

The Organization of Eukaryotic Chromosomes. (*a*) An electron micrograph showing a strand of chromatin. Nucleosomes appear as beads arranged sequentially on a thread of DNA. (*b*) A nucleosome consists of four pairs of histone proteins wound by a strand of DNA. Linker histone-proteins are associated with DNA between adjacent nucleosomes. (*c*) The nucleosome/DNA chain is wound into a cylinder, which then undergoes folding. When chromatin is active, nucleosomes are loosely associated with DNA, and the chromatin is found in the 10 nm in diameter form.

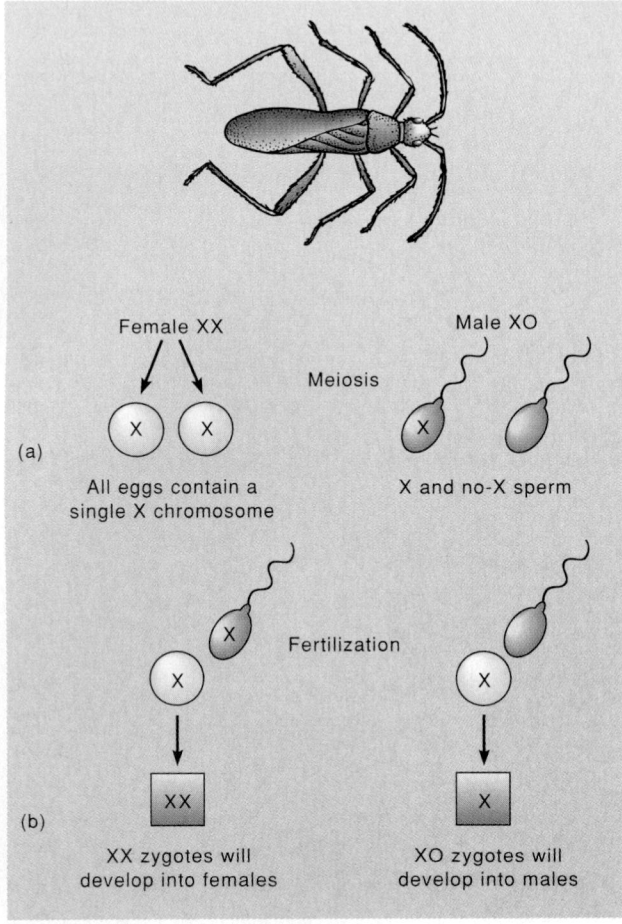

FIGURE 8.2

The XO-System of Sex Determination for the Insect *Protenor*.
(*a*) In females, all cells except gametes possess two X chromosomes. During meiosis, homologous X chromosomes segregate and all eggs contain one X chromosome. Males possess one X chromosome per cell. Meiosis results in ½ of all sperm cells having one X, and ½ of all sperm cells having no X. (*b*) Fertilization results in ½ of all offspring having one X chromosome—these offspring are males, and ½ of all offspring having two X chromosomes—these are females.

The number of X chromosomes, or the presence of a Y chromosome, is not the only genetic factor that determines sex. An individual's XO or XY status is often referred to as his or her "chromosomal sex." Genes that are not a part of sex chromosomes can influence, and even reverse, the chromosomal sex of some animals.

NUMBER OF CHROMOSOMES

Even though the number of chromosomes is constant within a species, there is great variation in chromosome number among species (table 8.1).

Chromosomes are present in sets, with the number in a set being characteristic of each kind of animal, and expressed as "N." N identifies the number of different kinds of chromosomes. The most common condition for animals is that there

TABLE 8.1	CHROMOSOME NUMBERS OF SELECTED ANIMALS	
COMMON NAME	**SCIENTIFIC NAME**	**NUMBER OF CHROMOSOMES (2N)**
Fruit fly	*Drosophila melanogaster*	8
Frog	*Rana pipiens*	26
Honeybee	*Apis mellifera*	32
Hydra	*Hydra vulguria attenuata*	32
Cat	*Felis domesticus*	38
Rat	*Rattus norvegicus*	42
Human	*Homo sapiens sapiens*	46
Chimpanzee	*Pan troglodytes*	48
Dog	*Canis familiaris*	78
Chicken	*Gallus domesticus*	78
Carp	*Cyprinus carpio*	104

are two sets, or 2N chromosomes. This condition is called the **diploid** (Gr. *di*, two + *eoides*, doubled) condition. Some animals may have only one set, or N chromosomes (like gametes) and are said to be **haploid** (Gr. *hapl*, single) (e.g., male honeybees and some rotifers).

Animals usually do not have more than the diploid number of chromosomes. When this condition does exist, it is called **polyploidy** (Gr. *polys*, more). The upset in numbers of sex chromosomes apparently interferes with reproductive success. When polyploidy does occur (e.g., in brine shrimp, snout beetles, some flatworms, and some sow bugs), it is often accompanied by asexual reproduction.

Stop and Ask Yourself

1. What is the difference between chromatin and chromosomes? What is a nucleosome?

2. Why are there approximately equal numbers of males and females in human offspring?

3. What is the name of the condition in which there is one set (*N*) of chromosomes? More than 2 sets of chromosomes (3*N*, 4*N*, etc.)?

LINKAGE RELATIONSHIPS

Within a few years of the rediscovery of Mendel's work, William Bateson and R. C. Punnett discovered that certain traits of the pea seemed to violate the principle of independent assortment in that they observed altered ratios in progeny from what they thought was a dihybrid cross. Bateson and Punnett suggested that their results could be explained by a physical connection between the genes. We now know that many genes are carried on the same chromosome and are called **linked genes.** Because they tend to be inherited together, these genes belong to a **linkage group,** which is the functional definition of a chromosome. Genes that are on the same chromosome are carried together to one pole of the cell during anaphase I of meiosis, and do not assort independently, although the chromosomes do. Linked genes, however, are not linked forever, because crossing-over can occur (*see figure* 6.9). In crossing-over, parts of homologous chromosomes can be exchanged and genetic variability among offspring can be increased during meiosis.

AUTOSOMAL LINKAGE

Genes that are linked to autosomal chromosomes tend to be inherited together, and the pattern of inheritance is similar in both males and females. Occasionally, genes are so closely linked that they are always inherited together. This is called **complete linkage.** More often, however, there is some crossing-over between linked genes, and such genes are said to show **incomplete linkage.**

Crossing-over of linked genes occurs during prophase I of meiosis and is also called recombination. Exactly where recombination occurs along a chromosome is random, but it is not accidental. A complex of proteins, called the synaptonemal complex, helps homologous chromosomes pair in a gene to gene fashion, and proteins within that complex are apparently responsible for snipping and rejoining homologous chromosomes. If chromatid fragments from homologous chromosomes are rejoined after snipping, crossing-over has occurred (*see figure* 6.9). Analysis of rates of crossing-over between linked genes has allowed geneticists to map the position of genes on chromosomes (figure 8.3).

SEX LINKAGE

Genes linked to sex chromosomes do not necessarily influence traits dealing with sexual characteristics, and inheritance patterns for sex-linked genes are different from those for autosomally linked genes.

X Linkage

The primary consideration concerning X linkage deals with the fact that females usually have two X chromosomes, and males usually have a single X chromosome. Therefore, females have two genes for each trait. Males, however, have only one gene to consider, and are said to be **hemizygous** for X-linked traits. Genes in the hemizygous state are always expressed, regardless of whether they are dominant or recessive, because there is no allele on a homologous chromosome with which to interact.

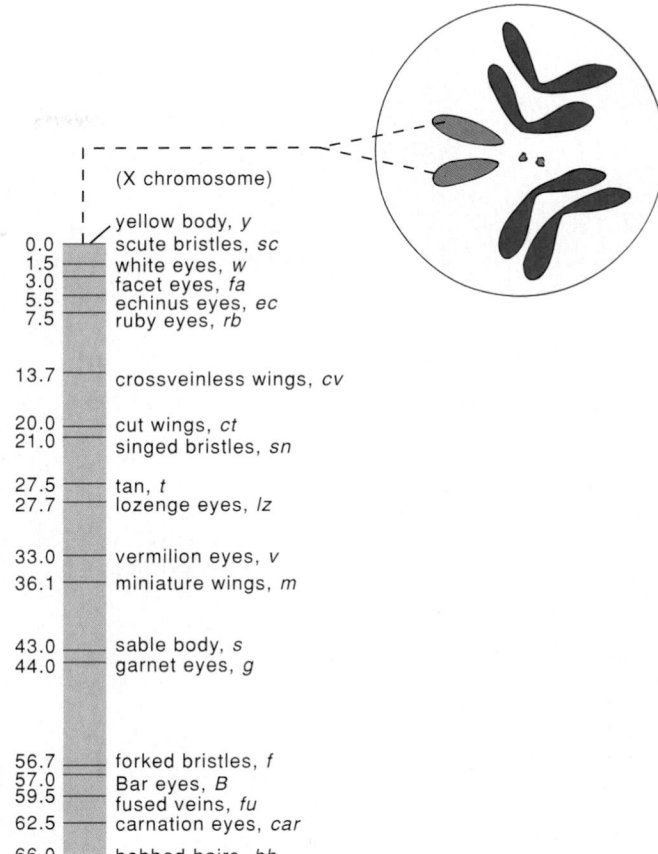

FIGURE 8.3

Partial Map of the X Chromosome of *Drosophila melanogaster*. Map units are shown to the left of the chromosome, and the name of each locus is indicated on the right.

In crosses involving X linkage, it is important to remember that the genes involved are carried on the X chromosome. These genes are customarily represented by an "X" to symbolize the X chromosome and superscript letters to symbolize the gene (e.g., X^a or X^A). A "Y" is used to designate the other sex chromosome; it will have no superscript since the gene is not present.

The following example will illustrate important considerations when working with crosses involving X linkage. The white eye color in *Drosophila* is produced by a recessive X-linked allele. Note that the two crosses in figure 8.4 involve white-eyed flies and red-eyed (wild-type) flies in the parental generation. The results of the two crosses illustrate how X linkage can affect the F_1 flies. In cross A, the male introduces the white eye allele, and in cross B, the female introduces the white eye allele. The results of a cross differ depending on the sex of the parent that introduces the mutant gene into a cross.

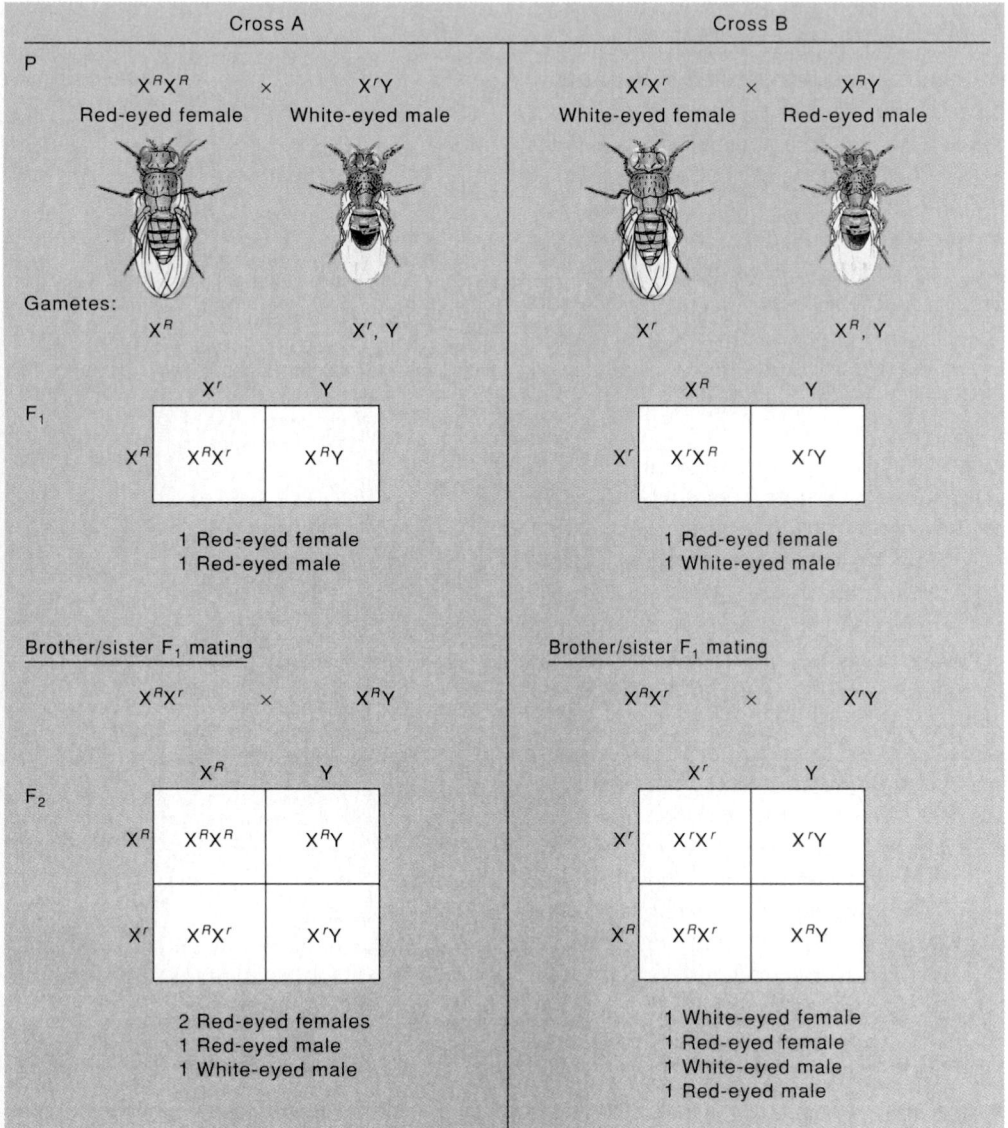

FIGURE 8.4

Patterns of Inheritance of X-linked Traits. Crosses A and B are called reciprocal crosses because they differ only in regard to the sex of the parent that introduces a trait (white eye) into the cross. These crosses illustrate several important considerations for working with crosses involving X linkage. X^R = red eye allele, X^r = white eye allele.

Therefore, it is important in crosses involving X linkage to keep track of the sex and phenotype of parents and offspring.

X-linked, recessive traits tend to be expressed in male offspring. If the mother is heterozygous (a carrier), she will not show the trait, but approximately ½ of her sons will (figure 8.4; cross A, F_2 and cross B, F_2). Male offspring always receive the X chromosome from their mother and the Y chromosome from their father, and thus X-linked traits tend to be passed to males from their mothers.

As illustrated in cross A, X-linked recessive genes are often expressed in males of alternate generations. A father who shows a recessive, X-linked trait will pass the gene to all of his daughters. The daughters will then be carriers and may pass the gene to ½ of their sons.

(2) X-linked traits show up more frequently in males than in females. For a female offspring to show an X-linked trait, her father must show the trait and her mother must at least be a carrier (cross B, F_2), or the gene in question must be dominant.

Many human traits are determined by genes carried on the X chromosome. One of these is red-green color blindness. Another, less common trait is hemophilia or "bleeder's disease."

The Lyon Hypothesis

The presence of unequal numbers of X chromosomes in males and females presents an interesting question. Why is it that females, with two X's, do not produce twice the amount of X-linked gene products than do males? Another interesting and related observation is that females, known to be heterozygous for an X-linked, recessive trait, occasionally express the recessive allele! Both of these observations were explained by Mary Lyon based on her work with mice.

In 1961, she suggested that at an early stage of development, one of the two X chromosomes present in mammalian body cells, except in some ovarian tissues, is inactivated. Much earlier, Murray L. Barr (1908–) discovered a densely staining patch of chromatin present in nuclei of cells of females but not males. Lyon suggested that each **Barr body** is really an X chromosome that has become entirely inactive, or heterochromatic. This X inactivation occurs early in development, and the X that is inactivated is determined by chance. Because inactivation is random, it should not be surprising that an occasional female, known to be heterozygous, should express a recessive X-linked trait (figure 8.5a). ③ Barr bodies are used in diagnosing certain diseases involving sex chromosome abnormalities, and they have also been used to check the sex of athletes competing in Olympic events that are open to only one sex (figure 8.5b). The procedure involves staining and examining cells scraped from the inside of the mouth.

Y Linkage

Y linkage is rare because the Y chromosome is small and carries few genes except those determining maleness. The pattern of transmission for Y-linked traits, when they occur, is relatively easy to diagnose. Y-linked traits are passed from a father to all of his sons because all sons must receive their father's Y chromosome.

SEX-INFLUENCED TRAITS

Autosomally determined traits can also be expressed differently in the two sexes. These **sex-influenced traits** are mentioned briefly in this section on sex linkage because inheritance patterns can superficially resemble patterns for X-linked traits. Consider, for example, the hypothetical family history in figure 8.6, showing a distribution of pattern baldness. As with X-linked traits, a majority of those affected with baldness are males; however, unlike X linkage, the transmission can be (as is the case in figure 8.6) from father to son. The preponderance of affected males is explained by gene physiology rather than by gene transmission. The gene for pattern baldness acts as a dominant gene in males because of high levels of testosterone, the male sex hormone. ④ Females, on the other hand, express the trait only when the gene is homozygous because no testosterone is present. When the genes are expressed, they result in extreme thinning of hair, not complete baldness. Because the dominance relationships of the two alleles are not fixed, upper- and lower-case letters cannot be used to symbolize alleles.

(a)

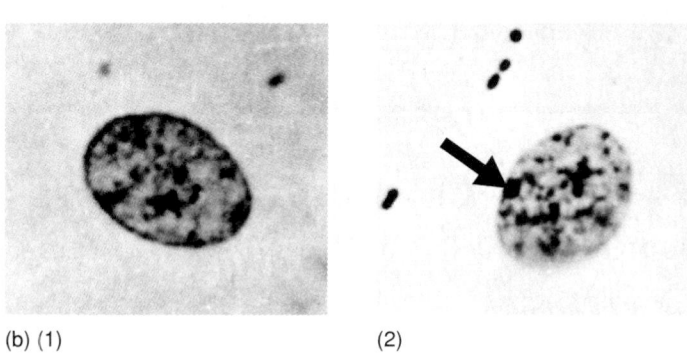

(b) (1)   (2)

FIGURE 8.5

X Inactivation. (a) X inactivation occurs early in development. Coat color in calico cats is an X-linked trait, and the calico coat occurs only in heterozygous females. The orange patches on this cat are made up of cells descended from cells in which the black allele was inactivated. The black patches consist of cells descended from cells in which the orange allele was inactivated. (b) A Barr body marks an inactivated X chromosome. Normally, one X chromosome is inactivated in the cells of a female mammal. A normal male cell (b1) has no Barr body, and a normal female cell (b2) has one Barr body (arrow). (b) From Wilson and Foster, Williams Textbook of Endocrinology 7th ed. © W. B. Saunders 1985.

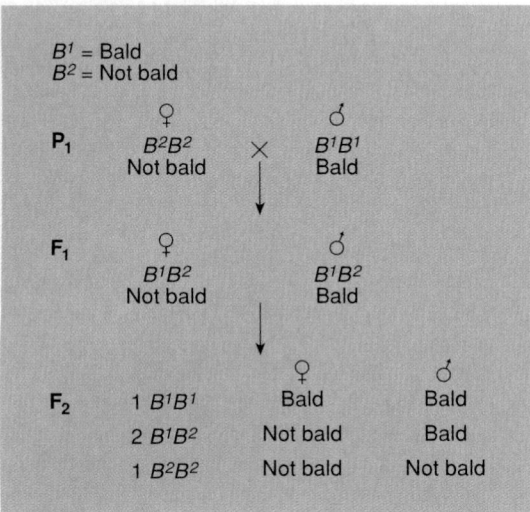

Figure 8.6

The Expression of a Sex-Influenced Trait. Pattern baldness is the result of a gene that acts as a dominant gene in males and a recessive gene in females.

Stop and Ask Yourself

4. What is a linkage group?
5. What accounts for the fact that a male with a single, recessive, X-linked allele usually shows the recessive trait?
6. What accounts for the fact that females heterozygous for an X-linked trait may show either the dominant or recessive phenotype?
7. What is the difference between sex-linked traits and sex-influenced traits?

CHANGES IN CHROMOSOME NUMBER AND STRUCTURE

The genetic material of a cell can change, and changes are important because they increase genetic variability and help increase the likelihood of survival in changing environments.

One kind of genetic rearrangement, recombination, has already been presented. Crossing-over permits linked genes to recombine and experience different genetic environments. Larger, cytologically visible changes include changes in chromosome number and structure.

DETECTING NUMBER AND STRUCTURE CHANGES

Modern tissue culture techniques permit biologists to examine chromosomes of humans and other animals. With tissue culture techniques, it is possible to obtain large numbers of rapidly dividing cells. Preparing and examining slides and photographs of metaphase chromosomes is called **karyotyping** (Gr. *karyo*, nucleus + *typos*, image) (figure 8.7). In karyotyping, a small quantity of blood is taken from a subject or from the umbilical vein of a fetus. This blood is cultured in a medium that promotes the rapid division of certain white blood cells. The cells are killed, applied to a slide, and stained. Well-spread metaphase chromosomes are analyzed by computer-aided techniques or photographed. Images of homologous chromosomes are arranged in order of decreasing size, by centromere position, and by banding patterns, and then numbered 1 to 22 plus X and Y (figure 8.8). Arranging the chromosomes in numbered homologous pairs allows detection of changes in the expected structure and number of the chromosomes. These techniques are applied in diagnosing changes in chromosome numbers and chromosome structure in both fetuses and postnatal individuals.

Changes in the number of X chromosomes can be easily detected by checking the number of Barr bodies present in cheek epithelial cells. The number of Barr bodies is always one less than the number of X chromosomes. Therefore, a female with no Barr bodies would be XO, a female with two Barr bodies would be XXX, and a male with one or more Barr bodies would have two or more X's as well as a Y.

VARIATION IN NUMBER

Changes in chromosome number may involve entire sets of chromosomes, as in polyploidy, which was discussed earlier. **Aneuploidy** (Gr. *a*, without), on the other hand, involves the addition or deletion of one or more chromosomes, not entire sets. The addition of one chromosome to the normal $2N$ chromosome number ($2N + 1$) is called a trisomy (Gr. *tri*, three + ME. *some*, a group of), and the deletion of a chromosome from the normal $2N$ chromosome number ($2N - 1$) is called a monosomy (Gr. *monos*, single).

Aneuploidy is usually caused by errors during meiosis. **Nondisjunction** occurs when a homologous pair fails to segregate during meiosis I, or when chromatids fail to separate at meiosis II (figure 8.8). Gametes produced will either be deficient in one chromosome or have an extra chromosome. If one of these gametes is involved in fertilization with a normal gamete, the monosomic or trisomic condition will result.

⑤ Trisomy 21, or Down syndrome, is a human trisomy involving chromosome number 21. Symptoms include short and broad hands, short stature, mental retardation, heart problems, and shortened life expectancy. Maternal age, and possibly paternal age, are important factors in the frequency of nondisjunction of these, and possibly other, chromosomes. Women between the ages of 35 and 39 are seven times more likely to have a Down syndrome child than women 15 to 19 years of age. The risk increases to a 20 times higher frequency for 40- to 45-year-old women, and a 50 times higher frequency for women over 45. This is an important consideration for couples who, for various reasons, delay having children. Other aneuploid variations usually result in severe consequences involving mental retardation and sterility.

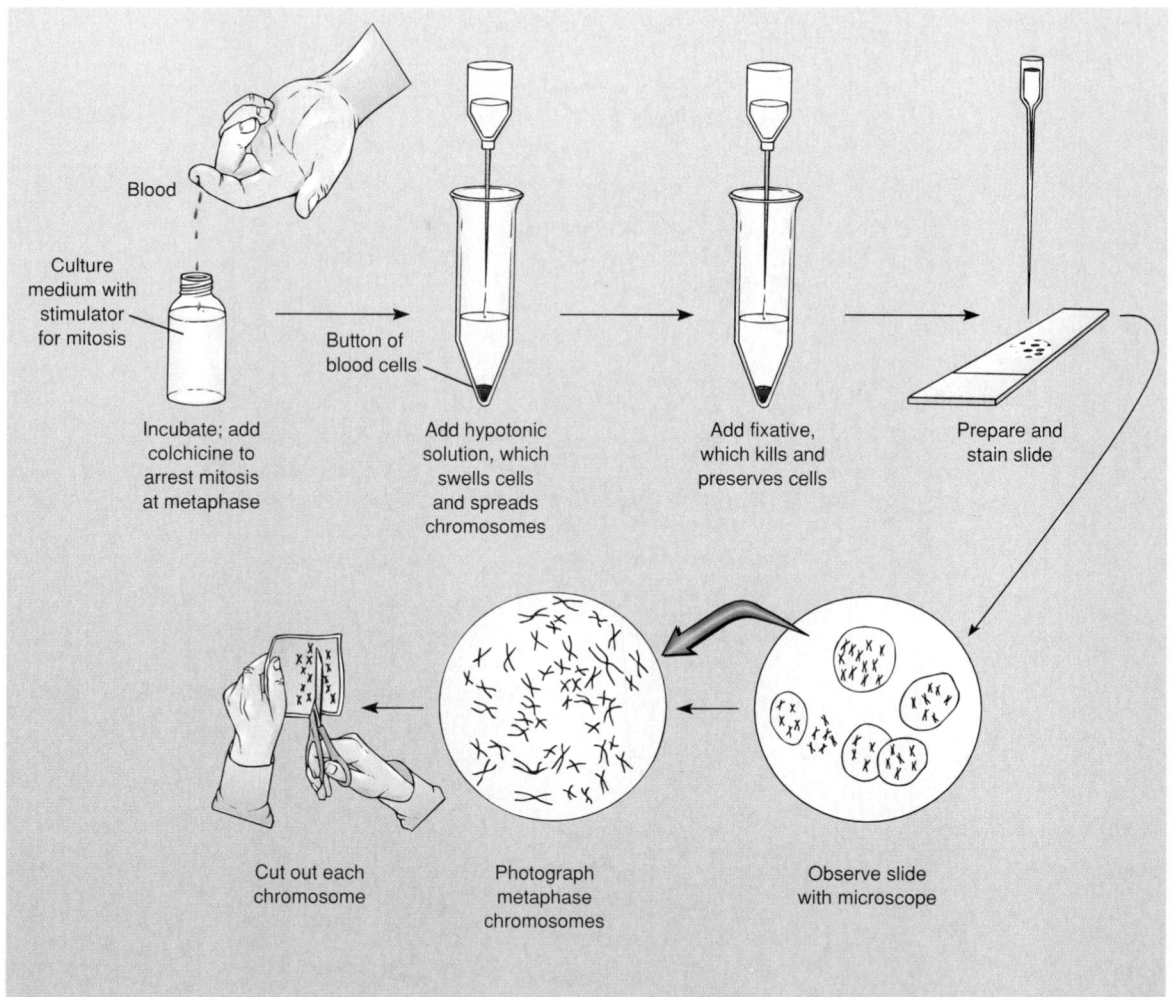

(a)

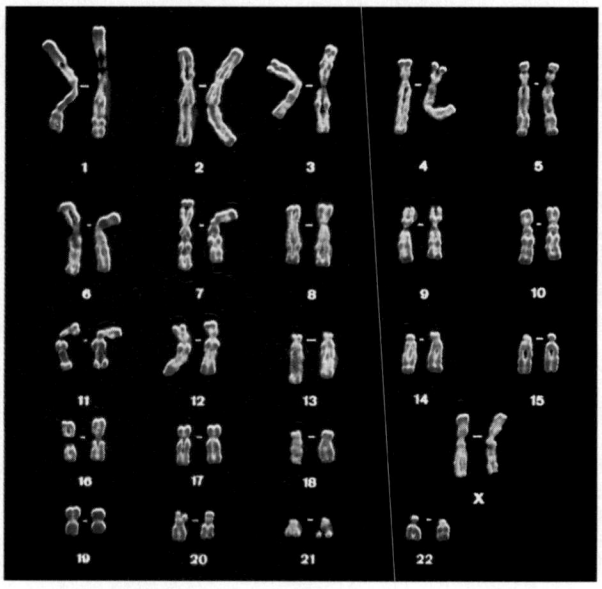

(b)

FIGURE 8.7

Karyotyping. (*a*) Karyotypes are routinely prepared from human white blood cells. Similar determinations can be made from samples of fetal blood drawn from an umbilical vein, from cells of the amniotic fluid bathing a fetus, or from samples of certain extraembryonic membranes (the chorion) surrounding a fetus. (Chorion sampling is relatively simple and has an advantage in that it can be performed at an earlier stage of development than sampling amniotic fluid.) Sampling fetal tissues is done only in individuals with a significant risk for a disease as all sampling procedures pose some risk for the fetus. (*b*) A human karyotype.

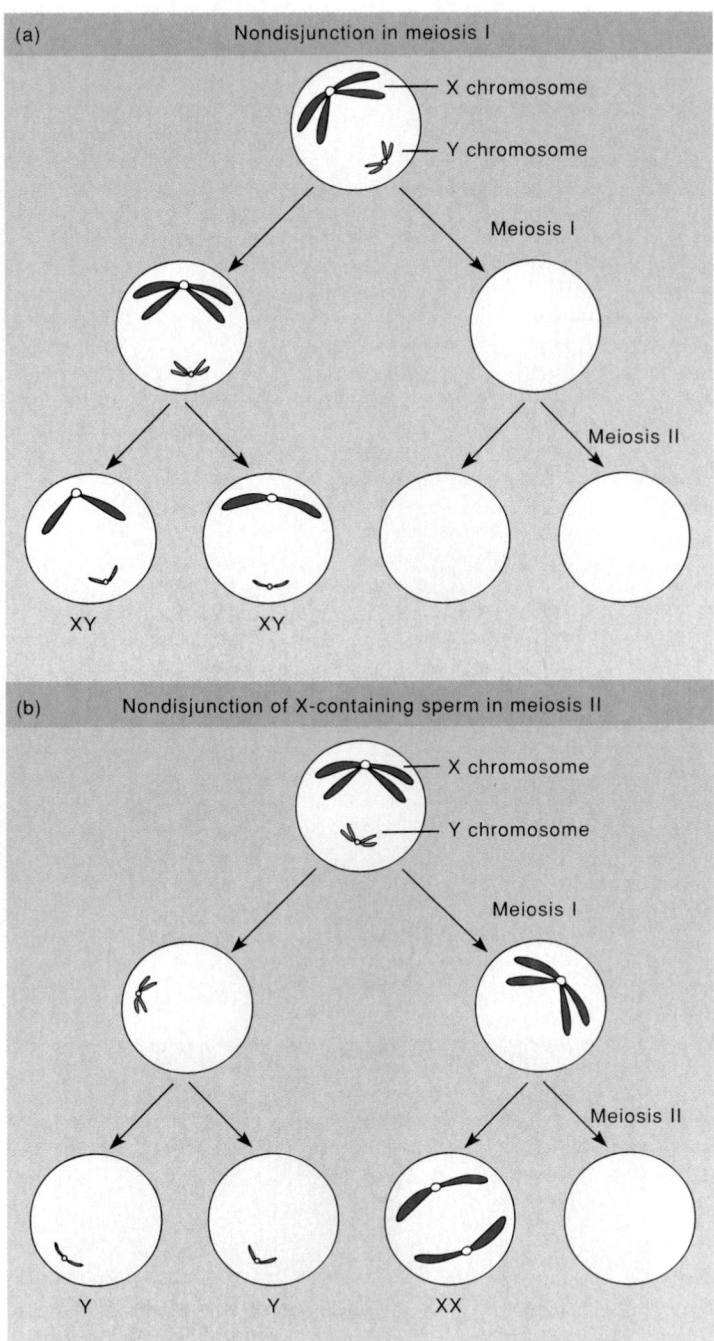

FIGURE 8.8

The Results of Primary and Secondary Nondisjunction in Sperm Formation. (*a*) Primary nondisjunction occurs in meiosis I and results in both the X and Y chromosomes ending up in one secondary spermatocyte. A normal second meiotic division results in ½ of all sperm having both X and Y chromosomes. The other ½ of all sperm lack any sex chromosomes. (*b*) Secondary nondisjunction occurs after a normal first meiotic division. Failure of the chromatids of the X chromosomes, for example, to separate in the second division means that ¼ of the sperm will have no sex chromosomes, ¼ will have two X chromosomes, and ½ will have one Y chromosome (from the normal separation of Y chromatids).

8.10

VARIATION IN STRUCTURE

The cell has a variety of protective and repair systems to make DNA a remarkably stable molecule. However, changes in its structure do occur. If these changes are cytologically invisible, they are called point mutations, which will be considered in the next chapter. Other changes may involve breaks in chromosomes. After breaking, pieces of chromosomes may be lost, or they may reattach, but not necessarily in their original position. The result is a chromosome that may have a different sequence of genes, multiple copies of genes, or missing genes. All of these changes can occur spontaneously. They can also be induced with various environmental agents, such as ionizing radiation and certain chemicals.

Translocations involve transfers of genetic material between nonhomologous chromosomes. Translocations may take a number of forms; the most common form involves a single break in each of two chromosomes and an exchange of broken pieces (figure 8.9a). Because translocations involve shifting, not deleting or adding, genetic material, they may not be too serious for the individual. The translocation can, however, cause chromosomal defects when gametes are formed (duplications and deletions).

In some instances, however, translocations are associated with certain phenotypic abnormalities. A form of Down syndrome, called translocation Down, results from a translocation. If the bottom third of chromosome 21 is translocated to another chromosome (most often chromosome 14), a gamete could end up with both the normal chromosome 21 and a portion of chromosome 21 being carried on chromosome 14. When fertilization occurs, the zygote contains three copies of some of the genes carried on chromosome 21. Another translocation that results in the movement of an arm of human chromosome 22 to chromosome 9 is the first chromosomal abnormality associated with a form of cancer. Myeloid leukemia is a malignancy of blood-forming tissues (bone marrow) that causes a proliferation of certain white blood cells.

Inversions involve two breaks in a chromosome, followed by the broken ends rejoining, with the central segment flip-flopped (figure 8.9b). The amount of DNA is not changed, but the order of some genes is reversed. Usually, there are no serious phenotypic effects.

Deletions result from breaks in chromosomes, followed by the loss of a portion of the chromosome. Deletions usually result from two breaks and the loss of an intervening segment of a chromosome (figure 8.9c). The effects of deletions increase in severity as the lost sections become larger. A human genetic disease, called Cri-du-chat (Fr., cry of the cat) results from a loss of part of chromosome 5. Symptoms include a very small head, wide-set eyes, mental retardation, and a catlike cry.

Duplications occur when portions of chromosomes are present in multiple copies. Duplications are difficult to detect in humans, although they probably exist. They are known in

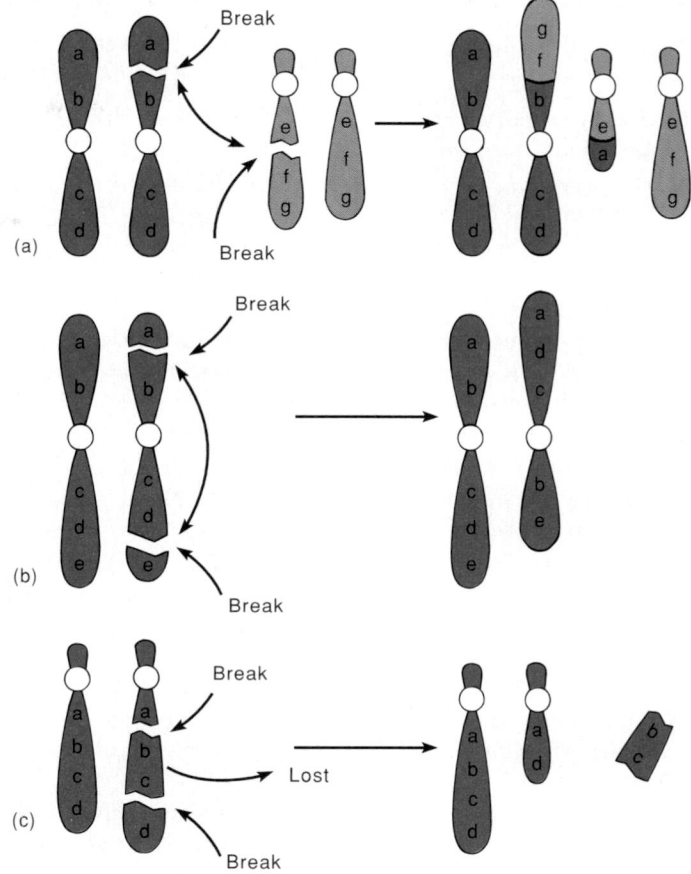

FIGURE 8.9

Common Kinds of Changes in Chromosome Structure.
(a) Translocations involve transfers of genetic material between nonhomologous chromosomes. (b) Inversions occur when a region of a chromatid is flip-flopped, resulting in gene order changes. (c) Deletions result from the loss of a segment of a chromosome.

many experimental organisms. The effects of duplications are probably less severe than for deletions. In fact, duplicated regions of chromosomes are believed to have had important evolutionary consequences. Because the duplicated genes are extra copies, they are not required for expression of the phenotype. Mutations of duplicated genes may be tolerated and may even prove beneficial.

Stop and Ask Yourself

8. What procedure is used in karyotyping?
9. What is aneuploidy and how is it likely to occur?
10. How would you describe the following kinds of chromosomal rearrangements: translocations, inversions, deletions, duplications?

SUMMARY

1. Eukaryotic chromosomes are complexly coiled associations of DNA and histone proteins.

2. Histone proteins help package DNA in the cell and have important gene regulation functions.

3. The sex of an animal is determined by the presence or absence of certain chromosomes that are represented differently in males and females. The X-Y system of sex determination is most common.

4. Numbers of chromosomes are constant for a given species. Although some examples of haploidy and polyploidy are cited, diploidy is most common in animals.

5. Genes carried on the same chromosome are said to be linked because they tend to be inherited together.

6. Crossing-over (recombination) results in parts of homologous chromosomes being exchanged during meiosis.

7. X-linked traits show up more frequently in males than females because males are hemizygous for any X-linked gene and males will show the trait regardless of whether the trait is determined by a dominant or a recessive gene.

8. Y-linked traits are transmitted exclusively from father to son.

9. Chromosome size, banding patterns, and centromere position can be used to identify particular chromosomes in microscopic preparations.

10. Aneuploidy occurs when one or more, but not entire sets of, chromosomes are added to or deleted from a genome. Aneuploidy results from nondisjunction during the first or second meiotic division. Changes in chromosome number almost always result in severe phenotypic consequences.

11. Changes in chromosome structure include translocations, inversions, deletions, and duplications. The severity of the phenotypic effect depends upon the amount of genetic material lost or duplicated.

SELECTED KEY TERMS

aneuploidy (p. 112)

autosomes (p. 106)

chromatin (p. 106)

diploid (p. 108)

haploid (p. 108)

hemizygous (p. 109)

karyotyping (p. 112)

linked genes (p. 109)

nondisjunction (p. 112)

polyploidy (p. 108)

sex chromosomes (p. 106)

translocation (p. 115)

CRITICAL THINKING QUESTIONS

1. Coat color in cats is determined by X-linked alleles, such that black (X^B) is dominant to orange (X^b). Calico cats, however, display patches of orange and black, and they are almost always female. Explain how the Lyon hypothesis can account for these observations.

2. Nondisjunction during the formation of a human sperm may result in XX, YY, XY, or no X- or Y-containing sperm depending upon when nondisjunction occurs. Diagram the meiotic events that could result in each of the above sperm. Assuming that each sperm fertilized a normal egg, how many Barr bodies would be present in the resulting zygotes?

3. How would the inheritance pattern for an X-linked, dominant trait be different from that of an X-linked, recessive trait?

4. In recent years, many couples have delayed starting a family until both partners have established a career. What factors should young couples consider before making their decision about when to start a family?

5. Explain why it is important that all regions of chromosomes are not continually active.

MOLECULAR GENETICS:
ULTIMATE CELLULAR CONTROL

Outline

Concepts

1. Deoxyribonucleic acid (DNA) is the genetic material of the cell. Its double helix structure suggests how it is able to replicate itself, and how it can code for the sequences of amino acids that make proteins.
2. The production of proteins involves two processes. Transcription is the production of a messenger RNA (mRNA) molecule that is complementary to a gene in DNA. Translation is the assembly of proteins at ribosomes based on the genetic information in the transcribed messenger RNA.
3. Substantial evidence for changing gene activity exists. The mechanisms for gene regulation in eukaryotic organisms are complex and well understood for a few genes.
4. Point mutations can drastically alter proteins. Some mutations occur spontaneously; however, various environmental agents can increase mutation rates.
5. Modern genetic technologies are being used to manipulate DNA. Recombinant DNA techniques are used to insert DNA into bacteria to produce large quantities of a desired protein. Gene insertion is the introduction of copies of desired genes into an organism lacking those genes.

Would You Like to Know:

These and other useful questions will be answered in this chapter.

This chapter contains evolutionary concepts, which are set off in this font.

Everyone reading this book has a unique combination of physical and personality traits. Many of these characteristics are traceable to genetic differences, and genetic differences are manifested in the kinds of proteins present in each reader. Some of these proteins contribute to observable traits, such as eye color, hair color, and height. Many other proteins contribute to one's uniqueness in more subtle, but just as important, ways. These proteins are enzymes (*see chapter 4*) that regulate rates of chemical reactions in organisms. Within certain environmental limits, we are who we are by the proteins that we synthesize! The purpose of this chapter is to explore the biochemical answers to such questions as What is a gene? How do genes control the expression of traits? How are the activities of genes controlled over the life of an organism? Much of the thrust of modern genetics revolves around questions such as these.

DNA: THE GENETIC MATERIAL

Twentieth-century biologists involved in the search for the genetic material realized that a molecule that serves as the genetic material must have certain characteristics in order to explain the properties of life. First, the genetic material must be able to code for the sequence of amino acids in proteins and control protein synthesis. Second, it must be able to replicate (produce an exact copy of) itself prior to cell division, so that daughter cells receive complete sets of genetic instructions. Third, the genetic material must be in the nucleus of eukaryotic cells. (The participation of the nucleus in fertilization and the chromosomal basis of heredity were described in the early 1900s.) Fourth, it must be able to change over time to account for evolutionary change. Only one molecule, DNA (deoxyribonucleic acid), fulfills all of these requirements.

THE DOUBLE HELIX MODEL

Two kinds of molecules participate in the production of proteins. By the early 1900s, scientists knew that both molecules are found in the nucleus and both are based on a similar building block, the nucleotide, giving them their name—nucleic acids. One of these molecules, **deoxyribonucleic acid** or **DNA,** is the genetic material and the other, **ribonucleic acid** or **RNA,** is produced in the nucleus and moves to the cytoplasm, where it participates in protein synthesis. The study of the how the information stored in DNA codes for RNA and protein is called **molecular genetics.**

Nucleic Acid Structure

DNA and RNA are large molecules made up of subunits called nucleotides (figure 9.1). A nucleotide consists of a nitrogen-containing organic base, either in the form of a double ring **(purine)** or a single ring **(pyrimidine).** Nucleotides also contain a pentose (five-carbon) sugar and a phosphate (–PO₄) group.

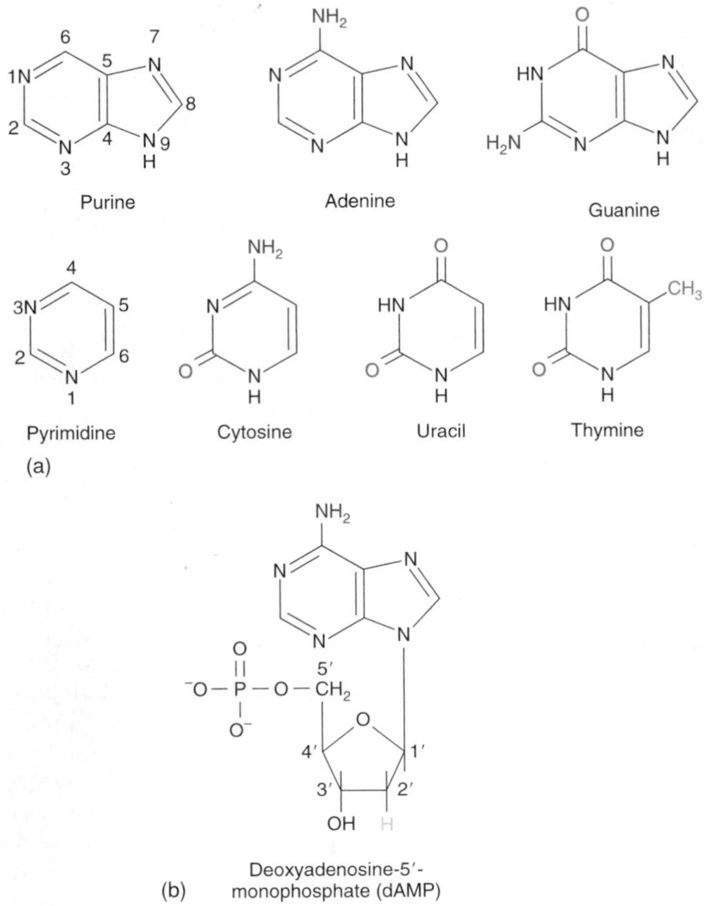

(a)

(b) Deoxyadenosine-5′-monophosphate (dAMP)

FIGURE 9.1

Components of Nucleic Acids. (*a*) The nitrogenous bases found in DNA and RNA. (*b*) Nucleotides are formed by attaching a nitrogenous base to the 1′ carbon of a pentose sugar and a phosphoric acid to the 5′ carbon of the sugar. (Carbons of the sugar are numbered with primes to distinguish them from the carbons of the nitrogenous base.) The sugar in DNA is deoxyribose, and the sugar in RNA is ribose. In ribose, a hydroxyl group (– OH) would replace the hydrogen shaded yellow.

The nucleotides of DNA and RNA, however, differ in several ways. Both DNA and RNA contain the purine bases adenine and guanine, and the pyrimidine base cytosine. The second pyrimidine in DNA, however, is thymine, whereas in RNA it is uracil. A second difference in the nucleotides of DNA and RNA involves the sugar. The pentose of DNA is deoxyribose, and in RNA it is ribose. A third important difference between DNA and RNA is that DNA is a double-stranded molecule and RNA is single stranded, although it may be folded back on itself and coiled.

The key to understanding the function of DNA is knowing how nucleotides are linked together into a three-dimensional structure. Research into the structure of DNA was propelled into a new era by James Watson (1928–), a U.S. biologist, and Francis Crick (1916–), from Great Britain.

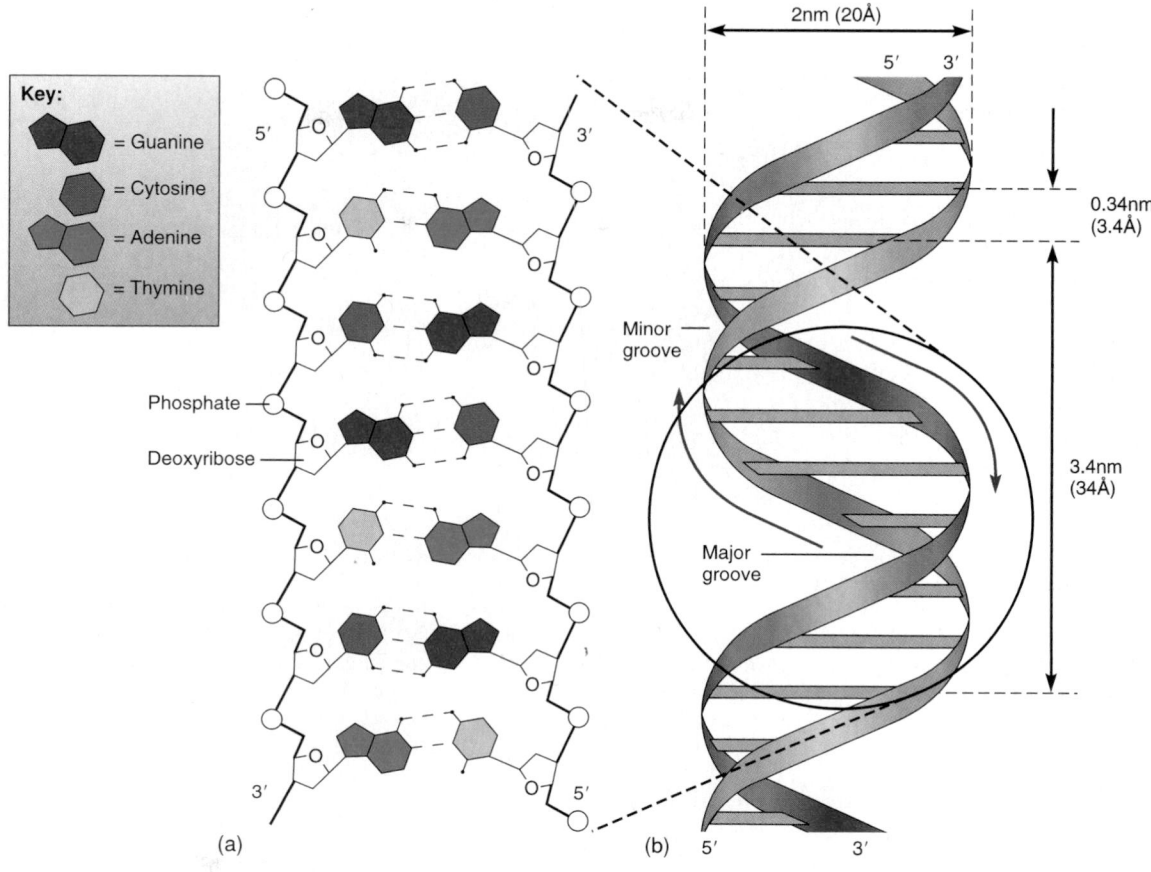

Figure 9.2

The Structure of DNA. (*a*) Nucleotides of one strand of nucleic acid are joined by linking the phosphate of one nucleotide to the 3′ carbon of an adjacent nucleotide. Hydrogen bonds are indicated with dashed lines between the nitrogenous bases. There are three hydrogen bonds between cytosine and guanine and two between thymine and adenine. The antiparallel orientation of the two strands is indicated by using the 3′ and 5′ carbons at the ends of each strand. (*b*) A three-dimensional representation of DNA. The antiparallel nature of the strand is indicated by the colored arrows.

① They proposed that the DNA molecule was ladderlike, with the rails of the ladder consisting of alternating sugar-phosphate groups (figure 9.2*a*). The phosphate of a nucleotide attaches at the fifth (5′) carbon of deoxyribose. Adjacent nucleotides attach to one another by a covalent bond between the phosphate of one nucleotide and the third (3′) carbon of deoxyribose. The two strands are held together by the pairing of nitrogenous bases between strands. Adenine (a purine) is hydrogen bonded to its complement, thymine (a pyrimidine), and guanine (a purine) is hydrogen bonded to its complement, cytosine (a pyrimidine) (figure 9.2*b*). Each strand of DNA is oriented such that the 3′ carbons of deoxyribose in one strand are oriented in the opposite directions from the 3′ carbons in the other strand. The strands' terminal phosphates are, therefore, at opposite ends, and the DNA molecule is thus said to be **antiparallel** (Gr. *anti*, against + *para*, beside + *allelon*, of one another). The entire molecule is twisted into a right-handed helix, with one complete spiral every 10 base pairs (figure 9.2*b*). Investigations have found that this description of DNA is accurate for DNA from nearly all organisms.

DNA Replication in Eukaryotes

An important aspect of DNA replication was worked out in the late 1950s by Matthew Meselson and Franklin Stahl. ② They elegantly demonstrated that each DNA strand serves as a template for a new strand. One strand can serve as a template for the synthesis of a second strand, because the pairing requirements between purine and pyrimidine bases dictate positioning of nucleotides in a new strand. Thus, each new molecule contains one strand from the old molecule and one newly synthesized strand. Because ½ of the old molecule is conserved in the new molecule, DNA replication is said to be semiconservative.

DNA replication in eukaryotic cells occurs in many chromosomes simultaneously, involves numerous enzymes, and requires the production of histone proteins that associate with the DNA in chromatin (*see figure 8.1*). Once the strands have been separated by enzymes, replication of DNA is initiated simultaneously at many sites along the strands. The replication units, which are the segments of DNA copied at each initiation

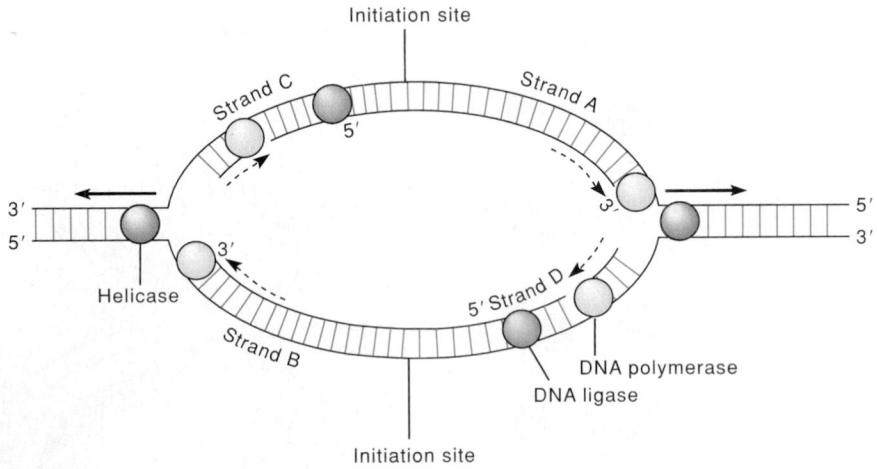

Figure **9.3**

DNA Replication. Recall that replication begins simultaneously at many initiation sites along the length of a chromosome. The DNA associated with each initiation site is called a replicon. Notice that synthesis of strands A and B is continuous from the initiation site, and that synthesis of strands C and D is discontinuous from the initiation site. These strands are produced in fragments because DNA polymerase can only produce new DNA strands in the 5' to 3' direction. Helicase enzymes aid in the untwisting of the double helix during replication, and DNA ligase enzymes join DNA fragments produced during replication. Replication is bidirectional from the initiation site. Dashed arrows indicate the direction of movement of DNA polymerase and strand fragment elongation. Solid arrows indicate the bidirectional progress of replication.

site, are called replicons (figure 9.3). Two new strands are synthesized simultaneously, going in both directions from the initiation site of a replicon. DNA polymerases—the enzymes that assemble nucleotides into DNA strands—copy an existing strand, beginning at the 3' end and working toward the 5' end. Because the replicated strand is complementary to the old strand, the new DNA strands are synthesized from their 5' end to their 3' end.

Stop and Ask Yourself

1. How are the nucleotides of DNA and RNA similar? How are they different?
2. Why is the DNA molecule said to be antiparallel?
3. Why is DNA replication said to be semiconservative?
4. What is the function of DNA polymerase?

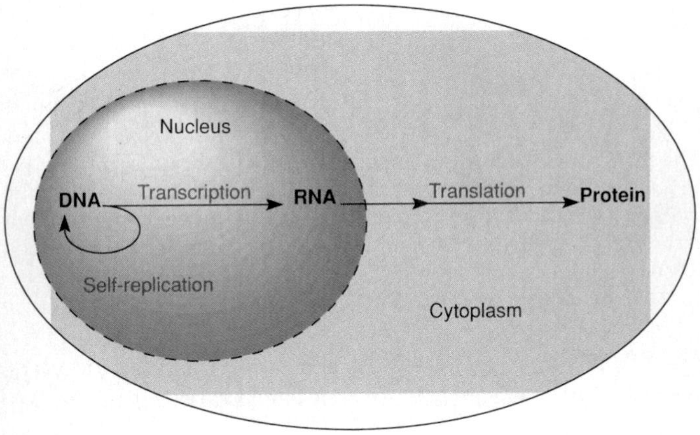

Figure **9.4**

The Central Dogma. Transcription involves the production of messenger RNA from DNA in the nucleus. Messenger RNA carries the transcribed code from the nucleus to the cytoplasm where translation occurs. Translation is the decoding of the message in messenger RNA and the production of a protein.

GENES IN ACTION

The important relationship between genes and enzymes was worked out by George Beadle and Edward Tatum in the 1930s. The culmination of their research was the one-gene-one-enzyme hypothesis, stating that one gene codes for one specific enzyme. This hypothesis has undergone some revisions as more has become known about proteins, and today is known as the **one-gene-one-polypeptide theory.** This early work indicated to

later researchers that the genetic material must carry instructions for the synthesis of proteins. A gene can be defined as a sequence of bases in DNA that codes for the synthesis of one polypeptide, and genes must somehow transmit their information from the nucleus to the cytoplasm, where protein synthesis occurs. The **central dogma** of molecular genetics describes the relationship among the steps from DNA to the production of a protein (figure 9.4). The synthesis of an RNA molecule is called **transcription** (L. *trans*, across + *scriba*, to write), and the decoding of the message at the ribosome is called **translation** (L. *trans*, to transfer + *latere*, to remain hidden).

Three Major Kinds of RNA

There are three major kinds of RNA, each with a specific role to play in protein synthesis. All three kinds of RNA are produced in the nucleus from DNA. **Messenger RNA (mRNA)** is a linear strand that is responsible for carrying a set of genetic instructions for synthesizing proteins to the cytoplasm. **Transfer RNA (tRNA)** picks up amino acids in the cytoplasm, carries them to ribosomes, and helps position them for incorporation into a polypeptide. **Ribosomal RNA (rRNA),** along with proteins, make up ribosomes.

The Genetic Code

DNA must code for the 20 different amino acids that are found in all organisms. 3 The information-carrying capabilities of DNA reside in the sequence of nitrogenous bases. The genetic code is represented by a sequence of three bases—a triplet code. Figure 9.5 shows the genetic code as reflected in the mRNA that will be produced from DNA. Each three-base combination is called a **codon,** and close examination of figure 9.5 reveals that more than one codon can specify the same amino acid because there are 64 possible codons, but only 20 amino acids. This characteristic of the code is referred to as **degeneracy.** Usually, when the first two bases are determined, the amino acid is determined. Note that not all codons code for an amino acid. The base sequences UAA, UAG, and UGA are all stop signals. As a period indicates the end of a sentence, the stop codons indicate where polypeptide synthesis should end. The base sequence AUG codes for the amino acid methionine, which serves as a start signal.

The genetic code is often referred to as a universal code because of its remarkable constancy in virtually all life-forms. Exceptions to the code have been found only in the DNA of mitochondria and a few single-celled organisms.

Transcription

The central dogma indicates that the genetic information in DNA is not translated directly into proteins, but is first transcribed into mRNA. Transcription involves numerous enzymes that unwind a region of a DNA molecule, initiate and end mRNA synthesis, and modify the mRNA after transcription has been completed. Unlike DNA replication, only one or a few genes are exposed, and only one of the two DNA strands is transcribed (figure 9.6).

One of the important enzymes of this process is RNA polymerase. After a section of DNA is unwound, RNA polymerase recognizes a specific sequence of DNA nucleotides called the promoter. RNA polymerase attaches at the promoter and begins joining ribose nucleotides, which are complementary to the 3′ end of the DNA strand. As in replication, the new nucleotide sequence (which now will be RNA) is formed in the 5′ to 3′ direction. In RNA, the same pairing of complementary bases that is seen in DNA occurs, except that in RNA, the base uracil replaces the base thymine as a complement to adenine. Thus, everywhere adenine occurs in the DNA being transcribed, uracil will be the complementary base added to the mRNA strand.

Newly transcribed mRNA must be modified before leaving the nucleus to carry out protein synthesis. Some base sequences in newly transcribed mRNA do not code for proteins. In eukaryotic organisms, the base sequences of a gene

Second position

First position	U		C		A		G		Third position
U	UUU	Phe	UCU	Ser	UAU	Tyr	UGU	Cys	U
	UUC		UCC		UAC		UGC		C
	UUA	Leu	UCA		UAA	STOP	UGA	STOP	A
	UUG		UCG		UAG		UGG	Trp	G
C	CUU	Leu	CCU	Pro	CAU	His	CGU	Arg	U
	CUC		CCC		CAC		CGC		C
	CUA		CCA		CAA	Gin	CGA		A
	CUG		CCG		CAG		CGG		G
A	AUU	Ile	ACU	Thr	AAU	Asn	AGU	Ser	U
	AUC		ACC		AAC		AGC		C
	AUA		ACA		AAA	Lys	AGA	Arg	A
	AUG	Met	ACG		AAG		AGG		G
G	GUU	Val	GCU	Ala	GAU	Asp	GGU	Gly	U
	GUC		GCC		GAC		GGC		C
	GUA		GCA		GAA	Glu	GGA		A
	GUG		GCG		GAG		GGG		G

Ala	=	Alanine	Leu	=	Leucine
Arg	=	Arginine	Lys	=	Lysine
Asn	=	Aparagine	Met	=	Methionine
Asp	=	Aspartic acid	Phe	=	Phenylalanine
Cys	=	Cysteine	Pro	=	Proline
Gin	=	Glutamine	Ser	=	Serine
Glu	=	Glutamic acid	Thr	=	Threonine
Gly	=	Glycine	Trp	=	Tryptophan
His	=	Histidine	Tyr	=	Tyrosine
Ile	=	Isoleucine	Val	=	Valine

Figure 9.5

The Genetic Code. Sixty-four messenger RNA codons are shown here. The first base of the triplet is on the left side of the figure. The second base is at the top, and the third base is on the right side of the figure. The abbreviations used for amino acids are shown above. In addition to coding for the amino acid methionine, the AUG codon also serves as the initiator codon. Three codons do not code for an amino acid but act as a signal to stop the synthesis of the protein.

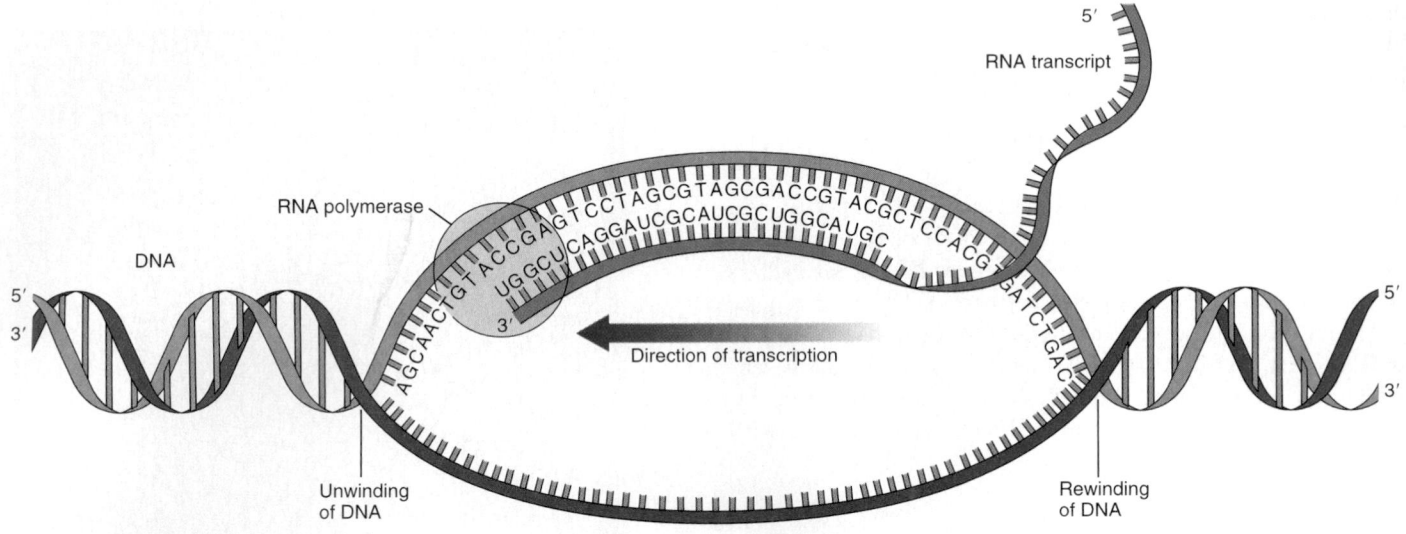

Figure 9.6

Transcription. Transcription involves the production of a messenger RNA molecule that is complementary to the coding strand of the segment of DNA. Note that transcription is similar to DNA replication in that the molecule is synthesized in the 5′ to 3′ direction.

that code for proteins, called exons, are broken up by non-coding regions called introns. The whole mRNA strand is called the primary transcript. RNA splicing involves cutting out introns so that the mRNA coding region can be read continuously at the ribosome.

TRANSLATION

Translation is the synthesis of proteins at the ribosomes in the cytoplasm, based on the genetic information contained in the transcribed mRNA.

Amino Acids and tRNA

Another type of RNA, called transfer RNA (tRNA), is important in the translation process. It brings the different amino acids coded for by the mRNA into alignment so that a polypeptide can be made. Transfer RNA is frequently represented as a two-dimensional cloverleaf (figure 9.7a), although the molecule actually undergoes helical twisting (figure 9.7b). Complementary pairing of bases across the molecule maintains tRNA's configuration. The shape of tRNA has important functional implications. The presence of some unusual bases (i.e., unusual for nucleic acids) disrupts the normal base pairing and forms loops in the molecule. The center loop (the "anticodon loop") has a sequence of three unpaired bases called the **anticodon**.

Pairing of the codon of the mRNA strand and its complementary anticodon of the tRNA positions the amino acid being carried by tRNA.

Ribosomes, mRNA, and Peptide Bonds

Ribosomes, the sites of protein synthesis, consist of large and small subunits that organize the pairing between the codon and the anticodon. Several sites on the ribosome serve as binding sites for mRNA and tRNA. At the initiation of translation, mRNA binds to a small, separate ribosomal subunit. Attachment of the mRNA requires that the initiation codon (AUG) of mRNA be aligned with the P (peptidyl) site of the ribosome. A tRNA with a complementary anticodon for methionine binds to the mRNA, and a large subunit joins, forming a complete ribosome.

The formation of a polypeptide is ready to begin. Another site, the A (aminoacyl) site, is next to the P site. A second tRNA, whose anticodon is complementary to the codon in the A site, is positioned. There are now two tRNA molecules with their attached amino acids side-by-side in the P and A sites (figure 9.8). This step requires enzyme aid and energy, in the form of guanine triphosphate (GTP). An enzyme (peptidyl transferase), which is actually a part of the larger ribosomal subunit, breaks the bond between the amino acid and tRNA in the P site, and catalyzes the formation of a peptide bond between

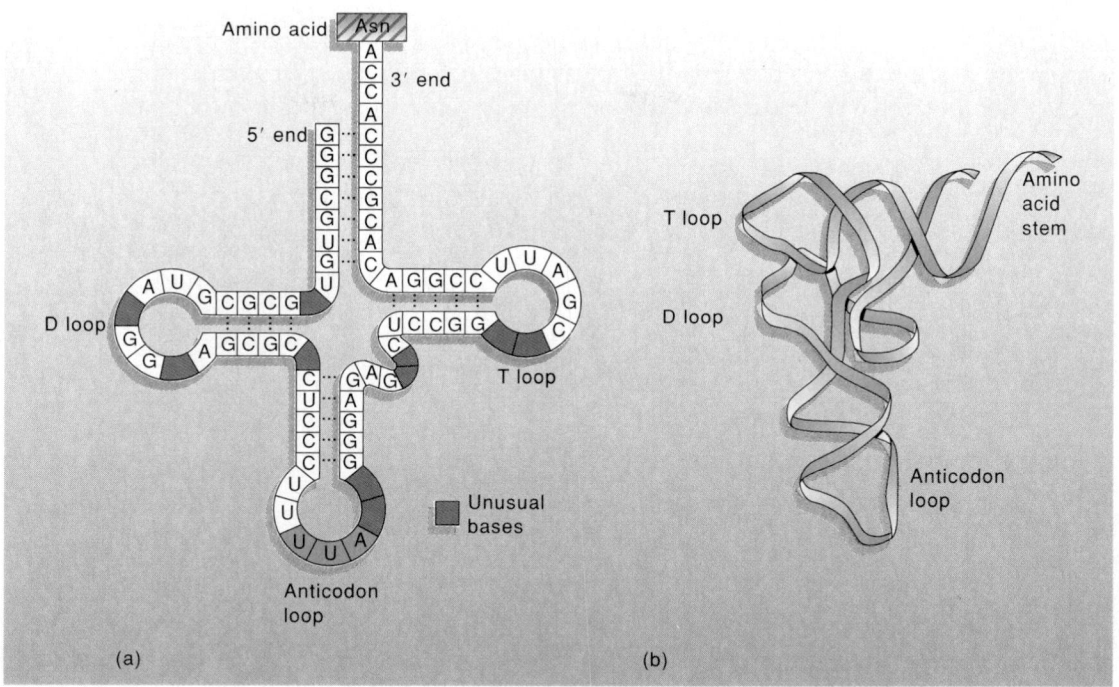

Figure 9.7

The Structure of Transfer RNA. (*a*) A diagrammatic representation of the secondary structure of transfer RNA. An amino acid attaches to the 3′ end of the molecule. The ACC base sequence at this end of the molecule is present in all tRNAs. The "t loop" helps position tRNA at the ribosome. The anticodon is the sequence of three bases that pairs with the codon in mRNA, thus positioning the amino acid that tRNA carries. Other aspects of tRNA structure position the tRNA in the enzyme that attaches the correct amino acid to the tRNA. (*b*) A more accurate representation of tRNA when its three-dimensional folding is considered.

that amino acid and the amino acid in the A site. (Recall the energy for this reaction was previously conferred to the bond between the amino acid and tRNA by ATP.)

The mRNA strand then moves along the ribosome a distance of one codon. This step requires more enzymatic action and more energy from GTP. The tRNA with two amino acids attached to it that was in the A site is now in the P site. A third tRNA can now enter the exposed A site. This process continues until the entire mRNA has been translated, and a polypeptide chain has been synthesized. Often many ribosomes will be translating a single mRNA strand simultaneously. Translation ends when a termination codon (e.g., UAA) is encountered. Proteins called release factors, as well as the hydrolysis of GTP to GDP + P$_i$, are involved in release of the ribosome from the mRNA.

In spite of the complexities of translation, the process is very rapid. Approximately 20 peptide bonds are formed every second. An average-sized protein can be synthesized in about 15 seconds at a cost of four high-energy bonds per peptide bond.

POSTTRANSLATIONAL MODIFICATIONS

Proteins synthesized in the translation process have a variety of destinations in an animal. Some are secreted from a cell, some are incorporated into lysosomes, some make up components of membranes, and some make up the structural framework of the cell. Others act as enzymes. Most proteins are synthesized as preproteins. Preproteins have a sequence of amino acids attached at one end that helps direct them to their destination.

Protein synthesis often occurs on the surface of the rough endoplasmic reticulum (ER; *see figure 3.15*). The synthesis of proteins on ribosomes bound to the ER allows preproteins to move into the ER as the protein is being translated. Once the preprotein or a portion of it is through the membrane, amino acids that do not contribute to the finished protein are cleaved from the molecule, and when the translation is finished, the protein can be moved to the Golgi apparatus for packaging into a secretory vesicle or a lysosome.

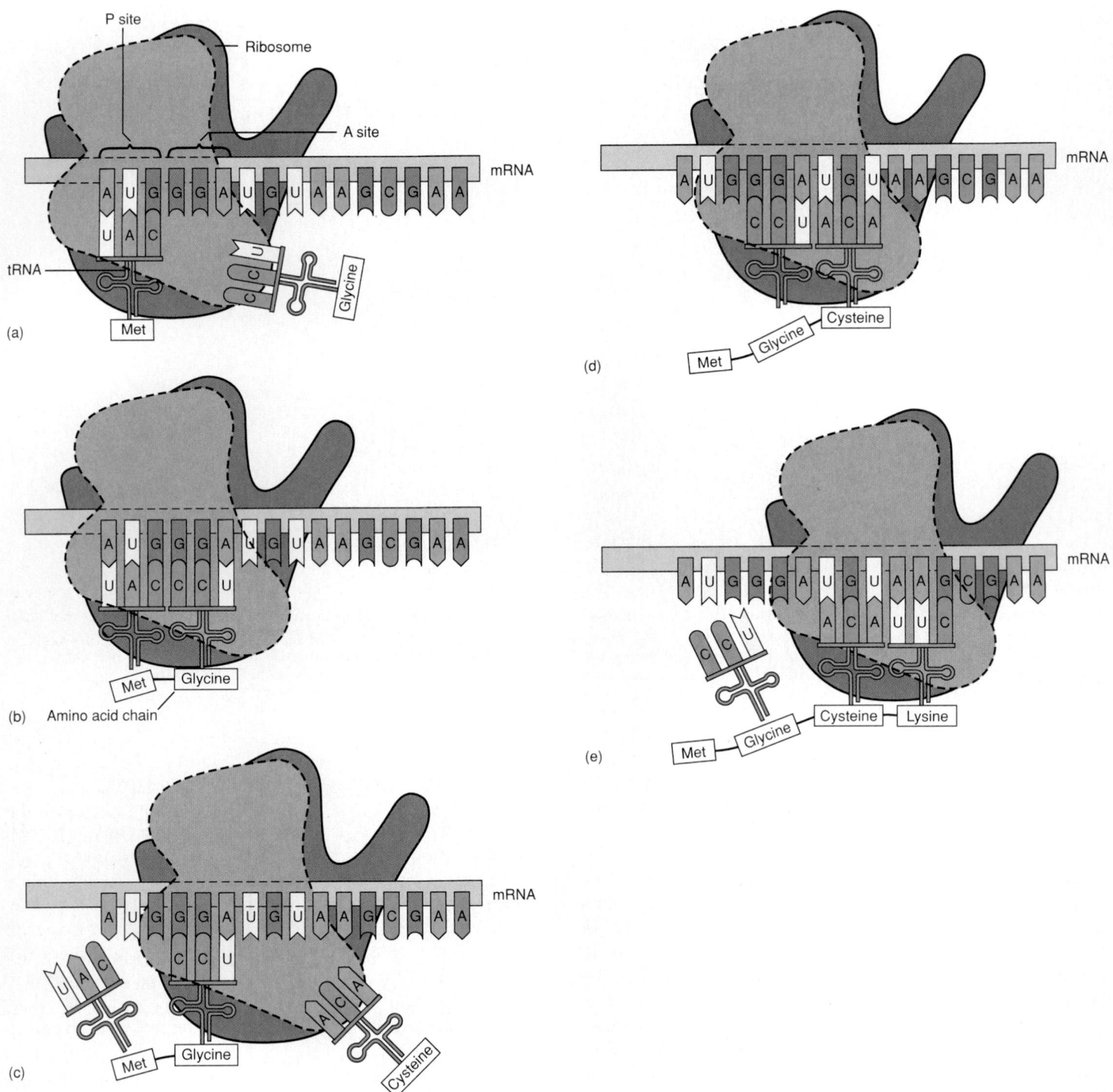

Figure 9.8

The Events of Translation. (*a*) Translation begins by a methionine tRNA associating with the P site of the smaller ribosomal subunit and the initiation codon of mRNA associated with that subunit. The larger ribosomal subunit attaches to the small subunit/tRNA complex. (*b*) A second tRNA carrying the next amino acid enters the A site. A peptide bond is formed between the two amino acids, freeing the first tRNA in the P site. (*c*) The mRNA, along with the second tRNA and its attached dipeptide, moves the distance of one codon. The first tRNA is discharged, leaving its amino acid behind. The second tRNA is now in the P site, and the A site is exposed and ready to receive another tRNA-amino acid. (*d*) A second peptide bond is formed. (*e*) This process continues until an mRNA stop signal is encountered.

Stop and Ask Yourself

5. The genetic code is a degenerate code. What does this mean?
6. How does a primary transcript differ from the mRNA molecule that leaves the nucleus?
7. What is the anticodon?
8. What is the role of the following in protein synthesis: A site? P site? Preprotein?

Control of Gene Expression in Eukaryotes

The gene control processes that function in prokaryotic organisms are well understood. Genes of prokaryotes are usually linked into functional units called operons. Operons consist of **structural genes,** which are genes that code for the desired end product; and **regulator genes,** which control transcription of the structural genes. Similar regulatory genes exist in eukaryotic organisms. The control of gene function in eukaryotic organisms is very complex, and details of gene regulation are well known for only a few genes.

4 Many genes are functional only during particular stages in the life history of an animal. Consider, for example, the changes that humans go through only during puberty. Other genes are turned on and off more frequently. Aldosterone, for example, is a steroid hormone produced in the cortex (outer region) of the adrenal gland. This hormone functions at the kidney to promote reabsorption of sodium from the urine and secretion of potassium into the urine. Aldosterone enters kidney cells by diffusion, combines with a cytoplasmic receptor, and enters the nucleus to alter gene activity.

There is ample cytological evidence that the activity of genes changes throughout the life of an animal cell. Observations of structural changes in chromosomes indicate that when gene activity changes, chromosomal structure may be altered. In addition, most animals have far more DNA in the nuclei of their cells than codes for all of their proteins. Some of this extra DNA may consist of regulatory genes.

Mutations

Genetic material must account for evolutionary change. Mutations are changes in the structure of genes and chromosomes. Changes in chromosome number and cytologically visible changes in structure were described in chapter 8. **Point mutations** are changes in nucleotide sequences and may result from the replacement, addition, or deletion of nucleotides. Mutations are always random events. Although certain environmental factors may change mutation rates, there is no way to predict what genes will be affected or what the nature of the change will be. 5 Some mutations may be unnoticed or even beneficial; however, the consequences of genetic changes are usually negative because they disturb the structure of proteins that are the products of millions of years of evolution.

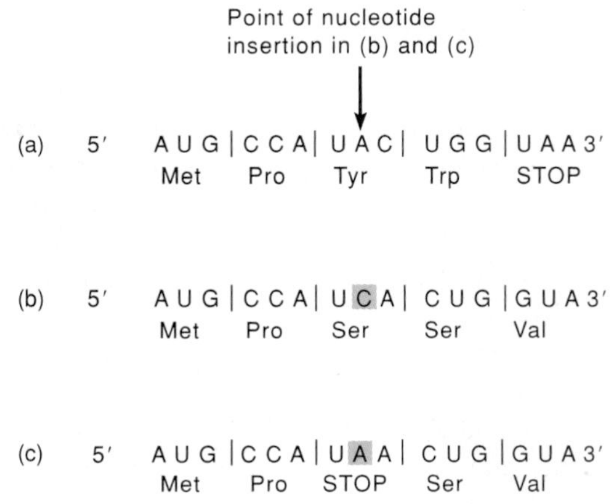
Point of nucleotide insertion in (b) and (c)
(a) 5′ AUG | CCA | UAC | UGG | UAA 3′
Met Pro Tyr Trp STOP
(b) 5′ AUG | CCA | UCA | CUG | GUA 3′
Met Pro Ser Ser Val
(c) 5′ AUG | CCA | UAA | CUG | GUA 3′
Met Pro STOP Ser Val

Figure 9.9

Frameshift Mutations. A segment of mRNA showing that insertion of a nucleotide can cause frameshift mutations. (*a*) Normal mRNA base sequence. (*b*) After the insertion of "C," the stop signal is deleted and the sequence of amino acids following the point of insertion is altered. (*c*) After the insertion of "A," a stop signal is created in the middle of a gene, causing premature termination.

Kinds of Point Mutations

Animals are protected from the negative effects of base changes when the changes occur in the third position of a DNA triplet. Because many amino acids are coded for by the first two bases of a DNA triplet, the third base can vary, and not change the amino acid specified. Thus, roughly 30% of all single base changes will never manifest themselves in altered protein structure and are referred to as silent mutations.

6 On the other hand, base changes in the first or second position of a DNA code, and sometimes base changes at the third position, will result in the substitution of one amino acid for another. Sickle cell anemia (*see chapter 7*) results in the reduced ability of hemoglobin to carry oxygen and the tendency of affected red blood cells to get stuck in, and clog, capillary beds. These dramatic changes in circulatory physiology result from a single base substitution in one of the polypeptides of hemoglobin. Valine (GUG) is substituted for glutamic acid (GAG) at one position. Mutations that result in single amino acid changes are called missense mutations.

Mutations that result in the most severe changes in protein structure are the result of the addition or deletion of a base. These mutations are called frameshift mutations, because adding or deleting a base causes all codons after the change to be misread. This kind of change is likely to create a useless protein (figure 9.9).

CAUSES OF MUTATIONS

Although mutation rates can be increased by various environmental agents, mutations are not unique to our modern world. Mutations have occurred throughout the history of life on earth. Many mutations are said to be spontaneous mutations because they have no obvious cause. Many of these are a result of base-pairing errors during replication, and result in a substitution of one base pair for another.

A variety of mutagenic agents affect mutation rates. Thousands of chemicals used in industry and in science laboratories are suspected mutagens. Some of these chemicals, such as 5-bromodeoxyuridine, have structures similar to normal DNA bases, but may pair differently during replication and cause a base substitution. Other chemicals change the structure of certain bases. Nitrous acid (HNO_2), a powerful mutagen, converts adenine to a guaninelike compound, and after replication, an A-T base pair would be changed to a G-C base pair.

Electromagnetic radiation (ultraviolet light, X rays, and gamma rays) and nuclear radiation (alpha and beta particles, protons, and neutrons) are also mutagenic. Ultraviolet light from the sun, for example, easily penetrates the outer epidermal cell layers and can cause base substitutions in DNA of cells in the germinal layers of the epidermis. These changes are a primary cause of skin cancer.

Fortunately, cells have DNA repair mechanisms, so that damage that occurs is often repaired, and no detrimental effects are experienced. Repair mechanisms involve enzyme systems that detect a base change by comparing the altered strand to the complementary strand and cut out and replace the altered base.

Stop and Ask Yourself

9. What evidence is there that many genes are active only at certain times?
10. What are silent mutations? Missense mutations? Frameshift mutations?
11. How does the fact that DNA is a double helix protect against the negative effects of point mutations?

APPLICATIONS OF GENETIC TECHNOLOGIES

Technologies that have allowed scientists to understand life are now being applied to manipulate life. Most scientists and many laypersons would agree that applications of these technologies have great potential for improving the quality of life on earth. Scientists can now assay individuals for some genetic abnormalities before birth, detect some abnormalities hidden in the genome of prospective parents, control fertilization, and manipulate DNA (figure 9.10). However, numerous ethical considerations are involved with the application of these technologies.

9.10

The remainder of this chapter focuses on two applications of genetic technologies, and briefly discusses ethical dilemmas presented by each application.

RECOMBINANT DNA

(7) **Recombinant DNA** techniques involve the incorporation of human, or other, DNA into bacteria in hopes that the bacteria will become a factory for the desired protein. For example, most of the growth hormone used to treat dwarfism is now produced using recombinant DNA.

Recombinant DNA techniques differ depending on whether one is interested in producing a protein of prokaryotic or eukaryotic origin. In either case, however, a vector must be used to incorporate foreign DNA into the bacteria. One kind of vector is a plasmid. Plasmids are small, extrachromosomal circles of DNA that occur naturally in bacteria. They replicate independently from a bacterial chromosome, can be isolated by gel electrophoresis, and can be incorporated back into bacteria using a calcium-enriched medium. Because plasmids are self-replicating, many copies of an engineered plasmid will be present in each bacterial cell. If one wishes to isolate prokaryotic DNA for transfer, the procedure involves cutting the DNA into fragments using restriction enzymes. The same kind of enzyme is used to cleave plasmids (figure 9.11a). When plasmid DNA and DNA fragments are mixed, and an enzyme called DNA ligase is added, the fragments and the plasmid DNA may join (figure 9.11b). The plasmids can then be reincorporated into bacteria (figure 9.11c).

After incorporating DNA into bacteria, the investigator must find the bacterial copies that contain the plasmids with the desired gene. Not all plasmids will have incorporated the desired gene, and not all bacteria will have incorporated plasmids. If the plasmid has genes that convey resistance to an antibiotic, culturing bacteria on a medium containing that antibiotic will select for bacteria containing the plasmid. Out of those bacteria that survive, only a few will have the desired gene. One technique for isolating these bacteria involves isolating mRNA from a cell culture actively synthesizing the desired protein and incorporating a radioactive label into that mRNA. The mRNA has a base sequence complementary to the desired gene, and one can induce hybridization (bonding) between mRNA and DNA. This procedure is done by transferring bacterial colonies to special filter paper, treating the filter paper with alkali to separate DNA strands, and flooding the filter paper with labeled mRNA. The filter paper is then placed on photographic film, and the hybridized DNA/mRNA will expose the film, identifying the bacterial colony containing the desired gene. Bacteria from that colony can be cultured, and their protein product recovered.

Techniques used for incorporating eukaryotic DNA into plasmids are slightly different. They begin by isolating mRNA rather than DNA, because mRNA from a cell undergoing protein synthesis will not have intron base sequences. An enzyme called reverse transcriptase is used to produce DNA from the mRNA. This DNA, called complementary

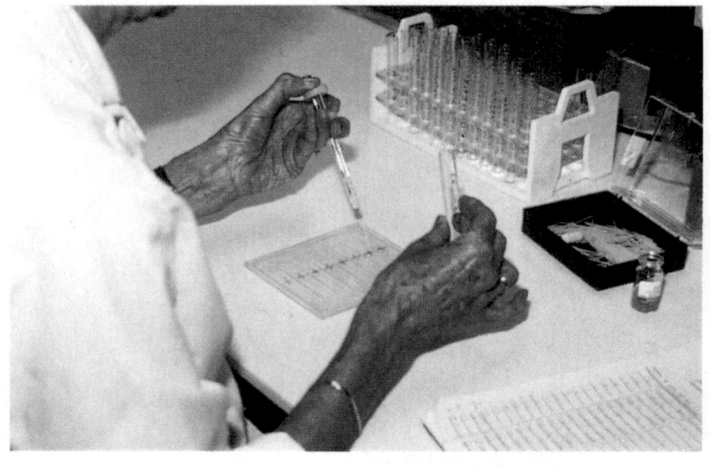
(a)

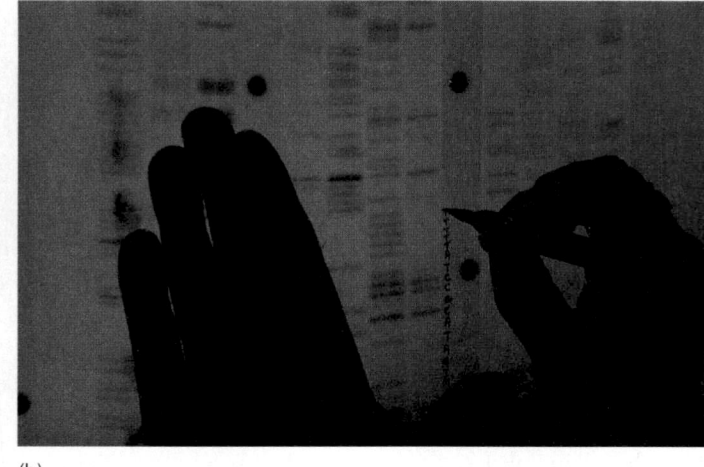
(b)

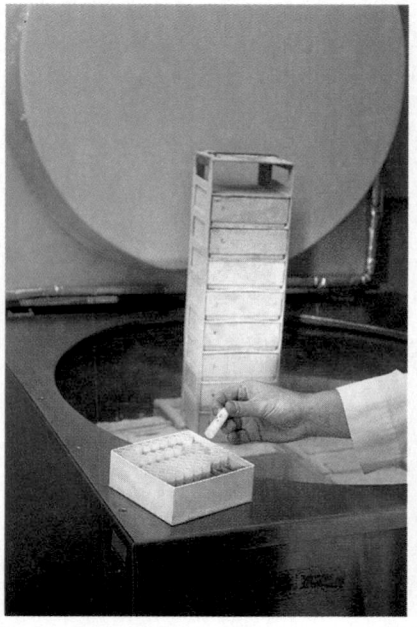
(c)

(d)

(e)

FIGURE 9.10

Manipulation of DNA. (*a*) Preparation of an electrophoretic gel for the analysis of nucleic acids. (*b*) Analysis of gel electrophoresis results and determination of DNA base sequences. (*c*) Hybridoma cells to be used in the production of monoclonal antibodies are stored at –34° C (–94° F). (*d*) Purification of a product by column chromatography. (*e*) The production of interferon in a large fermenter.

DNA (cDNA), can be incorporated into plasmids and into bacteria in the usual fashion. Culturing these bacteria can result in large quantities of protein at relatively low cost.

The Controversy

No one doubts that recombinant DNA technologies can provide supplies of valuable proteins and useful bacteria. Concerns regarding the application of these technologies center around recombinant organisms that eventually need to be tested outside the laboratory. Even though the scientists involved may take precautions to ensure that bacteria will have

little chance of harming the environment, many people have concerns about possibilities of the uncontrolled proliferation of engineered organisms. Thus, even though guidelines for laboratory applications have been relaxed, guidelines for field tests are stringent.

GENE INSERTION

Gene insertion involves the introduction of copies of desired genes into an organism that lacks those genes (box 9.1). In human applications, gene insertion, or gene therapy, has been used to insert normal genes into a patient with defective genes.

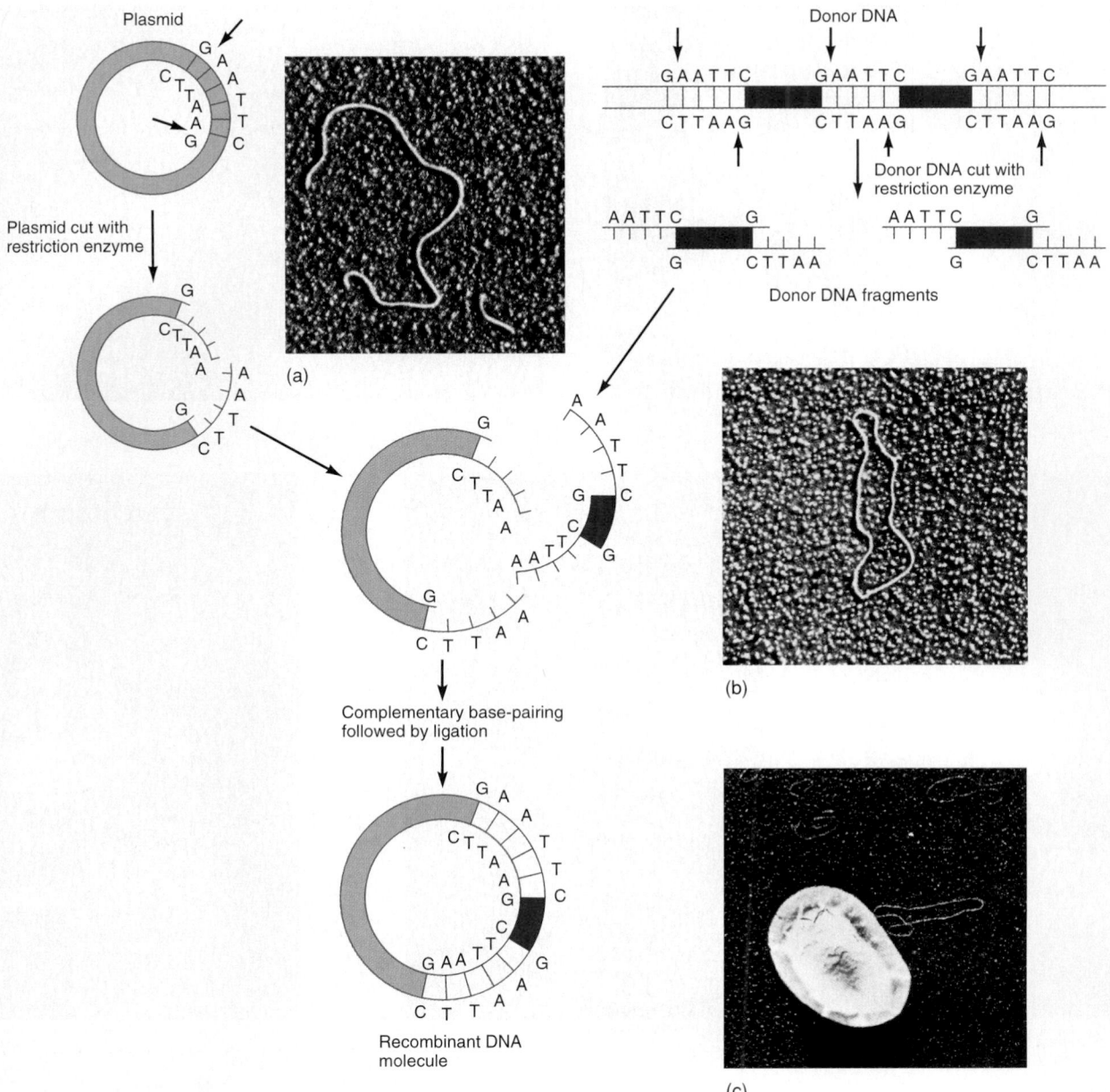

Figure 9.11

Recombinant DNA. (*a*) These techniques involve cutting plasmid DNA and donor DNA with restriction enzymes. This process leaves the ends of DNA fragments with complementary base sequences. (The electron micrograph shows a cleaved plasmid and a fragment of host DNA.) (*b*) Plasmid and host fragments are joined by ligase enzymes. (*c*) The plasmid, now containing host DNA, is introduced into bacteria. (Note the recombined plasmid lying next to the bacterium in the electron micrograph.)

BOX 9.1 | TRANSGENIC ANIMALS

Although recombinant DNA technology was pioneered in bacteria, it is now being applied to animals. When a cell of an animal receives a foreign gene, and then an individual develops from the engineered cell, the resulting organism is termed **transgenic** (L. *trans.* through + genes). The altered cell can be from an oocyte or fertilized egg of a sexually reproducing animal.

Because transgenic animals can produce large quantities of valuable drugs, they may revolutionize the pharmaceutical industry. For example, in Edinburgh, Scotland, a flock of sheep now exists that is a direct descendant of one ewe (a female sheep) named Ethel. When Ethel was a fertilized egg, she received a human gene for factor VIII. Factor VIII is a blood protein that animals and humans need in order for blood to clot. If it is absent, hemophilia results. As a result of the inserted human gene for factor VIII, Ethel and her progeny now produce large amounts of factor VIII in their milk. This valuable protein need only be separated from the sheep's milk to supply enough clotting factor for all of the hemophiliacs in the world.

Transgenic goats have been similarly engineered to secrete tissue-plasminogen activator (t-PA) in their milk (figure 1). Tissue-plasminogen activator dissolves blood clots in the treatment of heart attacks and arterial blockages. Transgenic mice have been engineered that contain the gene for breast cancer; thus, enabling scientists to study this human disease in an animal model. Other transgenic mice termed SCID (for severe combined immune deficiency) have been developed that lack an immune system. These mice are now serving as models for studying human diseases such as acquired immunodeficiency syndrome (AIDS), muscular dystrophy, and diabetes. Pig embryos injected with human hemoglobin genes develop into transgenic pigs that synthesize human hemoglobin. Current plans are to purify human hemoglobin and use it as a blood substitute.

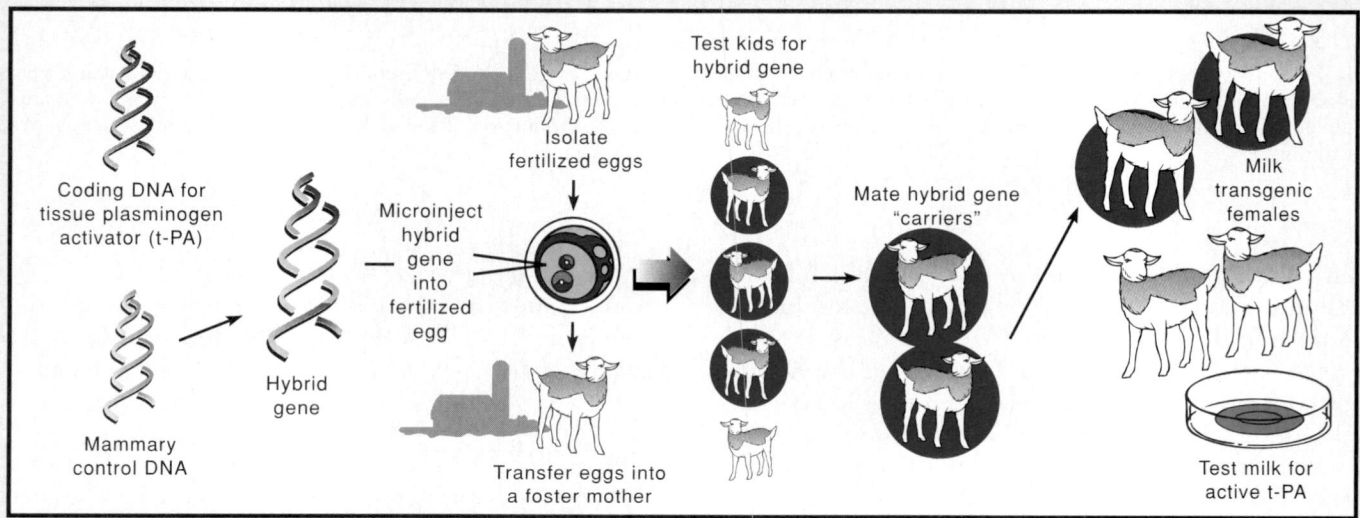

FIGURE 1 **How to Put t-PA into Goat's Milk.** Circled goats symbolize those goats found to carry the t-PA gene.

In other applications, it could involve the insertion of genes for disease resistance, faster growth, or increased size into plant or animal stocks.

The basic strategy of gene insertion is illustrated by a recent attempt at human gene therapy. SCID (severe combined immune deficiency) represents a group of diseases that affect one in 100,000 infants. Affected individuals are left with essentially no immune system, and they often die from otherwise mild childhood infections.

In one form of SCID, a group of white blood cells, called T lymphocytes, lack the ability to produce an enzyme called adenosine deaminase (ADA). This enzyme breaks down chemicals that destroy T lymphocytes. In the absence of ADA, T lymphocytes are destroyed, and the immune system does not function. Treatment for this form of SCID has involved receiving injections of ADA, which has been isolated from cattle, twice each week for the life of the individual.

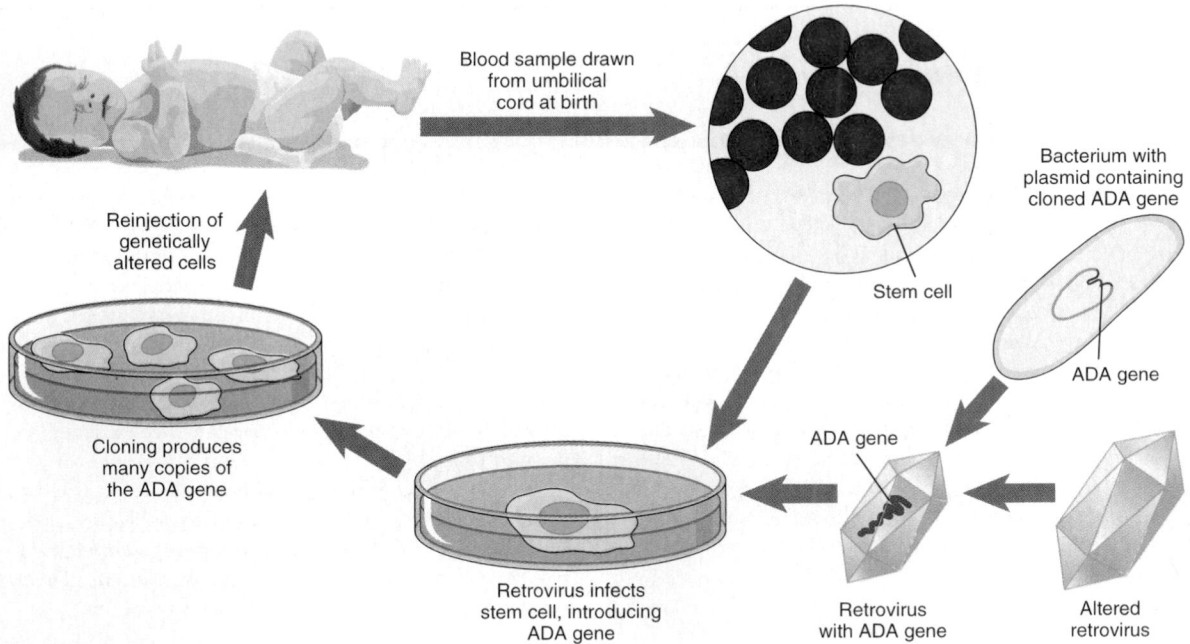

Figure 9.12

Genetic Treatment for SCID. A blood sample is drawn from the umbilical cord of a SCID newborn. Stem cells are isolated and incubated with retroviruses containing the ADA gene. After the ADA gene is incorporated into stem cells, the stem cells are allowed to multiply and then are reinjected into the infant. The hope is that genetically altered cells will take over the production of T lymphocytes, and a permanent supply of ADA will result.

In 1993, Donald Kohn and his colleagues at Children's Hospital in Los Angeles attempted a genetic cure for this disease in three SCID newborns (figure 9.12). They used recombinant DNA techniques to isolate and clone the normal ADA gene. The ADA gene was inserted into specially engineered viruses called retroviruses. Retroviruses can insert DNA into a human cell, but they do not damage the cell. When the three SCID infants were born, T lymphocyte precursor cells (stem cells) were isolated from the umbilical cord. Stem cells normally reside in the bone marrow and divide throughout one's life to produce T lymphocytes and other blood cells. These stem cells were incubated with the retroviruses, and then they were injected into the infants with the hope that transformed cells would make their way into the bone marrow and begin producing T lymphocytes capable of ADA synthesis.

The three children are still receiving ADA injections, but this attempt at a genetic cure seems to be on the road to success. There is evidence of ADA producing T lymphocytes in these children. The hope is that the T lymphocytes produced by the descendants of the originally transformed stem cells can take over the job of supplying ADA. If that happens a genetic cure will have been accomplished!

Germ-line gene therapy is much more difficult. ⑧ It involves introducing genes into early developmental stages of animals (figure 9.12). These genes could be incorporated into gametes and, thus, could eradicate genetic threats to a family's future.

The Controversy

Undoubtedly, gene insertion will become a reality; it has tremendous potential for good. Ethical concerns regard decision-making processes involved with these manipulations. Some individuals question whether humans have any business altering the human genome. Others simply wonder who will be trusted to make decisions about what genes are "good" and what genes are "bad."

Stop and Ask Yourself

12. How are the following used in recombinant DNA techniques: Restriction enzymes? Plasmids? DNA ligase? Reverse transcriptase?

13. What is gene insertion? How is gene insertion being used in the treatment of SCID patients?

SUMMARY

1. Deoxyribonucleic acid (DNA) is the hereditary material of the cell. Ribonucleic acid (RNA) participates in protein synthesis.

2. Nucleic acid building blocks are called nucleotides. Nucleotides consist of a nitrogenous (purine or pyrimidine) base, a phosphate, and a pentose sugar.

3. DNA consists of a double helix, in which the sugar-phosphate groups form the rails of the helix, and nitrogenous bases pair across the molecule, being held together by hydrogen bonds.

4. The replication of DNA is semiconservative. During replication, the DNA strands separate, and each strand serves as a template for a new strand. One-half of the old molecule is conserved in each new molecule.

5. A gene can be defined as a series of nucleotides of DNA that code for a single polypeptide.

6. Proteins are produced in a cell as a result of two processes. Transcription involves the production of a messenger RNA molecule from a DNA molecule. Translation involves the movement of messenger RNA to the cytoplasm where transfer RNA and ribosomes are involved with linking amino acids in a proper sequence to produce a polypeptide.

7. Proteins are often produced as preproteins. Sequences of amino acids attached at one end of the protein help direct proteins to their destination.

8. There is good evidence for changing gene activity. The details of gene regulation in eukaryotes are well known for only a few genes.

9. Point mutations are changes in nucleotide sequences in DNA. Mutations can occur spontaneously, although a variety of mutagenic agents affect mutation rates. These mutagens include various chemicals and electromagnetic and nuclear radiation.

10. Recombinant DNA techniques involve the incorporation of human, or other, DNA into bacteria in hopes that the bacteria will produce a desired protein. Gene insertion involves the introduction of desired genes into an organism that lacks those genes.

SELECTED KEY TERMS

anticodon (p. 122)
antiparallel (p. 119)
codon (p. 121)
deoxyribonucleic acid (DNA) (p. 118)
messenger RNA (mRNA) (p. 121)
molecular genetics (p. 118)
point mutations (p. 125)
regulator genes (p. 125)
ribonucleic acid (RNA) (p. 118)
ribosomal RNA (rRNA) (p. 121)
structural genes (p. 125)
transcription (p. 121)
transfer RNA (tRNA) (p. 121)
translation (p. 121)

CRITICAL THINKING QUESTIONS

1. Matthew Meselson and Franklin Stahl found that DNA replication was semiconservative. Explain the results they would have gotten in their experiments if replication were conservative. (That is, if replication resulted in one entirely new molecule and conserved the parental molecule.)

2. In a zoology laboratory experiment, you analyze the DNA from your own white blood cells. You determine that 15% of the nucleotide bases it contains is thymine. What percentage of the bases is cytosine?

3. Explain why degeneracy in the genetic code lessens the impact of mutations that result in base substitutions. Does degeneracy also lessen the impact of frameshifts? Explain.

4. Given the fact that most mutations are recessive and usually do not show up in natural populations, explain why zoos are concerned with the loss of genetic diversity by excessive inbreeding within the confines of the zoo.

5. Imagine that you are a prospective parent, and that it is the year 2010. You are told by a genetic counselor that you and your spouse both carry a rare recessive gene that could result in a severely deformed child. The chance of this trait showing up in your child is one in four. You have four choices.

   a. You may decide not to have a child.
   b. You may adopt a child.
   c. You may take your chances with nature.
   d. You may have corrective genes inserted into your own (your spouse's) ovum, which would then undergo in vitro fertilization with your spouse's (your) sperm. You can then be confident of having a normal child.

   Which option would you choose? Why? Which aspects of the decision are "scientific" and which are "nonscientific"?

DESCRIPTIVE EMBRYOLOGY

Concepts

1. Embryology is the study of the development of an organism from the fertilized egg to the time that all major organ systems have formed. Descriptive embryology focuses on describing developmental stages of an animal, and experimental embryology focuses on understanding the cellular controls for development.
2. Development of a new animal begins with fertilization of an egg by a sperm. Fertilization events help ensure that fertilization is successful, that multiple fertilization is prevented, and that the egg is prepared for development.
3. Patterns of development of different animals have important common themes. Some of the unique developmental patterns of different animals arise from differences in how yolk is distributed in animal eggs.
4. The development of echinoderms illustrates how eggs with very little, evenly distributed yolk may develop.
5. The development of amphibians illustrates how a moderate amount of unevenly distributed yolk influences development.
6. The embryos of reptiles, birds, and mammals require adaptations for long developmental periods in terrestrial environments.

Would You Like to Know:

1. why, although millions are produced, only one sperm usually penetrates an egg during fertilization? (p. 135)
2. why echinoderms (sea stars and sea urchins) are often used to study animal development? (p. 138)
3. why frog eggs are darkly pigmented on top and lightly pigmented on the bottom? (p. 141)
4. what a chicken egg contains? (p. 143)

These and other useful questions will be answered in this chapter.

This chapter contains evolutionary concepts, which are set off in this font.

How does one explain the complexity of form and function found in adult animals? Can all of this complexity arise from a single egg? Most biologists of the seventeenth and eighteenth centuries believed that gametes contained miniaturized versions of all of the elements present in the adult. This concept was known as **preformation.**

In the middle of the eighteenth century, the competing theory of **epigenesis** (Gr. *epi,* on + L. *genesis,* birth) gained in popularity. Biologists who favored this theory maintained that the egg contained the material from which the embryo is gradually built—much like a carpenter builds a building from lumber, nails, bricks, and mortar. The essence of this theory was described by Aristotle during the fourth century B.C., and depended on an unexplained "creative principle" to direct the assembly.

In separate experiments, Wilhelm Roux (1888) and Hans Driesch (1892) set out to determine whether epigenesis or preformation was correct. Both allowed a fertilized egg to divide to the two-cell stage. Roux, using amphibian embryos (frogs, toads, salamanders), killed one of the two cells with a hot needle. Driesch, using echinoderm embryos (sea stars, sea urchins, sea cucumbers), completely separated the divided cells. If an entire animal developed from a single cell, then epigenesis would be supported. If a portion of the animal developed, then preformation would be favored. What was the result? Interestingly, Roux described the formation of a half embryo (figure 10.1*a*), and Driesch found that each cell retained the potential to develop into an entire organism (figure 10.1*b*). We now know that Driesch was the more correct of the two, and that the killed cell, still attached to Roux's developing amphibian embryo, probably altered the development of the untreated cell.

This episode in history marks an important turning point in **embryology** (Gr. *embryo,* to be full + *logos,* discourse), the study of the development of an animal from the fertilized egg to the time that all major organ systems are formed. Early studies were descriptive in nature, documenting the stages an animal goes through in embryological development. Such material is the subject of this chapter. The works of Roux, Driesch, and others were the beginning of experimental embryology (or developmental biology). Developmental biologists use the tools of molecular biology (*see chapter 9*) to investigate the genetic controls of development.

FERTILIZATION

A variety of mechanisms are used by different animals to bring opposite sexes together, and to induce the release of eggs and/or sperm. Similarly, once gametes have been released, different mechanisms increase the likelihood of fertilization.

For fertilization to occur, a sperm must penetrate the gel coat of an egg, which consists of protein, or protein and polysaccharide (mucopolysaccharide). To penetrate this coating, the sperm of most animals possess enzymes called sperm lysins. These enzymes may be associated with a specialized organelle at the head of the sperm, called the **acrosome,** or with the plasma

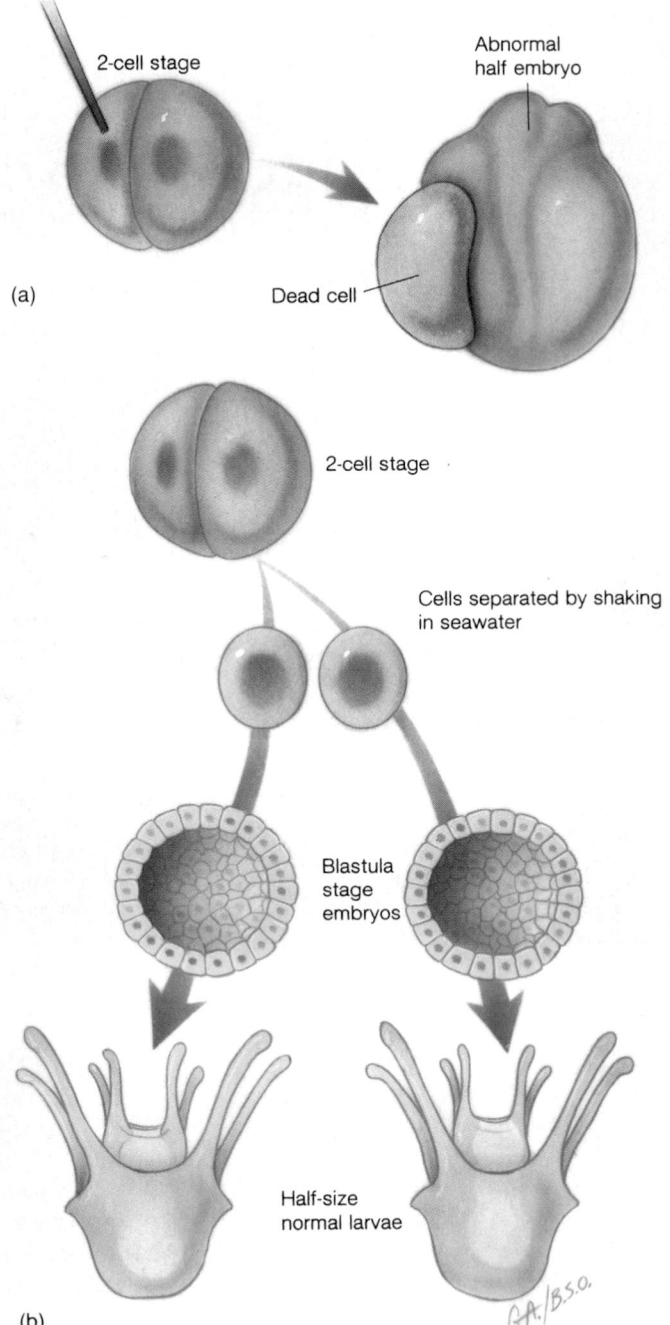

FIGURE 10.1

The Experiments of Wilhelm Roux and Hans Driesch. (*a*) A "hemiembryo" was produced by Wilhelm Roux by killing one blastomere of a two-celled amphibian embryo. (*b*) Driesch found that separating cells of a two-celled embryo resulted in the development of two small, but otherwise normal, larvae.

membrane of the anterior tip of the sperm. When a sperm contacts the gel coat, the acrosome releases lysins that dissolve a pathway for the sperm (figure 10.2). In humans, even 80 million sperm per ejaculation often means reduced fertility, because sperm lysins from many sperm are required to dissolve the gel coat of an egg. The acrosome of some species reorganizes

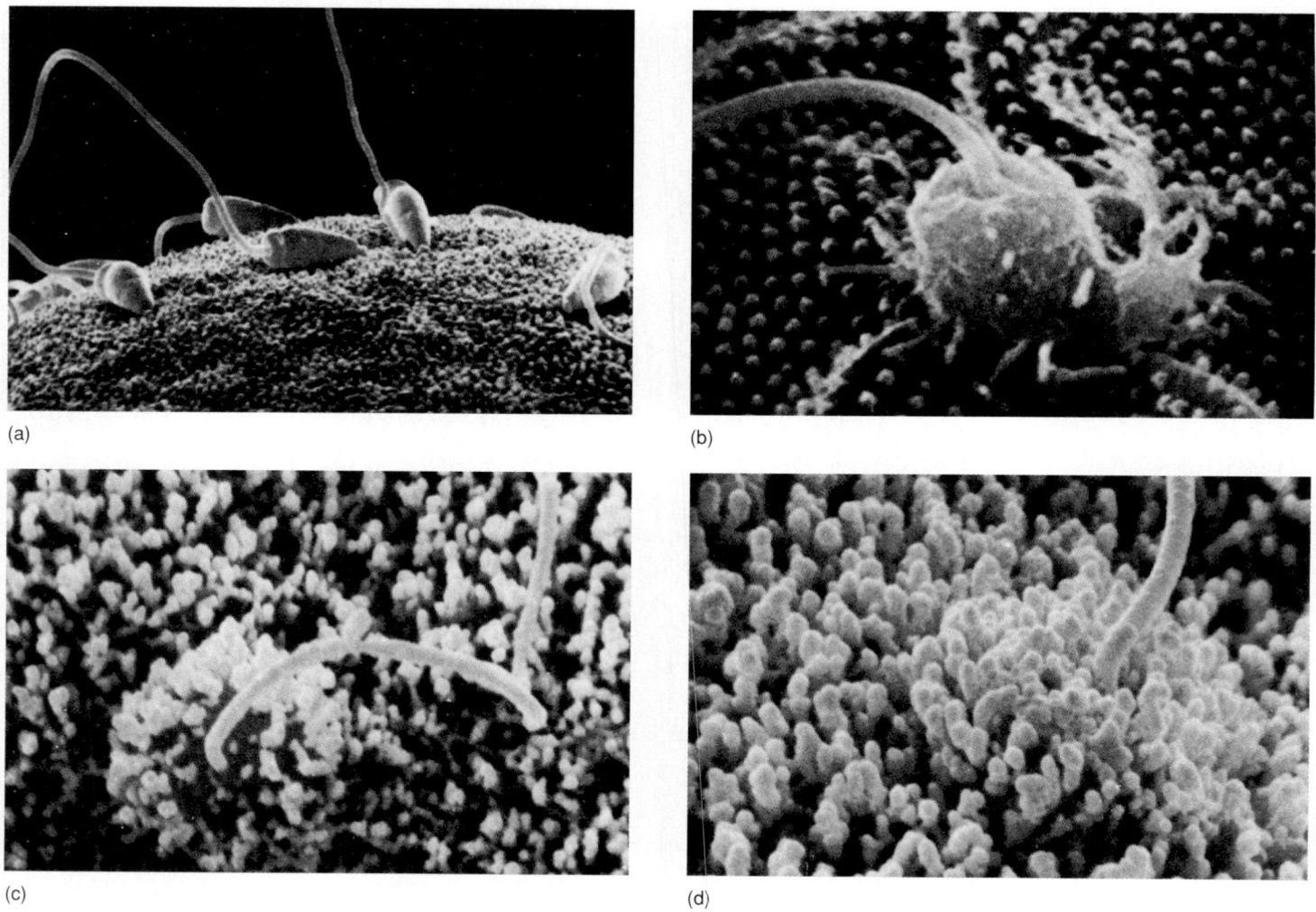

Figure 10.2

Scanning Electron Micrographs of the Fertilization of Sea Urchin Eggs. The fertilization membrane was removed before photomicrographs (*c*) and (*d*) were taken. (*a*) Sperm contacting the egg surface. (*b*) Microvilli of the egg plasma membrane begin to enfold the head of the sperm (×7,500). (*c,d*) Sperm penetration being completed (×4,800; ×7,125).

into an acrosomal process after releasing lysins (figure 10.3). Just outside the egg plasma membrane is a layer called the vitelline layer (or zona pellucida). Egg binding proteins (bindins) on the surface of the acrosomal process bind to sperm attachment molecules on the vitelline layer of the egg plasma membrane (figure 10.4). Acrosomal and egg plasma membranes then fuse. Other parts of the sperm (e.g., the mitochondria, centrioles, and flagellum) may or may not enter the egg, depending on the species involved.

EGG ACTIVATION

The fusion of acrosomal and egg membranes is the beginning of egg activation. Egg activation is a series of biochemical changes in the egg that ensure the completion of fertilization and initiates embryonic development. The events of egg activation have been studied extensively in echinoderms, and some of the findings of that work are discussed below.

Membrane and Cortical Events

Some of the earliest changes in the zygote occur at the plasma membrane, and in the outer region of the cell cytoplasm (called the cortex). ① The purpose of these early changes is to ensure fertilization by only a single sperm.

After contact by sperm, microvilli from the plasma membrane of the ovum wrap around a single sperm. The sperm then is drawn into the egg by contraction of microfilaments in the egg's cytoplasm (*see figures 10.2 and 10.3*).

A second series of events defends against multiple fertilization. Within milliseconds of penetration by a sperm, ionic changes make the plasma membrane unresponsive to other sperm, and initiate the formation of a protective envelope around the egg, called the **fertilization membrane.**

The fertilization membrane forms as granules in the cortex discharge into the region between the egg plasma membrane and the vitelline layer (*see figure 10.3c*). Enzymes released by the cortical granules loosen the vitelline layer's contact with the plasma

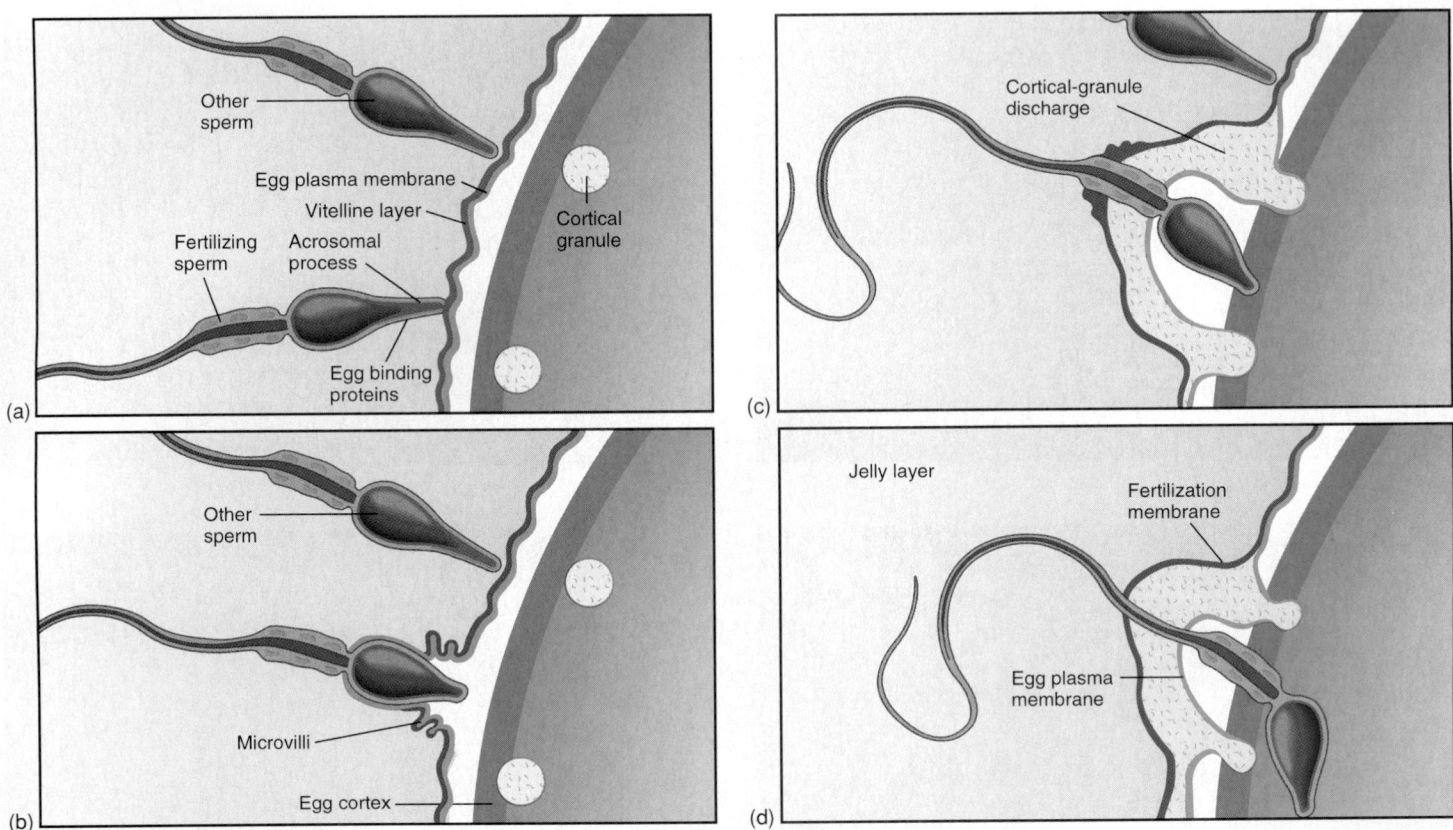

FIGURE 10.3

The Fertilization of Echinoderm Eggs. (*a*) Acrosomal process contacts the vitelline membrane. (*b*) Sperm lysins have created a hole in the vitelline membrane. Changes in the permeability of plasma membrane to sodium ions initiate changes in the membrane that permit only a single sperm to enter. (*c*) Cortical granules discharge, and the vitelline membrane begins to rise off the egg plasma membrane. (*d*) The fertilization membrane is formed.

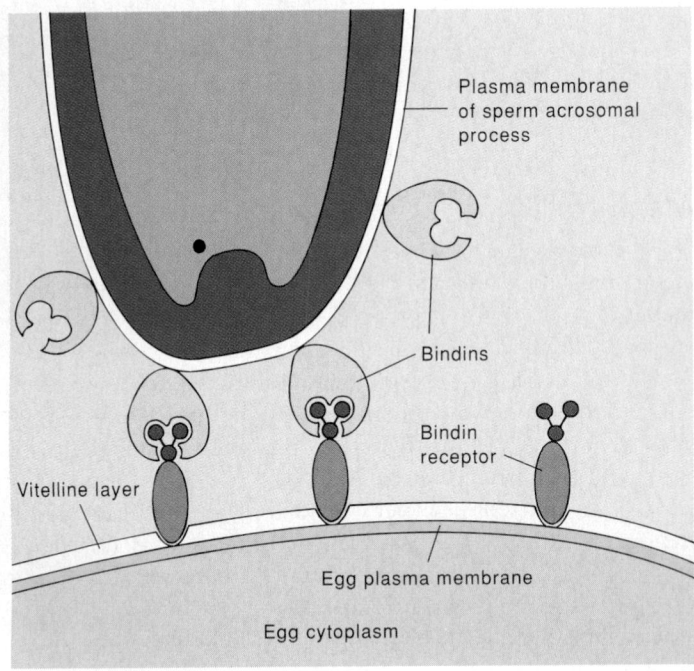

FIGURE 10.4

Sperm-Egg Adhesion is Mediated by Species-Specific Macromolecules. Schematic drawing of bindin proteins covering the surface of the acrosomal process of a sea urchin sperm. The bindin proteins bind to specific bindin receptor molecules (a carbohydrate) associated with the vitelline layer of the egg.

membrane. The granules allow water to enter the space between the vitelline layer and the egg plasma membrane, causing the vitelline layer to lift off the egg. Proteins of the cortical granules thicken and strengthen the vitelline layer. All of these reactions are completed in 1 or 2 minutes following fertilization. The above reactions are important, because multiple fertilization will usually result in genetic imbalances, and a nonviable embryo.

Other important changes occur in the egg cortex. After sperm penetration, the cortical layer thickens, and rotational and sliding movements of the outer egg cytoplasm begin. In amphibians, these cortical changes result in the formation of a **gray crescent** on the egg, opposite the point of sperm penetration, between the animal and vegetal hemispheres. As we will see, the gray crescent has an important influence on later development.

METABOLIC AND NUCLEAR EVENTS

Prior to nuclear fusion (called syngamy; *see chapter* 6), other nuclear events usually occur. Postfertilization changes help prepare the zygote for the ensuing mitotic divisions. Ionic changes raise the intracellular pH and initiate the following changes in zygote physiology. DNA replication occurs, and in most species investigated, rates of protein synthesis increase. Rapid protein synthesis following fertilization meets the needs of new cells for enzymes and structural proteins that make up the mitotic spindle and contribute to the structure of chromosomes. Little mRNA synthesis takes place in the zygote. Instead, existing maternal (egg) mRNA is activated, and it directs the formation of the bulk of the proteins synthesized in early stages of embryonic development. This influence is called maternal dominance.

The region of the egg referred to as the **animal pole** contains less yolk, more mitochondria, more ribosomes, and is more metabolically active than the opposite, **vegetal pole** of the egg.

CLEAVAGE AND EGG TYPES

Billions of cells that make up adult animals arise from the zygote. **Cleavage** is a term used to refer to cell divisions that occur during embryonic development, and the cells produced by it are called **blastomeres** (Gr. *blasto*, sprout + *mero*, part). The first cell division of the zygote results in two daughter cells. These blastomeres divide in synchrony, producing a four-celled embryo. As more blastomeres are produced, divisions become asynchronous. Throughout early embryology, the embryo does not increase in overall size. Instead, blastomeres become smaller, and the proportion of DNA to cytoplasm increases.

QUANTITY AND DISTRIBUTION OF YOLK

Egg sizes and cleavage patterns differ among animal species because of differences in the quantity and distribution of yolk in an egg. Yolk is a mixture of proteins, lipids, and glycogen and serves as the food reserve for the developing embryo. The quantity of yolk present is related to the length of the animal's independent development, which is defined as the development that occurs between the time of fertilization and the point at which the animal begins feeding on its own, or the point at which the embryo is nourished by a parent.

CLEAVAGE PATTERNS

The influence of yolk on cleavage patterns is evidenced by the relative size of the blastomeres that result from cleavage and the rate of cleavage. Eggs with evenly distributed yolk usually have cleavage patterns that result in uniformly sized blastomeres. Eggs with unevenly distributed yolk have cleavage patterns that result in unequal blastomeres.

Cleavages that completely divide an egg are said to be **holoblastic** (Gr. *holo*, whole + *blasto*, sprout). If cleavages cannot

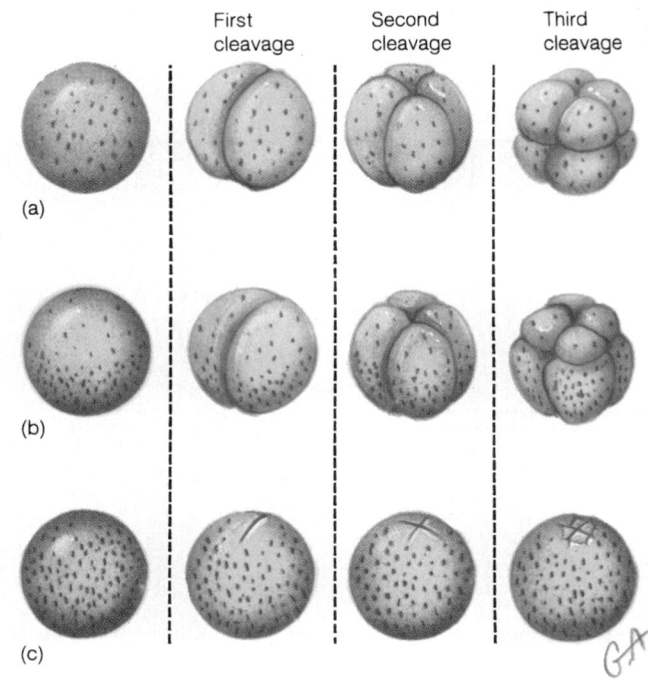

First cleavage   Second cleavage   Third cleavage

(a)

(b)

(c)

FIGURE 10.5

Early Cleavage Patterns. (*a*) Holoblastic cleavage of an embryo containing a small quantity of evenly distributed yolk results in uniformly sized blastomeres. (e.g., a sea urchin). (*b*) Holoblastic cleavage of an embryo containing moderate to large quantities of unevenly distributed yolk results in unequal blastomeres (e.g., an amphibian). (*c*) Meroblastic cleavage occurs when large quantities of yolk prevent the embryo from dividing completely (e.g., a reptile or bird).

completely divide the embryo because of large quantities of yolk, the cleavages are said to be **meroblastic** (Gr. *mero*, part). The development of these embryos occurs around, or on top of, the yolk (figure 10.5).

Other cleavage patterns result from differences in the orientation of the mitotic spindle during mitosis, and the degree to which the fate of early blastomeres is predetermined. Developmental differences are thought to reflect differences in the evolutionary history of animal groups that possess them. For example, the pattern of cleavage described above, where blastomeres are oriented directly over one another, is characteristic of the evolutionary lineage leading to the echinoderms and chordates. Another pattern of cleavage, where an upper tier of blastomeres is twisted out of line with a lower tier of blastomeres, is characteristic of the lineage leading to the annelids (segmented worms) and arthropods (insects and their relatives). Cleavage patterns, as well as other differences in the development of animals in these two evolutionary lineages, are compared in chapter 21.

THE PRIMARY GERM LAYERS AND THEIR DERIVATIVES

Tissues and organs of animals arise from layers, or blocks, of embryonic cells called **primary germ layers.** Their development from a nondescript form in the early embryo to their form

TABLE 10.1	THE PRIMARY GERM LAYERS AND THEIR DERIVATIVES IN VERTEBRATES	
GERM LAYER	**DERIVATIVE**	
Ectoderm	Nervous tissue	
	Epidermis of the skin	
	Sensory organs	
Endoderm	Gut tract lining	
	Digestive glands	
	Respiratory tract lining	
Mesoderm	Connective tissues	
	Circulatory system	
	Bones, tendons, ligaments	
	Dermis of the skin	
	Excretory structures	
	Reproductive structures	
	Muscle	

in late embryonic through adult stages is called **differentiation.** One layer, **ectoderm** (Gr. *ektos*, outside + *derm*, skin), gives rise to the outer body wall. **Endoderm** (Gr. *endo*, within) forms the inner lining of the digestive cavity. **Mesoderm** (Gr. *meso*, in the middle) gives rise to tissues that are located between ectoderm and endoderm. Undifferentiated mesoderm (called **mesenchyme**) develops into muscles, blood and blood vessels, skeletal elements, and (other) connective tissues (table 10.1).

Stop and Ask Yourself

5. What is the influence of yolk on cleavage patterns?
6. What is the difference between holoblastic and meroblastic cleavages?
7. What tissue is derived from each of the following germ layers: Ectoderm? Endoderm? Mesoderm?
8. What is mesenchyme?

ECHINODERM EMBRYOLOGY

The embryology of echinoderms has been extensively studied. Echinoderms are easily maintained in laboratories, and the ease with which one can obtain mature sperm and eggs makes them convenient models to illustrate principles of early animal development.

The eggs of echinoderms have relatively little yolk, and the yolk is evenly distributed throughout the egg (figure 10.6 *a*). Cleavages are holoblastic, and result in similarly sized blastomeres (figure 10.6*b–d*). In just a few hours, a solid ball of small cells, called the **morula** (L. *morum*, mulberry) (figure 10.6*e*), is produced.

As cell division continues, cells pull away from the interior of the embryo. A fluid-filled cavity, the **blastocoel,** is produced, and the cells form a single layer around the cavity. The embryo is now in the form of a hollow sphere and is called a **blastula** (figure 10.6*f*). In sea urchins, development through the blastula stage takes place within the fertilization membrane. When the cells of the blastula develop cilia, the blastula breaks out of the fertilization membrane and begins to swim. Late in the blastula stage, groups of cells break free of the animal end of the embryo, and position themselves within the blastocoel. These cells, called primary mesenchyme, will form skeletal elements (called spicules) of the embryo.

The next series of events in echinoderm embryology is called **gastrulation.** The first sign of gastrulation is the invagination of cells at a point in the vegetal half of the embryo (figure 10.6*g*). The point of invagination is the **blastopore,** and it will eventually form the anal opening of the larva. During invagination, an embryonic gut, the **archenteron** (Gr. *archeo*, ancient + *enteron*, gut), elongates and reduces the size of the blastocoel (figure 10.6*h*).

During gastrulation, the embryo also begins to lengthen and assumes a pyramidal shape. Although adult echinoderms do not have head and tail ends, larvae have a preferred direction of movement. The end of an animal that meets the environment during locomotion is called the anterior end, and is where the head of most animals is located. The opposite end is the posterior end. The shape changes that occur during gastrulation result in the establishment of the anteroposterior axis of the embryo.

Finally, a body cavity, or coelom, forms from outpockets of the archenteron, and the gut breaks through the anterior body wall. The opening thus produced is the mouth.

The cell movements that begin in gastrulation are the result of groups of cells changing their shapes, all at the same time. These shape changes are mediated by contractile microfilaments (*see figure 3.20*). The result of these precise, coordinated changes is the transformation of a single-layered sphere of cells into an embryo with several layers of cells. The progressive development of an animal's form that begins in gastrulation is called **morphogenesis.** In the case of the sea urchin, these changes result in the development of a pluteus larva that swims freely in the sea and feeds on even smaller plants and animals (figure 10.6*i*).

Stop and Ask Yourself

9. What are the changes that occur in an echinoderm egg that lead to the formation of the blastula?
10. How does the archenteron of an echinoderm gastrula form? What is the fate of the blastopore?
11. What is morphogenesis?

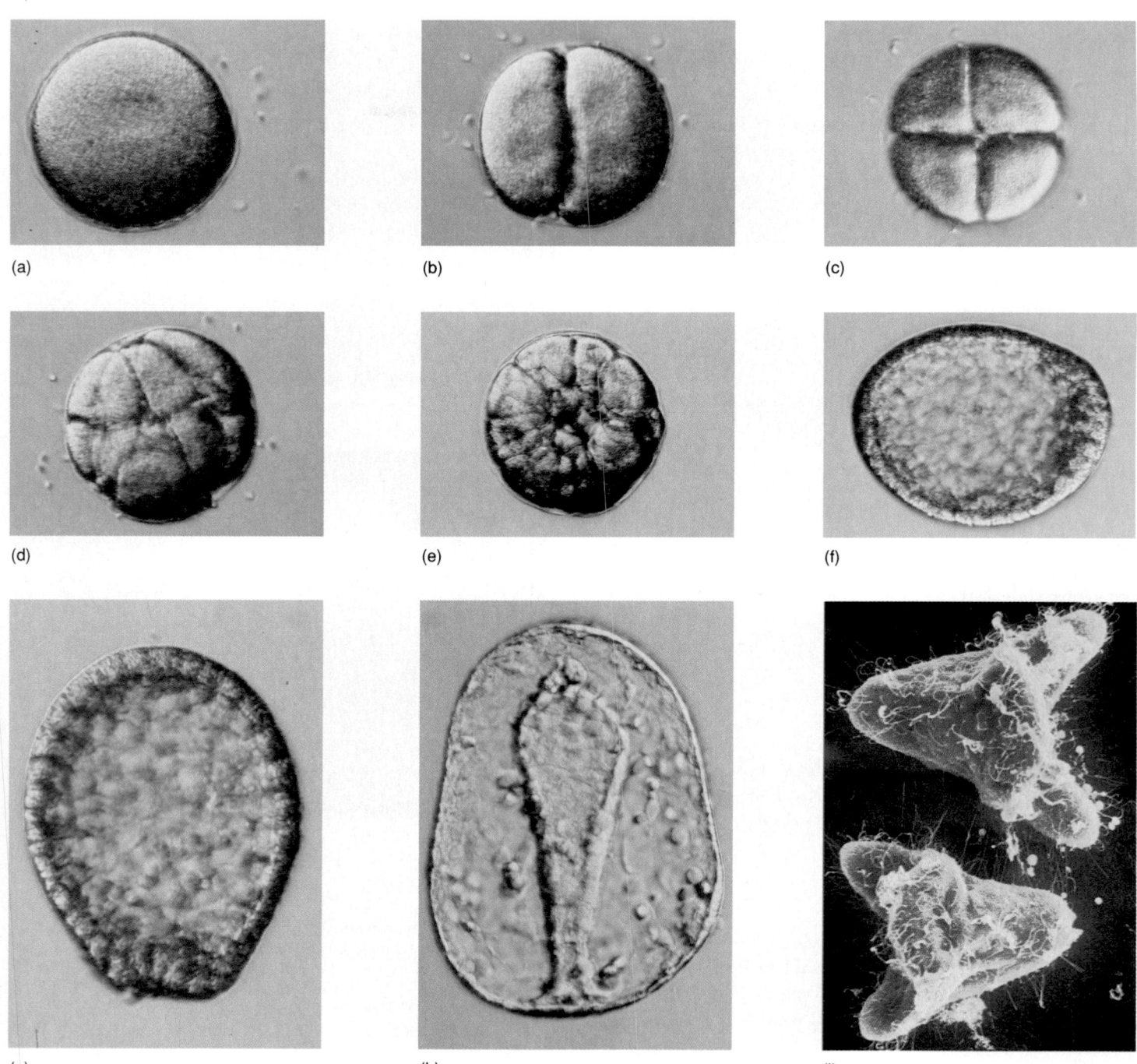

Figure 10.6

Stages in the Development of an Echinoderm. (*a*) Unfertilized egg. (*b*) The first two cleavages occur along the animal/vegetal axis. (*c*) The third cleavage occurs at right angles to the previous cleavages, midway between animal and vegetal poles. An eight-cell stage with approximately equal blastomeres results. Subsequent cleavages (*d* and *e*) result in the formation of the morula. (*f*) The blastula—a hollow sphere whose walls are a single cell-layer thick. (*g*) Gastrulation begins with invagination at a point on the surface of the blastula. (*h*) As gastrulation continues, the archenteron enlarges. (*i*) The pluteus. This scanning electron micrograph (×200) shows the pyramidal shape of the larva. Spicules are formed and the gut track is complete. Note the presence of cilia used in locomotion. (*a–h* photomicrographs are ×100.)

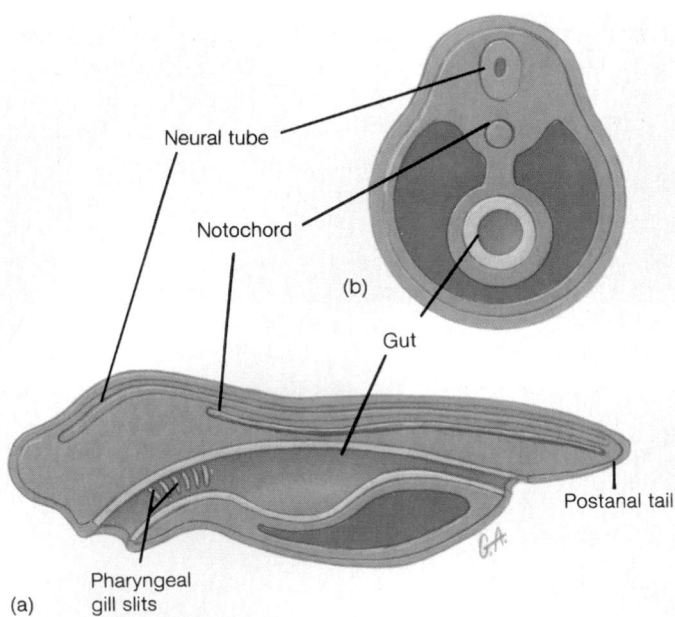

(a)

FIGURE 10.7

The Chordate Body Plan. The development of all chordates involves the formation of a neural tube, the notochord, gill slits, and a postanal tail. Derivatives of all three primary germ layers are present. (*a*) Side view. (*b*) Cross section.

VERTEBRATE EMBRYOLOGY

Early stages of vertebrate (animals with a vertebral column or "backbone") development are similar to those described for echinoderms. The differences that exist are the result of longer developmental periods, and for some vertebrates, adaptations for development on land.

THE CHORDATE BODY PLAN

Vertebrates are members of the phylum Chordata, and all chordates can be characterized by certain structures. The endpoint of our study of vertebrate embryology will be the point at which most of these characteristic structures have been formed (figure 10.7).

The nervous system of chordates develops from ectoderm, and is dorsal and hollow. The first evidence of a developing nervous system is the formation of the neural tube. Nervous tissue proliferates anteriorly into a brain.

The notochord is the primary axial supportive structure present in all chordate embryos, as well as many adults. It is a flexible, yet supportive, structure that lies just beneath the neural tube. The notochord is mesodermal in origin and consists of vacuolated cells packed into a connective tissue sheath.

In addition to the notochord and the dorsal hollow nerve cord, all chordates possess pharyngeal gill slits and a postanal tail at some point in their life history.

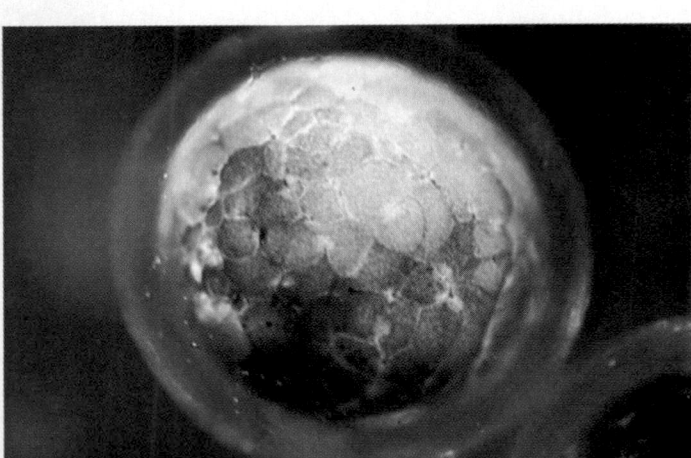

(b)

FIGURE 10.8

Fertilization of Amphibian Eggs. (*a*) Egg release and fertilization in frogs occur when the male (above) mounts and grasps the female (below). This positioning is called amplexus. Eggs are fertilized by the male as they are released by the female. (*b*) The egg of a frog shortly after fertilization. The egg has a jellylike coat. Note the darkly pigmented animal pole at the top and the yolk-laden vegetal pole at the bottom (×6).

AMPHIBIAN EMBRYOLOGY

The eggs of most amphibians are laid in watery environments and are fertilized as they are released from the female (figure 10.8*a*). Frog eggs have a pigmented animal pole. Because the vegetal pole is heavily laden with yolk, the eggs rotate in their jelly coats, so that the less dense, darkly pigmented animal pole is oriented up (figure 10.8*b*). This rather simple series of events has interesting adaptive significance. Given that amphibian eggs usually develop with little care or protection from the parents, one might wonder how they escape detection by predators. Certainly many do not. ③ The pigmentation, however, helps camouflage the developing embryos. When viewed from below, the light color of the vegetal end of floating eggs blends with the sky above. When viewed from above, the dark color of the animal end blends with the bottom of the pond, lake, or stream. The dark pigment of the animal pole also absorbs heat from the sun, and the warming that results may promote development.

Initial Cleavages

The first cleavage of the amphibian embryo, like that of echinoderms, is longitudinal. It begins at the animal pole, and divides the gray crescent in half. Because of the large amount of yolk in the vegetal end of the egg, cleavages are slower than in the animal end. The amphibian morula, therefore, consists of many small cells at the animal end of the embryo and fewer, larger cells at the vegetal end of the embryo (figures 10.9*a–d* and 10.10*a–d*). The amphibian blastula forms in much the same way as the echinoderm blastula, except that the yolky vegetal cells cause the blastocoel to form in the animal half of the embryo (figure 10.10*e; see also figure 10.9b*). Unlike that of echinoderms, the blastula wall of amphibians is composed of multiple cell layers.

Gastrulation

The cells of the blastula that will develop into specific structures are grouped together on the surface of the blastula. Gastrulation involves the movement of some of these cells into the interior of the embryo. Embryologists have used dyes or carbon particles to mark the surface of the blastula, and then have followed the movements of these cells during gastrulation. Embryonic cells are designated according to their future development by "presumptive notochord," "presumptive endoderm," and so forth.

The first sign that gastrulation is beginning is the formation of a groove between the gray crescent and the vegetal region of the embryo. This groove is the slitlike blastopore. The animal-pole margin of the blastopore is called the dorsal lip of the blastopore. Cells at the bottom of the groove move to the interior of the embryo, and the groove spreads transversely (figure 10.10*f*). This groove is similar to that which occurs during echinoderm blastopore formation. In amphibians, however, superficial cells now begin to roll over the dorsal lip of the blastopore in a process called **involution** (to curl inward). Cells spread from the animal pole toward the blastopore, and replace those moving into the interior of the embryo. In the process, the ends of the slitlike blastopore continue to spread transversely and downward toward the vegetal pole, until one end of the slit meets and joins the opposite end of the slit. A ringlike blastopore now surrounds the protruding, yolk-filled cells near the vegetal end of the embryo (*see figure 10.9c*). These

protruding cells are called the **yolk plug** (figure 10.10*g,h*). Eventually, the lips of the blastopore contract to completely enclose the yolk. The blastopore is said to have "closed."

During the closing of the blastopore, two other movements occur. First, the spreading of cells from the animal pole toward the dorsal lip of the blastopore, and the rolling of cells into the blastopore form the archenteron. As these mesodermal and endodermal cells roll into the interior of the embryo, the archenteron becomes larger, and the blastocoel becomes smaller (figure 10.10*f–h*). Because the large yolk-filled cells of the vegetal end are less active in these movements, their fate (making up the floor of the gut tract) is accomplished somewhat passively. Second, not only does gastrulation result in a spreading and thinning of ectodermal cells toward the blastopore, but it also results in ectoderm spreading over the entire embryo, a process called **epiboly.**

Mesoderm Formation

Some of the last cells to roll over the dorsal lip into the blastopore are presumptive notochord and presumptive mesoderm (figure 10.10*h*). Initially, these cells make up the dorsal lining of the archenteron near the blastopore. Later, they detach from the endoderm, and move to a position between the endoderm and ectoderm in the region of the dorsal lip of the blastopore. This mesoderm, referred to as **chordamesoderm,** spreads anteriorly (the embryo is now beginning to elongate) and laterally (to either side) between ectoderm and endoderm. Chordamesoderm is thicker dorsally in a region that will differentiate into notochord. As mesoderm spreads, it also thickens along the sides of the embryo. These thickenings are called **somites,** and are visible externally as a row of bumps on either side of the embryo (figure 10.10*k*). As mesoderm continues to spread ventrally, it splits to form the body cavity (coelom) and the mesodermal lining of the body wall and gut.

Neural Tube Formation

During late gastrulation, external changes along the upper surface of the embryo begin the formation of the neural tube—a process called **neurulation.** After gastrulation is completed, an oval-shaped area on the dorsal side (the future backside) of the embryo marks the presumptive neural tube. This region is called the neural plate (figure 10.10*i*). Microfilaments in neural plate cells cause a flattening and thickening of the neural plate. The edges of the neural plate roll up and over the midline of the neural plate. These longitudinal ridges, called neural folds, meet dorsally to form the neural tube (figure 10.10*i,j; see also figure 10.9d*). The portion of the neural tube that will become the brain is the last to close.

With further development of the mesoderm, the amphibian embryo will gradually take on the form of a tadpole larva. Yolk in cells lining the floor of the gut is gradually depleted, and the larva will begin feeding on algae and other plant material (*see figure 10.9e,f*).

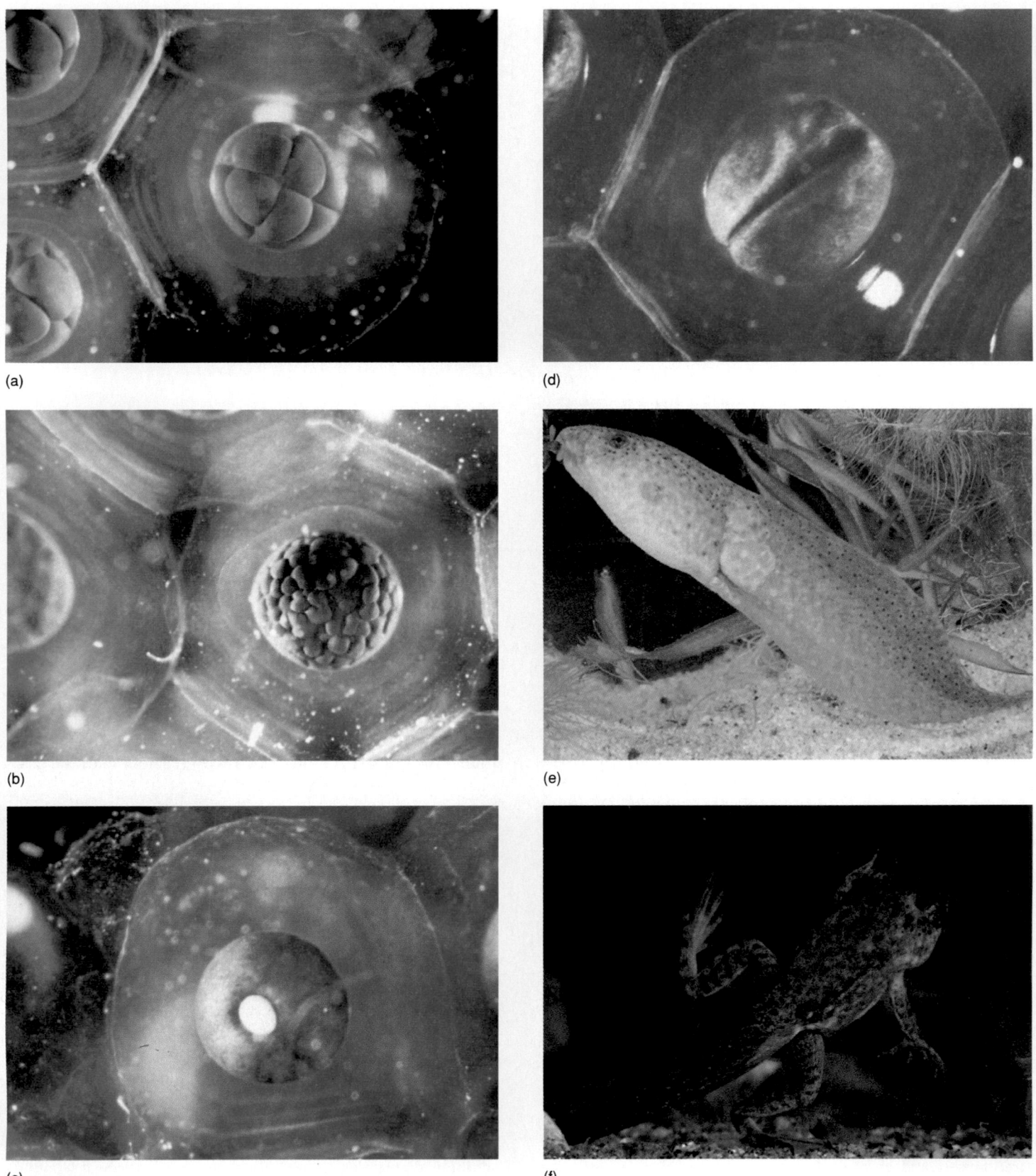

(a)

(b)

(c)

(d)

(e)

(f)

FIGURE 10.9

Frog Development. (*a*) Eight-cell stage. (*b*) Early blastula stage. (*c*) Late gastrula (yolk plug) stage. Note the circular blastopore with yolk protruding from within the embryo. (*d*) Neural groove stage. (Photomicrographs are ×6.) (*e*) A tadpole of the American bullfrog, *Rana catesbeiana*. (*f*) A tadpole of the American bullfrog undergoing metamorphosis. Note the presence of both legs and tail.

10.10

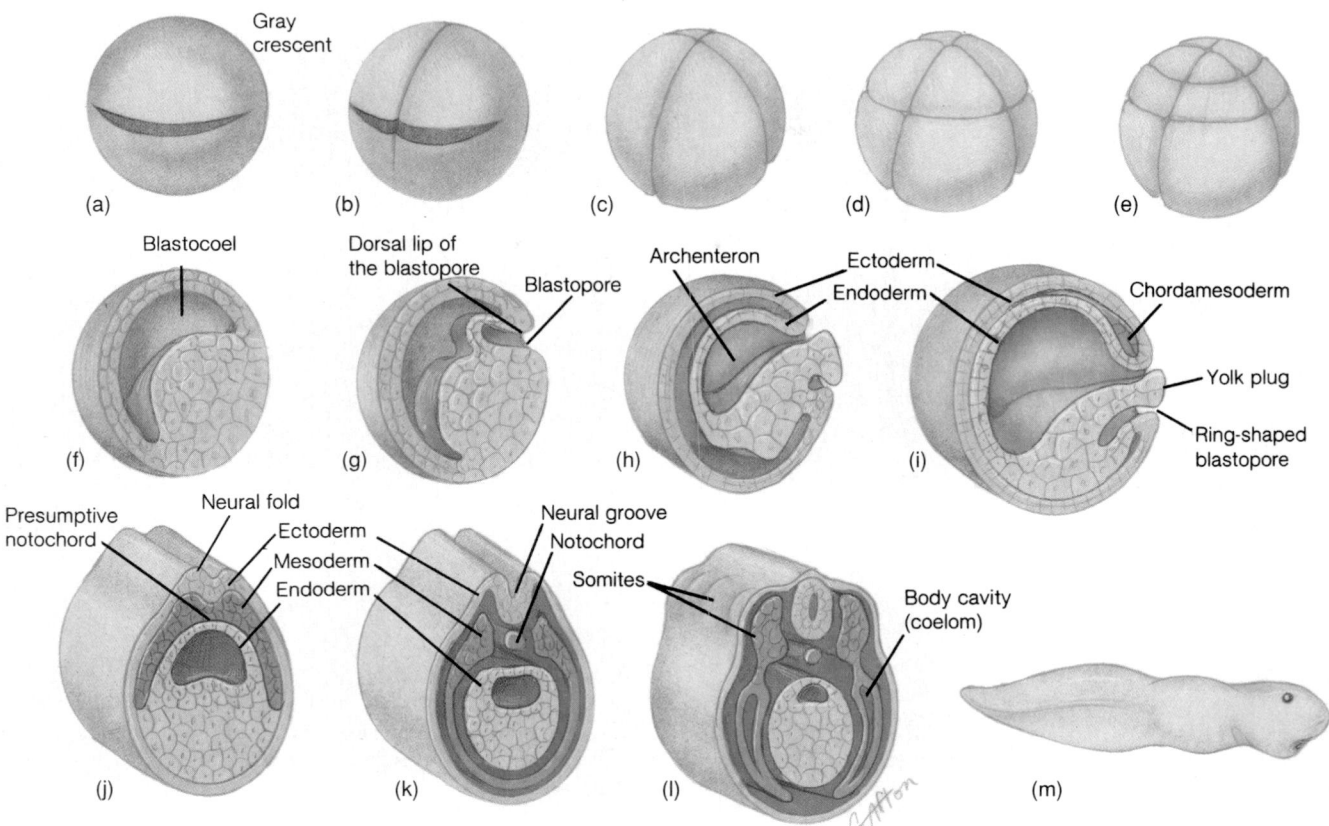

FIGURE 10.10

Stages in the Development of a Frog. (*a–c*) Early cleavages. The gray crescent is shown in (*a*). The first and second cleavages usually begin at the animal pole, and are at right angles to one another. The second cleavage begins before the first cleavage is completed. (*d*) The third cleavage is horizontal. Because of the dense, yolky cytoplasm at the vegetal pole, this third cleavage occurs closer to the animal pole, and results in unequal blastomeres. (*e*) The morula. (*f*) The blastula. Note the location of the blastocoel near the animal pole, and the multiple cell layers of the blastula. (*g–h*) Gastrulation. Involution begins as cells move into the interior of the embryo, forming a slitlike blastopore. The blastopore is extended to the sides, and toward the vegetal pole. Ectodermal cells spread into a thin layer over the surface of the embryo, gradually covering the vegetal end. The ends of the blastopore join, forming a yolk plug, and blastopore eventually closes. (*i*) Chordamesoderm begins the formation of the notochord, and spreads laterally. (*j–k*) The embryo lengthens during gastrulation, and when gastrulation is completed, nerve cord formation begins. The neural plate develops, its edges upfold, and the neural tube is formed. (*l*) The mesoderm proliferates, forming somites. Mesoderm along the sides of the embryo splits, forming the body cavity, or coelom. (*m*) The larval stage, or tadpole, gradually uses up the yolk stored in endodermal cells and begins to feed.

DEVELOPMENT IN TERRESTRIAL ENVIRONMENTS

Development of reptiles (class Reptilia), birds (class Aves), and mammals (class Mammalia) occurs on land rather than in the water. Development on land requires that the embryo be protected from desiccation, and in these animals, a series of extraembryonic membranes serve that purpose. The longer developmental periods of these animals reflect the fact that they lack independent larval stages. (Larval stages, such as those of amphibians, allow individuals to achieve increased complexity in spite of short embryonic periods.)

AVIAN EMBRYOLOGY

Chicken development can be used to model the development of birds and reptiles. ④ What is commonly referred to as the "egg" of a chicken is, in reality, the true egg, plus a variety of membranes that protect the egg. The yellow portion of the

chicken egg is the single cell produced in the chicken ovary. This egg is released into the oviduct, where fertilization may occur. Following fertilization, membranes and fluids are deposited around the egg (figure 10.11*a*). A vitelline membrane covers the surface of the true egg. The "white" consists of water, and a protein called albumen. This watery environment protects the egg from mechanical damage and drying. Albumen is a source of nutrients (in addition to the yolk of the egg), and is eventually consumed during development. Two denser strands of albumen (called chalazas) attach at the inside of the shell and at the egg, and keep the egg suspended in the center of the watery albumen. The shell is made of calcium carbonate impregnated with protein. Thousands of tiny pores (40 to 50 microns in diameter) in the shell permit exchange of gases between the embryo and the outside. On the inside of the shell are two shell membranes. An air pocket is formed between these membranes, at the rounded end of the shell. The air pocket enlarges during development, as air moves through

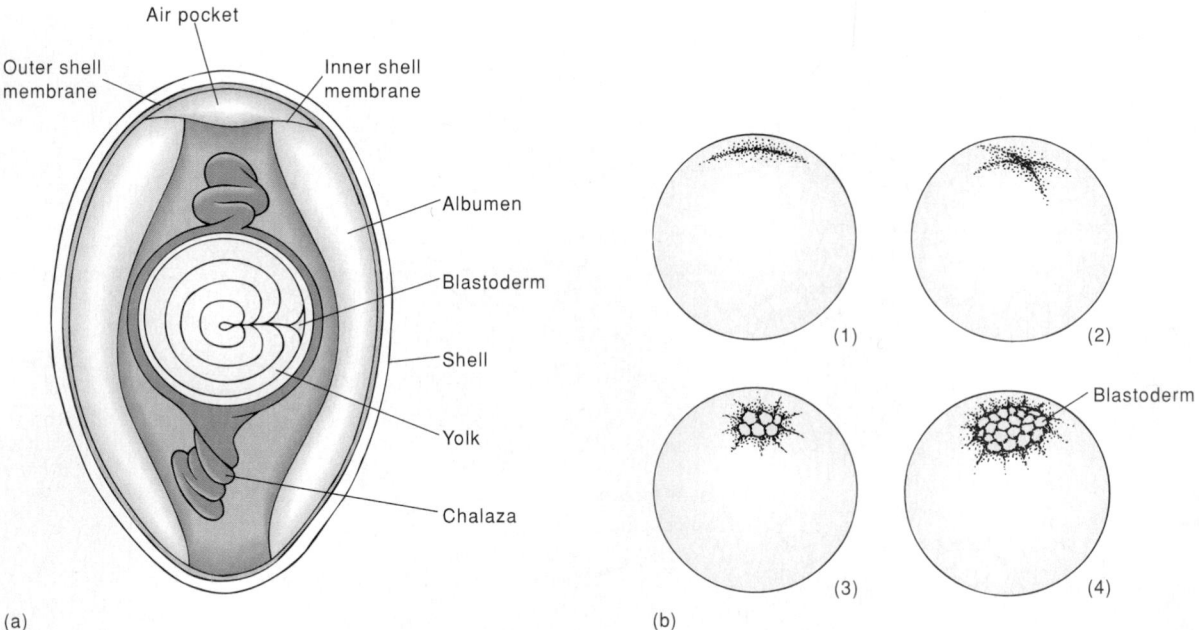

FIGURE 10.11

The Structure and Early Development of the Chicken Egg. (*a*) The egg and the egg membranes. Albumen is an accessory food source, and, along with egg membranes, protects the embryo and prevents the embryo from drying. (*b*) Initial cleavages result in the formation of a patch of cells at the animal pole of the egg, called the blastoderm. The numbers indicate a developmental sequence.

pores in the shell to replace water loss. As hatching approaches, the chick penetrates the air pocket with its beak, the lungs inflate, and the chick begins to breathe from the air sac, while still exchanging gases across vascular extraembryonic membranes.

Early Cleavages and Gastrulation

Cleavage of the chicken egg is meroblastic (figure 10.11*b*). A small disk of approximately 60,000 cells at the animal end of the egg develops and is called the **blastoderm.** The blastoderm is raised off the yolk, leaving a fluid-filled space analogous to the blastocoel of the amphibian blastula. The proliferation and movement of cells of the blastoderm result in a sorting of cells into two layers. The **epiblast** (Gr. *epi*, upon + *blast*, sprout) is the outer layer of cells, and the **hypoblast** (Gr. *hypo*, below) is the inner layer of cells (figure 10.12*a–c*). The movements of blastoderm cells are the beginning of gastrulation. The chicken egg is released from the reproductive tract of the female at about this time.

A medial, linear invagination, called the **primitive streak,** gradually extends anteriorly (figure 10.12*d*). A depression, called Henson's node, forms at the anterior margin of the primitive streak and marks the beginning of an inward migration of epiblast cells, comparable to involution of the amphibian gastrula. The primitive streak is, therefore, analogous to the dorsal lip of the blastopore. This migration occurs during a

dramatic posterior movement of Henson's node. Migrating cells form mesoderm and endoderm, and what is left of the epiblast on the surface of the embryo is the ectoderm. The three germ layers are now arranged on the surface of the yolk.

Following gastrulation, notochordal cells are separated from the overlying neural ectoderm, and the neural tube forms as described earlier for the amphibian embryo. In addition, mesoderm, which originally formed as solid blocks of cells, is organized into somites and splits to form the coelom.

Further development results in the embryo lifting off the yolk (figure 10.12*e*). This occurs when the margins of the embryo grow downward and meet below the embryo. A connection between the embryo and the yolk is retained and is called the yolk stalk. Blood vessels develop in the yolk stalk and carry nutrients from the yolk to the embryo.

The Development of Extraembryonic Membranes

Extraembryonic membranes of amniotes include the yolk sac, the amnion, the chorion, and the allantois (figure 10.13*a,b*). Reptiles and birds have a large quantity of yolk that becomes enclosed by a **yolk sac.** The yolk sac develops from a proliferation of the endoderm and mesoderm around the yolk. The yolk sac is highly vascular and distributes nutrients to the developing embryo.

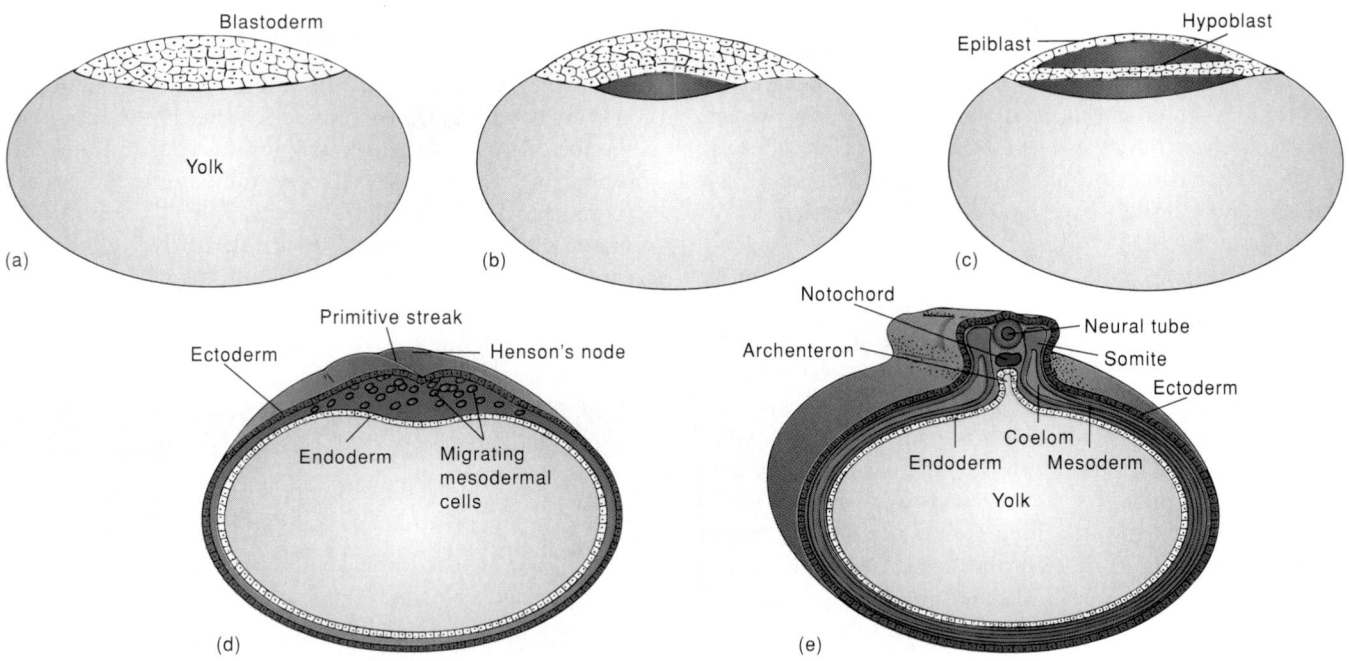

FIGURE 10.12

Gastrulation in the Chick Embryo. (*a–b*) Meroblastic cleavage results in the formation of the blastoderm. (*c*) Cells of the blastoderm rise off the yolk and rearrange into two layers—epiblast and hypoblast. (*d*) Gastrulation results from the migration of epiblast cells into a longitudinal groove called the primitive streak. These migrating cells form mesoderm and endoderm, and cells remaining in the epiblast form ectoderm. (*e*) The embryo lifts off the yolk when the margins of the embryo grow downward and meet below the embryo.

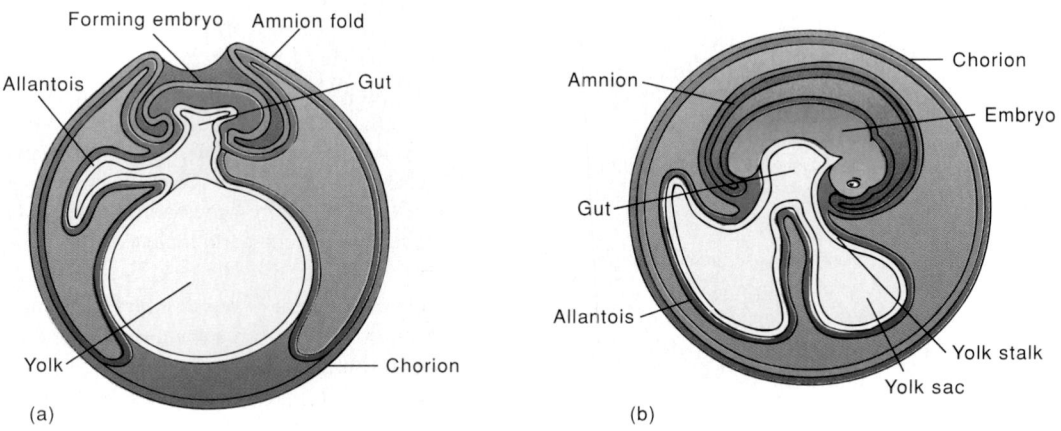

FIGURE 10.13

The Formation of Extraembryonic Membranes. (*a*) The embryo lifts off the yolk as hypoblast proliferates around the yolk to form the yolk sac. The amnion begins forming before the allantois. (*b*) Amnion folds fuse above the embryo enclosing the embryo in the amnion, and forming a continuous chorion on the inside of the shell. The allantois increases in size as uric acid accumulates. The yolk is being used up.

Following the neural tube stage, the ectoderm and mesoderm on both sides of the embryo lift off the yolk and grow dorsally over the embryo. As these membranes meet dorsally, they fuse and form an inner **amnion** and an outer **chorion.** The amnion encloses the embryo in a fluid-filled sac. This amniotic cavity provides protection against shock and drying. The chorion is nearer the shell, becomes highly vascular, and aids in gas exchange.

Development in a closed environment presents a problem of waste disposal. Accumulation of nitrogenous waste products in the embryo, or unconfined in the shell, would be lethal for the embryo. The immediate breakdown product of proteins is highly toxic ammonia. This ammonia is converted to a less toxic form, uric acid, which is excreted and stored in the **allantois,** a ventral outgrowth of the gut tract. Uric acid is a semisolid, and thus little water is wasted. The allantois gradually enlarges during development to occupy the region between the amnion and the chorion. In addition, the allantois becomes highly vascular and functions with the chorion in gas exchange.

THE FATE OF MESODERM

Following gastrulation in birds, reptiles, and mammals, all three primary germ layers have formed. Of the three layers, the fate of the mesoderm is the most complex. Mesoderm forms all of the supportive tissues of vertebrates, including connective tissues (bone, cartilage, and blood) and muscle. These supportive tissues are frequently associated with derivatives of other primary germ layers. For example, the inner lining of the gut is endodermal, but mesodermally derived structures, such as smooth muscle, blood, and blood vessels, make up the bulk of that system.

Stop and Ask Yourself

12. How would you define involution, epiboly, yolk plug, and chordamesoderm?
13. What are the initial phases of mesoderm formation in amphibians?
14. How does a chicken egg provide a suitable environment for terrestrial development?

SUMMARY

1. Embryology is the study of the development of an animal from the fertilized egg to the point that all major organ systems are formed. Descriptive embryology involves the documentation of these changes. Experimental embryology is the study of the cellular controls of development.

2. One of the goals of embryology is the description of the formation and fates of the primary germ layers: ectoderm, endoderm, and mesoderm.

3. Fertilization is the process by which gametes are brought together, forming a diploid zygote. A variety of mechanisms have evolved to ensure that fertilization takes place.

4. Eggs are activated by contact with sperm. Changes in the egg cytoplasm ensure that a single sperm penetrates the egg, male and female pronuclei are positioned for mitosis, and the cell is metabolically ready for mitosis.

5. Cleavage patterns are influenced by the quantity and distribution of yolk. Eggs that contain little yolk divide into blastomeres that are equal in size. Eggs that contain larger amounts of yolk either do not divide completely, or divide into blastomeres that are unequal in size.

6. Echinoderm development is representative of the development of a zygote that contains very little yolk. Cleavages are holoblastic and equal. Gastrulation occurs by invagination of the blastula. Mesoderm and the coelom form from simple outpockets of the archenteron.

7. Frog eggs have a large amount of unequally distributed yolk. As a result, their cleavage is holoblastic and unequal. The blastocoel forms near the animal pole, and gastrulation occurs by involution. Chordamesoderm forms between ectoderm and endoderm, and develops into somites, coelomic linings, and the notochord. Changes in the ectoderm include the formation of the tubular nerve cord.

8. The development of reptiles, birds, and mammals shows adaptations for terrestrialism, including the formation of extraembryonic membranes.

9. The initial cleavages of a chicken egg result in the formation of a disk of cytoplasm, the blastoderm, at the animal end of the embryo. Gastrulation involves the movement of cells toward a medial longitudinal groove, called the primitive streak.

SELECTED KEY TERMS

allantois (p. 146)   embryology (p. 134)
amnion (p. 146)   endoderm (p. 138)
blastula (p. 138)   gastrulation (p. 138)
chorion (p. 146)   mesoderm (p. 138)
differentiation (p. 138) morula (p. 138)
ectoderm (p. 138)

CRITICAL THINKING QUESTIONS

1. In what sense is fertilization a random event? Do you think random fertilization is adaptive for a species? Explain your answer.

2. What mechanisms prevent fertilization of an egg by more than one sperm? Why is this important?

3. Practical applications often follow quickly on the heels of basic research. How could basic research into the process of fertilization be applied to problems of contraception and infertility?

4. Evaluate the following statement: "The primary differences between early cleavages of most animal embryos are the result of the quantity and distribution of yolk."

5. Many terrestrial vertebrates have eggs that are protected by a shell and have large quantities of yolk. Why do most mammalian eggs lack these features?

SUGGESTED READINGS

BOOKS

Balinsky, B. 1982. *An Introduction to Embryology*. 6th ed. Philadelphia: W. B. Saunders Co.

Cohen, J. 1977. *Reproduction*. London: Butterworths.

Cummings, M. R. 1988. *Human Heredity*. Minnesota: West Publishing Co.

Dunn, L. C. 1965. *A Short History of Genetics*. New York: McGraw-Hill.

Ehrlich, P. R., and Feldman, S. S. 1977. *The Race Bomb: Skin Color, Prejudice, and Intelligence*. New York: Quandrangle.

Emery, A. E. H. 1984. *An Introduction to Recombinant DNA*. New York: John Wiley & Sons.

Farnsworth, M. W. 1988. *Genetics*. 2d ed. New York: Harper & Row Publishers.

Gilbert, S. 1988. *Developmental Biology*. 2d ed. Sunderland, Mass.: Sinauer Associates, Inc.

Giudice, G. 1986. *The Sea Urchin Embryo: A Developmental Biological System*. New York: Springer-Verlag.

Hopper, A. F., and Hart, N. H. 1985. *Foundations of Animal Development*. 2d ed. Boston: Oxford University Press.

Iltis, H. 1966. *Life of Mendel*. New York: Haffner.

John, P. C. L. (ed). 1985. *The Cell Cycle*. New York: Cambridge University Press.

Karp, B., and Berrill, N. J. 1981. *Development*. 2d ed. New York: McGraw-Hill.

Keller, E. F. 1983. *A Feeling for the Organism: The Life and Work of Barbara McClintock*. San Francisco: W. H. Freeman.

Klug, W. S., and Cummings, M. R. 1994. *Concepts of Genetics*. 4th ed. Columbus, Ohio: Charles E. Merrill Publishing Co.

Krimsky, S. 1982. *The Social History of the Recombinant DNA Controversy*. Cambridge, Massachusetts: MIT Press.

Levitan, M. 1988. *Textbook of Human Genetics*. 3d ed. New York: Oxford University Press.

Lewin, B. 1994. *Genes*. 5th ed. New York: John Wiley & Sons.

Margulis, L., and Sagan, D. 1986. *Origins of Sex: Three Billion Years of Genetic Recombination*. New Haven, Conn.: Yale University Press.

Mitchinson, J. 1972. *Biology of the Cell Cycle*. New York: Cambridge University Press.

Prescott, D. M. 1976. *Reproduction of Eukaryotic Cells*. New York: Academic Press.

Rothwell, N. 1988. *Understanding Genetics*. New York: Oxford University Press.

Russell, P. J. 1986. *Genetics*. Boston: Little, Brown & Co.

Saunders, J. W., Jr. 1982. *Developmental Biology*. New York: Macmillan.

Slack, J. M. W. 1983. *From Egg to Embryo: Determinative Events in Early Development*. Cambridge: Cambridge University Press.

Stern, C., and Sherwood, E. R. (eds.). 1966. *The Origin of Genetics, A Mendel Source Book*. San Francisco: W. H. Freeman. (Contains translations of Mendel's classic papers as well as other papers by early geneticists.)

Strickberger, M. W. 1985. *Genetics*. 3d ed. New York: Macmillan Publishing Co.

Suzuki, D. T., Griffiths, A. J. F., Miller, J. H., and Lewontin, R. C. 4th ed. 1989. *An Introduction to Genetic Analysis*. San Francisco: W. H. Freeman.

Tamarin, R. H. 1991. *Principles of Genetics*. 3d ed. Dubuque: Wm. C. Brown Publishers.

Trinkaus, J. P. 1984. *Cells into Organs.* 2d ed. Englewood Cliffs, N.J.: Prentice-Hall.

Weaver, R. F., and Hedrick, P. W. 1992. *Genetics.* 2d ed. Dubuque: Wm. C. Brown Publishers.

Zimmerman, A. M., and Forer, A. 1981. *Mitosis/Cytokinesis.* New York: Academic Press.

ARTICLES

Allison, A. Sickle cells and evolution. *Scientific American* August, 1956.

Beams, S. W., and Kessel, R. G. 1976. Cytokinesis: A comparative study of cytoplasm division in animal cells. *American Scientist* 64:279–290.

Beardsley, T. Sex switch: The gene determining maleness in human embryos is found. *Scientific American* March, 1988.

Belmont, L., and Marolla, F. A. 1973. Birth order, family size, and intelligence. *Science* 182:1096–1101.

Benditt, J. Genetic skeleton. *Scientific American* July, 1988.

Bouchard, T. J., Jr., and McGue, M. 1981. Familial studies of intelligence: A review. *Science* 212:1055–1059.

Cech, T. R. RNA as an enzyme. *Scientific American* November, 1986.

Chandley, A. C. 1988. Meiosis in man. *Trends in Genetics* 4:79–83.

Cooke, J. 1988. The early embryo and the formation of body pattern. *American Scientist* 76:3535–3542.

De Duve, C. 1988. The second genetic code. *Nature* 333: 117–118.

D'Eustachio, P., and Ruddle, R. H. 1983. Somatic cell genetics and gene families. *Science* 220:919.

Diamond, J. Blood, genes, and malaria. *Natural History* February, 1989.

Donelson, D. E., and Turner, M. J. How the trypanosome changes its coat. *Scientific American* February, 1985.

Doolittle, R. F. Proteins. *Scientific American* October, 1985.

Edelman, G. M. Topobiology. *Scientific American* May, 1989.

Epel, D. 1980. Fertilization. *Endeavour* 4:26.

———. The program of fertilization. *Scientific American* November, 1977.

Friedmann, T. Progress toward human gene therapy. *Scientific American* June, 1989.

Fuchs, F. Genetic amniocentesis. *Scientific American* June, 1980.

Gerhart, J., Black, S., Scharf, S., Gimlich, R., Vincent, J. P., Danilchik, M., Rowning, B., and Roberts, J. 1986. Amphibian early development. *BioScience* 36:541–549.

Gould, M., and Stephano, J. L. 1987. Electrical responses of eggs to acrosomal protein similar to those induced by sperm. *Science* 235:1654–1657.

Gould, S. J. Sex and size. *Natural History* August, 1983.

———. Down's syndrome. *Natural History* September, 1980.

Grunstein, M. Histones as regulators of genes. *Scientific American* October, 1992.

Inoue, S. 1981. Cell division and the mitotic spindle. *Journal of Cell Biology* 91:132s–137s.

John, B. 1976. Myths and mechanisms of meiosis. *Chromosoma* 54: 295–325.

Laskey, R. A. 1988. A role for the nuclear envelope in controlling DNA replication within the cell cycle. *Nature* 332:546–548.

Macalpine, I., and Hunter, R. Porphyria and King George III. *Scientific American* July, 1969.

Marx, J. L. 1985. Putting the human genome on the map. *Science* 229:150.

———. 1989. Detecting mutations in human genes. *Science* 243:737–738.

———. September, 1991. A "mitey" theory for gene jumping. *Science* 253:1092.

———. September, 1991. Getting a jump on gene transfer in *Drosophila. Science* 253:1093.

Mazia, D. The cell cycle. *Scientific American* January, 1974.

McIntosh, J. R., and McDonald, K. L. The mitotic spindle. *Scientific American* October, 1989.

McKnight, S. L. Molecular zippers in gene regulation. *Scientific American* April, 1991.

McKusick, V. A. The mapping of human chromosomes. *Scientific American* April, 1981.

Metz, C. 1978. Sperm and egg receptors involved in fertilization. *Current Topics in Developmental Biology* 12:107–119.

Murray, A. W., and Kirschner, M. W. What controls the cell cycle. *Scientific American* March, 1991.

Murray, A. W., and Szostak, J. W. Artificial chromosomes. *Scientific American* November, 1987.

Murray, J. How the leopard gets its spots. *Scientific American* March, 1988.

Pardee, A. B. 1978. Animal cell cycle. *Annual Review of Biochemistry* 47:715–750.

Patterson, D. The causes of Down syndrome. *Scientific American* August, 1987.

Ptashne, M. How gene activators work. *Scientific American* January, 1989.

Radman, M., and Wagner, R. The high fidelity of DNA duplication. *Scientific American* August, 1989.

Rahn, H., Ar, A., and Paganelli, V. How bird eggs breathe. *Scientific American* February, 1979.

Roberts, L. 1988. Chromosomes: The ends in view. *Science* 240:982–983.

———. 1988. The race for the cystic fibrosis gene. *Science* 240:141–144.

Silberner, J. Off on switch for cell division found. *Science News* August 24, 1985.

Sloboda, R. D. 1980. The role of microtubules in cell structure and cell division. *American Scientist* 68:290–298.

Special focus: Genetic engineering. 1984. *American Biology Teacher,* 46(8).

10.16

———. Genetic engineering. 1984. *American Biology Teacher,* 46(9).

Stahl, F. Genetic recombination. *Scientific American* February, 1987.

Steitz, J. A. "Snurps." *Scientific American* June, 1988.

Turnbull, A. 1988. Woman enough for the games? *New Scientist* 119:61–65.

Vaughan, C. 1988. Second thoughts on second genetic code. *Science News* 133:341.

Verma, I. M. Gene therapy. *Scientific American* November, 1990.

Wassaman, P. M. 1987. The biology and chemistry of fertilization. *Science* 235:553–560.

———. Fertilization in mammals. *Scientific American* December, 1988.

Weintraub, H. M. Antisense RNA and DNA. *Scientific American* January, 1990.

Weiss, R. 1989. Genetic testing possible before conception. *Science News* 136(21):326.

White, R., and Lalouel, J. Chromosome mapping with DNA markers. *Scientific American* February, 1988.

Winkler, M. 1988. Translational regulation in sea urchin eggs. *BioEssays* 8:157–161.

Yanieshevsky, R. M., and Stein, G. H. 1981. Regulation of the cell cycle in eukaryotic cells. *International Review of Cytology* 69:223–259.

Zeidler, J. P. 1988. Automated chromosome analysis. *Nature* 334:635.

part THREE

EVOLUTION

All organisms have an evolutionary history and a future that will be influenced by evolutionary forces. Evolution is a major unifying theme in biology because it helps us understand the life-shaping processes that all species experience.

Ground-breaking studies of evolution were carried out by Charles Darwin and Alfred Russel Wallace in the nineteenth century. Their historical work serves as an important introduction to evolutionary theory. The work of these and other pioneer evolutionary biologists is presented in chapter 11. Since these early studies, our knowledge of genetics, in particular the principles of population genetics, has greatly influenced evolutionary theory. These genetic ideas, along with the questions of direction and rate of change, are presented in chapter 12.

Even though Part Three ends with chapter 12, our coverage of evolution does not end there. In spite of organisms experiencing common evolutionary processes, evolution has resulted in a great diversity of animal life. An important goal of Part Five of this book is to present the diversity of animal life from an evolutionary perspective.

Land iguana, *Conolophus subcristate*.

EVOLUTION:
A HISTORICAL PERSPECTIVE

Concepts

1. Organic evolution is the change of a species over time.
2. Although the concept of evolution is very old, the modern explanation of how change occurs was formulated by Charles Darwin. Darwin began gathering his evidence of evolution during a worldwide mapping expedition on the HMS *Beagle* and spent the rest of his life formulating and defending his ideas.
3. Darwin's theory of evolution by natural selection, although modified from its original form, is still a highly regarded account of how evolution occurs.
4. Modern evolutionary theorists apply principles of genetics, ecology, and geographic and morphological studies when investigating evolutionary mechanisms.
5. "Adaptation" may refer to either a process of evolutionary change or to the result of a change. In the latter sense, an adaptation is a structure or a process that increases an animal's potential to survive and reproduce in specific environmental conditions.

Would You Like to Know:

1. whether the idea of evolutionary change originated with Charles Darwin? (*p. 154*)
2. what circumstances led Charles Darwin to become a naturalist on the HMS *Beagle*? (*p. 156*)
3. how Charles Darwin's experiences in South America convinced him that evolution occurs? (*p. 157*)
4. what prompted Charles Darwin to publish his work in 1859, 23 years after returning from his voyage on the HMS *Beagle*? (*p. 160*)
5. why geography is important for biologists? (*p. 161*)

These and other useful questions will be answered in this chapter.

Questions of earth's origin and life's origin have been on the minds of humans since prehistoric times, when accounts of creation were passed orally from generation to generation. For many people, these questions centered around concepts of purpose. Religious and philosophical writings help provide answers to questions such as: Why are we here? What is human nature really like? How do we deal with our mortality?

Many of us are also concerned with other, very different, questions of origin. How old is the planet earth? How long has life been on earth? How did life arise on earth? How did a certain animal species come into existence? Answers for these questions come from a different authority—that of scientific inquiry.

The purpose of this chapter is to present the history of the study of organic evolution, and to introduce the **theory of evolution by natural selection. Organic evolution** (L. *evolutus,* unroll), according to Charles Darwin, is "descent with modification." This statement simply means that species change over time. Evolution by itself does not imply any particular lineage or any particular mechanism, and virtually all scientists agree that the evidence for change in organisms over long time periods is overwhelming (*see chapter 1*). Further, most scientists agree that natural selection, the mechanism for evolution outlined by Charles Darwin, is one explanation of how evolution occurs. In spite of the scientific certainty of evolution and an acceptance of a general mechanism, much is still to be learned about the details of evolutionary processes. Scientists will be debating these details for years to come (box 11.1).

PRE-DARWINIAN THEORIES OF CHANGE

① The idea of evolution did not originate with Charles Darwin. Some of the earliest references to evolutionary change are from the ancient Greeks. The philosophers Empedocles (495–435 B.C.) and Aristotle (384–322 B.C.) described concepts of change in living organisms over time. Georges-Louis Buffon (1707–1788) spent many years studying comparative anatomy. His observations of structural variations in particular organs of related animals, and especially his observations of vestigial structures (*see chapter 1*), convinced him that change must have occurred during the history of life on earth. Erasmus Darwin (1731–1802), a physician and the grandfather of Charles Darwin, was intensely interested in questions of origin and change. He believed in the common ancestry of all organisms.

LAMARCK: AN EARLY PROPONENT OF EVOLUTION

Jean Baptiste Lamarck (1744–1829) was a distinguished French zoologist. His contributions to zoology include important studies of the classification of animals. Lamarck, however, is remembered more for a theory of how change occurs. He believed that species are not constant, and that existing species were derived from preexisting species.

Lamarck's rather elaborate explanation of how evolutionary change occurs involved a theory of inheritance that was widely accepted in the early 1800s called the **theory of inheritance of acquired characteristics.** Lamarck believed that organisms develop new organs or modify existing organs as environmental problems present themselves. In other words, organs change as the need arises. Lamarck illustrated this point with the often-quoted example of the giraffe. He contended that ancestral giraffes had short necks, much like those of any other mammal. Straining to reach higher branches during browsing resulted in their acquiring higher shoulders and longer necks. These modifications, produced in one generation, were passed on to the next generation. Lamarck went on to state that the use of any organ resulted in that organ becoming highly developed, and that disuse resulted in degeneration. Thus, the evolution of highly specialized structures, such as vertebrate eyes could be explained.

Lamarck published his theory in 1802 and defended it in the face of social and scientific criticism. Society in general was unaccepting of the ideas of evolutionary change, and evidence for evolution had not been developed thoroughly enough to convince most scientists that evolutionary change occurs. Thus, Lamarck was criticized in his day more for advocating ideas of evolutionary change than for the mechanism he proposed for that change. Today he is criticized for defending a mechanism of inheritance and evolutionary change that we now know lacks reasonable supporting evidence. For a change to be passed on to the next generation, it must be based on genetic changes in the germ cells. Changes in the giraffes' necks, as envisioned by Lamarck, could not be passed on because they did not originate as changes in the genetic material. Even though Lamarck's mechanism of change was incorrect, we should remember him for his steadfastness in promoting the idea of evolutionary change and his other accomplishments in zoology.

Stop and Ask Yourself

1. What is organic evolution?
2. What contributions to our concept of evolution were made by Buffon?
3. What is the theory of inheritance of acquired characteristics, and how did Lamarck use it to explain how evolution occurred?

DARWIN'S EARLY YEARS AND HIS JOURNEY

Charles Robert Darwin (1809–1882) was born on February 12, 1809. His father, like his grandfather, was a physician. During Charles Darwin's youth in Shrewsbury, England, his interests centered around dogs, collecting, and hunting birds—all popular pastimes in wealthy families of nineteenth century England.

BOX 11.1	THE ORIGIN OF LIFE ON EARTH—LIFE FROM NONLIFE

Geologists estimate from radioisotope dating that the earth is approximately 4.6 billion years old. The oldest fossils are of cyanobacteria that come from 3.5-billion-year-old rocks (stromatolites) from Australia and South Africa. Thus, it took no more than 1 to 1.5 billion years for life to originate.

In trying to explain how life may have arisen, scientists first needed to know the conditions that existed on the earth after its formation. In 1929, J. B. S. Haldane described the atmosphere of primordial earth as a reducing atmosphere (with little free oxygen present) containing primarily hydrogen, water, ammonia, and methane. In 1953, Stanley Miller and Harold Urey constructed a reaction vessel in which they duplicated the atmosphere described by Haldane. They heated the mixture to 80° C and provided the atmosphere with an electrical spark to simulate lightning. Over the course of a week, they removed samples from their system and found a variety of common amino acids and other organic acids.

The above scenario for the origin of the first organic compounds, although once widely accepted, is under increasing scrutiny. Recent evidence suggests that carbon dioxide and nitrogen gas, not methane and ammonia, were the major components of the earth's primitive atmosphere. These conditions are much less favorable for the formation of organic compounds using the Miller/Urey apparatus.

Scientists have begun to look for new explanations for the origin of the first organic chemicals and at older explanations, which are being revived. One of these is that life's beginnings may have occurred deep in the oceans, in underwater hot springs called hydrothermal vents. These vents could have supplied the energy and raw materials for the origin and survival of early life-forms. This vent hypothesis is supported by the presence of a group of bacteria, called archaebacteria, that tolerate temperatures up to 120° C and seem to have undergone less evolutionary change than any other living species.

Another explanation for the origin of the earth's first organic molecules is that they came from outer space. Astronomers are detecting an increasing diversity of organic compounds (such as amino acids and other hydrocarbons) in meteorites that have collided with the earth. Investigations of the most recent pass-by of Halley's comet revealed that comets may be relatively rich in organic compounds. Even though many scientists think it is possible that the first organic compounds could have come from space, no

microbial life-forms have been detected in space, and conditions in outer space are incompatible with life as we know it.

A second step in the origin of life must have been the hooking together of early organic molecules into the polymers of living organisms: polypeptides, polynucleotides, and carbohydrates. Organic molecules may have become isolated in tidepools or freshwater ponds, and as water was lost through evaporation, condensation reactions could have occurred. Alternatively, reacting molecules may have been concentrated by adsorption on the surfaces of clay or iron pyrite particles, where polymerization could occur.

The final steps in the origin of life are the subject of endless speculations. In some way, organic molecules were surrounded by a membranelike structure, self-replication occurred, and DNA became established as the genetic material. A "chicken-or-the-egg" paradox emerges if one thinks of DNA as the first genetic material. DNA codes for proteins, yet proteins are required for DNA replication, transcription, and translation. A possible way around this paradox was suggested by Thomas R. Cech and Sidney Altman in the early 1980s. They discovered a certain type of RNA, which acts like an enzyme that cuts and splices itself into a functional molecule. The first organisms could have been vesicles of self-replicating RNA molecules. Other scientists think that proteins may have served as the first genetic material, and that DNA was established as the code-carrying molecule secondarily. No self-replicating proteins, however, have been found.

Early life would have been limited by the nutrients produced in the primordial environment. If life were to continue, another source of nutrients was needed. Photosynthesis, which is the production of organic molecules using solar energy and inorganic compounds, probably freed living organisms from a dwindling supply of nutrients. The first photosynthetic organisms probably used hydrogen sulfide as a source of hydrogen for reducing carbon dioxide to sugars. Later, water served this same purpose and oxygen liberated by photosynthetic reactions began to accumulate in the atmosphere. Earth and its atmosphere slowly began to change. Ozone in the upper atmosphere began to filter ultraviolet radiation from the sun, the reducing atmosphere slowly became an oxidizing atmosphere, and at least some living organisms began to utilize oxygen. About 420 million years ago enough protective ozone had built up to make life on land possible. Ironically, the change from a reducing atmosphere to an oxidizing atmosphere also meant that life could no longer arise abiotically.

These activities captivated him far more than the traditional education he received at boarding school. In 1825, he entered medical school in Edinburgh, Scotland. For two years, he enjoyed the company of the school's well-established scientists. Darwin, however, was not interested in a career in medicine because he could not bear the sight of pain. This problem prompted his father to suggest that he train for the clergy in the

Church of England. With this in mind, Charles enrolled at Cambridge University in 1828 and graduated with honors in 1831. This training, like the medical training he received, was disappointing for Darwin. Again, his most memorable experiences were those with Cambridge scientists. During his stay at Cambridge, Darwin developed a keen interest in collecting beetles and made valuable contributions to beetle taxonomy.

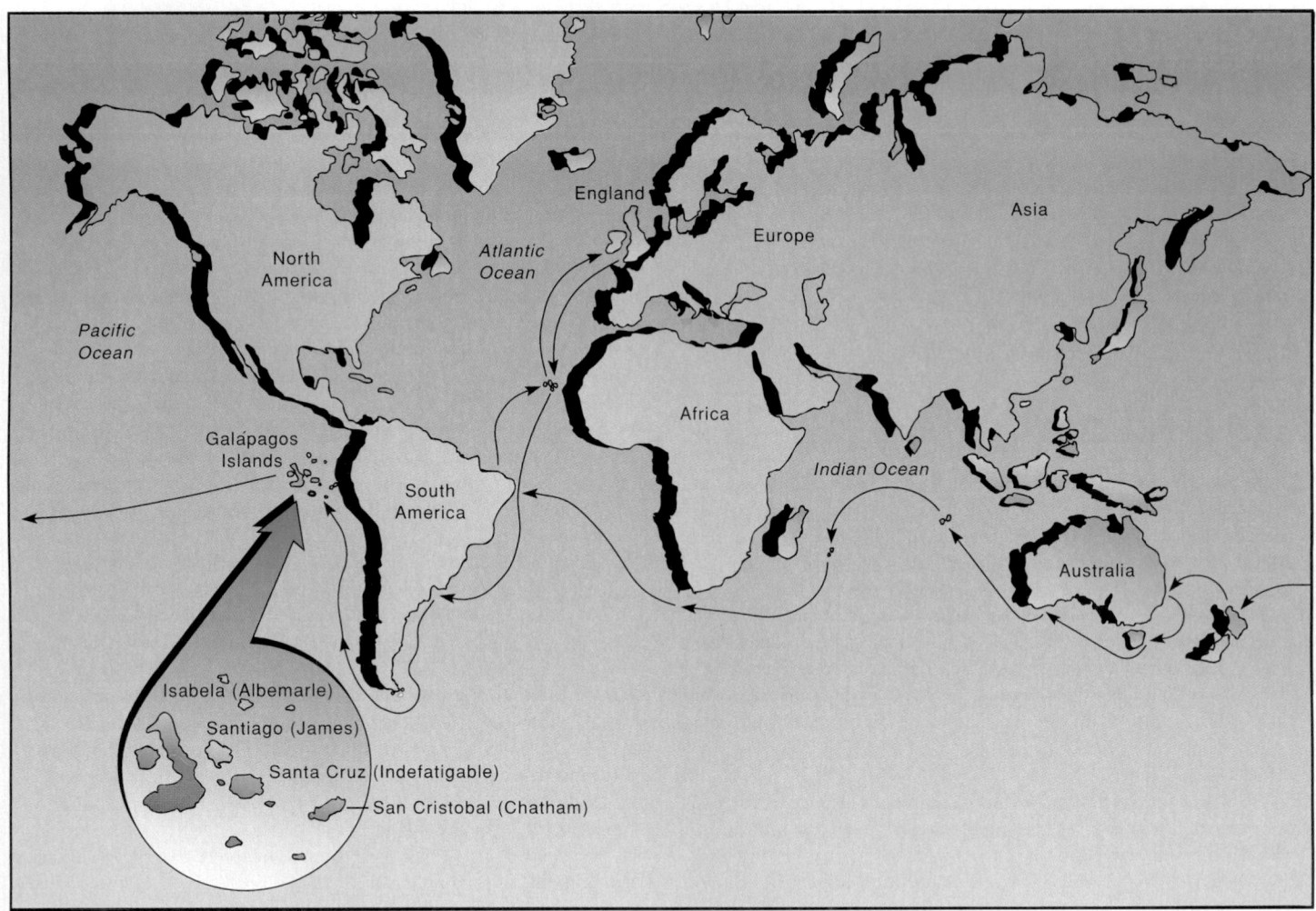

Figure 11.1

The Voyage of the *Beagle*. Charles Darwin served as a naturalist on a mapping expedition that lasted 5 years. Darwin's observations throughout those 5 years, especially those on the Galápagos Islands, served as the basis for the theory of evolution by natural selection.

Voyage of the HMS Beagle

One of his Cambridge mentors, a botanist by the name of John S. Henslow, nominated Darwin to serve as a naturalist on a mapping expedition that was to travel around the world. He was commissioned as a naturalist on the HMS *Beagle*, which set sail on December 27, 1831 on a voyage that lasted 5 years (figure 11.1). Darwin helped with routine seafaring tasks and made numerous collections, which he sent to Cambridge. The voyage gave him ample opportunity to explore tropical rain forests, fossil beds, the volcanic peaks of South America, and the coral atolls of the South Pacific. Most importantly, Darwin spent 5 weeks on the **Galápagos Islands,** a group of volcanic islands that lie 600 miles off the coast of Ecuador. Some of his most revolutionary ideas came from his observations of plant and animal life on these islands. At the end of the voyage, Darwin was just 27 years old. He spent the rest of

his life examining specimens, rereading notes, making new observations, and preparing numerous publications. His most important publication, *On the Origin of Species by Means of Natural Selection*, revolutionized biology.

Early Development of Darwin's Ideas of Evolution

The development of Darwin's theory of evolution by natural selection was a long, painstaking process. Darwin had to become convinced that change occurs over time. Before leaving on his voyage, Darwin accepted the prevailing opinion that the earth and its inhabitants had been created 6,000 years ago and had not changed since. Because his observations during his voyage suggested that change does occur, he realized that 6,000 years could not account for the diversity of modern species if they arose through gradual change. Once ideas of change were established in Darwin's thinking, it took about 20 years of study to conceive, and thoroughly document, the mechanism by which change occurs. Darwin died without knowing the genetic principles that support his theory.

Geology

Darwin began his voyage by reading Charles Lyell's (1779–1875) *Principles of Geology*. In this book, Lyell developed the ideas of another geologist, James Hutton, into the theory of **uniformitarianism.** His theory was based on the idea that the earth is shaped today by the forces of wind, rain, rivers, volcanoes, and geological uplift—just as it has been in the past. Lyell and Hutton contended that it was these forces, not catastrophic events, that shaped the face of the earth over hundreds of millions of years. This book planted two important ideas in Darwin's mind: (1) the earth could be much older than 6,000 years and (2) if the face of the earth changed gradually over long periods of time, could not living forms also change during that time?

Fossil Evidence

Once the HMS *Beagle* reached South America, Darwin spent time digging in the dry riverbeds of the pampas (grassy plains) of Argentina. He found the fossil remains of an extinct hippopotamuslike animal, now called *Toxodon*, and fossils of a horselike animal, *Thoantherium*. Both of these fossils were from animals that were clearly different from any other animal living in the region. Modern horses were in South America, of course, but they had been brought to the Americas by Spanish explorers in the 1500s. The fossils suggested that horses had been present and had become extinct long before the 1500s. Darwin also found fossils of giant armadillos and giant sloths. Except for their large size, these fossils were very similar to forms Darwin found living in the region.

Fossils were not new to Darwin. They were popularly believed to be the remains of animals that perished in catastrophic events, such as Noah's flood. ③ In South America, however, Darwin understood them to be evidence that the species composition of the earth had changed. Some species became extinct without leaving any descendants. Others became extinct, but not before giving rise to new species.

Galápagos Islands

On its trip up the western shore of South America, the HMS *Beagle* stopped at the Galápagos Islands, which are named after the very large tortoises that inhabit them (Sp. *galápago*, tortoise). The tortoises weigh up to 250 kg, have shells up to 1.8 m in diameter, and live for 200 to 250 years. It was pointed out to Darwin by the islands' governor that the shape

(a)

(b)

Figure 11.2

Galápagos Tortoises. (*a*) Shorter-necked subspecies of *Geochelone elephantopus* live in moister regions and feed on low-growing vegetation. (*b*) Longer-necked subspecies live in drier regions and feed on high-growing vegetation.

of the tortoise shells from different parts of Albemarle Island differed. Darwin noticed other differences as well. Tortoises from the drier regions had longer necks than tortoises from wetter habitats (figure 11.2). In spite of their differences, the tortoises were quite similar to each other and to the tortoises on the mainland of South America.

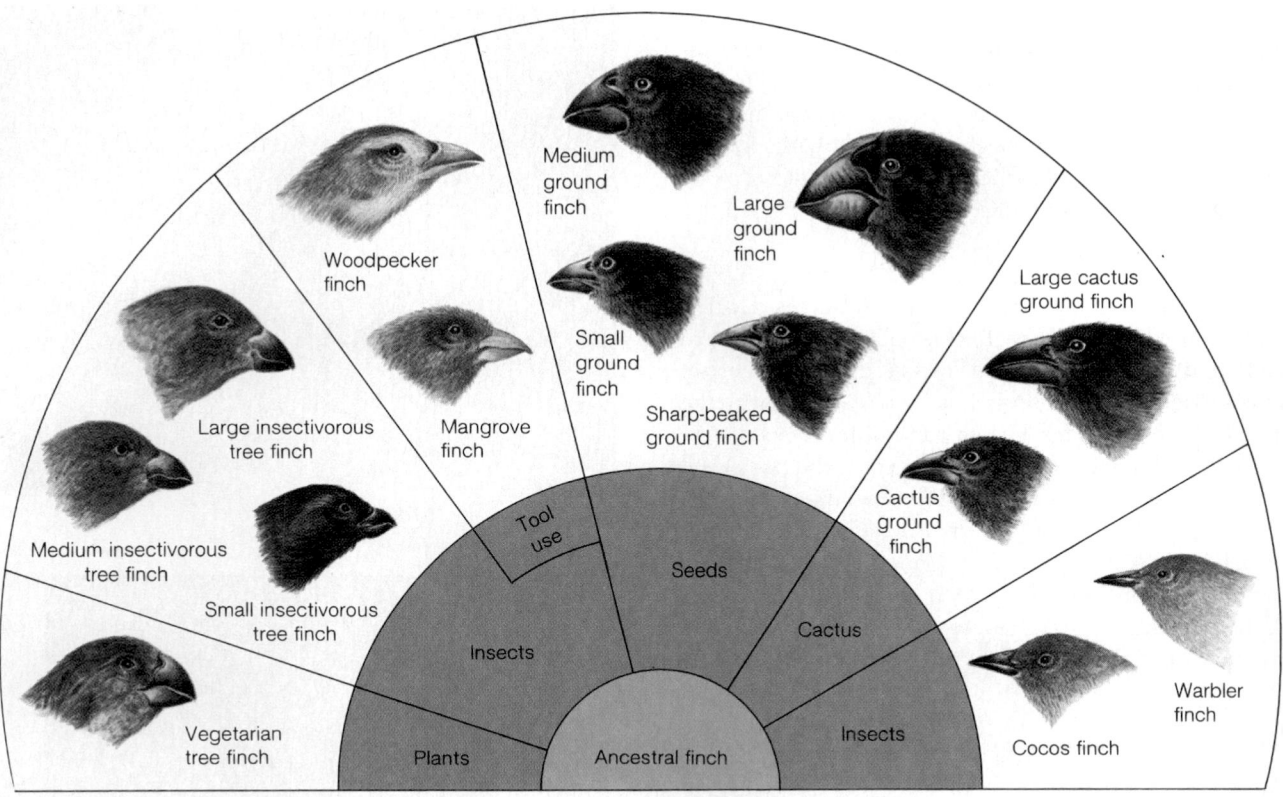

Figure 11.3

Adaptive Radiation of the Galápagos Finches. Ancestral finches from the South American mainland colonized the Galápagos Islands. Open habitats and few predators promoted the radiation of finches into most of the roles normally filled by birds.

How could these overall similarities be explained? Darwin reasoned that the island forms were derived from a few ancestral animals that managed to travel from the mainland, across 600 miles of ocean. (Because the Galápagos Islands are volcanic islands and arose out of the seabed, there was never any land connection with the mainland. One modern hypothesis is that tortoises floated from the mainland on mats of vegetation that regularly break free from coastal riverbanks during storms.) Without predators on the islands, tortoises gradually increased in number.

Darwin also explained some of the differences that he saw. In dryer regions, where vegetation was sparse, tortoises with longer necks would be favored because they could reach higher to get food. In moister regions, tortoises with longer necks would not necessarily be favored and the shorter-necked tortoises could survive.

Darwin made similar observations of a group of dark, sparrowlike birds. Although he never studied them in detail, Darwin noticed that the Galápagos finches bore similarities suggestive of common ancestry. Scientists now think that Galápagos finches also descended from an ancestral species that originally inhabited the mainland of South America. The chance arrival of a few finches, in either single or multiple colonization events, probably set up the first bird populations on the islands. Early finches encountered many different habitats,

all empty of other birds and predators. Ancestral finches, probably seed eaters, multiplied rapidly and filled the seed-bearing habitats most attractive to them. Fourteen species of finches arose from this ancestral group, including one species found on small Cocos Island northeast of the Galápagos Islands. Each species is adapted to a specific habitat on the islands. The most obvious difference between these finches relates to dietary adaptations and is reflected in the size and shape of their bills (figure 11.3).

Darwin's experiences in South America and the Galápagos Islands convinced him that animals change over time and that, in the course of the history of life on earth, many kinds of animals have become extinct. Although he would not document his hypothesis for many years, these experiences helped him formulate ideas of how evolutionary change occurs.

THE THEORY OF EVOLUTION BY NATURAL SELECTION

On his return to England in 1836 and for the next 17 years, Darwin worked diligently on the notes and specimens he had collected and made new observations. He was particularly interested in the obvious success of breeders in developing desired variations in plant and animal stocks (figure 11.4). He wondered if this artificial selection of traits could have a parallel in the natural world.

Initially, Darwin was unable to find a natural process similar to artificial selection. However, in 1838, he read an essay by Thomas Malthus (1766–1834) entitled *Essay on the Principle of Population*. Malthus believed that the human population has the potential to increase geometrically. However, because resources cannot keep pace with the increased demands of a burgeoning population, the influences of population-restraining factors, such as poverty, wars, plagues, and famine, begin to be felt. It occurred to Darwin that a similar struggle to survive occurs in nature. This struggle, when viewed over generations, could serve as a means of **natural selection.** Traits that were detrimental for an animal would be eliminated by the failure of the animal containing them to reproduce.

NATURAL SELECTION

By 1844 Darwin had formulated, but not yet published, his ideas on natural selection. The essence of his theory is as follows:

1. All organisms have a far greater reproductive potential than is ever realized. For example, a female oyster releases about 100,000 eggs with each spawning, a female sea star releases about 1 million eggs each season, and a female robin may lay four fertile eggs each season. What if all of these eggs were fertilized and developed to reproductive adults by the following year? A half million female sea stars (½ of the million eggs would produce females and ½ would produce males), each producing another million eggs, repeated over just a few generations would soon fill up the oceans! Even the adult female robins, each producing four more robins, would result in unimaginable resource problems in just a few years.
2. Inherited variations arise by mutation. Seldom are any two individuals exactly alike. Some of these genetic variations may confer an advantage to the individual possessing them. In other instances, variations may be harmful for an individual. In still other instances, particular variations may be neither helpful nor harmful. (These are said to be neutral.) These variations can be passed on to offspring.
3. Because resources are limited, there is a constant struggle for existence. Many more offspring are produced than resources can support; therefore, many individuals will die. Darwin reasoned that the individuals that die will be those with the traits (variations) that make survival and successful reproduction less likely. Other traits that promote successful reproduction are said to be adaptive.
4. Adaptive traits will be perpetuated in subsequent generations. Because organisms with maladaptive traits are less likely to reproduce, the maladaptive traits will become less frequent in a population, and eventually will tend to be eliminated.

(a)

(b)

FIGURE 11.4

Artificial Selection. The artificial selection of domestic fowl has resulted in the diverse varieties that we see today. Breeders perpetuated the variations they desired by allowing only certain offspring to breed. (*a*) Bearded white Polish fowl. (*b*) Jungle fowl.

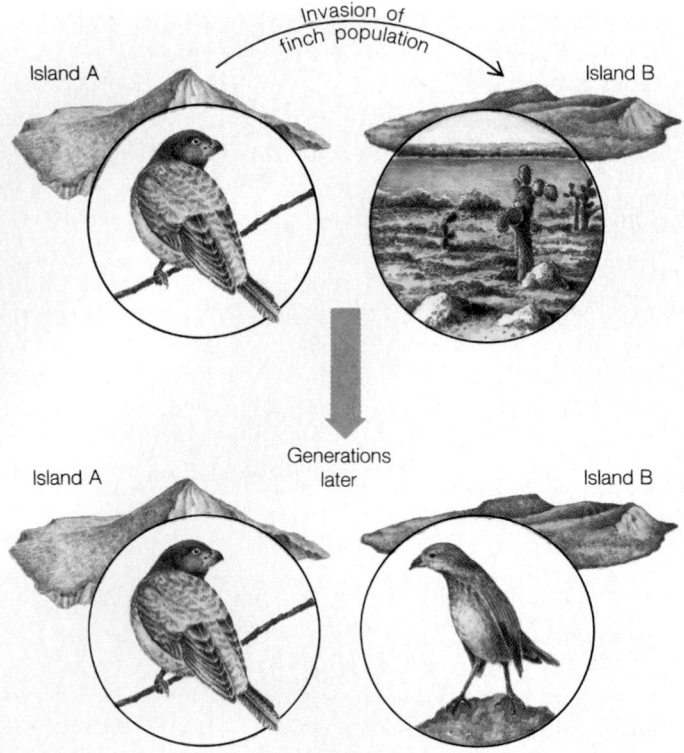

Invasion of finch population

Island A   Island B

Generations later

Island A   Island B

Figure 11.5

Natural Selection in Galápagos Finches. Natural selection of finches on the Galápagos Islands resulted in changes in bill shape. In this illustration, tree-feeding birds on island A invaded island B. The relatively treeless habitats of island B selected against birds most adapted to living in trees, and individuals that could exploit seeds on the ground in low-growing vegetation were more likely to survive and reproduce. Subsequent generations of finches on island B should show ground-feeding bill characteristics.

With these ideas, Darwin formulated a theory that explained how the tortoises and finches of the Galápagos Islands changed over time (figure 11.5). In addition, Darwin's theory explained how some animals, such as the ancient South American horses, could become extinct. What if a new environment is presented to a group of animals that are ill-adapted to that environment? Climatic changes, food shortages, and other environmental stressors could lead to extinction.

Adaptation

Adaptation occurs when a change in a phenotype increases an animal's chance of successful reproduction. It is likely to be expressed when an organism encounters a new environment, and may result in the evolution of multiple new groups if an environment can be exploited in different ways. No terms in evolution have been laden with more confusion than "adaptation"

and "fitness or adaptedness." Adaptation is sometimes used to refer to a process of change in evolution. That use of the term is probably less confusing than when "adaptation" is used to describe the result of the process of change. For our purposes, adaptations are defined as characteristics that increase an organism's, or a species', potential to successfully reproduce in a specified environment. In a similar fashion, adaptedness or fitness is a measure of the capacity for successful reproduction in a given environment.

There has been a tendency to view every characteristic as an adaptation to some kind of environmental situation. The view has been that if a structure is now performing a specific function, it must have arisen for that purpose, and is, therefore, an adaptation. An extreme extension of this incorrect view is that evolutionary adaptations lead to perfection.

Alfred Russel Wallace

Alfred Russel Wallace (1823–1913) was an explorer of the Amazon Valley, and led a zoological expedition to the Malay Archipelago, which is an area of great biogeographical importance. Wallace, like Darwin, was impressed with evolutionary change and had read the writings of Thomas Malthus on human populations. In the midst of a bout with malarial fever (*see box 17.2*), he synthesized a theory of evolution similar to Darwin's theory of evolution by natural selection. After writing the details of his theory, Wallace sent his paper to Darwin for criticism. ④ Darwin recognized the similarity of Wallace's ideas, and prepared a short summary of his own theory. Both Wallace's and Darwin's papers were published in the *Journal of the Proceedings of the Linnean Society* in 1859. Darwin's insistence on having Wallace's ideas presented along with his own shows Darwin's integrity. Darwin then shortened a manuscript he had been working on since 1856 and published it as *On the Origin of Species by Means of Natural Selection* in November, 1859. The 1,250 copies prepared in the first printing sold out the day the book was released.

In spite of the similarities in the theories of Wallace and Darwin, there were also important differences. Wallace, for example, believed that every evolutionary modification was a product of selection and, therefore, had to be adaptive for the organism. Darwin, on the other hand, admitted that natural selection may not explain all evolutionary changes. He did not insist on finding adaptive significance for every modification. Further, unlike Darwin, Wallace stopped short of attributing human intellectual functions and the ability to make moral judgments to evolution. On both of these matters, Darwin's ideas are closer to the views of most modern scientists.

Wallace's work provided an important spark that motivated Darwin to publish his own ideas. The theory of natural selection, however, is usually credited to Charles Darwin. The years of work given to the theory by Darwin, and the accumulation of massive evidence for the theory, led even Wallace to attribute the theory to Darwin. Wallace wrote to Darwin in 1864:

> I shall always maintain [the theory of evolution by natural selection] to be actually yours and yours only. You had worked it out in details I had never thought of years before I had a ray of light on the subject.

Stop and Ask Yourself

4. How did the following contribute to Charles Darwin's formulation of the theory of natural selection: Uniformitarianism? South American fossils? Galápagos tortoises?
5. What are four elements of the theory of evolution by natural selection?

EVOLUTIONARY THOUGHT AFTER DARWIN

The most significant changes that occurred in evolutionary thought began in the 1930s and have continued to the present. The combination of population genetics with evolutionary theory is called the **modern synthesis** or **neo-Darwinism.**

BIOGEOGRAPHY

5 In the tradition of Darwin and Wallace, biologists of the period of modern synthesis recognized the importance of geography as an explanation of the evolution and the distribution of plants and animals (*see chapter 1; figures 1.3 and 1.4*). One of the distribution patterns that biogeographers try to explain is how similar groups of organisms can live in places separated by seemingly impenetrable barriers. Recall that Darwin was struck by the presence of fossil horses in South America. This distribution was puzzling because modern horses were introduced to America from Europe. The fossil horses must have arisen in America or arrived by some unknown means, then became extinct and left no descendants. Biogeographers also try to explain why plants and animals, separated by geographical barriers, are often very different in spite of similar environments. For example, evolution may take different directions in different parts of the world; therefore, major predators in Africa and America might be expected to differ if they had no common ancestry. Finally, biogeographers try to explain why oceanic islands, such as the Galápagos, often have relatively few, but unique, resident species. They try to document island colonization and subsequent evolutionary events, which may be very different from evolutionary events in ancestral, mainland groups.

Modern evolutionary biologists recognize the importance of geological events, such as volcanic activity, the movement of great land masses, climatic changes, and geological uplift (mountain building), in creating or removing barriers to the movements of plants and animals. As scientists learned more about the geologic history of the earth, they understood more about animal distribution patterns and factors that played important roles in their evolution. Only in understanding how the surface of the earth came to its present form can we understand its inhabitants (box 11.2).

Information from the study of biogeography can be applied in the study of contemporary environmental problems. Prehistoric removal of geographic barriers allowed species from one region of the world to invade other regions, sometimes resulting in dramatic changes in species composition. Invading species tend to be highly competitive, with high reproductive potential, and have been important agents of extinction in regions that they invade. For example, during the Pliocene and Miocene epochs (about 10 million years ago) the Central American land bridge formed between North and South America (*see box 11.2*). Many species of plants and animals used this land bridge to move between continents. Information from the study of past events is now being applied to predict the effect of the removal of geographical barriers on native populations. For example, the proposed sea-level canal across Panama could bring an interchange of species between the Atlantic and Pacific Oceans, causing extinction of many fishes and other animals. In addition the voracious coral predator, *Acanthaster planci* (the crown-of-thorns sea star), could be introduced into the Caribbean region.

Evolution is one of the major unifying themes in biology because it helps explain both the similarities and diversity of life. In chapter 1 you learned of the sources of evidence for evolution—biogeography gives evidence of prehistoric climates, habitats, and animal distribution patterns; paleontology provides evidence of animals that existed in the past; comparative anatomy leads to the description of homologous structures; and molecular biology provides evidence of relatedness of animals based on their biochemical similarities. This evidence leaves little doubt that evolution has occurred in the past, and this chapter described the historical development of a theory that accounts for how evolution occurs. In chapter 12 you will learn how the incorporation of the principles of population genetics has affected scientific concepts of the mechanism of evolution.

Stop and Ask Yourself

6. What is modern synthesis or neo-Darwinism?
7. What are some of the distribution patterns that biogeographers attempt to explain?
8. How has the discovery of continental drift influenced our understanding of evolution?

BOX 11.2 CONTINENTAL DRIFT

It seems remarkable, but the earth's largest land masses are moving—about 1 cm a year! The 1960s revolutionized geology as **continental drift** became an accepted theory.

During the Permian period (about 250 million years ago), all of earth's land masses were united into a single continent called Pangaea (figure 1a). Soon after, Pangaea began to break up, as the huge crustal plates began to move apart. Approximately 200 million years ago, there were two great continents. The northern continent was Laurasia, and the southern continent was Gondwana (figure 1b). Seventy million years ago, Gondwana broke apart, followed later by the breakup of Laurasia (figure 1c).

Movement of these crustal plates continues today. Their study is known as **plate tectonics.** During these movements, new crustal material is thrust up from the ocean floor along the mid-Atlantic ridge, and flows in both directions from that ridge. The mid-Atlantic ridge runs from the Falkland Islands, at its southern end, to Iceland, at its northern end. As the huge crusts move away from each other in the Atlantic, old crustal material sinks back into the earth in deep

oceanic trenches in the Pacific Ocean. Evidence of these movements is seen in the earthquakes along the western coast of North America.

The drifting of the continents has important implications for biogeographers and paleontologists. Continental drift explains why some fossils have a worldwide distribution. Land organisms in existence during the time that all continents were united as Pangaea had access to most of the land masses of the world. It should not be surprising, therefore, to find some fossils that are similar in all parts of the world, such as the fossils that Charles Darwin found in South America that were very similar to animals living in Africa. Were it not for continental drift, this pattern would be very difficult to explain.

Continental drift also explains how differences in organisms may develop. Because oceanic barriers were created as a result of continental drift, plants and animals were separated from one another when continents separated. Evolution then proceeded independently in each biogeographical region and resulted in species characteristic of that region.

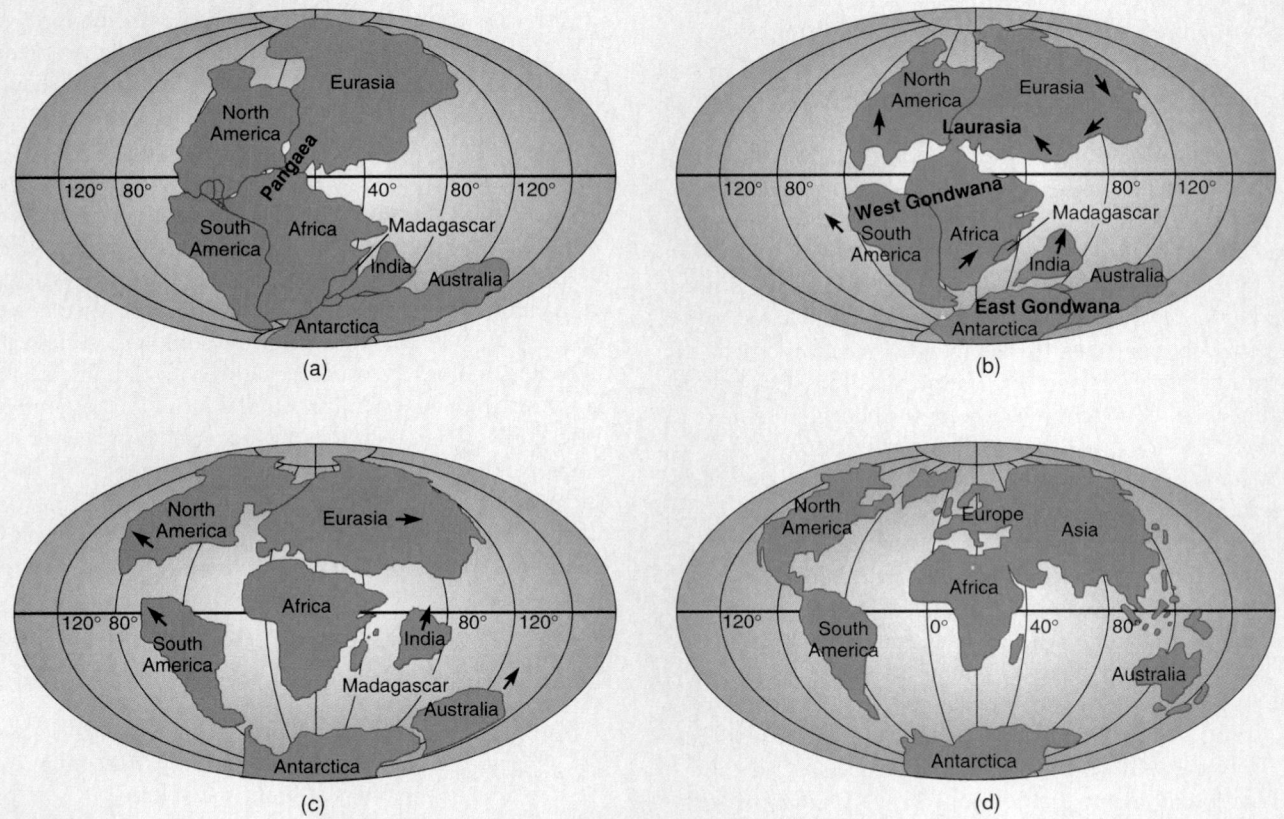

FIGURE 1   **Continental Drift.** (a) About 250 million years ago, the continents of the earth were joined into a single land mass that geologists call Pangaea. (b) About 150 million years ago, Pangaea broke up into the northern (Laurasia) and southern (Gondwana) continents. (c) This breakup was followed, about 70 million years ago, by the separation of continents in the Southern Hemisphere, and later by the separation of continents in the Northern Hemisphere. (d) The present position of continents. Note the complementary outlines of the eastern coast of South America and the western coast of Africa. The collision of India with Eurasia (c) resulted in the formation of the Himalaya Mountains.

Summary

1. Organic evolution is the change of a species over time.

2. Ideas of evolutionary change can be traced back to the ancient Greeks.

3. Jean Baptiste Lamarck was an eighteenth-century proponent of evolution, and proposed a mechanism—inheritance of acquired characteristics—to explain it.

4. Charles Darwin saw impressive evidence for evolutionary change while on a mapping expedition on the HMS *Beagle*. The theory of uniformitarianism, South American fossils, and observations of tortoises and finches on the Galápagos Islands convinced Darwin that evolution occurs.

5. After returning from his voyage, Darwin began formulating his theory of evolution by natural selection. In addition to his experiences on his voyage, later observations of artificial selection and Malthus' theory of human population growth helped shape his theory.

6. Darwin's theory of natural selection includes the following elements: (a) all organisms have a greater reproductive potential than is ever attained; (b) inherited variations arise by mutation; (c) there is a constant struggle for existence in which those organisms that are least suited to their environment will die; (d) the adaptive traits present in the survivors will tend to be passed on to subsequent generations, and the nonadaptive traits will tend to be lost.

7. "Adaptation" may refer to a process of change or a result of change. An adaptation is a characteristic that increases an organism's potential to survive and reproduce in a given environment.

8. All evolutionary changes are not adaptive, nor do all evolutionary changes lead to perfect solutions to environmental problems.

9. Alfred Russel Wallace outlined a theory similar to Darwin's, but never accumulated significant evidence documenting his theory.

10. Modern evolutionary theorists apply principles of genetics, ecological theory, and geographic and morphological studies to solving evolutionary problems.

11. The study of biogeography provides information on how similar groups of organisms can live in widely separated areas, accounts for the importance of geological events in evolution of plants and animals, and helps scientists predict the effects of removal of geographical barriers on extant populations.

Selected Key Terms

adaptation (*p. 160*)
continental drift (*p. 162*)
Galápagos Islands (*p. 156*)
modern synthesis (*p. 161*)
natural selection (*p. 159*)
neo-Darwinism (*p. 161*)

organic evolution (*p. 154*)
theory of evolution by natural selection (*p. 154*)
theory of inheritance of acquired characteristics (*p. 154*)
uniformitarianism (*p. 157*)

Critical Thinking Questions

1. Chapter 1 contains a discussion of the scientific method. Review that section and do the following: (a) outline a hypothesis and design a test of "inheritance of acquired characteristics" and (b) define what is meant by the word "theory" in the theory of evolution by natural selection.

2. Assuming that you have already studied chapter 9, describe the implications of inheritance of acquired characteristics for the central dogma of molecular genetics (*see figure 9.4*).

3. Review the definition of "adaptation" in the sense of a result of evolutionary change. Imagine that two deer, A and B, are identical twins. Deer A is shot by a hunter before it has a chance to reproduce. Deer B is not shot and goes on to reproduce. According to our definition of adaptation, is deer B more fit for its environment than deer A? Why or why not?

4. Why is the stipulation of "a specific environment" included in the definition of "adaptation"?

5. Imagine that you could go back in time and meet simultaneously with Charles Darwin and Gregor Mendel. Construct a dialogue in which you explain to both the effect of their ideas on each other's theory and their theories on modern biology. The dialogue should include their responses and questions throughout the conversation.

EVOLUTION AND GENE FREQUENCIES

Outline

Concepts

1. In modern genetic theory, organic evolution is defined as a change in the frequency of alleles in a population.
2. The principles of modern genetics help biologists understand how variation arises. This variation increases the chances of a population's survival in changing environments.
3. Population genetics is the study of events occurring in gene pools. The Hardy-Weinberg theorem helps scientists understand the circumstances under which evolution occurs. Evolution occurs when (a) genetic drift or neutral selection occurs, (b) gene flow occurs, (c) mutations introduce new genes into populations, or (d) natural selection occurs.
4. Balanced polymorphism occurs when two or more body forms are maintained in a population without a range of phenotypes between them.
5. The fundamental unit of classification is the species, and the process by which new species are formed is called speciation.
6. For speciation to happen, reproductive isolation must occur.
7. Different organisms, as well as structures within organisms, evolve at different rates. Evolution may also proceed in jumps rather than at a constant pace.
8. Molecular biologists study DNA and proteins to uncover evolutionary relationships.

Would You Like to Know:

These and other useful questions will be answered in this chapter.

One can envision natural selection operating in two ways, and both are important perspectives on evolution. In one way (e.g., the focus of chapter 11), we can look at characteristics of individual animals. When a bird acquires an adaptation through natural selection that permits it to feed more efficiently on butterflies, we often describe the trait in terms of physical characteristics (e.g., bill shape) or inherited behaviors. This description of natural selection recognizes that natural selection must act in the context of living organisms.

The organism, however, must be viewed as a vehicle that permits the phenotypic expression of genes. In chapter 12, you will learn the second way that natural selection operates is upon the gene. A bird or a butterfly is not permanent—they die. The genes that they carry, however, are potentially immortal. The result of natural selection (and evolution in general) is reflected in how common, or how rare, specific genes are in a group of animals that are interbreeding—and, therefore, sharing genes. A group of individuals of the same species that occupy a given area at the same time and share a unique set of genes is called a **population.**

A more precise definition of organic evolution is a change in the frequency of alleles in a population. The frequency of an allele in a population is the abundance of that particular allele in relation to the sum of all alleles at that locus. Another way to express the same idea is that organic evolution is a change in the total genetic makeup of a population (the **gene pool**). This chapter examines evolution from the perspective of changes in gene pools and covers some of the mechanisms by which evolution occurs, as well as processes by which new species arise.

THE MODERN SYNTHESIS: A CLOSER LOOK

Much of your background for understanding the modern synthesis comes from studying genetics because it explains why variations between individuals exist, and how they are passed to future generations. Genetic variation is important in evolution because some variations may confer an advantage to individuals, leading to natural selection. The potential for genetic variation in individuals of a population is unlimited. Even the relatively simple principles of inheritance described by Gregor Mendel provide for remarkable variation. In addition, crossing-over, multiple alleles, and mutations add to this variation. The result is that no two individuals, except identical twins, are genetically identical. Chance combinations of genes are likely to result in some individuals being better able to survive and reproduce in a given environment than other individuals.

MUST EVOLUTION HAPPEN?

Evolution is central to all of biology, but is evolution always occurring in a particular population? As we will see, there are certainly times when the rate of evolution is very slow, and there are times when the rate of evolution is very rapid. But, are there times when evolution does not occur at all?   ① The answer to this question lies in the theories of **population genetics,** the study of the genetic events that occur in gene pools.

THE HARDY-WEINBERG THEOREM

In 1908, an English mathematician, Godfrey H. Hardy, and a German physician, Wilhelm Weinberg, independently derived a mathematical model describing what happens to the frequency of alleles in a population over time. Their combined ideas became known as the Hardy-Weinberg theorem. It states that the mixing of alleles at meiosis and their subsequent recombination will not alter the frequencies of the alleles in future generations, as long as certain assumptions are met. If they are met, then evolution will not occur, because the allelic frequencies will not change from generation to generation, even though the specific mixes of alleles in individuals may vary.

The assumptions of the Hardy-Weinberg theorem are as follows:

1. The size of population must be very large. Large size ensures that the frequency of a gene will not change by chance alone.
2. Mating within the population must be random. Every individual must have an equal chance of mating with any other individual in the population. Expressed in a slightly different way, the choice of a mate must not be based on similarity or dissimilarity in a given trait. If this condition is not fulfilled, then some individuals are more likely to reproduce than others, and natural selection may occur.
3. There must not be any migration of individuals into, or out of, the population. Migration may introduce new genes into the gene pool, or add or delete copies of existing genes.
4. Mutations must not occur. If they do, mutational equilibrium must exist. Mutational equilibrium occurs when mutation from the wild-type allele to a mutant form is balanced by mutation from the mutant form back to the wild type. In either case, no new genes are introduced into the population from this source.

These assumptions must be met if allelic frequencies are not changing; that is, if evolution is not occurring. These assumptions are clearly very restrictive, and few, if any, real populations meet them.   ② This means that most populations are evolving. The theorem, however, does provide a

BOX 12.1   GENETIC EQUILIBRIUM

To illustrate the Hardy-Weinberg theorem, consider a hypothetical population that meets all of the assumptions listed on p. 166. In this population, a particular autosomal locus has two alleles; allele A has a frequency of 0.8 [$f(A) = 0.8$], and allele a has a frequency of 0.2 [$f(a) = 0.2$]. Another way to say the same thing is that, in this population, 80% of the genes for this locus are allele A, and 20% are allele a. For the purpose of our example, assume dominance; however, it is irrelevant to the Hardy-Weinberg theorem.

Because random mating is assumed, one can easily determine the genotypic and phenotypic frequencies of the next generation using a Punnett square type of analysis (figure 1). Because we are assuming dominance, the phenotypic frequencies of the F_1 generation are:

$$f(\text{phenotype } A) = 0.64 + 0.32 = 0.96$$
$$f(\text{phenotype } a) = 0.04$$

Gene frequencies of the F_1 generation can be determined by adding the frequency of each homozygote to ½ the frequency of the heterozygote. (The frequency of an allele in the heterozygote is reduced by ½ because heterozygotes contain only a single copy of each allele.)

	f(allele A)	f(allele a)
AA individuals	0.64	0
Aa individuals	½(0.32) = 0.16	½(0.32) = 0.16
aa individuals	0	0.04
Overall frequency	0.80	0.20

Note that the overall frequency of each allele in the F_1 generation has not changed from that assumed for the parental generation. This example illustrates that if the assumptions of the Hardy-Weinberg theorem are met, the frequency of genes does not change from generation to generation. In other words,

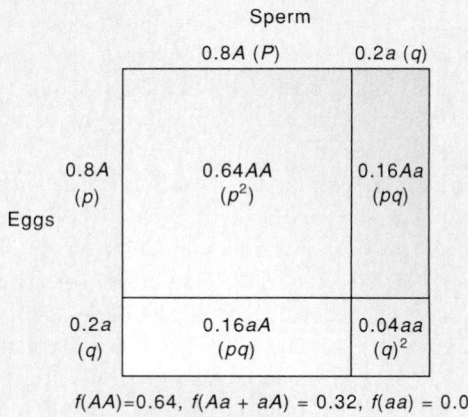

$$f(AA)=0.64,\ f(Aa + aA) = 0.32,\ f(aa) = 0.04$$
$$(p + q)^2 = p^2 + 2pq + q^2 = 1$$

FIGURE 1   Genotypic Frequencies. Determining the genotypic frequencies of offspring from allelic frequencies in a parental generation. This analysis assumes random mating, and that each allele is equally likely to be incorporated into a viable gamete. The frequency of each allele in a sperm or egg is simply the frequency of that allele in the parental population. Allelic frequencies are often represented by p and q, and genotypic frequencies can be found by expanding the binomial $(p + q)^2$.

Hardy-Weinberg equilibrium is achieved, and evolution does NOT occur!

The Hardy-Weinberg theorem can be stated in general mathematical terms. Considering a locus with two interacting alleles, if p = the frequency of one allele, and q = the frequency of a second allele, then $p + q = 1$. The frequency of genotypes in the next generation can be found by algebraically expanding the binomial equation $(p + q)^2 = p^2 + 2pq + q^2 = 1$.

useful theoretical framework for examining changes in gene frequencies in populations (box 12.1)

In the next section, we will see how, when the assumptions are not met, evolutionary change occurs.

Stop and Ask Yourself

1. What is a gene pool?
2. What are the four assumptions of the Hardy-Weinberg theorem?
3. Are the assumptions listed in your answer to question 2 realistic for animal populations?
4. What conclusion can be drawn from the Hardy-Weinberg theorem?

EVOLUTIONARY MECHANISMS

Evolution is neither a creative force working for progress, nor a dark force working to sacrifice individuals for the sake of the group. It is neither moral nor immoral. It has neither a goal, nor a mind to conceive a goal. Such goal-oriented thinking is said to be teleological. Evolution is simply a result of some individuals in a population surviving and being more effective at reproducing than others in the population, leading to changes in gene frequencies. In this section, we will examine some of the situations when the Hardy-Weinberg assumptions are not met—situations in which gene frequencies do change from one generation to the next and evolution occurs.

Population Size, Genetic Drift, and Neutral Selection

③ Chance often plays an important role in the perpetuation of genes in a population, and the smaller the population size, the more significant the effect of chance events may be. Fortuitous circumstances, such as a chance encounter between reproductive individuals, may promote reproduction. Some traits of a population survive, not because they convey increased fitness, but because they happened to be in gametes that were involved in fertilization. When chance events influence the frequencies of genes in populations, **genetic drift** is said to occur. Because gene frequencies are changing independently of natural selection, genetic drift is often referred to as **neutral selection.**

The process of genetic drift is analogous to flipping a coin. The likelihood of getting a head or a tail is equal. One is most likely to achieve the 50:50 ratio of heads and tails in a large number of tosses. In only ten tosses, one should not be surprised to get, for example, a disproportionate 7 heads and 3 tails. Similarly, the chance of one or the other of two equally adaptive alleles being incorporated into a gamete, and eventually into an individual in a second generation, is equal. In sampling gametes in a small population, unusual proportions of alleles may occur in any one generation of gametes because meiotic events, like tossing a coin, are random. Assuming that both alleles have equal fitness, these unusual proportions will be reflected in the phenotypes of the next generation. These chance events may result in a particular allele increasing in frequency or decreasing in frequency (figure 12.1a). In small populations, inbreeding is also common. Genetic drift and inbreeding are likely to reduce genetic variation within a population.

If a mutation introduces a new allele into a population and that allele is no more or less adaptive than existing alleles, genetic drift may permit the new allele to become established in the population (figure 12.1b), or the new allele may be lost because of genetic drift. The likelihood of genetic drift occurring in small populations suggests that a Hardy-Weinberg equilibrium will not occur in such a population.

Two special cases of genetic drift have influenced the genetic makeup of some populations. When a few individuals from a parental population colonize new habitats, they seldom carry a representative sample of the gene pool from which they came. The new colony that emerges from the founding individuals is likely to have a distinctive genetic makeup with far less variation than the larger population. This form of genetic drift is called the **founder effect.**

An often-cited example of the founder effect concerns the genetic makeup of the Dunkers of eastern Pennsylvania. They emigrated from Germany to the United States early in the eighteenth century, and for religious reasons, have not married outside their sect. Examination of certain traits (e.g., ABO blood type) in their population reveals very different gene frequencies from the Dunker populations of Germany.

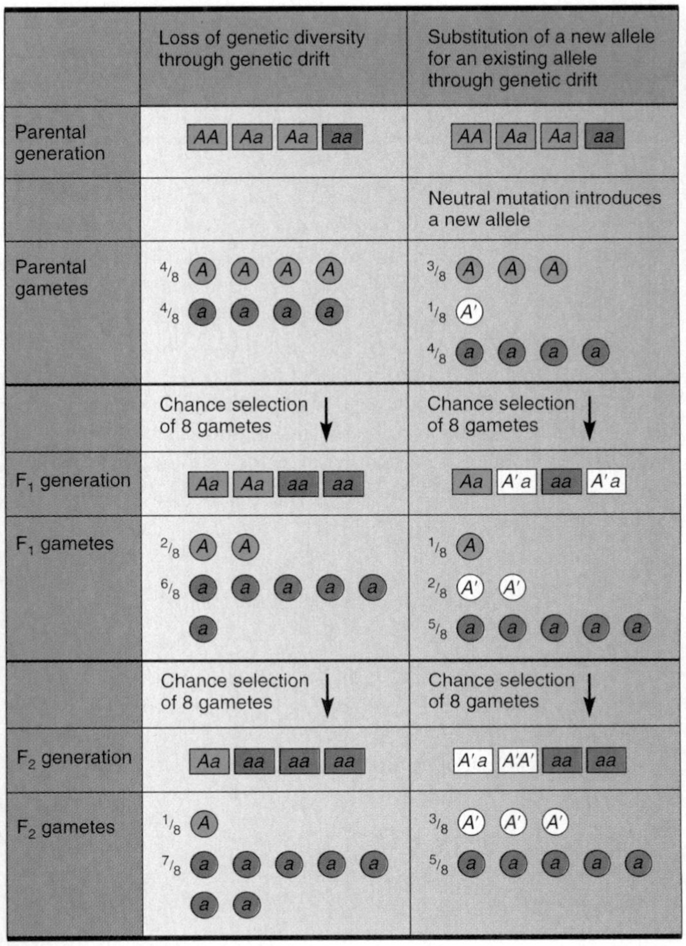

(a)   (b)

Figure 12.1

Genetic Drift. (a) Genetic diversity may be lost as a result of genetic drift. Assume alleles *a* and A are equally adaptive. Allele *a* might be incorporated into gametes more often than A, or it could be involved in more fertilizations. In either case, the frequency of *a* increases and the frequency of A decreases because of random events operating at the level of gametes. (b) A new, equally adaptive, allele may become established in a population as a result of genetic drift. In this example, the allele (A′) substitutes for an existing allele (A). The same mechanisms could also account for the loss of the newly introduced allele or the establishment of A′ as a third allele.

These differences are attributed to the chance absence of certain genes in the individuals that founded the original Pennsylvania Dunker population.

A similar effect can occur when the number of individuals in a population is drastically reduced. For example, cheetah populations in South and East Africa are endangered. The severe depletion in numbers experienced in these populations has reduced genetic diversity to the point that even if populations are restored, the recovered populations will have only a remnant of the original gene pool (figure 12.2). This form of

(a)

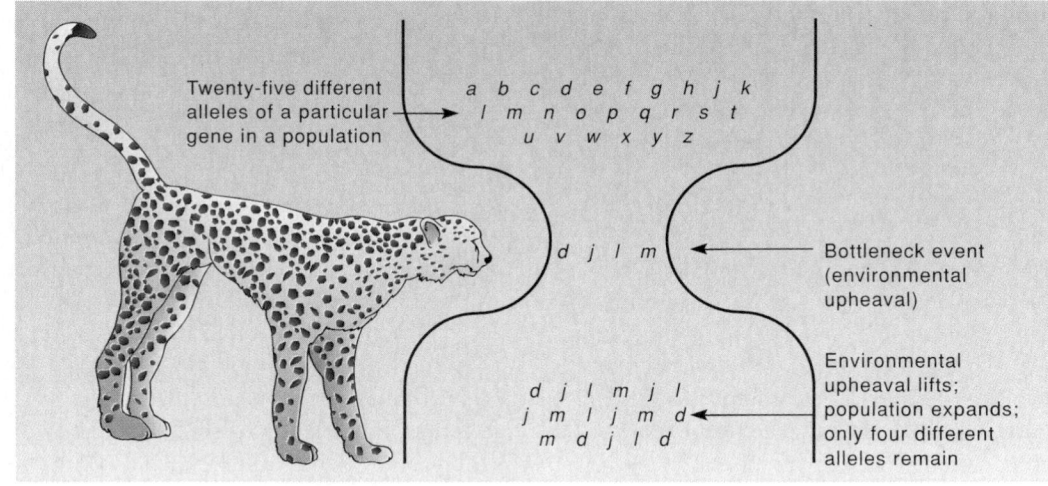

(b)

Figure 12.2

The Bottleneck Effect. (*a*) Cheetahs (*Acinonyx jubatus*) of South and East Africa have been endangered by human activities. (*b*) Severe reduction in the original population has caused a bottleneck effect that, even if population size recovers, has resulted in a loss of genetic diversity.

Figure 12.3

The Bottleneck Effect. The Northern elephant seal (*Mirounga angustirostris*) was severely overhunted in the late 1800s. Even though its population numbers are now increasing, its genetic diversity is very low.

genetic drift is called the **bottleneck effect.** A similar example concerns the Northern elephant seal (figure 12.3). It was hunted to near extinction in the late 1800s. Legislation to protect the seal was enacted in 1922, and now the population is greater than 100,000 individuals. In spite of this relatively large number, the genetic variability in the population is very low.

The effects of bottlenecks are somewhat controversial. The traditional interpretation is that decreases in genetic diversity make populations less likely to withstand environmental stress and more susceptible to extinction. That is, in a population with high genetic diversity, it is more likely that some individuals will have a combination of genes that allows them to withstand environmental changes. In the case of the cheetah, recent evidence indicates that this cat's current problems may be more a result of predation by lions and spotted hyenas on cheetah cubs than a result of low genetic diversity. Most evolutionary biologists agree, however, that over evolutionary time frames, high genetic diversity makes extinction less likely.

Gene Flow

The Hardy-Weinberg theorem assumes that no individuals enter a population from the outside (immigrate), and that no individuals leave a population (emigrate). If immigration or emigration occurs, the Hardy-Weinberg equilibrium is upset, and changes in gene frequency (evolution) occur. These changes in gene frequency from migration of individuals are called **gene flow.** Although there are certainly some natural populations for which gene flow may not be significant, most populations experience changes in allelic frequency from this source.

Mutation

Changes in the structure of genes and chromosomes are called mutations (*see chapters 8 and 9*). The Hardy-Weinberg theorem assumes that no mutations occur, or that mutational equilibrium exists. Mutations, however, are a fact of life. Most importantly, mutations are the origin of all new genes and a source of variation that may prove adaptive for an animal. Mutation counters the loss of genetic material that results from natural selection and genetic drift, and increases the likelihood that variations will be present that allow a group to survive future environmental shocks.

Mutations are random events, and the likelihood of a mutation is not affected by the usefulness of the mutation. Organisms have no special device to filter harmful genetic changes from advantageous changes before they occur. Mutations occur, and animals must take the bad along with the good. The effects of mutations vary enormously. Most are deleterious. Some mutations that are neutral or harmful in one environment may help an organism survive in another environment.

Mutational equilibrium occurs when a mutation from the wild-type allele to a mutant form is balanced by mutation from the mutant back to the wild type. This has the same effect on allelic frequency as if no mutation occurred. Mutational equilibrium rarely exists, however. **Mutation pressure** is a measure of the tendency for gene frequencies to change through mutation.

Natural Selection Reexamined

The theory of natural selection remains preeminent in modern biology. Natural selection occurs whenever some phenotypes are more successful at leaving offspring than other phenotypes, and the tendency for it to occur—and upset Hardy-Weinberg equilibrium—is called **selection pressure.** Although natural selection is simple in principle, it is quite diverse in actual operation.

Modes of Selection

Many populations have a range of phenotypes for certain traits. This range may be characterized using a bell-shaped curve, where phenotypic extremes are less common than the intermediate phenotypes. Natural selection may affect a range of phenotypes in three different ways.

Directional selection occurs when individuals at one phenotypic extreme are at a disadvantage compared to all other individuals in the population (figure 12.4a). In response to this selection, the deleterious gene(s) decreases in frequency and all other genes increase in frequency. Directional selection may occur when a mutation gives rise to a new gene, or when the environment changes to select against an existing phenotype.

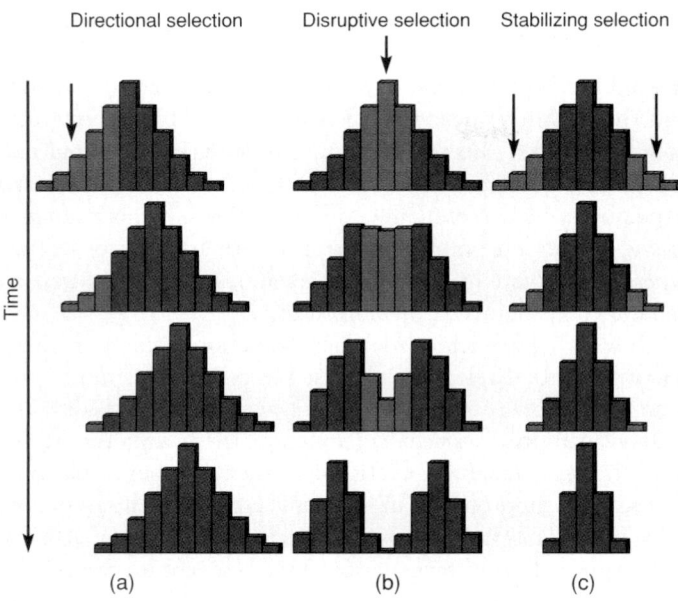

Directional selection   Disruptive selection   Stabilizing selection

Time

(a)   (b)   (c)

Figure 12.4

Modes of Selections. (*a*) Directional selection occurs when individuals at one phenotypic extreme are selected against. It results in a shift in phenotypic distribution toward the advantageous phenotype. (*b*) Disruptive selection occurs when an intermediate phenotype is selected against and results in the production of distinct subpopulations. (*c*) Stabilizing selection occurs when individuals at both phenotypic extremes are selected against, and results in a narrowing at both ends of the range. Arrows indicate selection against one or more phenotypes. The X-axis of each graph indicates the range of phenotypes for the trait in question.

Industrial melanism, a classic example of directional selection, occurred in England during the industrial revolution. Museum records and experiments document how environmental changes affected selection against one phenotype of the peppered moth, *Biston betularia.*

In the early 1800s, a gray form made up about 99% of peppered moth population. That form still predominates in nonindustrial northern England and Scotland. In industrial areas of England, the gray form was replaced by a black form over a period of about 50 years. In these areas, the gray form made up only about 5% of the population, and 95% of the population was black. The gray phenotype, previously advantageous, had become deleterious.

The nature of the selection pressure was understood when it was discovered that birds prey more effectively on moths resting on a contrasting background. Prior to the industrial revolution, the gray form was favored because gray moths blended with the bark of trees on which the moths rested. The black form contrasted with the lighter lichen-covered bark, and was easily spotted by birds (figure 12.5a). Early in the industrial revolution, however, factories used soft coal, and spewed soot and other pollutants into the air. Soot covered the tree trunks where the moths rested, and bird predators could easily pick out

(a)

(b)

Figure 12.5

Directional Selection. Two body forms of the peppered moth, *Biston betularia.* There is a gray and black form in each picture. (*a*) Prior to the industrial revolution, the black form was easily spotted by bird predators, and the gray form was camouflaged. (*b*) In industrial regions, after the industrial revolution, selection was reversed because of soot covering the bark of trees where moths rested. Note how clearly the gray form can be seen, whereas the black form is almost invisible.

gray moths against the black background. The black form was now effectively camouflaged (figure 12.5b).

In the 1950s, the British Parliament enacted air pollution standards that have helped reduce soot in the atmosphere. As would be expected, the gray form of the moth has had a small but significant increase in frequency.

Another form of natural selection may occur when circumstances select against individuals of an intermediate phenotype (figure 12.4b). ❹ **Disruptive selection** produces distinct subpopulations. Consider, for example, what could happen in a population of snails having a range of shell colors between white and dark brown. Their marine tidepool habitat provides two background colors. The sand, made up of pulverized mollusc shells, is white, and rock outcroppings are brown. In the face of predation by shorebirds, what phenotypes are going to be most common? Although white snails may not actively select a white background, those present on the sand are less likely to be preyed on than intermediate phenotypes on either sand or rocks. Similarly, brown snails are less likely to be preyed on than intermediate phenotypes on either substrate. Thus, two distinct subpopulations, one white and one brown, could be produced through disruptive selection.

A third form of natural selection occurs when both phenotypic extremes are deleterious. This process is called **stabilizing selection,** and results in a narrowing of the phenotypic range (figure 12.4c). During long periods of environmental constancy, new variations that arise, or new combinations of genes that occur, are unlikely to result in more fit phenotypes than the genes that have allowed a population to survive for thousands of years, especially when the new variations are at the extremes of the phenotypic range.

A good example of stabilizing selection is the horseshoe crab (*Limulus*), which occurs along the Atlantic coast of the United States (*see figure 23.8*). Comparison of the fossil record with living forms indicates that this body form has changed very little over 200 million years. Apparently, the combination of characteristics present in this group of animals represents a very successful combination of characteristics for the horseshoe crab's environment.

Neutralist/Selectionist Controversy

Most biologists recognize that both natural selection and neutral selection occur, but may not be equally important in all circumstances. For example, during long periods when environments are relatively constant, and stabilizing selection is acting on phenotypes, neutral selection may operate at the molecular level. Certain genes could be randomly established in a population. Occasionally, however, the environment shifts, and directional or disruptive selection begins to operate, resulting in gene frequency changes (often fairly rapid).

The relative importance of neutral selection and natural selection in natural populations is debated and is an example of the kind of debates occurring among evolutionists. These debates concern the mechanics of evolution and are the foundations of science. They lead to experiments that will ultimately present a clearer understanding of evolution.

BALANCED POLYMORPHISM AND HETEROZYGOTE SUPERIORITY

Polymorphism occurs in a population when two or more distinct forms exist without a range of phenotypes between them. **Balanced polymorphism** (Gr. *poly*, many + *morphe*, form) occurs when different phenotypes are maintained at relatively stable frequencies in the population and may resemble a population in which disruptive selection operates.

Sickle cell anemia (*see chapters 7 and 9*) results from a change in the structure of the hemoglobin molecule. Some of the red blood cells of persons with the disease are misshapen, and their ability to carry oxygen is reduced. In the heterozygous state, there are roughly equal quantities of normal and sickled cells. Sickle cell heterozygotes occur in some African populations with a frequency as high as 0.4. The maintenance of the sickle cell heterozygotes and both homozygous genotypes at relatively unchanging frequencies makes this trait an example of a balanced polymorphism.

Why hasn't such a seemingly deleterious gene been eliminated by natural selection? The sickle cell gene is most common in regions of Africa that are heavily infested with the malarial parasite, *Plasmodium falciparum*. Heterozygotes are less susceptible to malarial infections; if infected, they experience less severe symptoms than do homozygotes without sickled cells. Individuals homozygous for the normal allele are at a disadvantage because they experience more severe malarial infections, and individuals homozygous for the sickle cell allele are at a disadvantage because they suffer from severe anemia caused by the sickled cells. The heterozygotes, who usually experience no symptoms of anemia, are more likely to survive than either homozygote. This system is also an example of heterozygote superiority, which occurs when the heterozygote is more fit than either homozygote. Heterozygote superiority can lead to balanced polymorphism, because perpetuation of the alleles in the heterozygous condition maintains both alleles at a higher frequency than would be expected if natural selection acted only on the homozygous phenotypes.

Stop and Ask Yourself

5. What is neutral selection? Why are the effects of neutral selection more likely to show up in small populations, or in fringe groups of larger populations?

6. Why are mutations important evolutionary occurrences?

7. How would you define the terms directional selection, disruptive selection, and stabilizing selection? Which is more likely to occur in a time of climatic change?

SPECIES AND SPECIATION

Taxonomists classify organisms into groups based on their similarities and differences. This classification system is discussed in chapters 1 and 16. The fundamental unit of classification is the species. Unfortunately, it is difficult to formulate a universally applicable definition of species. According to a biological definition, a **species** is a group of populations in which genes are actually, or potentially, exchanged through interbreeding.

Although this definition is concise, it has problems associated with it. Taxonomists often work with morphological characteristics, and the reproductive criterion must be assumed based on morphological and ecological information. Also, some organisms do not reproduce sexually. Obviously, other criteria need to be applied in these cases. Another problem concerns fossil material. Paleontologists describe species of extinct organisms, but how are they to test the reproductive criterion? Finally, populations of similar organisms may be so isolated from each other that the exchange of genes is geographically impossible. To test a reproductive criterion, biologists can transplant individuals to see if mating can occur. Under such circumstances, however, one can never be certain that mating of transplanted individuals would really occur if animals were together in a natural setting.

Rather than trying to establish a definition of a species that solves all these problems, it is probably better to simply understand the problems associated with the biological definition. In describing species, taxonomists use morphological, physiological, embryological, behavioral, molecular, and ecological criteria, realizing that all of these have a genetic basis.

⑤   **Speciation** is the formation of new species. A requirement of speciation is that subpopulations are prevented from interbreeding. This is called **reproductive isolation.** When subpopulations are reproductively isolated, natural selection and genetic drift can result in evolution taking a different course in each subpopulation. Reproductive isolation can occur in different ways.

Premating isolation prevents mating from taking place. For example, subpopulations may be separated by impenetrable barriers such as rivers or mountain ranges. Other forms of premating isolation are more subtle. If courtship behavior patterns of two animals are not mutually appropriate, mating will not occur. Similarly, individuals that have different breeding periods, or that occupy different habitats, will be unable to breed with each other.

Postmating isolation prevents successful fertilization and development, even though mating may have occurred. For example, conditions in the reproductive tract of a female may not support the sperm of another individual, which prevents successful fertilization. Postmating isolation also occurs because hybrids are usually sterile (e.g., the mule produced from a mating of a male donkey and a mare is a sterile hybrid). Mismatched chromosomes cannot synapse properly during meiosis, and any gametes produced are not viable. Other kinds of postmating isolation include developmental failures of the fertilized egg or embryo.

ALLOPATRIC SPECIATION

Allopatric (Gr. *allos*, other + *patria*, fatherland) **speciation** occurs when subpopulations become geographically isolated from one another. For example, a mountain range or river may permanently separate members of a population. Adaptations to different environments or neutral selection in these separate populations may result in members not being able to mate successfully with each other, even if experimentally reunited. Allopatric speciation is believed by many biologists to be the most common kind of speciation (figure 12.6).

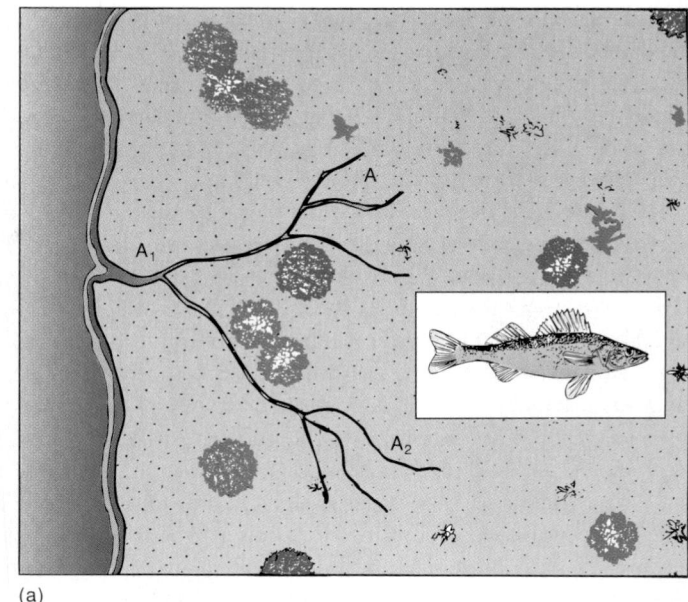

(a)

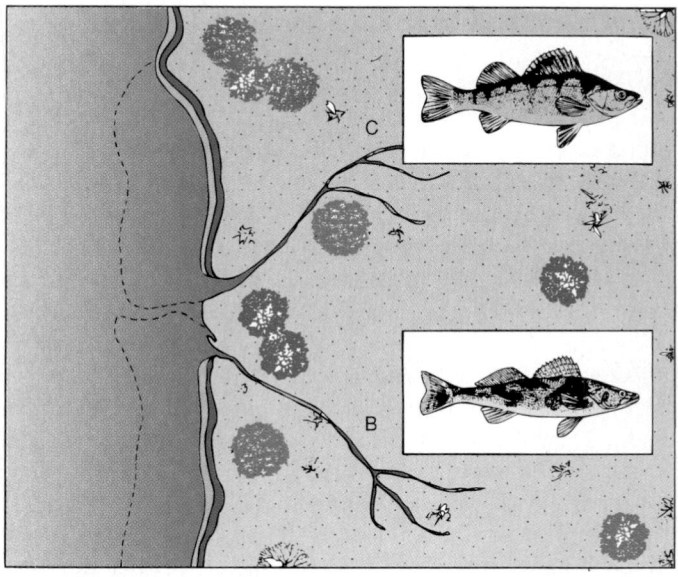

(b)

FIGURE 12.6

Allopatric Speciation. Allopatric speciation can occur when a geographic barrier divides a population. (*a*) In this hypothetical example, a population of freshwater fish in a river drainage system is divided into three subpopulations: A, A_1 and A_2. Genetic exchanges may occur between A and A_1, and between A_1 and A_2. Exchanges are less common between A and A_2. (*b*) A rise in the level of the ocean forces the breakup of A_1, and separates A and A_2 into separate populations. Genetic drift and different selection pressures in the two populations may eventually result in the formation of species B and C.

The finches that Darwin saw on the Galápagos Islands are a classic example of allopatric speciation, as well as an important evolutionary process called adaptive radiation. **Adaptive radiation** occurs when a number of new forms diverge from an ancestral form, usually in response to the opening of major new habitats.

Fourteen species of finches evolved from the original finches that colonized the Galápagos Islands. It is likely that ancestral finches, having emigrated from the mainland, were distributed among a few of the islands of the Galápagos. Populations became isolated on various islands over a period of time. Even though the original population probably displayed some genetic variation, even greater variation arose over time. The original finches were seed eaters, and after their arrival, they probably filled their preferred habitats very rapidly. Variations within the original finch population may have allowed some birds to exploit new islands and habitats where no finches had been. Mutations changed the genetic composition of the isolated finch populations, introducing further variations. Natural selection favored the retention of the variations that happened to promote successful reproduction.

The combined forces of isolation, mutation, and natural selection allowed the finches to diverge into a number of species with specialized feeding habits (*see figure 11.3*). Of the 14 species of finches, six have beaks specialized for crushing seeds of different sizes. Others feed on flowers of the prickly pear cactus or in the forests on insects and fruit.

PARAPATRIC SPECIATION

Another form of speciation is called **parapatric** (Gr. *para*, beside) **speciation,** which occurs in small, local populations, called **demes.** For example, all of the frogs in a particular pond, or all of the sea urchins in a particular tidepool, make up a deme. Individuals of a deme are more likely to breed with one another than with other individuals in the larger population, and because they experience the same environment, they are subject to similar selection pressures. Demes are not completely isolated from each other because individuals, developmental stages, or gametes can move between demes of a population. On the other hand, the relative isolation of a deme may mean that its members experience different selection pressures than other members of the population. If so, speciation can occur. Although most evolutionists theoretically agree that parapatric speciation can occur, no certain cases are known. Parapatric speciation is therefore considered of less importance in the evolution of animal groups than allopatric speciation.

SYMPATRIC SPECIATION

A third kind of speciation is called **sympatric** (Gr. *sym*, together) **speciation.** It occurs within a single population. Even though organisms are sympatric, they still may be reproductively isolated from one another. Many plant species are capable of producing viable forms with multiple sets of chromosomes. Such events could lead to sympatric speciation among groups in the same habitat. Sympatric speciation in animals, however, rarely, if ever, occurs.

Stop and Ask Yourself

8. Why is reproductive isolation necessary for speciation to occur?
9. What form of premating isolation is likely to promote allopatric speciation?
10. What is postmating isolation? What are three forms it may take?
11. What are sympatric, parapatric, and allopatric speciation?
12. What is adaptive radiation?

RATES OF EVOLUTION

Charles Darwin perceived evolutionary change as occurring gradually over millions of years. This concept, called **phyletic gradualism,** has been the traditional interpretation of the tempo, or rate, of evolution.

Some evolutionary changes, however, occur very rapidly. Studies of the fossil record show that many species do not change significantly over millions of years. These periods of stasis (Gr. *stasis*, standing still), or equilibrium, are interrupted when a group encounters an ecological crisis, such as a change in climate or a major geological event. Over the next 10,000 to 100,000 years, a variation might be advantageous that previously would have been selectively neutral or disadvantageous. Alternatively, geological events might result in new habitats becoming available. (Events that occur in 10,000 to 100,000 years are almost instantaneous in an evolutionary time frame.) This geologically brief period of change "punctuates" the previous million or so years of equilibrium, and eventually settles into the next period of stasis. In this model, the periods of stasis are characterized by stabilizing selection, and the periods of change are characterized by directional or disruptive selection (figure 12.7). This model of evolution in which long periods of stasis are interrupted by brief periods of change is called the **punctuated equilibrium model.**

Such rapid evolutionary changes in small populations have been observed in the field. The acquisition of pesticide and antibiotic resistance by insect pests and bacteria are examples of rapid natural selection that have been observed by humans. In a series of studies over a 20-year period, Peter R. Grant has shown that natural selection results in rapid morphological changes in the bills of Galápagos finches. A long, dry period from the middle of 1976 to early January 1978 resulted in birds with larger, deeper bills. Early in this dry period, smaller, easily cracked seeds were quickly consumed by birds. As birds were forced to turn to large seeds, birds with weaker bills were selected against, resulting in a measurable change in the makeup of the finch population of the island, Daphne Major.

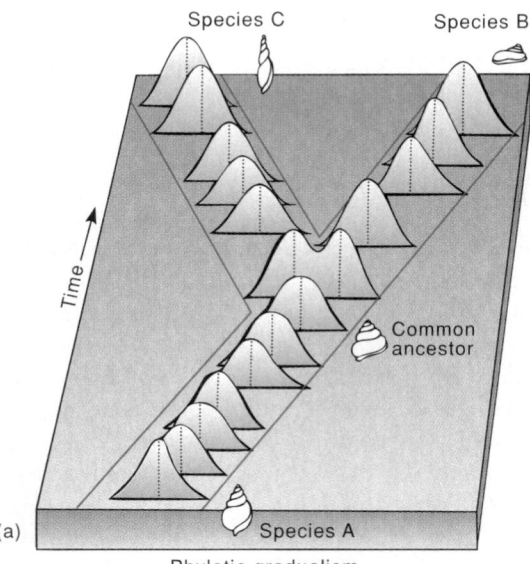

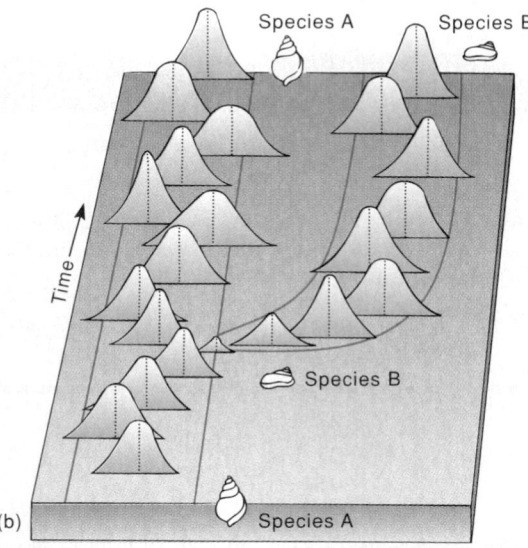

Figure 12.7

Rates of Evolution. A comparison of phyletic gradualism and punctuated equilibrium. (*a*) Phyletic gradualism is a model of evolution in which gradual changes occur over very long time periods. Notice that a continuous series of intermediate phenotypes are present as species B and species C gradually diverge from species A. (*b*) Punctuated equilibrium is a model of evolution in which long periods of stasis are interrupted by rapid periods of change. Notice the very rapid divergence of species B from species A, after which species B enters a period of relative stasis.

TABLE 12.1	AMINO ACID DIFFERENCES IN CYTOCHROME *c* FROM DIFFERENT ORGANISMS	
ORGANISMS	**NUMBER OF VARIANT AMINO ACID RESIDUES**	
Cow and sheep	0	
Cow and whale	2	
Horse and cow	3	
Rabbit and pig	4	
Horse and rabbit	5	
Whale and kangaroo	6	
Rabbit and pigeon	7	
Shark and tuna	19	
Tuna and fruit fly	21	
Tuna and moth	28	
Yeast and mold	38	
Wheat and yeast	40	
Moth and yeast	44	

One advantage of the punctuated equilibrium model is its explanation for why the fossil record does not always show transitional stages between related organisms. Gradualists attribute the absence of transitional forms to the fact that fossilization is an unlikely event, and, therefore, many transitional forms disappeared without leaving a fossil record. Since punctuated equilibrium involves rapid changes in small, isolated populations, preservation of intermediate forms in the fossil record would be even less likely. The rapid pace (geologically speaking) of evolution resulted in apparent "jumps" from one form to another.

MOLECULAR EVOLUTION

Many evolutionists study changes in animal structure and function that are observable on a large scale—for example, changes in the shape of a bird's bill or in the length of an animal's neck. All evolutionary change, however, results from changes in the sequence of bases in DNA and amino acids in proteins. ⑥ Molecular evolutionists investigate evolutionary relationships between organisms by studying DNA and proteins. For example, cytochrome *c* is a protein present in the pathways of cellular respiration in all eukaryotic organisms (table 12.1). Organisms shown to be closely related from using other investigative tools, have similar cytochrome *c* molecules. The fact that cytochrome *c* has changed so little during hundreds of millions of years suggests that mutations of the cytochrome *c* gene are nearly always detrimental, and will be selected against. Because it has changed so little, cytochrome *c* is said to have been conserved evolutionarily.

Not all proteins are conserved as rigorously as cytochrome *c*. Although variations in highly conserved proteins can be used to help establish evolutionary relationships between distantly related organisms, less conserved proteins are useful for looking at relationships between more closely related animals. Because some proteins are conserved and others are not, the best information regarding evolutionary relationships is obtained by comparing as many proteins as possible in any two species.

GENE DUPLICATION

Recall that most mutations are selected against. However, if an extra copy of a gene is present, one copy may be modified and, as long as the second copy is furnishing the essential protein, the organism is likely to survive. Gene duplication, the accidental duplication of a gene on a chromosome, is one way that extra genetic material can arise (*see chapter 8*).

Vertebrate hemoglobin and myoglobin are believed to have arisen from a common ancestral molecule. Hemoglobin carries oxygen in red blood cells, and myoglobin is an oxygen storage molecule in muscle. The ancestral molecule probably carried out both functions. However, about 1 billion years ago, gene duplication followed by mutation of one gene resulted in the formation of two polypeptides: myoglobin and hemoglobin. Further gene duplications over the last 500 million years probably explain the fact that most vertebrates, other than primitive fishes, have hemoglobin molecules consisting of four polypeptides.

MOSAIC EVOLUTION

A previous section described how rates of evolution can vary both in populations and in molecules and structures. A species might be thought of as a mosaic of different molecules and structures that have evolved at different rates. Some molecules or structures are conserved in evolution, others change more rapidly. The basic design of a bird provides a simple example. All birds are easily recognizable as birds because of highly conserved structures, such as feathers, bills, and a certain body form. Particular parts of birds, however, are less conservative and have a higher rate of change. Wings have been modified for hovering, soaring, and swimming. Similarly, legs have been modified for wading, swimming, and perching. These are examples of **mosaic evolution.**

Stop and Ask Yourself

13. How do phyletic gradualism and punctuated equilibrium models differ?
14. How can amino acid sequencing and DNA base sequencing provide evidence of evolutionary relationships?
15. What does it mean to say that cytochrome *c* is an evolutionarily conserved protein?

SUMMARY

1. Organic evolution is a change in the frequency of alleles in a population.
2. Unlimited genetic variation, in the form of new alleles and new combinations of alleles, increases the chances that a population will survive future environmental changes.
3. Population genetics is the study of events occurring in gene pools. The Hardy-Weinberg theorem describes the fact that, if certain assumptions are met, gene frequencies of a population remain constant from generation to generation.
4. The assumptions of the Hardy-Weinberg theorem, when not met, define circumstances under which evolution will occur.
   (a) Fortuitous circumstances may allow only certain alleles to be carried into the next generation. Such chance variations in allelic frequencies are called genetic drift or neutral selection. (b) Allelic frequencies may change as a result of individuals immigrating into, or emigrating from, a population. (c) Mutations are the source of new genetic material for populations. Mutational equilibrium rarely exists, and thus mutations usually result in changing allelic frequencies. (d) The tendency for allelic frequencies to change, due to differing fitness, is called selection pressure.

5. Selection may be directional, disruptive, or stabilizing.

6. Balanced polymorphism occurs when two or more body forms are maintained in a population. Heterozygote superiority can lead to balanced polymorphism.

7. According to a biological definition, a species is a group of populations within which there is potential for exchange of genes. Significant problems are associated with the application of this definition.

8. In order for speciation to happen, reproductive isolation must occur. Speciation may occur sympatrically, parapatrically, or allopatrically, although most speciation events are believed to be allopatric.

9. Premating isolation may prevent mating from occurring and/or postmating isolation may prevent the development of fertile offspring, if mating has occurred.

10. Phyletic gradualism is a model of evolution that depicts change as occurring gradually, over millions of years. Punctuated equilibrium is a model of evolution that depicts long periods of stasis interrupted by brief periods of relatively rapid change.

11. The study of rates of molecular evolution helps establish evolutionary interrelationships between organisms.

12. A duplicated gene may be modified by mutation, and by chance, come to serve a function other than its original role.

13. Any species can be thought of as a mosaic of different molecules and structures that have evolved at differing rates.

SELECTED KEY TERMS

adaptive radiation (*p. 173*)
Hardy-Weinberg equilibrium
    (*p. 167*)
neutral selection (*p. 168*)
phyletic gradualism (*p. 174*)
population genetics (*p. 166*)

punctuated equilibrium model
    (*p. 174*)
reproductive isolation (*p. 173*)
speciation (*p. 173*)
species (*p. 172*)

CRITICAL THINKING QUESTIONS

1. Can natural selection act on variations that are not inherited? (Consider, for example, deformities that arise from contracting a disease.) If so, what is the effect of that selection on subsequent generations?

2. In what way does overuse of antibiotics and pesticides increase the likelihood that these chemicals will eventually become ineffective? This is an example of which one of the three modes of natural selection?

3. What are the implications of the "bottleneck effect" for wildlife managers who try to help endangered species, such as the whooping crane, recover from near extinction?

4. What does it mean to think of evolutionary change as being goal-oriented? Explain why this way of thinking is wrong.

5. Imagine that two species of butterflies resemble one another closely. One of the species (the model) is distasteful to bird predators, and the other species (the mimic) is not. How could directional selection have resulted in the mimic species evolving a resemblance to the model species?

SUGGESTED READINGS

BOOKS

Ayala, F. J. 1982. *Population and Evolutionary Genetics: A Primer.* Menlo Park: Benjamin Cummings Publishing Company, Inc.

Bowler, P. 1984. *Evolution: The History of an Idea.* Berkeley: University of California Press.

Darwin, C. 1894. *On the Origin of Species.* Reprint. 1975. Cambridge: Cambridge University Press.

Dodson, E. O., and Dodson, P. 1985. *Evolution: Process and Product.* Belmont: Wadsworth Publishing Co.

Eldredge, N., and Cracraft, J. 1980. *Phylogenetic Patterns and the Evolutionary Process: Method and Theory in Comparative Biology.* New York: Columbia University Press.

Endler, J. A. 1986. *Natural Selection in the Wild.* Princeton: Princeton University Press.

Futuyma, D. J. 1986. *Evolutionary Biology*, 2d ed. Sunderland: Sinauer Associates, Inc.

Godfrey, L. R. 1985. *What Darwin Began.* Old Tappan: Allyn and Bacon, Inc.

Grant, P. R. 1986. *Ecology and Evolution of Darwin's Finches.* Princeton: Princeton University Press.

Hecht, M. K., Wallace, B., and Prance, G. T. (eds.). 1967–1988. *Evolutionary Biology*, Vols. 1–22. New York: Plenum Press.

Mayr, E. 1982. *The Growth of Biological Thought: Diversity, Evolution, and Inheritance.* Cambridge: Harvard University Press.

Menard, H. W. 1986. *The Ocean of Truth: A Personal History of Global Tectonics*. Princeton, N.J.: Princeton University Press.

Otte, D., and Endler, J. A. (eds.). 1989. *Speciation and its Consequences*. Sunderland: Sinauer Associates, Inc.

Smith, J. M. 1989. *Evolutionary Genetics*. New York: Oxford University Press.

Smith, J. M. (ed.). 1982. *Evolution Now: A Century After Darwin*. New York: W. H. Freeman.

Stebbins, G. L. 1982. *Darwin to DNA, Molecules to Humanity*. New York: W. H. Freeman.

Volpe, E. P. 1985. *Understanding Evolution*. 5th ed. Dubuque: Wm. C. Brown Publishers.

ARTICLES

Allegre, C. J., and Schneider, S. H. The evolution of the earth. *Scientific American* October, 1994.

Altman, S. A. 1989. The monkey and the fig. *American Scientist* 77(3):256–263.

Alvarez, W., and Asaro, F. What caused the mass extinction? An extraterrestrial impact. *Scientific American* October, 1990.

Amato, I. 1987. Tics in the tocks of molecular clocks: Comparing the DNA, RNA and proteins of different species may reveal the entire tree of life, but obstacles are emerging. *Science News* 131:74–75.

Briggs, D. E. G. 1991. Extraordinary fossils. *American Scientist* 79(2):130–141.

Callagan, C. A. 1987. Instances of observed speciation. *The American Biology Teacher* 49(1):34–36.

Carson, H. L. November 1987. The process whereby species originate. *BioScience* 37:715–720.

Cherfas, J. 1991. Ancient DNA: Still busy after death. *Science* 253:1354–1356.

Courtillot, V. E. What caused the mass extinction? A volcanic eruption. *Scientific American* October, 1990.

Coyne, J. A., and Barton, N. H. 1988. What do we know about speciation? *Nature* 331:485–486.

Dalziel, I. W. D. Earth before Pangea. *Scientific American* January, 1995.

Finchel, T., and Finlay, B. J. 1994. The evolution of life without oxygen. *American Scientist* 82 (1):22–29.

Freedman, W. L. The expansion rate and size of the universe. *Scientific American* November, 1992.

Gould, S. J. The evolution of life on the earth. *Scientific American* October, 1994.

Grant, P. R. Natural selection and Darwin's finches. *Scientific American* October, 1991.

Herbert, S. Darwin as a geologist. *Scientific American* May, 1986.

Horgan, J. In the beginning . . . *Scientific American* February, 1991.

Jermeij, G. J. 1991. When biotas meet: Understanding biotic interchange. *Science* 253:1099–1104.

Joyce, G. F. Directed molecular evolution. *Scientific American* December, 1992.

Kirshner, R. P. The earth's elements. *Scientific American* October, 1994.

Lewontin, R. C. Adaptation. *Scientific American* September, 1978.

Linde, A. The self-reproducing inflationary universe. *Scientific American* November, 1994.

May, R. R. The evolution of ecological systems. *Scientific American* September, 1987.

Myers, N. 1985. The ends of the lines. *Natural History* 94:2–6.

Peebles, J. E., Schramm, D. N., Turner, E. L., and Kron, R. G. The evolution of the universe. *Scientific American* October, 1994.

Ramos, V. A. 1989. The birth of southern South America. *American Scientist* 77(5): 444–459.

Rebek, J. Synthetic self-replicating molecules. *Scientific American* July, 1994.

Ross, P. E. Eloquent remains. *Scientific American* May, 1992.

Ruthen, R. Adapting to complexity. *Scientific American* January, 1993.

Ryan, M. J. 1990. Signals, species, and sexual selection. *American Scientist* 78(1):46–52.

Sheldon, P. 1988. Making the most of evolution diaries. *New Scientist* 117:52–54.

Weinberg, S. Life in the universe. *Scientific American* October, 1994.

York, D. The earliest history of the earth. *Scientific American* January, 1993.

part FOUR

BEHAVIOR AND ECOLOGY

Chapter 1 of this textbook stressed unity and diversity. All life is unified at molecular, cellular, and evolutionary levels. A fundamental unity also exists at an environmental level. All living organisms are partners in the use of the

earth's resources. In particular, humans have a responsibility to see that the resources of this planet are preserved for all organisms in all generations. It is only through studying the interactions of organisms with one another, and with the physical attributes of their environment, that this goal will ever be realized. Even in our "enlightened" generation, waste and misuse are unbridled. In many ways, our technologies have permitted abusive practices unheard of by previous generations. Scientists, theologians, and philosophers must lead the way in protecting our fragile ecosystems.

Part Four (chapters 13 through 15) presents some behavioral interactions among organisms and some of the other interactions between organisms and their environment. Many complex relationships exist, and zoologists can fully understand organisms only in the context of populations, communities, and ecosystems.

Cecropia moth larvae, *Hyalophora cecropia*.

ANIMAL BEHAVIOR

Outline

Concepts

1. Behavior refers to the varied activities that an animal performs during its lifetime. Internal physiological conditions, environmental stimuli, and social situations influence specific behavioral responses.
2. Proximate factors that influence the behavior of an animal include the following: genetics, developmental experiences, and the current environment, including photoperiod, season, and temperature. These effects are mediated by the nervous and endocrine systems of the animal.
3. The ultimate factor that influences the behavior of an animal is natural selection. Animals that possess certain traits are more successful at surviving and reproducing.
4. Two key problems that face each animal are finding a place to live and finding food.
5. The evolution of various social systems, in which animals live in groups, affects many aspects of their behavior.

Would You Like to Know:

1. if an earthworm placed on a hook feels any pain? (*p. 182*)
2. how tadpoles know how to swim? (*p. 182*)
3. how baby chicks know how to follow their mother? (*p. 184*)
4. how a trainer teaches an animal to do tricks? (*p. 185*)
5. how a fly processes information from its environment and feeds? (*p. 186*)
6. how male moths detect the presence of females who are ready to mate? (*p. 188*)
7. what decisions hummingbirds make while finding and visiting flower patches? (*p. 189*)
8. why some animals eat only a limited number of foods and others eat many different foods? (*p. 189*)
9. why some animals live in groups and others live alone? (*p. 190*)

These and other useful questions will be answered in this chapter.

This chapter contains evolutionary concepts, which are set off in this font.

Animal behavior can be defined as the activities animals perform during their lifetime. These activities include locomotion, feeding, breeding, capture of prey, avoidance of predators, and social behavior. Animals send signals, respond to signals or stimuli, carry out maintenance behavior, make choices, and interact with one another. This chapter examines some of these aspects of animal behavior.

FOUR APPROACHES TO ANIMAL BEHAVIOR

Observations of animal behavior have been made by naturalists and philosophers for centuries. Only in the last century, however, has there been significant progress in understanding this behavior.

One approach to the study of animal behavior is that of the **comparative psychologists,** who emphasize studies of the genetic, neural, and hormonal bases of animal behavior. Psychologists conduct experimental studies, in both laboratory and field settings, that relate to animal learning and to the development of behavior. They explore the manner in which information is received by animals, and the processes and nature of the behavior patterns constituting the animals' responses to their surroundings.

Ethology (Gr. *ethologica*, depicting character) is the study of animal behavior in which evolution and the natural environment are important considerations. The leaders of this approach have been Konrad Lorenz, Niko Tinbergen, and Karl von Frisch, who were awarded the Nobel Prize in Physiology or Medicine in 1973. **Ethologists** observe the behavior of a variety of animals in their natural environments, and study the behavior of closely related species in order to consider the evolution and origin of certain behavior patterns. Ethologists rarely deal with learning and are interested instead in questions of animal communication, mating behavior, and social behavior.

Behavioral ecology emphasizes the ecological aspects of animal behavior. Predator-prey interactions, foraging strategies, reproductive strategies, habitat selection, intraspecific and interspecific competition, and social behavior are topics of interest to behavioral ecologists.

Sociobiology is the study of the evolution of social behavior. It combines many aspects of ethology and behavioral ecology. Sociobiologists emphasize the importance of natural selection on individuals living in groups.

PROXIMATE AND ULTIMATE CAUSES

"Why do animals do what they do?" is a question frequently asked by behavioral scientists. More immediate ecological and physiological causes of behavior, such as eating to satisfy hunger, are called proximate causes. Another level of causation in behavior that occurs on the evolutionary time scale is that of ultimate causes. A display serves not only to attract a mate, but to increase the likelihood of passing genetic information to the next generation.

ANTHROPOMORPHISM

Anthropomorphism (Gr. *anthropos*, man + *morphe*, form) is the application of human characteristics to anything not human. When observing animals, one should avoid assigning human feelings to their behavior, because this is not likely to be accurate, especially with invertebrate animals. Consider the example of placing an earthworm on a fishhook. Does the fishhook hurt the earthworm, causing it to writhe in pain? Both of the descriptive words, hurt and pain, are based on human experience and conscious awareness. ① A better explanation that reduces the anthropomorphic interpretation is that when the earthworm is placed on the hook, certain receptors are stimulated, and nerve impulses are generated and travel along reflex neural circuits. The muscles are stimulated and the worm begins to wriggle in an attempt to escape from the hook. This explanation more closely describes what has been observed and does not attempt to suggest what the earthworm "feels."

DEVELOPMENT OF BEHAVIOR

For a normal behavior pattern to develop, the genes that code for the formation of the structures and organs involved in the behavior must be present. For example, in vertebrates, normal locomotion movements will not occur without proper development and growth of the limbs. This process requires some interaction with the animal's environment because proper nourishment, water balance, and other factors must be maintained for normal development to occur.

MATURATION

Some behavior patterns appear only after a specific developmental stage or time is reached. During **maturation,** there is improvement in the performance of the behavior pattern as parts of the nervous system and other structures complete development. ② A classic example is tail movement in frog embryos that are near hatching. While still in the egg membranes, they start moving their tails as they would if they were swimming, and the coordination of movements improves with time. These improved movements are due to maturation, not practice or experience.

INSTINCT/LEARNING INTERACTIONS

In recent years, many behavioral scientists have concluded that both instinct and learning are important in the behavior of animals. Interaction of inherited (i.e., instinctive) and learned components shapes a number of behavior patterns. For example, young bobcats raised in isolation without the chance to catch live prey did not attack a white rat placed with them, unless the rat tried to escape. At first, their attacks were not efficient, but after some experience, they were seizing prey by the neck and rapidly killing them. Apparently, inherited components of this behavior

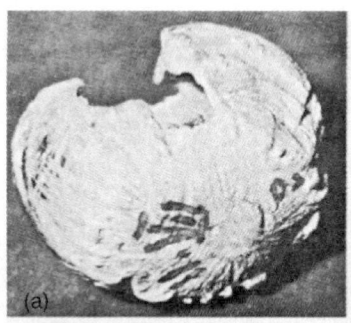
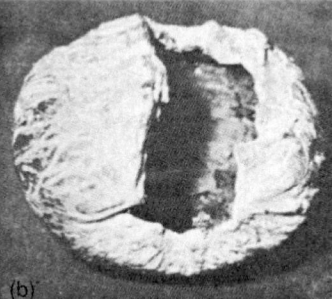

Figure 13.1

Instinctive and Learned Behavior. Nut-cracking behavior in squirrels involves instinctive and learned components. (*a, b*) An inexperienced squirrel has opened this hazelnut as evidenced by the many gnawing marks made at random. (*c, d*) An experienced squirrel has opened this hazelnut efficiently by gnawing and prying on the broad side of the nut to crack it open. *Courtesy of Prof. Dr. Eibl-Eibesfeldt.*

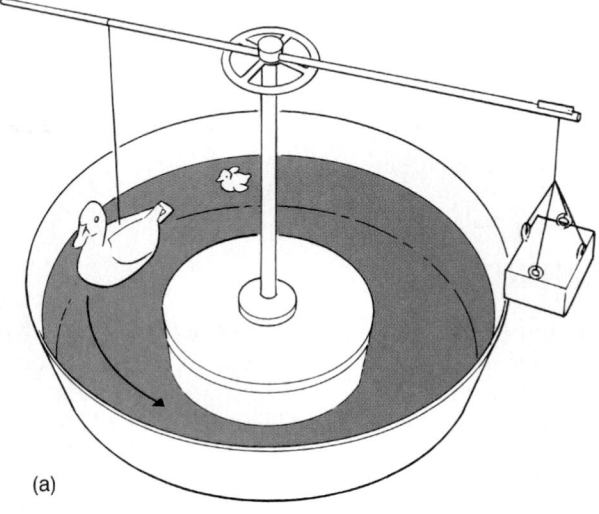

(a)

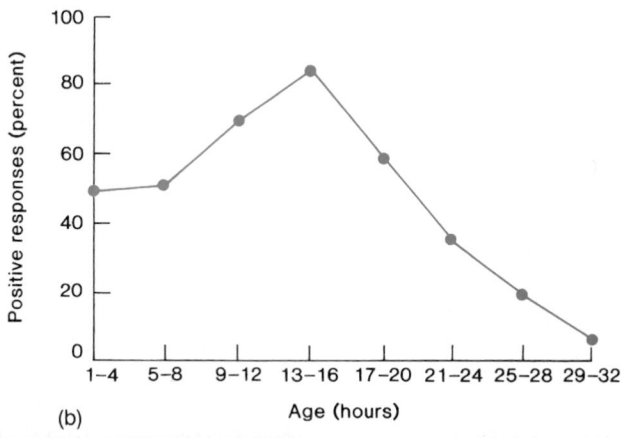

(b)

(c)

Figure 13.2

Imprinting in Young Birds. (*a*) A circular arena apparatus is used to imprint the young duckling on its "mother" (a stuffed model). (*b*) The critical period for imprinting is most likely to occur 13 to 16 hours after birth. (*c*) Imprinted geese following Konrad Lorenz.

pattern are refined by learning. Under normal conditions, the learning or experiences occur during play with littermates.

Another example involving instinctive and learned components to behavior may be seen in the nut-cracking behavior of squirrels. Squirrels gnaw and pry to open a nut. Inexperienced squirrels are not efficient; they gnaw and pry at random on the nut. Experienced squirrels, however, are very efficient. They gnaw a furrow on the broad side, then wedge their lower incisors into the furrow and crack the nut open (figure 13.1).

Imprinting

During **imprinting,** a young animal develops an attachment toward another animal or object (figure 13.2*a*). The attachment usually forms only during a specific critical period that occurs soon after hatching or birth and is not reversible (figure 13.2*b*). Imprinting is a rapid learning process that apparently occurs without reinforcement.

Some pioneering work on imprinting was done by Konrad Lorenz (1903–1989). He did experiments with geese in which he allowed the geese to imprint on him (figure 13.2*c*). The goslings followed him as though he was their mother.

3 In nature, many species of birds in which the young follow the parent soon after birth use imprinting so the young can identify with or recognize their parent(s). They can then be led successfully to the nest or to water. Both visual and auditory cues are important in imprinting systems.

LEARNING

Learning produces changes in the behavior of an individual that are due to experience. Learning is considered adaptive because it allows an animal to respond quickly to changes in its environment. Once an animal learns something, its behavioral choices are increased.

An animal's ability to learn may be correlated with the predictability of certain characteristics of its environment. Where certain changes in the habitat occur regularly and are predictable, the animal may respond to a stimulus with an instinctive behavior very rapidly and without modification. An animal would not necessarily benefit from learning in this situation. However, where certain environmental changes are unpredictable and cannot be anticipated, an animal may modify its behavioral responses through learning or experience. This modification is adaptive because it allows an animal to not only change its response to fit a given situation, but also to improve its response to subsequent, similar environmental changes.

Several different categories of learning have been identified, ranging from habituation (the simplest form of learning) to insight learning (the most complex form) that involves cognitive processes.

HABITUATION

Habituation is the simplest and perhaps most common type of behavior occurring in many different animals. Habituation involves a waning or decrease in response to repeated or continuous stimulation. Simply, an animal learns not to respond to stimuli in its environment that are constant and probably relatively unimportant. By habituating to unimportant stimuli, an animal conserves energy and time that might be better spent on other important functions. For example, after time, birds learn to ignore scarecrows that previously caused them to flee. Squirrels in a city park adjust to the movements of humans and automobiles. If the stimulus is withheld, then the response returns rapidly. Habituation does not involve any conditioning. Habituation is believed to be controlled through the central nervous system, and should be distinguished from sensory adaptation. Sensory adaptation involves repeated stimulation of receptors until they stop responding. For example, if one enters a room where there is an unusual odor, the olfactory sense organs soon stop responding to these odors.

FIGURE 13.3

The Apparatus Used by Pavlov to Demonstrate Classical Conditioning. If a ringing bell is presented just before a dog is given food, over several repetitions the dog will begin to associate the stimulus with the food. The dog becomes conditioned to salivate with the ringing of the bell alone.

CLASSICAL CONDITIONING

Classical conditioning is a type of learning documented by the Russian physiologist, Ivan Pavlov (1849–1936). In his classic experiment on the salivary reflex in dogs, he presented food right after the sound of a bell (figure 13.3). After a number of such presentations, the dogs were conditioned—they associated the sound of the bell with food. It was then possible to bring about the dog's usual response to food—salivation—with just the sound of the bell. The food was a positive reinforcement for salivating behavior, but responses could also be conditioned using negative reinforcement.

Classical conditioning is very common in the animal kingdom. Birds learn to avoid certain brightly colored caterpillars that have a noxious taste. Because birds may associate the color pattern with the bad taste, animals with a similar color pattern may also be avoided.

INSTRUMENTAL CONDITIONING

In **instrumental conditioning** (also known as trial-and-error learning), the animal shows appetitive behavior during which it carries out certain searching actions, such as walking and moving about. If the animal should, for example, find food during these activities, the food acts as reinforcement for the behavior and the reward is associated with the behavior. If this association is repeated several times, the animal has learned that the behavior leads to reinforcement.

fly or a young mammal at play may improve coordination of certain movements or behavior patterns by practice during these activities.

LATENT LEARNING

Latent learning, sometimes called exploratory learning, involves making associations without immediate reinforcement or reward. The reward is not obvious. There is, however, apparently some motivation for an animal to learn about its surroundings. For example, if a rat is placed in a maze that has no food or reward, it will explore the maze, although rather slowly. If food or another reward is provided, the rat quickly runs the maze. Apparently, previous learning of the maze had occurred, but remained latent or hidden until an obvious reinforcement was provided. Latent learning allows an animal to learn about its surroundings as it explores. Knowledge about an animal's home area may be important for its survival, perhaps enabling it to escape from a predator or capture prey.

INSIGHT LEARNING

In **insight learning,** the animal uses cognitive or mental processes to associate experiences and solve problems. The classic example is the work of Wolfgang Kohler (1887–1967) on chimpanzees that were trained to get food rewards by using tools (figure 13.5a). One chimpanzee was given some bamboo poles that could be joined together to make a longer pole. Some bananas were supported from the ceiling. Once a longer pole was formed, the chimp went right to the fruit and used the long pole to knock the bananas to the cage floor. Kohler believed that the animal used insight learning to get the bananas.

In addition, Jane van Lawick-Goodall (1934–) has observed chimpanzees in the wild using tools to accomplish various tasks. For example, they use crumpled leaves as a sponge for drinking water (figure 13.5b).

FIGURE 13.4
Instrumental Conditioning in a Skinner Box. The rat, through random movements, accidentally pressed the lever and received a reward. Through repetition the behavior of pressing the lever comes to be associated with the reward.

A classic example of instrumental learning is that of a rat in a "Skinner box," developed by B. F. Skinner (1904–1990), a prominent psychologist (figure 13.4). When placed in the box, the rat will begin to explore. It moves all about the box and, by accident, eventually presses a lever and is rewarded with a food pellet. Because food rewards are provided with each pressing of the lever, the reward is associated with the behavior. Through repetition, the rat learns to press the lever right away to receive the reward. In this type of learning, the animal is said to be instrumental in providing its own reinforcement.

In instrumental conditioning, a "shaping" of the behavior can be manipulated by providing the reinforcement (food) whenever the animal comes close to the lever and continuing to supply reinforcement when the animal touches the lever. Finally, the animal learns to press the lever to obtain food.

Learning of new motor patterns by young animals often involves instrumental conditioning. A young bird learning to

Stop and Ask Yourself

1. What are four ways to study animal behavior?
2. How would you differentiate proximate and ultimate causation?
3. Why is anthropomorphism a problem when describing the behavior of animals?
4. What happens during the maturation of a behavior pattern?
5. What is meant by "an inherited disposition to learn"?
6. What are some functions of imprinting in animals?
7. What are the five categories of learning? Give an example of each kind.

(a)

(b)

Figure 13.5

Insight Learning in Chimpanzees. (*a*) This chimpanzee (*Pan troglodytes*) put two sticks together and stood on stacked boxes to reach the bananas that had been suspended from the ceiling. (*b*) This chimpanzee is using a crumpled leaf as a sponge for drinking water.

CONTROL OF BEHAVIOR

The behavior of animals is regulated by internal mechanisms (proximate causes) that include the nervous system and the endocrine system. These systems function to receive information from the external environment via the sensory organs, process that information involving the brain and the endocrine glands, and initiate responses in terms of motor patterns or changes in the operations of internal organs. In general, more specific and rapid responses are mediated by the nervous system, and slower, more general responses occur through the endocrine system.

NERVOUS SYSTEM

The details of the structure of the nervous systems found in animals, and how the various parts function, are covered elsewhere (*see chapter 33*). Our main goal here is to examine the ways in which the nervous system is involved in behavior. One key role for the nervous system is to act as a **stimulus filter.** Each organism is being continuously bombarded by stimuli from many sources. The sensory organs and central nervous system of the animal act to block incoming stimuli that are unimportant or irrelevant. The information that passes through the sensory filters is then sorted and processed within the nervous system to ensure appropriate responses.

5 An excellent example of the various steps in the process by which the nervous system mediates behavior is the manner in which blowflies feed (figure 13.6). The blowfly has special sensory receptors on its feet. As the fly moves around and encounters different substrates, the receptors can detect the presence of certain sugars. The information from the feet is processed in the fly's nervous system and results in the extension of the proboscis, which, in turn, stimulates the oral taste receptors and the fly begins to feed. How does the fly know when to stop? Without some feedback mechanism to tell the proboscis to stop feeding, the fly could continue to consume the sugar solution until it burst! It turns out that there are receptors in the foregut of the blowfly (the first stop for the incoming food in the fly's digestive system), which, when the foregut swells sufficiently, send a message to the fly's brain. The message is relayed to the nerves that control the feeding response, and further intake of the sugar solution is halted.

Another example of how the nervous system regulates behavior concerns the control of aggressive behavior in rhesus monkeys. In one study, surgery was performed on the dominant male monkey in a group of four to six animals in order to implant electrodes into specific brain regions involved in either eliciting or inhibiting aggressive behavior. By providing very mild electrical stimulation to the monkey's brain, it was possible to produce either aggressive or passive behaviors, depending

Figure 13.6

Blowfly Feeding. Blowflies (*Lucilia* spp.) detect food with their feet, resulting in proboscis extension and feeding.

on which electrode was used to send the message. It was also possible to train the other monkeys in the group to press a lever whenever the dominant monkey became aggressive. Pressing the lever resulted in a message being sent to the brain of the dominant male that inhibited his aggression.

Endocrine System

For animals, the endocrine system is closely interrelated with the nervous system. Many receptors located on neurons in the brain or central nervous system are specialized for receiving input from hormones. In addition, the brain communicates with the endocrine system via neurons, as for example, the connections between the hypothalamus and pituitary gland of vertebrates (*see chapter 35*). Other endocrine glands (e.g., the adrenals and gonads) are located throughout the body of the organism. How do the **hormones,** the products from the endocrine glands, affect behavior? There are two major ways in which products from endocrine glands influence behavior: organizational effects and activational effects.

Organizational effects of hormones occur during development and are particularly important for sex differentiation. These effects involve the presence of hormones and critical time periods such that the developmental pathways for specific brain regions and developing gonadal tissues are influenced to become either female- or malelike. The major effect is such that at about the middle of gestation in most mammals (e.g., guinea pigs, monkeys), the testes produce a surge of male hormone (testosterone). This organizes both other developing tissues and certain regions of the brain. In the absence of the surge of testosterone, the organism develops more femalelike characteristics in terms of external anatomy and brain regions

important for sex differences. The surge of testosterone normally is initiated by genes that turn on the production and release of the hormone in the tissues of the developing animal's own body, but instances occur in which the testosterone comes from an external source.

Several examples should help us understand this organizational process. In cattle, a female embryo is masculinized if her twin is a male fetus—when his system turns on and releases testosterone during gestation, some of that hormone crosses over to affect the developing female. The result is a freemartin, a sterile heifer that exhibits a number of malelike behavior patterns. In humans, some hormone treatments that used to be given to pregnant women who were in danger of losing their fetus resulted in masculinization of female embryos, because the hormones injected as a medical treatment were converted to and acted like testosterone within the mother.

Activational effects of hormones are those events that occur where an external stimulus triggers a hormonally mediated response by the organism. Many male fishes change color patterns when their territory boundary is threatened; the color change is a prelude to aggressive behavior if such is necessary to defend the territory. Many animals, including domestic cats, roosters, and mice lose their aggressive fighting ability when they are castrated. This is caused by removing the gonads (the source of the testosterone, which acts by stimulating particular brain receptors to produce aggression).

Communication

Communication involves the transfer of information from one animal to another. Communication requires a sender and receiver that are mutually adapted to each other. The animal acting as the sender must send a clear signal to the receiver. Communication can occur within species (intraspecific) or between species (interspecific). Intraspecific communication in animals is especially important for reproductive success. Examples of interspecific communication include warning signals, such as the rattle of a rattlesnake's tail and the presentation of its hindquarters and tail by a skunk.

Animals use a variety of modalities for communication, including visual, auditory, tactile, and chemical signals. The characteristics of a signal system are shaped by natural selection. Animals have evolved combinations of signals that may be more effective than any single signal.

Visual Communication

Visual communication is important to many animals because a large amount of information can be conveyed in a short period of time. Most animals (e.g., cephalopod molluscs, arthropods, and most vertebrates other than mammals) that have well-developed eyes have color vision. Many fishes, reptiles, and birds exhibit brilliant color patterns that usually have a signaling function. Most mammals have plain, darker colors and lack color vision because they are nocturnal, as were their probable ancestors—nocturnal insectivores. A notable exception is primates in which color vision has appeared again along with colorful displays.

A visual signal may be present at all times, as are the bright facial markings of a male mandrill. The signal may be hidden, or located on a less exposed part of an animal's body and then suddenly presented. Some lizards, such as green anoles, can actually change their color through activities of pigment cells in the skin.

Visual signals have some disadvantages in that the line of sight may be blocked by various objects in the environment and/or may be difficult to see over a long distance. Also, the signals are usually not effective at night and may be detected by predators.

ACOUSTIC COMMUNICATION

Acoustic or sound communication is commonly used by arthropods and vertebrates. These animals must expend energy to produce sounds, but sounds can be used during night or day. Sound waves also have the advantage of traveling around objects and may be produced or received while an animal is in the open or concealed. Sounds may carry a large amount of information because of the many possible variations in frequency, duration, volume, and tone.

Communication systems are closely adapted to the environmental conditions in which they are used and the function of the signal. For example, tropical forest birds produce low-frequency calls that pass easily through dense vegetation. Many primates in tropical forests produce sounds that travel over long distances. Other examples include the calls of territorial birds that sit on a high perch to deliver the signal more effectively, and the alarm calls of many small species of birds. Some of the more complex acoustic signals that have been studied are birdsong and human speech.

TACTILE COMMUNICATION

Tactile communication refers to the communication between animals in physical contact with each other. The antennae of many invertebrates and the touch receptors in the skin of vertebrates function in tactile communication (*see figure 34.14*). Some examples of tactile communication are birds preening the feathers of other birds and primates grooming each other (figure 13.7).

CHEMICAL COMMUNICATION

Chemical communication is another common mode of communication. Unicellular organisms with chemoreceptors can recognize members of their own species. Chemical signals are well-developed in insects, fishes, salamanders, and mammals. Some advantages of chemical signals are that they (1) usually provide a simple message that can last for hours or days; (2) are effective

FIGURE 13.7

Tactile Communication. A subordinant male (on the left) chacma baboon (*Papio ursinus*) is grooming a dominant male (on the right).

night or day; (3) can pass around objects; (4) may be transported over long distances; and (5) take relatively little energy to produce. Disadvantages of chemical signals are that they cannot be changed quickly and are slow to act.

Chemicals that are synthesized by one organism and affect the behavior of another member of the same species are called **pheromones.** Chemical signals are usually detected by olfactory receptors in the receiving animal. Many animals mark their territories by depositing odors that act as chemical signals to other animals of the same species. For example, many male mammals mark specific points in their territories with pheromones that serve to warn other males of their presence in the area. The same pheromones may also attract females that are in breeding condition.

Differences in the chemical structure of pheromones may be directly related to their function. Pheromones used for marking territories and attracting mates usually last longer because of their higher molecular weights. Airborne signals have lower molecular weights and disperse easily. ⑥ For example, the sex attractant pheromones of female moths who are ready to mate are airborne and can be detected by males a few kilometers away.

Stop and Ask Yourself

8. Why are stimulus filters in the nervous system important?

9. How would you separate organizational and activational effects of hormones on behavior?

10. What differences would you expect between the communication system of animals that are active at night versus those that are active in the daytime?

11. What are the advantages of chemical communication?

FIGURE 13.8
Habitat Selection in Deer Mice. Deer mice inhabit a variety of habitats. The *Peromyscus maniculatus* (shown here) lives in forests, often nesting in trees.

BEHAVIORAL ECOLOGY

Behavioral ecologists investigate the ways animals find their way about (orientation and navigation), the process of finding a place to live (habitat selection), the choices made in selecting what foods to eat (foraging behavior), and the ways in which behavior can influence population biology.

HABITAT SELECTION

Habitat selection refers to the animal's choice of a place to live. Two types of factors affect where animals of a particular species live. First are the animal's physiological tolerance limits, which are set by evolution and may involve temperature, humidity, water salinity, and other environmental parameters. Within those constraints, a second set of psychological factors are important—animals make choices about where to reside based on available food resources, nest sites, lack of predators, and past experience. For example, woodland deer mice may be constrained to live in forests rather than fields because they cannot tolerate the high

temperatures in the field environment (figure 13.8). Within the forest, they may prefer (choose to live in) areas with larger trees (e.g., oak or beech) because these trees provide more food in the form of acorns and beechnuts, in addition to better shelter and more nest sites.

FORAGING BEHAVIOR

All animals must consume food to survive. For most organisms, a large portion of their daily routine involves finding and consuming food. The process of locating food resources is called **foraging behavior.** The choices that animals face involve the following:

1. What items should be included in the diet?
2. Given that food is not often distributed evenly in the environment, but occurs in patches or clumps, what path should an animal take between patches, and how should it locate new patches of food?
3. As the food in a patch is depleted, when should the organism depart from that location and seek another patch of food?

⑦ Hummingbirds and various species of bees that visit clumps of flowers to obtain nectar must make each of these decisions. Owls that forage for small rodents in different habitats, including fields and forests, must make similar decisions.

Although the animals certainly are not calculating their own energy budgets as they forage, we can gain some insight into the foraging process by examining the energy costs and gains involved in finding and consuming food. These considerations include energy needed to search for food, energy used to pursue or handle the food, and energy required to digest the food. If the animal is to survive, then the gain in energy from digesting a particular set of food items must exceed the costs. Thus, a praying mantis must expend energy to locate a moth, additional energy is used to strike the moth, still more energy goes toward removing the moth's wings and consuming them, and finally, metabolic energy will be necessary to digest the body of the moth. The mantis will survive if the energy derived from digesting the moth is greater than these costs. This will be particularly true if extra energy is needed for searching for a mate or laying eggs.

Specialists and Generalists

Some animals are **specialists** with respect to diet and habitat selection. Evolution has resulted in these animals being very efficient at utilizing a particular resource. The koala bear, an Australian marsupial, eats the leaves of only certain species of eucalyptus trees. ⑧ Its digestive system is adapted to derive energy from the leaves of these trees more efficiently than are other animals. Although being a specialist means there is the capacity to very successfully exploit a particular resource, there are risks involved. If a plant disease invades and kills trees of the eucalyptus species that form the koalas' diet, koalas may not be able to survive.

At the other end of the continuum are **generalists,** capable of eating a variety of foods or living in a variety of habitats. These animals can survive under a wide range of conditions. Humans are a good example of a generalist species. So, too, are some pest species, like European starlings, introduced into the United States a century ago and now living in almost every available type of habitat. The disadvantage for generalists is that almost everywhere they eat and live, they face competition from other organisms, something that is often avoided by specialists.

SOCIAL BEHAVIOR

Social behavior typically refers to any interactions among members of the same species, but it has also been applied to animals of different species, excluding predator-prey interactions.

LIVING IN GROUPS

Animal populations are often organized into groups. A group of animals may form an aggregation for some simple purpose, such as feeding, drinking, or mating. Several *Drosophila* flies on a piece of rotting fruit is an example of an aggregation. A true animal **society** is a stable group of individuals of the same species that maintains a cooperative social relationship. This association typically extends beyond the level of mating and taking care of young. Social behavior has evolved independently in many species of animals; complex social organizations may be found in invertebrates as well as vertebrates.

⑨　One major benefit of belonging to a group may be that it offers protection against predators (figure 13.9). There is safety in numbers, and the detection of predators may be enhanced by having several individuals on alert to warn against an intruder. In a group, some individuals can be on alert while others are free to be involved in other activities. Also, cooperative hunting and capture of prey would increase the feeding efficiency of predators. Living in social groups is also advantageous in some instances due to the ability to gain protection from the elements (e.g., huddling together in cold weather) and during the processes of mate finding and rearing of young. In many species, most notably the social insects, living in groups has resulted in the evolutionary division of labor, with specific individuals performing specialized tasks (e.g., defense, food procurement, feeding of young).

A disadvantage of group living may be competition for resources. Other disadvantages include the fact that diseases and parasites may spread more rapidly in group-living animals, and the fact that there may be some interference between individuals with regard to reproduction and rearing of young. The value of group living depends on the species and behaviors involved.

FIGURE 13.9

Group Living. A flock of starlings reacts to a bird of prey by forming a tight group, reducing the chances of the predator singling out any particular individual.

AGONISTIC BEHAVIOR, TERRITORIES, AND DOMINANCE HIERARCHIES

In a society of animals, there is usually some maintenance of social structure and spacing of group members. This pattern is often accomplished through agonistic behavior, in which one animal is aggressive or attacks another animal that responds by either returning the aggression or submitting. In rare cases, agonistic behavior is lethal, but usually the animals are not killed or even severely injured. In many species, males vent much of their aggression in the form of threat displays. Displays typically involve signals that serve to warn other males of an intention to defend an area or territory (figure 13.10). Although agonistic behavior may seem antisocial, it is important for maintaining the social order. Agonistic behavior is especially important in the maintenance of territories and dominance hierarchies.

A territorial animal uses agonistic behavior to defend a site or area against certain other individuals. The site is known

Figure 13.10

Agonistic Behavior. A baboon (*Comopithecus hamadryas*) exhibiting a threat display toward other members of the troop.

as its **territory,** and competing individuals are excluded from it. Many male birds and mammals occupy a breeding territory for part of the year. A male will actively defend his area against other males, so that he can attract a female and court her without interference from other males. Territories may offer certain advantages to the occupants, in addition to being a location for attracting a mate and rearing young. Territories may contain a food supply or provide shelter to avoid predators and unfavorable climate.

In **dominance hierarchies,** a group of animals is organized in such a way that some members of the group have greater access to resources, such as food or mates, than do others. Those near the top of the order have first choice of resources, whereas those near the bottom go last and may do without if resources are in short supply. An example of a dominance hierarchy is the "pecking-order" of chickens in a pen. When a small group of chickens is placed together, fights will occur among them until a linear hierarchy of dominance is established. Higher-ranked chickens are among the first to eat and may peck lower-ranked chickens. Once the hierarchy is set, peaceful coexistence is possible. Occasional fights will occur if a bird tries to move up in the order.

Dominance hierarchies exist in many vertebrate groups, the most common being in the form of linear relationships, although triangular relationships may form. In baboons, the strongest male is usually highest in the rank order. But, sometimes, older males may band together forming coalitions to subdue a stronger male and lead the troop.

ALTRUISM

In **altruism,** an individual gives up or sacrifices some of its own reproductive potential to benefit another individual. For example, one individual of a group of crows gives an alarm call to warn other individuals of the group of an approaching predator, even though the call may attract the predator to the sender of the signal. How is it possible that such behavior evolved? Are normal natural selection processes at work here?

To be successful in a biological sense, an animal must produce as many young as possible, thereby passing its genes to succeeding generations. However, passing on genes can be accomplished by aiding a relative and its young because they probably share some genes. In terms of reproductive potential or output, it is theoretically possible that an individual may pass more genes to the next generation by aiding the survival of relatives than it would rearing its own young.

A well-known example of altruism occurs in societies of hymenopteran insects, such as honeybees. The male drones are haploid, and the female workers and queen are diploid, resulting in a genetic asymmetry. Diploid workers share, on the average, 3/4 of their genes with their full sisters. If they reproduced, they would share only 1/2 of their genes with hypothetical offspring. Thus, female honeybees may have more genes in common with their sisters than they would with their own offspring. The workers may pass more genes to the next generation by helping their mother produce more full sisters, some of whom may become reproductive queens, than if they produce their own young.

William Hamilton (1936–) proposed the idea of **kin selection** to explain how selection acting on related animals can affect the fitness of an individual. In this way, a gene carried by a particular individual may pass to the next generation through a related animal. An individual's fitness is therefore based on both the genes it passes on, as well as those common genes passed on by relatives. A genetically based tendency to be altruistic could therefore be passed on by the individual carrying it or by a relative who also carries it. Obviously, for kin selection to work, individuals of a group must be able to identify relatives, as occurs in small groups of primates and in social insects.

Stop and Ask Yourself

12. How do the physiological constraints and preferences of an animal interact in the process of habitat selection?

13. What are some differences between specialists and generalists with respect to habitat selection and foraging behavior?

14. What are some benefits of being a member of a group?

15. Why is agonistic behavior so common in animal societies?

16. What are some benefits of having a territory?

17. How does a dominance hierarchy become established in a group of animals?

SUMMARY

1. Animal behavior includes the many activities of an animal during its lifetime. There are several approaches to the study of animal behavior: comparative psychology, ethology, behavioral ecology, and sociobiology.

2. Natural selection influences animal behavior just as it does other characteristics of an animal. Certain behavioral traits that allow animals to survive and reproduce are favored.

3. Certain behavior patterns require time for maturation, during which an improvement of the behavior occurs as parts of the nervous system and other structures complete development.

4. Many behavior patterns require an interaction of instinctive and learned components for efficient performance. In some instances, an animal may inherit a disposition to learn a specific behavior. Also, an animal may learn certain behavior patterns only during a specific sensitive period early in life.

5. Through learning, an animal can adjust quickly to changes in its environment. Learning is adaptive for animals in an environment where changes are not predictable. The types of learning known to occur in animals include habituation, classical conditioning, instrumental conditioning, latent learning, and insight learning.

6. The nervous system plays a role in regulating behavior through the process of sensory reception of information from the environment, processing and storing that information, and mediating appropriate motor responses.

7. Hormonal effects on behavior may either be organizational, affecting developmental processes such as sexual differentiation, or activational, involving more immediate behavioral responses, such as aggression.

8. Communication in animals requires the use of clear signals by one animal and their reception by another. Visual, acoustic, tactile, and chemical signals are important channels in communication systems.

9. Animals have evolved mechanisms for guiding their selection of habitats in which to live and reproduce, and their choices of foods to eat.

10. Many animal species live in groups in which various benefits are provided. Groups range from simple aggregations to more complex social organizations, or societies.

11. Agonistic behavior in the form of attacks or threat displays is important in spacing the members of a species or establishing and defending a territory. In some instances, a dominance hierarchy may exist in which the members may be ranked in order from the most dominant individual to the most subordinate individual. Once the hierarchy is established, agonistic behavior is reduced in the group.

12. In some societies, behavior in which one individual sacrifices its reproductive potential to help another individual occurs. Altruism may be a result of kin selection, in which aiding one's relatives enhances the spreading of these genes that are shared with relatives.

SELECTED KEY TERMS

behavioral ecology (p. 182)

classical conditioning (p. 184)

comparative psychologists (p. 182)

dominance hierarchies (p. 191)

ethology (p. 182)

foraging behavior (p. 189)

habitat selection (p. 189)

habituation (p. 184)

imprinting (p. 183)

insight learning (p. 185)

instrumental conditioning (p. 184)

latent learning (p. 185)

maturation (p. 182)

sociobiology (p. 182)

territory (p. 191)

CRITICAL THINKING QUESTIONS

1. How can you distinguish between classical and instrumental conditioning? What are some examples of each that might occur in nature?

2. How is kin selection related to natural selection?

3. Will a sea gull incubate an infertile chicken egg placed in her nest? Explain your answer.

4. An advertisement for Boone Trail Nugget Company features a hiker eating a bowl of cereal on a mountaintop. What type of learning does this type of advertisement rely on? Explain your answer.

5. What habitat features would a rattlesnake examine when looking for a place to live?

ECOLOGY I:
INDIVIDUALS AND POPULATIONS

Concepts

1. Ecology is the study of the relationships of organisms to their environment, and to other organisms. In part, it involves the study of how abiotic factors, such as energy, temperature, moisture, light, geology, and soils influence individuals.
2. Ecology also involves the study of populations. Populations grow, and growth is regulated by population density, the carrying capacity of the environment, and interactions between members of the same population.
3. Ecology also involves the study of individuals interacting with members of their own and other species. Herbivory, predator-prey interactions, competition for resources, and other kinds of interactions influence the makeup of animal populations.

Would You Like to Know:

1. whether or not some animals can tolerate colder temperatures than others in the same species? (p. 194)
2. why deer hunters in northern climates take larger animals than hunters in the south? (p. 195)
3. whether or not bears really hibernate? (p. 196)
4. why some animals never need to drink water? (p. 196)
5. how an animal can tell that winter is coming, and that it is time to accumulate food reserves? (p. 196)
6. how long a bird, like a robin, can expect to live? (p. 197)
7. why mosquitoes appear so quickly after a few days of rain? (p. 199)
8. why predators usually do not hunt their prey to extinction? (p. 200)
9. why a parasite usually does not kill its host? (p. 202)

These and other useful questions will be answered in this chapter.

This chapter contains evolutionary concepts, which are set off in this font.

All animals have certain requirements for life. In searching out these requirements, animals come into contact with members of their own species and other species. The interactions that result mold the lives of the animals involved. Sometimes these interactions are obvious and even violent, such as interactions that occur between predator and prey. Other interactions may occur without the participants seeing each other. The multitude of interactions of animals with their environment and other animals are the basis for chapter 14.

ANIMALS AND THEIR ABIOTIC ENVIRONMENT

An animal's **habitat** (environment) includes all living (biotic) and nonliving (abiotic) characteristics of the area in which the animal lives. Abiotic characteristics of a habitat include factors such as availability of oxygen and inorganic ions, light, temperature, and current or wind velocity. Physiological ecologists study abiotic influences and have found that animals live within a certain range of values for any environmental factor. This range is called the **tolerance range** for that factor. At either limit of the tolerance range, one or more essential functions cease. A certain range of values within the tolerance range, called the **range of optimum,** defines the conditions under which an animal is most successful (figure 14.1).

Combinations of abiotic factors are necessary for an animal to survive and reproduce. When one of these is out of the range of tolerance for an animal, that factor becomes a **limiting factor.** For example, even though a stream insect may have the proper substrate for shelter, adequate current to bring in food and aid in dispersal, and the proper ions to ensure growth and development, inadequate supplies of oxygen will make life impossible.

Often, the response of an animal to any of these factors is to orient itself with respect to it; such orientation is called **taxis.** For example, a response to light is called phototaxis. If an animal favors well-lighted environments, and moves toward a light source, it is said to display positive phototaxis. If it prefers low light intensities, it is said to display negative phototaxis.

Physiological ecologists have found that tolerance ranges often change in response to altered environmental conditions (e.g., changes in season). Catfish maintained at 25° C have a tolerance range for temperature that is 2 to 3° C lower than catfish maintained at 30° C. Such changes in tolerance ranges are called **acclimation.**

ENERGY

Energy is the ability to do work. For animals, work includes everything from foraging for food to moving molecules around within cells. To supply their energy needs, animals ingest other organisms—that is, animals are **heterotrophic** (Gr. *hetero,* other + *tropho,* feeder). **Autotrophic** (Gr. *autos,* self + *tropho,* feeder)

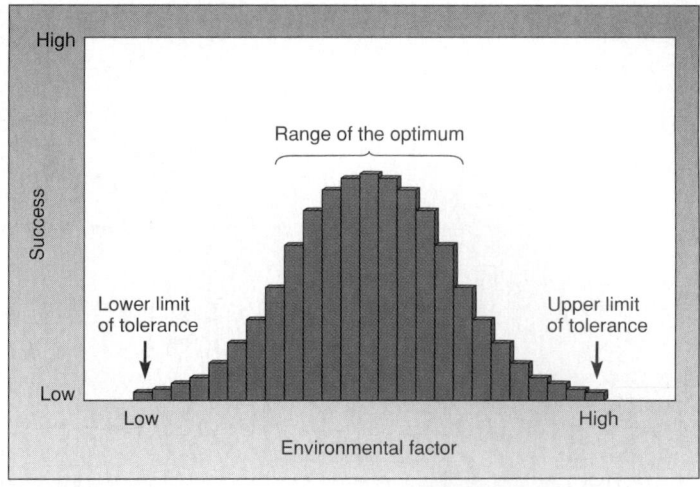

FIGURE 14.1

Tolerance Range of an Animal. The tolerance range of an animal can be depicted by plotting changes in an environmental factor versus some index of success (perhaps egg production, longevity, or growth). The graphs that result are often, though not always, bell-shaped. The range of the optimum is the range of values of the factor within which success is greatest. The range of tolerance and range of the optimum may vary depending on an animal's stage of life, health, and activity.

organisms (e.g., plants) carry on photosynthesis or other carbon-fixing activities that supply their food source. An accounting of the total energy intake of an animal, and a description of how that energy is used and lost, is referred to as an **energy budget** (figure 14.2).

The total energy contained in food eaten by an animal is called the gross energy intake. Some food is undigested, and some food that is digested may not be absorbed into the bloodstream. Energy in unabsorbed and undigested food is lost in the feces. Other food may be absorbed, but later lost to excretion in urine or perspiration. Energy lost in feces and through excretion is called excretory energy.

After excretory energy is accounted for, the remainder of gross energy intake is absorbed and is available for cell work. Some of this energy supports minimal maintenance activities, such as pumping blood; exchanging gases; supporting repair processes; and maintaining nervous, sensory, and endocrine functions. In addition to minimal maintenance activities, animals must support necessary activities, such as catching food, escaping predators, and finding shelter. The energy devoted to the sum of these activities is called existence energy.

After existence and excretory functions are accounted for, any energy that is left can be devoted to growth, mating, nesting, and caring for young. The portion of gross energy intake that exceeds excretory and existence energies is called productive energy. Survival requires that individuals acquire enough energy to supply these productive functions. Favorable energy budgets are sometimes difficult to attain, especially in temperate regions where winter often makes food supplies scarce.

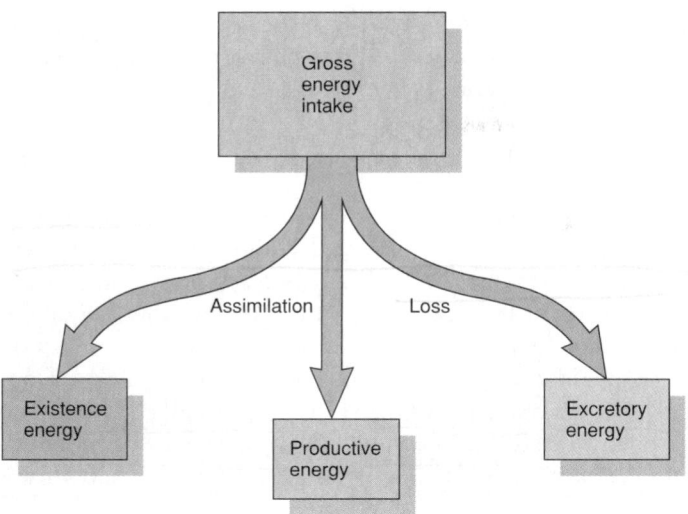

Figure 14.2

Energy Budgets of Animals. The gross energy intake of an animal is the sum of energy lost in excretory pathways, plus energy assimilated for existence and productive functions. The relative sizes of the boxes in this diagram are not necessarily proportional to the amount of energy devoted to each function. The total energy in an energy budget of an animal, and the amount of energy devoted to productive functions, depends upon various internal and external factors (e.g., time of year and reproductive status).

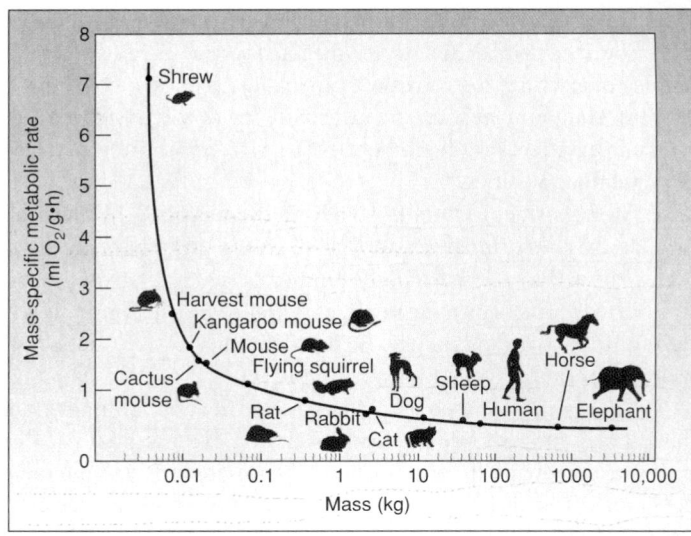

Figure 14.3

The Effects of Body Size on Metabolic Rate for Some Mammals. Metabolic rate is expressed in ml O_2 consumed/g of body weight/hour. Note that the X-axis has a logarithmic scale to compress the difference between the weights of shrew and elephant. Metabolic rates and body size are inversely related.

Temperature

Part of an animal's existence energy is expended in regulating body temperature. Temperature influences the rates of chemical reactions in animal cells (metabolic rate) and affects the overall activity of the animal. The body temperature of an animal seldom remains constant because of an inequality between heat loss and heat gain. Heat energy can be lost to objects in an animal's surroundings as infrared and heat radiation; to the air around the animal through convection; and as evaporative heat loss. On the other hand, heat is gained from solar radiation, infrared and heat radiation from objects in the environment, and relatively inefficient metabolic activities that generate heat as a by-product of cellular functions. Thermoregulatory needs influence many habitat requirements, such as the availability of food, water, and shelter.

Body size and metabolic rates are interrelated. In a particular taxonomic category, smaller animals have higher rates of metabolism than do larger animals. For example, the metabolic rate of a mouse is in excess of 20 times higher per gram of tissue than the metabolic rate of an elephant. The reason for this relationship between size and metabolic rate is not entirely clear. A traditional explanation is that small animals have a higher surface area to volume ratio, and thus as body size increases, there is relatively less body surface over which heat is lost (figure 14.3). This explanation, however, is less than satisfactory. Ectotherms (animals that use external heat sources for regulation of body temperature), whose rate of heat loss is less influenced

by body size, show the same relationship of metabolic rate to body mass as endotherms (animals that use internal heat sources for regulation of body temperature).

The surface-area explanation, however, probably does explain another observation. ② Members of a species living in cold climates tend to be larger than members of the same species in warm climates. The smaller surface area per unit of body mass of large animals reduces heat loss compared to smaller animals of the same species.

Animal Inactivity

When food becomes scarce, or when animals are not feeding for other reasons, they are subject to starvation. This problem is especially severe for small endotherms, whose metabolic rates are high and whose energy reserves are small. Under these circumstances, metabolic activities may decrease dramatically.

Torpor is a time of decreased metabolism and lowered body temperature that occurs in daily activity cycles. Hummingbirds and bats must feed almost constantly when they are active. To survive daily periods of inactivity, their body temperature and metabolic rate drop dramatically. A lower metabolic rate conserves energy and allows hummingbirds and bats to survive periods when they do not feed. At the end of a period of torpor, metabolic activity and body temperature rise quickly.

Hibernation is a time of decreased metabolism and lowered body temperature that may last for weeks or months. True hibernation occurs in small mammals, such as rodents, shrews, and bats. The set point of a hibernator's thermoregulatory center drops to about 20°C, but thermoregulation is not suspended.

This maintenance of thermoregulation distinguishes hibernation from the winter inactivity of ectotherms. Snakes, for example, overwinter in retreats that are unlikely to experience freezing temperatures. In an unusually cold winter, however, animals may freeze to death because they have no internal thermoregulatory abilities.

Winter sleep occurs in some larger animals. These mammals are sustained through periods of winter inactivity by large energy reserves. ③ Body temperatures do not drop substantially, and sleeping animals can wake and become active very quickly—a fact quickly learned by any rookie zoologist probing around the den of a sleeping bear!

Aestivation is a period of inactivity in some animals that must withstand extended periods of drying. The animal usually enters a burrow as its environment begins to dry. It generally does not eat or drink and emerges again after moisture returns. This is common in many invertebrates. For example, some arthropods enter the substrate of drying ponds and streams and remain inactive until the pond or stream fills with water again. The Australian burrowing frog (*Cyclorana alboguttatus; see figure 28.15b*) and the chuckwalla (*Sauromalus obesus; see figure 29.9*) are examples of vertebrates that live in dry habitats and withstand seasonal droughts by aestivating.

MOISTURE

All life's processes occur in the watery environment of the cell. Water loss is inevitable, and it must be replaced if life is to continue. Water is lost in urine, feces, gas exchange, and through evaporation from body surfaces. Animals display numerous adaptations to lower or reduce the impact of water loss. Some animals reduce water loss by producing essentially dry feces. Others produce a concentrated urine and utilize excretory products that can be excreted in semisolid form. Controlling evaporative water loss involves a difficult set of compromises between water conservation and evaporative cooling. Often environments that require water conservation also require cooling. The nocturnal (night-active) life-style of many desert animals is apparently an adaptation to reduce the need for evaporative cooling in a hot environment. Some animals, such as camels, can tolerate water losses of up to 25 to 40% of their total body weight (*see box 38.1*).

Water is acquired from food, drink, and metabolism. Metabolic water is water produced as a by-product of cellular metabolism. ④ Numerous arthropods, and some mammals, have such efficient water conservation mechanisms that metabolic water is sufficient for replacing water loss. For example, flour beetles (*Tribolium*) that live their entire lives in containers of dry flour survive on water produced by cellular metabolism.

Aquatic animals also face water-regulation problems. Maintaining proper ion and water balances in freshwater environments involves conserving ions that tend to be lost to the environment and countering the osmotic influx of water into animal tissues. The problem in marine environments is just the opposite. Seawater is hypertonic to the tissues of many marine animals. As on land, water tends to be lost to the environment, and ions tend to accumulate in body tissues.

LIGHT

Animals are also influenced by light conditions. A photoperiod is the length of the light period in a 24-hour day and is an accurate index of seasonal change. As spring approaches and the period of daylight increases, birds enter their breeding condition. Lengthening daylight hours indicate that conditions will soon be suitable for producing and rearing offspring. ⑤ Similarly, the changing photoperiod in autumn indicates that food supplies will soon be dwindling. This change may be an important cue to stockpile food reserves, or to find a suitable wintering site.

Light also influences cycles of daily activity, called **circadian** (L. *circa*, about + *diem*, day) **rhythms.** Many people have experienced air travel to different time zones and the accompanying upset in timing of daily activities. This upset, commonly known as "jet lag," is a result of our innate (biological) clock telling us it is time for one activity (e.g., sleep) and external cues (e.g., daylight) telling us it is time for another (daytime) activity. Similar problems result from a change between "day shift" and "night shift" at a job. Recent research indicates that the photoperiod is responsible for resetting our biological clocks so the new time of activity can seem normal.

Many animals have circadian rhythms. Freshwater and marine invertebrates have daily patterns of migration between the upper and lower levels of a water column. Many stream invertebrates (e.g., mayfly, stone fly, and caddis fly naiads) have periods of activity at dawn and dusk. Terrestrial animals are either diurnal or nocturnal. These cycles of activity are controlled by biological clocks that are probably influenced by the photoperiod.

Many animals have marked phototactic responses that help them find appropriate habitats. For example, many invertebrates living in the substrates of lakes and streams are negatively phototactic. Their daily activities are thus directed away from light sources and into sheltering substrates.

GEOLOGY AND SOILS

Geological formations and soils often directly or indirectly affect organisms living in an area. Soils reflect an area's geological and biological history and affect animal life directly and indirectly. Soils are homes for a large variety of protozoa, nematodes, earthworms, arthropods, and vertebrates, such as salamanders, snakes, and moles. Characteristics of the soil, such as texture, amount of organic matter, fertility, and water-holding ability directly influence the number and kinds of animals living in or on the soil. Soils also have obvious effects on the kinds of plants that grow in an area. This indirectly influences animal life because all animals, regardless of whether they live in the soil or on top of the soil, ultimately depend on plants for their food.

POPULATIONS

Populations are groups of individuals of the same species that occupy a given area at the same time, and have unique attributes. These attributes include growth rate, age structure, sex ratio, and mortality rate.

POPULATION GROWTH

Animal populations change over time as a result of birth, death, and dispersal. One way to characterize a population with regard to the death of individuals is with survivorship curves (figure 14.4). The Y-axis of a survivorship graph is a logarithmic plot of numbers of survivors, and the X-axis of the graph is a linear plot of age. Note that there are three kinds of survivorship curves. Individuals in type I (convex) populations survive to an old age, then die rapidly. Environmental factors are relatively unimportant in influencing mortality, and most individuals live their potential life span. Some human populations approach type I survivorship. Individuals in type II (diagonal) populations have a constant probability of death throughout their lives. The environment has an important influence on death, and the environment is no harsher on the young than on the old. Populations of birds and rodents often have type II survivorship curves. Individuals in type III (concave) populations experience very high juvenile mortality. Those reaching adulthood, however, experience a much lower mortality rate. Fishes and many invertebrates display type III survivorship curves.

Mortality in natural populations is often high. In birds, for example, it is not uncommon for each cohort to experience greater than 50% mortality each year. ⑥ The potential life span of the American robin, for example, is 11 years; however, the average robin probably lives only 1.4 years.

Exponential Growth

The potential for population growth can be demonstrated in the laboratory under conditions that provide abundant resources and space. For example, placing a few fruit flies in a large culture jar containing abundant food allows them to reproduce very rapidly.

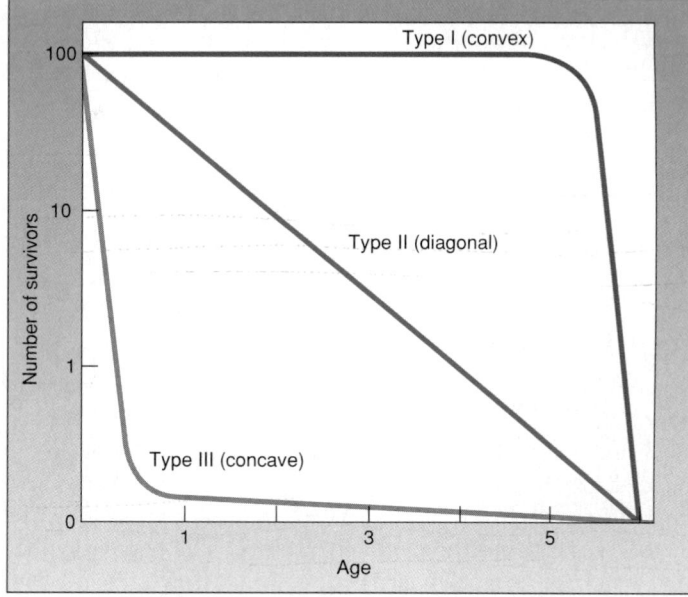

FIGURE **14.4**

Survivorship. Survivorship curves are a plot of number of survivors (usually a logarithmic plot) versus age. Type I curves apply to populations in which individuals are likely to live out their potential life span. Type II curves apply to populations in which mortality rates are constant throughout age classes. Type III curves apply to populations in which mortality rates are highest for the youngest cohorts.

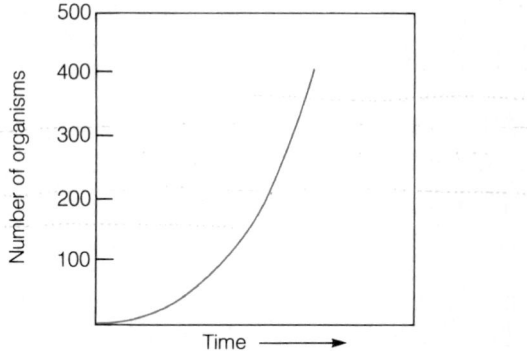

FIGURE **14.5**

Exponential Growth. The number of organisms (Y-axis) is plotted on an arithmetic scale and results in a curve with an increasing slope.

Source: Leland G. Johnson, Biology, 2d Ed. Copyright © 1987 Wm. C. Brown Communications, Inc. Dubuque, Iowa.

One female fruit fly will lay in excess of 50 eggs. Reproductive adults develop in about 14 days, with approximately equal numbers of male and female offspring. For each female that began the population, 50 flies would be expected 2 weeks later. For each female in the second generation, 50 more flies would be produced after 2 more weeks, and so on. In other words, the population is experiencing **exponential growth.** Exponential growth is shown in figure 14.5 in an arithmetic plot. Rather than increasing by adding a constant number of individuals to the population in every generation, the population increases by the same ratio per unit time.

All populations do not display the same capacity for growth. Factors such as the number of offspring produced, the likelihood of survival to reproductive age, the duration of the reproductive period, and the length of time it takes to reach maturity all influence reproductive potential. The capacity of a population to increase maximally is called its **biotic potential** or **intrinsic rate of growth.** It is symbolized by r and defined as the rate of population increase under optimal conditions.

Logistic Population Growth

It should be obvious that exponential growth cannot occur indefinitely. In some years, for example, American robin populations are larger than in other years; on average, however, robin populations are relatively constant. The constraints placed on a population by climate, food, space, and other environmental factors is called **environmental resistance.** The population size that a particular environment can support is called the environment's **carrying capacity,** and is symbolized by K. In these situations, growth curves assume a sigmoid, or flattened **S** shape (figure 14.6a).

The effects of environmental resistance are often not instantaneous. For example, a field of grain may support a large population of young field mice, but as mice mature and acquire larger appetites, resources may dwindle. Populations on the increase, therefore, may exceed the carrying capacity. Eventually, increased death rate will cause the population to decrease to, or go below, K. Growth curves may thus fluctuate around K, or become **J**-shaped (figure 14.6b,c).

POPULATION REGULATION

The conditions that must be met for an animal to survive are unique for every species. What many species have in common, however, is that population density and competition impact populations in predictable ways. In addition, unstable environmental conditions may prevent animal populations from ever reaching the carrying capacity of the environment.

Population Density

Some factors influence the number of animals in a population without regard to the number of individuals per unit space (density). For example, weather conditions often limit populations. An extremely cold winter with little snow cover may devastate a population of lizards sequestered beneath the litter of the forest floor. Regardless of the size of the population, a certain percentage of individuals will freeze to death. Activities of humans, such as construction and deforestation, often affect animal populations in a similar fashion. Such factors are said to regulate populations in a density-independent fashion.

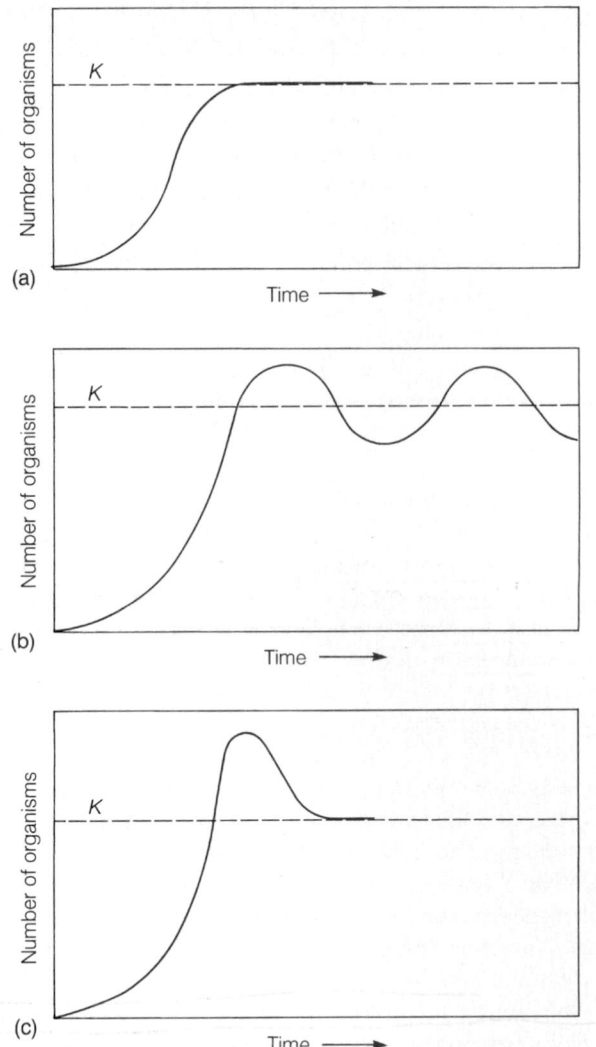

FIGURE 14.6

Logistic Population Growth. Logistic growth curves take into consideration the fact that limited resources place an upper limit on population size. (*a*) When carrying capacity (*K*) is reached, population growth levels off, creating an S-shaped curve. (*b,c*) During its exponential growth phase, a population may overshoot carrying capacity because demand on resources may lag behind population growth. When that happens, numbers may cycle on either side of *K*, or form a J-shaped curve.

Other regulatory factors are more severe when population density is high (or sometimes very low) than they are at other densities. Such regulatory factors are said to be density dependent. Animals often use territorial behavior, song, and scent marking to tell others to look elsewhere for reproductive space. These actions become more pronounced as population density increases, and are thus density dependent. Other density dependent factors include competition for resources, disease, predation, and parasitism.

Intraspecific Competition

Competition occurs when animals utilize similar resources and, in some way, interfere with each other's procurement of those resources. Competition between members of the same species is called **intraspecific competition** and is often intense, because the resource requirements of individuals are nearly identical. Intraspecific competition may occur without individuals coming into direct contact. (The "early bird that gets the worm" doesn't necessarily see later arrivals.) In other instances, the actions of one individual directly affect another. Territorial behavior and the actions of socially dominant individuals are examples of direct interference.

r and K Selection

In some instances, the logistic-growth model accurately characterizes a population. Populations whose size tends to evolve toward their carrying capacity are said to be **K-selected.** Individuals in these populations are regulated by density-dependent factors, and are found in relatively predictable environments. In K-selecting environments, populations tend to be made up of long-lived, slowly maturing species. Reproductive rates are relatively low, and the young may receive substantial parental care. Most populations of large mammals are produced through K selection.

At the opposite extreme are populations that are prevented from achieving their carrying capacity. When a trait is selected for that promotes rapid population growth, ecologists say that the population is **r-selected.** Regulation through r selection involves density-independent factors like climate. Individuals may occupy marginally adequate habitats and reproduce very quickly when conditions permit. One female produces many young, and developmental stages mature quickly with little parental care. Efficient dispersal systems distribute eggs, young, or adults. In other words, the biotic potential of individuals with r-selected traits has been maximized during evolution. ⑦ A mosquito population that increases rapidly a few days after a rainy period is a familiar example of r selection (table 14.1).

Stop and Ask Yourself

5. What does the survivorship curve of a type III population look like?

6. What factor(s) are taken into consideration in logistic growth calculations that place a limit on exponential growth?

7. What is the difference between density-independent and density-dependent population regulation? Give examples of each.

8. Are environmental factors, such as weather, very important, moderately important, or unimportant in determining survivorship of juvenile stages in r-selected species?

TABLE 14.1	CHARACTERISTICS OF r VERSUS K SELECTION	
r-Selected Traits	**K-Selected Traits**	
Early maturation increases reproductive potential	Late maturation avoids risks of breeding	
Many, smaller young produced	Fewer, larger young produced	
Short life spans (often less than 1 year)	Longer life spans	
Less parental care of offspring	More parental care increases individual offspring's chances of survival	
Uncrowded conditions require little competition for resources	Crowding nearly always results in intense competition for resources	

INTERSPECIFIC INTERACTIONS

Members of other species can affect all characteristics of a population. Interspecific interactions include herbivory, predation, competition, and symbiosis. Animals, however, are rarely limited by artificial categories that zoologists create to help organize life's complexity. As you study the following material, realize that animals often do not interact with other animals in only one way. The nature of interspecific interactions may change as an animal matures, as seasons change, or as the environment changes.

HERBIVORY

Animals that feed on plants by cropping portions of the plant, but usually not killing the plant, are called herbivores. Some are grazers (e.g., cattle and bison), which means they feed on grasses and other herbaceous vegetation. Browsers (e.g., deer and rabbits) feed on the leaves and twigs of woody plants. Other forms of herbivory include frugivory (feeding on fruits), seed eating, nectar and sap feeding, and pollen eating.

PREDATION

Predators are animals that feed by killing and eating other organisms. Predators influence the distribution and abundance of prey, and conversely, the distribution and abundance of prey influence predator populations. For example, the lake trout (*Salvelinus namaycush*) is the only freshwater fish whose native distribution included virtually all of North America but never crossed the narrow Bering Strait into Siberia. In contrast, lake trout have crossed larger expanses of ocean to the freshwater systems of islands in northern Canada. Predation by the Pacific

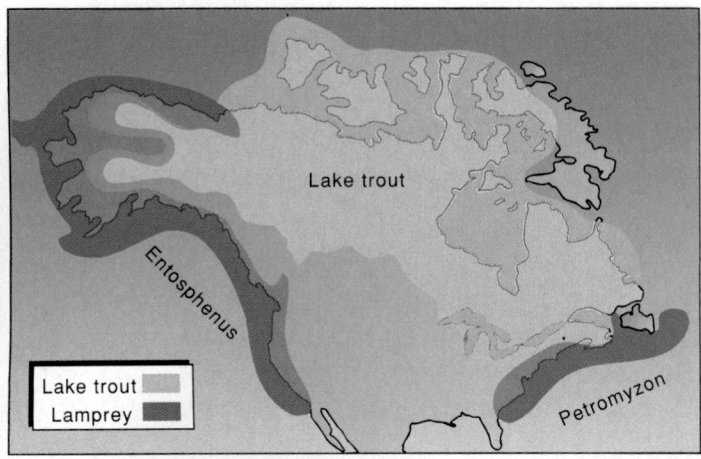

Figure **14.7**

Predator/Prey Interactions. The distribution of lake trout (shown in lighter green) (*Salvelinus namaycush*) in North America before the construction of the Welland Canal. Purple areas show the distribution of sea lampreys. *From C. C. Lindsey, "Problems in Zoology of the Lake Trout,* Salvelinus namaycush,*" Journal of Fisheries Research Board of Canada, 21:977–994, 1964. Used by permission.*

sea lamprey (*Entosphenus*) has probably prevented the movement of lake trout to Siberian freshwater systems (figure 14.7). This explanation is supported by the decline of lake trout in the Great Lakes after the construction of the Welland Canal allowed the Atlantic sea lamprey (*Petromyzon*) to move into the Great Lakes (*see box 27.1*).

Interactions between predators and prey are complex and are affected by many characteristics of the environment. ⑧ Coexistence of predator and prey apparently requires a habitat that allows prey to take refuge when their numbers are small. Under these conditions, predator populations decline, but some survive by finding other sources of food.

INTERSPECIFIC COMPETITION

When competition for resources occurs between members of different species, one species may be forced to move or become extinct, or the two species may share the resource and coexist.

Competitive Exclusion

The **competitive exclusion principle** has influenced the thinking of ecologists for over 50 years. It states that two species with exactly the same requirements for food, habitat, nest sites, and other conditions of life cannot coexist.

Numerous investigations in laboratories and observations in nature, however, have failed to document the universality of the competitive exclusion principle. Part of the reason for this

failure is the fact that two species rarely have identical requirements for food, space, and other conditions of life.

Although it is an exception to the results of most investigations, competitive exclusion apparently did occur in the citrus groves of southern California. California red scale is an insect pest of citrus trees. A wasp parasite of scale insects, called the golden-naveled scalesucker, lays its eggs under the scalelike citrus pest, and larvae feed on and eventually kill the scale insect. In hopes of more efficient pest control, a second scalesucker, the Lingnan scalesucker, was introduced to southern California from China. The Lingnan scalesucker was able to outcompete the golden-naveled scalesucker, and within 2 years, the Lingnan species completely replaced the native species at some plots.

Coexistence

Most studies have shown that competing species can coexist. Coexistence can occur when species utilize resources in slightly different ways, and when the effects of interspecific competition are less severe than the effects of intraspecific competition. These ideas can be illustrated by the studies of Robert MacArthur on five species of warblers that all used the same caterpillar prey. Warblers partitioned their spruce tree habitats by dividing a tree into preferred regions for foraging. Although there was some overlap of foraging regions, competition was limited, and the five species coexisted (figure 14.8).

Resources can be divided among competing species in many ways. Partitioning, however, cannot occur indefinitely because the total quantity of any resource is limited. If individuals in a population cannot obtain enough of a resource to support reproduction, then similarities between species become important limiting factors, and competitive exclusion may occur.

COEVOLUTION

The evolution of ecologically related species is sometimes coordinated such that each species exerts a strong selective influence on the other. This is called **coevolution.**

Coevolution may occur when species are competing for the same resource, or during predator-prey interactions. In the evolution of predator-prey relationships, for example, natural selection should favor the development of protective characteristics in prey species. Similarly, selection favors characteristics in predators that allow them to become better at catching and immobilizing prey. Coevolution in predator-prey relationships occurs when a change toward greater predator efficiency is countered by increased elusiveness of prey. If evolutionary rates are balanced, neither species would be expected to win this evolutionary "arms race." If not balanced, then one species could become extinct, and its role would likely be taken over

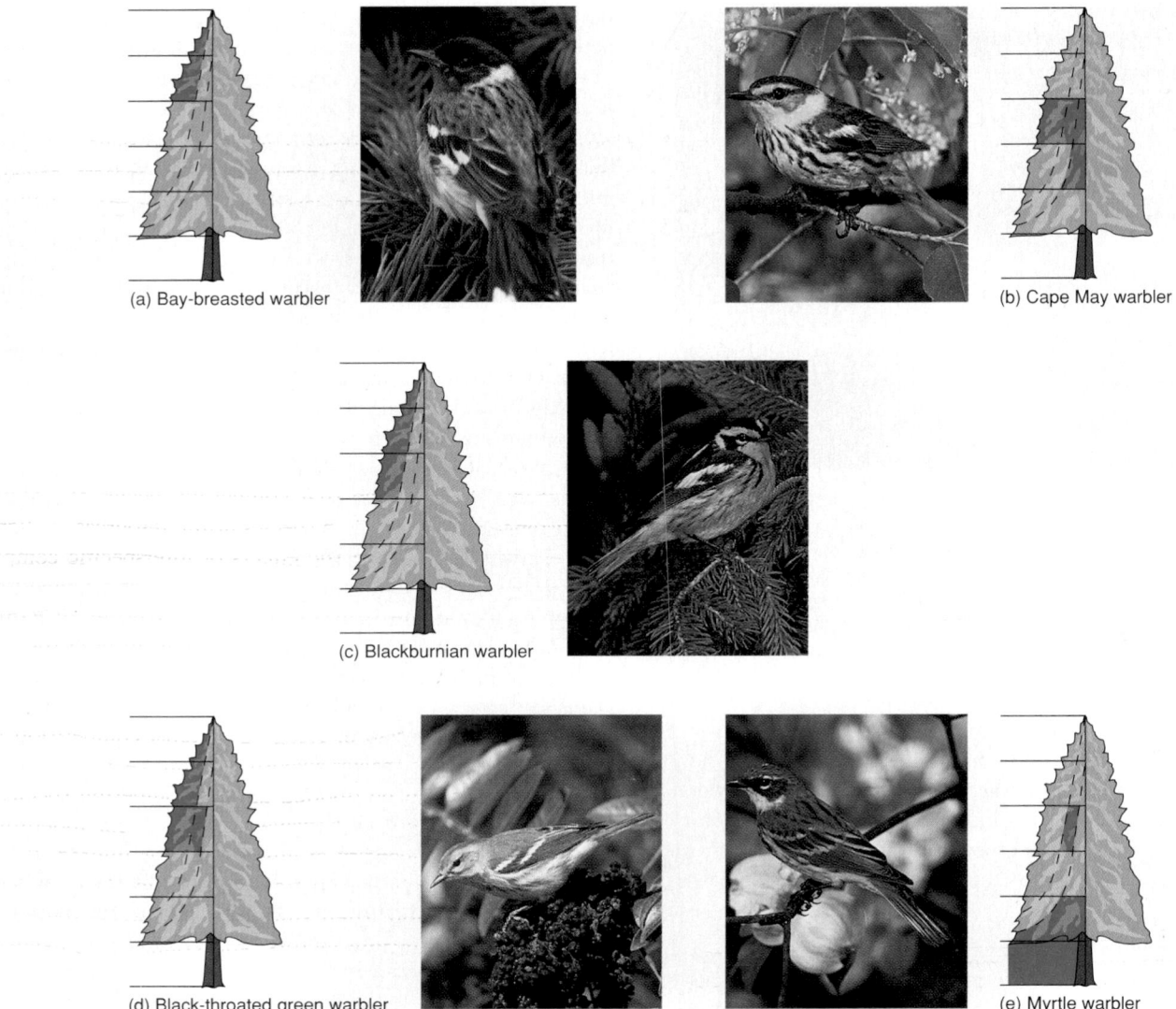

(a) Bay-breasted warbler

(b) Cape May warbler

(c) Blackburnian warbler

(d) Black-throated green warbler

(e) Myrtle warbler

FIGURE 14.8

Coexistence of Competing Species. Robert MacArthur found that five species of warblers (*a–e*) coexisted by partitioning resources. Partitioning occurred by dividing up spruce trees into preferred foraging regions. Preferred foraging regions are shown in dark green. (*a*) Bay-breasted warbler (*Dendroica castanea*), (*b*) Cape May warbler (*D. tigrina*), (*c*) Blackburnian warbler (*D. fusca*), (*d*) Black-throated green warbler (*D. virens*) (*e*) Myrtle warbler (*D. coronata*).

by another species. Although many examples of predator-prey relationships exist, the evidence documenting their development through coevolution is scanty.

Coevolution is obvious in the relationships between some flowering plants and their animal pollinators (figure 14.9). Early land plants were dependent on wind and rain to achieve pollination. Cross-pollination became more likely when pollen began to be carried from one flower to another by insects, birds, or bats. Coevolution is obvious in plants that display adaptations for attracting specific pollinators, or when animals display adaptations for extracting pollen and nectar from specific plants.

Flowers attract pollinators with a variety of elaborate olfactory and visual adaptations. Insect-pollinated flowers are usually yellow or blue, because insects best see these wavelengths of light. In addition, petal arrangements often provide perches for pollinating insects. Flowers pollinated by hummingbirds, on the other hand, are often tubular and red. Hummingbirds have a poor sense of smell, but see red very well. The long beak of hummingbirds is an adaptation that allows them to reach far into tubular flowers. Their hovering ability means they have no need of a perch. One particularly striking example of coevolution between a hummingbird and a flowering plant occurs in the tropics. *Ensifera ensifera* is a hummingbird with an extremely long

FIGURE **14.9**

Coevolution. Flowers and their pollinators have coevolved for millions of years. Typical hummingbird-pollinated flowers are red, and they produce large amounts of nectar. As a hummingbird feeds on the nectar with its long, thin bill, its head contacts the flower parts involved in pollination. The Cost's hummingbird (*Calypte costae*) is shown here.

bill (in excess of 8 cm). It feeds almost exclusively on passion flowers, which store their nectar deep within tubular flowers. The structure of the flower excludes virtually all other nectar-feeding animals, limiting competition for the hummingbird and reducing the chances of cross-pollination with other plant species.

SYMBIOSIS

Some of the best examples of adaptations arising through coevolution are seen when two different species live in continuing, intimate associations. These relationships are called **symbiosis** (Gr. *sym*, together + *bio*, life). Such interspecific interactions influence the species involved in dramatically different ways. In some instances, one member of the association benefits, and the other is harmed. In other cases, life without the partner would be impossible for both.

Parasitism

Parasitism is a very common form of symbiosis in which one organism lives in or on a second organism, called a host. The host usually survives at least long enough for the parasite to complete one or more life cycles.

The relationships between a parasite and its host(s) are often very complex. Some parasites have life histories involving multiple hosts. The definitive or final host is the host that

harbors the sexual stages of the parasite. A fertile female in a definitive host may produce and release hundreds of thousands of eggs in its lifetime. Each egg that is released gives rise to an immature stage that may be a parasite of a second host. This second host is called an intermediate host, and asexual reproduction occurs in this host. More than one intermediate host and more than one immature stage may be involved in some life cycles. For the life cycle to be completed, the final immature stage must have access to a definitive host. The likelihood that a particular egg will mature into a reproductive adult is usually remote. Producing large numbers of eggs is one of many parasitic adaptations that help ensure that a few individuals will eventually complete the life cycle. In any symbiotic relationship, however, half of the story is missed by focusing only on the parasite. Hosts may evolve mechanisms that help them resist parasitic infections. Many examples of coevolutionary interactions between host and parasite are cited in Part Five of this textbook.

Parasitoids are animals that deposit eggs or other developmental stages on another animal. As immatures develop, they live off host tissues and eventually kill the host. Because the death of the host is the usual outcome, parasitoids combine features of parasite and predator. For example, ichneumonid wasps lay eggs on or in other insects. The larvae feed on the host's tissues during larval development, eventually killing the host.

Commensalism

Commensalism is a symbiotic relationship in which one member of the relationship benefits, and the second is neither helped nor harmed. The distinction between parasitism and commensalism is somewhat difficult to apply in natural situations. Whether or not the host is harmed often depends on factors such as the nutritional state of the host. Thus, symbiotic relationships may be commensalistic in some situations and parasitic in others. One example of a commensalistic relationship involves *Entamoeba gingivalis*, a common amoeba that lives in the mouth of humans. Although it is often associated with tooth decay, it does not cause tooth or gum decay. It is passed from individual to individual by direct contact. Commensals may be provided with food, transportation (a relationship called phoresis), or shelter by their hosts.

Mutualism

Mutualism is a symbiotic relationship in which both members of the relationship benefit. Examples of mutualism abound in the animal kingdom. Clownfish and sea anemones live together in close association. The clownfish gain protection from the anemones and in turn provide some food to the anemones (figure 14.10a). Another example of mutualism is the cleaning of

(a)

(b)

FIGURE 14.10

Mutualism. (*a*) A mutualistic relationship between a clownfish (*Amphiprion perideraion*) and a sea anemone. The clownfish provides the anemone with scraps of its food and the anemone provides protection for the clownfish. The clownfish is apparently covered by mucus that does not elicit discharge of the anemone's stinging organelles called nematocysts. (*b*) Cleaning symbiosis is a common mutualistic relationship between marine animals. This Nassau grouper (*Epinephelus striatus*) is being cleaned by two gobies.

one animal by other animals. In cleaning mutualism, small fishes or invertebrates may swim into the mouth of larger fishes to remove ectoparasites. Characteristic markings and behavior identify cleaner species, which enjoy relative safety in the mouths of predatory species, such as barracudas and groupers (figure 14.10*b*).

Coevolution may occur in any symbiotic relationship. A host species that has a long history of association with a particular parasite may evolve greater resistance to the parasite. Similarly, parasites that are extremely virulent may kill their host before the parasite has a chance to reproduce. Thus, lower pathogenicity on the part of the parasite is advantageous for most parasites. Commensalistic or mutualistic symbiotic relationships, therefore, tend to be long-standing.

Commensalism or mutualism, however, is not a guaranteed outcome for all symbiotic relationships. It may be advantageous for a parasite to kill or weaken its host if perpetuation of a parasite species requires that a host be eaten. For example, certain acanthocephalans are larval parasites of freshwater crustaceans called amphipods and adult parasites of mallard ducks. Mallards acquire infections by eating amphipods. When infected by acanthocephalan larvae, the behavior of amphipods changes dramatically. Their usual negative phototaxis is reversed so that they leave the bottom substrates of a lake or river, and swim near the surface where they are easy prey for mallard ducks.

OTHER INTERSPECIFIC ADAPTATIONS

Many other characteristics of animals have been shaped by interspecific interactions. Predator-prey systems have led to some unusual adaptations, (e.g., coloration patterns) in either predator or prey species.

Camouflage

Camouflage occurs when an animal's color patterns help hide the animal, or a developmental stage, from another animal. **Cryptic coloration** (L. *crypticus*, hidden) is a type of camouflage that occurs when an animal takes on color patterns in its environment. Many animals blend in with their surroundings—some prey animals are camouflaged to prevent them from being seen by predators. For example, the Arctic hare acquires a white coat at its fall molt to blend in with its snowy background. In the spring, however, when the snow melts and bare ground is exposed, another molt produces a brown coat.

Countershading is a kind of camouflage common in eggs of frogs and toads. These eggs are darkly pigmented on top and lightly pigmented on the bottom (*see figure 10.8*). When viewed by a bird or other predator from above, the dark of the top side hides the eggs from detection against the darkness below. On the other hand, when viewed from below by a fish, the light undersurface blends with the bright air-water interface. Similar countershading occurs in many fish species, and decorator crabs mask themselves with algae and other concealing organisms to help themselves blend in with their environment.

Predators use camouflage to avoid detection by prey. The rufous-red coat overlaid with black stripes that breaks up the outline of a tiger in the forests of India, China, and Persia successfully hides the tiger as it stalks its prey (figure 14.11).

FIGURE 14.11

Camouflage. The color pattern of this tiger (*Panthera tigris*) provides effective camouflage that helps when stalking prey.

Aposematic Coloration and Mimicry

Some animals that protect themselves by being dangerous or distasteful to predators advertise their condition by conspicuous coloration. This coloration is a clear signal to predators to stay away. Certain dendrobatid frogs of Central and South America have toxic secretions in their skin, and are brightly colored to warn potential predators (*see box 28.1*). The sharply contrasting white stripe of a skunk and bright colors of poisonous snakes give similar messages. These color patterns are examples of warning or **aposematic coloration** (Gr. *apo*, away from + *sematic*, sign).

Resembling conspicuous animals may also be advantageous. **Mimicry** (L. *mimus*, to imitate) occurs when a species resembles one, or sometimes more than one, other species and gains protection by the resemblance. **Batesian mimicry** occurs when one species, called the mimic, resembles a second species,

FIGURE 14.12

Müllerian Mimicry. These six species of *Heliconius* are all distasteful to bird predators. A bird that consumes any member of the six species will be likely to avoid all six species in the future.

called the model, that is protected by aposematic coloration. An example of this form of mimicry occurs with monarch and viceroy butterflies. Monarch butterflies lay their eggs on milkweed plants, and as caterpillars grow, they incorporate toxins from the milkweed into their tissues. Jays or other birds that eat insects apparently learn about monarchs through experience. Jays that have experienced the taste of a monarch will not only refuse to eat monarchs, but they will also refuse to eat the viceroys that mimic the monarchs.

A second form of mimicry, called **Müllerian mimicry,** occurs when the model and the mimic are both distasteful. A predator does not have to taste both of the species involved to encounter the distasteful form (figure 14.12).

Stop and Ask Yourself

9. What is competitive exclusion? Under what circumstances is coexistence of competing species possible?

10. What is parasitism? How does it differ from commensalism and mutualism? What is coevolution?

11. How might coevolution of parasites and their hosts lead to mutualism?

12. Under what circumstances might it be advantageous for parasites to kill their hosts?

13. What is cryptic coloration? Give an example.

14. What is mimicry? What are two forms it may take?

SUMMARY

1. Many abiotic factors influence where an animal may live. Animals have a tolerance range and a range of optimum for environmental factors.
2. Energy for animal life comes from consuming autotrophs or other heterotrophs. It is expended in excretory, existence, and productive functions.
3. Temperature, water, light, and soils are important environmental factors that influence animal life-styles.
4. Animal populations change in size over time. Change can be characterized using life tables and survivorship curves.
5. Animal populations grow exponentially until the carrying capacity of the environment is achieved, at which point environmental resistance restricts population growth.
6. Population regulation may occur by density-independent or density-dependent mechanisms. Population control mechanisms may prevent some populations from achieving their carrying capacity.
7. Interspecific interactions influence animal populations. These interactions include herbivory, predator-prey interactions, interspecific competition, coevolution, mimicry, and symbiosis.

SELECTED KEY TERMS

autotrophic (*p. 194*)
carrying capacity (*p. 198*)
coevolution (*p. 200*)
energy budget (*p. 194*)
exponential growth (*p. 197*)
habitat (*p. 194*)
heterotrophic (*p. 194*)
limiting factor (*p. 194*)
mimicry (*p. 204*)
symbiosis (*p. 202*)

CRITICAL THINKING QUESTIONS

1. Explain how a 5 part per million level of dissolved oxygen might be a limiting factor for a fish in the summer, but may be completely suitable for that same fish in the winter.
2. Compare the survivorship curves for human populations of developed and Third-world countries.
3. Assuming a starting population of 10 individuals, a doubling time of 1 month, and no mortality, how many generations would it take a hypothetical population to achieve 10,000 individuals?
4. Why do you think that winter inactivity of many small mammals takes the form of hibernation, whereas winter inactivity in larger mammals is in the form of winter sleep?
5. Are most parasites *K*-selected or *r*-selected? Explain.

ECOLOGY II:
COMMUNITIES AND ECOSYSTEMS

Concepts

1. All populations living in an area make up a community. Communities have unique attributes that can be characterized by ecologists.
2. Communities and their physical surroundings are called ecosystems. Energy flowing through an ecosystem does not cycle. Energy that comes into an ecosystem must support all organisms living there before it is lost as heat. Nutrients and water, on the other hand, cycle through an ecosystem and are reused by organisms.
3. The earth can be divided into ecosystem types according to their characteristic plants, animals, and physical factors.
4. Concepts of community and ecosystem ecology provide a basis for understanding many of our ecological problems including human population growth, pollution, and resource depletion.

Would You Like to Know:

1. why we have an energy crisis? (p. 209)

2. why predators, such as hawks and eagles, are relatively uncommon, but other kinds of animals, such as robins and rabbits, are often so numerous? (p. 213)

3. where many of the atoms that make up your body's tissues were in the years before you were born? (p. 214)

4. what was one of the earliest natural applications of solar power? (p. 216)

5. whether or not the earth's current human population can be supported for many years to come? (p. 223)

6. why predators are often the first to feel the effects of poisons released into the environment? (p. 224)

These and other useful questions will be answered in this chapter.

All populations living in an area make up a **community.** When we take off our shoes to explore the animals living in streams we enter a foreign environment. However, we may have some ideas about what we will find because ecologists have found that community interactions, even in very different communities, have common themes.

Communities cannot be considered apart from their physical environment. Communities and their physical environment are called **ecosystems,** and by studying ecosystems, ecologists discover how communities are influenced by their physical surroundings. A stream community, for example, depends on supplies of carbon, phosphorus, nitrogen, water, and energy. At the same time, however, populations alter their physical environment. Stream animals reshape the stream by digging into its banks or by moving substrate. Even in the act of dying, a stream animal changes the characteristics of its environment by contributing organic matter to the stream bed.

This chapter examines the interactions occurring in communities and ecosystems. The principles that explain these interactions can help us understand many of today's environmental problems.

COMMUNITY STRUCTURE AND DIVERSITY

Stream communities are not just random mixtures of species; instead, they have a unique organization. Most communities have certain members that are of overriding importance in determining community characteristics. For example, a stream may have a large population of rainbow trout that helps determine the makeup of certain invertebrate populations on which the trout feed. Species that are responsible for establishing community characteristics are called **dominant species.**

Keystone species are species on which several other species depend. Removal of a keystone species would cause the death of the dependent species. The beaver, for example, constructs a dam that creates a habitat that supports many aquatic species.

Communities are also characterized by cycles of activity. Stream invertebrates are most active around sunset and sunrise. In other communities, some animals are nocturnal (night active). Nocturnal animals may avoid predators and the hot dry conditions of the daylight hours. Most birds (except owls), on the other hand, are diurnal (day active) and are dependent on keen vision for gathering food and avoiding predators. Other patterns of activity may follow the seasons, or conditions of temperature and moisture. Daily, seasonal, or other cycles of activity are referred to as a community's temporal structure.

Many communities also have a spatial structure, which is most obvious in the layering that occurs in a forest or a lake. Most photosynthesis occurs in the upper layers of forests and lakes. Animals feeding on this plant life must live in or visit these upper regions. Eventually, organic matter falls to the forest floor, or lake bottom, where it supports other organisms.

Community structure is also reflected in the variety of animals present in a community, called the **community**

(species) diversity or richness. Forces of nature and human activities influence community diversity. Factors that promote high diversity include a wide variety of resources, high productivity, climatic stability, moderate levels of predation, and moderate levels of disturbance from outside the community. Pollution often reduces the species diversity of ecosystems.

THE ECOLOGICAL NICHE

The **ecological niche** is an important concept of community structure. The niche of any species includes all the attributes of an animal's life-style: where it looks for food, what it eats, where it nests, and what conditions of temperature and moisture it requires. By measuring and plotting the tolerance ranges of an animal for environmental factors, a multidimensional image can be constructed that describes how an animal functions in a community (figure 15.1). Theoretically, competition results when the niches of two species overlap. Although niche overlap occurs in many communities, it tends to be minimized as communities mature. Niche overlap may be reduced if a common resource is divided in very specific ways. This mechanism is called niche diversification.

Although the niche concept is very difficult to quantify, it is valuable in helping us perceive community structure. It illustrates that members of a community tend to complement each other in resource use. They tend to partition resources rather than compete for them. It also helps us visualize the role of an animal in the environment.

COMMUNITY STABILITY

As with individuals, communities are born and they die. Between those events is a time of continual change. Some changes in the life of a community are not permanent changes. These include the replacement of old individuals by those of the next generation and seasonal fluctuations in the abundance of some animals. Other changes, however, are permanent and directional. Some permanent changes are the result of climatic or geological events. Others are brought about by the members of the community. It is the latter that are important for understanding community structure and diversity.

The dominant members of a community often change a community in predictable ways in a process called **succession** (L. *successio,* to follow). Communities may begin in areas nearly devoid of life. Geological events, such as the retreat of a glacier, may form a deep, nutrient-poor lake. This lake, however, will not remain in its early postglacial condition forever. Nutrients that can support new life wash into the lake from surrounding hillsides. The first community to become established in an area is called the **pioneer community.** Death, decay, and additional nutrients from the shore provide the raw materials that further enrich the lake. Animals (e.g., lake trout) that require deep, cold water can no longer survive, and are replaced by species that live in warmer, shallower waters. Over thousands of years, the lake is filled with organic matter and inorganic sediments. Eventually, what was once a lake is transformed into a marsh,

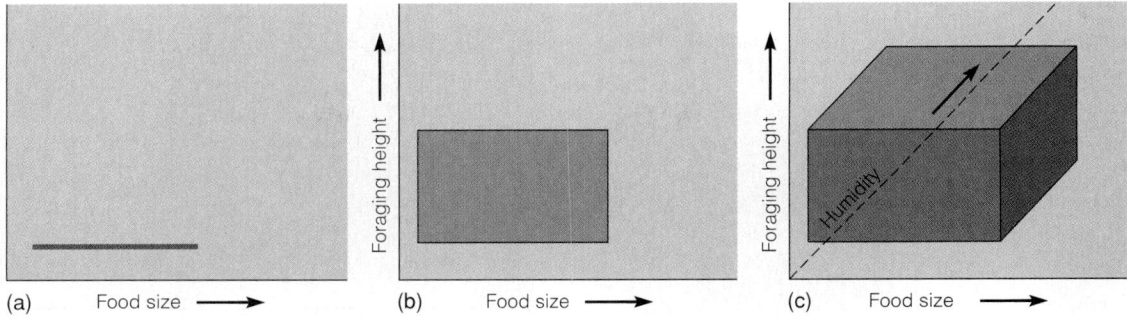

FIGURE 15.1

The Niche as a Multidimensional Space. Each characteristic of an animal's niche can be plotted on a separate axis of a graph. A visualization of a three-dimensional niche involving (*a*) food size, (*b*) foraging height, and (*c*) humidity is shown here. Additional dimensions would be added to portray the complete niche.

then a field, and finally a forest. Each successional stage is called a **seral stage,** and the entire successional sequence is a **sere** (ME. *seer,* to wither). Succession occurs because the dominant life-forms of a sere gradually make the area less favorable for themselves, but more favorable for organisms of the next successional stage.

The final community (the forest in our example) is called the **climax community.** It is different from the seral stages that preceded it because it can tolerate its own reactions. The accumulation of the products of life and death no longer make the area unfit for the individuals living there. Climax communities usually have complex structure and high species diversity. Species of climax communities tend to be *K*-selected. The stability of a climax community generally depends on a stable environment, although moderate, short-lived disturbances are tolerated.

If succession begins in an area that did not previously support a community, it is called primary succession. Examples include the establishment of a community on a newly exposed stretch of sandy beach or a new volcanic island (figure 15.2a). Succession also may occur in areas that previously supported a community, but where some outside disturbance (e.g., fire) upset the previous community. This kind of succession, called secondary succession, occurs more rapidly than primary succession because some organisms are already living there (figure 15.2b,c).

Stop and Ask Yourself

1. What are dominant species?
2. What is community diversity, and what factors promote high diversity?
3. In what way is succession brought about by the dominant members of a sere? How is the climax community different from a sere?
4. What is the difference between primary and secondary succession?

ECOSYSTEMS

In this section you will learn two important facts.   ① First, energy on this planet is not recyclable. Although energy is constantly coming to the earth from the sun, when we use energy stored in the earth's energy reserves it can never be reused. Second, everything else that we use comes from our planet. Eventually, materials we use will be returned to the earth, and will be reused by future generations.

TROPHIC STRUCTURE

There must be enough energy in an ecosystem to support the activities of all organisms living there. This energy enters an ecosystem as sunlight and is incorporated into the chemical bonds of the molecules within living and decaying tissues (*see figure 4.1*). The sum of all living and decaying tissues in an ecosystem is called the **biomass** (Gr. *bios,* life + ME. *masse,* to knead). Sooner or later, the energy in the biomass is lost from an ecosystem as heat.

The sequence of organisms through which energy moves in an ecosystem is called a **food chain.** One relatively simple food chain might look like the following:

grass → grazing insects → shrews → owls

It is more realistic to envision complexly interconnected food chains, called **food webs,** that involve many kinds of organisms (figure 15.3). Because food webs can become very complex, it is convenient to group organisms based on the form of energy used. These groupings are called **trophic levels.**

Producers

Producers (autotrophs) obtain food (complex organic compounds) from inorganic materials and an energy source. They form the first trophic level of an ecosystem. The producers that are most familiar to us are green plants. They are called

(a)

(b)

(c)

Figure 15.2

Succession. (*a*) Primary succession on a sand dune. Beach grass is the first species to become established on a sand dune. It stabilizes the dune so that shrubs, and eventually trees, can become established. (*b,c*) Secondary succession after fires in Yellowstone National Park. The lodgepole pine shown here is a fire-dependent species. The maintenance of a healthy forest requires periodic burning. Investigations reveal that fires reoccurring in 60- to 100-year intervals maintain these forests.

photoautotrophs (Gr. *photos*, light + *autos*, self + *trophe*, to feed); their source of energy is the sun, and they convert energy to food through the reactions of photosynthesis. Less than 1% of the sunlight reaching the earth's atmosphere is transformed by photosynthesis. The rest is reflected back into space by the atmosphere (30%), absorbed by the atmosphere (20%), or absorbed by the earth (50%). The total amount of energy fixed by producers is called **gross primary production.** A portion of

gross primary production is used for maintenance needs of the producers. The rest, called **net primary production,** is available to other trophic levels.

Few ecosystems obtain energy from sources other than the sun. Producers in ecosystems that get energy other than from the sun are called **chemolithoautotrophs** (Gr. *chemeai*, to alloy metals + *lithos*, stone + *autos*, self + *trophe*, to feed). They obtain energy by oxidizing inorganic compounds (box 15.1).

15.4

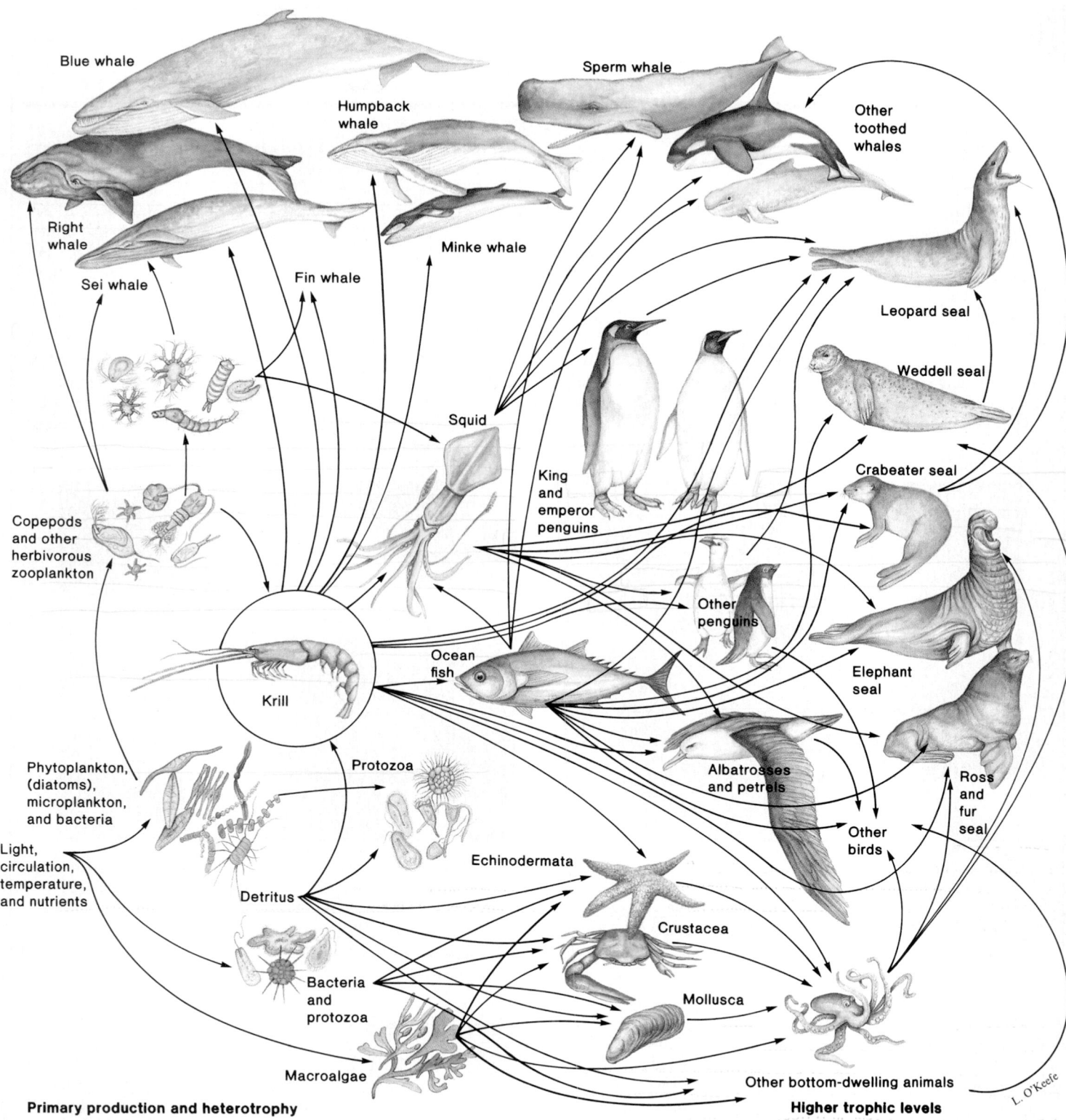

Blue whale

Sperm whale

Other toothed whales

Humpback whale

Right whale

Sei whale

Fin whale

Minke whale

Leopard seal

Weddell seal

Squid

King and emperor penguins

Crabeater seal

Copepods and other herbivorous zooplankton

Other penguins

Elephant seal

Ocean fish

Krill

Phytoplankton, (diatoms), microplankton, and bacteria

Protozoa

Albatrosses and petrels

Ross and fur seal

Light, circulation, temperature, and nutrients

Detritus

Echinodermata

Other birds

Crustacea

Bacteria and protozoa

Mollusca

Macroalgae

Other bottom-dwelling animals

L. O'Keefe

Primary production and heterotrophy

Higher trophic levels

Figure 15.3

Food Webs. An Antarctic food web. Small crustaceans called krill support nearly all life in Antarctica. Krill are eaten by 6 species of baleen whales, 20 species of squid, over 100 species of fish, 35 species of birds, and 7 species of seals. Krill feed on algae, protozoa, other small crustaceans, and various larvae. To appreciate the interconnectedness of food webs, trace the multiple paths of energy from light (lower left), through krill, to the leopard seal.

BOX 15.1   HYDROTHERMAL VENT COMMUNITIES

What some have called the oceanographic discovery of the century was made in 1977 by a Woods Hole Oceanographic Institute expedition to the Galápagos Rift, in the Pacific Ocean (figure 1a). The rift (an opening made by splitting) is over 2,700 m (over 1.5 mi) below the surface and part of an extensive mid-oceanic ridge system that has developed where the tectonic plates of the earth's crust are moving apart (*see box 11.2*). In such places, a flow of lava (magma) occasionally emerges and **hydrothermal vents** spew out hot water rich in hydrogen sulfide and other minerals.

One unusual finding of the expedition was that the life of a vent community is based not on the "rain" of material generated by the producers in the surface zones, but on a rich community of chemolithotrophic bacteria that derive all of the energy they need from the oxidation of inorganic compounds, such as hydrogen sul-

fide. They live in total darkness here, because the vents are far below the level of light penetration.

The expedition also noted that substrate around each vent was covered with many clams, crabs, polychaete annelids, and one species (*Riftia pachyptila*) of pogonophoran (figure 1b). Like other pogonophorans (tube worms), *Riftia* is nourished in part by the endosymbiotic bacteria found in its trophosome (*see endpaper 2*). These bacteria can oxidize hydrogen sulfide to sulfate and reduce carbon dioxide to organic compounds, which nourish both the symbiont and host. The worms' hemoglobin carries oxygen and hydrogen sulfide, tightly bound to another protein. This chemical bonding keeps these two molecules from reacting in an unproductive fashion before they are delivered to the bacteria. They also protect the host's tissue from the toxic hydrogen sulfide. These vent communities are among the few on earth that do not depend on solar energy for life.

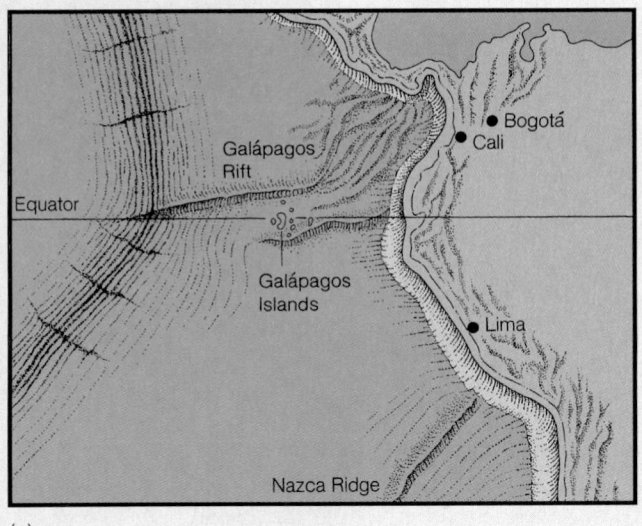

(a)

(b)

FIGURE 1   Hydrothermal Vent Communities. (a) The Galápagos Rift is the site of an extensive ocean-bottom community living on inorganic nutrients issuing from hydrothermal vents. (b) Life around these vents in the Galápagos Rift. Tube worms and crabs can be seen close to the vent.

Consumers

Other trophic levels are made up of consumers (heterotrophs). Consumers obtain their energy by eating other organisms. Herbivores (primary consumers) eat producers. Some carnivores (secondary consumers) eat herbivores, and other carnivores (tertiary consumers) eat the carnivores that ate the herbivores. Consumers also include scavengers that feed on large chunks of dead and decaying organic matter. Scavengers include earthworms and vultures.

Decomposers

Feeding at any consumer level is never 100% efficient. If herbivores crop 20% of net primary production, 80% is left behind. Eventually this primary production dies. Thanks to the decomposers, however, leftovers do not accumulate. Decomposers break down dead organisms and feces. Bacteria and fungi perform most of the decomposition by digesting organic matter extracellularly and absorbing the products of digestion. (They are said to be saprophytic.)

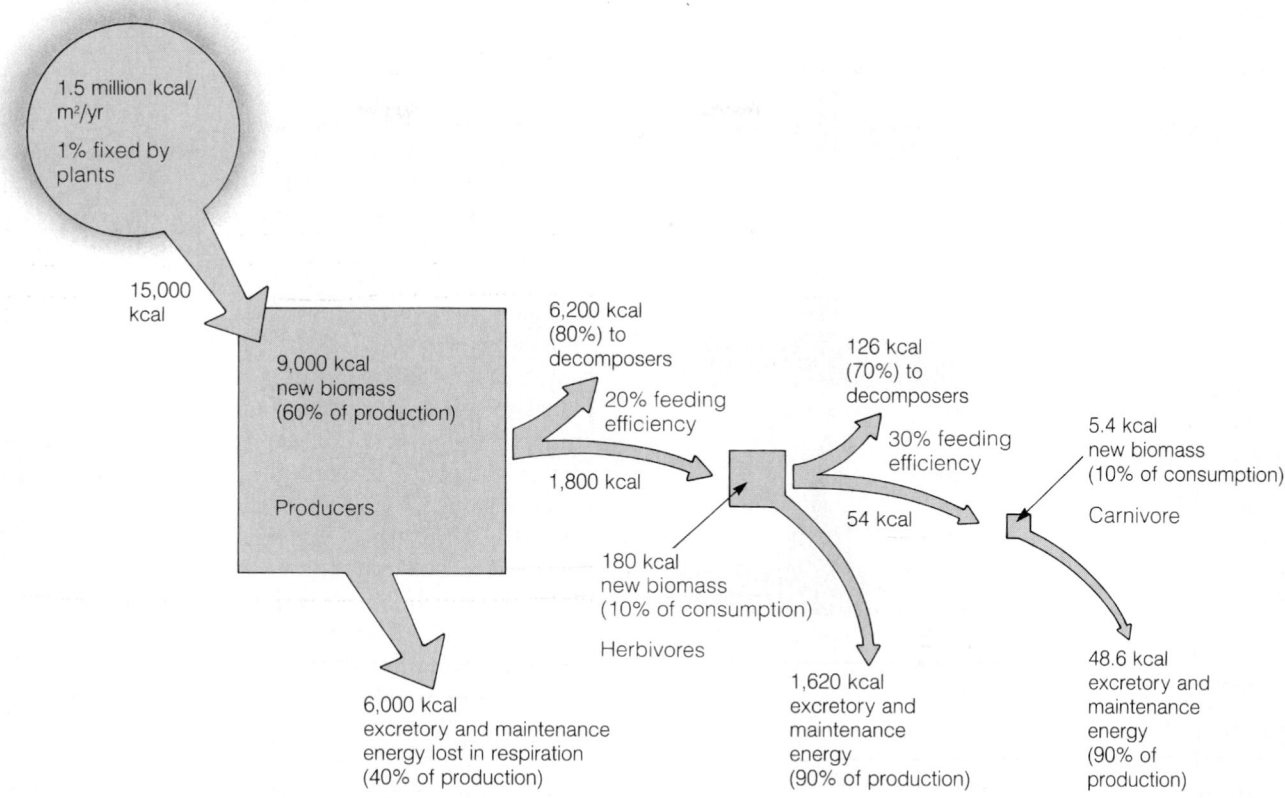

FIGURE 15.4

Energy Flow through Ecosystems. Approximately 1.5 million kilocalories of radiant energy strike a square meter of the earth's surface each year. Less than 1% (15,000 kcal/m²/yr) is converted into chemical energy by plants. Of this, approximately 60% is converted into new biomass, and 40% is lost in respiration. The herbivore trophic level harvests approximately 20% of net primary production, and decomposers get the rest. Of the 1,800 kcal moving into the herbivore trophic level, 10% (180 kcal) is converted to new biomass, and 90% (1,620 kcal) is lost in respiration. Carnivores harvest about 30% of the herbivore biomass, and 10% of that is converted to carnivore biomass. At subsequent trophic levels, harvesting efficiencies of about 30% and new biomass production of about 10% can be assumed. All of these percentages are approximations. Absolute values depend on the nature of the primary production (e.g., forest vs. grassland) and characteristics of the herbivores and carnivores (e.g., ectothermic vs. endothermic).

Efficiencies

The efficiency with which the animals of a trophic level convert food into new biomass depends on the nature of the food (figure 15.4). Much of the production of a forest is tied up in inedible, or undigestible, cellulose. On the other hand, a greater proportion of a grassland is available for herbivores. Carnivores are more efficient at assimilation than herbivores, because most of a herbivore's biomass is digestible. Further, the efficiency with which an animal converts food into new biomass depends on maintenance requirements of the animals involved. An average biomass conversion efficiency of 10% is usually cited, although efficiencies range from less than 1% for herbivorous endotherms to 35% for carnivorous ectotherms.

Ecological Pyramids

Ecological pyramids express the relationships between trophic levels in a graphic form. A **pyramid of numbers** shows the numbers of individuals at each trophic level of an ecosystem, a **pyramid of biomass** represents the biomass at each trophic level, and a **pyramid of energy** represents the amount of energy tied up in each trophic level (figure 15.5). All of these pyramids have the same shape. The area devoted to each level of the pyramid generally decreases from the producer to the highest consumer levels. ❷ Thus, predators (e.g., hawks and eagles) are much less common than animals such as squirrels and rabbits.

The trophic level concept is useful to help us visualize what happens to energy in ecosystems. In real ecosystems, however,

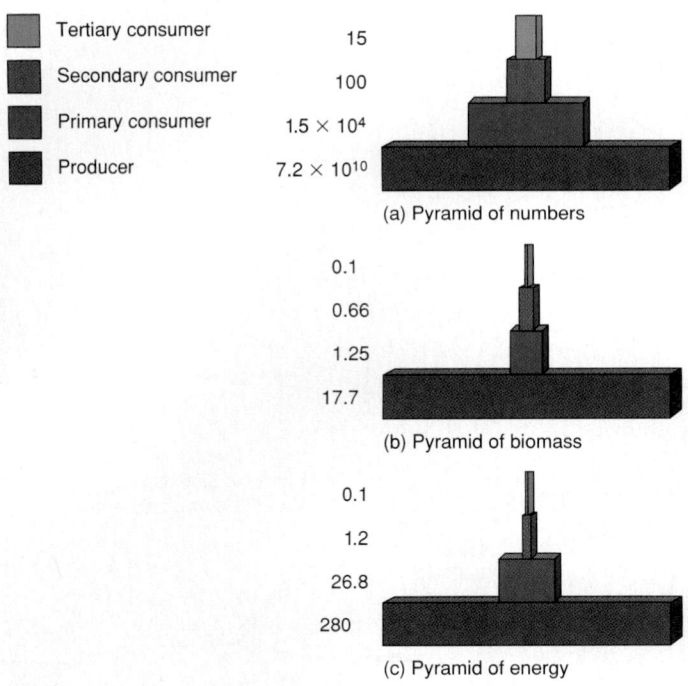

■ Tertiary consumer	15
■ Secondary consumer	100
■ Primary consumer	1.5×10^4
■ Producer	7.2×10^{10}

(a) Pyramid of numbers

0.1
0.66
1.25
17.7

(b) Pyramid of biomass

0.1
1.2
26.8
280

(c) Pyramid of energy

FIGURE 15.5

Ecological Pyramids for Data from an Experimental Pond. (*a*) Pyramid of numbers (individuals/m²). (*b*) Pyramid of biomass (dry g/m²). This figure represents a relatively long time interval. In open-water systems, instantaneous producer biomass is often less than herbivore biomass, because producers are small and reproduce rapidly, and consumers are large and longer lived. (*c*) Pyramid of energy (dry mg/m²).

trophic levels are difficult to describe. While the producer level is uniform, most animals function at more than one trophic level. Herbivores often consume insects when they graze, and carnivores move back and forth between secondary and tertiary consumer levels.

CYCLING

Did you ever wonder where the calcium atoms in your bones were 100 or even 100 million years ago?   ③ Perhaps they were in the bones of an ancient reptile, or in the sediments of prehistoric seas. Unlike energy, all matter is cycled from nonliving reservoirs to living systems, and back to nonliving reservoirs. Matter moves through ecosystems in biogeochemical cycles.

Nutrient Cycling

A nutrient is any element essential for life. Approximately 97% of living matter is made of oxygen, carbon, nitrogen, and hydrogen. Gaseous cycles involving these elements utilize the atmosphere or oceans as a reservoir. Elements such as sulfur, phosphorus, and calcium are less abundant in living tissues than those with gaseous cycles, but they are no less important

in sustaining life. The nonliving reservoir for these nutrients is the earth, and the cycles involving these elements are called sedimentary cycles.

Carbon Cycle

Carbon is very plentiful on our planet and is rarely a limiting factor. The reservoir for carbon is carbon dioxide (CO_2) in the atmosphere or water. Carbon enters the reservoir when organic matter is oxidized to CO_2. CO_2 is released to the atmosphere or water where autotrophs incorporate it into organic compounds. In aquatic systems, some of the CO_2 combines with water to form carbonic acid ($CO_2 + H_2O \rightleftharpoons H_2CO_3$). Because this reaction is reversible, carbonic acid can supply CO_2 to aquatic plants for photosynthesis when CO_2 levels in the water decrease. Carbonic acid can also release CO_2 to the atmosphere.

Some of the carbon in aquatic systems is tied up as calcium carbonate ($CaCO_3$) in the shells of molluscs and skeletons of echinoderms. Accumulations of mollusc shells and echinoderm skeletons have resulted in limestone formations that are the bedrock of much of the United States. Geological uplift, volcanic activities, and weathering returns much of this carbon to the earth's surface and the atmosphere.

A large supply of carbon is also tied up in fossil fuels. During the 65 million years of the Carboniferous period (which ended about 280 million years ago), organic matter accumulated in peat bogs. Incomplete decomposition and conditions of high temperature and pressure converted this carbon to coal, natural gas, and oil. Since the beginning of the Industrial Revolution (1760), humans have been burning fossil fuels and returning large quantities of this carbon to the atmosphere as CO_2 (figure 15.6).

Nitrogen Cycle

Nitrogen is an essential component of proteins, nucleic acids, and ATP. The reservoir for this nitrogen is the atmosphere, which is about 78% nitrogen (figure 15.7). Gaseous nitrogen, however, is not directly available to most plants. Instead, plants require nitrogen as ammonia (NH_3) or nitrate (NO_3^-). In these forms, nitrogen can be removed from the soil or water and incorporated into protein. Animals, of course, get their nitrogen by eating plants or other animals. When proteins and amino acids are metabolized, nitrogen is excreted as ammonia, urea, or uric acid. The latter two are readily converted to the ammonium ion (NH_4^+). Ammonia and the ammonium ion, in turn, are converted into nitrate and nitrite (NO_2^-) by bacteria in an energy-yielding reaction called nitrification. Nitrites and nitrates are then taken up by plants and incorporated into proteins.

In another part of the nitrogen cycle, the nitrogen in nitrates is returned to the air as gaseous nitrogen (N_2). Denitrifying bacteria live in anaerobic environments and use nitrates as a source of oxygen for cellular respiration. Denitrifying bacteria are offset by nitrogen fixation. Nitrogen-fixing

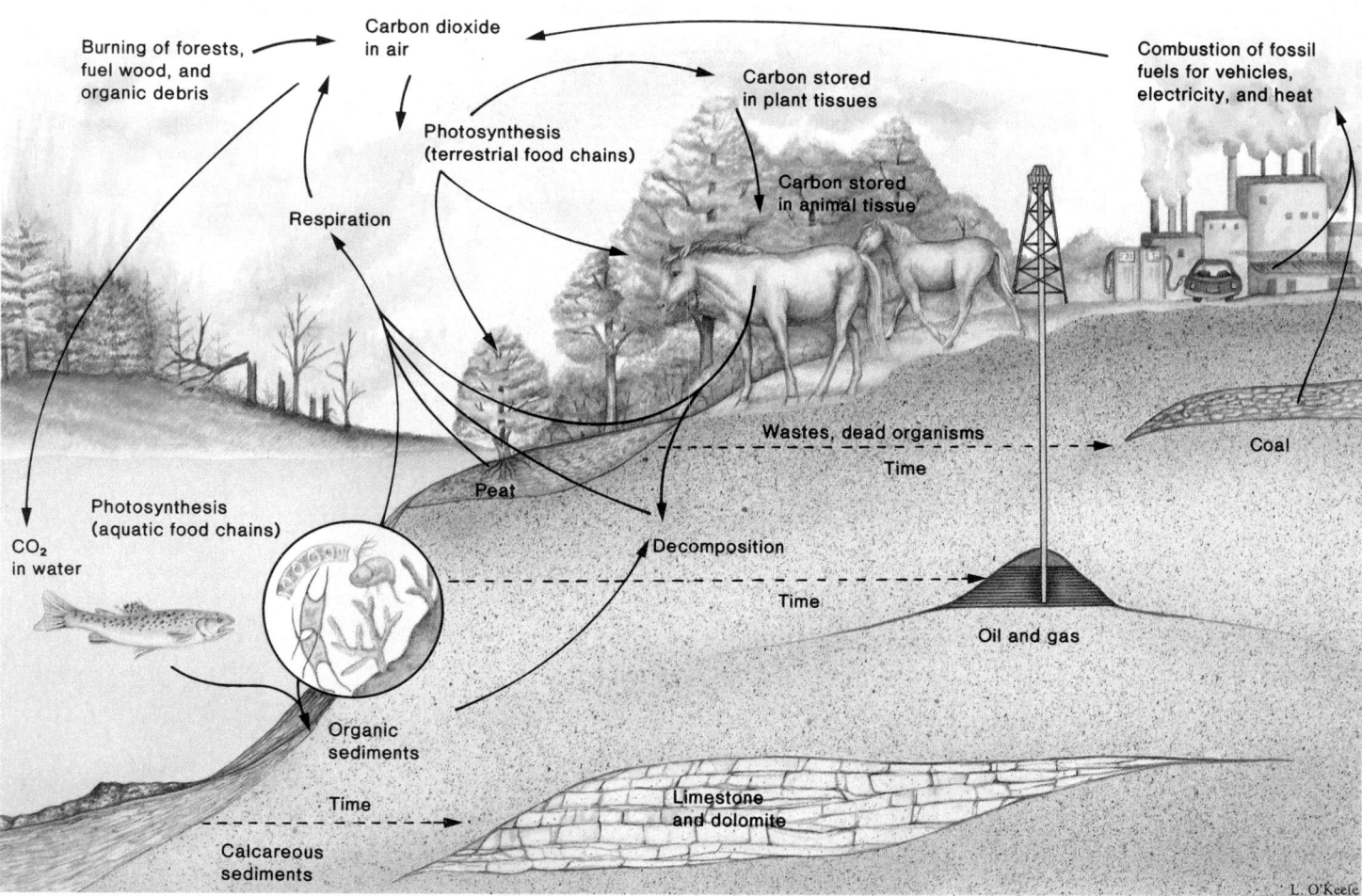

Figure 15.6

The Carbon Cycle. Carbon cycles between its reservoir in the atmosphere, living organisms, fossil fuels, and limestone bedrock.

bacteria (in association with leguminous plants such as soybeans) and cyanobacteria (blue-green algae), convert gaseous nitrogen to nitrates.

Other components of the nitrogen cycle include the industrial production of nitrates, the conversion by lightning of N_2 to nitrates, and volcanic activities that release nitrates from the earth's crust.

Other Nutrient Cycles

Phosphorus is an essential component of DNA, RNA, ATP, and vertebrate skeletons. Its cycle involves a sedimentary reservoir that contains about 0.000003% phosphorus. Animals acquire phosphorus in their diet, and phosphorus is returned to the soil in excretion and decay. Mining operations remove phosphates from the soil for the production of fertilizers and detergents. Overuse of these can promote algal growth in our rivers and lakes. Algal overgrowth leads to increased decomposition, oxygen depletion, and the early death of our waterways.

Sulfur is found in elemental form in the earth's crust, and as sulfate (SO_2) in the atmosphere. It is an essential component of amino acids but is rarely limiting. Animals acquire sulfur from plants, which extract it from the soil. Decaying plants and animals produce hydrogen sulfide and sulfate and return sulfur to the soil. The burning of high-sulfur coal also sends sulfate into the atmosphere.

Calcium is essential for muscle contraction, bone formation, nerve impulse conduction, and many other animal functions. The reservoir for calcium is the earth's crust (limestone beds) and our oceans. Animals acquire calcium in food and drink and return it to the soil in death, decay, and excretion.

Biogeochemical cycles have been disrupted by human activities. For example, the mining of phosphates for fertilizers increases the rate at which phosphates are lost through terrestrial runoff to ocean depths. Activities such as these can lead to serious shortages of some nutrients.

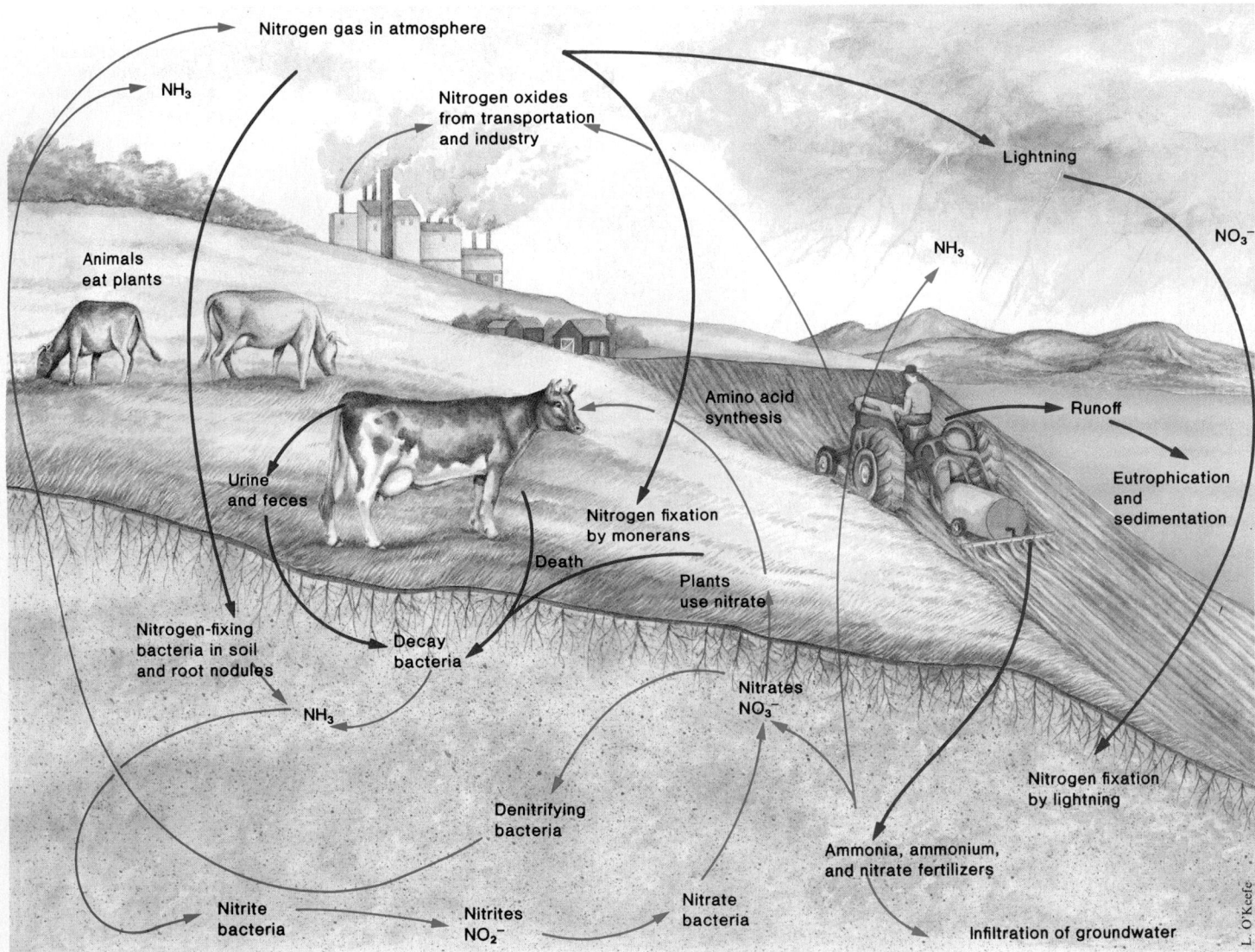

FIGURE 15.7

The Nitrogen Cycle. Nitrogen cycles between its reservoir in the atmosphere and living organisms. Nitrogen fixation converts gaseous nitrogen to nitrogen in nitrates.

Water Cycling

The cycling of water is one of the most basic of all cycles. Water moves between land, oceans, and the atmosphere. Oceans contain 97% of the earth's water, and water that evaporates from oceans eventually falls as rain, snow, ice, or fog. Some water that falls on land may return to the atmosphere by evaporation from soil, or from the leaves of plants. Other water is temporarily absorbed in the soil. Rain that does not evaporate or contribute to groundwater runs off into lakes and streams. Eventually, streams make their way to rivers, and rivers to oceans. In completing its cycle, water acts as a powerful force. It sculpts our land, transports nutrients to the sea, and powers electric generators. ④ The water cycle is called the **hydrological cycle** and is one of the earliest forms of solar power because it is powered entirely by sun-induced evaporation from our oceans.

Stop and Ask Yourself

5. What is the source of energy for individuals at the producer trophic level? At the secondary consumer trophic level?

6. Approximately what portion of the energy intake at one trophic level is converted into biomass at that trophic level? What happens to the rest of the energy?

7. What is the main reservoir for carbon in the carbon cycle?

8. What do nitrogen-fixing bacteria do?

15.10

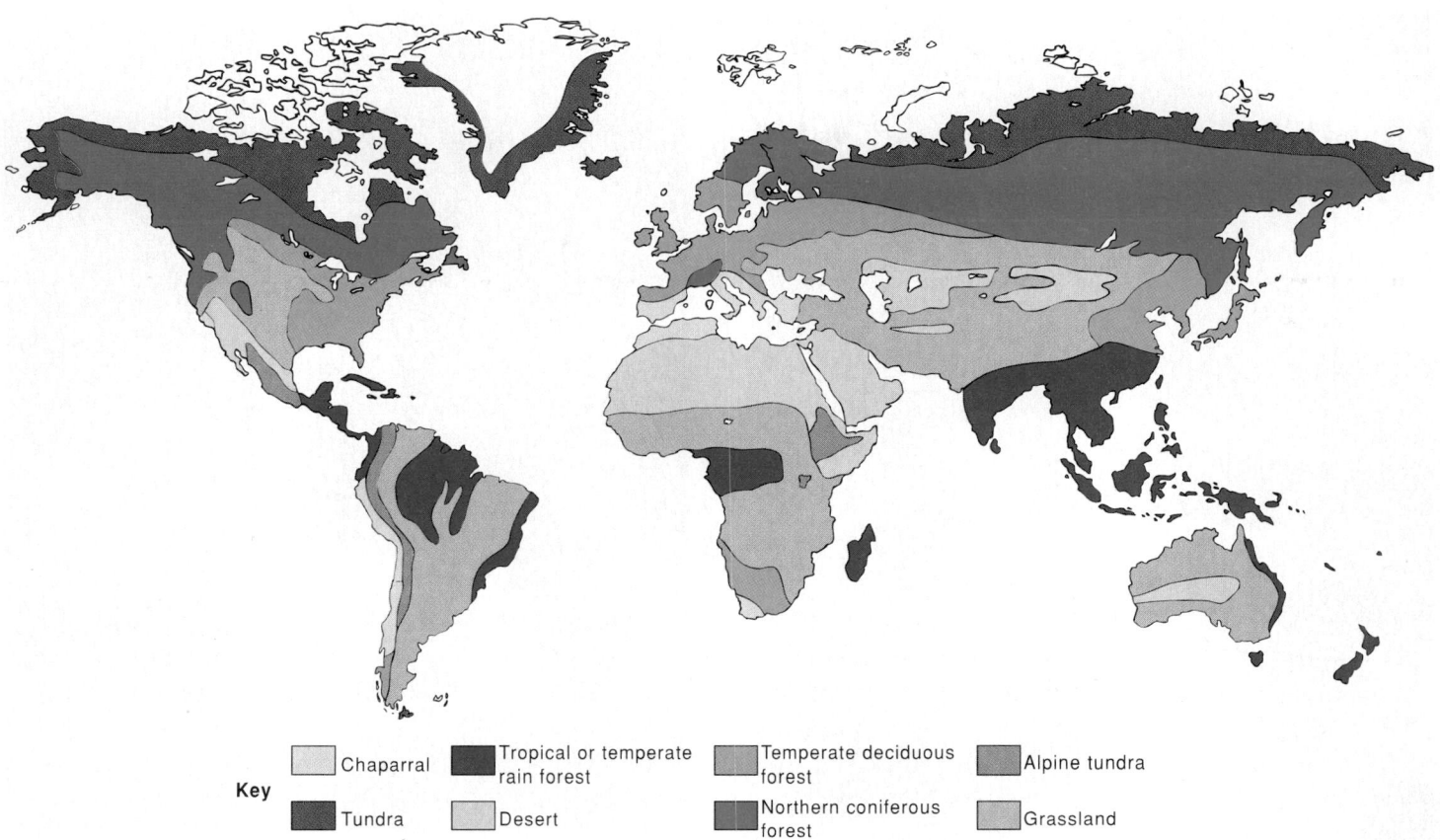

Figure 15.8

Biomes of the World. Biomes are distinctive associations of plant and animal populations dictated by climatic and geographical features.

Key — Chaparral — Tropical or temperate rain forest — Temperate deciduous forest — Alpine tundra — Tundra — Desert — Northern coniferous forest — Grassland

ECOSYSTEMS OF THE EARTH

The earth can be divided into ecosystem types according to characteristic plants, animals, and physical factors. Terrestrial ecosystems are divided into distinctive associations of plant and animal populations called **biomes** (figure 15.8). Biomes have certain geographical boundaries, but different parts of the world with similar climatic and geographical features have similar biome types. Aquatic ecosystems are subdivided into freshwater and marine ecosystems, each of which is further subdivided.

TERRESTRIAL ECOSYSTEMS

Tundra exists in two forms in North America. Arctic tundra occurs in the far northern reaches of North America (figure 15.9). For most of the year, it is covered with snow and ice. A very short summer provides only about 60 days during which mosses, lichens, grasses, and shrubs can grow. No trees occur here. Precipitation is a scanty 25 cm/year, yet the summer soils are wet and boggy. Just below the surface of the ground is a permanently frozen subsoil called permafrost. Productivity is low. The animal life of arctic tundra consists of rodents, musk oxen, caribou, owls, foxes, and weasels.

Alpine tundra occurs in mountains, above the altitude at which trees grow. Widely fluctuating temperatures, moderate precipitation, grasses, and shrubs characterize this ecosystem.

Northern coniferous forests are characterized by cool summers, cold winters, short (130 day) growing seasons, and moderate precipitation (40 to 100 cm/year). Most of the precipitation comes in the form of heavy winter snows. Soils are acidic and relatively infertile. Plants characteristic of the northern

Figure 15.9

Biomes—Arctic Tundra. Arctic tundra is dominated by mosses, lichens, grasses, and shrubs. Animal life includes rodents, caribou (*Rangifer caribou*, shown here), musk oxen, owls, weasels, and arctic foxes.

coniferous forests are spruce, fir, and pine. Because coniferous forests are "evergreen," some limited primary production can occur on warmer winter days. Pine needles that accumulate on the forest floor are very slow to decompose, and fire is important in promoting seed germination and release of nutrients locked in the pine needles. The diversity of animals in northern coniferous forests is not great, although population sizes can be quite large. Insects abound in the summer months, and other residents include snowshoe hares, lynx, wolves, caribou, and moose (figure 15.10).

Figure 15.10

Biomes—Northern Coniferous Forests. Northern coniferous forests are dominated by spruce and fir. Animal life includes snowshoe hares, wolves, and moose (*Alces americanus*, shown here).

Temperature deciduous forests occur in regions with moderate climate and well-defined summer and winter seasons. Precipitation ranges from 75 to 150 cm/year, and soils are relatively fertile. Deciduous trees, which lose their leaves in fall, dominate these forests. Decomposition of fallen leaves enriches forest soils. Vertical stratification of temperate deciduous forests is well developed, with most production occurring in the tops of the trees (the forest canopy). Insects are the most common herbivores, and white-tailed deer are the largest herbivores (figure 15.11). Carnivores of presettlement temperate deciduous forests included wolves and mountain lions.

The **grasslands** of North America are called prairies. Similar ecosystems in South America and Africa are called tropical savannas. A few scattered trees may be present in grasslands, but grasses, such as big and little bluestem, predominate. The nature of the vegetation of a grassland depends on the amount of moisture. Moist prairies in North America are called tall-grass prairies, and drier prairies are called short-grass prairies. As in northern coniferous forests, fire plays a role in maintaining grasslands by killing trees and shrubs that recover from disturbance very slowly. Because much of the primary production of a grassland dies each year,

FIGURE 15.12

Biomes—Grasslands. Grasslands of North America are dominated by grasses such as bluestem. They once provided abundant food for grazing animals, such as bison (*Bison bison*).

FIGURE 15.11

Biomes—Temperate Deciduous Forests. Temperate deciduous forests provide beautiful landscapes in the fall. Animal life includes white-tailed deer (*Odocoileus virginianus*).

organic matter accumulates quickly in grassland soils. The fertile soils of the prairies of North America have been exploited for agricultural purposes, and few tracts of virgin prairie remain. Because most of their primary production is edible, grasslands support large populations of herbivores, such as numerous insects and bison (figure 15.12).

Chaparral occurs in relatively dry (30 to 75 cm of rain per year) areas of the world, including the southwestern United States. Most precipitation comes during the winter, and temperatures fluctuate between 13 and 23°C. Plants of the chaparral are low and shrubby and have tough, waxy leaves. Animals include insects, rodents, rabbits, lizards, snakes, and mule deer (figure 15.13). The chaparral is another ecosystem in which fire is an important regulator of plant and animal populations.

Deserts occur around the world between the latitudes of 30° N and 30° S. Rainfall is less than 25 cm/year. Temperatures

FIGURE 15.13

Biomes—Chaparral. Chaparral occurs in the southwestern United States. It is characterized by low, shrubby vegetation, and animals such as mule deer (*Odocoileus hemionus*, shown here), rodents, rabbits, and many reptiles.

Figure 15.14

Biomes—Deserts. Deserts are dominated by cacti and desert shrubs. Animal life of deserts includes birds, rodents, numerous species of reptiles and arthropods, such as this giant hairy desert scorpion (*Hadrurus arizonensis*).

fluctuate widely; they are very high during daylight hours, and low at nighttime. Plants of very hot deserts are predominately cacti and desert shrubs. Cooler deserts are characterized by sagebrush. Animals of the desert include birds, rodents, reptiles, numerous insects, and other arthropods (figure 15.14). The evolution of desert animals has involved delicate compromises between the needs for evaporative cooling and water-based excretion, and the need to conserve water.

Tropical rain forests are found, among other places, in the equatorial regions of Central America, and northern South America. Their temperatures fluctuate between 20 and 25°C, and rainfall approaches 200 cm/year. Because of the high moisture, high temperatures, and the 12-month growing season, nutrient cycling occurs rapidly. Soils of tropical rain forests are relatively poor in nutrients because most of the nutrients are tied up in organisms. Life-forms of tropical rain forests are very diverse. Trees are broad-leaved and nondeciduous, and the forest is highly stratified. A nearly complete forest canopy creates a densely shaded forest floor. The rich diversity of plant life creates diverse food and habitat resources for animals. The stable temperatures and high humidity create ideal conditions for both soft- and hard-bodied ectothermic animals; so populations of annelids, arthropods, amphibians, and reptiles abound (figure 15.15).

Figure 15.15

Biomes—Tropical Rain Forests. Tropical rain forests provide the earth with a great variety of plant and animal species. The interior of the forest is dark and moist and is the last refuge on earth for many animals, such as this morpho butterfly (*Morpho achillaena*).

Aquatic Ecosystems

Aquatic environments are divided into freshwater and marine ecosystems, both of which have diverse habitats.

Freshwater Ecosystems

Freshwater ecosystems are classified according to water flow. **Lotic ecosystems** include brooks, streams, and rivers in which water is flowing. Some of the primary production of streams is provided by attached aquatic plants and algae. However, most of the primary production for lotic ecosystems comes from surrounding terrestrial

Figure 15.16

Lotic Ecosystems. Stream insects display a great variety of adaptations for living in moving water. This mayfly nymph (*Siphlonisca aerodromia*) shows streamlining and flattening, which allow the insect to maintain itself in strong currents.

habitats as runoff during rains and autumn leaf falls. Because most lotic ecosystems are relatively shallow and have long shorelines, terrestrial production is more than adequate to supply energy needs. Lotic ecosystems naturally have high oxygen levels. Water flowing over rocks, logs, and other objects causes turbulence that oxygenates the water. Numerous aquatic insects and other invertebrates divide resources. Some shred larger pieces of plant matter. Others, such as blackfly larvae and caddis fly larvae, filter floating microscopic debris from the water. Predators include numerous species of fish, as well as insects, such as stonefly larvae and dobsonfly larvae.

Current is probably the most important physical factor in lotic habitats. Some animals are strong swimmers, capable of negotiating rapids and waterfalls. Others retreat from the current by living on or in the substrate. The latter are called **benthic** (Gr. *benthos*, depth of the sea) **animals.** Many stream insects display adaptations for living in moving water. Adaptations include streamlining, flattening, and ballasting themselves with pebbles (figure 15.16).

Lentic ecosystems, including lakes and ponds, have standing water. Vertical stratification of lakes is common, especially in temperate regions. In the summer, the upper regions (the epilimnion) of a lake warm quickly. Because the deeper water (the hypolimnion) is cool, and because cool water is denser than warm water, mixing between upper and lower levels of the water column is prevented. Photosynthesis (and thus

oxygen production) occurs only in the upper levels of a lake because light is filtered by water with increasing depth. The main reactions occurring in the depths of a lake are those of decomposition. The deepest parts of a lake are often depleted of oxygen in the summer. In the fall, however, the surface waters cool, and winds cause mixing of the entire water column in what is called turnover. In the winter, the water again becomes layered under the ice, but winds and temperature changes cause another turnover in the spring.

A much greater share of the production of lentic ecosystems is from production occurring in the body of water. Most of this production is from microscopic algae floating near the surface. Organisms that swim or float in surface waters and are at the mercy of wind, waves, and current are a part of the **planktonic** (Gr. *planktos*, to wander) community. Deep, cold lakes that are nutrient-poor and relatively unproductive are said to be oligotrophic. Shallow, warm, nutrient-rich lakes are highly productive, and are said to be eutrophic. Succession in a lake, called **eutrophication,** was described earlier. The rate of eutrophication can be greatly increased by adding nutrients to a lake from fertilizers and other sources.

Other freshwater ecosystems include wet grassland areas called marshes; wet woodland areas called swamps; and peat bogs. They occur where the water table is near the surface of the land. Freshwater wetlands are important as hatcheries and rearing grounds for wildlife.

Marine Ecosystems

The most important physical characteristic that distinguishes marine ecosystems from freshwater ecosystems is the salinity of the water. Marine ecosystems have water containing a mixture of salts, which make up 3.5% of the mass of a quantity of seawater. This section briefly examines five marine ecosystems: estuaries, intertidal (littoral) zones, neritic zones, oceanic zones, and coral reefs.

Estuaries occur where fresh water meets seawater, and the salinity of seawater is diluted. Estuaries are very productive because freshwater streams carry nutrients into the estuary, and tidal currents bring nutrients from the ocean. The primary producers in estuaries include plankton, larger attached aquatic vegetation, and emergent vegetation, such as cordgrass. Animals and decomposers feed on this production, and find refuge in it. One of the very important functions of estuarine ecosystems is to serve as nursery grounds for many marine fishes, molluscs, and crustaceans. Estuaries are also important feeding grounds for wading and swimming birds.

Estuaries have suffered from human activities. They have been drained and filled to develop subdivisions and condominiums, and have been excavated to harbor pleasure boats. They have also been polluted by oil explorations and drilling. Their productivity is threatened by acid rain. In recent years, these activities have been slowed, but have not stopped.

Intertidal (littoral) zones extend from the splash zone of ocean waves to the low tide marks (figure 15.17). These regions are subject to the actions of both waves and tides. Some intertidal animals make their living in splash zones. These animals, such as periwinkle snails, may live on algae attached to the rocky shoreline (figure 15.18).

Animals use a variety of strategies to survive during low tide. More motile animals, such as fish and some crabs, can move in and out of intertidal zones with the tides. Other animals, such as amphipods, isopods, ghost crabs, and numerous polychaetes, burrow beneath the sand and mud of the intertidal areas. A shovelful of intertidal sand and mud will reveal thousands of hidden residents. Yet other inhabitants of the intertidal zone are found in tidal pools. Small basins in the rock may be completely submerged at high tide, but exposed at low tide. Water trapped in tidepools by ebbing tides supports a rich animal life including numerous echinoderms, barnacles, limpets, and chitons. Attached animals withstand periods of exposure by closing their shells to avoid drying.

Neritic ecosystems consist of relatively shallow water that extends from the littoral zone to the edge of the continental

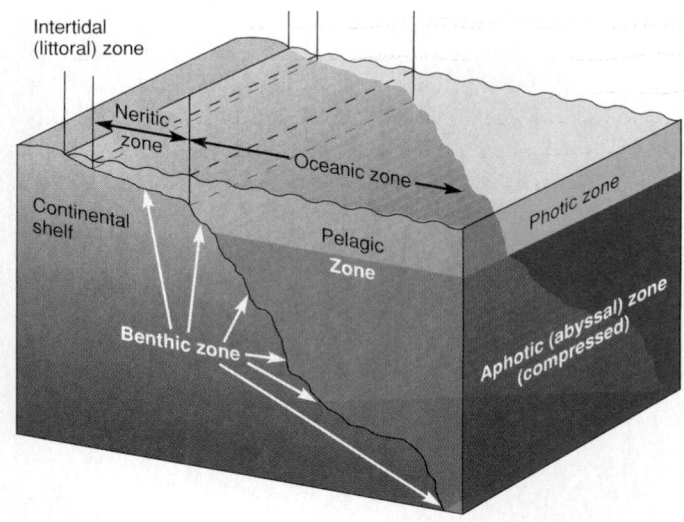

FIGURE 15.17

Marine Ecosystems. Diagrammatic section of an ocean, showing the distribution of major marine ecosystems.

FIGURE 15.18

Marine Ecosystems—The Intertidal Zone. Many members of the intertidal zone survive periods of low tide in water trapped in tidepools. These tidepools make rich habitats for exploration.

shelves. Oceanic currents bring nutrient-rich bottom waters to the surface, where they stimulate photosynthesis by planktonic algae (phytoplankton). In some communities, attached algae, such as the vast kelp beds of the north Pacific, are locally important in contributing to primary production. Animal members of the plankton (zooplankton), include the numerous crustaceans and larval stages of barnacles, echinoderms, and polychaetes. Neritic zones support some of the largest vertebrate predators and provide food for human consumption.

Oceanic ecosystems extend from the continental shelves into the relatively unproductive open ocean. Virtually all primary production in the open ocean occurs in the upper waters, a region called the photic zone. Phytoplankton again forms the base of the food web. There is continual darkness in the aphotic (abyssal) zone below 200 m. Life at these depths is dependent on production from the surface waters drifting to great depths. (The vent communities of the ocean floor are an exception that was described earlier; *see box 15.1.*) Animals found at these great depths may have luminescent organs that serve as searchlights, lures for prey, and sexual attractants.

In some parts of the world upwelling zones provide the highest productivity of all marine ecosystems. In these areas (e.g., off the coasts of California and Peru), surface currents carry water away from the shore, and nutrient-rich water rises from the depths to take its place. Nutrients in this water promote high rates of primary production, supporting some of the world's greatest fisheries.

Coral reefs are one of the most highly productive ecosystems in the world. They are associations of stony corals (phylum Cnidaria, class Anthozoa) and algae (called coralline algae and zooxanthellae). Reefs form over thousands of years in warm, clear, relatively shallow waters. The greatest depth at which they can grow is between 50 and 60 m. Below this depth, light is insufficient to support the growth of the dinoflagellates necessary for reef formation (*see box 18.2*).

Stop and Ask Yourself

9. What are the physical characteristics, dominant plants, and dominant animals of northern coniferous forests?

10. What are the physical characteristics, dominant plants, and dominant animals of tropical rain forests?

11. What is the source of most nutrients entering lotic ecosystems?

12. What is a definition for the following terms: Benthic animals, planktonic, intertidal (littoral) zone, neritic ecosystem, and oceanic ecosystem?

ECOLOGICAL PROBLEMS

In the last few hundred years of our history, humans have attempted to provide for the needs and wants of a growing human population. In our search for longer and better lives, however, humans have lost a sense of being a part of our

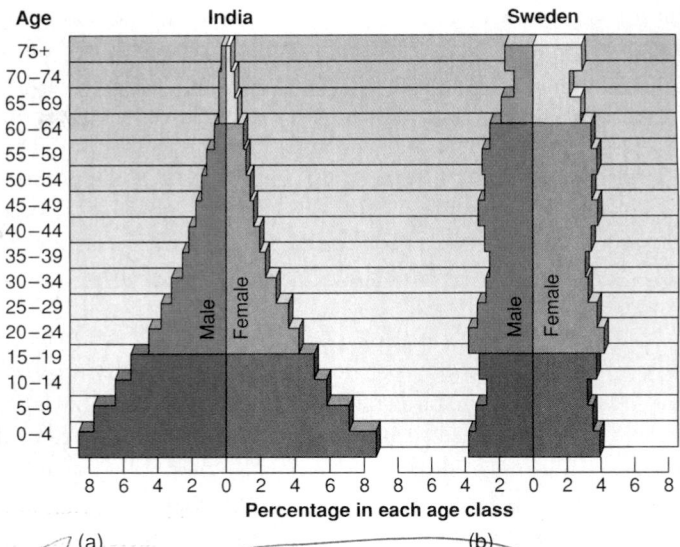

(a)   (b)

FIGURE 15.19

Human Age Pyramids. (*a*) In less developed countries, a greater proportion of the population is in the prereproductive age classes. High mortality in that age class compensates for high birth rates. As technologies reduce infant mortality and prolong the life span of the elderly, populations increase rapidly. (*b*) In developed countries, the age structure is more rectangular because of reduced mortality in all age classes. *Source: Robert Leo Smith,* The Ecology of Man, *2d ed., copyright 1976 Harper & Row, 1976.*

world's ecosystems. Now that you have studied some general ecological principles, it should be easier to understand many of our ecological problems.

HUMAN POPULATION GROWTH

An expanding human population is the root of most of our other environmental problems. Humans, like other animals, have a tendency to undergo exponential population growth. The earth, like any ecosystem on it, has a carrying capacity and a limited supply of resources. When human populations achieve that carrying capacity, populations should stabilize. If they do not stabilize in a fashion that limits human misery, then war, famine, and/or disease is sure to be the vehicle that accomplishes our ecological destiny.

5 What is our planet's carrying capacity? The answer to that question is not simple. In part, it depends on the standard of living that we desire for ourselves and whether or not we expect resources to be distributed equally among all populations. Currently, the earth's population stands at 5.6 billion people. Virtually all environmentalists agree that number is too high if all people are to achieve the affluence of developed countries.

Unless intense efforts are made to curb population growth, world populations could double in the next 50 years. Looking at the age characteristics of world populations helps to explain why human populations will grow rapidly. The **age structure** of a population is the proportion of a population that is in prereproductive, reproductive, and postreproductive classes. Age structure is often represented by an age pyramid. Figure 15.19 shows an age pyramid for a developed country and for a lesser developed country. In less developed countries, the age pyramid has a very broad base, indicating high birth rates. As in many natural populations, these high birth rates are offset by high infant mortality. However, what happens when less developed countries begin accumulating technologies that reduce prereproductive mortality and prolong the life of the elderly? Unless reproductive practices change, a population explosion occurs. Unfortunately, cultural practices change very slowly, and there has been a reluctance to use modern birth control practices.

In developed countries, population growth tends to be slower, and the proportion of the population in each reproductive class is balanced. Birth rates in the United States have decreased in recent years because of the use of modern birth control practices. In spite of decreased birth rate, the U.S. population, now at about 258 million, is still growing. Immigration is currently the biggest factor influencing population growth in the United States. If one assumes 2 million legal and illegal immigrants per year, then the U.S. population may increase to 500 million by 2050. Given our current standard of living, even 200 million people living in the United States is too many. Problems of homelessness, hunger, resource depletion, and pollution all stem from trying to support too many people at our current standard of living.

POLLUTION

Pollution is any detrimental change in an ecosystem. Most kinds of pollution are the results of human activities. When human populations are large, and affluence demands more and more goods and services, pollution problems are compounded. Because you have studied sections of this chapter on ecosystem productivity and nutrient cycling, you should now be able to understand why these problems exist.

Pollution of our waters takes many forms. Industries generate toxic wastes, heat, and plastics, some of which will persist for centuries. Every household in the world generates human wastes that must be disposed of. All too often, industrial and human wastes find their ways into groundwater or into streams, lakes, and oceans. When they do, water becomes unfit for human consumption and unfit for wildlife.

Air pollution also presents serious problems. Burning fossil fuels releases sulfur dioxide and nitrogen oxides into the atmosphere. Sulfur dioxide and water combine to produce sulfuric acid, which falls as **acid rain.** Acid rain lowers the pH of lakes, often many miles from the site of sulfur dioxide production. Carbon dioxide released in burning fuels has accumulated in the atmosphere, causing the **greenhouse effect.** Carbon dioxide reflects solar radiation back to the earth, causing an increase in world temperature, polar ice caps to melt, and ocean levels to rise. The release of chlorinated fluorocarbons from aerosol cans, air conditioners, and refrigerators contributes to the depletion of the earth's ultraviolet filter—the atmospheric ozone layer. As a result, the incidence of skin cancer is likely to increase.

When wastes and poisons enter food webs, organisms at the highest trophic levels usually suffer the most. ⑥ Very tiny amounts of a toxin incorporated into primary production can quickly build up as carnivores feed on herbivores that have concentrated toxins in their tissues. This problem is especially severe when the material is not biodegradable (not broken down by biological processes). The accumulation of matter in food webs is called **biological magnification.**

RESOURCE DEPLETION AND BIODIVERSITY

Other environmental problems arise because humans have been too slow to realize that an ecosystem's energy is used only once. When a quantity of energy is lost to outer space as heat, it is gone from the earth forever.

As with energy, other resources are also being squandered by human populations. Overgrazing and deforestation have led to the spread of our world's deserts. Exploitation of tropical rain forests has contributed to the extinction of many plant and animal species.

The variety of living organisms in an ecosystem is called **biodiversity.** No one knows for sure how many species there are in the world. About 1.4 million species have been described. Taxonomists estimate that there are 4 to 30 million more. Much of this unseen, or unnoticed, biodiversity is unappreciated for the free services it performs. Forests hold back flood waters and recycle CO_2 and nutrients. Insects pollinate crops and control insect pests, and subterranean organisms promote soil fertility through decomposition. Many of these undescribed species would, when studied, provide new food crops, petroleum substitutes, new fibers, and pharmaceuticals. All of these functions require not just remnant groups but large healthy populations. Large populations promote the genetic diversity required for surviving environmental changes. When genetic diversity is lost, it is lost forever. Our heroic attempts to save endangered species come far too late. Even when they succeed, they salvage only a tiny portion of an original gene pool.

The biodiversity of all natural areas of the world is threatened. Acid rain, pollution, urban development, and agriculture know no geographic or national boundaries. The main threats to biological diversity arise from habitat destruction by expanding human populations. Humans are either directly or indirectly exploiting about 40% of the earth's net primary production. Often this involves converting natural areas to agricultural uses, frequently substituting less efficient crop plants for native species. Habitat loss displaces thousands of native plants and animals.

Some of the most important threatened natural areas include tropical rain forests, coastal wetlands, and coral reefs. Of these, tropical rain forests have been an important focus of attention. Tropical rain forests cover only 7% of the earth's land surface, but they contain more than 50% of the world's species. Tropical rain forests are being destroyed rapidly, mostly for agricultural production. About 76,000 km^2 (an area greater than

Figure 15.20
Tropical Deforestation. Severe erosion quickly followed the removal of the tropical rain forest on these slopes in Madagascar.

the area of the country of Costa Rica) is being cleared each year (*see figure 1.9*). At current rates of destruction, most tropical rain forests will be gone in the twenty-first century. According to some estimates, we are losing 17,500 rain forest species each year. Clearing of tropical rain forests achieves little, because the thin, nutrient-poor soils of tropical rain forests are exhausted within 2 years (figure 15.20). Sadly, rain forests are a

nonrenewable resource. Seeds of rain forest plants germinate rapidly, but seedlings are unprotected on sterile, open soils. Even if a forest were able to become reestablished, it would take many centuries to return to a climax rain forest.

There are solutions to the problems of threatened biodiversity. None of the solutions, however, is quick and easy. First, more money needs to be appropriated for training taxonomists and ecologists, and for supporting their work. Second, all countries of the world need to realize that biodiversity, when preserved and managed properly, is a source of economic wealth. Third, we need a system of international ethics that values natural diversity for the beauty it brings to our lives. Anything short of these steps will surely lead to severe climatic changes and mass starvation.

Stop and Ask Yourself

13. What is an age pyramid? How do age pyramids help predict future population trends?

14. What is acid rain? What kinds of pollutants contribute to its formation?

15. Why are chlorinated fluorocarbons thought to contribute to skin cancer?

16. Why are higher trophic levels often most severely affected by poisons in the food web?

SUMMARY

1. All populations living in an area make up a community.
2. Communities can be characterized by dominant members, cycles of activity, and the variety of organisms present.
3. Organisms have roles in their community. The niche concept helps ecologists visualize those roles.
4. Communities often change in predictable ways. Successional changes often lead to a stable climax community.
5. Energy that supports ecosystem reactions is not recyclable. Energy that is fixed by producers is eventually lost as heat.
6. Unlike energy, nutrients and water are cycled through ecosystems. Cycles involve movements of material from nonliving reservoirs in the atmosphere or the earth to biological systems and back to the reservoirs again.
7. The earth is divided into ecosystem types according to characteristic plants, animals, and physical factors. Terrestrial ecosystems are called biomes. Aquatic ecosystems are subdivided into freshwater and marine ecosystems.
8. Human population growth is the root of most of our environmental problems. Trying to support too many people at the standard of living present in developed countries has resulted in air and water pollution and resource depletion.
9. Pollution and resource depletion are important environmental problems that threaten life as we know it. Biodiversity is an important resource that is threatened by human activities.

SELECTED KEY TERMS

CRITICAL THINKING QUESTIONS

1. What is the usefulness of the concept of an ecological niche?
2. Which of the following would be a more energetically efficient strategy for supplying animal protein for human diets? Explain your answers.
    a. Feeding people beef raised in feedlots on grain or feeding people beef that has been raised in pastures.
    b. Feeding people sardines and herrings or processing sardines and herrings into fishmeal that is subsequently used to raise poultry, which is used to feed people.
3. Explain why the biomass present at one trophic level of an ecosystem decreases at higher trophic levels.
4. What is the role of fire in grassland and coniferous forest ecosystems? Should fires be allowed to burn themselves out in land managed by the U.S. Park Service?
5. Why are wetlands and estuaries important ecosystems?

SUGGESTED READINGS

BOOKS

Alcock, J. 1989. *Animal Behavior*. Sunderland, Mass.: Sinauer Associates, Inc.

Brewer, R. 1994. *The Science of Ecology*. 2d ed. Philadelphia: Saunders College Publishing.

Drickamer, L. C., and Vessey, S. H. 1986. *Animal Behavior: Concepts, Processes, and Methods*. Boston: Prindle, Weber, and Schmidt.

Ehrlich, P. R., and Roughgarden, J. 1987. *The Science of Ecology*. New York: Macmillan Publishing Co.

Hunt, C. E. 1988. *Down by the River: The Impact of Federal Water Projects and Policies on Biological Diversity*. Washington, D.C.: Island Press.

Kennedy, I. R. 1988. *Acid Soil and Acid Rain*. Champaign: Research Studies Press.

Krebs, C. J. 1985. *Ecology: The Experimental Analysis of Distribution and Abundance*. New York: Harper & Row.

Manning, A., and Partridge, L. 1992. *An Introduction to Animal Behaviour*. New York: Cambridge University Press.

Norton, B. G. 1988. *The Preservation of Species: The Value of Biological Diversity*. Princeton: Princeton University Press.

Schmidt-Nielsen, K. 1984. Scaling: *Why Is Animal Size So Important?* Boston: Cambridge University Press.

Shair, H. N., Barr, G. A., and Hofer, M. A. 1991. *Developmental Psychology: New Methods and Changing Concepts*. New York: Oxford University Press.

Trivers, R. 1985. *Social Evolution*. Menlo Park, Calif.: Benjamin Cummings.

Wilson, E. O. 1975. *Sociobiology: The New Synthesis*. Cambridge, Mass.: Belknap Press.

Wilson, E. O. (ed.) 1988. *Biodiversity*. Washington, D.C.: National Academy Press.

ARTICLES

Axelrod, R., and Hamilton, W. D. 1981. The evolution of cooperation. *Science* 211:1390–1396.

Bertness, M. D. 1992. The ecology of a New England salt marsh. *American Scientist* 80(3):260–268.

Bongaarts, J. Can the growing human population feed itself? *Scientific American* March, 1994.

Bray, F. Agriculture for developing nations. *Scientific American* July, 1994.

Charlson, R. J. Sulfate aerosol and climatic change. *Scientific American* February, 1994.

Energy for planet earth. *Scientific American* September, 1990 (special issue).

Fingeman, M. (ed.). 1988. Energetics and Animal Behavior (a symposium). *American Zoologist* 28(3):813–938.

Gould, J., and Marler, P. Learning by instinct. *Scientific American* January, 1987.

Harden, G. 1986. Cultural carrying capacity: A biological approach to human problems. *BioScience* 36:599–607.

Hess, E. H. Imprinting in a natural laboratory. *Scientific American* February, 1972.

Holloway, M. Soiled shores. *Scientific American* October, 1991.

Holloway, M. Sustaining the Amazon. *Scientific American* July, 1993.

Holloway, M. Nurturing nature. *Scientific American* April, 1994.

Jones, R. D., and Wigley, T. M. L. Global warming trends. *Scientific American* August, 1990.

Kusler, J. A., Mitsch, W. J., and Larson, J. S. Wetlands. *Scientific American* January, 1994.

Lewin, R. 1988. Food scarcity hones competitive edge. *Science* 241:165.

Managing planet earth. *Scientific American* September, 1989 (special issue).

May, R. M. How many species inhabit the earth? *Scientific American* October, 1992.

May, R. M., and Seger, J. 1986. Ideas in ecology. *American Scientist* 74:256.

Moore, J. A. 1985. Science as a way of knowing: Human ecology. *American Zoologist* 25:483.

Nicol, S. J., and de la Mare, W. 1993. Ecosystem management and the Antarctic krill. *American Scientist* 81(1):36–47.

Nordhaus, W. D. 1994. Expert opinion on climatic change. *American Scientist* 82(1):45–51.

Page, R. E. 1989. Genetic specialists, kin recognition, and nepotism in honeybee colonies. *Nature* 338:576-579.

Pearce, F. 1988. Gaia: A revolution comes of age. *New Scientist* 117:32–33.

Peterson, I. 1986. Ecological energy: Bigger is better. *Science News* 130:341.

Repetto, R. Deforestation in the tropics. *Scientific American* April, 1990.

Repetto, R. Accounting for environmental assets. *Scientific American* June, 1992.

Romme, W. H., and Despain, D. G. The Yellowstone fires. *Scientific American* November, 1989.

Scheller, R. H., and Axel, R. How genes control an innate behavior. *Scientific American* March, 1984.

Schindler, D. W. 1988. Effects of acid rain on freshwater ecosystems. *Science* 239:149–157.

Scott, J. M., Csuti, B., Jacobi, J. D., and Estes, J. E. 1987. Species richness: A geographic approach to protecting future biological diversity. *BioScience* 37:782–788.

Terborgh, J. Why American songbirds are vanishing. *Scientific American* May, 1992.

Trivers, R. L. 1971. The evolution of reciprocal altruism. *Quarterly Review Biology* 46:35.

Wallace, A. June 16, 1988. Mechanisms of coexistence. *Nature* 333:597.

part FIVE

ANIMALLIKE PROTISTS AND ANIMALIA

One person can never fully appreciate the impressive diversity in the animal kingdom. Zoologists, therefore, must specialize—devoting their lives to the study of particular animal groups. Knowledge of all aspects of the biology of

animals is invaluable because it reveals the delicate balances in nature and gives clues to how we can preserve those balances. Furthermore, as zoologists learn more about animal groups, information that directly affects human welfare emerges. For example, from research on the nervous systems of squid and cockroaches comes much of what we know about nerve cells and many human nervous disorders. In spite of the work of generations of zoologists, there remains a wealth of unanswered questions about animals. Many species, especially in the tropics, have not been described. Some species may hold keys to unlocking the secrets of cancer, AIDS, and other diseases. Other species may provide insight into managing world resources.

Chapters 16 to 31 present an overview of the known animallike protists and animal phyla. Specifically, chapter 16 is an introduction to animal taxonomy, which is the study of the naming of organisms and their evolutionary relationships, and to the basic organization of animal bodies. Chapter 17 then covers the animallike protists and chapters 18 to 31 survey the animal phyla. These chapters are the beginning of an exciting journey into the diversity of the animal kingdom. Perhaps one of these chapters will captivate your attention, and you will join the thousands of zoologists who have spent their lives studying a portion of the animal kingdom.

Nautilus, *Nautilus pompilius*.

ANIMAL CLASSIFICATION, PHYLOGENY, AND ORGANIZATION

Concepts

1. Order in nature allows systematists to name animals and discern evolutionary relationships among them.
2. All organisms can be placed in one of five kingdoms based on whether their cells are prokaryotic or eukaryotic; whether they are truly multicellular or not; and whether they get their food through absorption, ingestion, or autotrophy.
3. Animal systematists use a variety of methods to discern evolutionary relationships. Evolutionary systematics and phylogenetic systematics (cladistics) are two widely used approaches in the study of evolutionary relationships.
4. Animal relationships are represented by branching evolutionary tree diagrams.
5. Animal body plans can be categorized based upon how cells are organized into tissues and how body parts are distributed within and around an animal.

Would You Like to Know:

1   why zoologists use scientific names, rather than common names, for the animals they study? (*p. 231*)

2   why zoology courses often cover organisms such as *Amoeba* and *Paramecium* when these organisms are really not animals? (*p. 231*)

3   why evolutionary tree diagrams can be misleading? (*p. 236*)

4   why sedentary animals, such as sea anemones, do not have heads and tails? (*p. 237*)

5   why body cavities are advantageous to animals that possess them? (*p. 239*)

These and other useful questions will be answered in this chapter.

This chapter contains evolutionary concepts, which are set off in this font.

One of the cornerstones of science that is virtually unchallenged is that there is order in nature. The order found in living systems is a natural consequence of the shared evolutionary processes that influence life. This chapter describes how the classification of animals and the basic organization of their bodies reflect that order.

CLASSIFICATION OF ORGANISMS

One of the characteristics of modern humans is our ability to communicate with a spoken language. Language not only allows us to communicate, but it also helps us encode and classify concepts, objects, and organisms that we encounter. To make sense out of life's diversity, we need more than just names for organisms. A potpourri of over a million animal names is of little use to anyone. To be useful, a naming system must reflect the order and relationships that arise from evolutionary processes. The study of the kinds and diversity of organisms and the evolutionary relationships among them is referred to as **systematics** (Gr. *systema*, system + *ikos*, body of facts) or **taxonomy** (Gr. *taxis*, arrangement + L. *nominalis*, belonging to a name). These studies result in the description of new species and the organization of animals into groups (taxa) based on degree of evolutionary relatedness. (Some biologists distinguish between systematics and taxonomy. These biologists prefer to think of taxonomy as the work involved with the original description of species, and systematics as the assignment of species into evolutionary groups. In this textbook, we will not make this distinction because of the extensive overlap between the two tasks.) **Nomenclature** (L. *nominalis*, belonging to a name + *calator*, to call) is the assignment of a distinctive name to each species.

A TAXONOMIC HIERARCHY

Our modern classification system is rooted in the work of Karl von Linné (1707–1778). His binomial system (*see chapter 1*) is still used today. Von Linné also recognized that different species could be grouped into broader categories based on shared characteristics. A group of animals that shares a particular set of characteristics forms an assemblage called a **taxon.** For example, a housefly (*Musca domestica*), although obviously unique, shares certain characteristics with other flies (the most important of these being a single pair of wings). Based on these similarities, all true flies form a logical, more inclusive group. Further, all true flies share certain characteristics with bees, butterflies, and beetles. Thus, these animals form an even more inclusive taxonomic group. They are all insects.

Von Linné recognized five taxa. Modern taxonomists use those five, and have added two other major taxa. They are arranged hierarchically (from broader to more specific): **kingdom, phylum, class, order, family, genus,** and **species** (table

TABLE 16.1	TAXONOMIC CATEGORIES OF A HUMAN AND A DOG	
TAXON	**HUMAN**	**DOMESTIC DOG**
Kingdom	Animalia	Animalia
Phylum	Chordata	Chordata
Class	Mammalia	Mammalia
Order	Primates	Carnivora
Family	Hominidae	Canidae
Genus	*Homo*	*Canis*
Species	*sapiens*	*familiaris*

FIGURE 16.1

Classification of Organisms. Animals belong to one of five large groups of organisms called kingdoms. The grouping of organisms according to evolutionary relationships helps scientists make sense of life's diversity. The Sumatran tiger cubs shown here belong to the species *Panthera tigris*.

16.1). Even though von Linné did not accept evolution, many of his groupings reflect evolutionary relationships. Morphological similarities between two animals have a genetic basis and are the result of a common evolutionary history. Thus, in grouping animals according to shared characteristics, von Linné grouped them according to their evolutionary relationships (figure 16.1). Ideally, members of the same taxonomic group are more closely related to each other than to members of different taxa (*see figure 1.10*).

Above the species level, there are no precise definitions of what constitutes a particular taxon. (The species concept was discussed in chapter 12.) Disagreements as to whether two species should be grouped into the same taxon or different taxa are common.

NOMENCLATURE

Do you call certain freshwater crustaceans crawdads, crayfish, or crawfish? Do you call a common sparrow an English sparrow, a barn sparrow, or a house sparrow?   ① The binomial system of nomenclature brings order to a chaotic world of common names. There are two problems with common names. First, common names vary from country to country, and from region to region within a country. Some species have literally hundreds of different common names. Biology transcends regional and nationalistic boundaries, and so must the names of what biologists study. Second, many common names refer to taxonomic categories higher than the species level. A superficial examination will simply not distinguish most different kinds of pillbugs (class Crustacea, order Isopoda) or most different kinds of crayfish (class Crustacea, order Decapoda). A common name, even if one recognizes it, often does not specify a particular species.

The binomial system of nomenclature is universal, and one always knows what level of classification is involved in any description. No two kinds of animals are given the same binomial name, and every animal has only one correct name, as required by the *International Code of Zoological Nomenclature*. The confusion caused by common names, therefore, is avoided. When writing the scientific name of an animal, the genus begins with a capital letter, the species designation begins with a lowercase letter, and the entire scientific name is italicized or underlined because it is latinized. Thus, the scientific name of humans is written *Homo sapiens*, and when the genus is understood, the binomial name can be abbreviated *H. sapiens*.

KINGDOMS OF LIFE

In the 1960s, a system of classification that uses five kingdoms gained widespread acceptance (figure 16.2). It distinguishes between kingdoms based on cellular organization and mode of nutrition. According to this system, members of the kingdom **Monera** are the bacteria and the cyanobacteria. They are distinguished from all other organisms by being prokaryotic. (Prokaryotic organisms lack a membrane-bound nucleus and other membranous organelles [*see table 3.1*].) Members of the kingdom **Protista** are eukaryotic and consist of single cells, or colonies of cells. This kingdom includes *Amoeba*, *Paramecium*, and many others. Members of the kingdom **Plantae** are eukaryotic, multicellular, and photosynthetic. Plants are characterized by walled cells and are usually nonmotile. Members of the kingdom **Fungi** are also eukaryotic and multicellular. Like plants, they have walled cells and are usually nonmotile. Fungi are distinguished from plants by mode of nutrition. They digest organic matter extracellularly and absorb the breakdown products. Members of the kingdom **Animalia** are eukaryotic, multicellular, and feed by ingesting other organisms or parts of other organisms. Their cells lack walls and they are usually motile.

In recent years, the five-kingdom classification system has been challenged by new information regarding the evolutionary relationships among the monerans and protists. Much of this information comes from molecular studies of ribosomal RNA from bacteria and protists. One system of classification that has the support of many microbiologists divides organisms into three domains (a taxonomic level above the kingdom level). All eukaryotic organisms are members of one domain and the eubacteria and archaebacteria make up the two other domains.

This textbook is primarily devoted to the animals. The next chapter, however, covers the animallike protists (protozoa). Its inclusion is a part of a tradition that originated with an old two-kingdom classification system.   ② Animallike protists (e.g., *Amoeba*, *Paramecium*) were once considered a phylum (Protozoa) in the animal kingdom, and general zoology courses usually include them.

ANIMAL SYSTEMATICS

The goal of animal systematics is to arrange animals into groups that reflect evolutionary relationships. Ideally, these groups should include a single ancestral species and all of its descendants. Such a group is called a **monophyletic group.** In searching out monophyletic groups, taxonomists look for attributes of animals, referred to as characters, that indicate relatedness. A character is virtually anything that has a genetic basis and that can be measured—from an anatomical feature to a sequence of nitrogenous bases in DNA or RNA. **Polyphyletic groups** that sometimes result from systematic studies reflect insufficient knowledge regarding the particular group because it is impossible for a species to evolve through two separate evolutionary pathways.

As in any human endeavor, disagreements have arisen in animal systematics. These disagreements revolve around methods of investigation and whether or not data may be used in describing distant evolutionary relationships. Three contemporary schools of systematics exist: evolutionary systematics, numerical taxonomy, and phylogenetic systematics (cladistics).

Evolutionary systematics is the oldest of the three approaches to systematics. It is sometimes called the "traditional approach," although it has certainly changed since the beginnings of animal systematics. **A basic assumption of evolutionary systematists is that organisms closely related to an ancestor will resemble that ancestor more closely than they resemble distantly related organisms.** Two kinds of similarities between organisms are recognized (*see also the discussion of homology and analogy in chapter 1*). Homologies are resemblances that result from common ancestry and are useful in classifying animals. An example is the similarity in the arrangement of bones in the wing of a bird and the arm of a human (*see figure 1.7*). Analogies are resemblances that result from organisms adapting under similar evolutionary pressures. The latter process is sometimes called convergent evolution. Analogies do not reflect common ancestry and are not used in animal taxonomy. The similarity between the wings of birds and insects is an analogy.

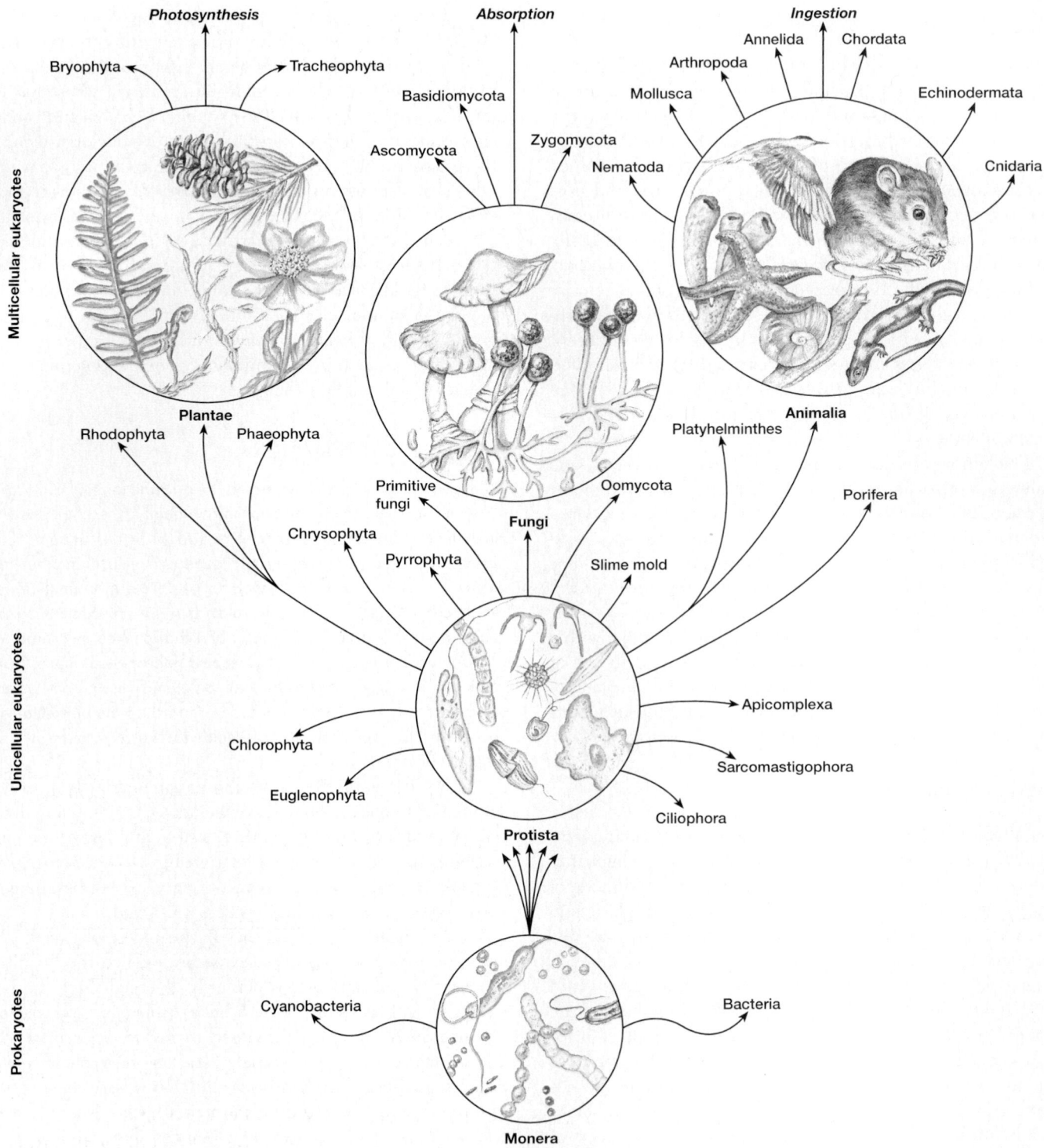

FIGURE 16.2
The Kingdoms of Life. In 1969 Robert H. Whittaker described a five-kingdom classification system that is widely used today.

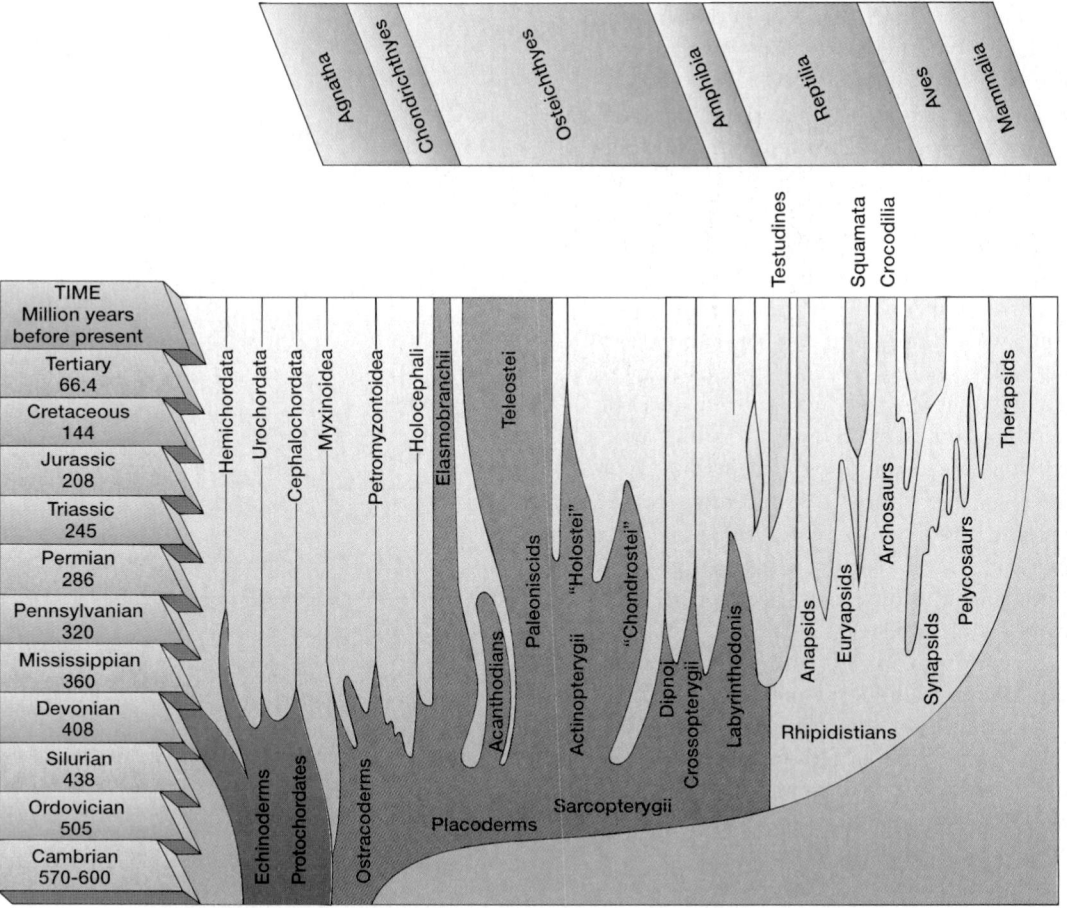

FIGURE 16.3

A Phylogenetic Tree Showing Vertebrate Phylogeny. A phylogenetic tree derived from evolutionary systematics depicts the degree of divergence since branching from a common ancestor, which is indicated by the time periods on the vertical axis. The width of the branches indicates the number of recognized genera for a given time period. Note that this diagram shows the birds (Aves) as being closely related to the reptiles (Reptilia), and both groups as having class-level status.

Evolutionary systematists often portray the results of their work on phylogenetic trees, where organisms are ranked according to their evolutionary relationships. Figure 16.3 is a phylogenetic tree showing vertebrate evolutionary relationships. In addition to depicting ancestry, time scales and relative abundance of animal groups are shown. These diagrams reflect judgments made about rates of evolution and the relative importance of certain key characters (e.g., feathers in birds).

Numerical taxonomy emerged during the 1950s and 1960s and represents the opposite end of the spectrum from evolutionary systematics. The founders of numerical taxonomy believed that the criteria for grouping taxa had become too arbitrary and vague. They tried to make taxonomy more objective. Numerical taxonomists use mathematical models and computer-aided techniques to group samples of organisms according to overall similarity. There is no attempt to distinguish

between homologies and analogies. Numerical taxonomists admit that analogies exist. They contend, however, that it is sometimes impossible to tell one from the other and analogies will be overshadowed by the numerous homologies used in data analysis. A second major difference between evolutionary systematics and numerical taxonomy is that numerical taxonomists limit discussion of evolutionary relationships to closely related taxa. Numerical taxonomy is the least popular of the three taxonomic schools; however, computer programs developed for use by numerical taxonomists are used by all taxonomists.

Phylogenetic systematics (cladistics) is a third approach to animal systematics. The goal of cladistics is similar to that described for evolutionary systematics—the generation of hypotheses of genealogical relationships among monophyletic groups of organisms. Cladists contend, however, that their methods are more scientific than those of evolutionary systematists because cladists' methods are more open to analysis and testing.

As do evolutionary systematists, cladists differentiate between homologies and analogies. Cladists contend, however, that homologies that are of recent origin are most useful in phylogenetic studies. Characters that are shared by all members of a group are referred to as **symplesiomorphies** (Gr. *sym*, together + *plesio*, near + *morphe*, form). These characters are homologies that may indicate a shared ancestry, but they are useless in describing relationships within the group. **Synapomorphies** (Gr. *syn*, together + *apo*, away + *morphe*, form), on the other hand, are characters that have arisen within the group since it diverged from a common ancestor. Synapomorphies are also called shared, derived characters and are more useful in cladistic analysis because they give information regarding degrees of relatedness. The identification of synapomorphies is a fundamental task for cladists.

In order to illustrate the difference between shared, ancestral characteristics (symplesiomorphies) and shared, derived characteristics (synapomorphies), we can consider the presence of hair and mammary glands in members of the class Mammalia. These characters are present in all mammals but are not in any other animal group. Hair and mammary glands indicate a common ancestry, but they cannot be used to distinguish between different groups of mammals because they are present in all mammals. On the other hand, a characteristic like teeth arrangement can be used as a synapomorphy because that characteristic is variable within the class. It is important to realize that a synapomorphy at one level of taxonomy may be a symplesiomorphy at a lower taxonomic level. Within the mammals, for example, all members of the class Rodentia (the rodents) have a characteristic arrangement of teeth. The arrangement of teeth, therefore, cannot be used to distinguish different rodents and is a common, ancestral character (a symplesiomorphy) for members of the order. Figure 16.4 illustrates the concepts of symplesiomorphy and synapomorphy in a hypothetical lineage.

Cladograms are evolutionary diagrams that depict a sequence in the origin of unique, derived characteristics. Cladograms are interpreted as a family tree depicting a hypothesis regarding monophyletic lineages. New data in the form of newly investigated characters, or reinterpretation of old data, are used to test the hypothesis described by the cladogram. Figure 16.5 is a cladogram depicting the evolutionary relationships among the reptiles, birds, and mammals.

Cladistics has become very widely accepted among zoologists. This acceptance has resulted in some nontraditional interpretations of animal phylogeny. One example of different interpretations derived through evolutionary systematics and cladistics can be seen by comparing figures 16.3 and 16.5. The birds have been assigned class-level status (Aves) by generations of taxonomists. Reptiles also have had class-level status (Reptilia). Cladistic analysis has shown, however, that birds are

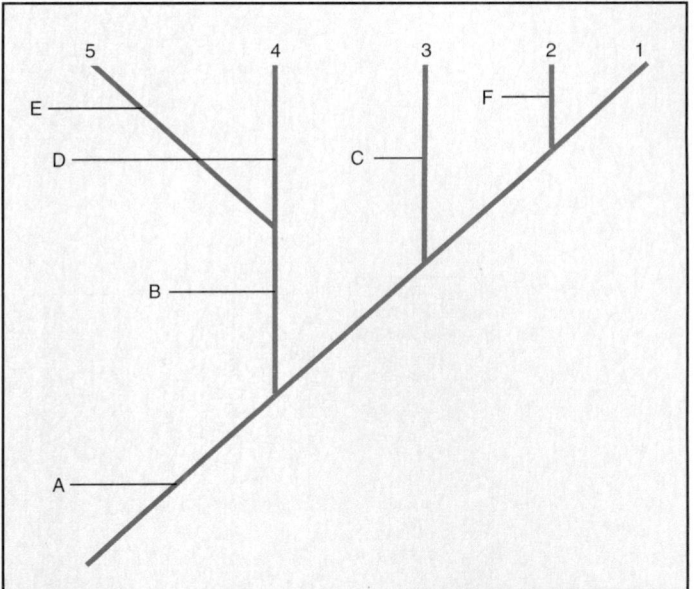

Figure 16.4

Interpreting Cladograms. This hypothetical cladogram shows five taxa (1–5) and the characters (A–F) used in deriving the taxonomic relationships. Character A is a symplesiomorphy (shared, ancestral characteristic) because it is shared by members of all five taxa. Because it is present in all taxa, character A cannot be used to distinguish members of this monophyletic lineage from each other. Character B is a synapomorphy (derived, ancestral character) because it is present in taxa 4 and 5 and can be used to distinguish these taxa from 1–3. Character B, however, is on the common branch giving rise to taxa 4 and 5. Character B is, therefore, symplesiomorphic for those two taxa. Characters D and E can be used to distinguish members of taxa 4 and 5.

more closely tied by common ancestry to the alligators and crocodiles than to any other group. According to this interpretation, birds and crocodiles would be assigned by cladists to a group that reflects this close common ancestry. Birds would become a subgroup within a larger group that included both birds and reptiles. Crocodiles would be depicted more closely related to the birds than they would be to snakes and lizards. Traditional evolutionary systematists maintain that the traditional interpretation is still correct because it takes into account the greater importance of key characteristics of birds (e.g., feathers and endothermy) that make the group unique. Cladists support their position by making the point that the designation of "key characteristics" involves value judgments that cannot be tested.

As debates between cladists and evolutionary systematists continue, our knowledge of evolutionary relationships among animals will become more complete. Debates like these are the fuel that force scientists to examine and reexamine old assumptions. Animal systematics is certain to be a lively and exciting field in future years.

The chapters that follow are a survey of the animal kingdom. The organization of these chapters reflects the traditional taxonomy that makes most zoologists comfortable. Cladograms

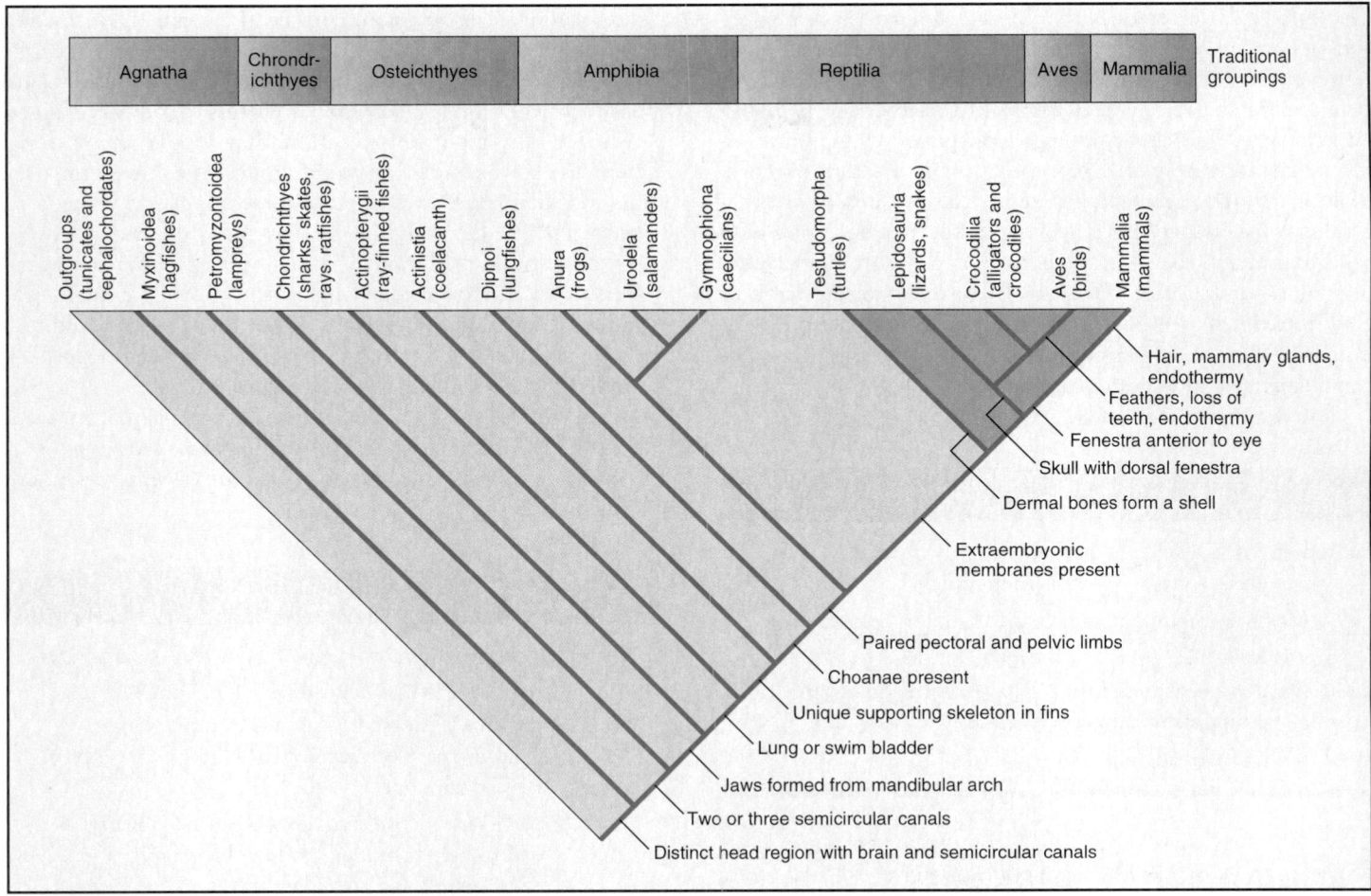

FIGURE 16.5

A Cladogram Showing Vertebrate Phylogeny. A cladogram is constructed by identifying points at which two groups diverged. Animals that share a branching point are included in the same taxon. Notice that timescales are not given or implied. The relative abundance of taxa is also not shown. Notice that this diagram shows the birds and crocodilians sharing a common branch, and that these two groups are more closely related to each other than either is to any other group of animals.

are usually included in the "Further Phylogenetic Considerations" at the end of most chapters, and any different interpretations of animal phylogeny implicit in these cladograms are discussed.

MOLECULAR APPROACHES TO ANIMAL SYSTEMATICS

In recent years, molecular biological techniques (*see chapter 9*) have provided important information for taxonomic studies. The relatedness of animals is reflected in the gene products (proteins) animals produce and in the genes themselves (the sequence of nitrogenous bases in DNA). Related animals have DNA derived from a common ancestor. Genes and proteins of related animals, therefore, are more similar than genes and proteins from distantly related animals. By comparing the sequence

of amino acids in proteins, or the sequence of nitrogenous bases in DNA or RNA, and assuming a relatively constant mutation rate (referred to as a molecular clock), taxonomists can estimate the time elapsed since divergence from a common ancestor. Sequencing the nuclear DNA and the mitochondrial DNA of animals has become commonplace. Mitochondrial DNA is useful in taxonomic studies because mitochondria have their own genetic systems and are inherited cytoplasmically. That is, mitochondria are transmitted from parent to offspring through the egg cytoplasm and can be used to trace maternal lineages. Using mitochondrial DNA involves relatively small quantities of DNA that change at a relatively constant rate. The sequencing of ribosomal RNA has been used extensively in studying taxonomic relationships within the protists. Ribosomal RNA is ideal because it makes up an essential organelle (the ribosome) in all organisms, and ribosomal RNA's structure changes slowly with time.

Molecular techniques have provided a wealth of new information useful to animal taxonomists. These techniques, however, are not a panacea that will replace traditional taxonomic methods. The molecular clocks that are used to determine rates of evolutionary change have provided important information that helps fill in time gaps in the fossil record. Molecular clocks, however, apparently run at different rates depending on whether one is looking at the sequence of amino acids in proteins, the sequence of bases in DNA from organelles like mitochondria, the sequence of bases in nuclear DNA, or data from different evolutionary lineages. Molecular and traditional methods of investigation will probably always be used to complement each other in taxonomic studies.

Stop and Ask Yourself

1. What does it mean when one says that our classification system is hierarchical?

2. Why are common names inadequate for scientific purposes?

3. What is a synapomorphy? Why are synapomorphies essential for the work of cladists?

4. What is a cladogram?

EVOLUTIONARY RELATIONSHIPS AND TREE DIAGRAMS

Although evolutionary tree diagrams can help one appreciate evolutionary relationships and timescales, they are often a source of misunderstanding. Evolutionary tree diagrams often illustrate relationships among levels of classification above the species (*see figure 16.5*). ③ Depicting phyla or classes as ancestral is misleading because evolution occurs in species groups (populations), not at higher taxonomic levels. Also, when phyla or classes are depicted as ancestral, one should remember that modern representatives of these "ancestral phyla" have had just as long an evolutionary history as animals in other taxonomic groups that may have descended from the common ancestor. All modern representatives of any group of animals should be visualized at the tips of a "tree branch," and they may be very different from ancestral species. We use modern representatives to help visualize general characteristics of an ancestral species, but never to specify details of the ancestor's structure, function, or ecology.

In addition to these problems of interpretation, evolutionary trees often imply a ladderlike progression of increasing complexity. This is misleading because evolution has often resulted in reduced complexity and body forms that are evolutionary failures. In many cases, evolution has led to extinction,

not evolutionary progression. Further, the common representation of a phylogeny as an inverted cone, or a tree with a narrow trunk and many higher branches, is often misleading. This implies that evolution is a continuous process of increasing diversification. The fossil records show that this is often wrong. There are, for example, 20 to 30 groups of echinoderms (sea stars and their relatives) in the fossil record and only 5 modern groups. This evolutionary lineage, like many others, underwent very rapid initial evolutionary diversification. After the initial diversification, extinction—not further diversification—was the rule. Contemporary paleontologist Stephen J. Gould uses the term contingency to refer to rapid evolutionary explosion followed by a high likelihood of extinction.

In spite of these problems, tree diagrams persist in scientific literature and are used in this textbook. As long as we keep their limitations in mind, they can help us visualize evolutionary relationships.

Stop and Ask Yourself

5. Why is it misleading to depict taxonomic groups higher than species on evolutionary tree diagrams?

6. Are the animals depicted along the trunk of an evolutionary tree diagram those that we see today? Why or why not?

7. What is meant by the term contingency? How can it be used to help us understand evolutionary relationships and tree diagrams?

PATTERNS OF ORGANIZATION

One of the most strikingly ordered series of changes in evolution is reflected in body plans in the animal kingdom and the protists. We can look at evolutionary changes in animal body plans and see what might be likened to a road map through a mountain range. What is most easily depicted are the starting and ending points and a few of the "attractions" along the route. What one cannot see from this perspective are the torturous curves and grades that must be navigated, and the extra miles that must be traveled, as one tries uncharted back roads. Unlike what we depict on a grand scale, evolutionary changes do not always mean "progress" and increased complexity. Evolution frequently results in backtracking, in experiments that fail, and in inefficient or useless structures. Evolution results in frequent dead ends, even though the route to that dead end may be filled with grandeur. The account that follows is a look at patterns of animal organization. As far as evolutionary pathways are concerned, one should view this account as an inexplicit road map through the animal kingdom. On a grand scale, it can be viewed as portraying evolutionary trends, but it should never be thought of as depicting an evolutionary sequence.

TABLE 16.2	ANIMAL SYMMETRY	
TERM	MEANING	
Asymmetry	The arrangement of body parts without a central axis or point (e.g., the sponges).	
Bilateral symmetry	The arrangement of body parts such that a single plane passing dorsoventrally through the longitudinal axis divides the animal into right and left mirror images (e.g., the vertebrates).	
Radial symmetry	The arrangement of body parts such that any plane passing through the oral-aboral axis divides the animal into mirror images (e.g., the cnidarians). Radial symmetry can be modified by the arrangement of some structures in pairs, or other combinations, around the central axis (e.g., biradial symmetry in the ctenophorans and some anthozoans, and pentaradial symmetry in the echinoderms).	

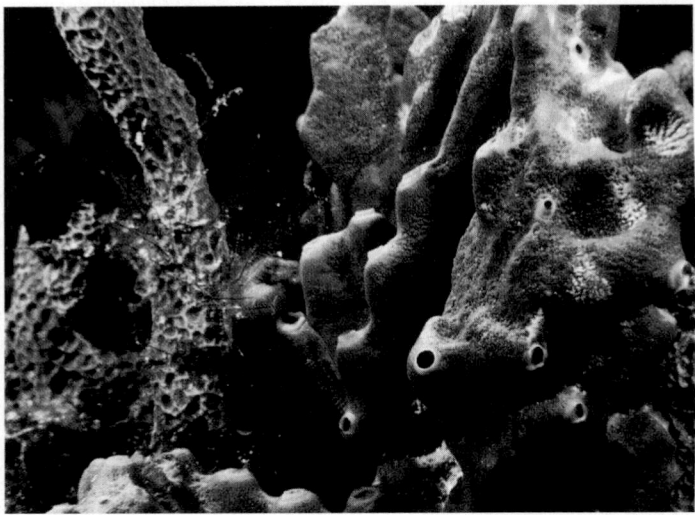

FIGURE 16.6

Asymmetry. Sponges display a cell-aggregate organization, and as seen in this brown volcano sponge (*Hemectyon ferox*), many are asymmetrical.

SYMMETRY

The bodies of animals and protists are organized into almost infinitely diverse forms. Within this diversity, however, certain patterns of organization can be described. The concept of symmetry is fundamental to understanding animal organization. **Symmetry** describes how the parts of an animal are arranged around a point or an axis (table 16.2).

Asymmetry, which is the absence of a central point or axis around which body parts are equally distributed, is characteristic of most protists and many sponges (figure 16.6). Asymmetry cannot be said to be an adaptation to anything or advantageous to an organism. Asymmetrical organisms do not develop complex communication, sensory, or locomotor functions. It is clear, however, that protists and animals whose bodies consist of aggregates of cells have flourished.

A sea anemone can move along a substrate, but only very slowly (figure 16.7). How is it to gather food? How does it detect and protect itself from predators? For this animal, a blind side would leave it vulnerable to attack and cause it to miss many meals. The sea anemone, as is the case for most sedentary animals, has sensory and feeding structures uniformly distributed around its body.   ④   Sea anemones do not have distinct head and tail ends. Instead, one point of reference is the end of the animal that possesses the mouth (the oral end), and a second point of reference is the end opposite the mouth (the aboral end). Animals such as the sea anemone are said to be radially symmetrical. **Radial symmetry** is the arrangement of

FIGURE 16.7

Radial Symmetry. Radially symmetrical animals, such as this tube coral polyp (*Tubastraea*), can be divided into equal halves by planes that pass through the oral/aboral axis. Sea anemones have their radial symmetry modified by certain arrangements of internal structures.

body parts such that any plane passing through the central oral-aboral axis divides the animal into mirror images. Radial symmetry is often modified by the arrangement of some structures in pairs, or in other combinations, around the central oral-aboral axis. The paired arrangement of some structures in radially symmetrical animals is referred to as biradial symmetry. The arrangement of structures in fives around a radial animal is referred to as pentaradial symmetry.

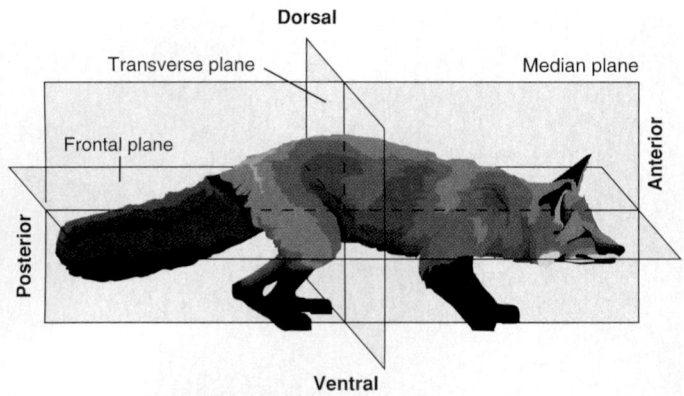

FIGURE 16.8

Bilateral Symmetry. Planes and terms of direction that are useful in locating parts of a bilateral animal are indicated. A bilaterally symmetrical animal, such as this fox, has only one plane of symmetry. An imaginary median plane is the only plane through which the animal could be cut to yield mirror-image halves.

Although the sensory, feeding, and locomotor structures found in radially symmetrical animals could never be called "simple," one never sees structures comparable to the complex sensory, locomotor, and feeding structures found in many other animals. The evolution of such structures in radially symmetrical animals would require repeated distribution of very specialized structures around the animal.

Bilateral symmetry is the arrangement of body parts such that there is only a single plane, passing dorsoventrally through the longitudinal axis of an animal, that divides the animal into right and left mirror images (figure 16.8). Bilateral symmetry is characteristic of active, crawling, or swimming animals. Because bilateral animals move primarily in one direction, one end of the animal is continually encountering the environment. The end that meets the environment is usually where complex sensory, nervous, and feeding structures evolve and develop. These developments result in the formation of a distinct head, and are called **cephalization** (Gr. *kephale*, head). The anterior end of an animal is where cephalization occurs. Posterior is opposite anterior; it is the animal's tail end. Other important terms of direction and terms describing body planes and sections are applied to bilateral animals. These terms are used for locating body parts relative to a point of reference or an imaginary plane passing through the body (tables 16.2 and 16.3; figure 16.8).

OTHER PATTERNS OF ORGANIZATION

In addition to body symmetry, there are other recognizable patterns of animal organization. In a broad context, these patterns of organization may reflect evolutionary trends. As explained earlier, however, one should not view these trends as exact sequences in animal evolution.

TABLE 16.3	TERMS OF DIRECTION
TERM	**DESCRIPTION**
Aboral	The end opposite the mouth
Oral	The end containing the mouth
Anterior	The head end; usually the end of a bilateral animal that meets its environment
Posterior	The tail end
Caudal	Toward the tail
Cephalic	Toward the head
Distal	Away from the point of attachment of a structure on the body (e.g., the toes are distal to the knee)
Proximal	Toward the point of attachment of a structure on the body (e.g., the hip is proximal to the knee)
Dorsal	The back of an animal; usually the upper surface; synonymous with posterior for animals that walk upright
Ventral	The belly of an animal; usually the lower surface; synonymous with anterior for animals that walk upright
Inferior	Below a point of reference (e.g., the mouth is inferior to the nose in humans)
Superior	Above a point of reference (e.g., the neck is superior to the chest)
Lateral	Away from the plane that divides a bilateral animal into mirror images
Medial (median)	On or near the plane that divides a bilateral animal into mirror images

The Unicellular (Cytoplasmic) Level of Organization

Organisms whose bodies consist of single cells or cellular aggregates display the unicellular level of organization. Unicellular body plans are characteristic of the Protista. Some zoologists prefer to use the designation "cytoplasmic" to emphasize the fact that all living functions are carried out within the confines of a single plasma membrane. It is a mistake to consider unicellular organization "simple." All unicellular organisms must provide for the functions of locomotion, food acquisition, digestion, water and ion regulation, sensory perception, and reproduction in a single cell.

Cellular aggregates (colonies) consist of loose associations of cells in which there is little interdependence, cooperation, or coordination of function—therefore, cellular aggregates cannot be considered tissues (*see chapter 3*). In spite of the absence of interdependence, some division of labor is found in these organisms. Some cells may be specialized for reproductive, nutritive, or structural functions.

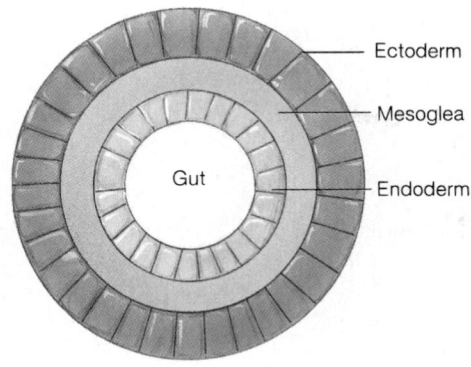

Figure 16.9

The Diploblastic Body Plan. Diploblastic animals have tissues derived from ectoderm and endoderm. Between these two layers is a noncellular mesoglea.

Diploblastic Organization

Cells are organized into tissues in most animal phyla. **Diploblastic** (Gr. *dis*, twice + *blaste*, to sprout) organization is the simplest, tissue-level organization (figure 16.9). Body parts are organized into layers that are derived from two tissue layers of the embryo. Ectoderm gives rise to the epidermis, the outer layer of the body wall. Endoderm gives rise to the gastrodermis, the tissue that lines the gut cavity. Between the epidermis and the gastrodermis is a noncellular layer called mesoglea. In some diploblastic organisms, cells occur in the mesoglea, but they are always derived from ectoderm or endoderm.

The cells in each tissue layer are functionally interdependent. The gastrodermis consists of nutritive (digestive) and muscular cells, and the epidermis contains epithelial and muscular cells. You may already be familiar with the feeding movements of *Hydra* or the swimming movements of a jellyfish. These kinds of functions are only possible when groups of cells cooperate, showing tissue-level organization.

Triploblastic Organization

Animals described in chapters 19 to 31 are **triploblastic** (Gr. *treis*, three + *blaste*, to sprout). That is, their tissues are derived from three embryological layers. As with diploblastic animals, ectoderm forms the outer layer of the body wall, and endoderm lines the gut. In addition to these two layers, a third embryological layer is sandwiched between the ectoderm and endoderm. This layer is mesoderm, which gives rise to supportive, contractile, and blood cells. Most triploblastic animals have an organ system level of organization. Tissues are organized together to

form excretory, nervous, digestive, reproductive, circulatory, and other systems. Triploblastic animals are usually bilaterally symmetrical (or have evolved from bilateral ancestors) and are relatively active animals.

Triploblastic animals are organized into several subgroups based on the presence or absence of a body cavity and, for those that possess one, the kind of body cavity present. A body cavity is a fluid-filled cavity in which the internal organs can be suspended and separated from the body wall.   ⑤   Body cavities are advantageous because they

1. Provide more room for organ development.
2. Provide more surface area for diffusion of gases, nutrients, and wastes into and out of organs.
3. Provide an area for storage.
4. Often act as hydrostatic skeletons.
5. Provide a vehicle for eliminating wastes and reproductive products from the body.
6. Facilitate increased body size.

Of these, the hydrostatic skeleton deserves further comment. Body cavity fluids give support while allowing the body to remain flexible. Hydrostatic skeletons can be illustrated with a water-filled balloon, which is rigid yet flexible. Because the water in the balloon is incompressible, squeezing one end causes the balloon to lengthen. Compressing both ends causes the middle of the balloon to become fatter. In a similar fashion, body-wall muscles, acting on coelomic fluid, are responsible for movement and shape changes in many animals.

The Triploblastic Acoelomate Pattern

Triploblastic animals whose mesodermally derived tissues form a relatively solid mass of cells between ectodermally and endodermally derived tissues are referred to as being **acoelomate** (Gr. *a*, without + *kilos*, hollow) (figure 16.10*a*). Some cells between the ectoderm and endoderm of acoelomate animals are loosely organized cells called parenchyma. Parenchymal cells are not specialized for a particular function.

The Triploblastic Pseudocoelomate Pattern

A **pseudocoelom** (Gr. *pseudes*, false) is a body cavity not entirely lined by mesoderm (figure 16.10*b*). No muscular or connective tissues are associated with the gut tract, no mesodermal sheet covers the inner surface of the body wall, and no membranes suspend organs in the body cavity. Embryologically, the pseudocoelom is derived from the blastocoel of the embryo (*see chapter 10*).

The Triploblastic Coelomate Pattern

A **coelom** is a body cavity that is completely surrounded by mesoderm (figure 16.10*c*). The inner body wall is lined by a thin mesodermal sheet, the peritoneum, and visceral organs are

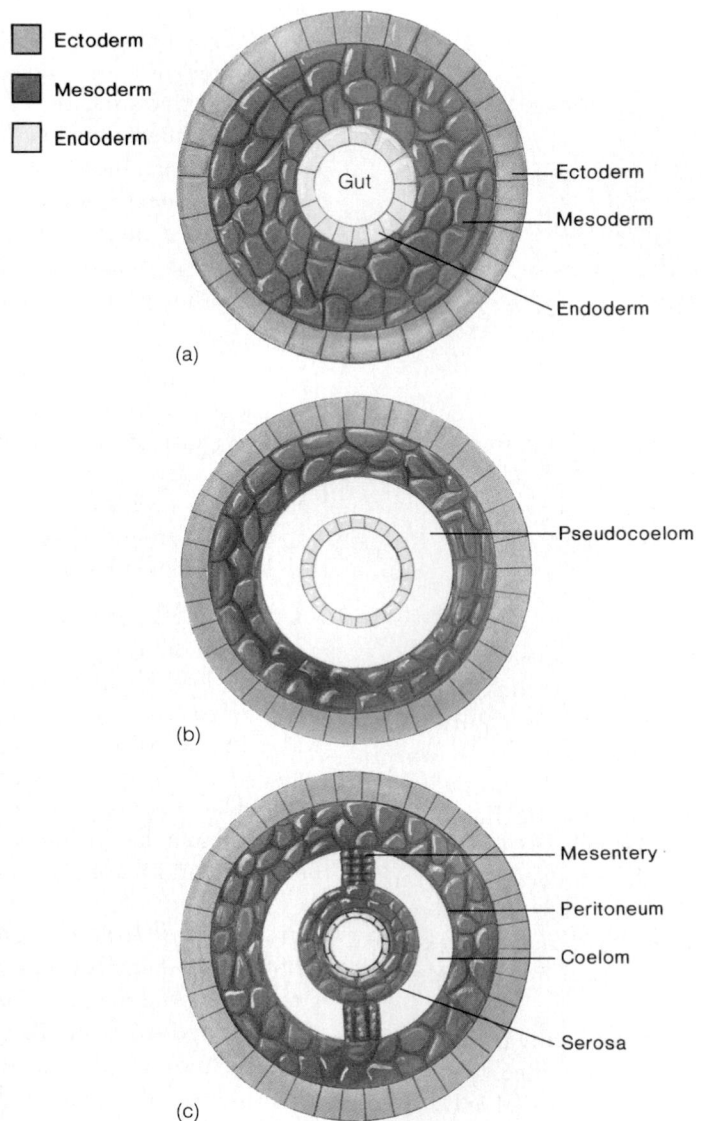

■ Ectoderm
■ Mesoderm
□ Endoderm

Gut

Ectoderm
Mesoderm
Endoderm

(a)

Pseudocoelom

(b)

Mesentery
Peritoneum
Coelom
Serosa

(c)

FIGURE 16.10

Triploblastic Body Plans. Triploblastic animals have tissues derived from ectoderm, mesoderm, and endoderm. (*a*) The triploblastic acoelomate pattern. (*b*) The triploblastic pseudocoelomate pattern. Note that there is no mesodermal lining on the gut track. (*c*) The triploblastic coelomate pattern. The coelom is completely surrounded by mesodermally derived tissues.

lined on the outside by a mesodermal sheet, the serosa. The peritoneum and the serosa are continuous, and suspend visceral structures in the body cavity. These suspending sheets are called mesenteries. Having mesodermally derived tissues, such as muscle and connective tissue, associated with internal organs enhances the function of virtually all internal body systems. In the chapters that follow, you will find many variations on the triploblastic coelomate pattern.

Stop and Ask Yourself

8. How would you distinguish between radial symmetry and bilateral symmetry? Why is radial symmetry advantageous for sedentary animals?

9. Why does cephalization usually accompany bilateral symmetry?

10. What kinds of tissues form from the mesoderm?

11. What advantages do body cavities confer to coelomate animals?

SUMMARY

1. Systematics is the study of the evolutionary history and classification of organisms. The binomial system of classification originated with von Linné and is used throughout the world in classifying organisms.
2. Organisms are classified into very broad categories called kingdoms. The five-kingdom classification system used in recent years is being challenged as new information regarding evolutionary relationships among the monerans and protists is discovered.
3. There are three modern approaches to systematics. They are evolutionary systematics, numerical taxonomy, and phylogenetic systematics (cladistics). Systematists believe that the ultimate goal of systematics is to establish evolutionary relationships in monophyletic groups. Evolutionary systematists use homologies and rank the importance of different characteristics in establishing evolutionary relationships. These taxonomists take into consideration differing rates of evolution in taxonomic groups. Phylogenetic systematists (cladists) look for shared, derived characteristics that can be used to investigate evolutionary relationships. Cladists do not attempt to weigh the importance of different characteristics. Wide acceptance of cladistic methods has resulted in some nontraditional taxonomic groupings of animals.
4. Evolutionary tree diagrams are useful for depicting evolutionary relationships, but their limitations must be understood.
5. The bodies of animals are organized into almost infinitely diverse forms. Within this diversity, however, certain patterns of organization can be described. Symmetry describes how the parts of an animal are arranged around a point or an axis.
6. Other patterns of organization reflect how cells are associated together into tissues, and how tissues are organized into organs and organ systems.

SELECTED KEY TERMS

bilateral symmetry (*p. 238*)
class (*p. 230*)
coelom (*p. 239*)
family (*p. 230*)
genus (*p. 230*)
kingdom (*p. 230*)
order (*p. 230*)
phylum (*p. 230*)
radial symmetry (*p. 237*)
species (*p. 230*)

CRITICAL THINKING QUESTIONS

1. In one sense, our classification system above the species level is artificial. In another sense, however, it is real. Explain this paradox.
2. Give proper scientific names to 10 hypothetical animal species. Assume that you have four different genera represented in your group of 10. Be sure your format for writing scientific names is correct.
3. Describe hypothetical synapomorphies that would result in an assemblage of one class, two orders, and three families (in addition to the four genera and 10 species).
4. Construct a cladogram, similar to that shown in figure 16.5, using your hypothetical animals from questions 2 and 3. Make drawings of your animals.
5. Describe the usefulness of evolutionary tree diagrams in zoological studies. Describe two problems associated with their use.

ANIMALLIKE PROTISTS: THE PROTOZOA

Concepts

1. The kingdom Protista is a polyphyletic group with origins in ancestral members of the kingdom Monera.
2. Protozoa display unicellular or colonial organization. All functions must be carried out within the confines of a single plasma membrane.
3. According to the most widely accepted classification scheme, there are seven protozoan phyla: Sarcomastigophora, Labyrinthomorpha, Apicomplexa, Microspora, Acetospora, Myxozoa, and Ciliophora.
4. Certain members of the above phyla have had, and continue to have, important influences on human health and welfare.

Would You Like to Know:

1. whether or not all protozoan phyla can be traced back to a single moneran ancestor? (p. 244)
2. whether some protozoa should be considered single cells, multicellular organisms, or both? (p. 245)
3. what causes "red tides"? (p. 248)
4. what protozoan causes dysentery in humans? (p. 252)
5. what protozoan has caused more deaths in armies throughout history than actual combat? (p. 254)
6. why sandboxes should always be kept covered when not in use? (p. 255)
7. what group of protozoa has members that are considered the most complex of all protists? (p. 256)

These and other useful questions will be answered in this chapter.

This chapter contains evolutionary concepts, which are set off in this font.

EVOLUTIONARY PERSPECTIVE

Where are your "roots"? Although most people are content to go back into their family tree a few hundred years, scientists look back millions of years to the origin of all life-forms. The fossil record indicates that virtually all protist and animal phyla living today were present during the Cambrian period, about 550 million years ago (*see table 1.1*). Unfortunately, there is little fossil evidence of the evolutionary pathways that gave rise to these phyla. Instead, evidence is gathered from examining the structure and function of living species. The "evolutionary perspective" in chapters 17 to 31 presents hypotheses regarding the origin of protist and animal phyla. These hypotheses seem reasonable to most zoologists; however, they are untestable, and alternative interpretations can be found in the scientific literature.

Ancient members of the kingdom Monera were the first living organisms on this planet. The Monera gave rise to the kingdom Protista (also called Protoctista) about 1.5 billion years ago. The endosymbiont hypothesis is one of a number of explanations of how this could have occurred (*see box 3.1*). ① Most scientists agree that the protists probably arose from more than one ancestral moneran group. Depending on the classification system used, between 7 and 45 phyla of protists are recognized today. These phyla represent numerous evolutionary lineages. When groups of organisms are believed to have had separate origins, they are said to be **polyphyletic** (Gr. *polys*, many + *phylon*, race). Some protists are plantlike because they are primarily autotrophic (they produce their own food). Others are animallike because they are primarily heterotrophic (they feed on other organisms). This chapter covers seven phyla of protists commonly called the protozoa (figures 17.1, 17.2).

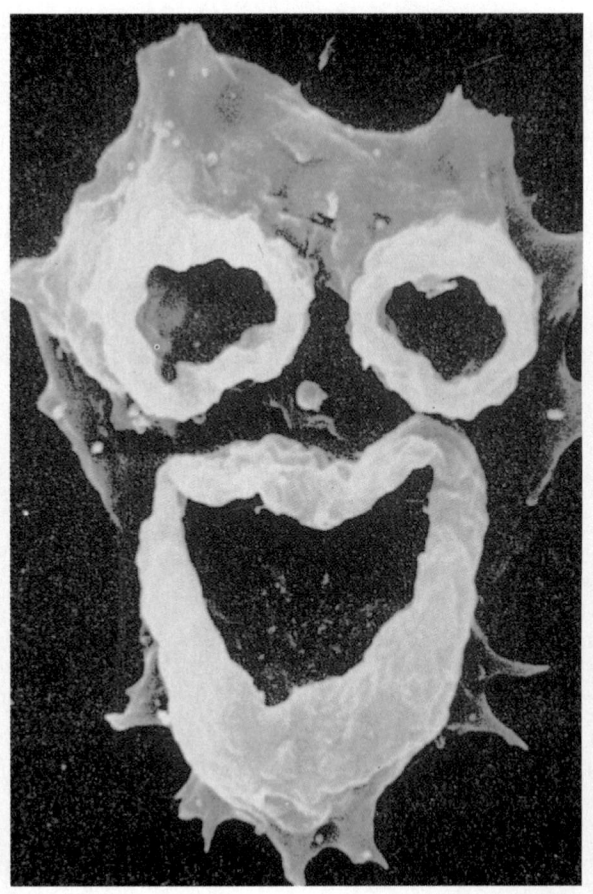

FIGURE 17.1

A Protozoan. Scanning electron micrograph of *Naegleria fowleri*, the cause of primary amebic meningoencephalitis in humans. The facelike structures are used for attack and engulfment of food sources (× 600).

FIGURE 17.2

Animallike Protists: The Protozoa. A generalized evolutionary tree depicting the major events and possible lines of descent for the protozoa (shaded in orange).

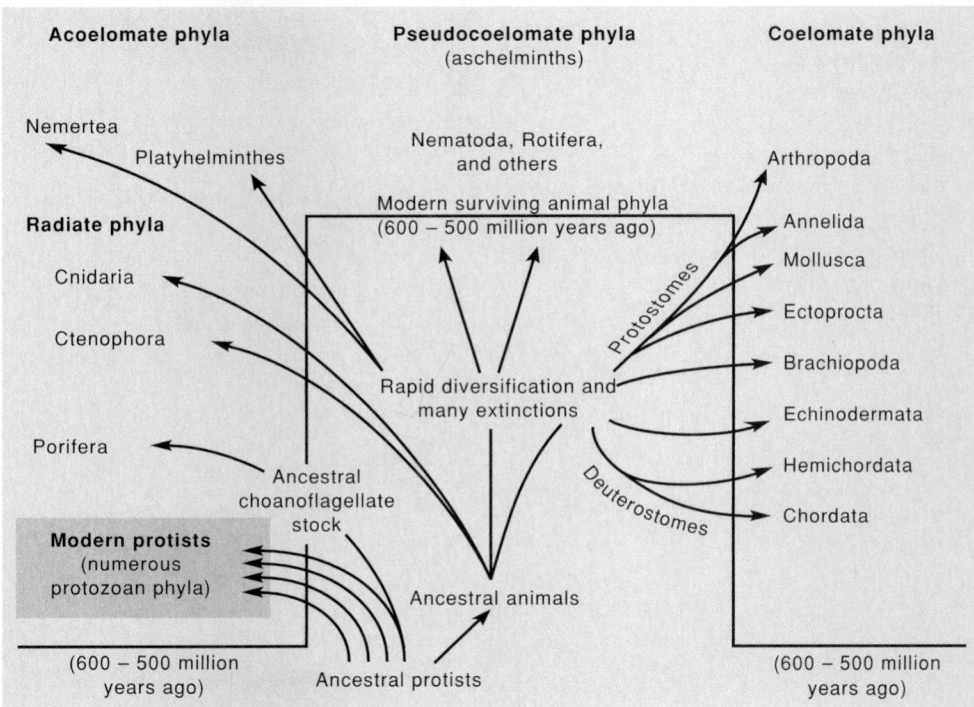

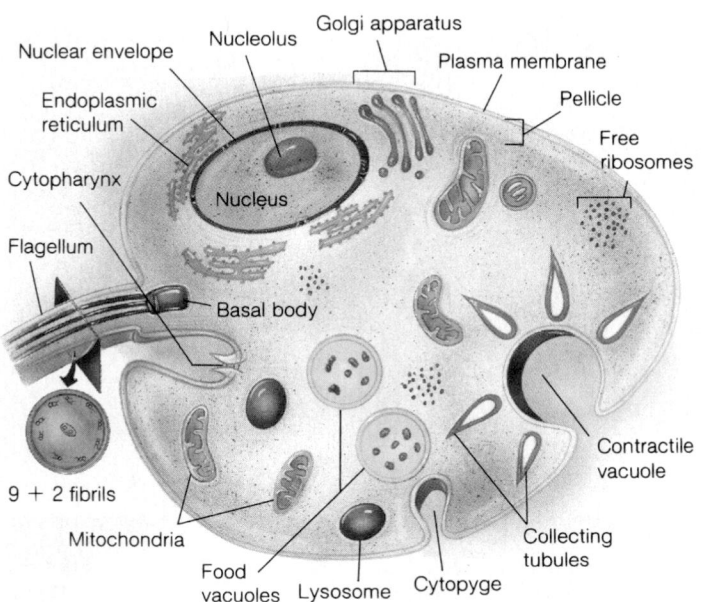

FIGURE 17.3

A Protozoan Protist. This drawing of a stylized protozoan with a flagellum illustrates the basic protozoan morphology. *From:* "A LIFE OF INVERTEBRATES" © 1979 W. D. Russell-Hunter.

LIFE WITHIN A SINGLE PLASMA MEMBRANE

Protozoa (Gr. *proto*, first + *zoa*, animal) display unicellular (cytoplasmic) organization. Their single-celled organization does not necessarily imply that they are simple organisms. ② Often, they are more complex than any particular cell in higher organisms. In some protozoan phyla, individuals may group together to form colonies, which are associations of individuals that are not dependent on one another for most functions. Protozoan colonies, however, can become very complex, with some individuals becoming so specialized that it becomes difficult to tell whether one is observing a colony or a multicellular organism.

MAINTAINING HOMEOSTASIS

Specific functions are carried out in protozoa by organelles that are similar to the organelles of other eukaryotic cells (figure 17.3; *see also figure 3.2*). Some protozoan organelles, however, reflect specializations for unicellular life-styles.

The plasma membrane of many protozoa is underlaid by a regular arrangement of microtubules. Together, they are called the **pellicle.** The pellicle is rigid enough to maintain the shape of the protozoan, but it is also flexible.

The cytoplasm of a protozoan is differentiated into two regions. The portion of the cytoplasm just beneath the pellicle is called **ectoplasm** (Gr. *ectos*, outside + *plasma*, to form). It is relatively clear and firm. The inner cytoplasm is called **endoplasm** (Gr. *endon*, within). It is usually granular and more fluid.

The conversion of cytoplasm between these two states is important in one kind of protozoan locomotion and is discussed later.

Most marine protozoa have solute concentrations similar to that of their environments. Freshwater protozoa, however, must regulate the water and solute concentrations of their cytoplasm. Water enters freshwater protozoa by osmosis because of higher solute concentrations in the protozoan than in the environment. This excess water is removed by **contractile vacuoles** (figure 17.3). In some protozoa, contractile vacuoles are formed by coalescence of smaller vacuoles. In others, the vacuoles are permanent organelles that are filled by collecting tubules that radiate into the cytoplasm. The contraction of microfilaments (*see figure 3.20*) has been implicated in the emptying of contractile vacuoles.

Most protozoa ingest other organisms or products of other organisms—either by absorbing dissolved nutrients by active transport or by ingesting whole or particulate food through endocytosis (*see figure 3.14*). In some protozoa, food may be ingested in a specialized region analogous to a mouth, called the **cytopharynx.** Digestion and transport of food occurs in **food vacuoles** that form during endocytosis. Digestion is mediated by enzymes and acidity changes. Food vacuoles fuse with enzyme-containing lysosomes and circulate through the cytoplasm, distributing the products of digestion. After digestion is completed, the vacuoles are called **egestion vacuoles.** They release their contents by exocytosis, sometimes at a specialized region of the plasma membrane or pellicle called the **cytopyge.**

Because protozoa are small, they have a large surface area in proportion to their volume. This high surface area-to-volume ratio (*see figure 3.3*) facilitates two other maintenance functions. Gas exchange involves acquiring quantities of oxygen needed for cellular respiration and eliminating the carbon dioxide that is produced as a by-product. Excretion is the elimination of the nitrogenous by-products of protein metabolism. The principal nitrogenous waste in protozoa is ammonia. Both gas exchange and excretion occur by diffusion across the plasma membrane.

REPRODUCTION

Both asexual and sexual reproduction occur among the protozoa. One of the simplest and most common forms of asexual reproduction is **binary fission.** In binary fission, mitosis produces two nuclei that are distributed into two similar-sized individuals when the cytoplasm divides. During cytokinesis, some organelles are also duplicated to ensure that each new protozoan will possess the needed organelles to begin life. Depending on the group of protozoa, cytokinesis may be longitudinal or transverse (figures 17.4 and 17.5).

Other forms of asexual reproduction are common. During **budding,** mitosis is followed by the incorporation of one nucleus into a cytoplasmic mass that is much smaller than the parent cell. **Multiple fission** or **schizogony** (Gr. *schizein*, to split) occurs when a large number of daughter cells are formed from

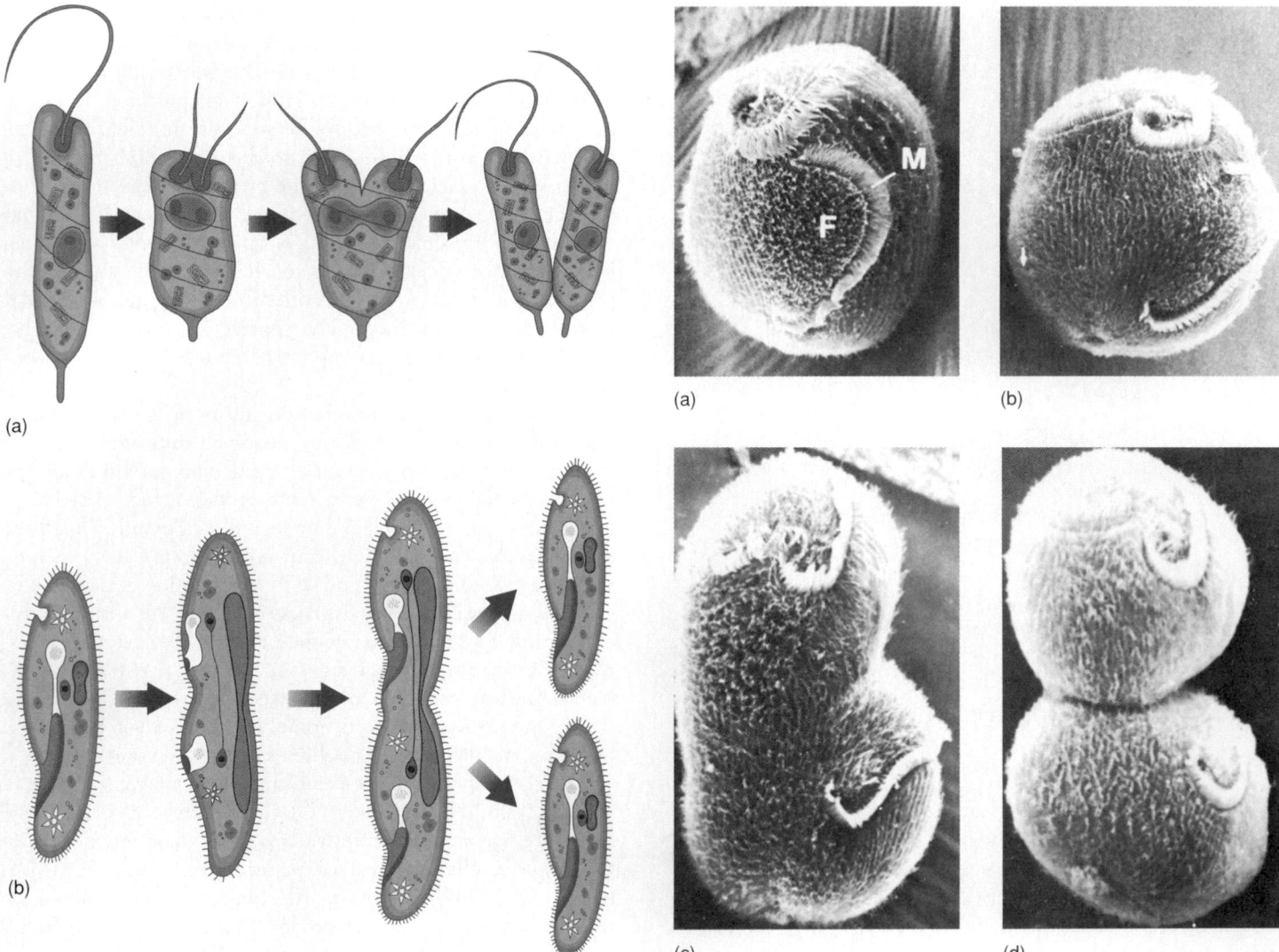

Figure 17.4

Asexual Reproduction in Protozoa. Binary fission begins with mitosis. Cytoplasmic division (cytokinesis) divides the organelles between the two cells and results in two similarly sized protozoa. Binary fission is (*a*) longitudinal in some protozoa (e.g., mastigophorans) and (*b*) transverse in other protozoa (e.g., ciliates).

Figure 17.5

Binary Fission of the Ciliate, *Stentor coeruleus*. Fission includes the division of some surface features (*a,b*), in this case cilia modified into a bandlike structure called a membranelle (M). F designates the frontal field, and the beginning of a fission furrow is shown by the arrow in (*b*). Fission is completed by division of the cytoplasm (*c,d*). (Scanning electron micrographs × 250.)

the division of a single protozoan. Schizogony begins with multiple mitotic divisions in a mature individual. When a certain number of nuclei have been produced, cytoplasmic division results in the separation of each nucleus into a new cell.

Sexual reproduction involves the formation of gametes and the subsequent fusion of gametes to form a zygote. In most protozoa, the sexually mature individual is haploid. Gametes are produced by mitosis, and meiosis occurs following union of gametes. Ciliated protozoa are an exception to this pattern. Specialized forms of sexual reproduction will be covered as individual protozoan groups are discussed.

Symbiotic Life-Styles

Symbiotic life-styles are important for many protozoa. **Symbiosis** (Gr. *syn*, with + *bios*, life) occurs when one organism lives in an intimate association with another. For many protozoa, these interactions involve a form of symbiosis called **parasitism,** in which one organism lives in or on a second organism, called a **host.** The host is harmed but usually survives, at least long enough for the parasite to complete one or more life cycles.

The relationships between a parasite and its host(s) are often complex. Some parasites have life histories involving multiple hosts. The **definitive host** is the host that harbors the sexual stages of the parasite. The sexual stages may produce offspring that enter another host. This second host is called an **intermediate host,** and asexual reproduction occurs here. More than one intermediate host and more than one immature stage may be involved in some life cycles. For the life cycle to be completed, the final, asexual stage must have access to a definitive host.

Other kinds of symbiosis involve relationships that do not harm the host. **Commensalism** is a symbiotic relationship in which one member of the relationship benefits, and the second member is neither benefited nor harmed. **Mutualism** is a symbiotic relationship in which both species benefit.

PROTOZOAN TAXONOMY

Zoologists who specialize in the study of protozoa are called **protozoologists.** Most protozoologists now regard the Protozoa as a subkingdom, consisting of seven separate phyla within the kingdom Protista. These are the phylum Sarcomastigophora, consisting of flagellates and amoebae with a single type of nucleus; the phyla Labyrinthomorpha, Apicomplexa, Microspora, Ascetospora, and Myxozoa, consisting of either saprozoic or parasitic species; and the phylum Ciliophora, containing ciliated protozoa with two types of nuclei. The classification of this subkingdom into phyla is based primarily on types of nuclei, mode of reproduction, and mechanism of locomotion (table 17.1). These taxa are further discussed in subsequent sections of this chapter.

Stop and Ask Yourself

1. Ancestral members of what kingdom of organisms gave rise to the protozoa?
2. What is the function of the following structures: pellicle? contractile vacuoles? cytopharynx? egestion vacuoles?
3. What are three forms of asexual reproduction in protozoa?
4. Why are gametes produced by mitosis rather than by meiosis in most protozoa?

PHYLUM SARCOMASTIGOPHORA

With over 18,000 described species, Sarcomastigophora (sar′ko-mas-ti-gof″o-rah) (Gr. *sarko*, fleshy + *mastigo*, whip + *phoros*, to bear) is the largest protozoan phylum. Characteristics of the phylum Sarcomastigophora include the following:

1. Unicellular or colonial
2. Locomotion by flagella, pseudopodia, or both
3. Autotrophic, saprozoic, or heterotrophic
4. Single type of nucleus
5. Sexual reproduction usually occurs

TABLE 17.1	SUMMARY OF PROTOZOAN CLASSIFICATION

Phylum Sarcomastigophora (sar′ko-mas-ti-gof′o-rah)
Protozoa that possess flagella, pseudopodia, or both for locomotion and feeding; single type of nucleus.
   Subphylum Mastigophora (mas-ti-gof′o-rah)
   One or more flagella used for locomotion; autotrophic, heterotrophic, or saprozoic.
      Class Phytomastigophorea (fi′to-mas-ti-go-for′ah)
      Chloroplasts usually present; mainly autotrophic, some heterotrophic. *Euglena, Volvox, Chlamydomonas.*
      Class Zoomastigophorea (zo′o-mas-tigo-for′ah)
      Lack chloroplasts; heterotrophic or saprozoic. *Trypanosoma, Trichonympha, Trichomonas, Giardia, Leishmania.*
   Subphylum Sarcodina (sar′ko-din″ah)
   Pseudopodia for movement and food gathering; naked or with shell or test; mostly free living.
      Superclass Rhizopoda (ri-zop′o-dah)
      Lobopodia, filopodia, reticulopodia, or no distinct pseudopodia. *Amoeba, Entamoeba, Naegleria, Arcella, Difflugia;* forminiferans (*Gumbelina*).
      Superclass Actinopoda (ak′ti-nop″o-dah)
      Spherical, planktonic; axopodia supported by microtubules; includes marine radiolarians with siliceous tests and freshwater heliozoans (*Actinophrys*).
   Subphylum Opalinata (op′ah-li-not′ah)
   Cylindrical; covered with cilia. *Opalina, Zelleriella.*
Phylum Labyrinthomorpha (la′brinth-o-morp′ha)
Trophic stage as ectoplasmic network with spindle-shaped or spherical, nonamoeboid cells; saprozoic and parasitic on algae and seagrass; mostly marine and estuarine. *Labyrinthula.*
Phylum Apicomplexa (a′pi-kom-plex′ah)
Parasitic with an apical complex used for penetrating host cells; cilia and flagella lacking, except in certain reproductive stages. The gregarines (*Monocystis*), coccidians (*Eimeria, Isospora, Sarcocystis, Toxoplasma*), *Plasmodium.*
Phylum Microspora (mi-cro-spor′ah)
Unicellular spores; intracellular parasites in nearly all major animal groups. The microsporeans (*Nosema*).
Phylum Acetospora (ah-seat-o-spor′ah)
Multicellular spore; all parasitic in invertebrates. The acetosporans (*Paramyxa, Haplosporidium*).
Phylum Myxozoa (myx-o-zoo-ah)
Spores of multicellular origin; all parasitic. The myxozoans (*Myxosoma*).
Phylum Ciliophora (sil-i-of′or-ah)
Protozoa with simple or compound cilia at some stage in the life history; heterotrophs with a well-developed cytostome and feeding organelles; at least one macronucleus and one micronucleus present. *Paramecium, Stentor, Euplotes, Vorticella, Balantidium.*

SUBPHYLUM MASTIGOPHORA: FLAGELLAR LOCOMOTION

Members of the subphylum Mastigophora (mas-ti-gof′o-rah) use flagella in locomotion. Movements of flagella may be

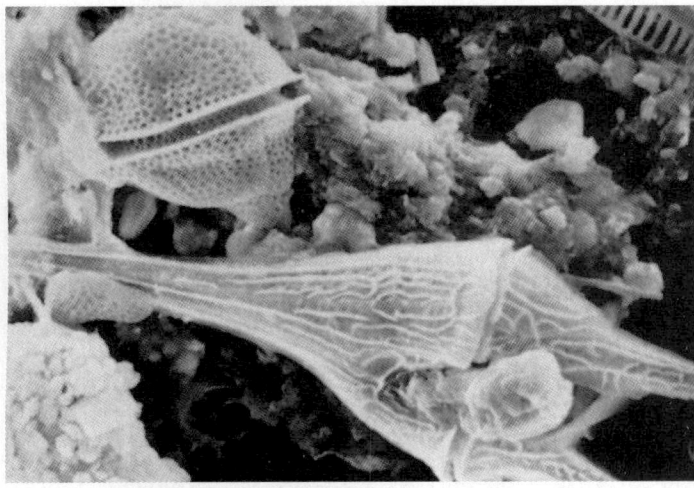

FIGURE 17.6

Class Phytomastigophorea: Dinoflagellates. Scanning electron micrograph of two species of dinoflagellates, *Peridinium* in the upper left and *Ceratium* in the lower half. The transverse grooves in the center of each dinoflagellate are the location for one of the two flagella (scanning electron micrograph × 800).

two-dimensional, whiplike movements or helical movements that result in the protozoan being pushed or pulled through its aquatic medium.

CLASS PHYTOMASTIGOPHOREA

The subphylum Mastigophora is divided into two classes. Members of the class Phytomastigophorea (fi'to-mas-ti-go-for'ah) (Gr. *phytos,* plant) possess chlorophyll and one or two flagella. Phytomastigophoreans are responsible for producing a large portion of the food in marine food webs. Much of the oxygen in our atmosphere also comes from photosynthesis by these marine organisms.

Marine phytomastigophoreans include the dinoflagellates (figure 17.6). Dinoflagellates have one flagellum that wraps around the organism in a transverse groove. The primary action of this flagellum causes the organism to spin on its axis. A second flagellum is a trailing flagellum that pushes the organism forward. In addition to chlorophyll, many dinoflagellates contain xanthophyll pigments, which give them a golden-brown color. At times, dinoflagellates become so numerous that they color the water. One genus, *Gymnodinium,* has representatives that produce toxins.   3   Periodic "blooms" of these organisms are called "red tides" and result in fish kills along the continental shelves. Human deaths may result from consuming tainted molluscs or fish. The Bible reports that the first plague Moses visited upon the Egyptians was a blood-red tide that

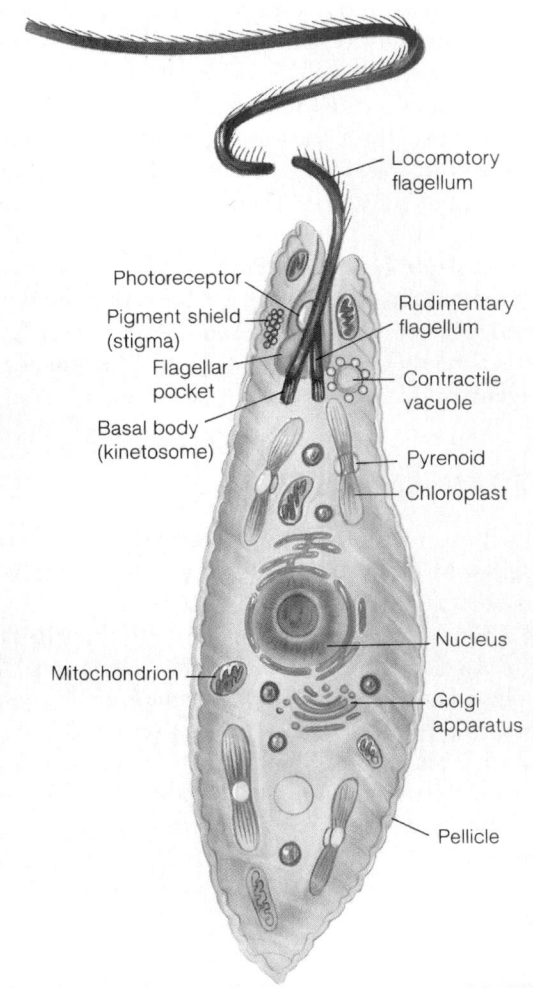

FIGURE 17.7

Phytomastigophorean Anatomy: The Structure of *Euglena.* Note the large, well-organized chloroplasts. The photoreceptor allows the organism to swim toward light.

killed fish and fouled water. Indeed, the Red Sea is probably named after these toxic dinoflagellate blooms.

Euglena is a phytomastigophorean found in fresh water (figure 17.7). Each chloroplast has a **pyrenoid,** which synthesizes and stores polysaccharides. If cultured in the dark, euglenoids feed by absorption and lose their green color. Some euglenoids (e.g., *Peranema*) lack chloroplasts and are always heterotrophic.

Euglena orients toward light of certain intensities. A pigment shield (**stigma**) covers a photoreceptor at the base of the flagellum. The stigma permits light to strike the photoreceptor from only one direction, allowing *Euglena* to orient and move in relation to a light source.

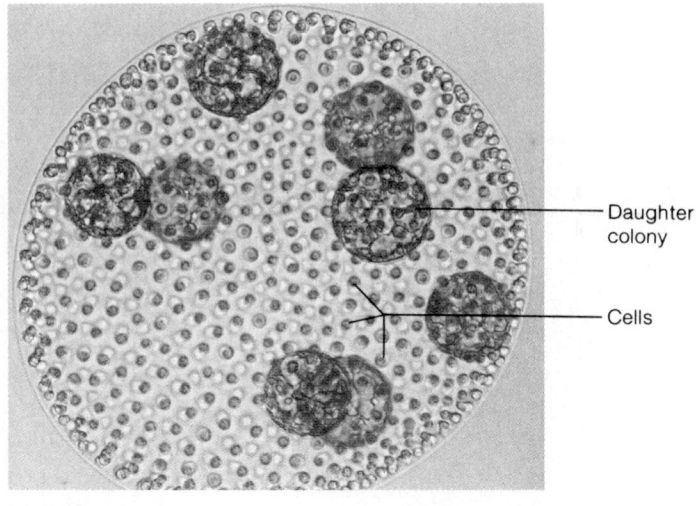

(a)

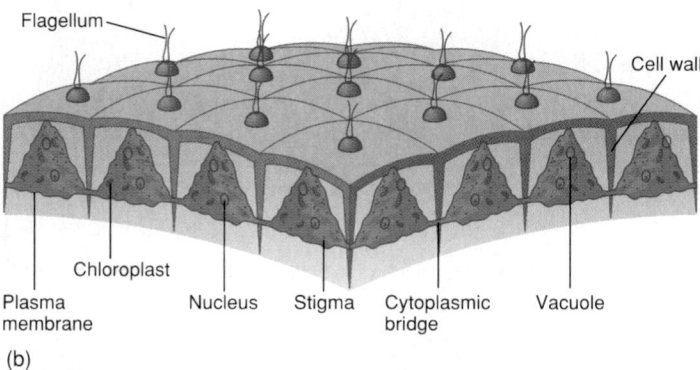

(b)

Figure 17.8

Class Phytomastigophorea: *Volvox*, a Colonial Flagellate. (*a*) A *Volvox* colony showing asexually produced daughter colonies (light micrograph × 400). (*b*) An enlargement of a portion of the colony wall.

Euglenoid flagellates are haploid and reproduce by longitudinal binary fission (*see figure 17.4a*). Sexual reproduction in these species is unknown.

Volvox is a colonial flagellate consisting of up to 50,000 cells embedded in a spherical, gelatinous matrix (figure 17.8a). Cells possess two flagella, which cause the colony to roll and turn gracefully through the water (figure 17.8b).

Although most cells of *Volvox* are relatively unspecialized, reproduction is dependent upon certain specialized cells. Asexual reproduction occurs in the spring and summer when certain cells withdraw to the watery interior of the parental colony and form daughter colonies. When the parental colony dies and ruptures, daughter colonies are released.

Sexual reproduction in *Volvox* occurs during autumn. Some species are **dioecious** (having separate sexes), other

species are **monoecious** (having both sexes in the same colony). In autumn, specialized cells differentiate into macrogametes or microgametes. Macrogametes are large, filled with nutrient reserves, and nonmotile. Microgametes form as a packet of flagellated cells that leaves the parental colony and swims to a colony containing macrogametes. The packet then breaks apart and syngamy occurs between macro- and microgametes. The zygote, an overwintering stage, secretes a resistant wall around itself and is released when the parental colony dies. Because the parental colony consists of haploid cells, the zygote must undergo meiosis to reduce the chromosome number from the diploid zygotic condition. One of the products of meiosis then undergoes repeated mitotic divisions to form a colony consisting of just a few cells. The other products of meiosis degenerate. This colony is released from the protective zygotic capsule in the spring.

Class Zoomastigophorea

Members of the class Zoomastigophorea (zo´o-mas-ti-go-for´ah) (Gr. *zoion*, animal) lack chloroplasts and are heterotrophic. Some members of this class are important parasites of humans (box 17.1).

One of the most important species of zoomastigophoreans is *Trypanosoma brucei*. This species is divided into three subspecies: *T. b. brucei*, *T. b. gambiense*, and *T. b. rhodesiense*. The first of these three subspecies is a parasite of nonhuman mammals of Africa. The latter two cause sleeping sickness in humans. Tsetse flies (*Glossina* spp.) are intermediate hosts and vectors of all three subspecies. When a tsetse fly bites an infected human or mammal, parasites are picked up with the meal of blood. Trypanosomes multiply asexually in the gut of the fly for about 10 days, then migrate to the salivary glands. While in the fly, the trypanosomes are transformed, in 15 to 35 days, through a number of body forms. When the infected tsetse fly bites another vertebrate host, the parasites travel with salivary secretions into the blood of a new definitive host. The parasites multiply asexually in the new host and are again transformed through a number of body forms. Parasites may live in the blood, lymph, spleen, central nervous system, and cerebrospinal fluid (figure 17.9a,b).

When trypanosomes enter the central nervous system, they cause general apathy, mental dullness, and lack of coordination. "Sleepiness" develops and the infected individual may fall asleep during normal daytime activities. Death results from any combination of the above symptoms, from heart failure, malnutrition, and other weakened conditions. If detected early, sleeping sickness is curable. However, if an infection has advanced to the central nervous system, recovery is unlikely.

BOX 17.1   GIARDIASIS: "BACKPACKER'S DISEASE" IN THE ROCKY MOUNTAINS

Many of the pristine rivers, streams, and lakes in the Rocky Mountains now harbor the mastigophorean *Giardia lamblia* (figure 1). *Giardia* can inhabit the intestine of humans, and wild and domestic animals. In the intestine, the parasites multiply by binary fission and thickly carpet the intestinal wall. Because the parasites are so numerous, a person or animal can shed millions of *Giardia* cysts in the feces. If a human or animal infected by the parasite defecates close to a body of water, the durable cysts can infect someone else who drinks the water even 2 to 3 months later. Dogs, cattle, beavers, deer, bear and other *Giardia* hosts add to the reservoir of contaminated feces and have helped to create the current situation.

In animals and humans, *Giardia* causes the disease **giardiasis,** commonly called "backpacker's disease." Giardiasis is exceedingly unpleasant and usually involves severe diarrhea and painful intestinal cramps that can last for days or weeks. Antiparasitic drugs can quickly cure the disease. However, the best advice is to avoid giardiasis in the first place by not drinking water from wilderness streams or lakes.

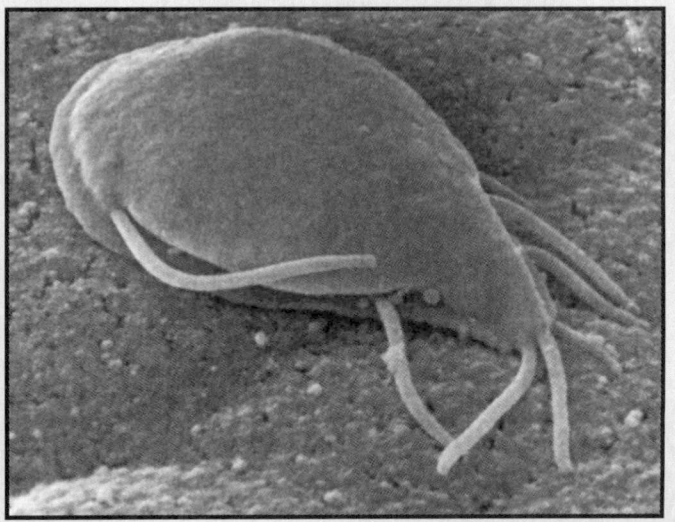

FIGURE 1   Scanning Electron Micrograph of *Giardia lamblia* Adhering to the Wall of the Intestine. The organism is 12 to 15 μm long.

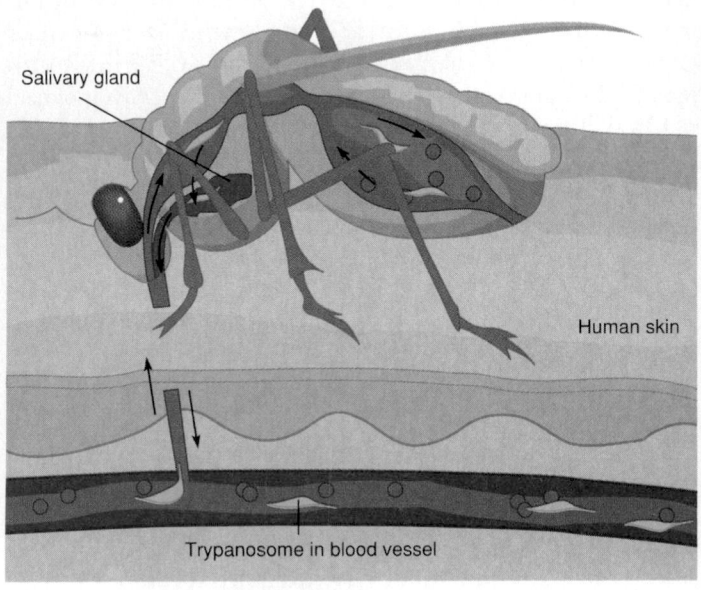

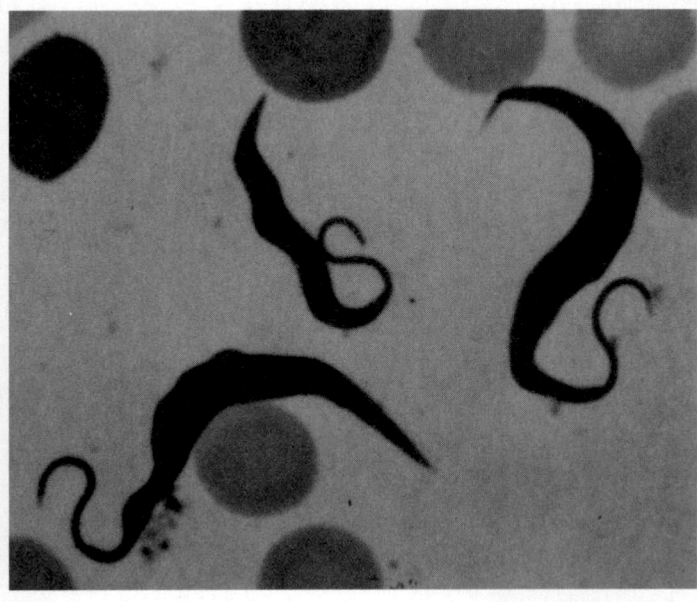

(a)   (b)

FIGURE 17.9

Class Zoomastigophorea: The Life Cycle of *Trypanosoma brucei.* (*a*) When a tsetse fly feeds on a vertebrate host, trypanosomes enter the vertebrate's circulatory system with the fly's saliva. Trypanosomes multiply in the circulatory and lymphatic systems by binary fission. When another tsetse fly bites this vertebrate host again, trypanosomes move into the gut of the fly, and undergo binary fission. Trypanosomes then migrate to the fly's salivary glands, where they are available to infect a new host. (*b*) Light micrograph showing trypanosomes among red blood cells (× 1,200).

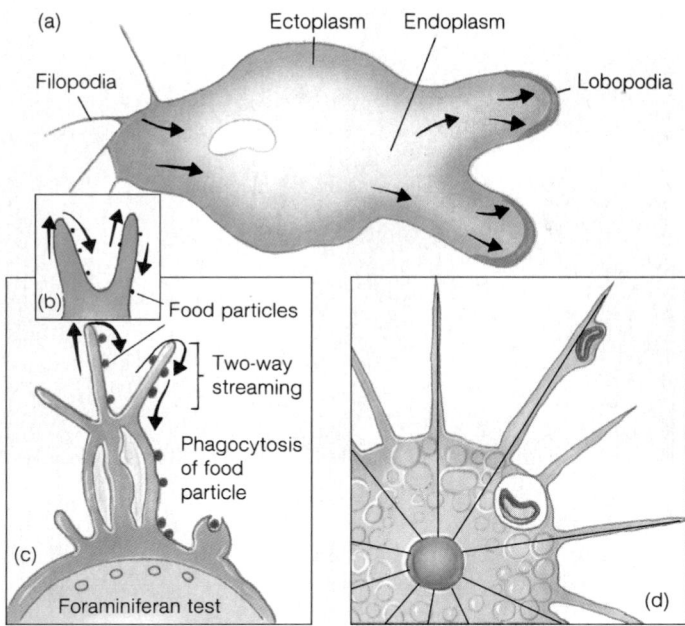

Figure **17.10**

Variations in Pseudopodia. (*a*) Lobopodia of *Amoeba* contain both ectoplasm and endoplasm and are used for locomotion and engulfing food. (*b*) Filopodia of a shelled amoeba contain ectoplasm only and provide constant two-way streaming that delivers food particles to this protozoan in a conveyor-belt fashion. (*c*) Reticulopodia are similar to filopodia except that they branch and rejoin to form a netlike series of cell extensions. They occur in foraminiferans such as *Globigerina*. (*d*) Axopodia on the surface of a heliozoan such as *Actinosphaerium* deliver food to the central cytoplasm.

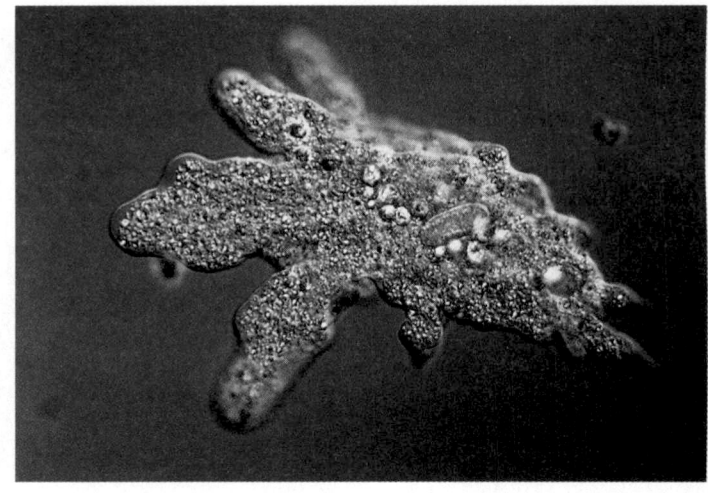

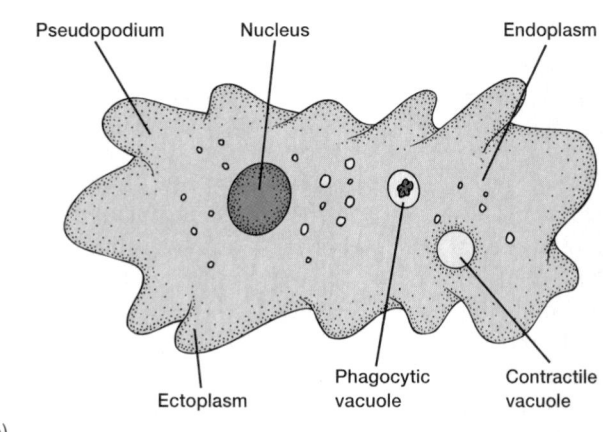

Figure **17.11**

Subphylum Sarcodina: Class Lobosea. (*a*) Light micrograph of *Amoeba proteus* showing blunt lobopodia (× 160). (*b*) Drawing showing the anatomy of *Amoeba proteus*.

Subphylum Sarcodina: Pseudopodia and Amoeboid Locomotion

Members of the subphylum Sarcodina (sar′ko-din″ah) are the amoebae (singular amoeba). When feeding and moving, they form temporary cell extensions called **pseudopodia** (s., pseudopodium) (Gr. *pseudes*, false + *podion*, little foot). Pseudopodia exist in a variety of forms. **Lobopodia** (Gr. *lobos*, lobe; s., lobopodium) are broad cell processes containing ectoplasm and endoplasm and are used for locomotion and engulfing food (figure 17.10*a*). **Filopodia** (L. *filum*, thread; s., filopodium) contain ectoplasm only and provide a constant two-way streaming that delivers food in a conveyor-belt fashion (figure 17.10*b*). **Reticulopodia** (L. *reticulatus*, netlike; s., reticulopodium) are similar to filopodia, except that they branch and rejoin to form a netlike series of cell extensions (figure 17.10*c*). **Axopodia** (L. *axis*, axle; s., axopodium) are thin, filamentous, and supported by a central axis of microtubules. The cytoplasm covering the central axis is adhesive and movable. Food caught on axopodia can be delivered to the central cytoplasm of the amoeba (figure 17.10*d*).

Class Lobosea

The most familiar amoebae belong to the class Lobosea (lo-bo′sah) (Gr. *lobos*, lobe) and the genus *Amoeba* (figure 17.11). These amoebae are naked (they have no test or shell) and are normally found on substrates in shallow water of freshwater ponds, lakes, and slow-moving streams, where they feed on other protists and bacteria. Food is engulfed by phagocytosis, a process that involves the cytoplasmic changes described earlier for amoeboid locomotion (*see figure 3.14*). In the process, food is incorporated into food vacuoles. Binary fission occurs when an amoeba reaches a certain size limit. As with other amoebae, no sexual reproduction is known to occur.

Other members of the class Lobosea possess a test or shell. **Tests** are protective structures secreted by the cytoplasm. They may be calcareous (made of calcium carbonate),

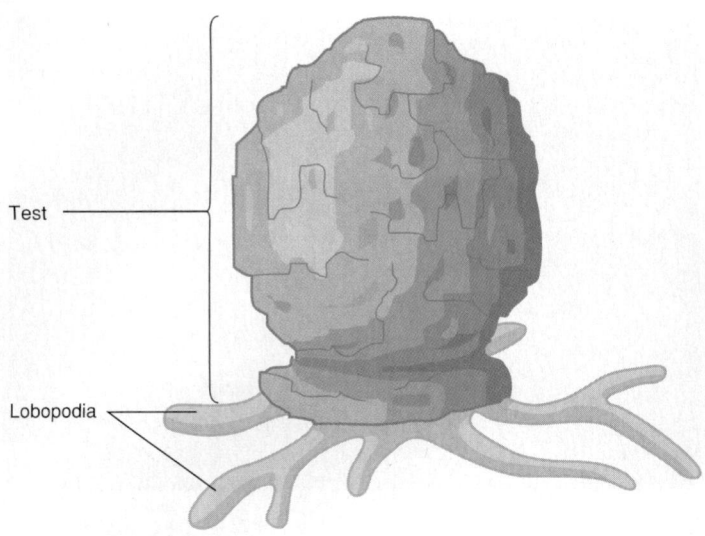

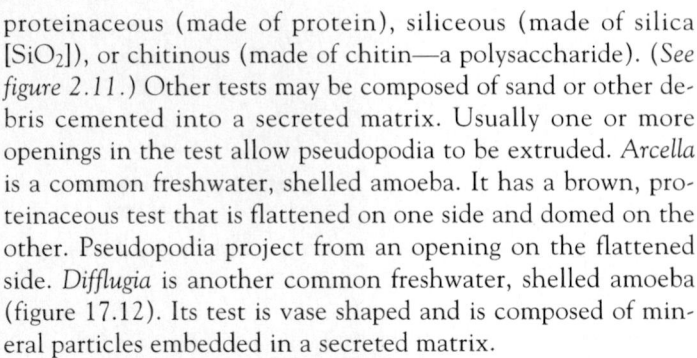

Test

Lobopodia

FIGURE 17.12

Subphylum Sarcodina. *Difflugia oblongata,* a common freshwater, shelled amoeba. The test is composed of cemented mineral particles.

FIGURE 17.13

Subphylum Sarcodina: Foraminiferan Test (*Polystomella*). As this foraminiferan grows, it secretes new, larger chambers that remain attached to older chambers, making this protozoan reminiscent of a tiny snail (light micrograph × 63).

proteinaceous (made of protein), siliceous (made of silica [SiO_2]), or chitinous (made of chitin—a polysaccharide). (*See figure 2.11.*) Other tests may be composed of sand or other debris cemented into a secreted matrix. Usually one or more openings in the test allow pseudopodia to be extruded. *Arcella* is a common freshwater, shelled amoeba. It has a brown, proteinaceous test that is flattened on one side and domed on the other. Pseudopodia project from an opening on the flattened side. *Difflugia* is another common freshwater, shelled amoeba (figure 17.12). Its test is vase shaped and is composed of mineral particles embedded in a secreted matrix.

Most amoebae are symbiotic; a few are pathogenic. For example,   4   *Entamoeba histolytica* causes one form of dysentery in humans. Dysentery is marked by inflammation and ulceration of the lower intestinal tract, accompanied by a debilitating diarrhea that includes blood and mucus. Amoebic dysentery is a worldwide problem that plagues humans in crowded, unsanitary conditions.

A significant problem in the control of *Entamoeba histolytica* is the fact that an individual can be infected and contagious without experiencing symptoms of the disease. Amoebae live in the folds of the intestinal wall, feeding on starch and mucoid secretions. Amoebae are passed from one host to another in the form of cysts that are transmitted by fecal contamination of food or water. Amoebae leave the cysts after a host ingests contaminated food or water and take up existence in the intestinal wall.

FORAMINIFERANS, HELIOZOANS, AND RADIOLARIANS

Foraminiferans (commonly called forams) are primarily a marine group of amoebae. Foraminiferans possess reticulopodia and secrete an exoskeleton called a test that is mostly calcium carbonate. As foraminiferans grow, they secrete new, larger chambers that remain attached to the older chambers (figure 17.13). Test enlargement follows a symmetrical pattern that may result in a straight chain of chambers or spiral arrangement that resembles a snail shell. Many of these tests may reach relatively large sizes; for example, "Mermaid's pennies," found in Australia, may be several centimeters in diameter.

Foraminiferan tests have left an abundant fossil record that began in the Cambrian period. Foram tests make up a large component of marine sediments, and the accumulation of foram tests on the floor of primeval oceans has resulted in our limestone and chalk deposits. The white cliffs of Dover are one example of a foraminiferan-chalk deposit. Oil geologists use fossilized forams to identify geologic strata when taking exploratory cores.

Heliozoans are freshwater amoebae that are either planktonic or live attached by a stalk to some substrate. (The plankton of a body of water consists of those organisms that float freely in the water.) Heliozoans are either naked or enclosed within a test that contains openings for axopodia (figure 17.14*a*).

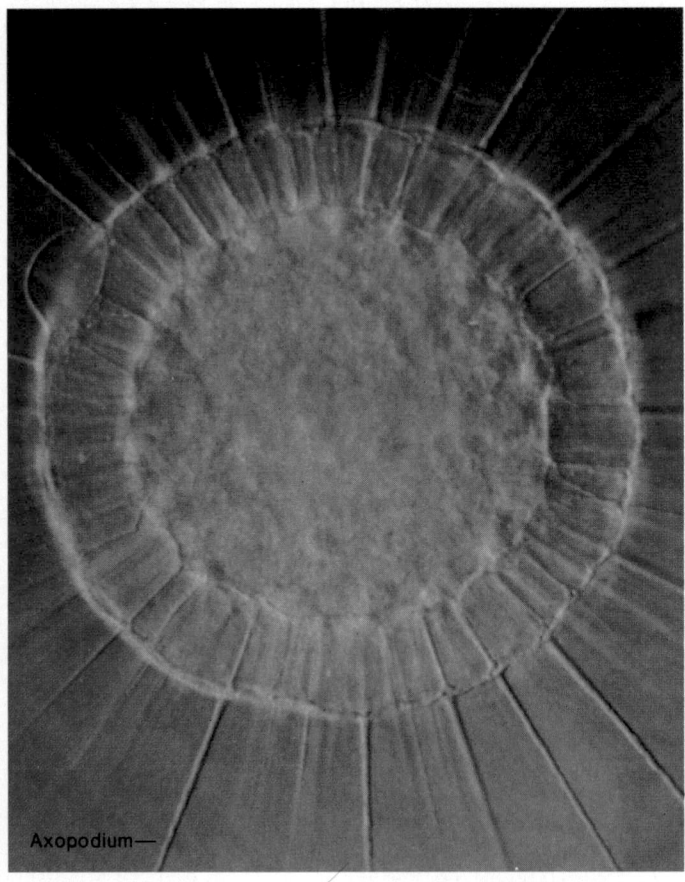

Axopodium—

(a)

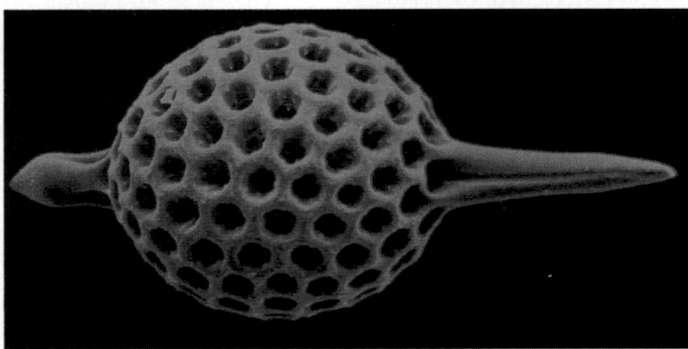

(b)

FIGURE 17.14

Subphylum Sarcodina: Heliozoan and Radiolarian Tests.
(*a*) *Actinosphaerium sol* has a spherical body covered with fine, long axopodia made up of numerous microtubules and surrounded by streaming cytoplasm. Following phagocytosis by the axopodium, waves of cytoplasmic movement carry trapped food particles into the main body of this protozoan (light micrograph × 450). (*b*) The radiolarian *Spaerostylus* is typically spherical with a highly sculptured test (light micrograph × 480).

Radiolarians are planktonic, marine amoebae. They are relatively large; some colonial forms may reach several centimeters in diameter. They possess a test (usually siliceous) of either long, movable spines and needles or a highly sculptured and ornamented lattice (figure 17.14*b*). When radiolarians die, their tests drift to the ocean floor. Some of the oldest known fossils of eukaryotic organisms are radiolarians.

PHYLUM LABYRINTHOMORPHA

The very small phylum Labyrinthomorpha (la′brinth-o-morp′ha) consists of protozoa that have spindle-shaped non-amoeboid vegetative cells. In some genera, amoeboid cells move within a network of mucous tracks using a typical gliding motion. Most members are marine and either saprozoic or parasitic on algae or seagrass. Several years ago, *Labyrinthula* killed most of the "eel grass" on the Atlantic coast, starving many ducks that feed on the grass.

Stop and Ask Yourself

5. How and when does sexual reproduction occur in *Volvox*?
6. How do trypanosomes gain entry to their human hosts?
7. What mechanism explains amoeboid locomotion?
8. How is *Entamoeba histolytica* transmitted among humans? *Giardia lamblia*?

PHYLUM APICOMPLEXA

Members of the phylum Apicomplexa (a″pi-kom-plex′ah) (L. *apex*, point + *com*, together, + *plexus*, interweaving) are all parasites. Characteristics of the phylum include the following:

1. Apical complex that aids in the penetration of host cells
2. Single type of nucleus
3. Cilia and flagella lacking, except in certain reproductive stages
4. Life cycles typically include asexual (schizogony, sporogony) and sexual (gametogony) phases

CLASS SPOROZOEA

The most important species in this phylum are members of the class Sporozoea (spor′o-zo″e). The class name derives from the fact that most sporozoeans produce a resistant spore or oocyst following sexual reproduction. Some members of this class, including *Plasmodium* and coccidians, cause a variety of diseases in domestic animals and humans.

Although there is considerable variability in life cycles of sporozoeans, certain generalizations are possible. Many are intracellular parasites, and their life cycles may be divided into three phases. **Schizogony** is multiple fission of an asexual stage in host cells, resulting in the formation of many more (usually asexual) individuals, called merozoites, that leave the host cell and infect many other cells.

Some of the merozoites produced (as described above) undergo **gametogony,** which begins the sexual phase of the life cycle. In so doing, the parasite forms either microgametocytes or macrogametocytes. Microgametocytes undergo multiple fission to produce biflagellate microgametes that emerge from the infected host cell. The macrogametocyte develops directly into a single macrogamete. Fertilization of the macrogamete by a microgamete produces a zygote that becomes enclosed and is called an oocyst.

The zygote undergoes meiosis, and the resulting cells divide repeatedly by mitosis. This process, called **sporogony,** produces many rodlike sporozoites in the oocyst. Sporozoites infect the cells of a new host when the oocyst is ingested and digested by the new host, or sporozoites are otherwise introduced (e.g., by a mosquito bite).

One sporozoean genus, *Plasmodium,* causes malaria and has been responsible for more human suffering than most other diseases. Accounts of the disease go back as far as 1550 B.C. ⑤ Malaria was a significant contributor to the failure of the Crusades during the medieval era, and it has contributed more to the devastation of armies than has actual combat. Recently (since the early 1970s), there has been a resurgence of malaria throughout the world. It is estimated that over 100 million humans annually contract the disease.

The life cycle of *Plasmodium* involves vertebrate and mosquito hosts (figure 17.15). Schizogony occurs first in liver cells and later in red blood cells, and gametogony also occurs in red blood cells. Gametocytes are taken into a mosquito during a meal of blood and subsequently fuse. The zygote penetrates the gut of the mosquito and is transformed into an oocyst. Sporogony forms haploid sporozoites that may enter a new host when the mosquito bites the host.

The symptoms of malaria recur periodically and are called paroxysms (box 17.2). Chills and fever are correlated with the maturation of parasites, the rupture of red blood cells, and the release of toxic metabolites.

Four species of *Plasmodium* are the most important human malarial species. *P. vivax* causes malaria in which the paroxysms recur every 48 hours. This species occurs in temperate regions and has been nearly eradicated in many parts of the world. *P. falciparum* causes the most virulent form of malaria in humans. Paroxysms occur more irregularly than in the other species. It was once worldwide, but is now mainly tropical and subtropical in distribution. It remains one of the greatest killers of humanity, especially in Africa. *P. malariae* is worldwide in distribution and causes malaria with paroxysms that recur every 72 hours. *P. ovale* is the rarest of the four human malarial species, and is primarily tropical in distribution.

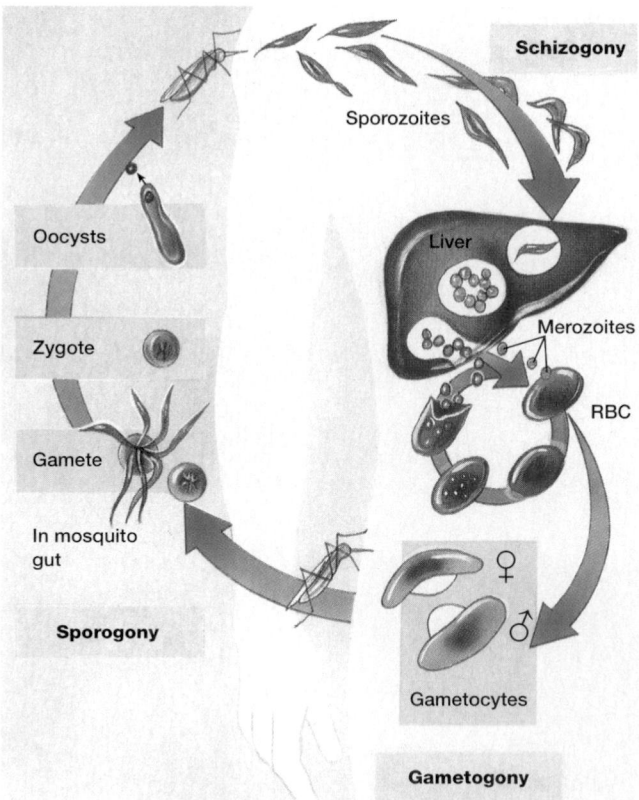

Figure 17.15

Phylum Apicomplexa: The Life Cycle of *Plasmodium*. Schizogony occurs in liver cells and, later, in the red blood cells of humans. Gametogony occurs in red blood cells. Microgametes and macrogametes are taken into a mosquito during a blood meal and fuse to form zygotes. Zygotes penetrate the gut of the mosquito and form the oocysts. Meiosis and sporogony form many haploid sporozoites that may enter a new host when the mosquito bites the host.

Other members of the class Sporozoea also cause important diseases. Coccidiosis is primarily a disease of poultry, sheep, cattle, and rabbits. Two genera, *Isospora* and *Eimeria,* are particularly important parasites of poultry. Yearly losses to the poultry industry in the United States from coccidiosis have approached 35 million dollars. Another coccidian, *Cryptosporidium,* has become more well-known with the advent of AIDS. It causes chronic diarrhea. Toxoplasmosis is a disease of mammals, including humans, and birds. Sexual reproduction of *Toxoplasma* occurs primarily in cats. Infections occur when oocysts are ingested with food contaminated by cat feces, or when meat containing encysted sporozoites is eaten raw or poorly cooked. Most infections in humans are asymptomatic and once infected an effective immunity develops. However, if a woman is infected near the time of pregnancy, or during pregnancy, congenital toxoplasmosis may develop in a fetus. Congenital toxoplasmosis is a major cause of stillbirths and spontaneous abortions. Fetuses that survive frequently show signs of mental retardation and epileptic seizures. There is no cure for congenital toxoplasmosis.

BOX 17.2   MALARIA CONTROL—A GLIMMER OF HOPE

The following quotation is from *The Lake Regions of Central Africa* by Sir Richard Burton (1821–1890). Sir Richard Burton was an adventurer whose visits to the Far East and Africa brought him into contact with the greatest killer of humanity, *Plasmodium falciparum*.

> The approach of malignant fever is very insidious. An attack begins mostly with an ordinary chill, attended by no unusual or marked symptoms. Sometimes the patient has had a light chill a day or two before this, which he has neglected. Sometimes he has felt slightly unwell for ten or fourteen days; has complained of loss of appetite and general weakness; but as these symptoms are not very marked, they are very apt to be overlooked, especially with newcomers.
>
> The real attack may begin with a chill or with a fever, but its effects are, in either case, at once evident in a peculiarly yellow skin and haggard countenance. In fever there is profuse perspiration, a rush of blood to the head, high and irregular pulse, and general prostration. Sometimes the body is hot, but dry. Thirst is urgent, but the stomach rejects whatever is drunk.
>
> If the paroxysm [sudden attack] of fever returns, it is with renewed force, and the third attack is commonly fatal. Before death the patient becomes insensible; there is violent vomiting, which is, in fact, regurgitation of ingesta, mixed with green and yellow fluid. Immediately after the chill, and even before this has passed off, the urine becomes dark red or black. The pulse is very irregular, the breathing slow and finally the patient sinks away into a state of coma, and dies without a struggle.

Malaria is still a fact of life—especially in Africa. Nearly 300 million people are afflicted annually, and 1/3 of them die. The fight against this disease has centered on two fronts: elimination of the mosquito species known to carry *Plasmodium* parasites and treatment of infected persons with antimalarial drugs. In the fight against mosquitoes, DDT (dichloro-diphenyl-trichloroethane) was employed successfully in the 1950s and 1960s. Its use greatly reduced the incidence of malaria by the middle 1960s. Mosquito-control programs, however, began to lose their effectiveness, largely because mosquitoes developed resistance to DDT. DDT has also been found to be a highly persistent pesticide. It retains its toxicity for many years and can build up to lethal levels in aquatic and terrestrial environments. Its use became less effective and more expensive—both in economic and environmental terms. Other pesticides are now being used, but mosquito resistance is becoming a problem with these pesticides too.

Even more serious is the worldwide development of resistance by *Plasmodium* parasites to antimalarial drugs, such as chloroquine.

As bleak as this picture sounds, scientists and health officials are optimistic that malaria will eventually be conquered. Recent advancements in molecular biology and immunology are being employed in the development of antimalarial vaccines. Some vaccines are now being tested. Researchers have found that the complexity of the disease presents special problems in the development of vaccines. Not only do each of the *Plasmodium* species require a separate vaccine, but each stage of the life cycle of a single species requires a separate immunological component in a vaccine.

Toxoplasmosis also ranks high amongst the opportunistic diseases afflicting AIDS patients. ⑥ Steps can be taken to avoid infections by *Toxoplasma*. Precautions include keeping stray and pet cats away from children's sandboxes; using sandbox covers; and awareness, on the part of couples considering having children, of the potential dangers of eating raw or very rare pork, lamb, and beef.

PHYLUM MICROSPORA

Members of the phylum Microspora (mi-cro-spor'ah), commonly called microsporidia, are small obligatory intracellular parasites. Included in this phylum are several species that parasitize beneficial insects. *Nosema bombicus* parasitizes silkworms (figure 17.16) causing the disease **pebrine,** and *N. apis* causes serious dysentery (foul brood) in honeybees. There has been an increased interest in these parasites because of their possible role as biological control agents for insect pests. For example, *N. locustae* has been approved and registered with the United States Environmental Protection Agency (EPA) for use in residual control of rangeland grasshoppers. Recently, four

microsporidian genera have been implicated in secondary infections of immunosuppressed and AIDS patients.

PHYLUM ACETOSPORA

Acetospora (ah-seat-o-spor'ah) is a relatively small phylum that consists exclusively of obligatory extracellular parasites characterized by spores lacking polar caps or polar filaments. The acetosporeans (e.g., *Haplosporidium*) primarily are parasitic in the cells, tissues, and body cavities of molluscs.

PHYLUM MYXOZOA

The phylum Myxozoa (myx-o-zoo-ah), commonly called myxosporeans, are all obligatory extracellular parasites in freshwater and marine fish. They have a resistant spore with one to six coiled polar filaments. The most economically important myxosporean is *Myxosoma cerebralis*, which infects the nervous system and auditory organ of trout and salmon causing whirling or tumbling disease.

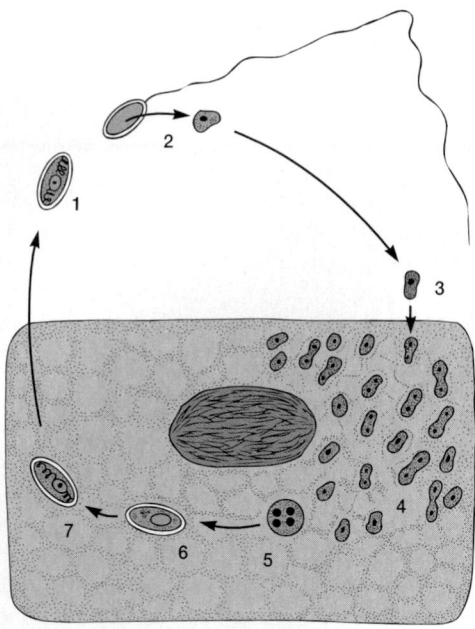

Figure 17.16

Phylum Microspora. Drawing of the Microsporean *Nosema bombicus*, which Is Fatal to Silkworms. The cell of a silkworm infected with *N. bombicus* is shown here. (*1*) A typical spore with one coiled filament: (*2*) When ingested, it extrudes the filament, which is used in locomotion. (*3*) The parasite enters an epithelial cell in the intestine of the silkworm and (*4*) divides many times to form small amoebae that eventually fill the cell and kill it. During this phase, some of the amoebae with four nuclei become spores (*5,6,7*). Silkworms are infected by eating leaves contaminated by the feces of infected worms.

Stop and Ask Yourself

9. What is an apical complex? What is it used for?
10. What is schizogony?
11. Members of which protozoan genus have caused the most human suffering since antiquity?
12. What are the three stages in the life cycle of *Plasmodium?*
13. How are infections of *Toxoplasma* acquired?
14. What are the dangers of toxoplasmosis for a fetus?
15. What are the four most important sporozoean parasites and the diseases they cause?
16. What is one economically important disease caused by a microsporidian? What group of animals do myxosporeans usually parasitize?

Phylum Ciliophora

7 The phylum Ciliophora (sil-i-of′or-ah) includes some of the most complex protozoa (*see table 17.1*). Ciliates are widely distributed in freshwater and marine environments. A few ciliates are symbiotic. Characteristics of the phylum Ciliophora include the following:

1. Cilia for locomotion and for the generation of feeding currents in water
2. Relatively rigid pellicle and more or less fixed shape
3. Distinct cytostome (mouth) structure
4. Dimorphic nuclei, typically a larger macronucleus and one or more smaller micronuclei

Cilia and Other Pellicular Structures

Cilia are generally similar to flagella, except that they are much shorter, more numerous, and widely distributed over the surface of the protozoan (figure 17.17). Ciliary movements are coordinated, so that ciliary waves pass over the surface of the ciliate. Many ciliates can reverse the direction of ciliary beating and the direction of cell movement.

Basal bodies (kinetosomes) of adjacent cilia are interconnected with an elaborate network of fibers that are believed to anchor the cilia and give shape to the organism.

The evolution of some ciliates has resulted in the specialization of cilia. Cilia may cover the outer surface of the protozoan. They may be joined together to form **cirri,** which are used in movement. Alternatively, cilia may be lost from large regions of a ciliate.

Trichocysts are pellicular structures primarily used for attachment. They are rodlike or oval organelles oriented perpendicular to the plasma membrane. In *Paramecium,* they have a "golf tee" appearance. Trichocysts can be discharged from the pellicle and, after discharge, they remain connected to the body by a sticky thread (figure 17.18).

Nutrition

Some ciliates, such as *Paramecium,* have a ciliated oral groove along one side of the body (*see figure 17.17*). Cilia of the oral groove sweep small, organic particles toward the cytopharynx where a food vacuole is formed. When a food vacuole reaches an upper size limit, it breaks free and circulates through the endoplasm.

Some free-living ciliates prey upon other protists or small animals. Prey capture is usually a case of fortuitous contact. *Didinium* is a ciliate that feeds principally on *Paramecium,* a prey item that is bigger than itself. The *Didinium* forms a temporary opening that can greatly enlarge to consume its prey (figure 17.19).

Suctorians are ciliates that live attached to their substrate by a stalk. They possess tentacles to which prey adhere. Their prey, often ciliates or amoebae, are paralyzed by secretions of the tentacles. The tentacles digest an opening in the pellicle of the prey, and prey cytoplasm is drawn into the suctorian through tiny channels in the tentacle. The mechanism for this probably involves tentacular microtubules (figure 17.20).

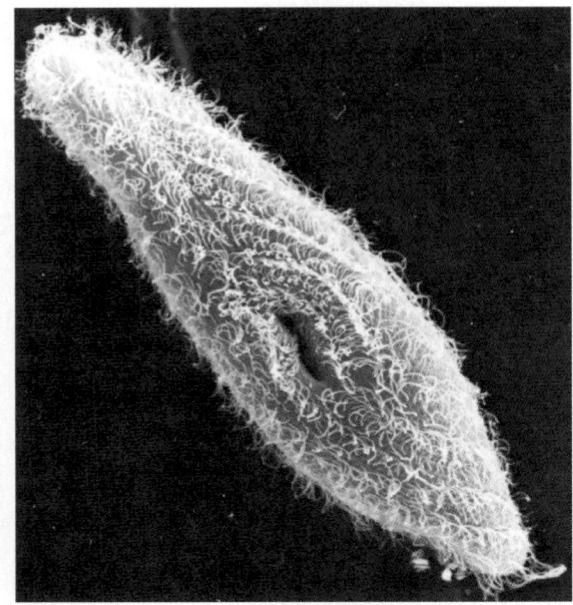

(a)

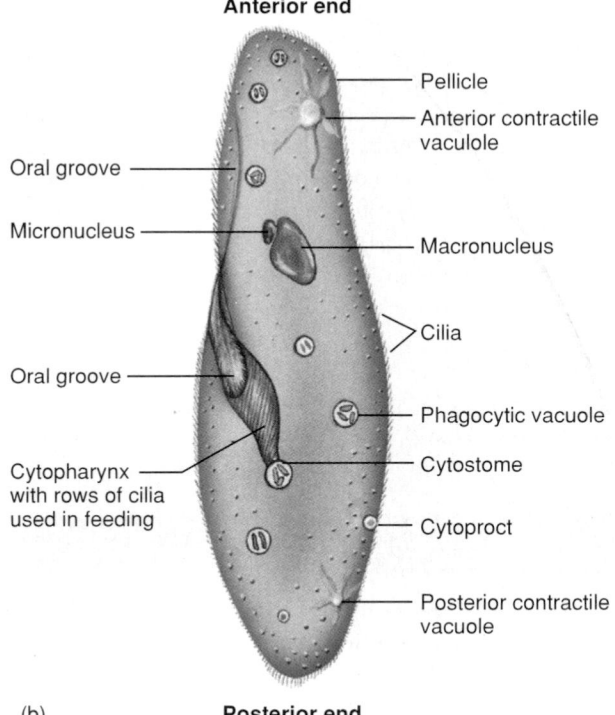

Anterior end

Pellicle

Anterior contractile
vaculole

Oral groove

Micronucleus

Macronucleus

Cilia

Oral groove

Phagocytic vacuole

Cytopharynx
with rows of cilia
used in feeding

Cytostome

Cytoproct

Posterior contractile
vaculole

(b)   **Posterior end**

Figure **17.17**

Phylum Ciliophora. (*a*) Scanning electron micrograph of the ciliate, *Paramecium sonneborn*. This paramecium is 40 μm in length. Note the oral groove near the middle of the body that leads into the cytopharynx (× 1,600). (*b*) The structure of a typical ciliate such as *Paramecium*.

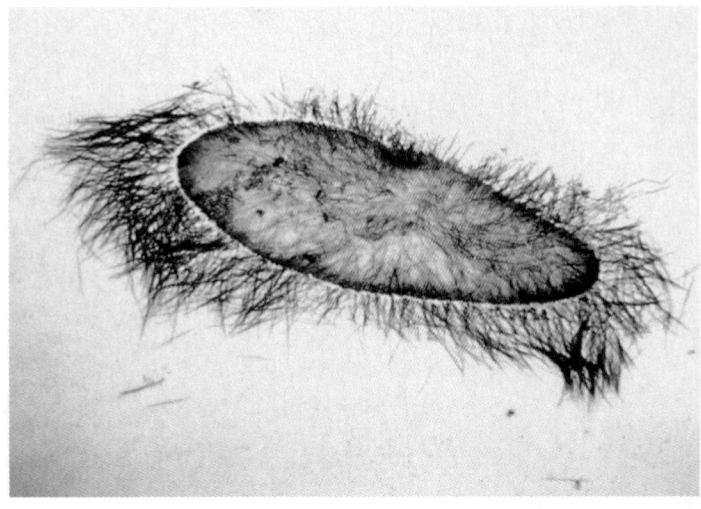

Figure **17.18**

The Discharged Trichocysts of *Paramecium*. Each trichocyst is able to produce a long, sticky proteinaceous thread when discharged. This thread connects the trichocyst in the body of the protozoan (light micrograph × 150).

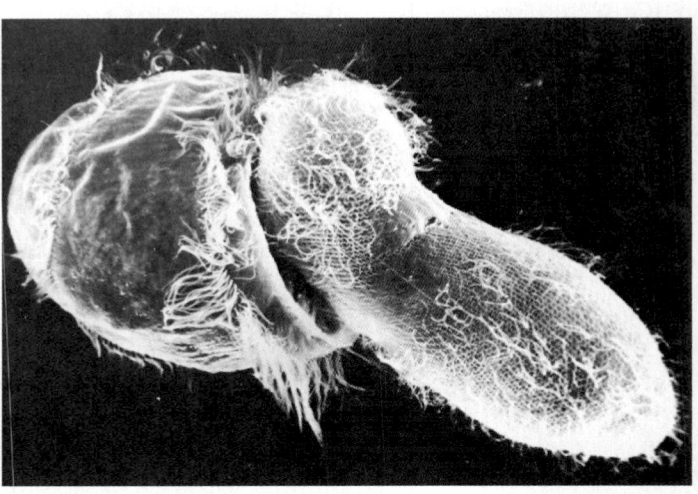

Figure **17.19**

A Single-Celled Hunter and Its Prey. The juglike *Didinium* (left) is shown swallowing a slipper-shaped *Paramecium* (right) (scanning electron micrograph × 550).

Genetic Control and Reproduction

Ciliates have two kinds of nuclei. A large, polyploid **macronucleus** regulates the daily metabolic activities. One or more smaller **micronuclei** serve as the genetic reserve of the cell.

Asexual reproduction of ciliates occurs by transverse binary fission and occasionally by budding. Budding occurs in suctorians

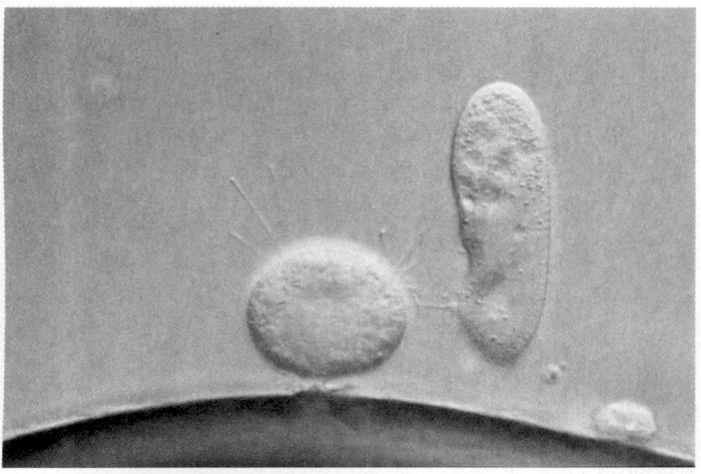

FIGURE 17.20

Suctorian (*Tokophrya* spp.) Feeding. A ciliate (right) is held by the knobbed tip of a tentacle. Tentacles discharge enzymes that immobilize the prey and dissolve the pellicle. Pellicles of tentacle and prey fuse, and the tentacle enlarges and invaginates to form a feeding channel. Prey cytoplasm is moved down the feeding channel and incorporated into endocytic vacuoles at the bottom of the tentacle (light micrograph × 181).

and results in the formation of ciliated, free-swimming organisms that attach to the substrate and take the form of the adult.

Sexual reproduction of ciliates occurs by **conjugation** (figure 17.21). The partners involved are called conjugants. Many species of ciliates have numerous mating types, not all of which are compatible with one another. The initial contact between individuals apparently occurs randomly, and adhesion is facilitated by sticky secretions of the pellicle. Fusion of ciliate plasma membranes occurs and lasts for several hours.

The macronucleus does not participate in the genetic exchange that follows. Instead, the macronucleus breaks up during or after micronuclear events and is reformed from micronuclei of the daughter ciliates.

After separation, the exconjugants undergo a series of nuclear divisions to restore the nuclear characteristics of the particular species, including the formation of a macronucleus from one or more micronuclei. These events are accompanied by cytoplasmic divisions which form daughter cells.

SYMBIOTIC CILIATES

Most ciliates are free living; however, some are commensalistic or mutualistic and a few are parasitic. *Balantidium coli* is an important parasitic ciliate that lives in the large intestines of humans, pigs, and other mammals. At times, it is a ciliary feeder; at other times, it produces proteolytic enzymes that digest host epithelium, causing a flask-shaped ulcer. (Its pathology resembles that of *Entamoeba histolytica*.) *B. coli* is passed from one host to another in cysts that are formed as feces begin to dehydrate in the large intestine. Fecal contamination of food or water is the most common form of transmission. It is potentially worldwide in distribution, but is most common in the Philippines.

Large numbers of different species of ciliates also inhabit the rumen of many ungulates (hoofed animals). These ciliates contribute to the digestive processes of their hosts.

FURTHER PHYLOGENETIC CONSIDERATIONS

The origin of protozoa probably took place about 1.5 billion years ago. Although there are over 30,000 known fossil species, they are of little use in investigations of the origin and evolution of the various protozoan groups. Only protozoa with hard parts (tests) have left much of a fossil record, and only the foraminiferans and radiolarians have well-established fossil records in Precambrian rocks. Recent evidence from the study of base sequences in ribosomal RNA (figure 17.22) indicates that each of the seven protozoan phyla probably had separate origins, and that each is sufficiently different from the others to warrant elevating all of these groups to phylum status as has been done in this chapter. Additional modifications to the present scheme of protozoan classification are continually being proposed as the results of new ultrastructural and molecular studies are published. For example, in 1993, T. Cavalier-Smith proposed that the protozoa be elevated to kingdom status with 18 phyla. The acceptance of this new classification by protozoologists, however, remains to be determined.

Stop and Ask Yourself

17. What are four characteristics of the phylum Ciliophora?
18. What are trichocysts used for in ciliates?
19. What occurs during conjugation in *Paramecium*?
20. Why is it difficult to find protozoan fossils?

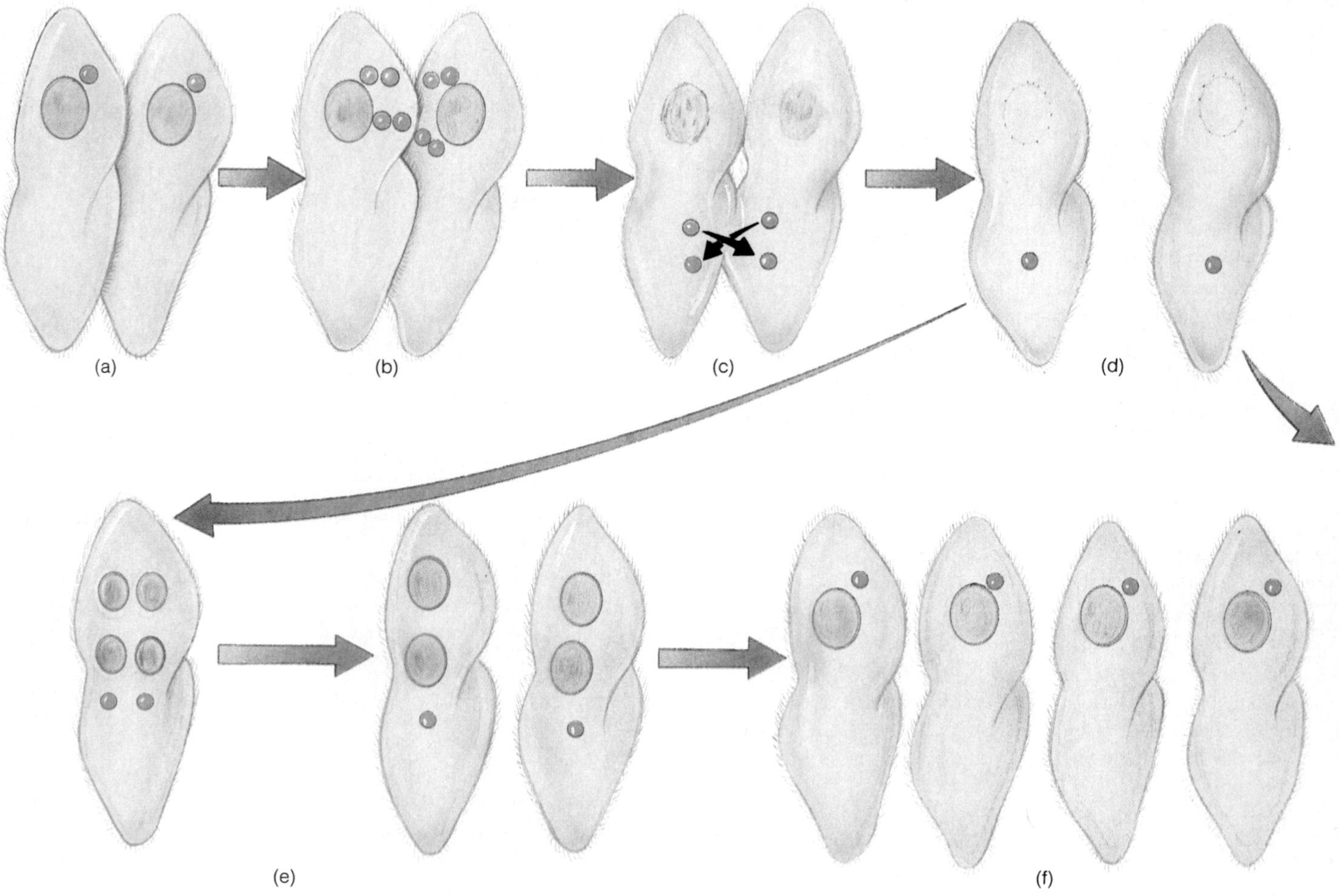

FIGURE 17.21

Conjugation in *Paramecium.* (*a*) Random contact brings individuals of opposite mating types together. (*b*) Meiosis results in four haploid pronuclei. (*c*) Three pronuclei and the macronucleus degenerate. Mitosis and mutual exchange of pronuclei is followed by fusion of pronuclei. (*d–f*) Separation of conjugants is followed by nuclear divisions that restore nuclear characteristics of the species. These events may be accompanied by cytoplasmic divisions.

FIGURE 17.22

A Cladogram Showing the Evolutionary Relationships of Protozoa and Other Eukaryotes Based on 18S Ribosomal RNA Sequence Comparisons. This cladogram suggests that evolution along the nuclear line of descent was not a continuous process, but instead occurred in major epochs (an epoch is a particular period of time marked by distinctive features and events). Five major evolutionary radiations (colored boxes) are apparent for the protozoa. As shown, it is clear that the Mastigophora (e.g., *Giardia*) and Microspora (e.g., *Nosema*) are modern relatives of the earliest major eukaryotic cell lines. Following the development of these protozoa, the other groups of protozoa radiated off the nuclear line of descent.

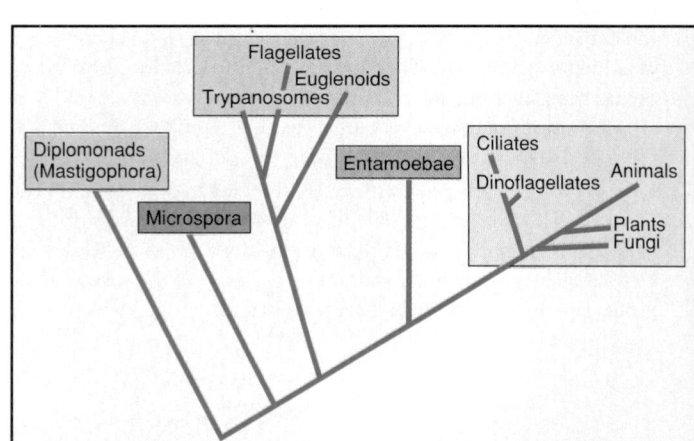

SUMMARY

1. The kingdom Protista is a polyphyletic group that arose about 1.5 billion years ago from the Monera. The evolutionary pathways leading to modern protozoa are uncertain.

2. Protozoa are both single cells and entire organisms. Many of their functions are carried out by organelles specialized for the unicellular life-style.

3. Many protozoa live in symbiotic relationships with other organisms, often in a host-parasite relationship.

4. Members of the phylum Sarcomastigophora possess pseudopodia and/or one or more flagella.

5. Members of the class Phytomastigophorea are photosynthetic and include the genera *Euglena* and *Volvox*. Members of the class Zoomastigophorea are heterotrophic and include *Trypanosoma*, which causes sleeping sickness.

6. Amoebae use pseudopodia for feeding and locomotion.

7. Members of the subphylum Sarcodina include the freshwater genera *Amoeba*, *Arcella*, and *Difflugia*, and the symbiotic genus *Entamoeba*. Foraminiferans and radiolarians are common marine amoebae.

8. Members of the phylum Apicomplexa are all parasites. The phylum includes *Plasmodium* and *Toxoplasma*, which cause malaria and toxoplasmosis, respectively. Many apicomplexans have a three-part life cycle involving schizogony, gametogony, and sporogony.

9. The phylum Microspora consists of very small protozoa that are intracellular parasites of every major animal group. They are transmitted from one host to the next as a spore, the form from which the group obtains its name.

10. The phylum Acetospora contains protozoa that produce spores lacking polar capsules. These protozoa are primarily parasitic in molluscs.

11. The phylum Myxozoa consists entirely of parasitic species, usually found in fishes. The spore is characterized by one to six polar filaments.

12. The phylum Ciliophora contains some of the most complex of all protozoa. Its members possess cilia, a macronucleus, and one or more micronuclei. Cilia are coordinated by mechanical coupling of cilia and can be specialized for different kinds of locomotion. Sexual reproduction occurs in ciliates by conjugation. Diploid ciliates undergo meiosis of the micronuclei to produce haploid pronuclei that are exchanged between two conjugants.

13. Precise evolutionary relationships are difficult to determine for the protozoa. The fossil record is sparse, and what does exist is not particularly helpful in deducing relationships. However, ribosomal RNA sequence comparisons indicate that each of the seven protozoan phyla probably had separate origins.

SELECTED KEY TERMS

ectoplasm (*p. 245*)
endoplasm (*p. 245*)
giardiasis (*p. 250*)
macronucleus (*p. 257*)
micronuclei (*p. 257*)

multiple fission (schizogony) (*p. 245*)
pellicle (*p. 245*)
protozoa (*p. 245*)
protozoologists (*p. 247*)
trichocysts (*p. 256*)

CRITICAL THINKING QUESTIONS

1. If it is impossible to know for certain the evolutionary pathways that gave rise to protozoa and animal phyla, do you think it is worth constructing hypotheses about those relationships? Why or why not?

2. In what ways are protozoa similar to animal cells? In what ways are they different?

3. If sexual reproduction is unknown in *Euglena*, how do you think this lineage of organisms has survived through evolutionary time? (Recall that sexual reproduction provides the genetic variability that allows species to adapt to environmental changes.)

4. The use of DDT has been greatly curtailed for ecological reasons. In the past, it has proven to be the greatest malaria deterrent known throughout the world. Many organizations would like to see this form of mosquito control resumed. Do you agree or disagree? Explain your reasoning.

5. If you were traveling out of this country and you were concerned about contracting amoebic dysentery, what steps could you take to prevent acquiring the disease? How would the precautions differ if you were going to a country where malaria was a problem?

18

MULTICELLULAR AND TISSUE LEVELS OF ORGANIZATION

Outline

Concepts

1. How multicellularity originated in animals, and whether the animal kingdom is monophyletic, diphyletic, or polyphyletic, are largely unknown.
2. Animals whose bodies consist of aggregations of cells, but whose cells do not form tissues, are found in the phylum Porifera as well as some lesser known phyla.
3. Animals that show diploblastic, tissue-level organization are found in the phyla Cnidaria and Ctenophora.
4. Members of the phylum Cnidaria are important in zoological research because of their relatively simple organization and their contribution to coral reefs.

Would You Like to Know:

1. how multicellularity could have arisen in the animal kingdom? (*p. 262*)
2. how natural sponges are prepared for use in cleaning applications? (*p. 267*)
3. what value the intricate branching canal systems are to a sponge? (*p. 267*)
4. whether cells of a sponge body can communicate with one another? (*p. 268*)
5. how soft-bodied cnidarians support themselves? (*p. 272*)
6. why one should avoid touching blue, gas-filled floats washed up on beaches of temperate and tropical waters? (*p. 275*)
7. which jellyfish should be avoided when swimming in coastal waters? (*p. 275*)
8. what organisms are responsible for the formation of coral reefs? (*p. 279*)

These and other useful questions will be answered in this chapter.

This chapter contains evolutionary concepts, which are set off in this font.

EVOLUTIONARY PERSPECTIVE

Animals with multicellular and tissue levels of organization have captured the interest of scientists and laypersons alike. A description of some members of the phylum Cnidaria, for example, could fuel a science fiction writer's imagination.

> From a distance I was never threatened, in fact I was infatuated with its beauty. A large, inviting, bright blue float lured me closer. As I swam nearer I could see that hidden from my previous view was an infrastructure of tentacles, some of which dangled nearly nine meters below the water's surface! The creature seemed to consist of many individuals and I wondered whether or not each individual was the same kind of being because, when I looked closely, I counted eight different body forms!
>
> I was drawn closer and the true nature of this creature was painfully revealed. The beauty of the gas-filled float hid some of the most hideous weaponry imaginable. When I brushed against those silky tentacles I experienced the most excruciating pain. Had it not been for my life vest, I would have drowned. Indeed, for some time, I wished that had been my fate.

This fictitious account is not far from reality for swimmers of tropical waters who have come into contact with *Physalia physalis*, the Portuguese man-of-war (figure 18.1). In organisms such as *Physalia physalis*, cells are grouped together, specialized for various functions, and are interdependent. This chapter covers three animal phyla with multicellular organization that varies from a loose association of cells to cells organized into two distinct tissue layers. These phyla include the Porifera, Cnidaria, and Ctenophora (figure 18.2).

ORIGINS OF MULTICELLULARITY

Multicellular life has been a part of the earth's history for approximately 550 million years. Although this seems a very long period of time, it represents only 10 percent of the earth's geological history. Multicellular life arose very quickly—in the 100 million years prior to the Precambrian/Cambrian boundary. What occurred during this 100 million years is often viewed as an evolutionary explosion. These evolutionary events resulted not only in the appearance of all of the 20 to 30 animal phyla recognized today, but also another 15 to 20 animal groups that are now extinct. Following this initial evolutionary explosion, most of the history of multicellular life has been one of extinction.

The evolutionary events leading to multicellularity are shrouded in mystery. ① Many zoologists believe that multicellularity could have arisen as dividing cells remained together, in the fashion of many colonial protists. Although there are a number of variations of this hypothesis, they are all treated here as the **colonial hypothesis** (figure 18.3a).

FIGURE 18.1

Physalia physalis, **the Portuguese Man-of-War.** The bluish float is about 12 cm long, and the nematocyst-laden tentacles can be up to 9 m long. Nematocysts are lethal to small vertebrates and are dangerous to humans. Note the fish that has been captured by the tentacles. Digestion will eventually leave only the fish's skeletal remains.

A second proposed mechanism is called the **syncytial hypothesis** (figure 18.3b). A syncytium is a large, multinucleate cell. The formation of plasma membranes in the cytoplasm of a syncytial protist could have formed a small, multicellular organism. These hypotheses are supported by the fact that colonial and syncytial organization occurs in some protist phyla.

ANIMAL ORIGINS

A fundamental question concerning animal origins is whether animals are monophyletic (derived from a single ancestor), diphyletic (derived from two ancestors), or polyphyletic (derived from many ancestors). The view that animals are polyphyletic is attractive to a growing number of zoologists. The nearly simultaneous

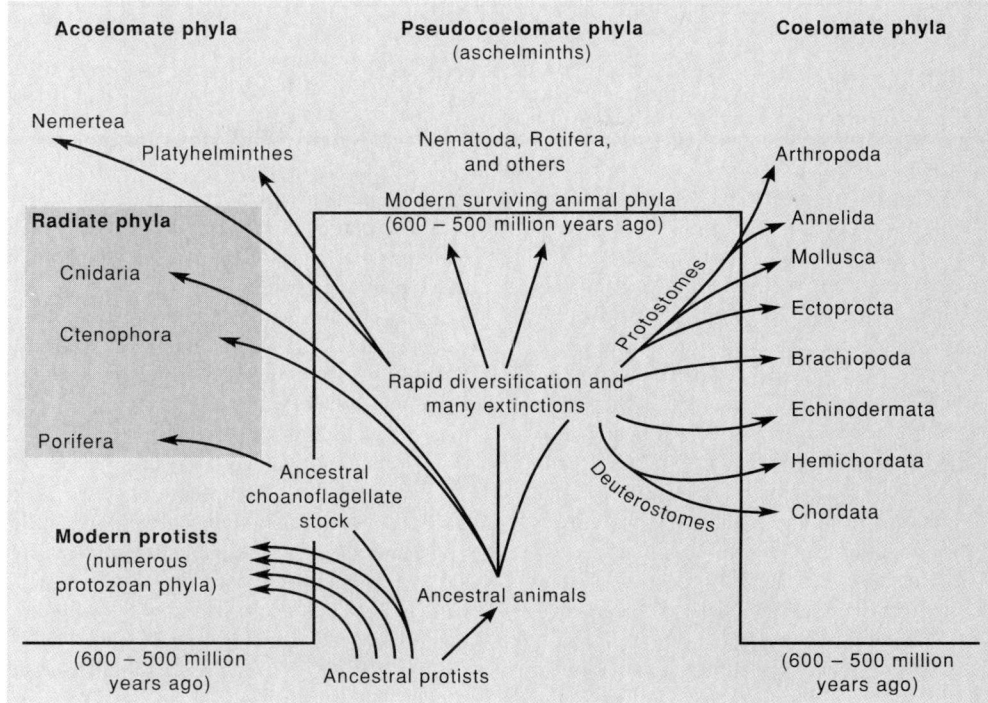

FIGURE 18.2

Evolutionary Relationships of the Poriferans and the Radiate Phyla. Members of the phylum Porifera are derived from ancestral protozoan stocks independently of other animal phyla. The radiate animals (shaded in orange) include members of the phyla Cnidaria and Ctenophora. This figure shows a diphyletic origin of the animal kingdom in which sponges are depicted as arising from the protists separate from other animals. Other interpretations of sponge origins are discussed in the text.

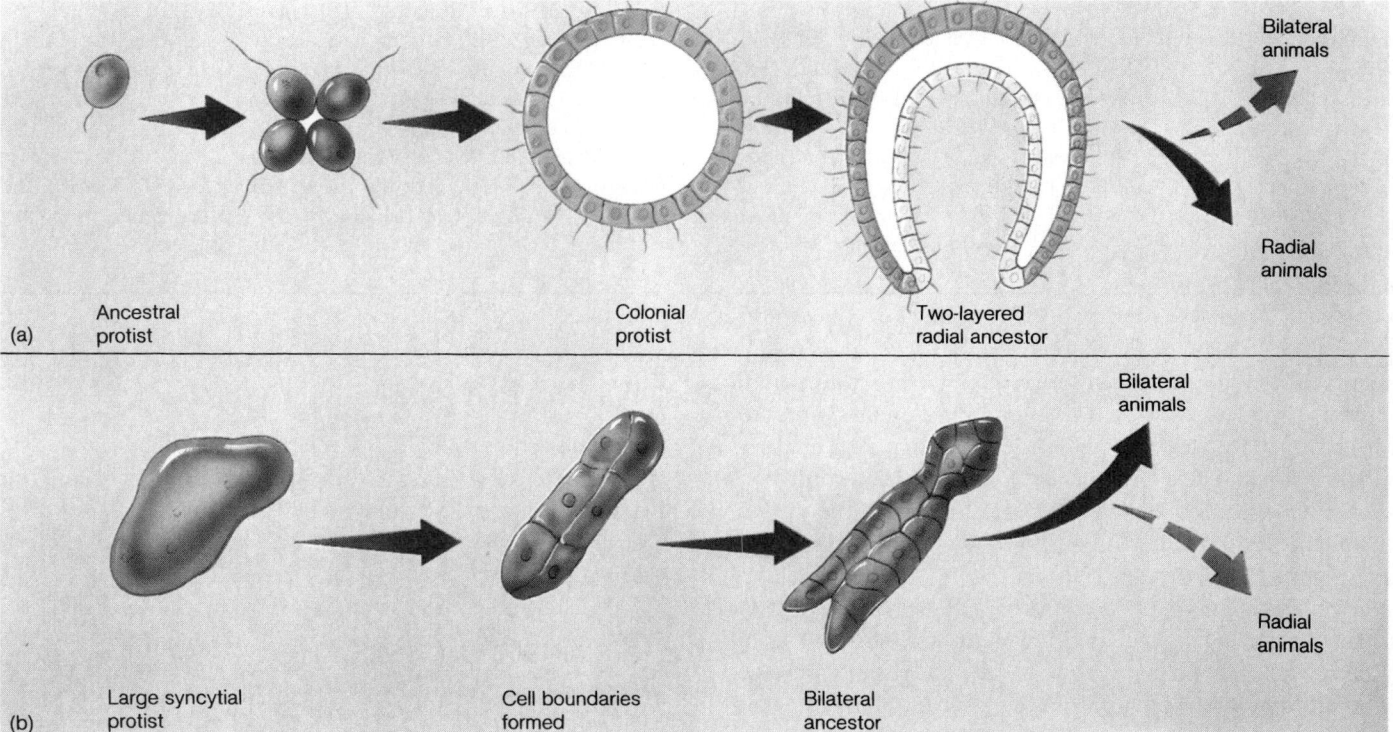

FIGURE 18.3

Two Hypotheses Regarding the Origin of Multicellularity. (a) The colonial hypothesis. Multicellularity may have arisen when cells produced by a dividing protist remained together. Invagination of cells could have formed a second cell layer. This hypothesis is supported by colonial organization of some Sacromastigophora. (The colonial protist and the two-layered radial ancestor are shown in sectional views.) (b) The syncytial hypothesis. Multicellularity could have arisen when plasma membranes were formed within the cytoplasm of a large, multinucleate protist. This hypothesis is supported by multinucleate, bilateral ciliates.

ANIMAL ORIGINS—THE CAMBRIAN EXPLOSION

The geological timescale (*see table 1.1*) is marked by significant geological and biological events including the origin of the earth about 4.6 billion years ago, the origin of life about 3.5 billion years ago (*see box 11.1*), the origin of eukaryotic life-forms about 1.5 billion years ago (*see box 3.1*), and the origin of animals about 0.6 billion years ago. The latter event marks the beginning of the Cambrian period. The origin of animals came relatively late in the history of the earth—only about 10% of the earth's history is marked by the presence of animals. During a geologically brief 100 million-year period, all modern animal phyla (along with other animals that are now extinct) evolved. This rapid origin and diversification of animals is often referred to as "the Cambrian explosion."

Important questions about this explosion have been asked ever since the time of Charles Darwin. Why did it occur so late in the history of the earth? The origin of multicellularity would seem a relatively simple step in comparison to the origin of life itself. Why are there no fossil records that document the series of evolutionary changes that occurred during the evolution of the animal phyla? Why did the evolution of animal life occur so quickly? Paleontologists continue to search the fossil records for answers to these kinds of questions.

One interpretation regarding the absence of fossils during this important 100 million-year period is that early animals were soft-bodied and simply did not fossilize. Fossilization of soft-bodied animals is less likely than fossilization of hard-bodied animals, but it does occur. Conditions that promote fossilization of soft-bodied animals include very rapid covering by sediments that creates an anoxic environment that discourages decomposition. In fact, fossil beds containing soft-bodied animals have been known for many years.

The Ediacara fossil formation, which contains the oldest known animal fossils, is made up exclusively of soft-bodied forms. Although it is named after a site in Australia, the Ediacara formation is worldwide in distribution and dates into Precambrian times.

This 700 million-year-old formation gives us few clues to the origin of modern animals, however, because it is believed to represent an evolutionary experiment that failed. It contains no ancestors of modern animal phyla.

A slightly younger fossil formation containing animal remains is called the Tommotian formation—named after a locale in Russia. It dates to the very early Cambrian period and it also contains only soft-bodied forms. At one time, the animals present in these fossil beds were assigned to various modern phyla, including the Porifera and Cnidaria, but most paleontologists now agree that all Tommotian fossils represent unique body forms that arose early in the Cambrian period and disappeared before the end of the period, leaving no descendants in the modern animal phyla.

A third fossil formation containing soft-bodied animals provides evidence of the results of the Cambrian explosion. This fossil formation, called the Burgess Shale, is in Yoho National Park in the Canadian Rocky Mountains of British Columbia. Shortly after the Cambrian explosion, mud slides rapidly buried thousands of marine animals under conditions that favored fossilization. These fossil beds provide evidence of virtually all of the 31 phyla described in this textbook plus about 20 other animal body forms. These animal body forms are so different from any modern animals that they cannot be assigned to any modern phyla (figure 1). These unassignable animals include a large swimming predator called *Anomalocaris* and a soft-bodied detritus-eating or algae-eating animal called *Wiwaxia*. Not only are there unique body forms in the Burgess Shale, but there are also fossils of many extinct representatives of modern phyla. For example, a well-known Burgess Shale animal called *Sidneyia* is a representative of a previously unknown group of arthropods (insects, spiders, mites, crabs).

There are many lessons that have been, and will be, learned from fossil formations like the Burgess Shale. One of these is that evolution cannot always be thought of as a slow progression. The story of the Cambrian explosion involves very rapid evolutionary

---

appearance of all animal phyla in fossils from the Precambrian/Cambrian boundary is difficult to explain if animals are monophyletic. If animals are polyphyletic, more than one explanation of the origin of multicellularity could be possible and more than one body form could be ancestral. Conversely, the impressive similarities in cellular organization in all animals support the view that all or most animals are derived from a single ancestor. For example, asters (*see figure 6.4*) are formed during mitosis in most animals, certain cell junctions are similar in all animal cells, flagellated sperm are produced by most animals, and the proteins that accomplish movement are similar in most animal cells. These common features are difficult to explain, assuming polyphyletic origins. If one assumes one or two ancestral lineages, then only one or two hypotheses regarding the origin of multicellularity can be correct (box 18.1).

PHYLUM PORIFERA

The Porifera (po-rif´er-ah) (L. *porus*, pore + *fera*, to bear), or sponges, are mostly marine animals consisting of loosely organized cells (figure 18.4; table 18.1). There are about 9,000 species of sponges, which vary in size from less than a centimeter to a mass that would fill one's arms.

Characteristics of the phylum Porifera include the following:

1. Asymmetrical or radially symmetrical
2. Three cell types: pinacocytes, mesenchyme cells, and choanocytes
3. Central cavity, or a series of branching chambers, through which water is circulated during filter feeding
4. No tissues or organs

diversification. A remarkable diversity of forms is seen in the Burgess Shale, but this diversity did not last. After an initial diversification, the story of evolution involved the extinction of many unique animals. Why was this evolution so very rapid? No one really knows. Many zoologists believe it was because there were so many ecological niches available and virtually no competition from existing species. Will we ever know the evolutionary sequences involved in the Cambrian explosion? Perhaps another ancient fossil bed of soft-bodied animals from 600 million-year-old seas is waiting for discovery.

FIGURE 1   The Burgess Shale. An artist's reconstruction of the Burgess Shale. The Burgess Shale contained numerous unique forms of animal life as well as representatives of most animal phyla described in this textbook. A trilobite is shown on the lower left. Tall sponges are shown on the right and left in the foreground. *Sidneyia* is shown on the seafloor in the middle foreground and in the middle left.

CELL TYPES, BODY WALL, AND SKELETONS

In spite of their relative simplicity, sponges are more than colonies of independent cells. As in all animals, sponge cells are specialized for particular functions. This organization is often referred to as division of labor.

Thin, flat cells, called **pinacocytes,** line the outer surface of a sponge. Pinacocytes may be mildly contractile, and their contraction may change the shape of some sponges. In a number of sponges, some pinacocytes are specialized into tubelike, contractile **porocytes,** which can regulate water circulation (figure 18.5a). Openings through porocytes are pathways for water moving through the body wall.

Just below the pinacocyte layer of a sponge is a jellylike layer referred to as the **mesohyl** (Gr. *meso*, middle + *hyl*, matter). Amoeboid cells are found moving about in the mesohyl and are specialized for reproduction, secreting skeletal elements, transporting food, storing food, and forming contractile rings around openings in the sponge wall.

Below the mesohyl and lining an inner chamber(s) are choanocytes, or collar cells. **Choanocytes** (Gr. *choane*, funnel + *cyte*, cell) are flagellated cells that have a collarlike ring of microvilli surrounding a flagellum. Microfilaments connect the microvilli, forming a netlike mesh within the collar. The flagellum creates water currents through the sponge, and the collar filters microscopic food particles from the water (figure 18.5b).

18.5

(a)   (b)

Figure 18.4

Phylum Porifera. Many sponges are brightly colored, commonly with hues of red, orange, green, or yellow. (*a*) *Verongia.* (*b*) *Axiomella.*

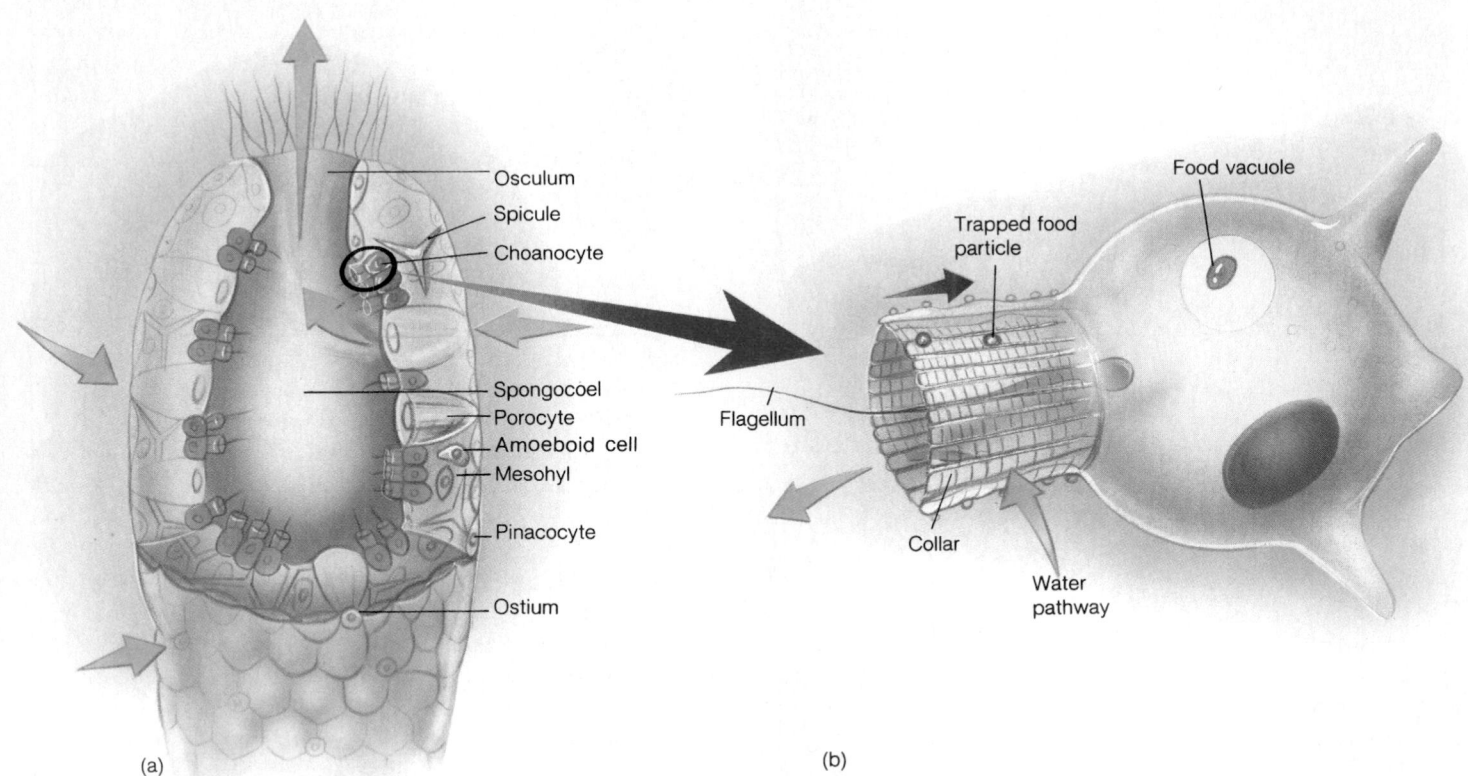

(a)   (b)

Figure 18.5

Morphology of a Simple Sponge. (*a*) In this example, pinacocytes form the outer body wall, and mesenchyme cells and spicules are found in the mesohyl. Ostia are formed by porocytes that extend through the body wall. (*b*) Choanocytes are cells with a flagellum surrounded by a collar of microvilli that traps food particles. Food is moved toward the base of the cell, where it is incorporated into a food vacuole and passed to amoeboid mesenchyme cells, where digestion takes place. Blue arrows show water flow patterns. The brown arrow shows the direction of movement of trapped food particles.

TABLE 18.1	CLASSIFICATION OF THE PORIFERA*

Phylum Porifera (po-rif'er-ah)
The animal phylum whose members are sessile and either asymmetrical or radially symmetrical; body organized around a system of water canals and chambers; cells not organized into tissues or organs.

Class Calcarea (kal-kar'ea)
Spicules composed of calcium carbonate; spicules needle shaped or with three or four rays; ascon, leucon, or scyon body forms; all marine. Calcareous sponges. *Grantia (Scypha), Leucosolenia.*

Class Hexactinellida (hex-act'in-el'id-ah)
Spicules composed of silica and usually six rayed; spicules often fused into an intricate lattice; cup or vase shaped; sycon or leucon body form; found at 450 to 900 m depths in tropical West Indies and eastern Pacific. Glass sponges. *Euplectella* (Venus flower-basket).

Class Demospongiae (de-mo-spun'je-e)
Brilliantly colored sponges with needle-shaped or four-rayed siliceous spicules or spongin or both; leucon body form; up to 1 m in height and diameter. Includes one family of freshwater sponges, Spongillidae, and the bath sponges. *Cliona, Spongilla.*

*The class Sclerospongiae has been recently abandoned and its members assigned to Calcarea and Demospongiae.

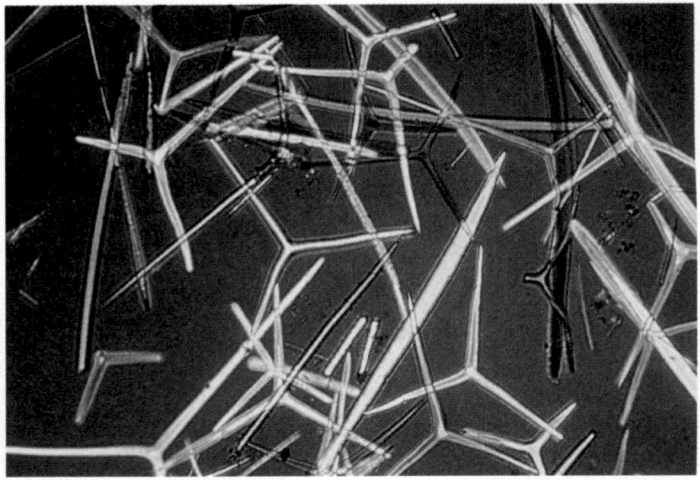

FIGURE 18.6
Sponge Spicules. Photomicrograph of a variety of sponge spicules (× 150).

The presence of choanocytes in sponges suggests an evolutionary link between the sponges and a group of protists called choanoflagellates. This link is discussed further at the end of this chapter.

Sponges are supported by a skeleton that may consist of microscopic needlelike spikes called **spicules.** Spicules are formed by ameboid cells, are made of calcium carbonate or silica, and may take on a variety of shapes (figure 18.6). ② Alternatively, the skeleton may be made of **spongin** (a fibrous protein made of collagen), which is dried, beaten, and washed until all cells are removed to produce a commercial sponge. The nature of the skeleton is an important characteristic in sponge taxonomy.

WATER CURRENTS AND BODY FORMS

The life of a sponge depends on the water currents created by choanocytes. Water currents bring food and oxygen to a sponge and carry away metabolic and digestive wastes. The way in which food filtration and circulation are accomplished is reflected in the body forms present in the phylum. Zoologists have described three sponge body forms.

The simplest and least common sponge body form is the **ascon** (figure 18.7a). Ascon sponges are vaselike. Ostia are the outer openings of porocytes and lead directly to a chamber called the spongocoel. Choanocytes line the spongocoel, and their flagellar movements draw water into the spongocoel through the ostia. Water exits the sponge through the osculum, which is a single, large opening at the top of the sponge.

In the **sycon** body form, the sponge wall appears folded (figure 18.7b). Water enters a sycon sponge through openings called dermal pores. Dermal pores are the openings of invaginations of the body wall, called incurrent canals. Pores in the body wall connect incurrent canals to radial canals, and the radial canals lead to the spongocoel. Choanocytes line radial canals (rather than the spongocoel), and the beating of choanocyte flagella moves water from ostia, through incurrent and radial canals, to the spongocoel, and out the osculum.

Leucon sponges have an extensively branched canal system (figure 18.7c). Water enters the sponge through ostia and moves through branched incurrent canals, which lead to choanocyte chambers. Canals leading away from the chambers are called excurrent canals. Proliferation of chambers and canals has resulted in the absence of a spongocoel, and often multiple exit points (oscula) for water leaving the sponge. ③ In complex sponges, an increased surface area for choanocytes results in large volumes of water being moved through the sponge and greater filtering capabilities. Although the evolutionary pathways in the phylum are complex and incompletely described, most pathways have resulted in the leuconoid body form.

MAINTENANCE FUNCTIONS

Sponges feed on particles that are in the 0.1 to 50 µm size range. Their food consists of bacteria, microscopic algae, protists, and other suspended organic matter. Recent investigations have discovered that a few sponges are carnivorous. These deep-water sponges (*Asbestopluma*) can capture small crustaceans using spicule-covered filaments. The prey are slowly drawn into the sponge and consumed. Large populations of sponges play an important role in reducing turbidity of coastal waters. A single leuconoid sponge, 1 cm in diameter and 10 cm high, can filter in excess of 20 liters of water every day!

18.7

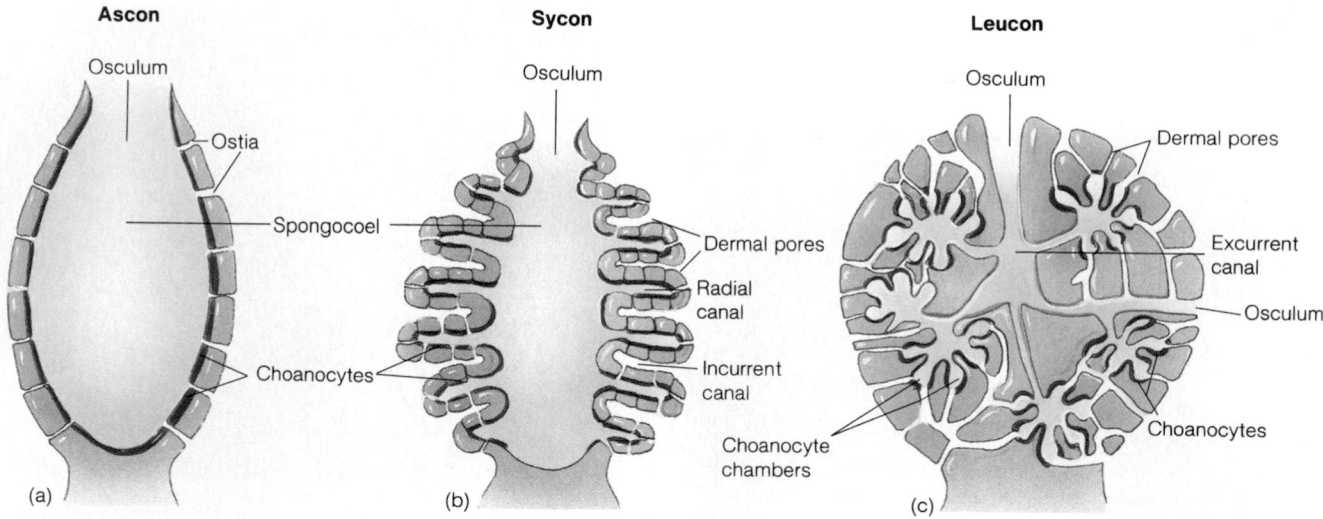

FIGURE 18.7

Sponge Body Forms. (*a*) An asconoid sponge. Choanocytes line the spongocoel in ascon sponges. (*b*) A syconoid sponge. The body wall of sycon sponges appears folded. Choanocytes line radial canals that open into the spongocoel. (*c*) A leuconoid sponge. The proliferation of canals and chambers has resulted in the loss of the spongocoel as a distinct chamber. Multiple oscula are frequently present.

Choanocytes filter small, suspended food particles. Water passes through their collar near the base of the cell then moves into a sponge chamber at the open end of the collar. Suspended food is trapped on the collar and moved along microvilli to the base of the collar, where it is incorporated into a food vacuole (*see figure 18.5b*). Digestion begins in the food vacuole by lysosomal enzymes and pH changes. Partially digested food is passed to amoeboid cells, which distribute it to other cells.

Filtration is not the only way that sponges feed. Larger food particles (up to 50 μm in size) may be phagocytized (*see figure 3.14*) by pinacocytes lining incurrent canals. Nutrients dissolved in seawater may also be absorbed by active transport.

Because of extensive canal systems and the circulation of large volumes of water through sponges, all sponge cells are in close contact with water. Thus, the loss of nitrogenous wastes (principally ammonia) and gas exchange occur by diffusion.

Sponges do not have nerve cells to coordinate body functions. Most reactions are the result of individual cells responding to a stimulus. For example, water circulation through some sponges is at a minimum at sunrise and at a maximum just before sunset because light inhibits the constriction of porocytes and other cells surrounding ostia, keeping incurrent canals open.   ❹   Other reactions, however, suggest some communication between cells. For example, the rate of water circulation through a sponge can drop suddenly without any apparent external cause. This reaction can be due only to choanocytes ceasing activities more or less simultaneously and implies some form of internal communication. The nature of this communication is unknown. Chemical messages transmitted by amoeboid cells and ion movement over cell surfaces are possible control mechanisms.

REPRODUCTION

Most sponges are monoecious (both sexes occur in the same individual) but do not usually undergo self-fertilization because they produce eggs and sperm at different times. Certain choanocytes lose their collars and flagella and undergo meiosis to form flagellated sperm. Other choanocytes (and amoeboid cells in some sponges) probably undergo meiosis to form eggs. Eggs are retained in the mesohyl of the parent. Sperm cells exit one sponge through the osculum and enter another sponge with the incurrent water. Sperm are trapped by choanocytes and incorporated into a vacuole. The choanocytes lose their collar and flagellum, become ameboid, and transport sperm to the eggs.

In most sponges, early development occurs in the mesohyl. Cleavage of a zygote results in the formation of a flagellated larval stage. (A **larva** is an immature stage that may undergo a dramatic change in structure before attaining the adult body form.) The larva breaks free and is carried out of the parent sponge by water currents. After no more than 2 days of a free-swimming existence, the larva settles to the substrate and begins development of the adult body form (figure 18.8*a,b*).

Asexual reproduction of freshwater and some marine sponges involves the formation of resistant capsules containing masses of amoeboid cells. These capsules, called **gemmules,** are released when the parent sponge dies in the winter and can survive both freezing and drying (figure 18.8*c*). When favorable conditions return in the spring, amoeboid cells stream out of a tiny opening, called the micropyle, and organize themselves into a sponge.

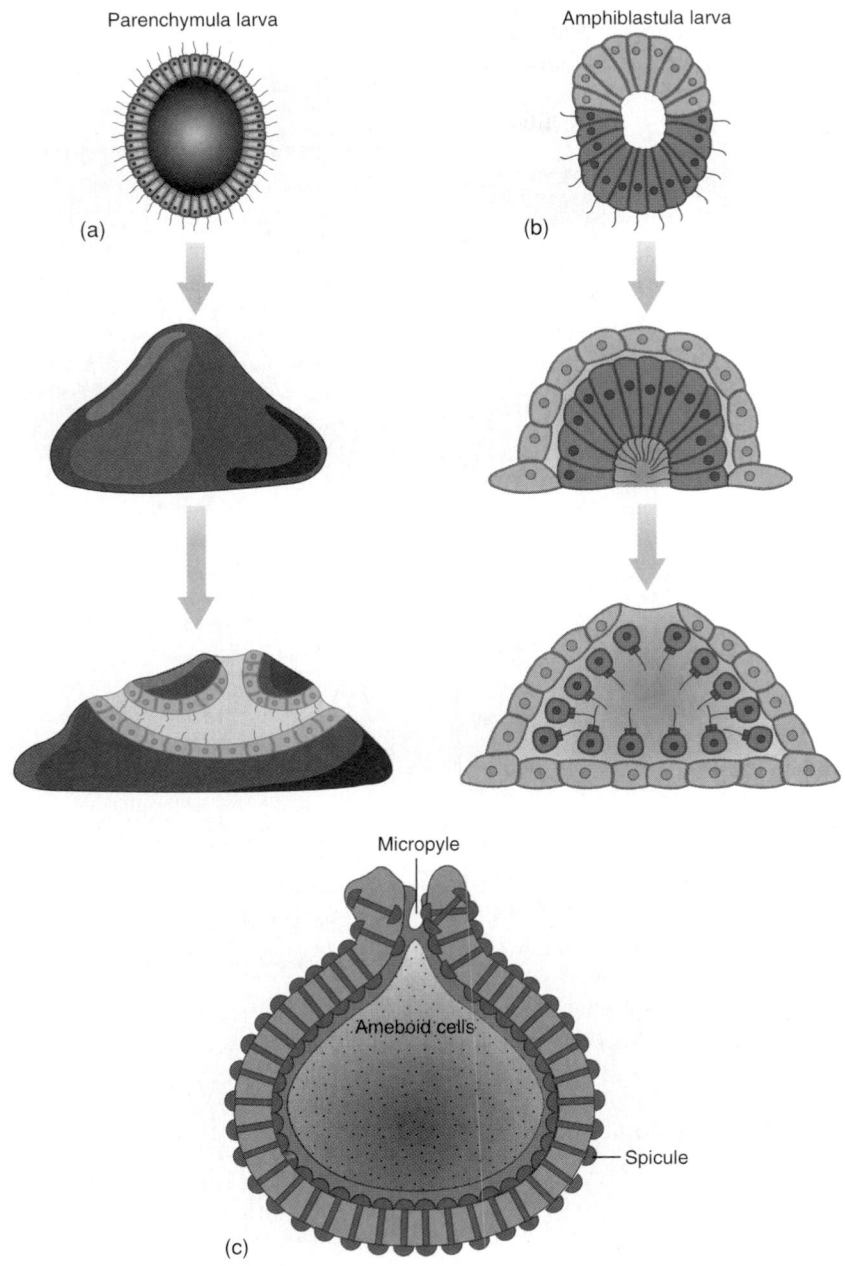

Parenchymula larva

(a)

Amphiblastula larva

(b)

Micropyle

Ameboid cells

Spicule

(c)

FIGURE 18.8

Development of Sponge Larval Stages. (*a*) Most sponges have a parenchymula larva. Flagellated cells cover most of the outer surface of the larva. After the larva settles and attaches, the outer cells lose their flagella, move to the interior, and form choanocytes. Interior cells move to the periphery and form pinacocytes. (*b*) Some sponges have an amphiblastula larva, which is hollow and has ½ of the larva composed of flagellated cells. On settling, the flagellated cells invaginate into the interior of the embryo and will form choanocytes. Nonflagellated cells overgrow the choanocytes and form the pinacocytes. (*c*) Gemmules are resistant capsules containing masses of amoeboid cells. Gemmules are released when a parent sponge dies (e.g., in the winter) and amoeboid cells form a new sponge when favorable conditions return.

Some sponges possess remarkable powers of regeneration. Portions of a sponge that are cut or broken from one individual will regenerate new individuals.

Stop and Ask Yourself

1. How do the "colonial" and "syncytial" hypotheses account for the origin of multicellularity?
2. What evidence supports the idea that the kingdom Animalia is polyphyletic?
3. What are three kinds of cells found in the Porifera and what are their functions?
4. What is the path of water circulating through an ascon sponge? Through a sycon sponge? Through a leucon sponge?

PHYLUM CNIDARIA (COELENTERATA)

Members of the phylum Cnidaria (ni-dar′e-ah) (Gr. *knide,* nettle) possess radial or biradial symmetry. Biradial symmetry is a modification of radial symmetry in which a single plane, passing through a central axis, divides the animal into mirror images. It results from the presence of a single or paired structure in a basically radial animal and differs from bilateral symmetry in that there is no distinction between dorsal and ventral surfaces. Radially symmetrical animals have no anterior or posterior ends. Thus, terms of direction are based on the position of the mouth opening. Recall that the end of the animal that contains the mouth is the oral end, and the opposite end is the aboral end. Radial symmetry is advantageous for sedentary animals because sensory receptors are evenly distributed around the body. These organisms can respond to stimuli that come from all directions.

The Cnidaria include over 9,000 species, are mostly marine, and are very important in coral reef ecosystems (table 18.2).

Characteristics of the phylum Cnidaria include the following:

1. Radial or biradial symmetry
2. Diploblastic, tissue-level organization
3. Gelatinous mesoglea located between the epidermal and gastrodermal tissue layers
4. Gastrovascular cavity
5. Nervous system in the form of a nerve net
6. Specialized cells, called cnidocytes, used in defense, feeding, and attachment

TABLE 18.2	CLASSIFICATION OF THE CNIDARIA

Phylum Cnidaria (ni-dar′e-ah)
Radial or biradial symmetry, diploblastic organization, a gastrovascular cavity, and cnidocytes.
 Class Hydrozoa (hi′dro-zo″ah)
 Cnidocytes present in the epidermis; gametes produced epidermally and always released to the outside of the body; no wandering mesenchyme cells in mesoglea; medusae usually with a velum; many polyps colonial; mostly marine with some freshwater species. *Hydra, Obelia, Gonionemus, Physalia.*
 Class Scyphozoa (si′fo-zo″ah)
 Medusa prominent in the life history; polyp small; gametes gastrodermal in origin and released into the gastrovascular cavity; cnidocytes present in the gastrodermis as well as epidermis; medusa lacks a velum; mesoglea with wandering mesenchyme cells of epidermal origin; marine. *Aurelia.*
 Class Cubozoa (ku′bo-zo″ah)
 Medusa prominent in life history; polyp small; gametes gastrodermal in origin; medusa cuboidal in shape with tentacles that hang from each corner of the bell; marine. *Chironex.*
 Class Anthozoa (an′tho-zo″ah)
 Colonial or solitary polyps; medusae absent; cnidocytes present in the gastrodermis; gametes gastrodermal in origin; gastrovascular cavity divided by mesenteries that bear nematocysts; internal biradial or bilateral symmetry present; mesoglea with wandering mesenchyme cells; marine. Anemones and corals. *Metridium.*

THE BODY WALL AND NEMATOCYSTS

Cnidarians possess diploblastic, tissue-level organization (*see* figure 16.9). Cells are organized into tissues that carry out specific functions, and all cells are derived from two embryological layers. The ectoderm of the embryo gives rise to an outer layer of the body wall, called the **epidermis,** and the inner layer of the body wall, called the **gastrodermis,** is derived from endoderm (figure 18.9). Cells of the epidermis and gastrodermis are differentiated into a number of cell types that function in protection, food gathering, coordination, movement, digestion, and absorption. Between the epidermis and gastrodermis is a jellylike layer called **mesoglea.** Cells are present in the middle layer of some cnidarians, but they have their origin in either the epidermis or the gastrodermis.

One kind of cell is characteristic of the phylum. Epidermal and/or gastrodermal cells called **cnidocytes** produce structures

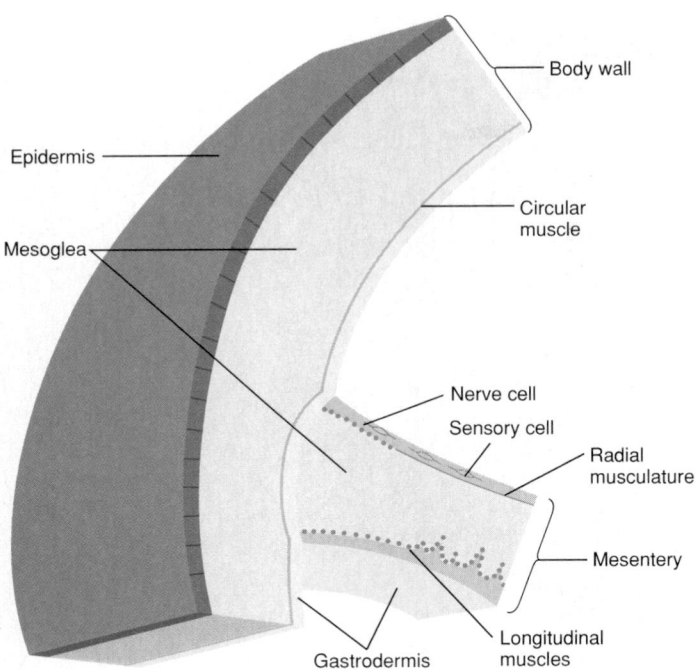

FIGURE 18.9

The Body Wall of a Cnidarian (Class Anthozoa). Cnidarians are diploblastic (two tissue layers). The epidermis is derived embryologically from ectoderm and the gastrodermis is derived embryologically from endoderm. Between these layers is mesoglea.
Source: After Bullock and Horridge.

called nematocysts, which are used for attachment, defense, and feeding. A **nematocyst** is a fluid-filled capsule enclosing a coiled, hollow tube (figure 18.10). The capsule is capped at one end by a lidlike operculum. The cnidocyte has a modified cilium, called a cnidocil. When the cnidocil is stimulated, the operculum is forced open and the coiled tube is discharged—as one would evert a sweater sleeve that had been turned inside out.

Nearly 30 kinds of nematocysts have been described. Nematocysts used in food gathering and defense may discharge a long tube armed with spines that penetrates the prey. The spines have hollow tips that discharge paralyzing toxins. Other nematocysts contain unarmed tubes that wrap around prey or a substrate. Still other nematocysts have sticky secretions that help the animal anchor itself. Six or more kinds of nematocysts may be present in one individual.

ALTERNATION OF GENERATIONS

Most cnidarians possess two body forms in their life histories (figure 18.11). The **polyp** is usually asexual and sessile. It is attached to a substrate at the aboral end, has a cylindrical body, called the column, and a mouth surrounded by food-gathering tentacles. The **medusa** (plural medusae) is dioecious

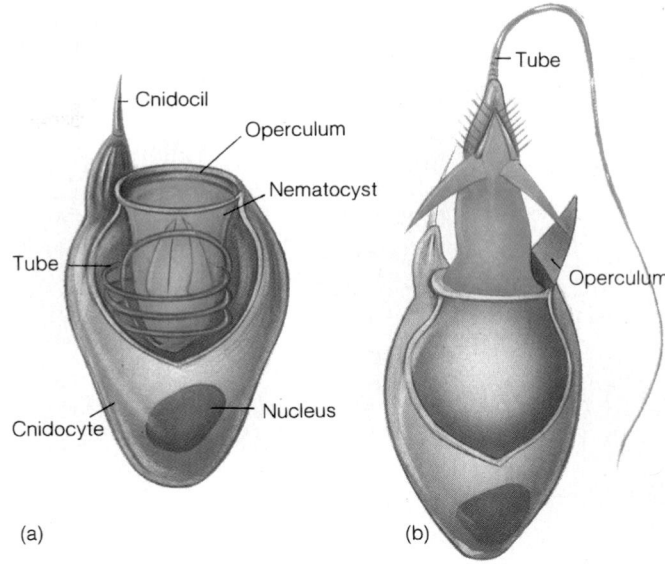

FIGURE 18.10

Cnidocyte Structure and Nematocyst Discharge. (*a*) A nematocyst develops in a capsule in the cnidocyte. The capsule is capped at its outer margin by an operculum (lid) that is displaced upon discharge of the nematocyst. The triggerlike cnidocil is responsible for nematocyst discharge. (*b*) A discharged nematocyst. When the cnidocil is stimulated, there is a rapid (osmotic) influx of water, causing the nematocyst to evert, first near its base, and then progressively along the tube from base to tip. The tube revolves at enormous speeds as the nematocyst is discharged. In nematocysts that are armed with barbs, the advancing tip of the tube is aided in its penetration of the prey as barbs spring forward from the interior of the tube and then flick backward along the outside of the tube.

and free swimming. It is shaped like an inverted bowl and has tentacles dangling from its margins. The mouth opening is centrally located facing downward, and the medusa swims by gentle pulsations of the body wall. The mesoglea is more abundant in a medusa than in a polyp, giving the former a jellylike consistency.

MAINTENANCE FUNCTIONS

The gastrodermis of all cnidarians lines a blind-ending cavity, called the **gastrovascular cavity.** This cavity functions in digestion, the exchange of respiratory gases and metabolic wastes, and for discharge of gametes. Food, digestive wastes, and reproductive stages enter and leave the gastrovascular cavity through the mouth.

The food of most cnidarians consists of very small crustaceans. Nematocysts entangle and paralyze prey, contractile cells in the tentacles cause the tentacles to shorten, and food is drawn

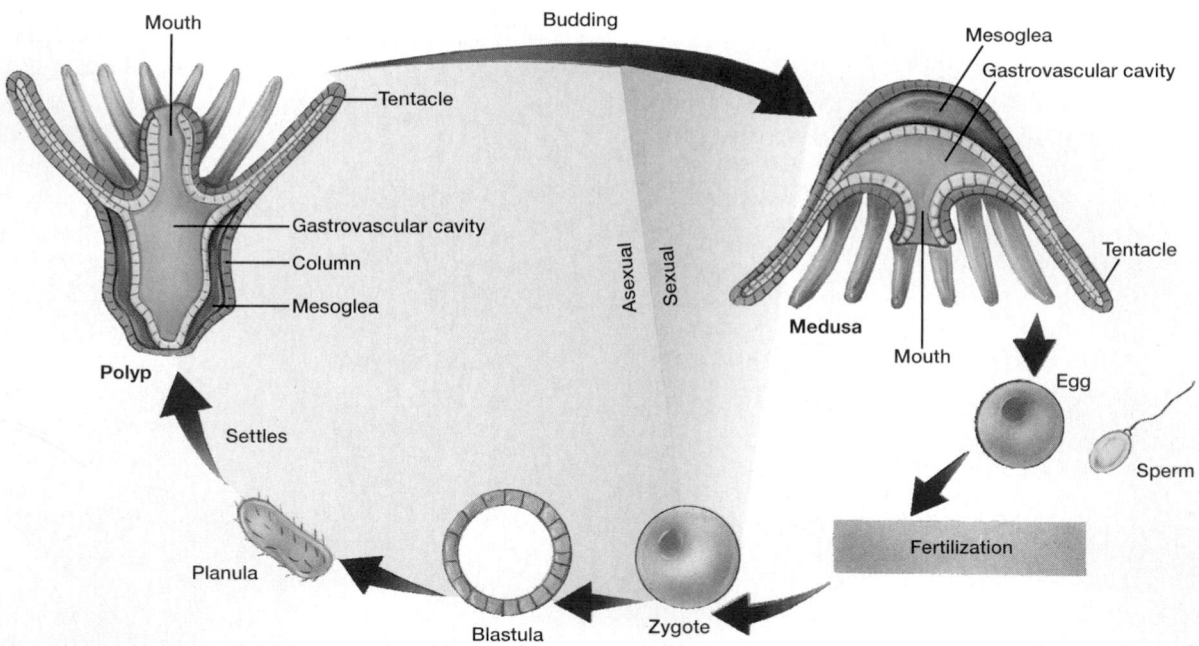

Figure 18.11

A Generalized Cnidarian Life Cycle. This figures show alternation between medusa and polyp body forms. Dioecious medusae produce gametes that may be shed into the water, where fertilization takes place. Early development forms a ciliated planula larva. After a brief free swimming existence, the planula settles to the substrate and forms a polyp. Budding of the polyp produces additional polyps and medusa buds. Medusae break free of the polyp and swim away. The polyp or medusa stage of many species is either lost or reduced and the sexual and asexual stages have been incorporated into one body form.

toward the mouth. As food enters the gastrovascular cavity, gastrodermal gland cells secrete lubricating mucus and enzymes, which reduce food to a soupy broth. Certain gastrodermal cells, called nutritive-muscular cells phagocytize partially digested food and incorporate it into food vacuoles, where digestion is completed. Nutritive-muscular cells also have circularly oriented contractile fibers that help move materials into or out of the gastrovascular cavity by peristaltic contractions. During peristalsis, ringlike contractions move along the body wall, pushing contents of the gastrovascular cavity ahead of them, expelling undigested material through the mouth.

⑤   Cnidarians derive most of their support from the buoyancy of water around them. In addition, they have a hydrostatic skeleton to aid in support and movement. A **hydrostatic skeleton** is water or body fluids confined in a cavity of the body and against which contractile elements of the body wall act. In the Cnidaria, the water-filled gastrovascular cavity acts as a hydrostatic skeleton. Certain cells of the body wall, called epithelio-muscular cells, are contractile and aid in movement. When a polyp closes its mouth (to prevent water from escaping) and contracts longitudinal epithelio-muscular cells on one side of the body, the polyp bends toward that side. If these cells contract while the mouth is open, water escapes from the gastrovascular cavity, and the polyp collapses.

Contraction of circular epithelio-muscular cells causes constriction of a part of the body and, if the mouth is closed, water in the gastrovascular cavity is compressed, and the polyp elongates.

Polyps use a variety of forms of locomotion. They may move by somersaulting from base to tentacles and from tentacles to base again, or move in an inchworm fashion, using their base and tentacles as points of attachment. Polyps may also glide very slowly along a substrate while attached at their base or walk on their tentacles.

Medusae move by swimming and floating. Most horizontal movements are from being passively carried by water currents and wind. Vertical movements are the result of swimming. Contractions of circular and radial epitheliomuscular cells cause rhythmic pulsations of the bell and drive water from beneath the bell, propelling the medusa through the water.

Cnidarian nerve cells have been of interest to zoologists for many years because they may be the most primitive nervous elements in the animal kingdom. By studying these cells, zoologists may gain insight into the evolution of animal nervous systems. Nerve cells are located below the epidermis, near the mesoglea, and interconnect to form a two-dimensional nerve net. This net conducts nerve impulses around the body in response to a localized stimulus. The extent to which a nerve impulse spreads over the body depends on the strength of a stimulus. For example, a weak stimulus applied to a polyp's tentacle may cause the tentacle to be retracted. A strong stimulus at the same point may cause the entire polyp to withdraw from the stimulus.

Sensory structures of cnidarians are distributed throughout the body and include receptors for perceiving touch and certain chemicals. More specialized receptors are located at specific sites on a polyp or medusa.

Because cnidarians have large surface area to volume ratios (see figure 3.3), all cells are a short distance from the body surface, and oxygen, carbon dioxide, and nitrogenous wastes can be exchanged by diffusion.

REPRODUCTION

Most cnidarians are dioecious. Sperm and eggs may be released into the gastrovascular cavity or to the outside of the body. In some instances, eggs are retained in the parent until after fertilization.

A blastula forms early in development, and migration of surface cells to the interior fills the embryo with cells that will eventually form the gastrodermis. The embryo elongates to form a ciliated, free-swimming larva, called a **planula.** The planula attaches to a substrate, interior cells split to form the gastrovascular cavity, and a young polyp develops (see figure 18.11).

Medusae are nearly always formed by budding from the body wall of a polyp, and polyps may form other polyps by budding. Buds may detach from the polyp or they may remain attached to the parent to contribute to a colony of individuals. Variations on this general pattern will be discussed in the survey of cnidarian classes that follows.

Stop and Ask Yourself

5. What are the three layers of the cnidarian body wall?
6. What is a nematocyst? What are several functions of nematocysts?
7. How would you characterize the nervous organization of cnidarians?
8. What is a hydrostatic skeleton? How does this function in cnidarians?

CLASS HYDROZOA

Hydrozoans (hi′dro-zo″anz) are small, relatively common cnidarians. The vast majority are marine, but this is the one cnidarian class with freshwater representatives. Most hydrozoans have life cycles that display alternation of generations; however, in some the medusa stage is lost, while in others the polyp stage is very small.

Hydrozoans can be distinguished from other cnidarians by three features (see table 18.2). Nematocysts are only in the epidermis; gametes are epidermal and released to the outside of the body rather than into the gastrovascular cavity; and the mesoglea never contains amoeboid mesenchyme cells.

Most hydrozoans have colonial polyp forms, some of which may be specialized for feeding, producing medusae by budding, or defending the colony. In *Obelia,* a common marine cnidarian, the planula develops into a feeding polyp, called a **gastrozooid** (gas′tra-zo′oid) (figure 18.12). The gastrozooid has tentacles, feeds on microscopic organisms in the water, and secretes a skeleton of protein and chitin called the perisarc, around itself.

Growth of an *Obelia* colony results from budding of the original gastrozooid. Rootlike processes grow into and horizontally along the substrate. They anchor the colony and give rise to branch colonies. The entire colony has a continuous gastrovascular cavity, body wall, and perisarc, and is a few centimeters high. Gastrozooids are the most common type of polyp in the colony; however, as an *Obelia* colony grows, gonozooids are produced. A **gonozooid** (gon′o-zo′oid) is a reproductive polyp that produces medusae by budding. *Obelia*'s small medusae are formed on a stalklike structure of the gonozooid. When medusae mature, they break free of the stalk and swim out an opening at the end of the gonozooid. Medusae reproduce sexually to give rise to more colonies of polyps.

Gonionemus (figure 18.13a) is a hydrozoan in which the medusa stage predominates. It lives in shallow marine waters, where it is often found clinging to seaweeds by adhesive pads on its tentacles. The biology of *Gonionemus* is typical of most hydrozoan medusae. The margin of the *Gonionemus* medusa projects inward to form a shelflike lip, called the velum. A velum is found on most hydrozoan medusae but is absent in all other cnidarian classes. The velum concentrates water expelled from beneath the medusa to a smaller outlet, creating a jet-propulsion system. The mouth is at the end of a tubelike **manubrium** that hangs from the medusa's oral surface. The gastrovascular cavity leads from the inside of the manubrium into four radial canals that extend to the margin of the medusa. Radial canals are connected at the margin of the medusa by an encircling ring canal.

In addition to a nerve net, *Gonionemus* has a concentration of nerve cells, called a nerve ring, that encircles the margin of the medusa. The nerve ring coordinates swimming movements. Embedded in the mesoglea around the margin of the medusa are sensory structures called statocysts (figure 18.13b). A **statocyst** consists of a small sac surrounding a calcium carbonate concretion called a statolith. When *Gonionemus* tilts, the statolith moves in response to the pull of gravity, and nerve impulses are initiated, which may change the animal's swimming behavior.

Gonads of *Gonionemus* medusae hang from the oral surface, below the radial canals. *Gonionemus* is dioecious, and the

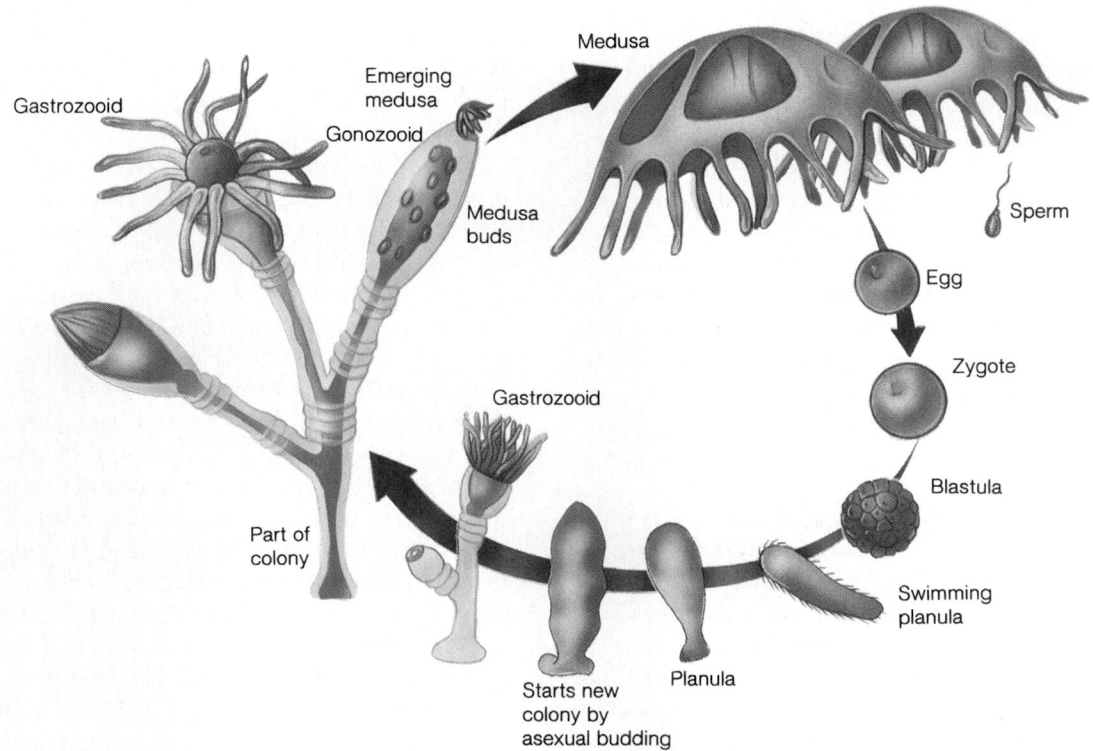

FIGURE 18.12

Obelia Structure and Life Cycle. This hydrozoan displays alternation between polyp and medusa stages. Unlike *Obelia*, the majority of colonial hydrozoans have medusae that remain attached to the parental colony and gametes or larval stages are released from the medusa through the gonozooid. The medusa often degenerate and may be little more than gonadal specializations in the gonozooid.

(a)

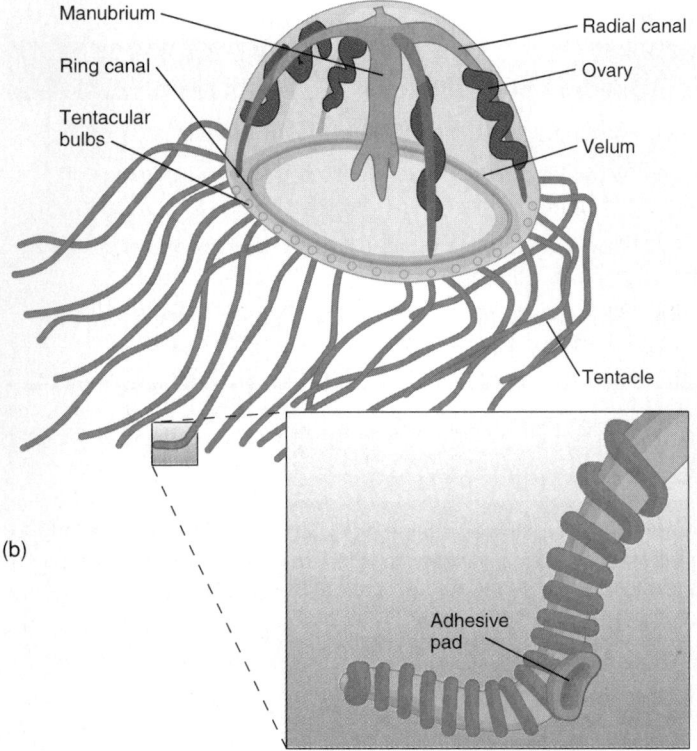

(b)

FIGURE 18.13

A Hydrozoan Medusa. (*a*) A *Gonionemus* medusa. (*b*) The structure of *Gonionemus*.

gametes are shed directly into seawater. A planula larva develops and attaches to the substrate, eventually forming a polyp (about 5 mm tall). The polyp reproduces by budding to make more polyps and medusae.

Hydra is a common freshwater hydrozoan that is found hanging from the underside of floating plants in clean streams and ponds. *Hydra* lacks a medusa stage and reproduces both asexually by budding from the side of the polyp and sexually. Hydras are somewhat unusual hydrozoans, because sexual reproduction occurs in the polyp stage. Testes are conical elevations of the body surface that form from mitosis of certain epidermal cells called interstitial cells. Sperm form by meiosis in the testes. Mature sperm exit the testes through temporary openings. Ovaries also form from interstitial cells. One large egg is formed per ovary. During egg formation, yolk is incorporated into the egg cell from gastrodermal cells. As ovarian cells disintegrate, the egg is left attached to the body wall by a thin stalk of tissue. After fertilization and early development, epithelial cells lay down a resistant chitinous shell. The embryo drops from the parent, overwinters, hatches in the spring, and develops into an adult.

Large oceanic hydrozoans belong to the order Siphonophora. These colonies are associations of numerous polypoid and medusoid individuals. Some polyps, called dactylozooids, possess a single, long (up to 9 m) tentacle armed with cnidocytes that are used in capturing prey. Other polyps are specialized for digesting prey. Various medusoid individuals form swimming bells, sac floats, oil floats, leaflike defensive structures, and gonads.

Physalia, commonly called the Portuguese man-of-war, is a very large, colonial siphonophore. It lacks swimming capabilities and moves at the mercy of wind and waves. ⑥ Its cnidocyte-laden dactylozooids are lethal to small vertebrates and dangerous to humans.

Class Scyphozoa

Members of the class Scyphozoa (si′fo-zo″ah) are all marine and are called "true jellyfish" because the dominant stage in their life history is the medusa (figure 18.14). Unlike hydrozoan medusae, scyphozoan medusae lack a velum, the mesoglea contains amoeboid mesenchyme cells, cnidocytes occur in the gastrodermis as well as the epidermis, and gametes are gastrodermal in origin (table 18.2).

Many scyphozoans are harmless to humans; others can deliver unpleasant and even dangerous stings. ⑦ For example, *Mastigias quinquecirrha*, the so-called stinging nettle, is a common Atlantic scyphozoan whose populations increase in late summer and become hazardous to swimmers (figure 18.14*a*). A rule of thumb for swimmers is to avoid helmet-shaped jellyfish with long tentacles and fleshy lobes hanging from the oral surface.

Aurelia is a common scyphozoan in both Pacific and Atlantic coastal waters of North America (figure 18.14*b*). The

(a)

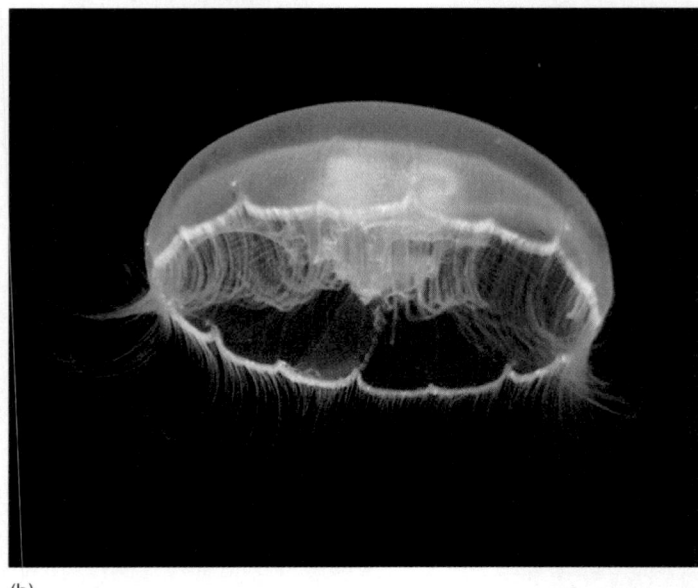

(b)

Figure 18.14

Representative Scyphozoans. (*a*) *Mastigias quinquecirrha*. (*b*) *Aurelia*.

margin of its medusa has a fringe of short tentacles and is divided by notches. The mouth of *Aurelia* leads to a stomach with four gastric pouches, which contain cnidocyte-laden gastric filaments. Radial canals lead from gastric pouches to the margin of the bell. In *Aurelia*, but not all scyphozoans, the canal system is extensively branched and leads to a ring canal around the margin of the medusa. Gastrodermal cells of all scyphozoans possess cilia for the continuous circulation of seawater and partially digested food.

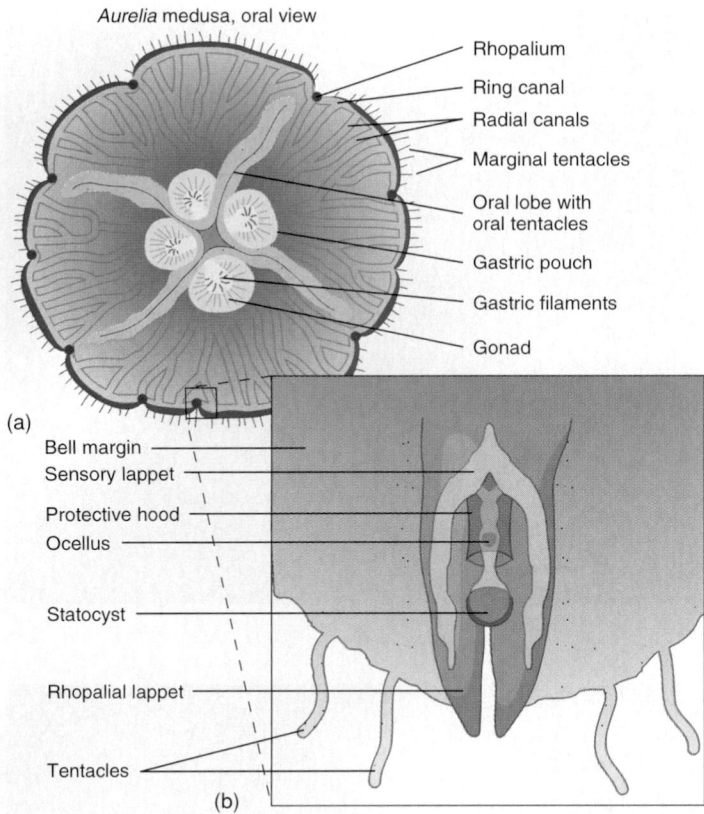

Aurelia medusa, oral view

- Rhopalium
- Ring canal
- Radial canals
- Marginal tentacles
- Oral lobe with oral tentacles
- Gastric pouch
- Gastric filaments
- Gonad

(a)

- Bell margin
- Sensory lappet
- Protective hood
- Ocellus
- Statocyst
- Rhopalial lappet
- Tentacles

(b)

Figure 18.15

The Structure of a Scyphozoan Medusa. (*a*) Internal structure of *Aurelia*. (*b*) A section through a rhopalium of *Aurelia*. Each rhopalium consists of two sensory (olfactory) lappets, a statocyst, and a photoreceptor called an ocellus. (*b*) *Source: After L. H. Hyman,* Biology of the Invertebrates, *copyright 1940 McGraw-Hill Publishing Co.*

Aurelia is a plankton feeder. At rest, it sinks slowly in the water, and microscopic animals are trapped in mucus on its epidermal surfaces. This food is carried by cilia to the margin of the medusa. Four fleshy lobes, called oral lobes, hang from the manubrium and are used to scrape food from the margin of the medusa (figure 18.15*a*). Cilia on the oral lobes carry food to the mouth.

In addition to sensory receptors located on the epidermis, *Aurelia* has eight specialized structures, called rhopalia, located in the notches at the margin of the medusa. Each **rhopalium** (figure 18.15*b*) consists of two sensory pits (presumed to be olfactory), lappets (probably touch receptors), and a statocyst. Photoreceptors, called ocelli, are also associated with rhopalia. *Aurelia* displays a distinct negative phototaxis, coming to the surface at twilight and descending to greater depths during bright daylight.

Scyphozoans are dioecious. *Aurelia*'s eight gonads are located in gastric pouches, two per pouch. Gametes are released into the gastric pouches. Sperm swim through the mouth to the outside of the medusa. In some scyphozoans, eggs are fertilized

in the female's gastric pouches, and early development occurs there. In *Aurelia*, eggs lodge in the oral lobes, where fertilization and development to the planula stage occurs.

The planula develops into a polyp called a **scyphistoma** (figure 18.16). The scyphistoma lives a year or more, during which time budding produces miniature medusae, called **ephyrae.** Repeated budding of the scyphistoma results in ephyrae being stacked on the polyp—as one might pile saucers on top of one another. After ephyrae are released, they gradually attain the adult form.

Class Cubozoa

The class Cubozoa (ku′bo-zo″ah) was formerly classified as an order in the Scyphozoa. The medusa is cuboidal, and tentacles hang from each of its corners. Polyps are very small and, for some species, polyps are unknown. Cubozoans are very active swimmers and feeders in warm tropical waters. Some possess dangerous nematocysts (figure 18.17).

Class Anthozoa

Members of the class Anthozoa (an′tho-zo″ah) are colonial or solitary and lack medusae. They include anemones and stony and soft corals. Anthozoans are all marine and are found at all depths.

Anthozoan polyps differ from hydrozoan polyps in three respects. (1) The mouth of an anthozoan leads to a pharynx, which is an invagination of the body wall that leads into the gastrovascular cavity. (2) The gastrovascular cavity is divided into sections by mesenteries (membranes) that bear cnidocytes and gonads on their free edges. (3) The mesoglea contains amoeboid mesenchyme cells (table 18.2).

Externally, anthozoans appear to show perfect radial symmetry. Internally, the mesenteries and other structures convey biradial symmetry to members of this class.

Sea anemones are solitary, frequently large, and colorful (figure 18.18*a*). Some attach to solid substrates, some burrow in soft substrates, and some live in symbiotic relationships (figure 18.18*b*). The polyp attaches to its substrate by a pedal disk (figure 18.19). An oral disk contains the mouth and hollow, oral tentacles. At one or both ends of the slitlike mouth is a siphonoglyph, which is a ciliated tract that moves water into the gastrovascular cavity to maintain the hydrostatic skeleton.

Mesenteries are arranged in pairs. Some attach at the body wall at their outer margin and to the pharynx along their inner margin. Other mesenteries attach to the body wall, but are free along their entire inner margin. Openings in mesenteries near the oral disk permit circulation of water between compartments set off by the mesenteries. The free lower edges of the mesenteries form a trilobed mesenterial filament. Mesenterial filaments bear cnidocytes, cilia that aid in water circulation, gland cells that secrete digestive enzymes, and absorptive cells that absorb products of digestion. Threadlike acontia at

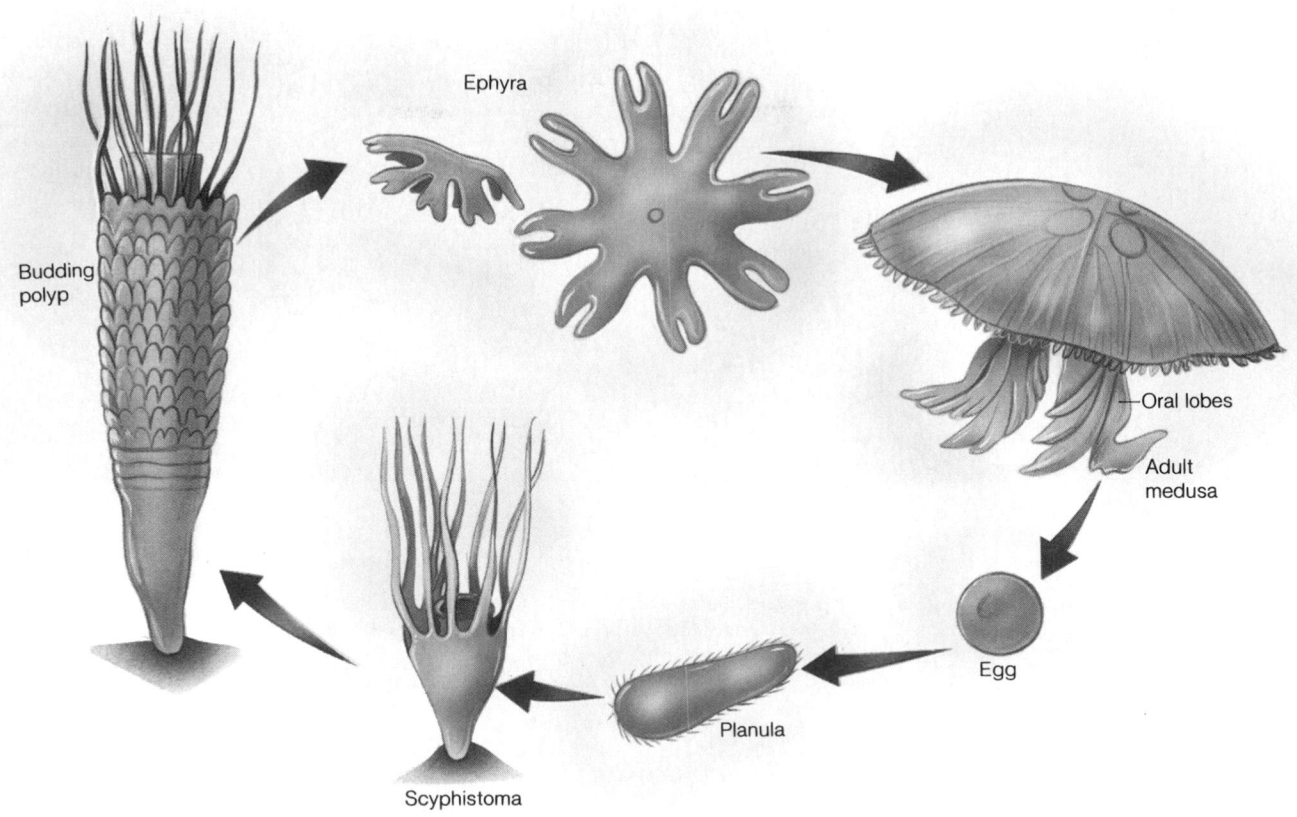

Figure 18.16

***Aurelia* Life History.** *Aurelia* is dioecious and, like all scyphozoans, the medusa predominates in the life history of the organism. The planula develops into a polyp called a scyphistoma, which produces young medusae, or ephyrae, by budding.

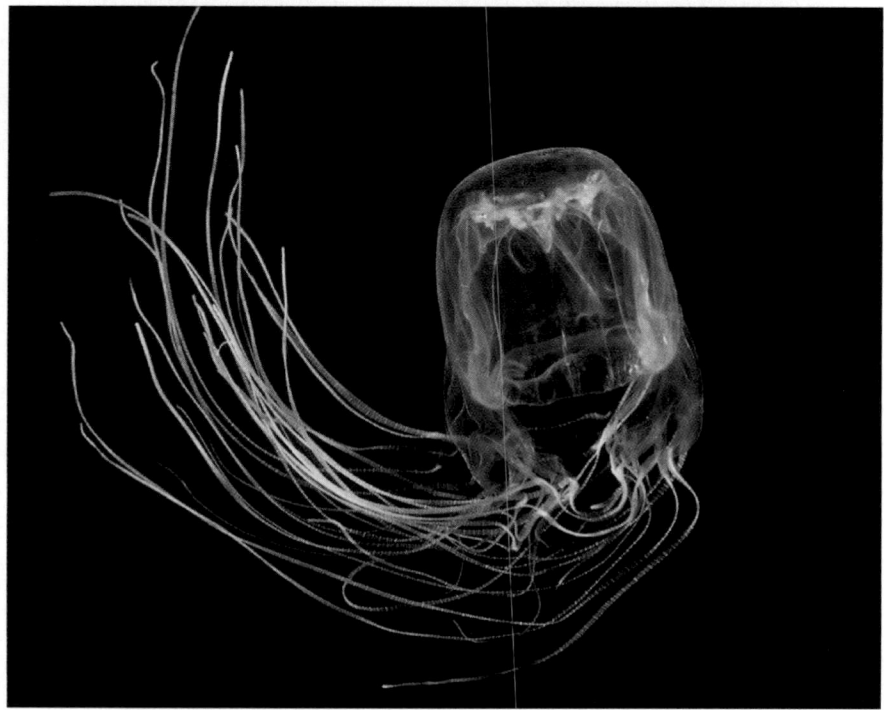

Figure 18.17

Class Cubozoa. The sea wasp, *Chironex fleckeri*. The medusa is cuboidal in shape; note the tentacles that hang from the corners of the bell. *Chironex fleckeri* has caused more human suffering and death off Australian coasts than the Portuguese man-of-war has in any of its home waters. Death from heart failure and shock is not likely unless one is repeatedly stung.

18.17

(a)

(b)

Figure 18.18

Representative Sea Anemones. (*a*) Giant sea anemone (*Anthopleura xanthogrammica*). (*b*) This sea anemone lives in a mutualistic relationship with a hermit crab (*Petrochirus diobenes*). Hermit crabs lack a heavily armored exoskeleton over much of their bodies and seek refuge in empty snail shells. When this crab outgrows its present home it will take its anemone with it to a new snail shell. This anemone, riding on the shell of the hermit crab, has a degree of mobility that is unusual for other anemones. The crab, in turn, is protected from predators by the anemone's nematocysts.

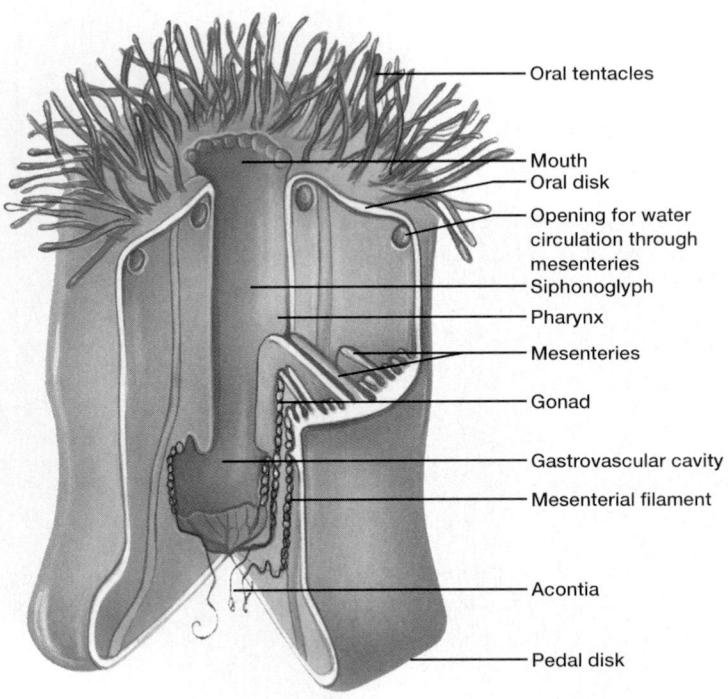

Oral tentacles

Mouth
Oral disk
Opening for water
circulation through
mesenteries
Siphonoglyph
Pharynx
Mesenteries
Gonad
Gastrovascular cavity
Mesenterial filament
Acontia
Pedal disk

Figure 18.19

Class Anthozoa. The structure of the anemone, *Metridium*.

the ends of mesenterial filaments bear cnidocytes. Acontia are used in subduing live prey in the gastrovascular cavity and can be extruded through small openings in the body wall or through the mouth when an anemone is threatened.

Muscle fibers are largely gastrodermal. Longitudinal muscle bands are restricted to the mesenteries. Circular muscles are in the gastrodermis of the column. When threatened, anemones contract their longitudinal fibers, allowing water to escape from the gastrovascular cavity. This action causes the oral end of the column to fold over the oral disk, and the anemone appears to collapse. The reestablishment of the hydrostatic skeleton depends on gradual uptake of water into the gastrovascular cavity via the siphonoglyphs.

Anemones are capable of limited locomotion. Movement is accomplished by gliding on their pedal disk, crawling on their side, and walking on their tentacles. When disturbed, some "swim" by thrashing their body or tentacles. Some anemones float using a gas bubble held within folds of the pedal disk.

Anemones feed on invertebrates and fishes. Tentacles capture prey and draw it toward the mouth. Radial muscle fibers in the mesenteries open the mouth to receive the food.

Both sexual and asexual reproduction are shown by anemones. In asexual reproduction, a piece of pedal disk may break away from the polyp and grow into a new individual in a process called pedal laceration. Alternatively, longitudinal or

BOX 18.2 | CORAL REEFS

Not all corals build coral reefs. Those that do not are called soft corals and often live at great depths in cold seawater. Stony corals are reef-building species. Coral reefs are built as calcium carbonate exoskeletons of one generation of stony corals are secreted on the exoskeletons of preceding generations. It requires millions of years for massive reefs, such as those found in warm, shallow waters of the Indian Ocean, the south Pacific Ocean, and the Caribbean Sea to develop (figure 1). Reef formation requires constantly warm (20°C), shallow water (less than 90 m), and constant salinity near 3.5%.

Most reef-building activities are the result of stony corals living in a mutualistic relationship (*see chapter 17*) with a group of dinoflagellate protists called **zooxanthellae** (*see figure 18.20*). Stony corals depend on photosynthetic activities of zooxanthellae as a principal source of carbohydrates. Predatory activities serve mainly as a source of protein for polyps. Zooxanthellae also promote exceptionally high rates of calcium deposition. As zooxanthellae carry on photosynthesis, they remove CO_2 from the environment of the polyp. Associated pH changes induce the precipitation of dissolved $CaCO_3$ as aragonite (coral limestone). It is thought that the 90 m depth limit for reef building corresponds to the limits to which sufficient light penetrates to support dinoflagellate photosynthesis.

Certain algae, called **coralline algae,** live outside the coral organisms and create their own calcium carbonate masses. These algae contribute to the reef by cementing together larger coral formations.

Reefs can extend hundreds of meters below the ocean's surface; however, only the upper and outer layer includes coral animals and algae. Most of the reef formation consists of exoskeletons of previous generations of stony corals. (The depth of the reef mass is evidence of changing oceanic levels during glacial periods and of the subsidence of the ocean floor.) In addition to the outer layer of photosynthetic and cnidarian life-forms, the reef supports a host of other organisms, including fishes, molluscs, arthropods, echinoderms, soft

FIGURE 1   **Coral Reefs.** A fringing reef surrounding an island off the eastern coast of Australia. Note the human-made shipping channel cut through the reef.

corals, and sponges. The exceptionally high productivity of reef communities depends on the ability of reef organisms to recycle nutrients rather than to lose them to the ocean floor.

There are three types of coral reefs. (1) Fringing reefs are built up from the sea bottom so close to a shoreline that no navigable channel exists between the shoreline and the reef. This reef formation frequently creates a narrow, shallow lagoon between the reef and the shore. Surging water creates frequent breaks and irregular channels through these reefs. (2) Barrier reefs are separated from shore by wide, deep channels. The Great Barrier Reef of Australia is 1,700 km long with a channel 20 to 50 m deep and up to 48 km wide. (The Great Barrier Reef actually consists of a number of different reef forms, including barrier reefs.) (3) Atolls are circular reefs that enclose a lagoon in the open ocean. One hypothesis regarding their origin, first described by Charles Darwin, is that atolls were built up around islands that later sank.

---

transverse fission may divide one individual into two, with missing parts being regenerated. Unlike other cnidarians, anemones may be either monoecious or dioecious. In monoecious species, male gametes mature earlier than female gametes so that self-fertilization does not occur. This is called **protandry** (Gr. *protos*, first + *andros*, male). Gonads occur in longitudinal bands behind mesenterial filaments. Fertilization may be external or within the gastrovascular cavity. Cleavage results in the

formation of a planula, which develops into a ciliated larva that settles to the substrate, attaches, and eventually forms the adult.

Other anthozoans are corals.   (8)   Stony corals are responsible for the formation of coral reefs (box 18.2) and, except for lacking siphonoglyphs, are similar to the anemones. Their common name derives from a cuplike calcium carbonate exoskeleton secreted around their base and the lower portion of

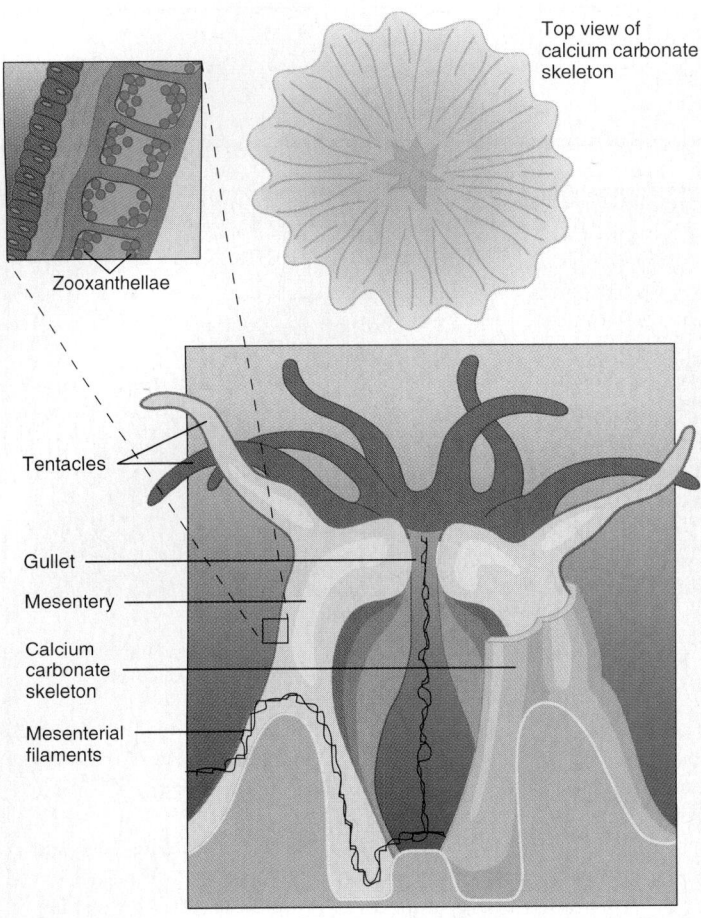

Top view of calcium carbonate skeleton

Zooxanthellae

Tentacles

Gullet

Mesentery

Calcium carbonate skeleton

Mesenterial filaments

Figure 18.20

Class Anthozoa. A stony coral polyp in its calcium carbonate skeleton (longitudinal section).

their column by epithelial cells (figure 18.20). When threatened, polyps retract into their protective exoskeletons. Sexual reproduction is similar to that of anemones, and asexual budding produces other members of the colony.

The colorful octacorallian corals are common in warm waters. They have eight pinnate (featherlike) tentacles, eight mesenteries, and one siphonoglyph. The body walls of members of a colony are connected, and mesenchyme cells secrete an internal skeleton of protein or calcium carbonate. Sea fans, sea pens, sea whips, red corals, and organ-pipe corals are members of this group (figure 18.21).

Stop and Ask Yourself

9. What hydrozoan has well-defined alternation of generations? What hydrozoan has reduced alternation of generations?

10. What kinds of sensory structures occur in cnidarians?

11. How do the following fit into the life history of a scyphozoan: scyphistoma? ephyra? planula?

12. What is protandry? How does it apply to the Anthozoa?

(a)

(b)

Figure 18.21

Representative Octacorallian Corals. (*a*) Fleshy sea pen (*Ptilosaurus gurneyi*). (*b*) Purple sea fan (*Gorgonia ventalina*).

Phylum Ctenophora

Animals in the phylum Ctenophora (ti-nof′er-ah) (Gr. *kteno*, comb + *phoros*, to bear) are called sea walnuts or comb jellies (table 18.3). There are approximately 90 described species, all of which are marine (figure 18.22*a*). Most ctenophorans have a spherical form, although several groups are flattened and/or elongate.

TABLE 18.3	CLASSIFICATION OF THE CTENOPHORA

Phylum Ctenophora (ti-nof'er-ah)
The animal phylum whose members are biradially symmetrical, diploblastic, usually ellipsoid or spherical in shape, possess colloblasts, and have meridionally arranged comb rows.
   Class Tentaculata (ten-tak'u-lata)
   With tentacles that may or may not be associated with sheaths, into which the tentacles can be retracted. *Pleurobranchia*.
   Class Nuda (nuda)
   Without tentacles; flattened; a highly branched gastrovascular cavity. *Beroe*.

(a)

Characteristics of the phylum Ctenophora include the following:

1. Diploblastic, tissue-level organization
2. Biradial symmetry
3. Gelatinous mesoglea located between the epidermal and gastrodermal tissue layers
4. Gastrovascular cavity
5. Nervous system in the form of a nerve net
6. Adhesive structures called colloblasts
7. Eight rows of ciliary bands, called comb rows, that are used in locomotion

Pleurobranchia has a spherical or ovoid, transparent body about 2 cm in diameter. It occurs in the colder waters of the Atlantic and Pacific Oceans (figure 18.22b). *Pleurobranchia*, like most ctenophorans, has eight meridional bands of cilia, called **comb rows,** that run between the oral and aboral poles. Comb rows are locomotor structures that are coordinated through a statocyst at the aboral pole. *Pleurobranchia* normally swims with its aboral pole oriented downward. Tilting is detected by the statocyst, and the comb rows adjust the animal's orientation. Two long, branched tentacles arise from pouches near the aboral pole. Tentacles possess contractile fibers that retract the tentacles and adhesive cells, called **colloblasts,** which are used for prey capture (figure 18.22c).

Ingestion occurs as the tentacles wipe the prey across the mouth. The mouth leads to a branched gastrovascular canal system. Some canals are blind; however, two small, anal canals open to the outside near the apical sense organ. Thus, unlike the cnidarians, ctenophores have an anal opening. Some undigested wastes are eliminated through these canals, and some are probably also eliminated through the mouth (*see figure 18.22b*).

Pleurobranchia is monoecious, as are all ctenophores. Two bandlike gonads are associated with the gastrodermis. One of these is an ovary and the other a testis. Gametes are shed through the mouth, fertilization is external, and a slightly flattened larva develops.

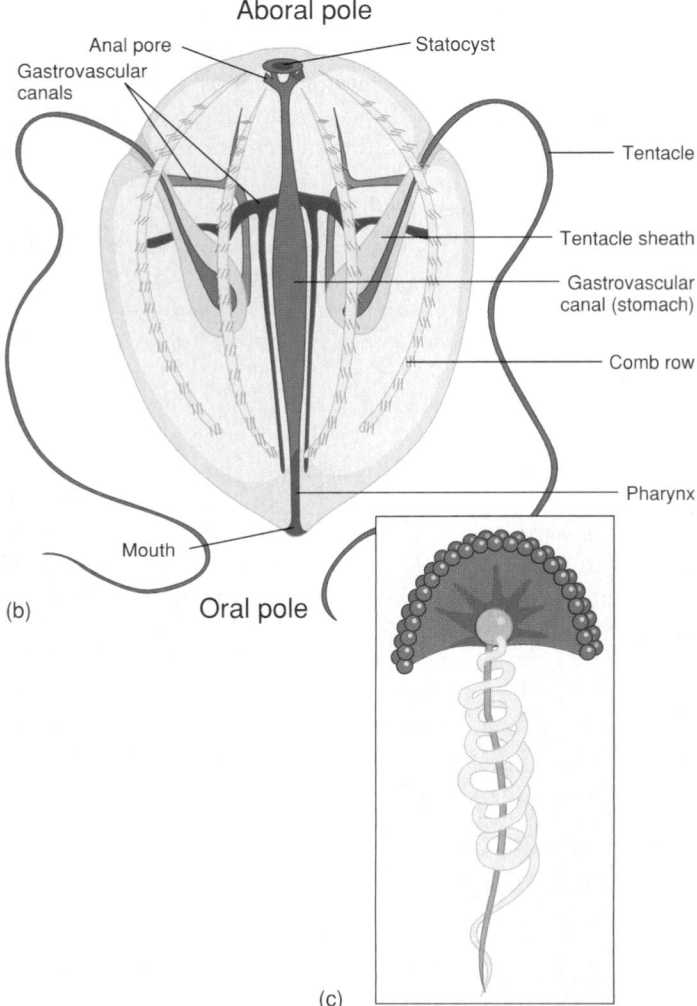

(b)

(c)

FIGURE 18.22

Phylum Ctenophora. (*a*) The ctenophore *Mnemiopsis*. Ctenophorans are well known for their bioluminescence. Light-producing cells are located in the walls of their digestive canals, which are located beneath comb rows. (*b*) The structure of *Pleurobranchia*. The animal usually swims with the oral end forward or upward. (*c*) Colloblasts consist of a hemispherical sticky head that is connected to the core of the tentacle by a straight filament. A contractile spiral filament coils around the straight filament. Straight and spiral filaments prevent struggling prey from escaping.

FURTHER PHYLOGENETIC CONSIDERATIONS

The evolutionary position of the phyla covered in this chapter is subject to debate. If the animal kingdom is polyphyletic, then all phyla could have had separate origins, although scientists who believe in multiple origins agree that the number of independent origins is probably small. Some zoologists believe it to be at least diphyletic, with the Porifera being derived separately from all other phyla. The similarity of poriferan choanocytes and choanoflagellate protists suggests evolutionary ties between these groups. Many other zoologists believe that the sponges have a common, although remote, ancestry with other animals. The presence of amoeboid and flagellated cells in sponges and higher animals is used to support this view. One thing that nearly everyone agrees upon, however, is that the Porifera are evolutionary "dead ends." They gave rise to no other animal phyla.

If two origins are assumed, the origin of the nonporiferan lineage is also debated. One interpretation is that the ancestral animal was derived from a radially symmetrical ancestor, which in turn may have been derived from a colonial flagellate similar in form to *Volvox* (*see figure 17.8*). If this is true, then the radiate phyla (Cnidaria and Ctenophora) could be closely related to that ancestral group. Other zoologists contend that bilateral symmetry is the ancestral body form, and a bilateral ancestor gave rise to both the radiate phyla and bilateral phyla. In this interpretation, the radiate phyla are further removed from the base of the evolutionary tree.

The probable evolutionary relationships of the cnidarian classes are shown in figure 18.23. The classical interpretation is that primitive Hydrozoa were the ancestral radial animals, and that the medusoid body form is the primitive body form. This ancestry is suggested by the fact that the medusa is the adult body form in the Hydrozoa, and that the medusa is the only body form present in some trachyline hydrozoans. The polyp may have evolved secondarily as a larval stage. In the evolution of the other three orders, septa appeared—dividing the gastrovascular cavity—and gonads became endodermal in origin. The Scyphozoa and Cubozoa are distinguished from the Anthozoa by the evolutionary reduction of the polyp stage in the former classes and the loss of the medusa stage in the latter class. The Scyphozoa and Cubozoa are distinguished from each other by budding of the polyp (Scyphozoa) and the cuboidal shape of the medusa (Cubozoa).

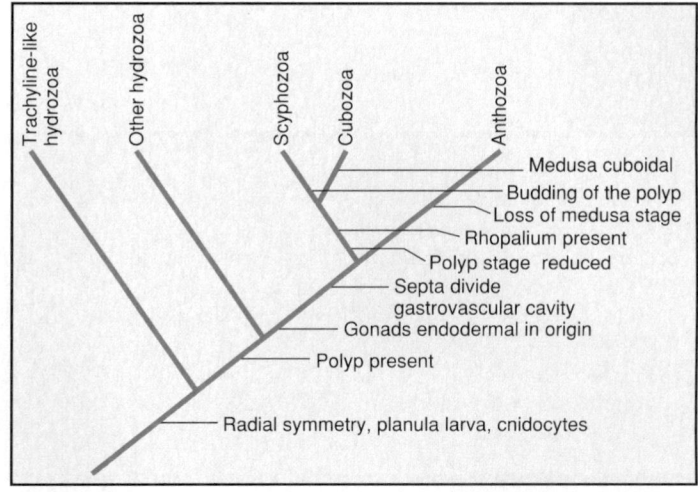

FIGURE 18.23

A Cladogram Showing Cnidarian Taxonomy. Selected synapomorphic characters are shown. Hydrozoans are believed by most zoologists to be ancestral to other cnidarians.

The relationships of the Ctenophora to any other group of animals are uncertain. The Ctenophora and Cnidaria share important characteristics such as radial (biradial) symmetry, diploblastic organization, nerve nets, and gastrovascular cavities. In spite of these similarities, differences in adult body forms and embryological development make it very difficult to derive the Ctenophora from any group of cnidarians. Relationships between the Cnidaria and Ctenophora are probably very distant.

Stop and Ask Yourself

13. What characteristics are shared by the Ctenophora and the Cnidaria?

14. What are colloblasts?

15. How are a statocyst and comb rows used by ctenophores to maintain an upright position in the water?

16. The sponges are considered evolutionary "dead ends." Why?

SUMMARY

1. Although the origin of multicellularity in animals is unknown, the colonial hypothesis and the syncytial hypothesis are explanations of how animals could have arisen. Whether the animal kingdom had origins in one, two, or many ancestors is debated.

2. Animals in the phylum Porifera are the sponges. Cells of sponges are specialized to perform functions, such as creating water currents, filtering food, producing gametes, forming skeletal elements, and lining the sponge body wall.

3. Sponges circulate water through their bodies to bring in food and oxygen and to carry away wastes and reproductive products. Evolution has resulted in most sponges having complex canal systems and large water-circulating capabilities.

4. Members of the phylum Cnidaria are radially or biradially symmetrical and possess diploblastic, tissue-level organization. Cells are specialized for food gathering, defense, contraction, coordination, digestion, and absorption.

5. The Hydrozoa differ from members of other cnidarian classes in having no nematocysts in their gastrodermis, ectodermal gametes, and mesoglea without mesenchyme cells. Most hydrozoans have well-developed polyp and medusa stages.

6. The class Scyphozoa contains the jellyfish. The polyp stage of scyphozoans is usually very small.

7. Members of the class Cubozoa are found in warm, tropical waters. Some possess dangerous nematocysts.

8. The Anthozoa lack the medusa stage. They include sea anemones and corals.

9. Members of the phylum Ctenophora are biradially symmetrical and diploblastic. They are characterized by bands of cilia, called comb rows.

10. Whether or not the Porifera had a common origin with other animals is debated. The Cnidaria and Ctenophora are distantly related phyla. Within the Cnidaria, the ancient hydrozoans are believed to be the stock from which modern hydrozoans and other cnidarians evolved.

SELECTED KEY TERMS

choanocytes (*p. 265*)

cnidocytes (*p. 270*)

epidermis (*p. 270*)

gastrodermis (*p. 270*)

gastrovascular cavity (*p. 271*)

hydrostatic skeleton (*p. 272*)

medusa (*p. 271*)

mesoglea (*p. 270*)

polyp (*p. 271*)

statocyst (*p. 273*)

CRITICAL THINKING QUESTIONS

1. If most animals are derived from a single ancestral stock, and if that ancestral stock was radially symmetrical, would the "colonial hypothesis" or the "syncytial hypothesis" of animal origins be more attractive to you? Explain.

2. Colonies were defined in chapter 16 as "loose associations of independent cells." Why are sponges considered to have surpassed that level of organization? In your answer, compare a sponge with a colonial protist like *Volvox*.

3. Evolution is often viewed as a continuous process of increasing diversification of body forms and species. What evidence is there in early animal evolution that contradicts this viewpoint?

4. Most sponges and sea anemones are monoecious, yet sexual reproduction usually occurs between separate individuals. Why is this advantageous for these animals? What ensures that self-fertilization does not occur in sea anemones?

5. Do you think that the polyp stage or the medusa stage predominated in the ancestral cnidarian? Support your answer. What implications does your answer have when interpreting the evolutionary relationships among the cnidarian classes?

SOME LESSER KNOWN INVERTEBRATES: MESOZOA AND PLACOZOA

TWO MULTICELLULAR PHYLA OF UNCERTAIN AFFINITIES

The phyla Mesozoa and Placozoa are small groups of animals that most of us will never encounter outside of textbook descriptions and illustrations. Even though these phyla are of uncertain evolutionary affinities, the placozoan body form is considered by some zoologists to be similar to that present in (at least one group of) the first animals.

PHYLUM MESOZOA

There are approximately 100 species in the phylum Mesozoa (mez'o-zo''ah) (Gr. *mesos* middle + *zoin,* animal). As larvae and/or adults, mesozoans are parasites of other marine invertebrates (brittle stars, bivalved molluscs, and cephalopod molluscs). They have two layers: an inner layer of reproductive cells and an outer layer of ciliated cells. Mesozoans are dioecious (sexes are separate) with complex life histories involving both sexual and asexual cycles. Some zoologists now believe that the mesozoans actually represent two phyla, Orthonectida and Dicyemedia (figure 1).

PHYLUM PLACOZOA

Members of the phylum Placozoa (plak'o-zo''ah) (Gr. *plak,* flattened + *zoin,* animal) are small (2 to 5 mm) marine organisms. The phylum's one species, *Tricoplax adherans,* was first described in the 1800s, largely forgotten, and then rediscovered in the 1960s on algae from the Red Sea. *Tricoplax* consists of two epithelial layers with fiber cells (possibly locomotor in function) between them. The upper epithelium consists of flagellated cells and transparent spheres of fatty material. The lower epithelium consists of flagellated cylinder cells and gland cells of nutritive function (figure 2). When *Tricoplax* feeds, it forms a temporary, ventral digestive cavity by raising its body off the substrate and secreting enzymes into the cavity. The similarity of this animal to a hypothetical ancestor proposed in the syncytial hypothesis of animal origins causes some zoologists to wonder if this group could be closely related to the first animals.

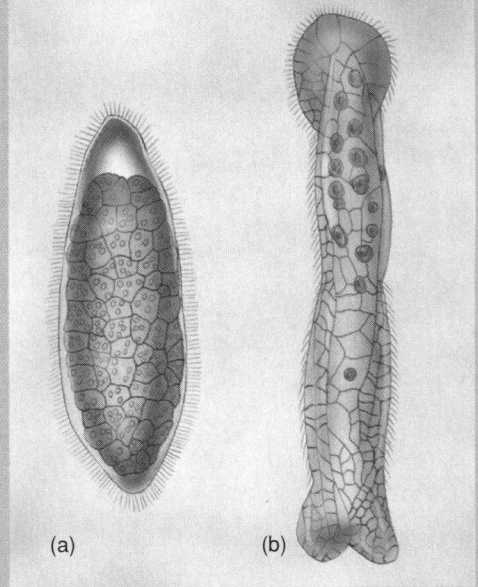

FIGURE 1
Phylum Mesozoa.
(*a*) *Rhopalura,* an orthnectid parasite of clams.
(*b*) *Pseudicyema,* a dicyemid parasite of cuttlefish.

(a)   (b)

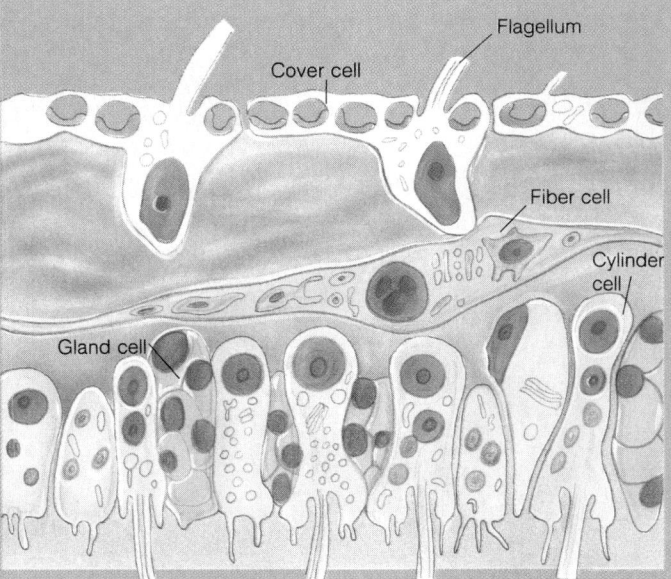

Flagellum
Cover cell
Fiber cell
Cylinder cell
Gland cell

FIGURE 2   **Phylum Placozoa.** *Tricoplax adherans* consists of two epithelial layers with fiber cells sandwiched in between those layers.

THE TRIPLOBLASTIC, ACOELOMATE BODY PLAN

Outline

Concepts

1. The acoelomates are represented by the phyla Platyhelminthes and Nemertea. These phyla are phylogenetically important because they are transitional between radial animals and the more complex bilateral animals. Three important characteristics appeared initially in this group: bilateral symmetry, a true mesoderm that gives rise to muscles and other organs, and a nervous system with a primitive brain and nerve cords.
2. Because the mesodermal mass completely fills the area between the outer epidermis and digestive tract, these animals lack a body cavity; hence the name, acoelomates.
3. The phylum Platyhelminthes is a large group of dorsoventrally flattened animals commonly called the flatworms.
4. Members of the class Turbellaria are mostly free living. Representatives of the classes Monogenea, Trematoda, and Cestoidea are parasitic.
5. The phylum Nemertea (proboscis or ribbon worms) contains predominantly marine, elongate, burrowing worms that possess digestive and vascular systems.
6. Acoelomates may have evolved from a primitive organism resembling a modern turbellarian.

Would You Like to Know:

1. what sexual maturity in a larval body form is called? (*p. 288*)
2. why monoecious animals exchange sperm? (*p. 292*)
3. how monogenetic flukes got their name? (*p. 293*)
4. how parasites called "flukes" got their name? (*p. 293*)
5. why *Fasciola hepatica* is called the sheep liver fluke? (*p. 295*)
6. how 10 m long tapeworms feed, even though they lack a mouth and digestive tract? (*p. 298*)

These and other useful questions will be answered in this chapter.

This chapter contains evolutionary concepts, which are set off in this font.

EVOLUTIONARY PERSPECTIVE

Members of the phyla Platyhelminthes and Nemertea are the first animals to exhibit bilateral symmetry and a body organization more complex than that of the cnidarians. All the animals covered in this chapter are triploblastic (have three primary germ layers), acoelomate (without a coelom), and classified into two phyla: the phylum Platyhelminthes includes the flatworms (figure 19.1) that are either free living (e.g., turbellarians) or parasitic (e.g., flukes and tapeworms), and the phylum Nemertea includes a small group of elongate, unsegmented, soft-bodied worms that are mostly marine and free living.

The evolutionary relationship of the major phylum in this chapter (Platyhelminthes) to other phyla is controversial. One interpretation is that the triploblastic acoelomate body plan is an important intermediate between the radial, diploblastic plan and the triploblastic coelomate plan. The flatworms would thus represent an evolutionary side branch from a hypothetical triploblastic acoelomate ancestor. Evolution from radial ancestors could have involved a larval stage that became sexually mature in its larval body form. ❶ Sexual maturity in a larval body form is called **paedomorphosis** (Gr. *pais*, child + *morphe*, form) and has occurred many times in animal evolution.

Other zoologists envision the evolution of the triploblastic, acoelomate plan from a bilateral ancestor. Primitive acoelomates, similar to flatworms, would have preceded the radiate phyla, and the radial, diploblastic plan would be secondarily derived.

The recent discovery of a small group of worms (Lobatocercebridae, Annelida) that shows both flatworm and annelid characteristics (annelids are a group of coelomate animals, such as the earthworm) suggests that the acoelomate body plan is a secondary characteristic. In this case, the flatworms would represent a side branch that resulted from the loss of a body cavity (figure 19.2).

FIGURE 19.1

Flatworms: Animals with Primitive Organ Systems. The marine tiger flatworm (*Prostheceraeus bellustriatus*) shows brilliant markings and bilateral symmetry. This flatworm inhabits the warm shallow waters around the Hawaiian Islands.

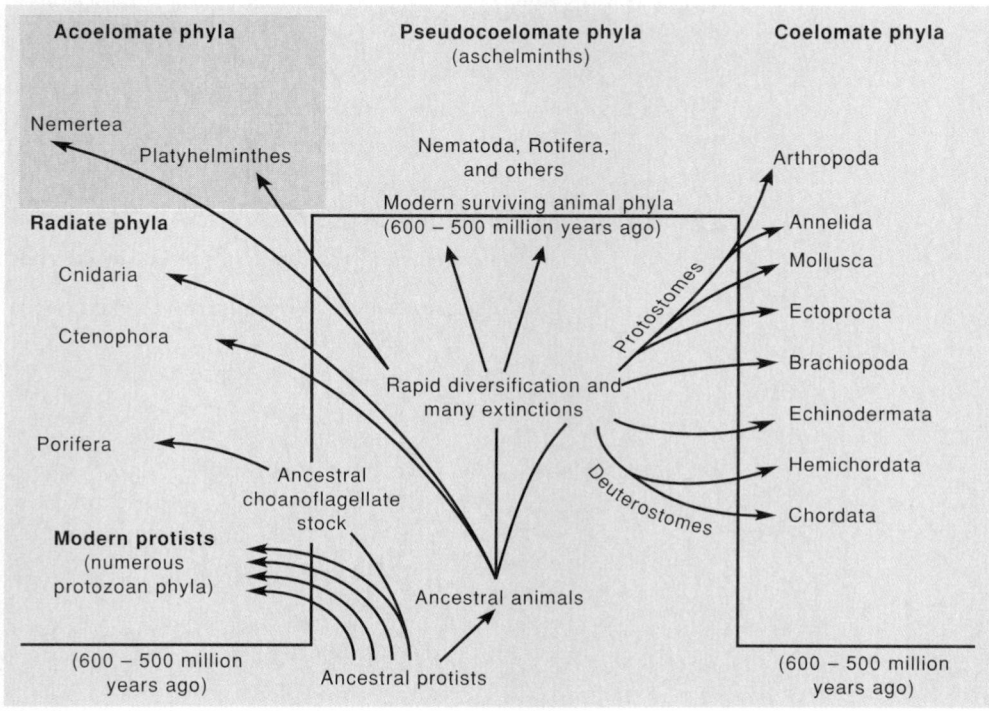

FIGURE 19.2

Acoelomate Phyla. A generalized evolutionary tree depicting the major events and possible lines of descent for the acoelomates (shaded in orange).

19.2

PHYLUM PLATYHELMINTHES

There are over 20,000 animal species in the phylum Platyhelminthes (plat″e-hel-min′thez) (Gr. *platys*, flat + *helmins*, worm). Flatworms range in adult size from 1 mm or less to several meters in length. Their mesodermally derived tissues include a loose tissue called **parenchyma** (Gr. *parenck*, anything poured in beside) that fills spaces between other more specialized tissues, organs, and the body wall. Depending on the species, parenchyma may function in providing skeletal support, nutrient storage, motility, reserves of regenerative cells, transport of materials, structural interactions with other tissues, modifiable tissue for morphogenesis, oxygen storage, and perhaps other functions that have yet to be determined. This is the first phylum covered that has an organ system level of organization—a significant evolutionary advancement over the tissue level of organization. The phylum is divided into four classes (table 19.1): (1) the Turbellaria consists of mostly free-living flatworms, whereas the (2) Monogenea, (3) Trematoda, and (4) Cestoidea contain solely parasitic species. Characteristics of the phylum Platyhelminthes include the following:

1. Usually flattened dorsoventrally, triploblastic, acoelomate, bilaterally symmetrical
2. Unsegmented worms (members of the class Cestoidea are strobilated)
3. Incomplete gut usually present; gut absent in Cestoidea
4. Somewhat cephalized, with an anterior cerebral ganglion and usually longitudinal nerve cords
5. Protonephridia as excretory/osmoregulatory structures
6. Hermaphroditic; complex reproductive systems

CLASS TURBELLARIA: THE FREE-LIVING FLATWORMS

Members of the class Turbellaria (tur′bel-lar′e-a) (L. *turbellae*, a commotion + *aria*, like) are mostly free-living bottom dwellers in freshwater and marine environments where they crawl on stones, sand, or vegetation. Turbellarians were named for the turbulence created in the water by the beating of their cilia. Over 300 species have been described. Turbellarians feed as predators and scavengers. The few terrestrial turbellarians known live in the humid tropics and subtropics. Although most turbellarians are less than 10 mm long, the terrestrial, tropical ones may reach 60 cm in length. Coloration is mostly in shades of black, brown, and gray, although some groups display brightly colored patterns.

Body Wall

As in the Cnidaria, the ectodermal derivatives include an epidermis that is in direct contact with the environment (figure 19.3). Some epidermal cells are ciliated and others contain microvilli. A basement membrane of connective tissue separates the epidermis from mesodermally derived tissues. An outer layer of circular muscle and an inner layer of longitudinal muscle lie

TABLE 19.1	CLASSIFICATION OF THE PLATYHELMINTHES

Phylum Platyhelminthes (plat″e-hel-min′thez)
Flatworms; bilateral acoelomates.
 Class Turbellaria (tur′bel-lar′e-a)
 Mostly free living and aquatic; external surface usually ciliated; predaceous; possess rhabdites, protrusible proboscis, frontal glands, and many mucous glands; mostly hermaphroditic. *Convoluta, Notoplana, Dugesia.*
 Class Monogenea (mon′oh-gen′ee-uh)
 Monogenetic flukes; mostly ectoparasites on vertebrates (usually on fishes; occasionally on turtles, frogs, copepods, squids); one life-cycle form in only one host; bear opisthaptor. *Disocotyle, Gyrodactylus, Polystoma.*
 Class Trematoda (trem′a-to′da)
 Trematodes; all are parasitic; several holdfast devices present; have complicated life cycles involving both sexual and asexual reproduction.
  Subclass Aspidogastrea
  Mostly endoparasites of molluscs; possess large opisthaptor; most lack an oral sucker. *Aspidogaster, Cotylaspis, Multicotyl.*
  Subclass Digenea
  Adults endoparasites in vertebrates; at least two different life-cycle forms in two or more hosts; have oral sucker and acetabulum. *Schistosoma, Fasciola, Clonorchis.*
 Class Cestoidea (ses-toid′da)
 All parasitic with no digestive tract; have great reproductive potential; tapeworms.
  Subclass Cestodaria
  Body not subdivided into proglottids; larva in crustaceans, adult in fishes. *Amphilina, Gyrocotyle.*
  Subclass Eucestoda
  True tapeworms; body divided into scolex, neck, and strobila; strobila composed of many proglottids; both male and female reproductive systems in each proglottid; adults in digestive tract of vertebrates. *Protocephalus, Taenia, Echinococcus, Taeniarhynchus, Diphyllobothrium.*

beneath the basement membrane. Other muscles are located dorsoventrally and obliquely between the dorsal and ventral surfaces. Between the longitudinal muscles and the gastrodermis are the loosely organized parenchymal cells.

The innermost tissue layer is the endodermally derived gastrodermis. It consists of a single layer of cells that comprise the digestive cavity. The gastrodermis secretes enzymes that aid in digestion, and it absorbs the end products of digestion.

On the ventral surface of the body wall there are several types of glandular cells that are of epidermal origin. **Rhabdites** are rodlike cells that swell and form a protective mucous sheath around the body. **Adhesive glands** open to the epithelial surface and produce a chemical that attaches part of the turbellarian to a substrate. **Releaser glands** secrete a chemical that dissolves the attachment as needed.

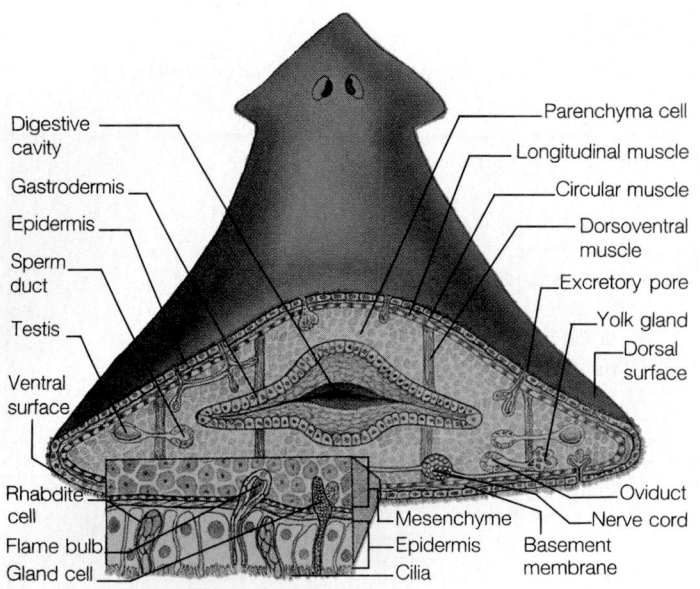

FIGURE 19.3

Phylum Platyhelminthes: Class Turbellaria. Cross section through the body wall of a sexually mature turbellarian (the planarian, *Dugesia*) showing the relationships of the various body structures.

Locomotion

Turbellarians are the first group of bilaterally symmetrical animals. Recall that bilateral symmetry is usually characteristic of animals that have an active life-style. Turbellarians are primarily bottom dwellers that glide over the substrate. They move using cilia and muscular undulations. As they move, turbellarians lay down a sheet of mucus that aids in adhesion and helps the cilia gain traction. The densely ciliated ventral surface and the flattened body of turbellarians enhance the effectiveness of this locomotion.

Digestion and Nutrition

Some marine turbellarians lack the digestive cavity (figure 19.4*a*) that is characteristic of other turbellarians. This blind cavity varies from a simple, unbranched chamber (figure 19.4*b*), to a highly branched system of digestive tubes (figure 19.4*d,e*). Others have digestive tracts that are lobed or diverticulated (figure 19.4*c*). From an evolutionary perspective, highly branched digestive systems are an advancement that results in more gastrodermis closer to the sites of digestion and absorption, reducing the distance the nutrients must diffuse. This aspect of digestive tract structure is especially important in some of the larger turbellarians and partially compensates for the absence of a circulatory system.

The turbellarian pharynx functions as an ingestive organ. It varies in structure from a simple, ciliated tube to a complex organ developed from the folding of muscle layers. In the latter, the free end of the tube lies in a pharyngeal sheath and can project out of the mouth when feeding (figure 19.5).

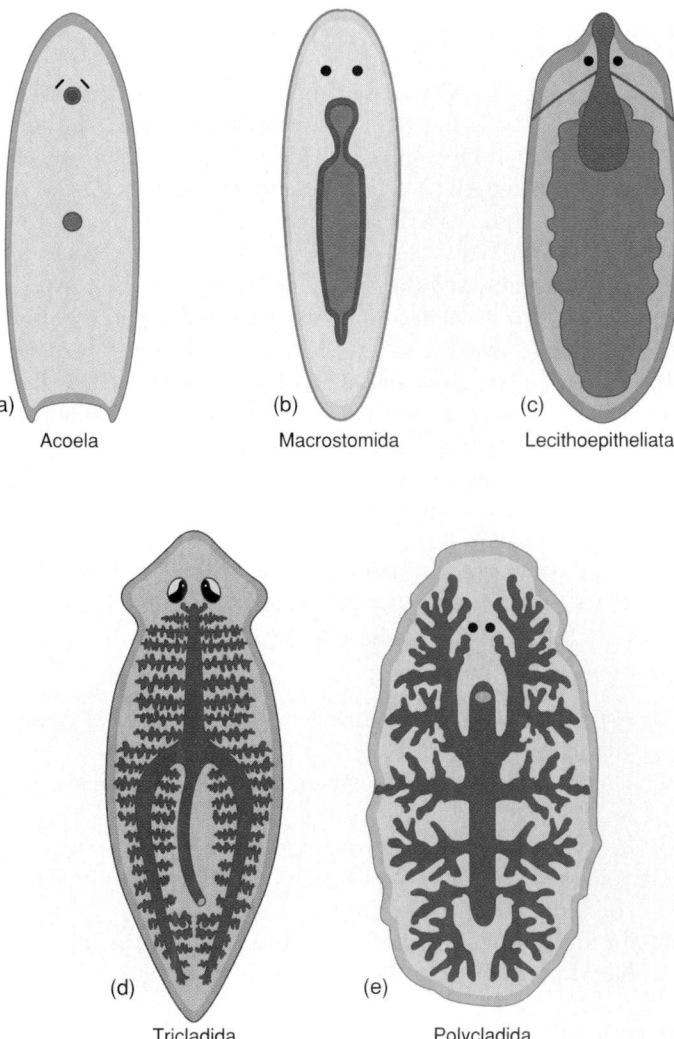

FIGURE 19.4

Digestive Systems in Some Orders of Turbellarians. (*a*) No pharynx and digestive cavity. (*b*) A simple pharynx and straight digestive cavity. (*c*) A simple pharynx and unbranched digestive cavity. (*d*) A branched digestive cavity. (*e*) An extensively branched digestive cavity in which the branches reach almost all parts of the body.

Most turbellarians, such as the common planarian, are carnivores and feed on small, live invertebrates or scavenge on larger, dead animals; some are herbivores and feed on algae that they scrape from rocks. They can detect the presence of food from a considerable distance by means of sensory cells (chemoreceptors) located on their heads.

Digestion of the food is partially extracellular. Enzymes are secreted from pharyngeal glands that help break down food into smaller units that can be taken into the pharynx. Once inside the digestive cavity, small units of food are engulfed by phagocytic cells that line it, and digestion is completed in intracellular vesicles.

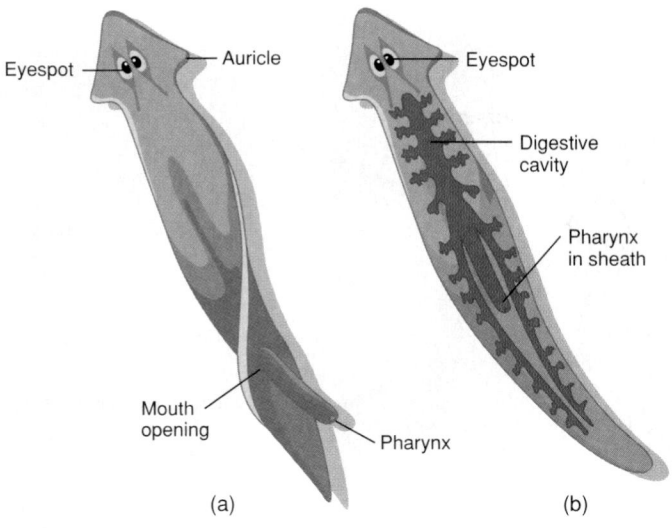

(a)   (b)

FIGURE 19.5

The Turbellarian Pharynx. (*a*) A planarian turbellarian with its pharynx extended in the feeding position, and (*b*) retracted within the pharyngeal sheath.

Exchanges with the Environment

There are no respiratory organs in the turbellarians; thus, respiratory gases (CO_2 and O_2) are exchanged by diffusion through the body wall. Most metabolic wastes (e.g., ammonia) are also removed by diffusion through the body wall.

In marine environments, invertebrates are often in an osmotic equilibrium with their environment. In fresh water, invertebrates are hypertonic to their aquatic environment and thus must regulate the osmotic concentration (water and ions) of their body tissues. It is the evolution of osmoregulatory structures in the form of protonephridia that enabled turbellarians to invade fresh water.

Protonephridia (Gr. *protos*, first + *nephros*, kidney; s. protonephridium) are a network of fine tubules that run the length of the turbellarian, along each of its sides (figure 19.6a). Numerous, fine side branches of the tubules originate in the parenchyma as tiny enlargements called **flame cells** (figure 19.6b). Flame cells (so named because in the living organism, they resemble a candle flame) have numerous cilia that project into the lumen of the tubule. The tubule wall surrounding the flame cell is perforated by slitlike fenestrations (openings). The beating of the cilia drives fluid down the tubule, creating a negative pressure in the tubule. As a result, fluid from the surrounding tissue is sucked through the fenestrations into the tubule. The tubules eventually merge and open to the outside of the body wall through a minute opening called a **nephridiopore.**

Nervous System and Sense Organs

The most primitive type of flatworm nervous system, found in worms in the order Acoela (e.g., *Convoluta* spp.), is a subepidermal nerve plexus (figure 19.7a). This plexus resembles the nerve net of cnidarians. A statocyst in the anterior end functions as a

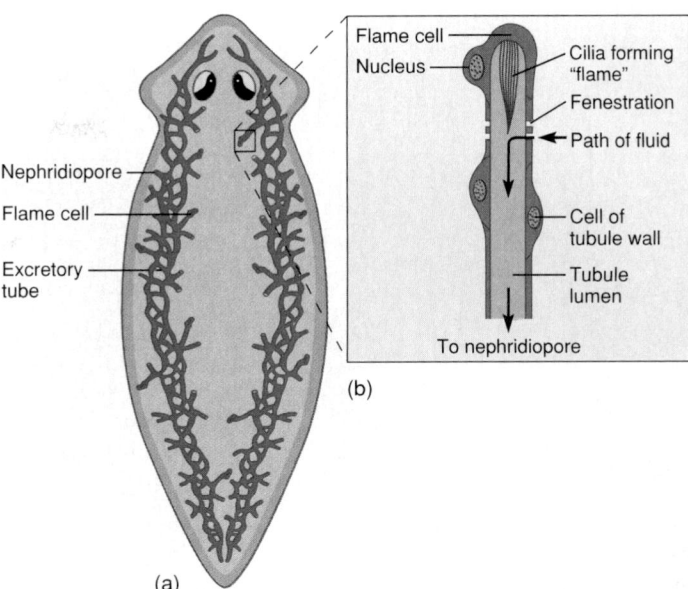

(a)

FIGURE 19.6

Protonephridial System in a Turbellarian. (*a*) The protonephridial system lies in the parenchyma and consists of a network of fine tubules that run the length of the animal on each side and open to the surface by minute nephridiopores. (*b*) Numerous fine, side branches from the tubules originate in the parenchyma in enlargements called flame cells. Small arrows indicate the direction of fluid movement.

mechanoreceptor (a receptor that is excited by pressure) that detects the position of the turbellarian's body in reference to the direction of gravity. Some turbellarians have a more centralized nerve net with cerebral ganglia (figure 19.7b). The nervous system of most other turbellarians, such as the planarian *Dugesia*, consists of a subepidermal nerve net and several pairs of long nerve cords (figure 19.7c). The nerve cords are connected by lateral branches called commissures (points of union). Nerve cords and their commissures give a ladderlike appearance to the turbellarian nervous system. These neurons are organized into sensory (going to the primitive brain), motor (going away from the primitive brain), and association (connecting) types—an important evolutionary advance with respect to the nervous system. Anteriorly, the nervous tissue is concentrated into a pair of cerebral ganglia (s., ganglion) that is called a primitive brain.

Turbellarians are capable of responding to a variety of stimuli in their external environment. Many tactile and sensory cells are distributed over the body. These cells detect touch, water currents, and chemicals. **Auricles** (sensory lobes) may project from the side of the head (figure 19.7c). Chemoreceptors that aid in the location of food are especially dense in these auricles.

Most turbellarians have two simple eyespots called **ocelli** (s., ocellus; *see figure 19.5*). These ocelli are used in orienting the animal with respect to the direction of light. (Most turbellarians are negatively phototropic and move away from light.) Each ocellus consists of a cuplike depression lined with black

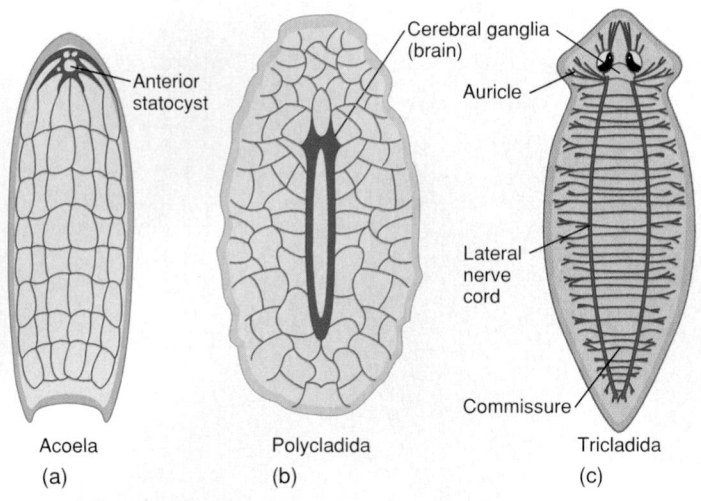

Figure 19.7

Nervous Systems in Three Orders of Turbellaria. (*a*) *Convoluta* has a nerve net with a statocyst. (*b*) The nerve net in a turbellarian in the order Polycladida has cerebral ganglia and two lateral nerve cords. (*c*) The cerebral ganglia and nerve cords in the planarian, *Dugesia*.

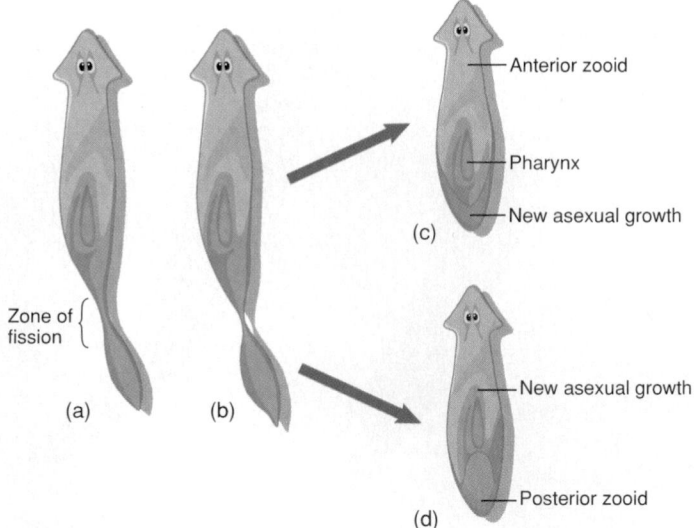

Figure 19.8

Asexual Reproduction in a Turbellarian. (*a*) Just before division and (*b*) just after. The posterior zooid will soon develop a head, pharynx, and other structures. (*c,d*) Later development.

pigment. Photoreceptor nerve endings in the cup are part of the neurons that leave the eye and connect with a cerebral ganglion.

Reproduction and Development

Many turbellarians reproduce asexually by transverse fission. Fission usually begins as a constriction behind the pharynx (figure 19.8). The two (or more) animals that result from fission are called **zooids** (Gr., *zoon*, living being or animal), and they will regenerate missing parts after separating from each other. Sometimes, the zooids remain attached until they have attained a fairly complete degree of development, at which time they detach as independent individuals.

Turbellarians are monoecious, and reproductive systems arise from the mesodermal tissues in the parenchyma. Numerous paired testes lie along each side of the worm and are the site of sperm production. Sperm ducts (vas deferens) lead to a seminal vesicle (a sperm storage organ) and a protrusible penis (figure 19.9). The penis projects into a genital chamber.

The female system has one to many pairs of ovaries. Oviducts lead from the ovaries to the genital chamber, which opens to the outside through the genital pore.

② Even though turbellarians are monoecious, reciprocal sperm exchange between two animals is usually the rule. This cross-fertilization ensures greater genetic diversity than does self-fertilization. During cross-fertilization, the penis of each individual is inserted into the copulatory sac of the partner. After copulation, sperm move from the copulatory sac to the genital chamber and then through the oviducts to the ovaries, where fertilization occurs. Yolk may either be directly incorporated into the egg during egg formation, or yolk cells may be laid around the zygote as it passes down the female reproductive tract past the vitellaria (yolk glands).

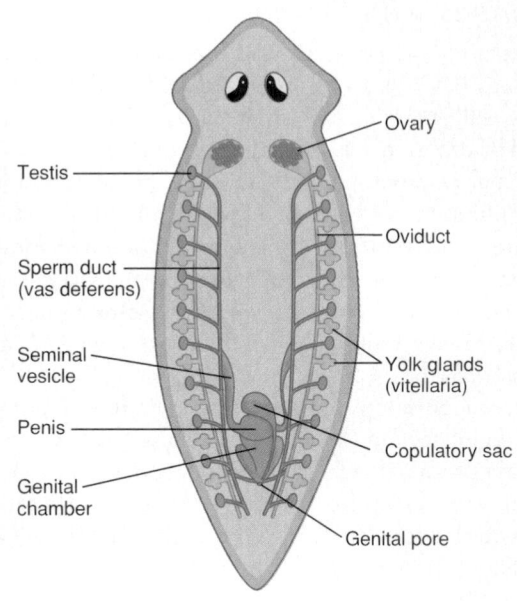

Figure 19.9

Triclad Turbellarian Reproductive System. Note the presence of both male and female reproductive organs in a single individual.

Eggs are laid with or without a gellike mass. In many turbellarians, eggs are enclosed in a hard capsule called a **cocoon** (L., *coccum*, eggshell). These cocoons are attached to the substrate by a stalk and contain several embryos per capsule. Two kinds of capsules are laid. Summer capsules hatch in 2 to 3 weeks, and immature animals emerge. Autumn capsules have thick walls that can resist freezing and drying, and hatch after overwintering.

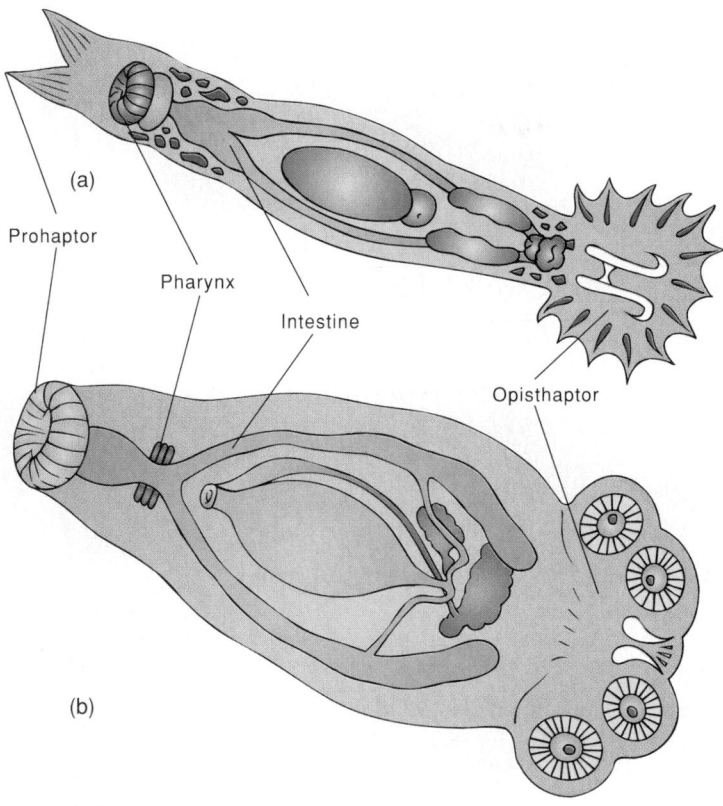

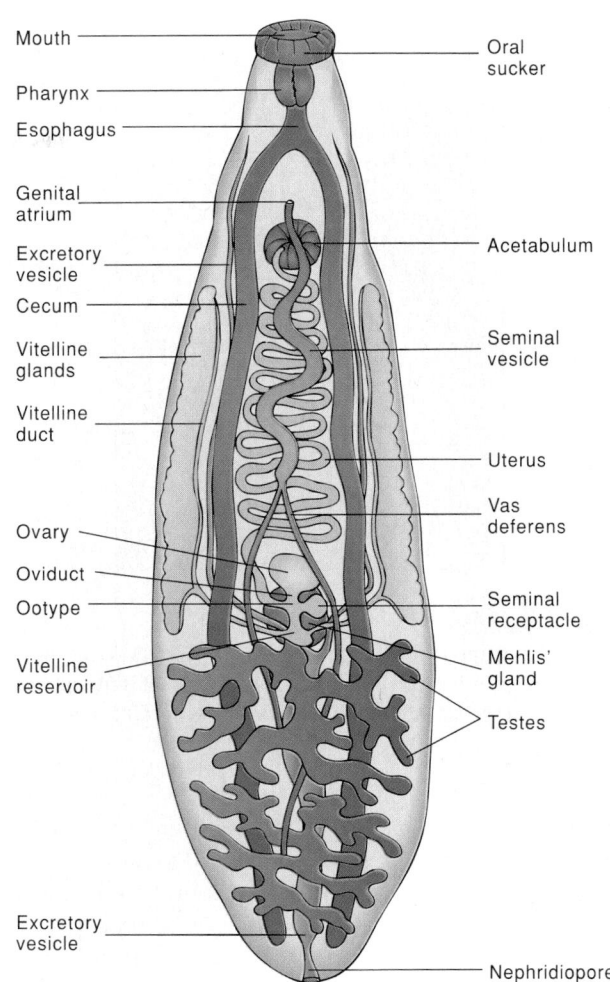

Figure 19.10
Class Monogenea. Drawing of two monogeneid trematodes.
(a) *Gyrodactylus* and (b) *Sphyranura*. Note the opisthaptors by which these ectoparasites cling to the gills of their fish host.

Development of most turbellarians is direct—a gradual series of changes transform the embryos into adults. A few turbellarians have a free-swimming stage called a **Muller's larva.** It has ciliated arms that it uses in feeding and locomotion. The larva eventually settles to the substrate and develops into a young turbellarian.

Stop and Ask Yourself

1. What are several general characteristics of the phylum Plathyhelminthes?
2. What is a cocoon? Muller's larva? Zooid?
3. How does a turbellarian move? Feed? Reproduce?

Class Monogenea

Monogenetic flukes are so named because there is but one generation in their life cycle; that is, one adult develops from one egg. Monogeneans are mostly external parasites (ectoparasites) of freshwater and marine fishes, where they attach to the gill filaments and feed on epithelial cells, mucus, or blood. Attachment is facilitated by a large, posterior opisthaptor (figure 19.10).

Figure 19.11
A Generalized Fluke (Digenetic trematode). Note the large percentage of the body devoted to reproduction. The Mehlis' gland is a conspicuous feature of the female reproductive tract; its function in trematodes is uncertain.

When eggs are produced, they are released by the adult and contain one or more threads. These threads are sticky and attach the eggs to the fish gill. Eventually, a ciliated larva called an **oncomiracidium** hatches from the egg and swims to another host fish, where it attaches by its opisthaptor and develops into an adult.

Class Trematoda

The approximately 8,000 species of parasitic flatworms in the class Trematoda (trem'a-to'da) (Gr. *trematodes*, perforated form) are collectively called **flukes,** a word that describes their wide, flat shape. Almost all adult flukes are parasites of vertebrates, whereas immature stages may be found in vertebrates, invertebrates, or encysted on plants. Many species are of great economic and medical importance.

Most flukes are flat and oval to elongate and range from less than 1 mm to 6 cm in length (figure 19.11). They feed on

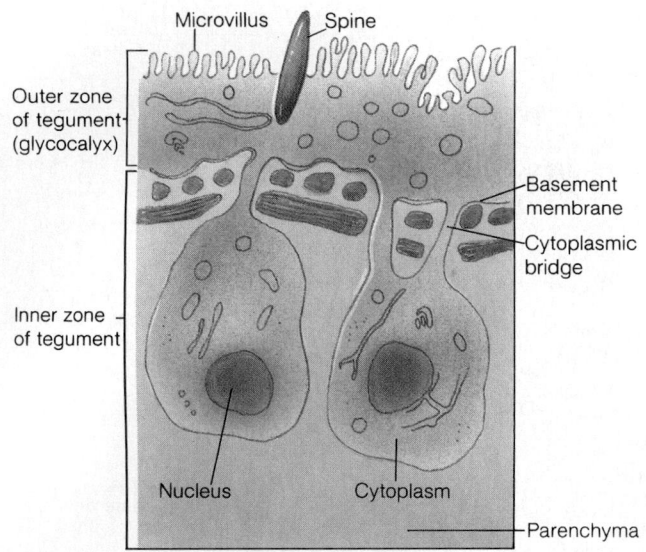

FIGURE 19.12

The Trematode Tegument. Drawing showing the fine structure of the tegument of a fluke. This figure represents an evolutionary adaptation that is highly efficient at absorbing nutrients and for protection.

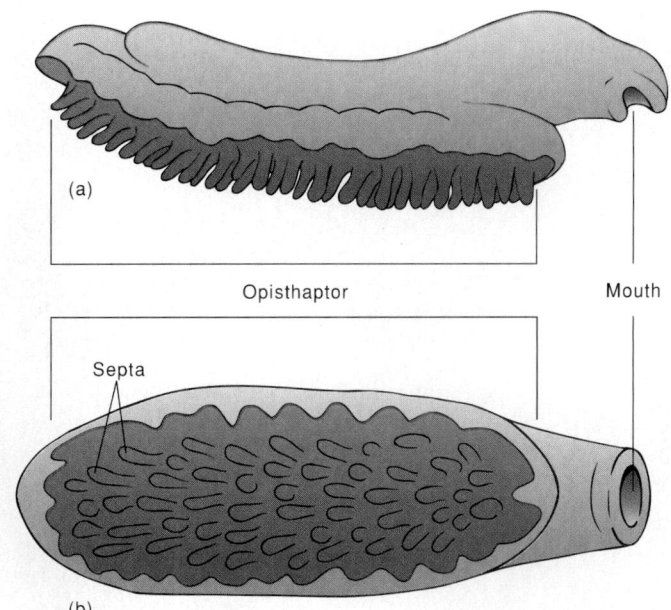

FIGURE 19.13

Class Trematoda: Subclass Aspidogastrea. A representative aspidogastrean fluke. (*a*) Lateral and (*b*) ventral views showing the large opisthaptor and numerous septa.

host cells and cell fragments. The digestive tract includes a mouth and muscular, pumping pharynx. Posterior to the pharynx, the digestive tract divides into two blind-ending, variously branched cecae (s., cecum). Some flukes may supplement their feeding by absorbing nutrients across their body wall.

The structure of the body wall is similar for all flukes and represents an evolutionary adaptation to the parasitic way of life. The epidermis consists of an outer layer called the **tegument** (figure 19.12), which forms a syncytium (a continuous layer of fused cells). The outer zone of the tegument consists of an organic layer of proteins and carbohydrates called the glycocalyx. The glycocalyx aids in the transport of nutrients, wastes, and gases across the body wall, and protects the fluke against enzymes and the host's immune system. Also found in this zone are microvilli that facilitate nutrient exchange. Cytoplasmic bodies that contain the nuclei and most of the organelles lie below the basement membrane. Slender cell processes called cytoplasmic bridges connect the cytoplasmic bodies with the outer zone of the tegument.

Subclass Aspidogastrea

This subclass consists of a small group of flukes that are primarily internal parasites (endoparasites) of molluscs. All aspidogastreans are characterized by the presence of a large, oval holdfast organ called the **opisthaptor** that covers the entire ventral surface of the animal (figure 19.13). The opisthaptor functions as an extremely strong attachment organ and is usually subdivided by

ridges or septa. The oral sucker, characteristic of most other trematode mouths, is absent. The life cycle of aspidogastreans may involve only one host (a mollusc), or two hosts. In the latter case, the final host is usually a vertebrate that becomes infected by ingesting a mollusc that contains immature aspidogastreans.

Subclass Digenea

The vast majority of all flukes belong to the subclass Digenea. In this subclass, at least two different forms, an adult and one or more larval stages, develop—a characteristic from which the name of the subclass was derived. Because digenetic flukes require at least two different hosts to complete their life cycles, these animals possess the most complex life cycles in the entire animal kingdom. As adults, they are all endoparasites in the bloodstream, digestive tract, ducts of the digestive organs, or other visceral organs in a wide variety of vertebrates that serve as definitive, or final, hosts. The one or more intermediate hosts (the hosts that harbor immature stages) may harbor several larval stages. The adhesive organs are two large suckers. The anterior sucker is the **oral sucker** and surrounds the mouth. The other sucker, the **acetabulum,** is located ventrally on the middle portion of the body (*see figure 19.11*).

The eggs of digenetic trematodes are oval and usually possess a lidlike hatch called an **operculum** (figure 19.14*a*). When an egg reaches fresh water, the operculum opens and a ciliated larva called a **miracidium** (pl., miracidia) swims out

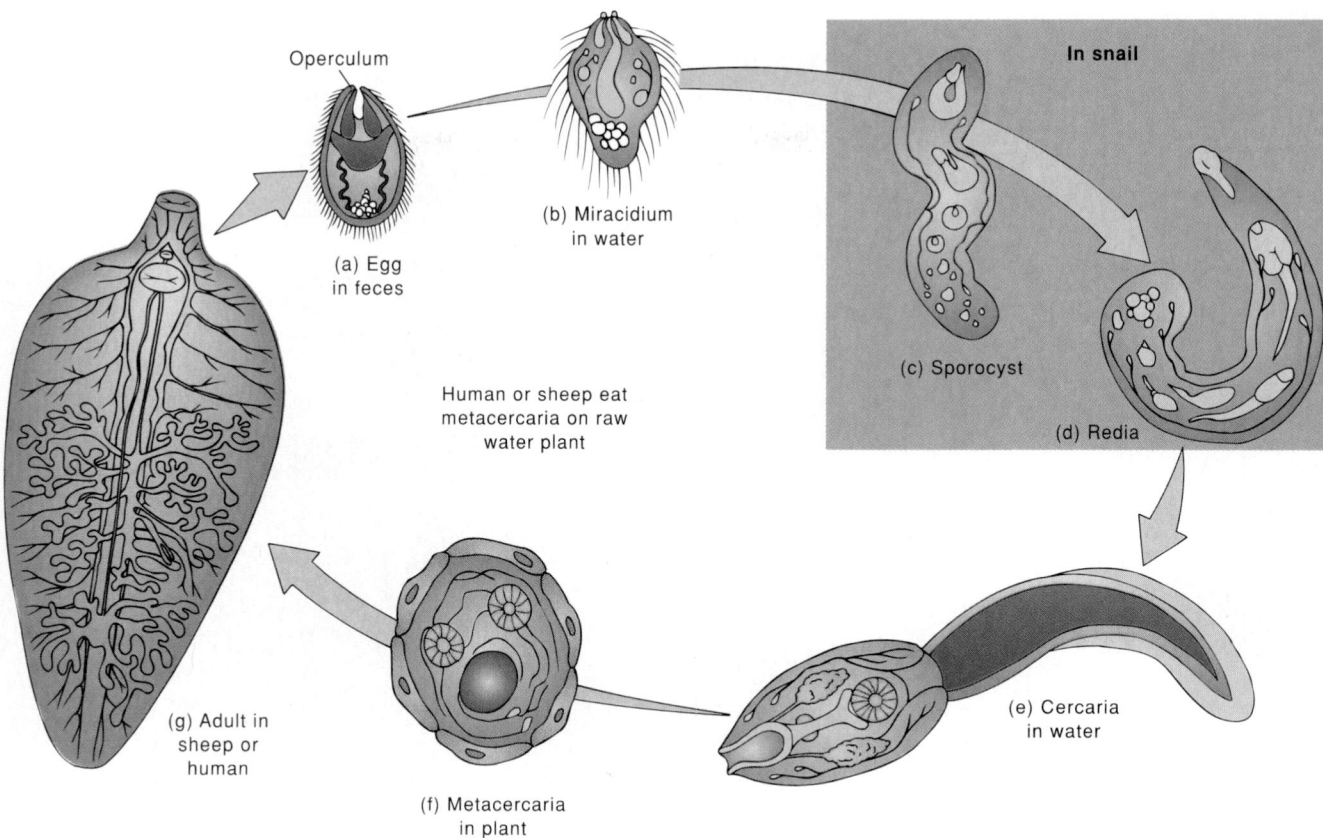

Figure 19.14

Class Trematoda: Subclass Digenea. The life cycle of the digenetic trematode, *Fasciola hepatica* (the common liver fluke).

(figure 19.14*b*). The miracidium swims until it finds a suitable first intermediate host (a snail) to which it is chemically attracted. The miracidium penetrates the snail, loses its cilia, and develops into a **sporocyst** (figure 19.14*c*). (Alternately, the miracidium may remain in the egg and hatch after being eaten by a snail.) Sporocysts are baglike and contain embryonic cells that develop into either **daughter sporocysts,** or **rediae** (s., redia) (figure 19.14*d*). At this point in the life cycle, asexual reproduction first occurs. From a single miracidium, hundreds of daughter sporocysts, and in turn, hundreds of rediae can form by asexual reproduction. Embryonic cells in each daughter sporocyst or redia produce hundreds of the next larval stage, called **cercariae** (s., cercaria) (figure 19.14*e*). (This phenomenon of producing many cercariae is called polyembryony. It enhances greatly the chances that one cercaria will further the life cycle.) A cercaria has a digestive tract, suckers, and a tail. Cercariae leave the snail and swim freely until they encounter a second intermediate or final host, which may be a vertebrate or invertebrate. The cercaria penetrates this host and encysts as a **metacercaria** (pl., metacercariae) (figure 19.14*f*). When the second intermediate host is eaten by the definitive host, the metacercaria excysts and develops into an adult (figure 19.14*g*).

Some Important Trematode Parasites of Humans

The Chinese liver fluke, *Clonorchis sinensis,* is a common parasite of humans in the Orient, where over 50 million people are infected. The adult lives in the bile ducts of the liver, where it feeds on epithelial tissue and blood (figure 19.15*a*). Embryonated eggs are released by the adults into the common bile duct, make their way to the intestine, and are eliminated with feces (figure 19.15*b*). The miracidia are released when a snail ingests the eggs. Following sporocyst and redial stages, cercariae emerge into the water. If the cercaria contacts a fish (the second intermediate host), it penetrates the epidermis of the fish, loses its tail, and encysts. The metacercaria develops into an adult in a human who eats raw or poorly cooked fish, a delicacy in the Orient and gaining in popularity in the Western world.

⑤   *Fasciola hepatica* is called the sheep liver fluke (*see figure 19.14*a) because it is common in sheep-raising areas and uses sheep or humans as its definitive host. The adults live in the bile duct of the liver. Eggs pass via the common bile duct to the intestine, from which they are eliminated. When eggs are

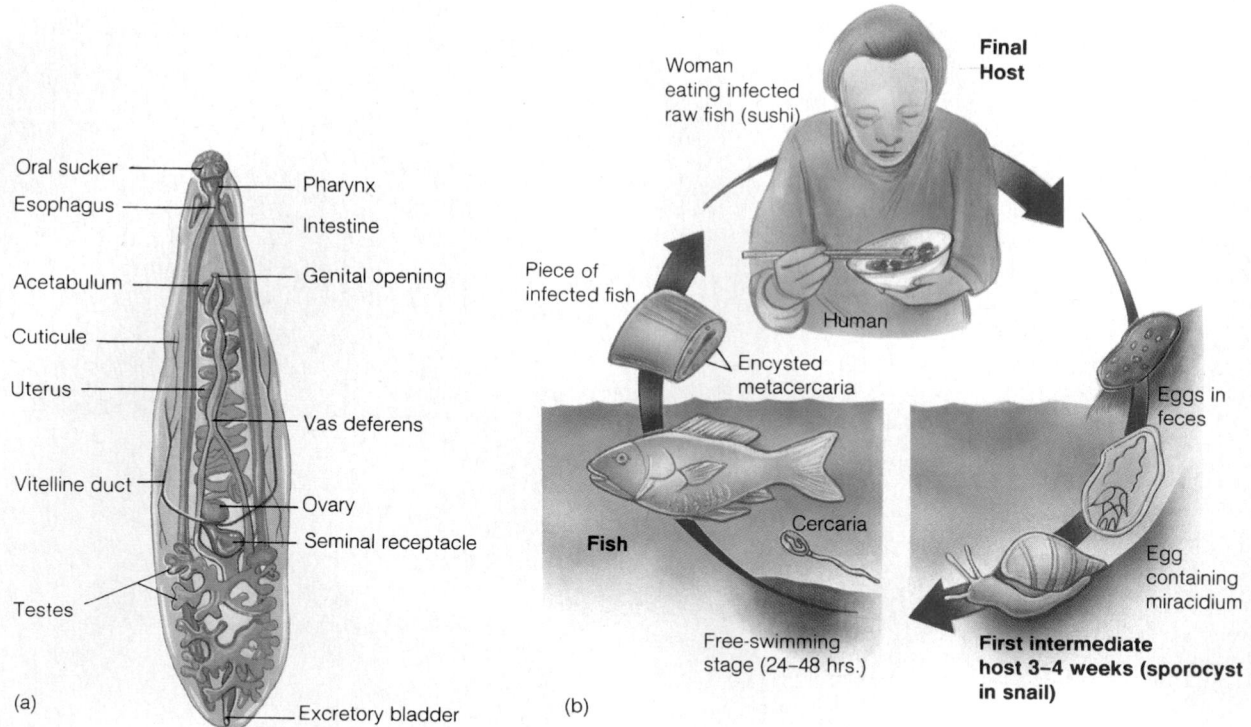

FIGURE 19.15

The Chinese Liver Fluke. *Clonorchis sinensis.* (*a*) Dorsal view and (*b*) life cycle.

deposited in fresh water, they hatch, and the miracidia must locate the proper species of snail. If a snail is found, miracidia penetrate the snail's soft tissue and develop into sporocysts that develop into rediae and give rise to cercariae. After the cercariae emerge from the snail, they encyst on aquatic vegetation. Sheep or other animals become infected when they graze on the aquatic vegetation. Humans may become infected with *Fasciola hepatica* by eating a freshwater plant called watercress that contains the encysted metacercaria.

Schistosomes are blood flukes that are of vast medical significance. The impact these flukes have had on history is second only to that of *Plasmodium* (malaria; *see box 17.2*). They infect over 200 million people throughout the world. Infections are most common in Africa (*Schistosoma haematobium* and *S. mansoni*), South and Central America (*S. mansoni*), and Southeast Asia (*S. japonicum*). The adult dioecious worms live in the bloodstream of humans (figure 19.16*a*). The male fluke is shorter and thicker than the female, and the sides of the male's body are curved under to form a canal along the ventral surface ("schistosoma" means "split body"). The female fluke is long and slender, and is carried in the canal of the male (figure 19.16*b*). Copulation is continuous, and the female produces thousands of eggs. Each egg contains a spine that aids it in moving through host tissue until it is eliminated in either the

feces or urine (figure 19.16*c*). Unlike other flukes, schistosome eggs lack an operculum. The miracidium escapes through a slit that develops in the egg when the egg reaches fresh water (figure 19.16*d*). The miracidium seeks a snail (figure 19.16*e*), penetrates it, develops into a sporocyst (figure 19.16*f*), daughter sporocysts (figure 19.16*f*), and then forked-tailed cercariae (figure 19.16*f*). There is no redial generation. The cercariae leave the snail and penetrate the skin of a human (figure 19.16*g*). Penetration is aided by anterior digestive glands that secrete digestive enzymes. Once in a human, the cercariae lose their tails and develop into adults in the intestinal veins, skipping the metacercaria stage (box 19.1).

Stop and Ask Yourself

4. What is unique about the trematode tegument?
5. What is the function of an opisthaptor?
6. What is the major difference between the life cycle of a monogenean and that of a digenean fluke?
7. How can each of the following be described: miracidium? sporocyst? redia? cercaria? metacercaria? operculum?

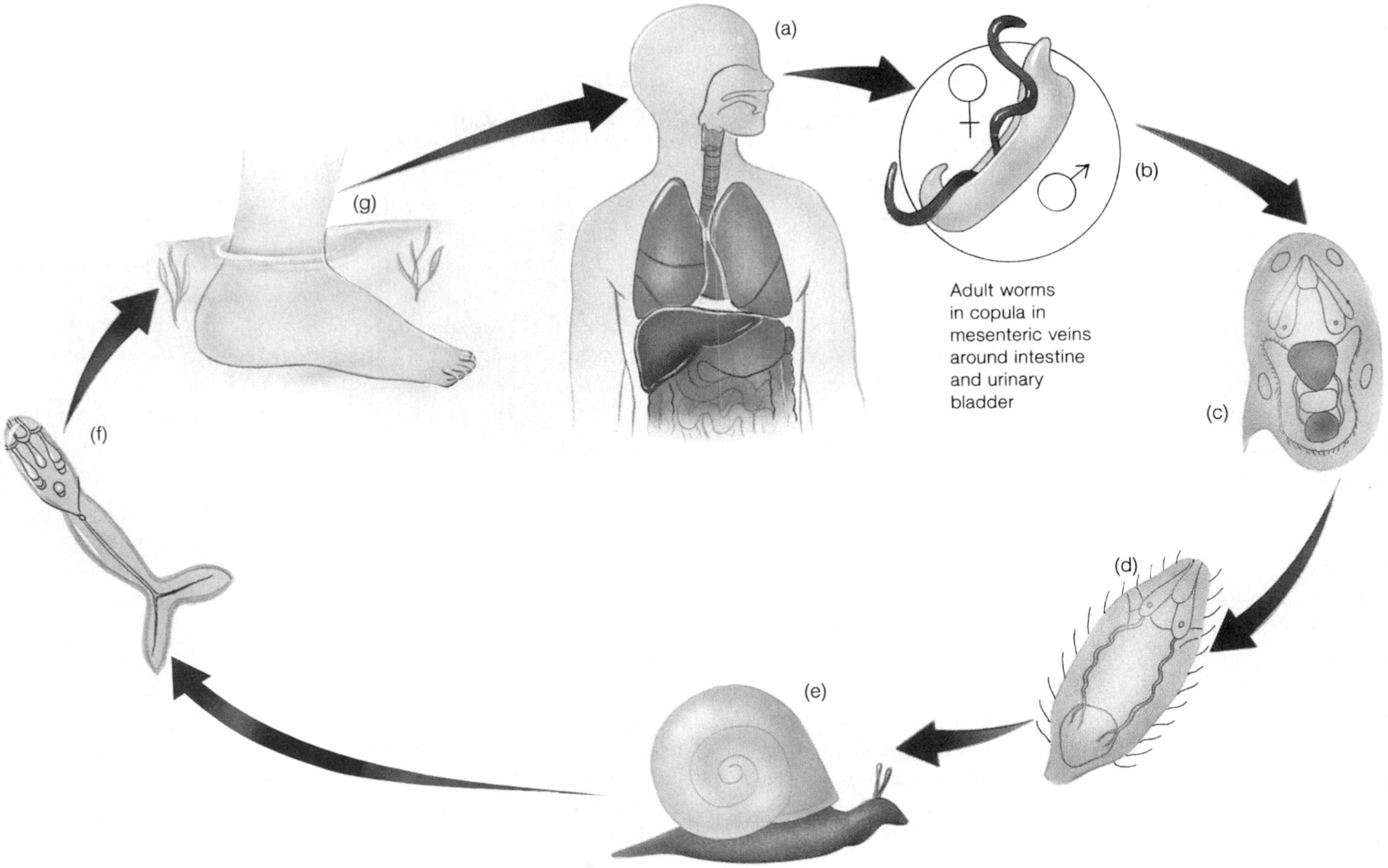

Adult worms
in copula in
mesenteric veins
around intestine
and urinary
bladder

FIGURE 19.16

A Representative Life Cycle of a Schistosome Fluke. The cycle begins in a human (*a*) when the female fluke lays eggs (*b,c*) in the thin-walled, small vessels of the small intestine (*S. mansoni* and *S. japonicum*) or urinary bladder (*S. haematobium*). Secretions from the eggs weaken the walls, and the blood vessels rupture, releasing eggs into the intestinal lumen or urinary bladder. From there the eggs leave the body. If they reach fresh water, the eggs hatch into ciliated, free-swimming larvae called miracidia (*d*). A miracidium burrows into the tissues of an aquatic snail (*e*), losing its cilia in the process, and develops into a sporocyst, then daughter sporocysts. Eventually forked-tailed larvae (cercariae) are produced (*f*). After the cercariae leave the snail, they actively swim about. If they encounter human skin (*g*), they attach to it and release tissue-degrading enzymes. The larvae enter the body and migrate to the circulatory system, where they mature. They end up at the intestinal vessels, where sexual reproduction takes place and the cycle begins anew.

BOX 19.1   SWIMMER'S ITCH

An interesting phase of schistosome biology concerns cercarial dermatitis or "swimmer's itch." Cercariae of species that normally infect birds (waterfowl and shorebirds) and other vertebrates, especially certain mammals (e.g., muskrats and mink), attempt to penetrate the skin of humans, and in doing so, sensitize the area of attack, resulting in itchy rashes. Because humans are not suitable definitive hosts for these cercariae, the flukes do not enter the bloodstream and mature, but perish after penetrating the skin. One of the most common causative agents of marine swimmer's itch on both the east and west coasts of North America is a blood parasite of sea gulls, the cercariae of which develop in a common mudflat snail.

CLASS CESTOIDEA: THE TAPEWORMS

The most highly specialized class of flatworms are members of the class Cestoidea (ses-toid' da) (Gr. *kestos*, girdle + *eidos*, form), commonly called either tapeworms or cestodes. All of the approximately 3,500 species are endoparasites that usually reside in the digestive system of vertebrates. Their color is often white with shades of yellow or gray. Adult tapeworms range in size from 1 mm to 15 m in length.

Tapeworms are characterized by two unique adaptations to their parasitic way of life.   ⑥   (1) Tapeworms lack a mouth and digestive tract in all of their life-cycle stages; they absorb nutrients directly across their body wall. (2) Most adult tapeworms consist of a long series of repeating units called **proglottids.** Each proglottid contains a complete set of reproductive structures.

As with most endoparasites, adult tapeworms live in a very stable environment. The intestinal tract of a vertebrate has very few environmental variations that would require the development of great anatomical or physiological complexity in any single tapeworm body system. Homeostasis (internal constancy) of a tapeworm is maintained by the physiology of the tapeworm's host. In adapting to such a specialized environment, tapeworms have lost some of the structures believed to have been present in ancestral turbellarians. Tapeworms are, therefore, a good example of the fact that evolution does not always result in greater complexity.

Subclass Cestodaria

Representatives of the subclass Cestodaria are all endoparasites in the intestine and coelom of primitive fishes. About 15 species have been identified. They possess some digenetic trematode features in that only one set of both reproductive systems is present in each animal, some bear suckers, and their bodies are not divided into proglottids as in other cestodes. Yet the complete absence of a digestive system, the presence of larval stages similar to those of cestodes, and the presence of parenchymal muscle cells, which are not present in any other platyhelminth, all suggest strong phylogenetic affinities with other cestodes.

Subclass Eucestoda

Almost all of the cestodes belong to the subclass Eucestoda and are called true tapeworms. They represent the ultimate degree of specialization of any parasitic animal. The body is divided into three regions (figure 19.17*a*). At one end is a holdfast structure called the **scolex** that contains circular or leaflike suckers and sometimes a rostellum of hooks (figure 19.17*b*). It is via the scolex that the tapeworm firmly anchors itself into the intestinal wall of its definitive vertebrate host. No mouth is present.

Posteriorly, the scolex narrows to form the neck. Transverse constrictions in the neck give rise to the third body region, the **strobila** (Gr. *strobilus*, a linear series; pl., strobilae). The strobila consists of a series of linearly arranged proglottids,

which function primarily as reproductive units. As a tapeworm grows, new proglottids are added in the neck region, and older proglottids are gradually pushed posteriorly. As they move posteriorly, proglottids mature and begin producing eggs. Thus, anterior proglottids are said to be immature, those in the midregion of the strobila are mature, and those at the posterior end that have accumulated eggs are gravid (L. *gravida*, heavy, loaded, pregnant).

The outer body wall of tapeworms consists of a tegument similar in structure to that of trematodes (*see figure 19.12*). It plays a vital role in the absorption of nutrients because tapeworms have no digestive system. The tegument even absorbs some of the host's own enzymes to facilitate digestion.

With the exception of the reproductive systems, the body systems of tapeworms are reduced in structural complexity. The nervous system consists of only a pair of lateral nerve cords that arise from a nerve mass in the scolex and extend the length of the strobila. A protonephridial system also runs the length of the tapeworm (*see figure 19.6*).

Tapeworms are monoecious and most of their physiology is devoted to producing large numbers of eggs. Each proglottid contains a complete set of male and female reproductive organs (figure 19.17*a*). Numerous testes are scattered throughout the proglottid and deliver sperm via a duct system to a copulatory organ called a cirrus. The cirrus opens through a genital pore, which is an opening shared with the female system. The male system of a proglottid matures before the female system, so that copulation usually occurs with another mature proglottid of the same tapeworm or with another tapeworm in the same host. As previously mentioned, the avoidance of self-fertilization leads to hybrid vigor.

Eggs in each proglottid are produced in a single pair of ovaries. Sperm stored in a seminal receptacle fertilize eggs as they move through the oviduct. After passing the vitelline (yolk) gland to pick up yolk cells, the eggs move into the ootype, which is an expanded region of the oviduct that shapes the capsules around the eggs. The ootype is surrounded by Mehlis' gland, which aids in the formation of the egg capsule. Most tapeworms have a blind-ending uterus where eggs accumulate (figure 19.17*a*). As eggs accumulate, the reproductive organs degenerate; thus, gravid proglottids can be thought of as "bags of eggs." Eggs are released when gravid proglottids break free from the end of the tapeworm and pass from the host with the feces. In a few tapeworms, the uterus opens to the outside of the worm, and eggs are released into the intestine of the host. Because the proglottids are not continuously lost in these worms, the adult tapeworms usually become very long.

Some Important Tapeworm Parasites of Humans

One medically important tapeworm of humans is the beef tapeworm, *Taeniarhynchus saginatus* (figure 19.18). Adults live in the small intestine and may reach lengths of 3 m. About 80,000 eggs per proglottid are released as proglottids break free of the

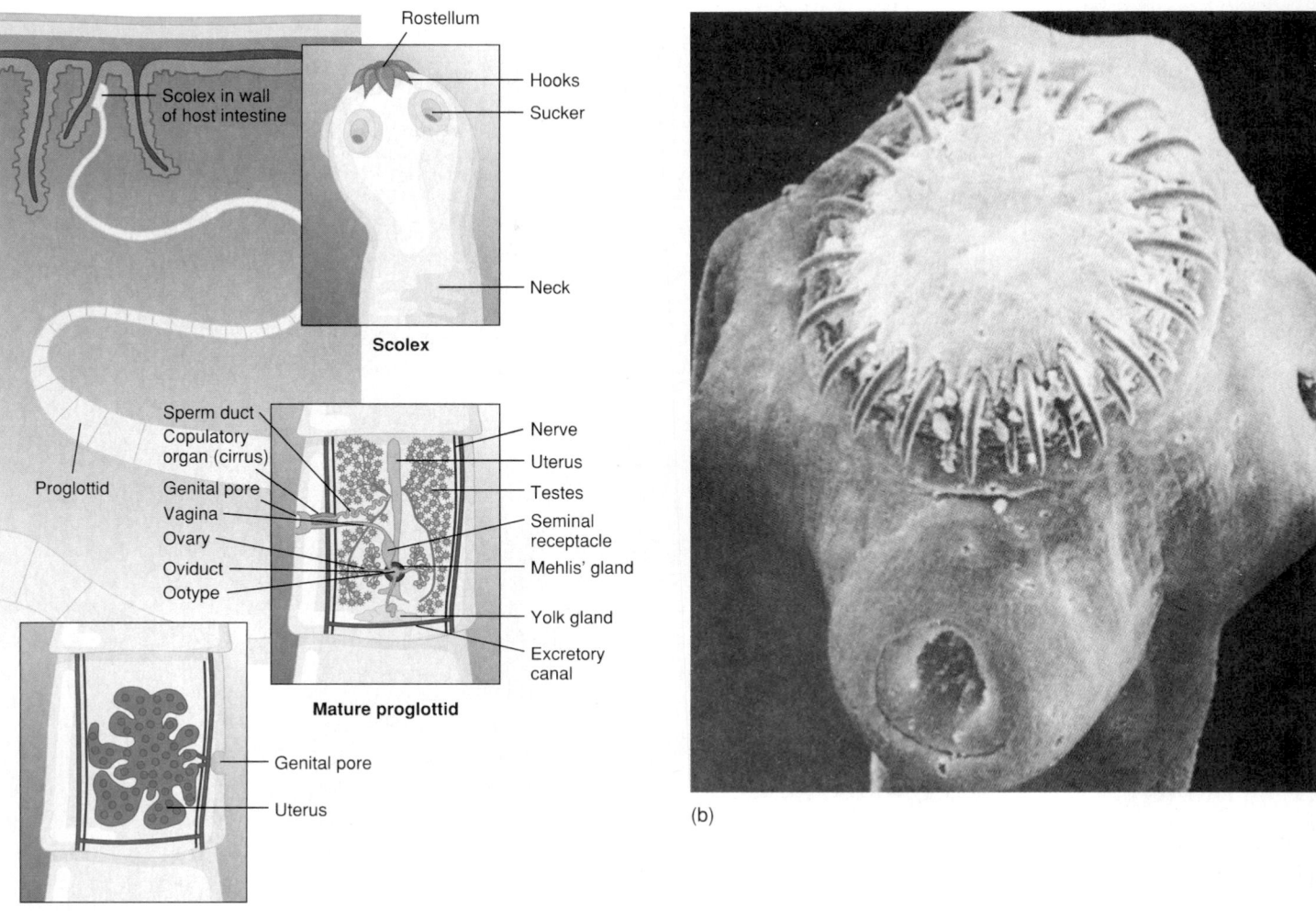

FIGURE 19.17

Class Cestoidea: A Tapeworm. (*a*) Diagram showing the scolex, neck, and proglottids of the pork tapeworm, *Taenia solium*. Included is a detailed view of a mature proglottid with a complete set of male and female reproductive structures. (*b*) A scanning electron micrograph (×100) of the scolex of the cestode *Taenia solium*. Notice the rostellum with two circles of hooks.

adult worm. As an egg develops, it forms a six-hooked (hexacanth) larva called the **onchosphere.** As cattle (the intermediate host) graze on pastures contaminated with human feces, the oncospheres (or proglottids) are ingested. Digestive enzymes of the cattle free the oncospheres, and the larvae use their hooks to bore through the intestinal wall into the bloodstream. The bloodstream carries the larvae to skeletal muscles, where they encyst and form a fluid-filled bladder called a **cysticercus** (pl., cysticerci) or **bladder worm.** When a human eats infected meat (termed "measly beef") that is raw or improperly cooked, the cysticercus is released from the meat, the scolex attaches to the human intestinal wall, and the tapeworm matures.

A closely related tapeworm, *Taenia solium* (the pork tapeworm), has a life cycle similar to *Taeniarhynchus saginatus,* except that the intermediate host is the pig. The strobila has been reported as being 10 m long, but 2 to 3 m is more common. The

pathology is more serious in the human than in the pig. Oncospheres are frequently released from gravid proglottids before the proglottids have had a chance to leave the small intestine of the human host. When these larvae hatch, they move through the intestinal wall, enter the bloodstream and are distributed throughout the body where they eventually encyst in human tissue as cysticerci. The disease that results is called **cysticercosis** and can be fatal if the cysticerci encyst in the brain.

The broad fish tapeworm, *Diphyllobothrium latum,* is relatively common in the northern parts of North America and in the Great Lakes area of the United States. This tapeworm has a scolex with two longitudinal grooves (bothria; s., bothrium; figure 19.19) that act as holdfast structures. The adult worm may attain a length of 10 m and shed up to a million eggs a day. Many proglottids release eggs through uterine pores. When eggs are deposited in fresh water, they hatch,

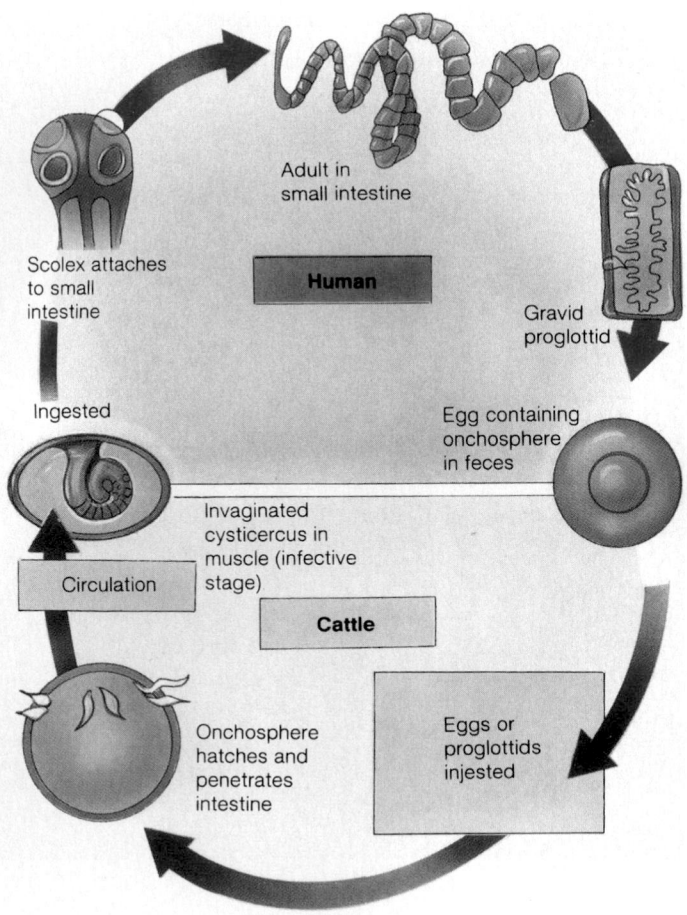

Figure 19.18

The Life Cycle of the Beef Tapeworm, *Taeniarhynchus saginatus.*
Source: Redrawn from Centers for Disease Control, Atlanta.

and ciliated larvae called **coracidia** (s., coracidium) emerge. These coracidia swim about until they are ingested by small crustaceans called copepods. The larvae shed their ciliated coats in the copepods and develop into **procercoid larvae.** When copepods are eaten by a fish, the procercoids burrow into the muscle of the fish and become **plerocercoid larvae.** Larger fishes that eat smaller fishes become similarly infected with plerocercoids. When infected, raw, or poorly cooked fishes are eaten by a human (or other carnivore), the plerocercoids attach to the small intestine and grow into adult worms.

Stop and Ask Yourself

8. What is a proglottid? A scolex? A strobila?
9. How do tapeworms obtain nutrients?
10. What is the life cycle of a typical tapeworm?
11. What is each of the following: coracidium? cysticercus? procercoid larva? plerocercoid larva?

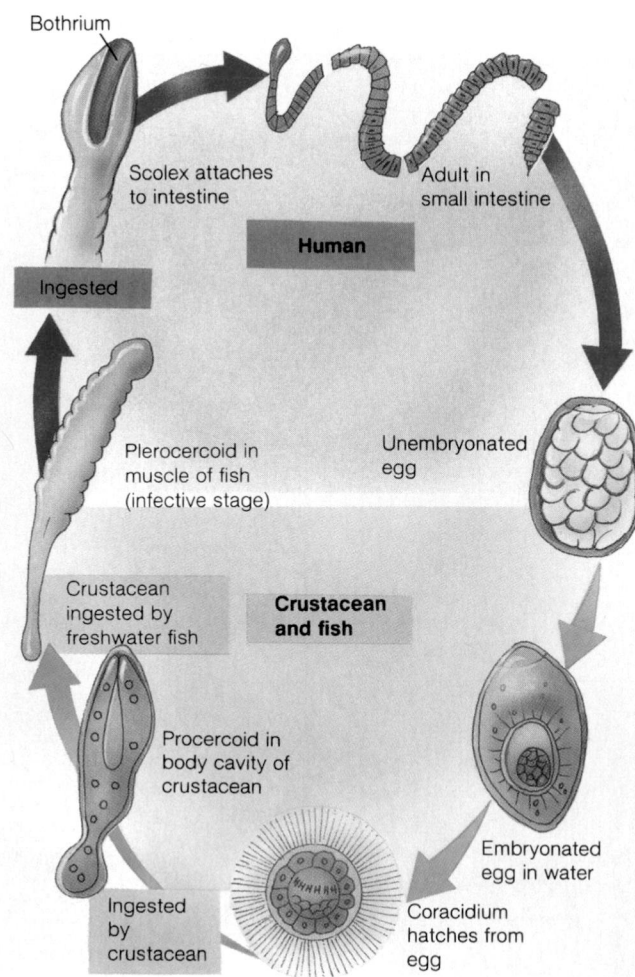

Figure 19.19

The Life Cycle of the Broad Fish Tapeworm, *Diphyllobothrium latum.*   *Source: Redrawn from Centers for Disease Control, Atlanta.*

PHYLUM NEMERTEA

Most of the approximately 900 species of nemerteans (nemer'te-ans) (Gr. *Nemertes*, a Mediterranean sea nymph; the daughter of Nereus and Doris) are elongate, flattened worms found in marine mud and sand. Due to the presence of a long proboscis, nemerteans are commonly called proboscis worms. Adult worms range in size from a few millimeters to several centimeters in length. Most nemerteans are pale yellow, orange, green, or red. Characteristics of the phylum Nemertea include the following:

1. Triploblastic, acoelomate, bilaterally symmetrical unsegmented worms possessing a ciliated epidermis containing mucous glands
2. Complete digestive tract with an anus

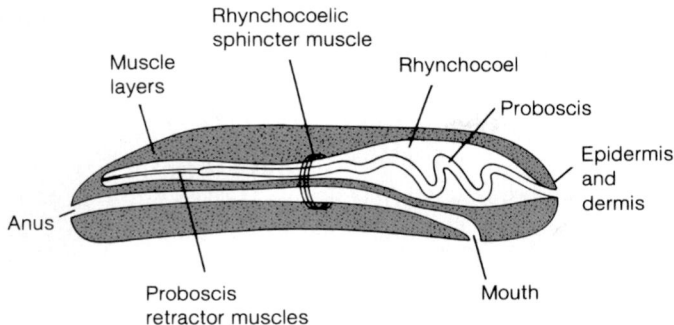

FIGURE 19.20

Phylum Nemertea. Diagram of a nemertean; longitudinal section, showing the tubular gut and proboscis. *Source: Modified from Turbeville and Ruppert, 1983, Zoomorphology, 103:103, Copyright 1983, Springer-Verlag, Heidelberg, Germany.*

3. Protonephridia
4. Cerebral ganglion, longitudinal nerve cords, and transverse commissures
5. Closed circulatory system
6. Body musculature organized into two or three layers

The most distinctive feature of nemerteans is a long proboscis that is held in a sheath called a **rhynchocoel** (figure 19.20). The proboscis may be tipped with a barb called a stylet. Carnivorous species use the proboscis to capture annelid (segmented worms) and crustacean prey.

Unlike the platyhelminths, nemerteans have a complete one-way digestive tract. They have a mouth for ingesting food and an anus for eliminating digestive wastes. This characteristic enables mechanical breakdown of food, digestion, absorption, and feces formation to proceed sequentially from an anterior to posterior direction—a major evolutionary innovation found in all higher bilateral animals.

Another major innovation found in all higher animals evolved first in the nemerteans—a circulatory system consisting of two lateral blood vessels and often, tributary vessels that branch from lateral vessels. However, no heart is present, and contractions of the walls of the large vessels help to propel blood along. Blood does not circulate but simply moves forward and backward through the longitudinal vessels. Blood cells are present in some species. This combination of blood vessels with their capacity to serve local tissues, and a one-way digestive system with its greater efficiency at processing nutrients, allows nemerteans to reach lengths much larger than most flatworms.

Nemerteans are dioecious. Male and female reproductive structures develop from parenchymal cells along each side of the body. External fertilization results in the formation of a helmet-shaped, ciliated **pilidium larva.** After a brief free-swimming existence, the larva develops into a young worm that settles to the substrate and begins feeding.

When they move, adult nemerteans glide on a trail of mucus. Cilia and peristaltic contractions of body muscles provide the propulsive forces.

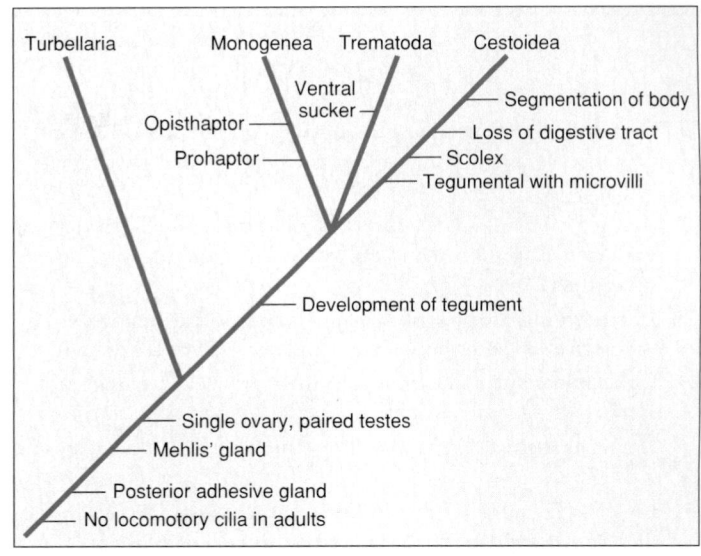

FIGURE 19.21

A Cladogram Showing Evolutionary Relationships between the Classes of Platyhelminthes. The absence of synapomorphies for the Turbellaria suggests that the ancestral platyhelminth was itself a turbellarian, and that some member of that class was ancestral to the three living parasitic groups. *Source: Data from D. R. Brooks, Journal of Parasitology, 1989, pp. 606-616.*

FURTHER PHYLOGENETIC CONSIDERATIONS

Zoologists who believe that the platyhelminth body form is central to animal evolution envision an ancestral flatworm similar to a turbellarian. Figure 19.21 illustrates a cladogram emphasizing the uniqueness of the tegument as a synapomorphy (a shared, evolutionarily derived character that is used to describe common descent among two or more species) uniting the Monogenea, Trematoda, and Cestoidea.

More conclusive evidence exists linking the parasitic flatworms to ancient, free-living ancestors. The divergence between the free-living and parasitic ways of life probably occurred in the Cambrian period, 600 million years ago. The first flatworm parasites were probably associated with primitive molluscs, arthropods, and echinoderms. It must have been much later that they acquired the vertebrate hosts and complex life cycles that have been described in this chapter.

Stop and Ask Yourself

12. Why are the nemerteans called proboscis worms?
13. What is a rhynchocoel?
14. What major body system developed for the first time in the nemerteans?

SUMMARY

1. The free-living platyhelminths, members of the class Turbellaria, are small, bilaterally symmetrical acoelomate animals with some cephalization.

2. Most turbellarians move entirely by cilia and are predators and scavengers. Digestion is initially extracellular and then intracellular.

3. Protonephridia are present in many flatworms and are involved in osmoregulation. A primitive brain and nerve cords are present.

4. Turbellarians are monoecious with the reproductive systems adapted for internal fertilization.

5. The mongenetic flukes (class Monogenea) are mostly ectoparasites of fishes.

6. The class Trematoda is divided into two subclasses (Aspidogastrea and Digenea) and most are external or internal parasites of vertebrates. A gut is present and most of these flukes are monoecious.

7. Cestodes, or tapeworms, are gut parasites of vertebrates. They are structurally more specialized than flukes, having a scolex with attachment organs, a neck region, and a strobila, which consists of a chain of segments (proglottids) budded off from the neck region. A gut is absent, and the reproductive system is repeated in each proglottid.

8. Nemerteans are similar to platyhelminths but can be much larger. They are predatory on other invertebrates, which they capture with a unique proboscis. They have a one-way digestive tract, a blood-vascular system, and the sexes are separate.

SELECTED KEY TERMS

acetabulum (p. 294)
cercariae (p. 295)
coracidia (p. 300)
cysticercus (p. 299)
daughter sporocysts (p. 295)
metacercaria (p. 295)
miracidium (p. 294)

onchosphere (p. 299)
oncomiracidium (p. 293)
plerocercoid larvae (p. 300)
procercoid larvae (p. 300)
rediae (p. 295)
sporocyst (p. 295)

CRITICAL THINKING QUESTIONS

1. Describe the morphological and developmental similarities and differences between nemerteans and turbellarians.

2. How do parasitic flatworms evade their host's immune system?

3. How would a zoologist go about documenting the complex life cycle of a digenetic trematode?

4. Describe some of the key features of acoelomate animals.

5. Consider the cestode body form and respond to the following statement: "Many very successful animals are anything but highly complex organisms. In fact, for some, evolution has meant a reduction in complexity." In what ways would this statement accurately describe the cestode body form? In what ways would it not be accurate?

THE PSEUDOCOELOMATE BODY PLAN:
ASCHELMINTHS

Outline

Concepts

1. Nine phyla are grouped together into the aschelminths: Gastrotricha, Rotifera, Kinorhyncha, Nematoda, Nematomorpha, Acanthocephala, Loricifera, Priapulida, and Entoprocta. Because most of these phyla have had a separate evolutionary history, this grouping is mostly one of convenience.
2. The major unifying aschelminth feature is a pseudocoelom. The pseudocoelom is a type of body cavity that develops from the blastocoel (the primitive cavity in the embryo) and is not fully lined by mesoderm, as in the true coelomates. In the pseudocoelomates, the muscles and other structures of the body wall and internal organs are in direct contact with fluid in the pseudocoelom (figure 20.1).
3. Other common aschelminth features include a complete digestive tract, a muscular pharynx, constant cell numbers (eutely), protonephridia, cuticle, and adhesive glands.

Would You Like to Know:

1. why worms molt? (p. 305)
2. how rotifers got their name? (p. 306)
3. in what animal the reproductive organ called a penis first developed? (p. 308)
4. what some of the most abundant animals on earth are? (p. 310)
5. why roundworms move in an undulating, wavelike fashion? (p. 310)
6. why all nematodes are round? (p. 311)
7. what the most common roundworm parasite in the United States is? (p. 313)
8. why you should not eat improperly cooked pork products? (p. 315)
9. what causes the disease elephantiasis? (p. 315)
10. what causes heartworm disease in dogs? (p. 315)
11. why horsehair worms were thought to arise from horses' tails? (p. 315)
12. how spiny-headed worms got their name? (p. 316)
13. what the most recently described animal phylum is? (p. 317)

These and other useful questions will be answered in this chapter.

This chapter contains evolutionary concepts, which are set off in this font.

EVOLUTIONARY PERSPECTIVE

The nine different phyla that are grouped for convenience as the **aschelminths** (Gr. *askos*, bladder + *helmins*, worm) are very diverse animals. They have obscure phylogenetic affinities, and their fossil record is meager. Two hypotheses have been proposed for their phylogeny. The first hypothesis contends that the phyla are related based on the presence of the following structures: a pseudocoelom, a cuticle, a muscular pharynx, and adhesive glands. The second hypothesis contends that the various aschelminth phyla are not related to each other. The absence of any single unique feature found in all groups strongly suggests independent evolution of each phylum. The similarities among the living aschelminths may simply be the result of convergent evolution as these various animals adapted to similar environments.

The correct phylogeny may actually be something between the two hypotheses. All phyla are probably distantly related to each other based on the few anatomical and physiological features they share (figures 20.1, 20.2). True convergent evolution may have also produced some visible analogous similarities, but each phylum probably arose from a common acoelomate ancestor, and diverged very early in evolutionary history (figure 20.3). Such an ancestor might have been a primitive, ciliated, acoel turbellarian (*see figure 19.4a*), from which it would follow that the first ancestor was ciliated, acoelomate, marine, probably monoecious, and lacked a cuticle.

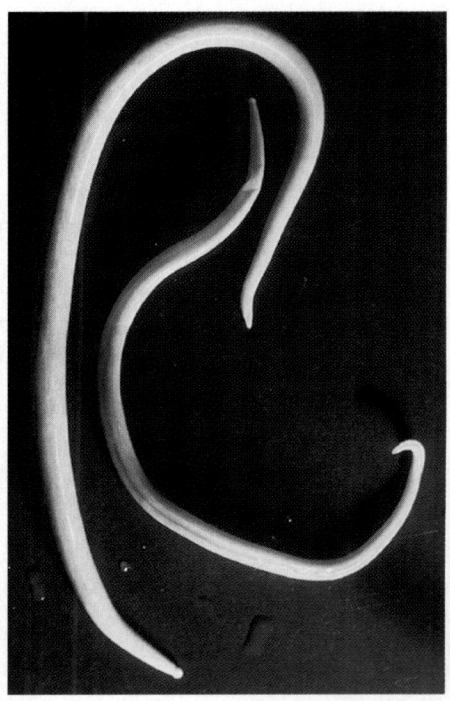

FIGURE 20.1

Roundworm Characteristics: A Fluid-Filled Body Cavity and a Complete Digestive System. *Ascaris lumbriocoides* inhabits the intestines of both pigs and humans. Male ascarid worms are smaller than females and have a curved posterior end.

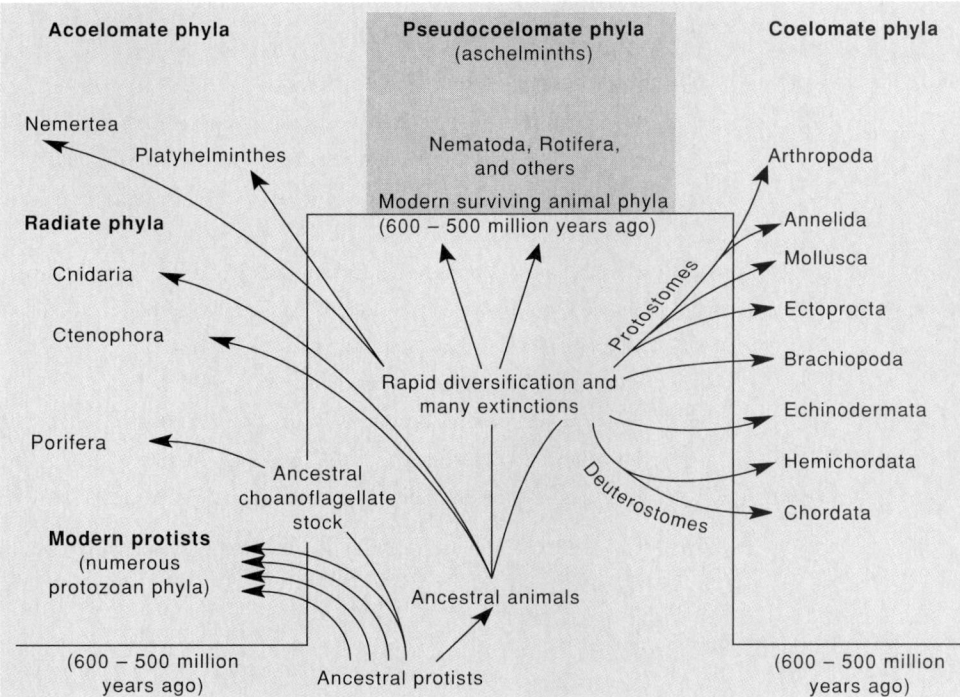

FIGURE 20.2

Pseudocoelomate Phyla. A generalized evolutionary tree depicting the major events and possible lines of descent for the pseudocoelomates (shaded in orange).

Extracellular cuticle   Intracellular cuticle

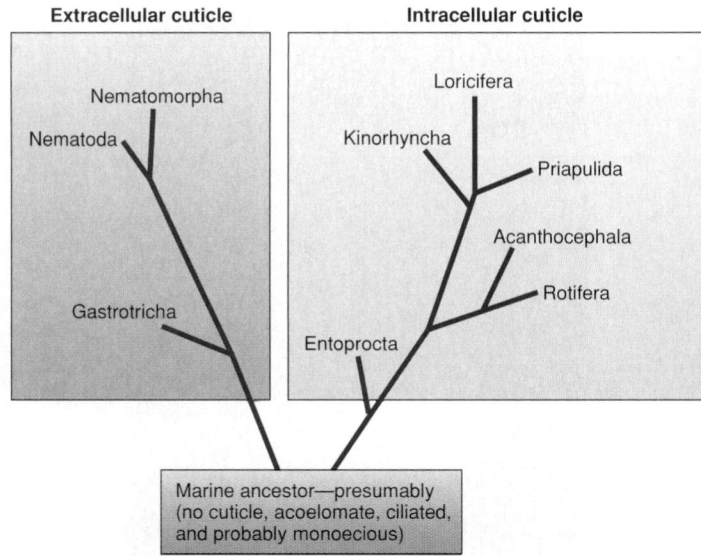

FIGURE 20.3

The Possible Phylogenetic Relationships among the Nine Aschelminth Phyla. Notice that the pseudocoelomate condition has probably been derived several times. That is to say, "aschelminths" are almost certainly a polyphyletic taxon. This may be seen in the structure of the aschelminth cuticle. For example, the cuticle of gastrotrichs, nematodes, and nematomorphs is extracellular, whereas the other members have an intracellular cuticle.

GENERAL CHARACTERISTICS

The aschelminths are the first assemblage of animals to possess a distinct body cavity, but one that lacks the peritoneal linings and membranes called mesenteries that are found in more advanced animals. As a result, the various internal (visceral) organs lie free in the cavity. Such a cavity is called a pseudocoelom or **pseudocoel** (*see figure 16.10b*), and the animals are called **pseudocoelomates.** The pseudocoelom is often fluid filled or may contain a gelatinous substance with mesenchyme cells, serves as a cavity for circulation, aids in digestion, and acts as an internal hydrostatic skeleton that functions in locomotion.

Most aschelminths (the acanthocephalans and nematomorphs are exceptions) have a complete tubular digestive tract that extends from an anterior mouth to a posterior anus. This tube-within-a-tube body plan was first encountered in the nemerteans (*see figure 19.20*) and is characteristic of almost all other higher animals. It permits, for the first time, the mechanical breakdown of food, digestion, absorption, and feces formation to proceed sequentially and continually from an anterior to posterior direction—an evolutionary advancement over the blind-ending digestive system. Most aschelminths also have a specialized muscular pharynx that is adapted for feeding.

20.1   AN APPLICATION OF EUTELY

The science of aging is called **gerontology** (Gr. *gerontos,* old man). The eutelic characteristic of aschelminths makes them excellent research animals for studies on aging because (1) none of the cells of aschelminths are being continually renewed; (2) aschelminths are devoid of the capacity to repair cells; and (3) a specific number of cells is present and their exact lineage is known. In a eutelic animal, cellular longevity appears to be a simple, measurable parameter, and the onset of aging can be easily studied. Some of the characteristics of aging that have been studied in these animals include the progressive disorganization of muscle and nerve cells, mitochondrial degeneration, decrease in cellular motility, accumulation of age pigments, and increase in specific gravity.

Many aschelminths show **eutely** (Gr. *euteia,* thrift), a condition in which the number of cells (or nuclei in syncytia) are constant both for the entire animal and for each given organ, in all the animals of that species (box 20.1). For example, the number of body (somatic) cells in all adult *Caenorhabditis elegans* nematodes is 959, and the number of cells in the pharynx of every worm in the species is precisely 80.

Most aschelminths are microscopic, although some grow to a length of over a meter. They are bilaterally symmetrical, unsegmented, triploblastic, and cylindrical in cross section. An osmoregulatory system of protonephridia (*see figure 19.6*) is found in most aschelminths. This system is best developed in freshwater forms in which osmotic problems are the greatest. No separate blood or gas exchange systems are present. There is some cephalization, with the anterior end containing a primitive brain, sensory organs, and a mouth. The vast majority of aschelminths are dioecious. Both reproductive systems are relatively uncomplicated; life cycles are usually simple, except in parasites. Cilia are generally absent from the external surface, but a thin, tough external cuticle is present for the first time in any animal group. The **cuticle** (L. *cutis,* skin) may bear spines, scales, or other forms of ornamentation that protect the animal and are useful to taxonomists.   ① Some aschelminths shed this cuticle in a process called **molting** or **ecdysis** (Gr. *ekdysis,* to strip off) in order to grow. Beneath the cuticle is a syncytial epidermis that actively secretes the cuticle. Several longitudinal muscle layers lie beneath the epidermis.

Most aschelminths are freshwater animals; only a few are found in marine environments. The nematomorphs, acanthocephalans, and many nematodes are parasitic. The remainder of this assemblage is mostly free living; some rotifers are colonial.

PHYLUM GASTROTRICHA

The gastrotrichs (gas-tro-tri′ks) (Gr. *gastros*, stomach + *trichos*, hair) are members of a small phylum of about 500 free-living marine and freshwater species that inhabit the space between bottom sediments. They range from 0.01 to 4 mm in length. Gastrotrichs move over the substrate using cilia on their ventral surface. The phylum contains a single class divided into two orders.

The dorsal cuticle often contains scales, bristles, or spines, and a forked tail is often present (figure 20.4). A syncytial epidermis is found beneath the cuticle. Sensory structures include tufts of long cilia and bristles on the rounded head. The nervous system includes a brain and a pair of lateral nerve trunks. The digestive system is a straight tube with a mouth, a muscular pharynx, a stomach-intestine, and an anus. Microorganisms and organic detritus from the bottom sediment and water are ingested by the action of the pumping pharynx. Digestion is mostly extracellular. Adhesive glands in the forked tail secrete materials that anchor the animal to solid objects. Paired protonephridia occur in freshwater species, rarely in marine ones. Gastrotrich protonephridia, however, are morphologically different from those found in the acoelomates. Each protonephridium possesses a single flagellum instead of the cilia found in flame cells.

Most of the marine species reproduce sexually and are hermaphroditic. Most of the freshwater species reproduce asexually by parthenogenesis; the females can lay two kinds of unfertilized eggs. Thin-shelled eggs hatch into females during favorable environmental conditions, whereas thick-shelled, resting eggs can withstand unfavorable conditions for long periods before hatching into females. There is no larval stage: development is direct, and the juveniles have the same form as the adults.

PHYLUM ROTIFERA

The rotifers (ro-tif′ers) (L. *rota*, wheel + *fera*, to bear) derive their name from the characteristic ciliated organ, the **corona** (Gr. *krowe*, crown), located around lobes on the head of these animals (figure 20.5*a*). The cilia of the corona do not beat in synchrony; instead, each cilium is at a slightly earlier stage in the beat cycle than the next cilium in the sequence. A wave of beating cilia thus appears to pass around the periphery of the ciliated lobes and gives the impression of a pair of spinning wheels. (Interestingly, the rotifers were first called "wheel animalicules.")

Rotifers are small animals (0.1 to 3 mm in length) that are abundant in most freshwater habitats; a few (less than 10%) are marine. There are about 2,000 species in three classes (table 20.1). The body is composed of approximately 1,000 cells, and the organs are eutelic. Rotifers are usually solitary free-swimming animals, although some colonial forms are known. Others occur interstitially in sediments.

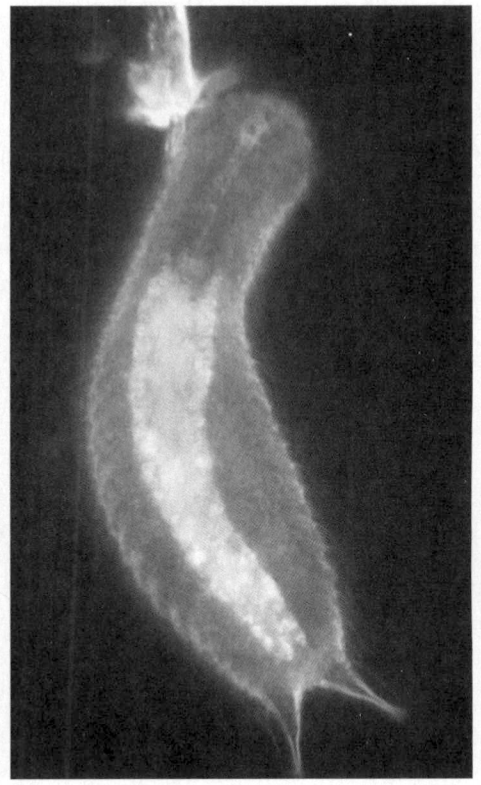

(a)

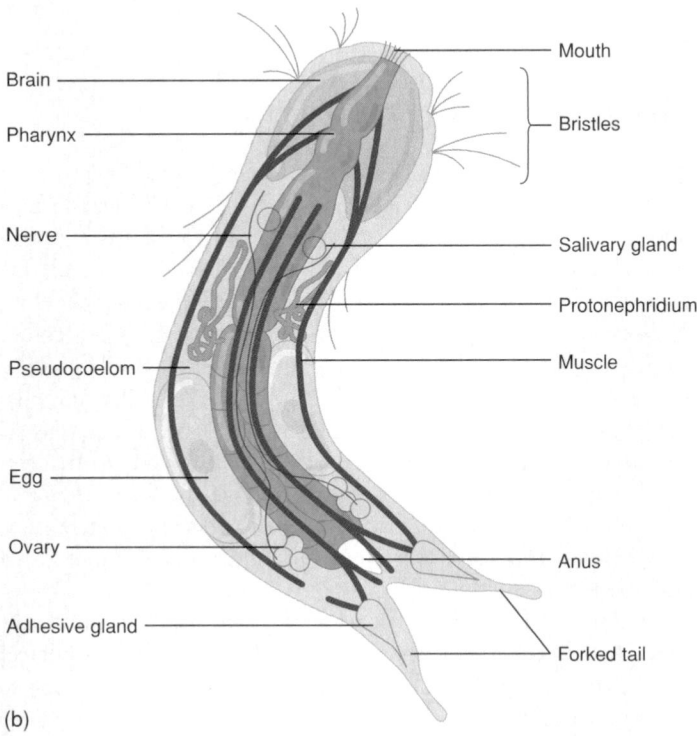

Brain —
Pharynx —
Nerve —
Pseudocoelom —
Egg —
Ovary —
Adhesive gland —

— Mouth
— Bristles
— Salivary gland
— Protonephridium
— Muscle
— Anus
— Forked tail

(b)

FIGURE 20.4

Phylum Gastrotricha. (*a*) Light micrograph of a gastrotrich *Chaetonotus*. Notice the transparent dorsoventrally flattened body. (*b*) Illustration of the internal anatomy of a freshwater gastrotrich.

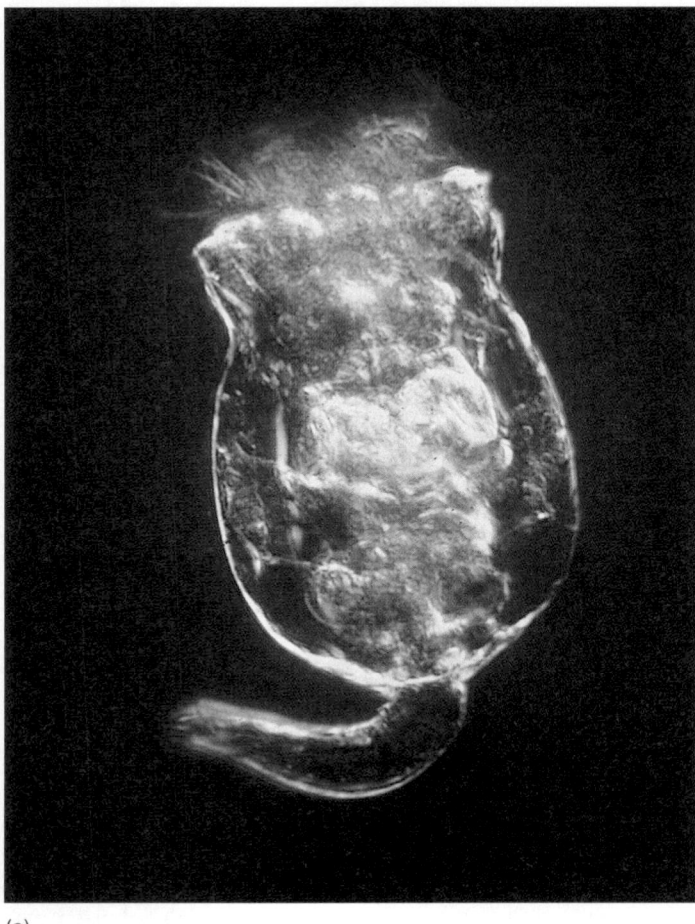

(a)

Figure 20.5

Phylum Rotifera. (*a*) Light micrograph of a rotifer, *Brachionus* (×150). (*b*) Illustration of the internal anatomy of a typical rotifer, *Philodina*.

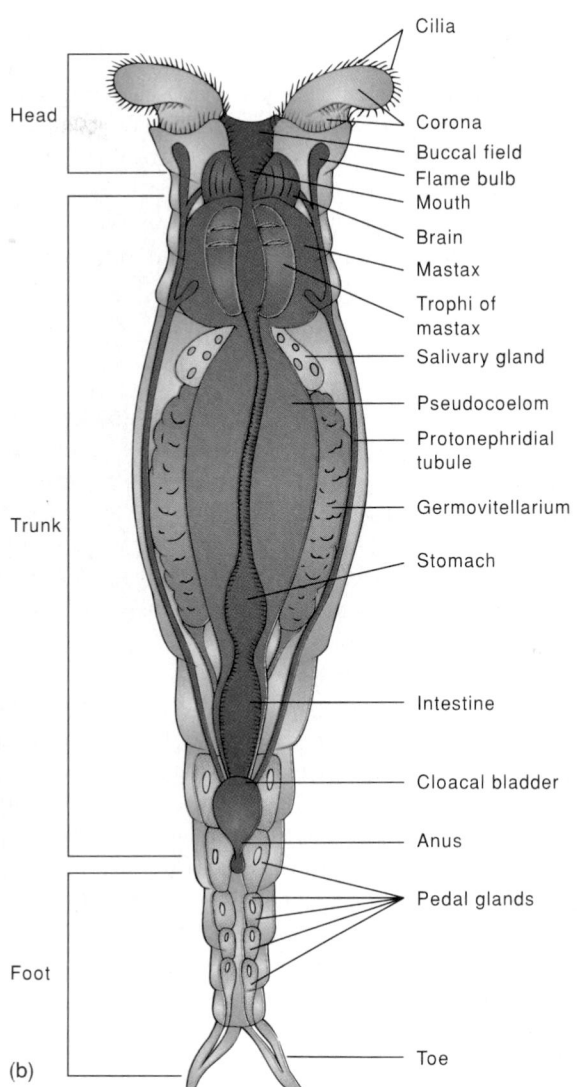

(b)

TABLE 20.1	CLASSIFICATION OF THE ROTIFERA

Phylum Rotifera (ro-tif′e-ra)
A cilated corona surrounding a mouth; muscular pharynx (mastax) present with jawlike features; nonchitinous cuticle; parthenogenesis is common; both freshwater and marine species.
  Class Seisonidea (sy′son-id′ea)
  A single genus of marine rotifers that are commensals of crustaceans; large and elongate body with reduced corona. *Seison.*
  Class Bdelloidea (Digonota) (del-oid′e-a)
  Anterior end retractile and bearing two trochal disks; mastax adapted for grinding; paired ovaries; cylindrical body; males absent. *Adineta, Philodina, Rotaria.*
  Class Monogononta (mon′o-go-no′ta)
  Rotifers with one ovary; mastax not designed for grinding; produce mictic and amictic eggs. Males appear only sporadically. *Conochilus, Collotheca, Notommata.*

Characteristics of the phylum Rotifera include the following:

1. Triploblastic, bilateral, unsegmented, pseudocoelomate
2. Complete digestive system, regionally specialized
3. Anterior end often has a ciliated organ called a corona
4. Posterior end with toes and adhesive glands
5. Well-developed cuticle
6. Protonephridia
7. Males generally reduced in number or absent; parthenogenesis common

EXTERNAL FEATURES

The external surface of a rotifer is covered by an epidermally secreted cuticle. In many species, the cuticle is thickened to form an encasement called a **lorica** (L. *corselet*, a loose-fitting case). The cuticle or lorica provides protection and is the main supportive element, although fluid in the pseudocoelom also provides hydrostatic support. The epidermis is syncytial; that is, there are no cell membranes between nuclei.

The head contains the corona, mouth, sensory organs, and brain (figure 20.5b). The corona surrounds a large ciliated area called the buccal field. The trunk is the largest part of a rotifer and is elongate and saclike. The anus occurs dorsally on the posterior trunk. The posterior, narrow portion is called the foot. The terminal portion of the foot usually bears one or two toes. At the base of the toes are many pedal glands whose ducts open on the toes. Secretions from these glands aid in temporary attachment of the foot to a substratum.

FEEDING AND THE DIGESTIVE SYSTEM

Most rotifers feed on small microorganisms and suspended organic material. The coronal cilia create a current of water that brings food particles to the mouth. The pharynx contains a unique structure called the **mastax** (Gr. *jaws*). The mastax is a muscular organ in which food is ground. The inner walls of the mastax contain several sets of jaws called *trophi* (figure 20.5b). The trophi vary in morphological detail and are used by taxonomists to distinguish species.

From the mastax, food passes through a short, ciliated esophagus to the ciliated stomach. Salivary and digestive glands secrete digestive enzymes into the pharynx and stomach. The complete extracellular digestion of food and its absorption occur in the stomach. In some species, a short ciliated intestine extends posteriorly and becomes a cloacal bladder, which receives water from the protonephridia and eggs from the ovaries, as well as digestive waste. The cloacal bladder opens to the outside via an anus at the junction of the foot with the trunk.

OTHER ORGAN SYSTEMS

All visceral organs lie in a pseudocoelom that is filled with fluid and interconnecting amoeboid cells. Osmoregulation is accomplished by protonephridia that empty into the cloacal bladder. Rotifers, like other pseudocoelomates, exchange gases and dispose of nitrogenous wastes across body surfaces. The nervous system is composed of two lateral nerves and a bilobed, ganglionic brain that is located on the dorsal surface of the mastax. Sensory structures include numerous ciliary clusters and sensory bristles concentrated on either one or more short antennae or the corona. One to five photosensitive eyespots may be found on the head.

REPRODUCTION AND DEVELOPMENT

Some rotifers reproduce sexually, although several types of parthenogenesis occur in most species. Smaller males appear only sporadically in one class (Monogononta) and no males are known in another class (Bdelloidea). In the class Seisonidea, fully developed males and females are equally common in the population. Most rotifers have a single ovary and an attached syncytial vitellarium, which produces yolk that is incorporated into the eggs. The ovary and vitellarium often fuse to form a single germovitellarium (figure 20.5b). After fertilization, each egg travels through a short oviduct to the cloacal bladder and out its opening.

In males, the mouth, cloacal bladder, and other digestive organs are either degenerate or absent. A single testis produces sperm that travel through a ciliated vas deferens to the gonopore. ③ Male rotifers typically have an eversible penis that injects sperm, like a hypodermic needle, into the pseudocoelom of the female (hypodermic impregnation).

In one class (Seisonidea), the females produce haploid eggs that must be fertilized to develop into either males or females. In another class (Bdelloidea), all females are parthenogenetic and produce diploid eggs that hatch into diploid females. In the third class (Monogononta), two different types of eggs are produced (figure 20.6). **Amictic eggs** (Gr. *a*, without + *miktos*, mixed or blended; thin-shelled summer eggs) are produced by mitosis, are diploid, cannot be fertilized, and develop directly into amictic females. Thin-shelled, **mictic** (Gr. *miktos*, mixed or blended) **eggs** are haploid. If the mictic egg is not fertilized, it develops parthenogenetically into a male; if fertilized, mictic eggs secrete a thick, heavy shell and become dormant or resting winter eggs. Dormant eggs always hatch with melting snows and spring rains into amictic females which begin a first amictic cycle, building up large populations quickly. By early summer, some females have begun to produce mictic eggs, males appear, and dormant eggs are produced. Another amictic cycle, as well as the production of more dormant eggs, occurs before the yearly cycle is over. Dormant eggs are often dispersed by winds or birds, accounting for the unique distribution patterns of many rotifers. Most females lay either amictic or mictic eggs, but not both. Apparently, during oocyte development, the physiological condition of the female determines whether her eggs will be amictic or mictic.

Stop and Ask Yourself

1. How do the cilia of a rotifer beat?
2. How can the anatomy of a rotifer be described?
3. How do rotifers feed? Reproduce?
4. What is the difference between a mictic and an amictic rotifer egg?

PHYLUM KINORHYNCHA

Kinorhynchs (kin'o-rink's) are small (less than 1 mm long), elongate bilaterally symmetrical worms found exclusively in marine environments, where they live in mud and sand. Because they have no external cilia or locomotor appendages, they simply burrow through the mud and sand with their snout.

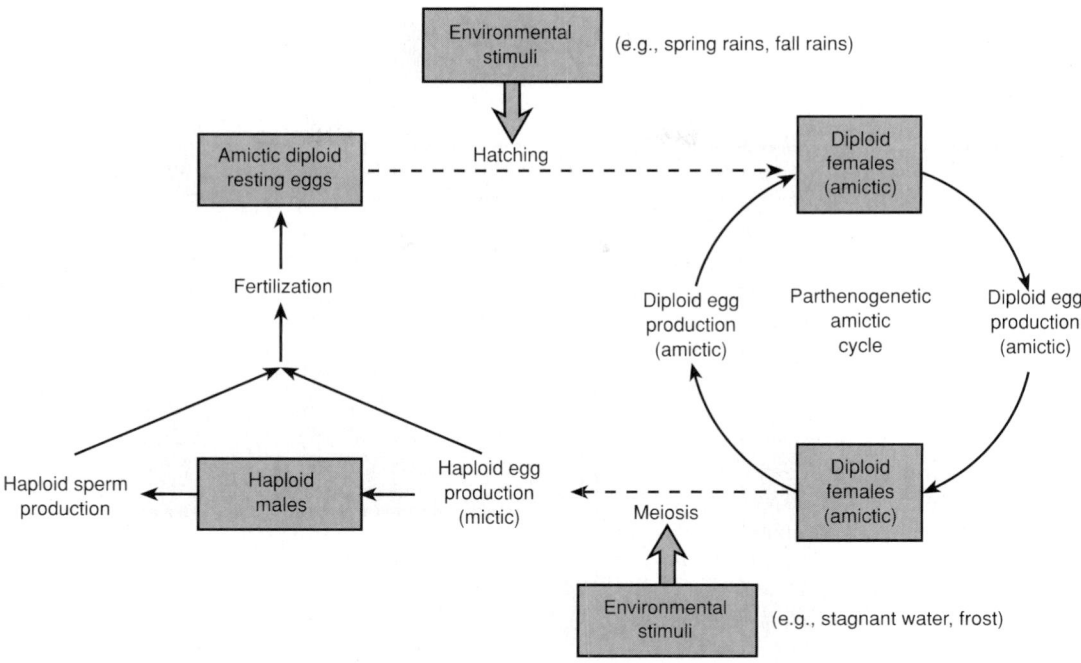

Figure 20.6

The Life Cycle of a Monogonont Rotifer. Dormant, diploid, resting eggs hatch in response to environmental stimuli (e.g., melting snows and spring rains) to begin a first amictic cycle. Other environmental stimuli (e.g., population density, stagnating water) later stimulate the production of haploid mictic eggs that lead to the production of dormant eggs that carry the species through the summer (e.g., when the pond dries up). With autumn rains, there is a second amictic cycle. Frost stimulates the production of mictic eggs again and the eventual dormant resting eggs that allow the population of rotifers to overwinter.

In fact, the phylum takes its name (Kinorhyncha, Gr. *kinein*, motion + *rhynchos*, snout) from this method of locomotion. The phylum Kinorhyncha contains about 150 known species.

The body surface of a kinorhynch is devoid of cilia and is composed of 13 or 14 definite units called **zonites** (figure 20.7). The head, represented by zonite 1, bears the mouth, an oral cone, and spines. The neck, represented by zonite 2, contains spines called **scalids** and plates called **placids.** The head can be retracted into the neck. The trunk consists of the remaining 11 or 12 zonites and terminates with the anus. Each trunk zonite bears a pair of lateral spines and one dorsal spine.

The body wall consists of a cuticle, epidermis, and two pairs of muscles: a dorsolateral and ventrolateral pair. The pseudocoelom is large and contains amoeboid cells.

A complete digestive system is present, consisting of a mouth, buccal cavity, muscular pharynx, esophagus, stomach-intestine (where digestion and absorption take place), and anus. Most kinorhynchs feed on diatoms, algae, and organic matter.

A pair of protonephridia is located in zonite 11. The nervous system consists of a brain and single ventral nerve cord with a ganglion (a mass of nerve cells) in each zonite. Eyespots and sensory bristles are found in some species. Kinorhynchs are dioecious with paired gonads. The male gonopore is surrounded by several spines that may be used in copulation. The young

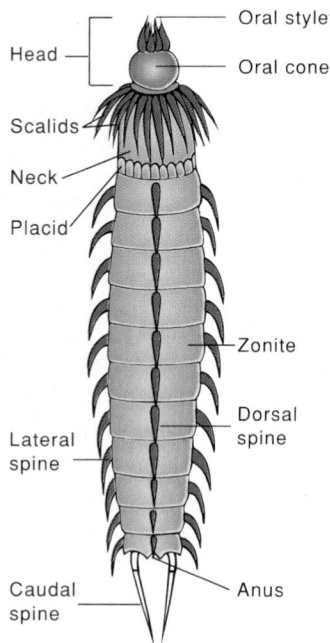

Figure 20.7

Phylum Kinorhyncha. An illustration of the external anatomy of an adult kinorhynch (dorsal view).

<table>
<tr><td>

BOX 20.2 | THE ECOLOGY OF SOIL NEMATODES

</td></tr>
</table>

Nematodes are incredibly abundant and diverse in soils. Some are parasitic on the roots of various plants, where they do considerable damage. Their large reproductive potential is generated at the expense of the plants on whose tissues they feed. The result is millions of dollars worth of damage to garden, truck farm, woody, and ornamental plants.

The vast majority of soil nematodes, however, are free living. They move between soil particles and are very important in the ecology of the soil. For example, some nematodes are voracious feeders on soil bacteria and fungi; they help control the populations of these microorganisms. Other nematodes feed, in turn, on the microbial feeders and also play an important role in biological control. Still other nematodes are eminently important in the entire process of decomposition. Many of these species are omnivorous or saprophytic (eat decomposing organic matter). The abundant soil nematodes are fed on by soil arthropods, some fungi, and earthworms. Overall, nematodes are essential to the energy flow and nutrient cycling in soil ecosystems.

TABLE 20.2 | CLASSIFICATION OF THE NEMATODES

Phylum Nematoda (nem-a-to′da)
Nematodes, or roundworms.
   Class Secernentea (Phasmidea) (ses-er-nen′te-a)
   Paired glandular or sensory structures called phasmids in the tail region; similar pair of structures (amphids) poorly developed in anterior end; excretory system present; both free-living and parasitic species. *Ascaris, Enterobius, Rhabditis, Turbatrix, Necator, Wuchereria.*
   Class Adenophorea (Aphasmidia) (a-den″o-for′e-a)
   Phasmids absent; most free living, but some parasitic species occur. *Dioctophyme, Trichinella, Trichuris.*

3. Complete digestive tract; mouth usually surrounded by lips bearing sense organs
4. Most with unique excretory system comprised of one or two renette cells or a set of collecting tubules
5. Body wall has only longitudinal muscles

EXTERNAL FEATURES

A typical nematode body is slender, elongate, cylindrical, and tapered at both ends (figure 20.8a,b). Much of the success of nematodes is due to their outer, noncellular, collagenous cuticle (figure 20.8c) that is continuous with the foregut, hindgut, sense organs, and parts of the female reproductive system. The cuticle may be either smooth or contain spines, bristles, papillae (small, nipplelike projections), warts, or ridges, all of which are of taxonomic significance. Three primary layers make up the cuticle: cortical, matrix, and basal. The cuticle functions to maintain internal hydrostatic pressure, provide mechanical protection, and aid in resisting digestion by the host in parasitic species. The cuticle is usually molted four times during maturation.

Beneath the cuticle is the epidermis, or hypodermis, which surrounds the pseudocoelom (figure 20.8d). The epidermis may be syncytial, and its nuclei are usually located in the four epidermal cords (one dorsal, one ventral, and two lateral) that project inward. The longitudinal muscles are the principal means of locomotion in nematodes.   ⑤   Contraction of these muscles results in undulatory waves that pass from the anterior to posterior end of the animal, creating characteristic thrashing movements. Nematodes lack circular muscles and therefore cannot crawl as do worms with more complex musculature.

Some nematodes have lips surrounding the mouth, and some species bear spines or teeth on or near the lips. In others, the lips have disappeared. Some roundworms have head shields that afford protection. Sensory organs include amphids, phasmids, or ocelli. **Amphids** are anterior depressions in the cuticle that contain modified cilia and function in chemoreception. **Phasmids** are located near the anus and also function in chemoreception. The presence or absence of these

hatch into larvae that do not have all of the zonites. As the larvae grow and molt, the adult morphology appears. Once adulthood is attained, molting no longer occurs.

PHYLUM NEMATODA

④   Nematodes (nem-a-to′des) (Gr. *nematos,* thread) or roundworms are some of the most abundant animals on earth—there may be some 5 billion in every acre of fertile garden soil. Zoologists estimate that there are anywhere from 10,000 to 500,000 roundworm species, feeding on every conceivable source of organic matter—from rotting substances to the living tissues of other invertebrates, vertebrates, and plants (box 20.2). They range in size from microscopic to several meters long. Many nematodes are parasites of plants or animals; others are free living in marine, freshwater, or soil habitats. Some nematodes play an important role in recycling nutrients in soils and bottom sediments.

Except in their sensory structures, nematodes lack cilia; a characteristic they share with arthropods. Also in common with some arthropods, the sperm of nematodes is amoeboid. Two classes of nematodes are recognized (table 20.2).

Characteristics of the phylum Nematoda include the following:

1. Triploblastic, bilateral, vermiform (resembling a worm in shape; long and slender), unsegmented, pseudocoelomate
2. Body round in cross section and covered by a layered cuticle; growth in juveniles usually accompanied by molting

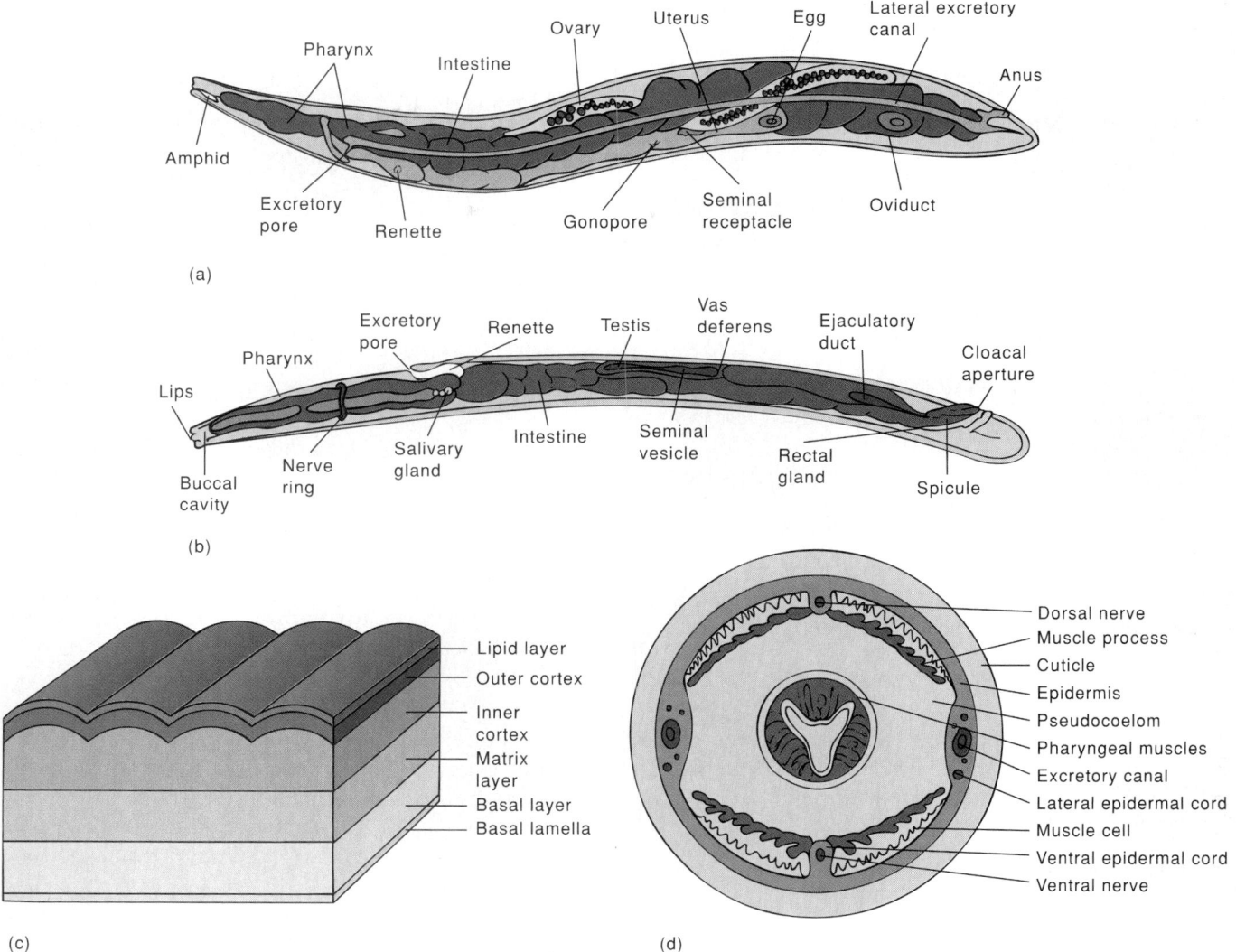

Figure 20.8

Phylum Nematoda. (*a*) Internal anatomical features of a female and (*b*) male *Rhabditis.* (*c*) A section through a nematode cuticle showing the various layers. (*d*) A cross section through the region of the muscular pharynx of a nematode. The hydrostatic pressure in the pseudocoelom acts to maintain the rounded body shape of a nematode and also to collapse the intestine, which aids in food and waste material moving from the mouth to the anus.

organs determines the taxonomic class (*see table 20.2*) to which nematodes belong. Paired ocelli (eyes) are present in aquatic nematodes.

INTERNAL FEATURES

The nematode pseudocoelom is a spacious, fluid-filled cavity that contains the visceral organs and forms a hydrostatic skeleton.   ⑥   All nematodes are round because of the equal outward force generated in all directions by the body muscles contracting against the pseudocoelomic fluid (figure 20.8*d*).

FEEDING AND THE DIGESTIVE SYSTEM

Depending on the environment, nematodes are capable of feeding on a wide variety of foods—they may be carnivores, herbivores, omnivores, saprobes that consume decomposing organisms, or parasitic species that feed on blood and tissue fluids of their hosts.

Nematodes have a complete digestive system consisting of a mouth, which may have teeth, jaws, or stylets; buccal cavity; muscular pharynx; long tubular intestine where digestion and absorption occur; short rectum; and anus. Hydrostatic

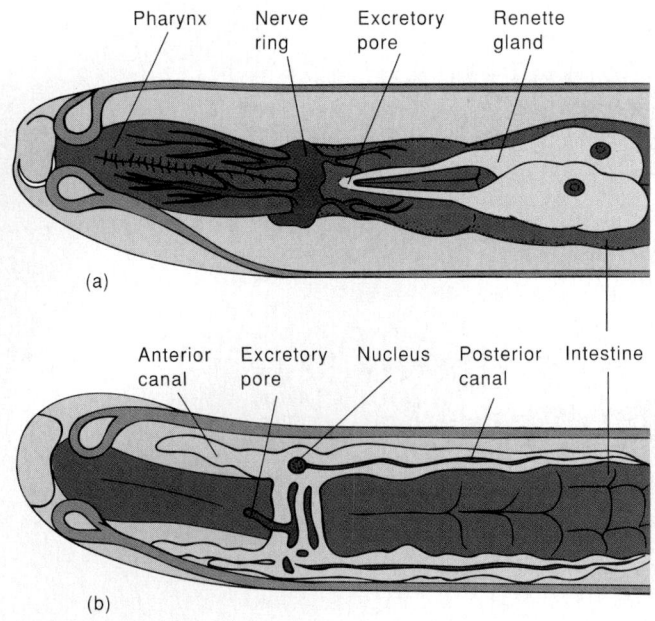

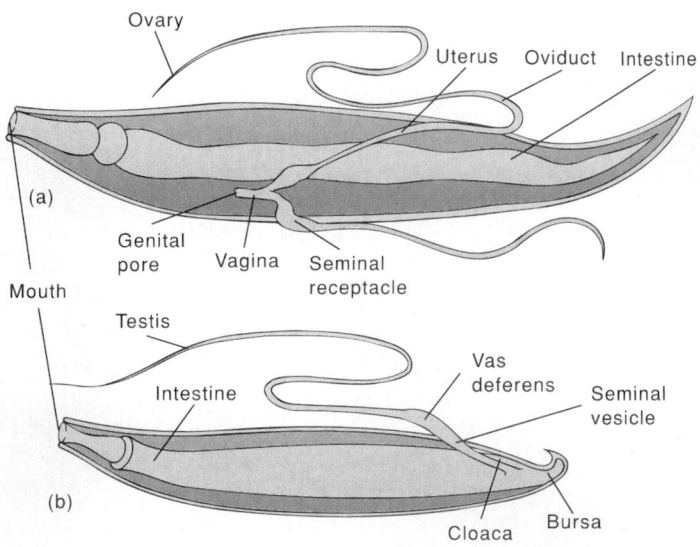

FIGURE 20.9
Nematode Excretory Systems. (*a*) Glandular, as found in *Rhabditis*.
(*b*) Tubular, as found in *Ascaris*.

FIGURE 20.10
Nematode Reproductive Systems. Illustrations showing the
reproductive systems of a (*a*) female and (*b*) male nematode such as
Ascaris. The sizes of the reproductive systems are exaggerated to show
details.

pressure in the pseudocoelom and the pumping action of the
pharynx are responsible for the passage of food through the alimentary canal.

OTHER ORGAN SYSTEMS

Nematodes accomplish osmoregulation and excretion of nitrogenous waste products (ammonia, urea) with two unique systems.
The glandular system (figure 20.9*a*) is found in aquatic species,
and consists of ventral gland cells, called **renettes,** that are located posterior to the pharynx. Each gland absorbs waste material
from the pseudocoelom and empties it to the outside through
an excretory pore. Parasitic nematodes have a more advanced
system, called the tubular system (figure 20.9*b*), that develops
from the renette system. In this system, the renettes unite to form
a large canal, which opens to the outside via an excretory pore.

The nervous system consists of an anterior nerve ring (*see*
figure 20.8b). Nerves extend anteriorly and posteriorly; many
connect to each other via commissures. Certain neuroendocrine secretions are involved in growth, molting, cuticle formation, and metamorphosis.

REPRODUCTION AND DEVELOPMENT

Most nematodes are dioecious and dimorphic, with the males
being smaller than the females. The long, coiled gonads lie free
in the pseudocoelom.

The female system consists of a pair of convoluted
ovaries (figure 20.10*a*). Each ovary is continuous with an
oviduct whose proximal end is swollen to form a seminal receptacle. Each oviduct becomes a tubular uterus; the two uteri
unite to form a vagina that opens to the outside through a
genital pore.

The male system consists of a single testis, which is
continuous with a vas deferens that eventually expands into
a seminal vesicle (figure 20.10*b*). The seminal vesicle connects to the cloaca. Males are commonly armed with a posterior flap of tissue called a bursa. The bursa aids the male
in the transfer of sperm to the female genital pore during
copulation.

After copulation, each fertilized egg is moved to the
gonopore by hydrostatic forces in the pseudocoelom (*see*
*figure 20.8*d). The number of eggs produced varies with the
species; some nematodes produce only several hundred,
whereas others may produce 200,000 daily. Some nematodes give birth to larvae (ovoviviparity). The development and hatching of the eggs are influenced by external
factors, such as temperature and moisture. Hatching produces a larva (also referred to by some parasitologists as a
juvenile) that has most adult structures. The larva (juvenile) undergoes four molts, although in some species, the
first one or two molts may take place before the eggs
hatch.

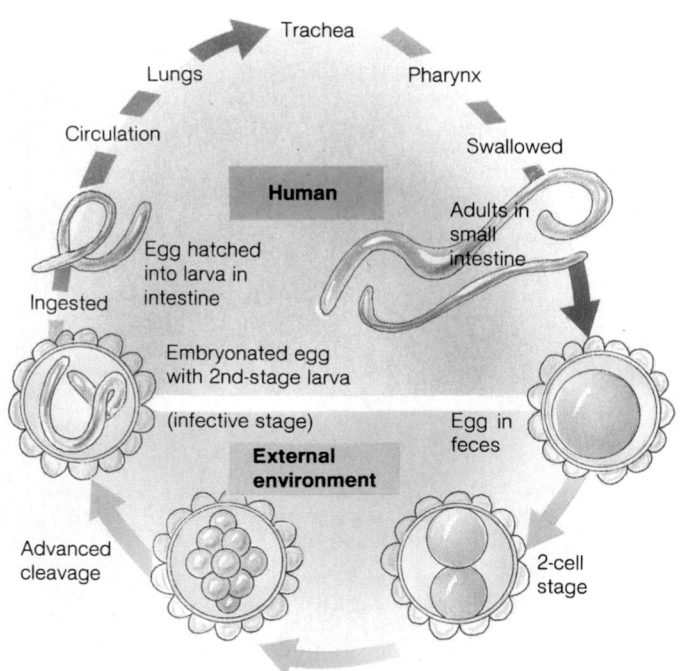

FIGURE 20.11

The Life Cycle of *Ascaris lumbricoides*. (See text for details.) *Source: Redrawn from Centers for Disease Control, Atlanta.*

SOME IMPORTANT NEMATODE PARASITES OF HUMANS

Parasitic nematodes possess a number of evolutionary adaptations to their way of life. These include a high reproductive potential, life cycles that make transmission from one host to another more likely, an enzyme-resistant cuticle, resistant eggs, and encysted larvae. The life cycles of nematodes are not as complicated as those of cestodes or trematodes because only one host is usually involved. Discussions of the life cycles of five important human parasites follow.

Ascaris lumbricoides: The Giant Intestinal Roundworm of Humans

It has been estimated that as many as 800 million people throughout the world may be infected with *Ascaris lumbricoides*. Adult *Ascaris* (Gr. *askaris*, intestinal worm) live in the small intestine of humans (*see figure 20.1*). Large numbers of eggs are produced and exit with the feces (figure 20.11). A first-stage larva develops rapidly in the egg, molts, and matures into a second-stage larva, the infective stage. When a human ingests embryonated eggs, they hatch in the intestine, the larvae penetrate the intestinal wall, and are carried via the circulation to the lungs. They molt twice in the lungs, migrate up the trachea, and are swallowed. The worms attain sexual maturity in the intestine, mate, and begin egg production.

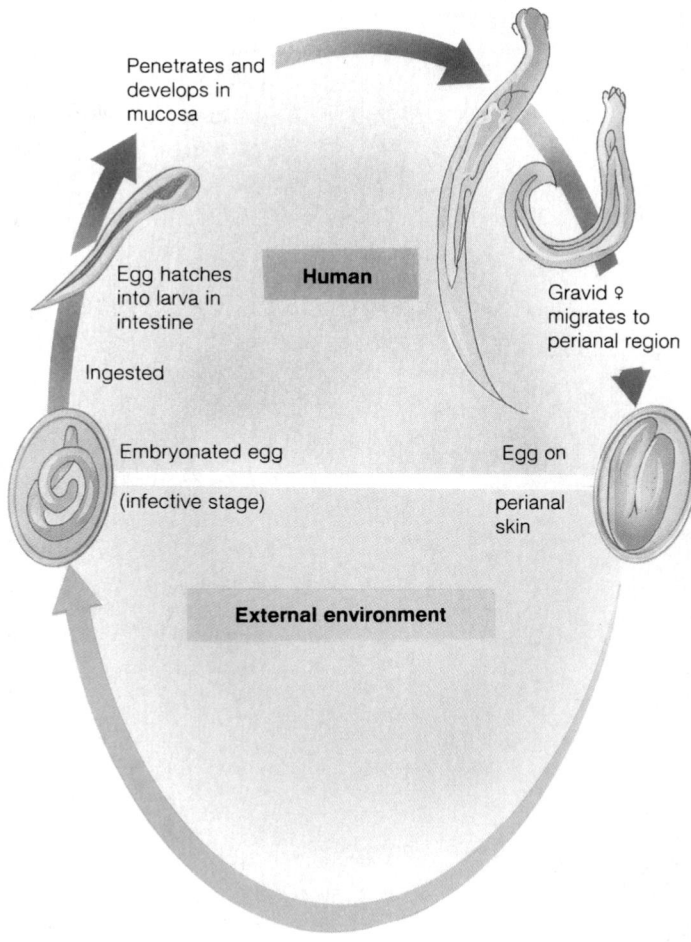

FIGURE 20.12

The Life Cycle of *Enterobius vermicularis*. (See text for details.) *Source: Redrawn from Centers for Disease Control, Atlanta.*

Enterobius vermicularis: The Human Pinworm

7   Pinworms (*Enterobius*; Gr. *enteron*, intestine + *bios*, life) are the most common roundworm parasites in the United States. Adult *Enterobius vermicularis* are located in the lower region of the large intestine. At night, gravid females migrate out of the cecum to the perianal area, where they deposit eggs containing a first-stage larva (figure 20.12). When humans ingest these eggs, the eggs hatch, the larvae molt four times in the small intestine and migrate to the large intestine. Adults mate, and females begin egg production in a short period of time.

Necator americanus: The New World Hookworm

The New World or American hookworm, *Necator americanus* (L. *necator*, killer), can be found in the southern United States. The adults live in the small intestine, where they hold onto the intestinal wall with teeth and feed on blood and tissue fluids

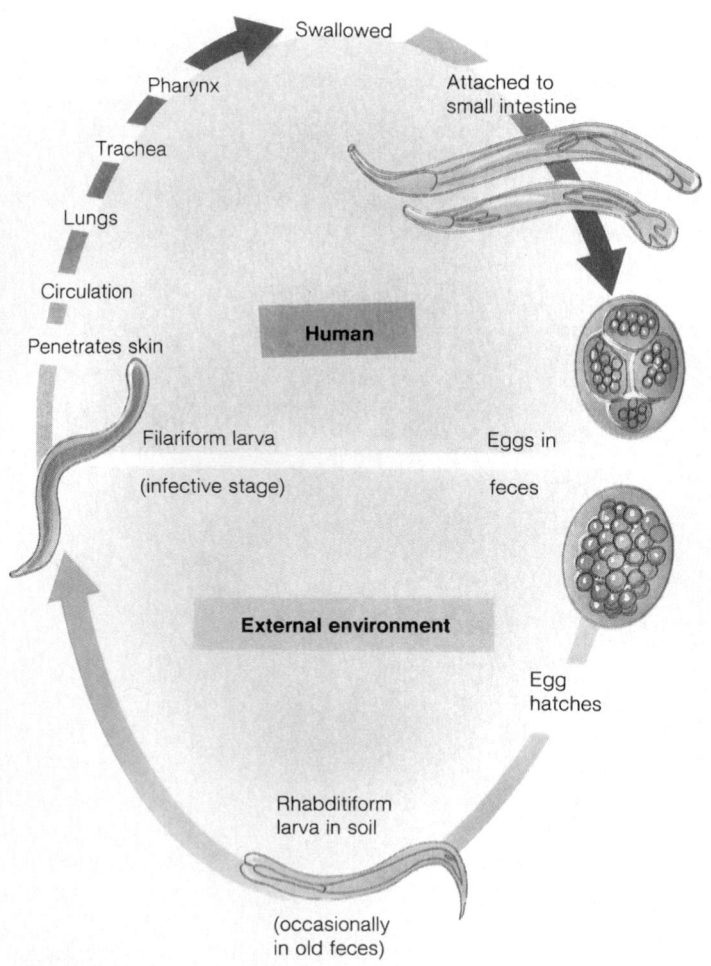

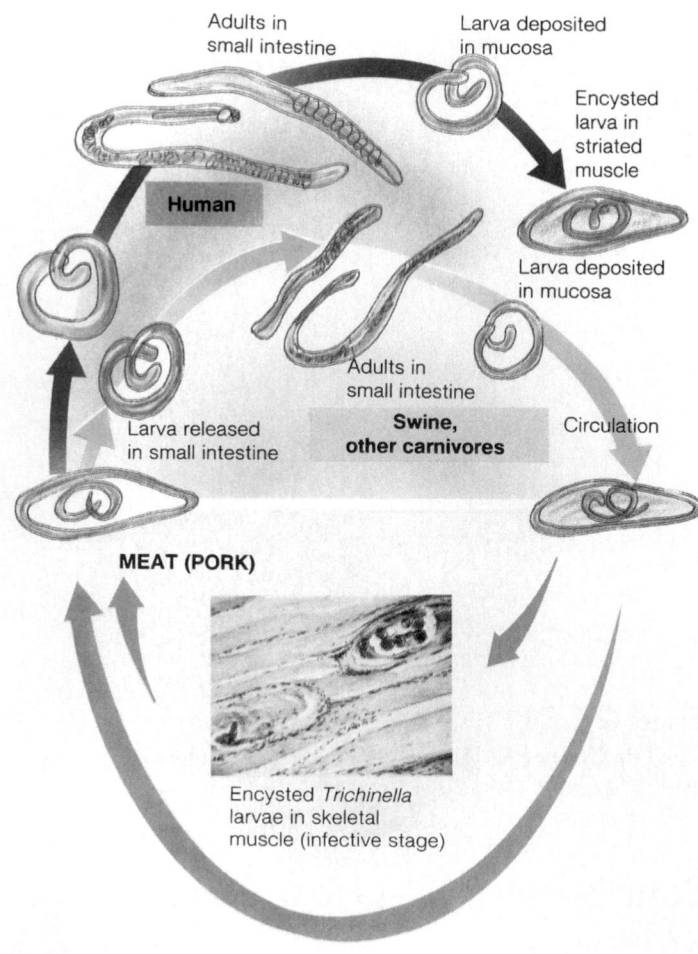

FIGURE 20.13

The Life Cycle of *Necator americanus*. (See text for details.) *Source: Redrawn from Centers for Disease Control, Atlanta.*

(figure 20.13). Individual females may produce as many as 10,000 eggs daily, which pass out of the body in the feces. The eggs hatch on warm, moist soil and release a small rhabditiform larva. It molts and becomes the infective filariform larva. Humans become infected when the filariform larva penetrates the skin, usually on the foot. (Outside defecation and subsequent walking barefoot through the immediate area maintains the life cycle in humans.) After the larva burrows through the skin, it reaches the circulatory system. The rest of its life cycle is similar to that of *Ascaris* (*see figure 20.11*).

Trichinella spiralis: The Porkworm

Adult *Trichinella* (Gr. *trichinos,* hair) *spiralis* live in the mucosa of the small intestine of humans and other carnivores (e.g., the pig). In the intestine, adult females give birth to young larvae that then enter the circulatory system and are carried to skeletal (striated) muscles of the same host (figure 20.14). The

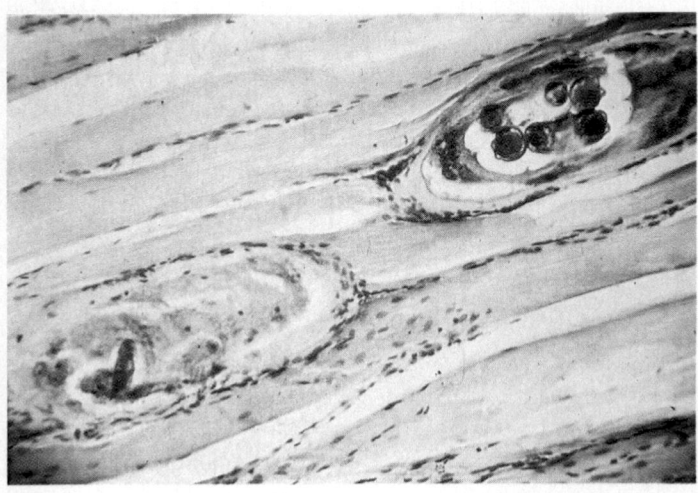

FIGURE 20.14

The Life Cycle of *Trichinella spiralis*. (*a*) See text for details. (*b*) An enlargement of the insert in (*a*) showing two encysted larvae in skeletal muscle (light micrograph ×450). (*a*) *Source: Redrawn from Centers for Disease Control, Atlanta.*

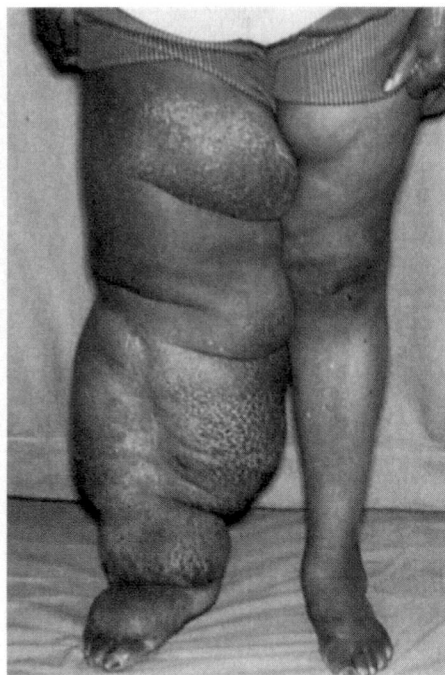

FIGURE 20.15

Elephantiasis. An Example of Elephantiasis Caused by the Filarial Worm, *Wuchereria bancrofti.* It takes years for this condition to become as shown in this figure.

young larvae encyst in the skeletal muscles and remain infective for many years. The disease caused by this nematode is called **trichinosis.** Infective meat (muscle) must be ingested by another host to continue the life cycle. ⑧ Humans most often become infected by eating improperly cooked pork products. Once ingested, the larvae excyst in the stomach and make their way to the small intestine, where they molt four times and develop into adults.

Wuchereria spp.: The Filarial Worms

In tropical countries, over 250 million humans are infected with filarial (L. *filium,* thread) worms. Two examples of human filarial worms are *Wuchereria bancrofti* and *W. malayi*. These elongate, threadlike nematodes live in the lymphatic system, where they block the vessels. Because lymphatic vessels return tissue fluids to the circulatory system, when the filiarial nematodes block these vessels, fluids tend to accumulate in peripheral tissues. ⑨ This fluid accumulation causes the enlargement of various appendages, a condition called **elephantiasis** (figure 20.15).

In the lymphatic vessels, adults copulate and produce larvae called **microfilariae** (figure 20.16). The microfilariae are released into the bloodstream of the human host and migrate to the peripheral circulation at night. When a mosquito feeds on a human, it ingests the microfilariae. The microfilariae migrate to the mosquito's thoracic muscles, where they molt

twice and become infective. When the mosquito takes another meal of blood, the infective third-stage larvae are injected into the blood of the human host through the mosquito's proboscis. The final two molts take place as the larvae enter the lymphatic vessels.

A filarial worm prevalent in the United States is *Dirofilaria immitis,* a parasite of dogs. ⑩ Since the adult worms live in the heart and large arteries of the lungs, the infection is called **heartworm disease.** Once established, these filarial worms are difficult to eliminate, and can be fatal; prevention with heartworm medicine is thus advocated for all dogs.

PHYLUM NEMATOMORPHA

Nematomorphs (nem′a-to-mor′phs) (Gr. *nema,* thread + *morphe,* form) are a small group (about 250 species) of elongate worms commonly called either **horsehair worms,** or **Gordian worms.** ⑪ The hairlike nature of these worms is so striking that they were formerly thought to arise spontaneously from the hairs of a horse's tail in drinking troughs or other stock-watering places. The adults are free living, but the juveniles are all parasitic in arthropods. They have a worldwide distribution and can be found in both running and standing water.

The body of a nematomorph is extremely long and threadlike and has no distinct head (figure 20.17). The body wall has a thick cuticle, a cellular epidermis, longitudinal cords, and a muscle layer of longitudinal fibers. The nervous system contains an anterior nerve ring and a vental cord.

Nematomorphs have separate sexes; two long gonads extend the length of the body. After copulation, the eggs are deposited in water. When an egg hatches, a small larva that has a protrusible proboscis armed with spines emerges. Terminal stylets are also present on the proboscis. The larva must quickly enter an arthropod (e.g., a beetle, cockroach) host, either by penetrating the host or being eaten. Lacking a digestive system, the larva feeds by absorbing material directly across its body wall. Once mature, the worm leaves its host only when the arthropod is near water. Sexual maturity is attained during the free-living adult phase of the life cycle.

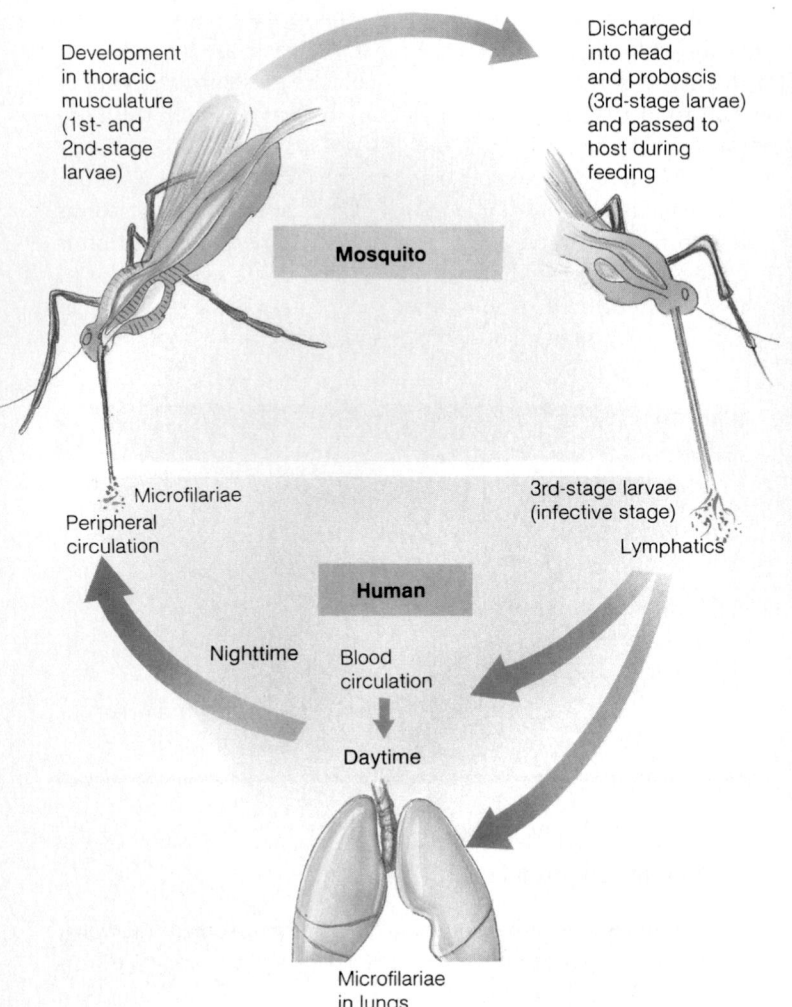

Development
in thoracic
musculature
(1st- and
2nd-stage
larvae)

Discharged
into head
and proboscis
(3rd-stage larvae)
and passed to
host during
feeding

Mosquito

Microfilariae
Peripheral
circulation

3rd-stage larvae
(infective stage)

Lymphatics

Human

Nighttime

Blood
circulation

Daytime

Microfilariae
in lungs

FIGURE 20.16

The Life Cycle of *Wuchereria* spp. (See text for details.) *Source: Redrawn from Centers for Disease Control, Atlanta.*

PHYLUM ACANTHOCEPHALA

Adult acanthocephalans (a-kan'tho-sef'a-lans) (Gr. *akantha*, spine or thorn + *kephale*, head) are endoparasites in the intestinal tract of vertebrates (especially fishes). Two hosts are required to complete the life cycle. The juveniles are parasites of crustaceans and insects. Acanthocephalans are generally small (less than 40 mm long), although one important species that occurs in pigs, *Macracanthorhynchus hirudinaceus*, can be up to 80 cm long. The body of the adult is elongate and composed of a short anterior proboscis, a neck region, and a trunk (figure 20.18*a*). ⑫ The proboscis is covered with recurved spines (figure 20.18*b*); hence the name "spiny-headed worms." The retractible proboscis provides the means of attachment in the host's intestine. Females are always larger than males and there are about 1,000 species.

The body wall of acanthocephalans is covered by a living syncytial tegument that has been adapted to the parasitic way

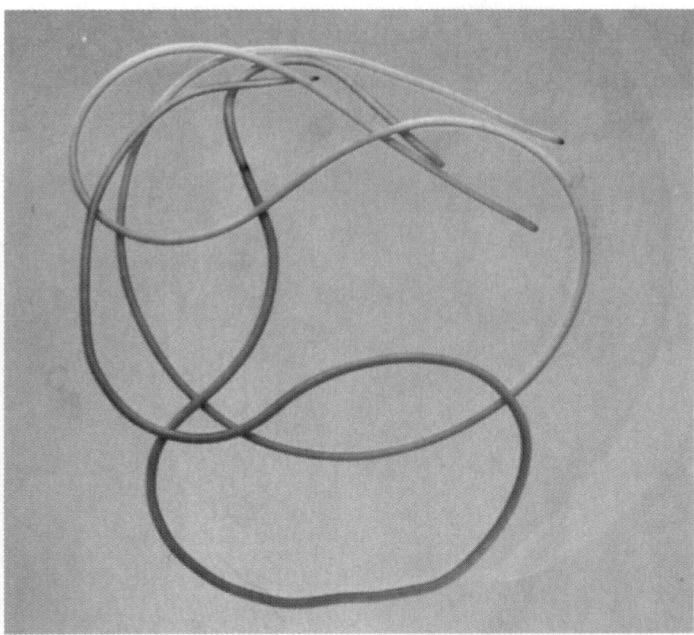

FIGURE 20.17

Phylum Nematomorpha. Photomicrograph of two adult worms. As illustrated, these worms tend to twist and turn upon themselves, giving the appearance of complicated knots, thus the name "Gordian worms." (Legend has it that King Gordius of Phrygia tied a formidable knot—the Gordian knot—and declared that whoever might undo it would be the ruler of all Asia. No one could accomplish this until Alexander the Great cut through it with his broadsword.)

of life. A glycocalyx (*see figure 3.6*) consisting of mucopolysaccharides and glycoproteins covers the tegument and protects against host enzymes and immune defenses. No digestive system is present; food is absorbed directly through the tegument from the host by specific membrane transport mechanisms and pinocytosis. Protonephridia may be present. The nervous system is composed of a ventral, anterior ganglionic mass from which anterior and posterior nerves arise. Sensory organs are poorly developed.

The sexes are separate, and the male has a protrusible penis. Fertilization is internal, and development of eggs takes place in the pseudocoelom. The biotic potential of certain acanthocephalans is great; for example, a gravid female *Macroacanthorhynchus hirudinaceus* may contain up to 10 million embryonated eggs. The eggs pass out of the host with the feces and must be eaten by certain insects (e.g., cockroaches or grubs), or by aquatic crustaceans (e.g., amphipods, isopods, ostracods). Once in the invertebrate, the larva emerges from the egg and is now called an **acanthor.** It burrows through the gut wall and lodges in the hemocoel, where it develops into an **acanthella** and eventually into a **cystacanth.** When the intermediate host is eaten by a mammal, fish, or bird, the cystacanth excysts and attaches to the intestinal wall with its spiny proboscis.

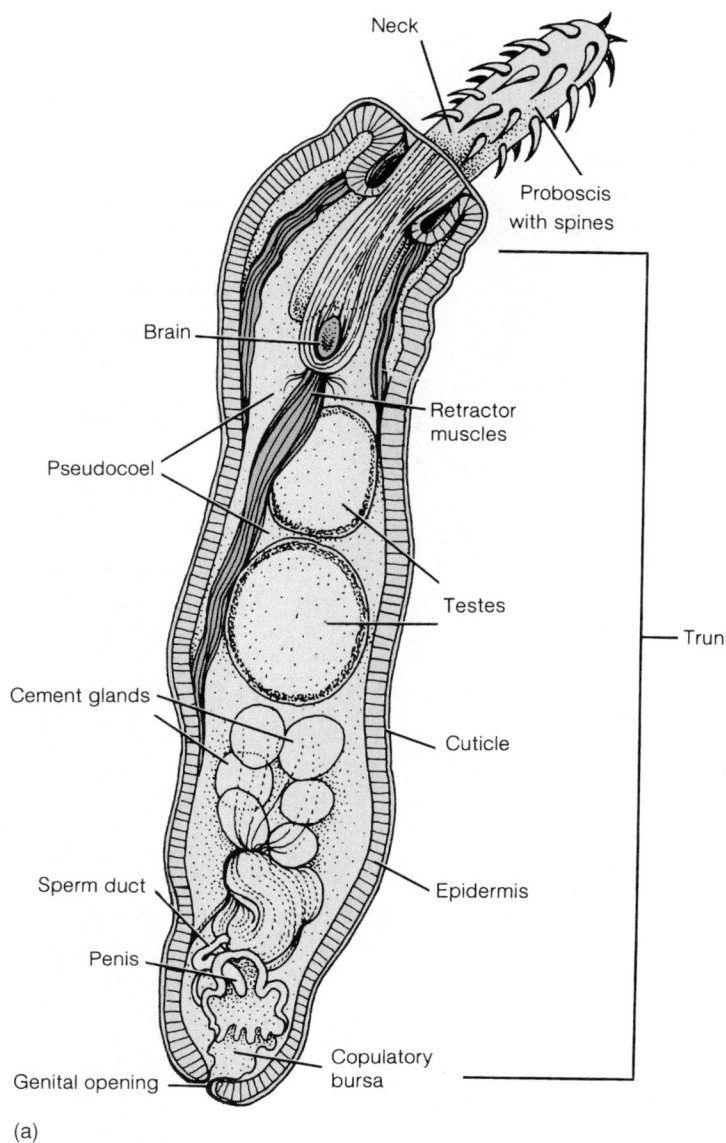

(a)

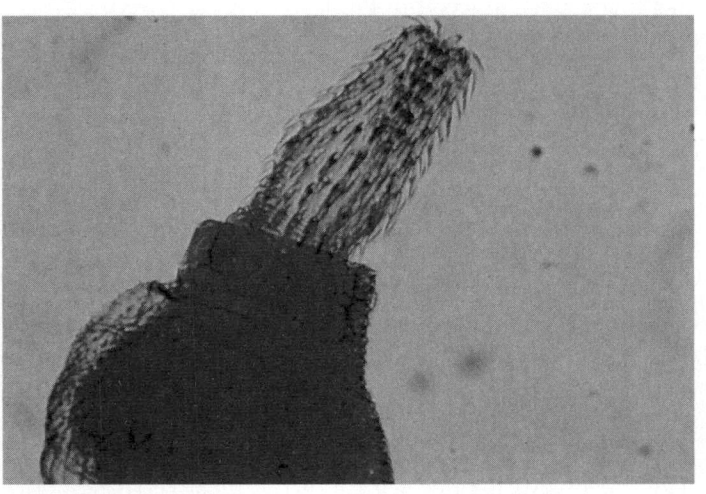

(b)

FIGURE 20.18

Phylum Acanthocephala. (*a*) Drawing of an adult male, dorsal view.
(*b*) Light micrograph of the proboscis of a spiny-headed worm (×50).

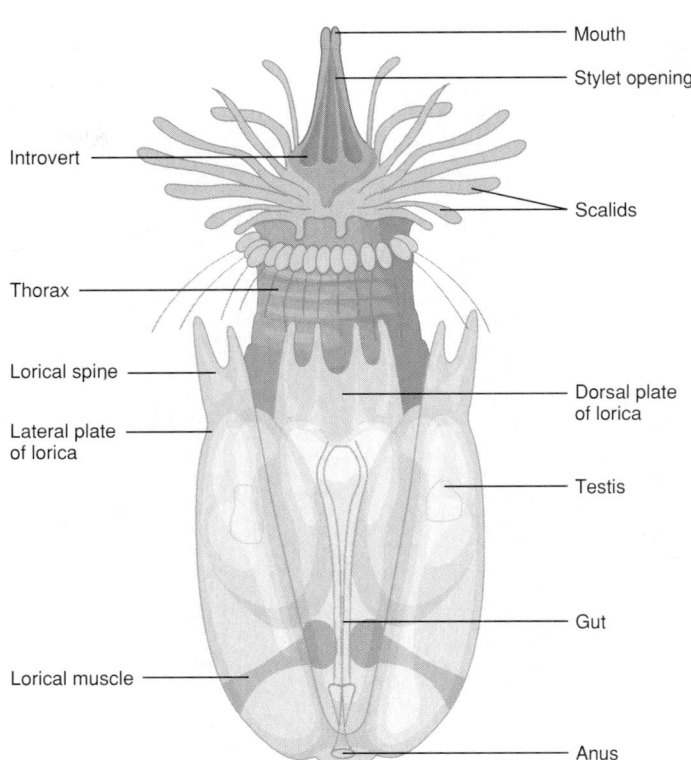

FIGURE 20.19

Phylum Loricifera. The anatomy of an adult male *Nanaloricus* (dorsal view).

Stop and Ask Yourself

9. Why are nematomorphs called horsehair worms or Gordian worms?
10. What is the life cycle of a nematomorph?
11. What is unique about the tegument of an acanthocephalan?
12. What is the life cycle of an acanthocephalan?

PHYLUM LORICIFERA

13 The phylum Loricifera (lor'a-sif-er-a) (L. *lorica*, clothed in armor + *fero*, to bear) is the most recently described animal phylum. Its first members were identified and named in 1983. Loriciferans occur in spaces between marine gravel. A characteristic species is *Nanaloricus mysticus*. It is a small, bilaterally symmetrical worm that has a spiny head called an **introvert**, a thorax, and an abdomen surrounded by a lorica (figure 20.19). Both the introvert and thorax can be retracted into the anterior end of the lorica. The introvert bears eight oral stylets that surround the mouth. The lorical cuticle is periodically molted. A pseudocoelom is present and contains a short digestive system, brain, and several ganglia. Loriciferans are dioecious with paired gonads. About 14 species have been formally described.

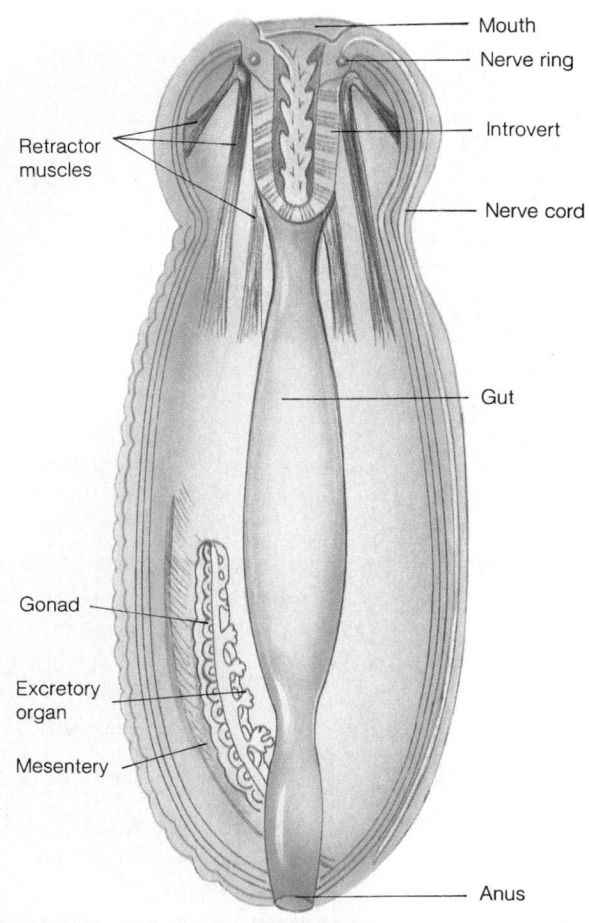

FIGURE 20.20

Phylum Priapulida. The internal anatomy of the priapulid, *Priapulus*. In this drawing, the introvert is shown withdrawn into the body.

PHYLUM PRIAPULIDA

The priapulids (pri′a-pyu-lids) (Gr. *priapos*, phallus + *ida*, pleural suffix; from *Priapos*, the Greek god of reproduction, symbolized by the penis) are a small group (only 16 species) of marine worms found in cold waters. They live buried in the mud and sand of the seafloor, where they feed on small annelids and other invertebrates.

The body (figure 20.20) is cylindrical in cross section, and ranges in length from 2 mm to about 8 cm. The anterior part of the body is an introvert (proboscis), which can be drawn into the longer, posterior trunk. The introvert functions in burrowing and is surrounded by spines. The muscular body is covered with a thin cuticle that bears spines and the trunk bears superficial annuli. A straight digestive tract is suspended in a large pseudocoelom that acts as a hydrostatic skeleton. In some species, the pseudocoelom contains amoeboid cells that probably function in gas transport. The nervous system consists of a nerve ring around the pharynx and a single midventral nerve cord. The sexes are separate but not superficially distinguishable. A pair of gonads is suspended in the pseudocoelom and shares a common duct with

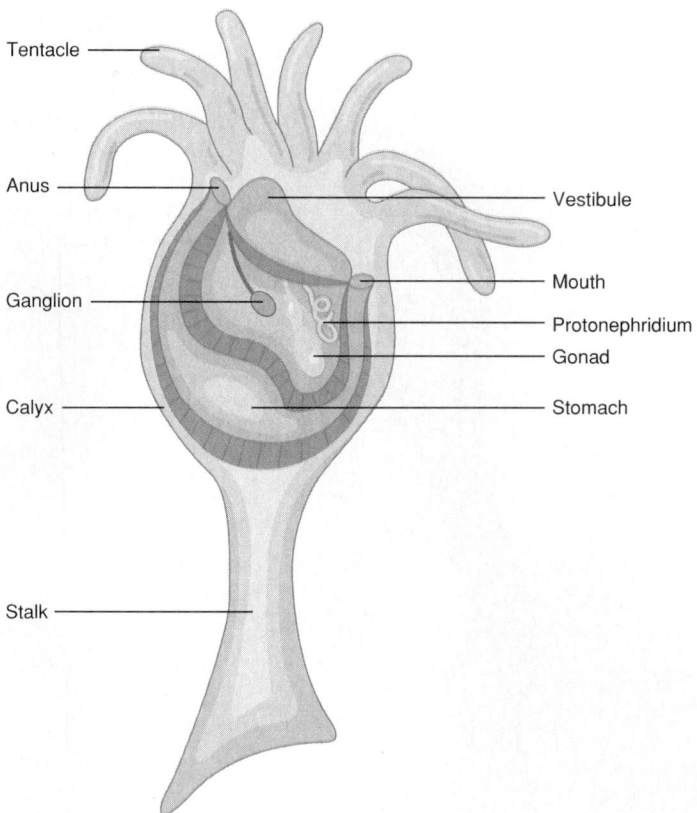

FIGURE 20.21

Phylum Entoprocta. Some morphological features of a typical entoproct.

the protonephridia. The duct opens near the anus, and gametes are shed into the sea. Fertilization is external, and the eggs eventually sink to the bottom, where the larvae develop into adults. The cuticle is repeatedly molted throughout life. The most commonly encountered species is *Priapulus caudatus*.

PHYLUM ENTOPROCTA

The entoprocts (en′to-prok′s) (Gr. *entos*, within + *proktos*, anus) comprise a small phylum of about 100 species of sedentary marine filter feeders. They are either solitary or colonial and are found in coastal waters. One group is commensalistic on the body surface of various invertebrates. Most entoprocts are microscopic in size. Entoprocts may form large, matlike colonies on rocks. An individual entoproct consists of a muscular stalk bearing a cup-shaped **calyx** with a crown of ciliated tentacles (figure 20.21). The stalk is surrounded by a chitinous cuticle and may bear an attachment disk with adhesive glands. The pseudocoel is filled with loose connective tissue. Entoprocts are filter feeders, and when they feed, the cilia on the tentacles convey food into the mouth. The digestive tract forms a U-shaped gut located in the calyx. Also found in the calyx is a pair of protonephridial tubules that open through a single pore into the mouth. The nervous system consists of a small, central ganglion and radiating nerves. Exchange of gases occurs across the body surface.

Entoprocts reproduce by asexual budding and also sexually. Most entoprocts are hermaphroditic, but usually eggs and sperm are produced at different times in one animal. Sperm are released freely into the water, and fertilization occurs internally. Embryos develop in a brood chamber, from which free-swimming larvae are released. Eventually, the larvae settle to the substrata and develop into adults.

FURTHER PHYLOGENETIC CONSIDERATIONS

The aschelminths are clearly a diverse assemblage of animals. Despite the common occurrence of a cuticle, pseudocoelom, a muscular pharynx, and adhesive glands, there are no distinctive features that occur in every phyla.

The gastrotrichs show some distant relationships to the acoelomates. For example, many gastrotrichs lack a body cavity, are monoecious, are small, and their ventral cilia may have been derived from the same ancestral sources as those of the turbellarian flatworms.

The rotifers also have certain features in common with the acoelomates. The protonephridia of rotifers closely resemble those of some freshwater turbellarians, and it is generally believed that rotifers originated in freshwater habitats. Both flatworms and rotifers have separate ovaries and vitellaria. Rotifers probably had their origins from the earliest acoelomates and may have had a common bilateral, metazoan ancestor.

The kinorhynchs, acanthocephalans, loriciferans, and priapulids all have a spiny anterior end that can be retracted; thus, they are probably related. Loriciferans and kinorhynchs appear to be most closely related.

The affinities of the nematodes to other phyla are vague. No other living group is believed to be closely related to these worms. Nematodes probably evolved in freshwater habitats and then colonized the oceans and soils. The ancestral nematodes may have been sessile, attached at the posterior end, with the anterior end protruding upward into the water. The nematode cuticle, feeding structures, and food habits probably preadapted these worms for parasitism. In fact, free-living species could become parasitic without substantial anatomical or physiological changes.

Nematomorphs may be more closely related to nematodes than to any other group by virtue of both groups being cylindrical in shape, having a cuticle, dioecious, and sexually dimorphic. However, because the larval form of some nematomorphs has a resemblance to the Priapulida, the exact affinity to the nematodes is questionable.

The phylogenetic position of the entoprocts is still controversial. Some zoologists consider entoprocts more closely related to a phylum of coelomates called the Ectoprocta. However, because entoprocts have a pseudocoelom and protonephridia similar to flatworms and rotifers, they are discussed with the aschelminths.

Stop and Ask Yourself

13. What are the characteristics of a typical loriciferan?
14. How can a typical priapulan be described?
15. How can a typical entoproct be described?
16. What evidence is there that the individual aschelminth phyla exhibit diverse phylogenetic relationships?

SUMMARY

1. Nine phyla are grouped together as the aschelminths. Most have a well-defined pseudocoelom, a constant number of body cells or nuclei (eutely), protonephridia, and a complete digestive system with a well-developed pharynx. No organs are developed for gas exchange or circulation. The body is covered with a cuticle that may be molted. Only longitudinal muscles are often present in the body wall.

2. The phylogenetic affinities among the nine phyla and with other phyla are uncertain.

3. Gastrotrichs are microscopic, aquatic animals with a head, neck, and trunk. Numerous adhesive glands are present. The group is generally hermaphroditic, although males are rare and female parthenogenesis is common in freshwater species.

4. The majority of rotifers inhabit fresh water. The head of these animals bears a unique ciliated corona used for locomotion and food capture. Males are smaller than females and unknown in some species. Females may develop parthenogenetically.

5. Kinorhynchs are minute worms living in marine habitats. Their bodies are comprised of 13 zonites, which have cuticular scales, plates, and spines.

6. Nematodes live in aquatic and terrestrial environments; many are parasitic and of medical and agricultural importance. They are all elongate, slender, and circular in cross section. Two sexes are present.

7. Nematomorpha are threadlike and free living in fresh water. They lack a digestive system.

8. Acanthocephalans are also known as spiny-headed worms because of their spiny proboscis. All are endoparasites in vertebrates.

9. The phylum Loricifera was described in 1983. These microscopic animals have a spiny head and thorax and are found in gravel in marine environments.

10. The phylum Priapulida contains only 15 known species of cucumber-shaped, wormlike animals that live buried in the bottom sand and mud in marine habitats.

11. The phylum Entoprocta contains about 100 species of sessile or sedentary filter feeders; most are hermaphroditic.

Selected Key Terms

amictic eggs (*p. 308*)

aschelminths (*p. 304*)

corona (*p. 306*)

cuticle (*p. 305*)

eutely (*p. 305*)

mastax (*p. 308*)

mictic eggs (*p. 308*)

zonites (*p. 309*)

Critical Thinking Questions

1. Discuss the limitations placed on shape changes in nematodes by the structure of the body wall.

2. What characteristics set the Nematomorpha apart from the Nematoda? What characteristics do the Nematomorpha share with the Nematoda?

3. In what respects are the kinorhynchs like nematodes? Like rotifers?

4. How are gastrotrichs related to the rotifers?

5. What are some environmental factors that appear to trigger the production of mictic females in monogonont rotifers?

21

MOLLUSCAN SUCCESS

Outline

Concepts

1. Triploblastic animals are often assembled into two groups, the protostomes and deuterostomes, based on certain developmental features.
2. Molluscs have a coelom, as well as a head-foot, visceral mass, mantle, and a mantle cavity. Most also have a radula.
3. Members of the class Gastropoda are the snails and slugs. They include the only terrestrial molluscs. Their bodies are modified by torsion and shell coiling.
4. Clams, oysters, mussels, and scallops are members of the class Bivalvia. They are all aquatic filter feeders and are often found burrowing in soft substrates or attached to hard substrates.
5. The class Cephalopoda includes the octopuses, squids, cuttlefish, and nautili. They are the most complex of all invertebrates and are adapted for predatory life-styles.
6. Other molluscs include members of the classes Scaphopoda (tooth shells), Monoplacophora, Aplacophora (solenogasters), and Polyplacophora (chitons). Members of these classes are all marine.
7. The exact relationship of molluscs to other animal phyla is debated. Specializations of molluscs have obscured evolutionary relationships among molluscan classes.

Would You Like to Know:

1. what characteristics can be used to identify molluscs? (*p. 325*)
2. how coiling of a snail's shell affects the arrangement of the snail's internal organs? (*p. 328*)
3. how a snail extends its tentacles? (*p. 328*)
4. how a pearl is formed? (*p. 330*)
5. how a clam feeds? (*p. 330*)
6. how some bivalves burrow through limestone and coral? (*p. 333*)
7. what invertebrate preys on whales? (*p. 335*)
8. what molluscs have the most advanced nervous and sensory functions among invertebrates? (*p. 335*)

These and other useful questions will be answered in this chapter.

This chapter contains evolutionary concepts, which are set off in this font.

EVOLUTIONARY PERSPECTIVE

Octopuses, squids, and cuttlefish (the cephalopods) may be considered some of the invertebrate world's most adept predators. Predatory life-styles have resulted in the evolution of large brains (by invertebrate standards), complex sensory structures (by any standards), rapid locomotion, grasping tentacles, and tearing mouthparts. In spite of these adaptations, cephalopods rarely make up a major component of any community. Once numbering about 9,000 species, the class Cephalopoda now includes only about 550 species (figure 21.1).

Zoologists do not know why the cephalopods have declined so dramatically. Cephalopods may have been outcompeted by vertebrates, because the vertebrates were also making their appearance in prehistoric seas, and some vertebrates acquired active, predatory life-styles. Alternatively, the cephalopods may have declined simply because of random evolutionary events.

The same has not been the case for all molluscs. This group has, as a whole, been very successful. If success is measured by numbers of species, the molluscs can be considered twice as successful as vertebrates! The vast majority of its nearly 100,000 living species belong to two classes: Gastropoda, the snails and slugs; and Bivalvia, the clams and their close relatives.

Molluscs are triploblastic, as are all the remaining animals covered in this textbook. In addition, they are the first animals described in this textbook that possess a coelom, although the coelom of molluscs is only a small cavity (the pericardial cavity) surrounding the heart and gonads. A coelom is a body cavity that arises in mesoderm and is lined by a sheet of mesoderm called the peritoneum (*see figure 16.10c*).

RELATIONSHIPS TO OTHER ANIMALS

Comparative embryology is the study of similarities and differences in early development of animals. Events in embryology of animals may be similar because of shared ancestry; however, similarities in development can also reflect adaptations of distantly related, or unrelated, species to similar environments. Comparative embryologists, therefore, have a difficult task of sorting homologous developmental sequences from analogous developmental sequences (*see chapter 1*). This difficulty is well illustrated in the attempt to determine the phylogenetic relationships of the molluscs to other phyla.

The phyla described in the following chapters are divided into two large groups, and many of the reasons for this separation stem from comparative embryology. Although there are exceptions to the following generalizations, most zoologists are convinced that these two groups are true evolutionary assemblages (figure 21.2).

Protostomes include animals in the phyla Mollusca, Annelida, Arthropoda, and others. The developmental characteristics that unite these phyla are shown in figure 21.3*a–d*. One

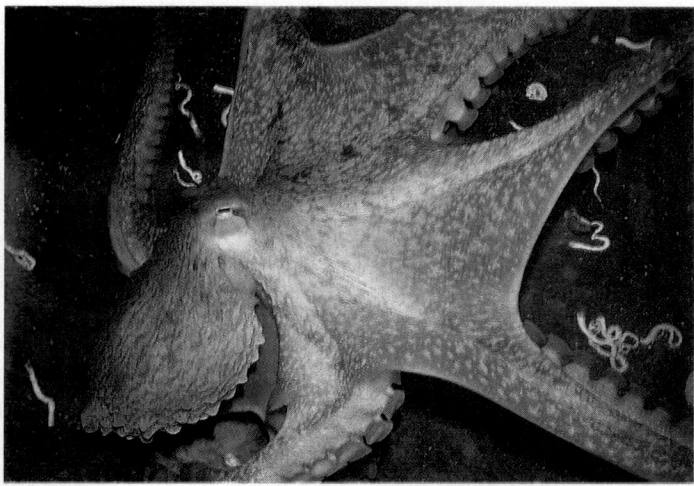

FIGURE 21.1

Phylum Mollusca. The phylum Mollusca includes nearly 100,000 living species including members of the class Cephalopoda—some of the invertebrate world's most adept predators. A member of the genus *Octopus* is shown here.

characteristic is the pattern of the early cleavages of the zygote. In spiral cleavage, the mitotic spindle is oriented obliquely to the animal/vegetal axis of a cell (*see chapters 6 and 10*). For example, division of the four-celled embryo produces an eight-celled embryo in which the upper tier of cells is twisted out of line with the lower cells. A second characteristic that is common to many protostomes is that early cleavage is determinate, meaning that the fate of cells is established very early in development. If blastomeres of a two- or four-celled embryo are separated, none will develop into a complete organism. A third characteristic is reflected in the term "protostome" (Gr. *protos*, first + *stoma*, mouth). The blastopore, which forms during an embryonic process called gastrulation (*see chapter 10*), usually remains open and forms the mouth. Other attributes of many protostomes include a top-shaped larva called a **trochophore larva** and a pattern of coelom and mesoderm formation, called schizocoelous, in which the mesoderm splits to form the coelom.

The other group, the **deuterostomes**, includes animals in the phyla Echinodermata, Hemichordata, Chordata, and others. The developmental characteristics that unite these phyla are shown in figure 21.3*e–h*. Radial cleavage occurs when the mitotic spindle is oriented perpendicularly to the animal/vegetal axis of a cell and results in blastomeres oriented directly over one another. Cleavage is indeterminate, meaning that the fate of blastomeres is determined late in embryology and, if blastomeres are separated, they can develop into entire individuals. In deuterostomes (Gr. *deutero*, second + *stoma*, mouth), the blastopore either forms the anus, or the blastopore closes, and the anus forms in the region of the blastopore. Mesoderm and coelom formation also differ from that of protostomes. The

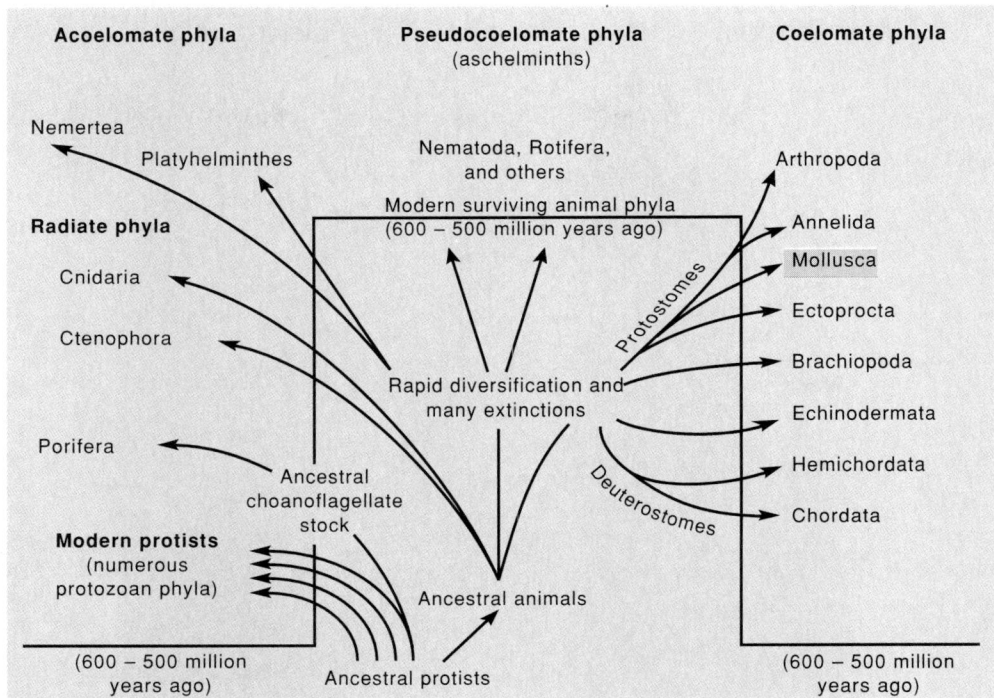

Figure 21.2

Evolutionary Relationships of the Molluscs. Molluscs (shaded in orange) share certain developmental characteristics with annelids, arthropods, ectoprocts, and brachiopods. These groups are placed into a larger assemblage called the protostomes. These developmental characteristics are discussed in this chapter.

mesoderm pinches off as pouches of the gut, and the coelom forms inside the mesodermal pouches. This method of coelom formation is called enterocoelous. A kidney-bean-shaped larva, called a dipleurula, is often represented as being characteristic of deuterostomes. There is, however, no single kind of deuterostome larval stage.

Origin of the Coelom

There are a number of hypotheses regarding the origin of the coelom. These hypotheses are important because they influence how one pictures the evolutionary relationships among triploblastic phyla.

The schizocoel hypothesis (Gr. *schizen,* to split + *koilos,* hollow) is patterned after the method of mesoderm development and coelom formation in many protostomes (figure 21.3*a*), in which all mesoderm is derived from a particular ectodermal cell of the blastula. Mesoderm derived from this cell fills the area between ectoderm and endoderm. The coelom arises from a splitting of this mesoderm. If the coelom formed in this way during evolution, mesodermally derived tissues would have preceded the coelom, implying that a triploblastic, acoelomate (flatworm) body form could be the forerunner of the coelomate body form (*see figure 16.10a*).

The enterocoel hypothesis (Gr. *enteron,* gut + *koilos,* hollow) suggests that the coelom may have arisen as outpocketings of a primitive gut tract. This hypothesis is patterned after the method of coelom formation in deuterostomes (other than vertebrates; *figure 21.3*b). The implication of this hypothesis is that mesoderm and the coelom formed from the gut of a diploblastic animal. If this is true, the triploblastic, acoelomate body form would have been secondarily derived by mesoderm filling the body cavity of a coelomate animal.

Unfortunately zoologists may never know which, if either, of these hypotheses is accurate. Some zoologists believe that the coelom may have arisen more than once in different evolutionary lineages, in which case, more than one explanation could be correct.

Molluscan Characteristics

Molluscs range in size and body form from the giant squid, measuring 18 m in length, to the smallest garden slug, less than 1 cm long. In spite of this diversity, the phylum Mollusca (mol-lus'kah) (L. *molluscus,* soft) is not difficult to characterize (table 21.1).

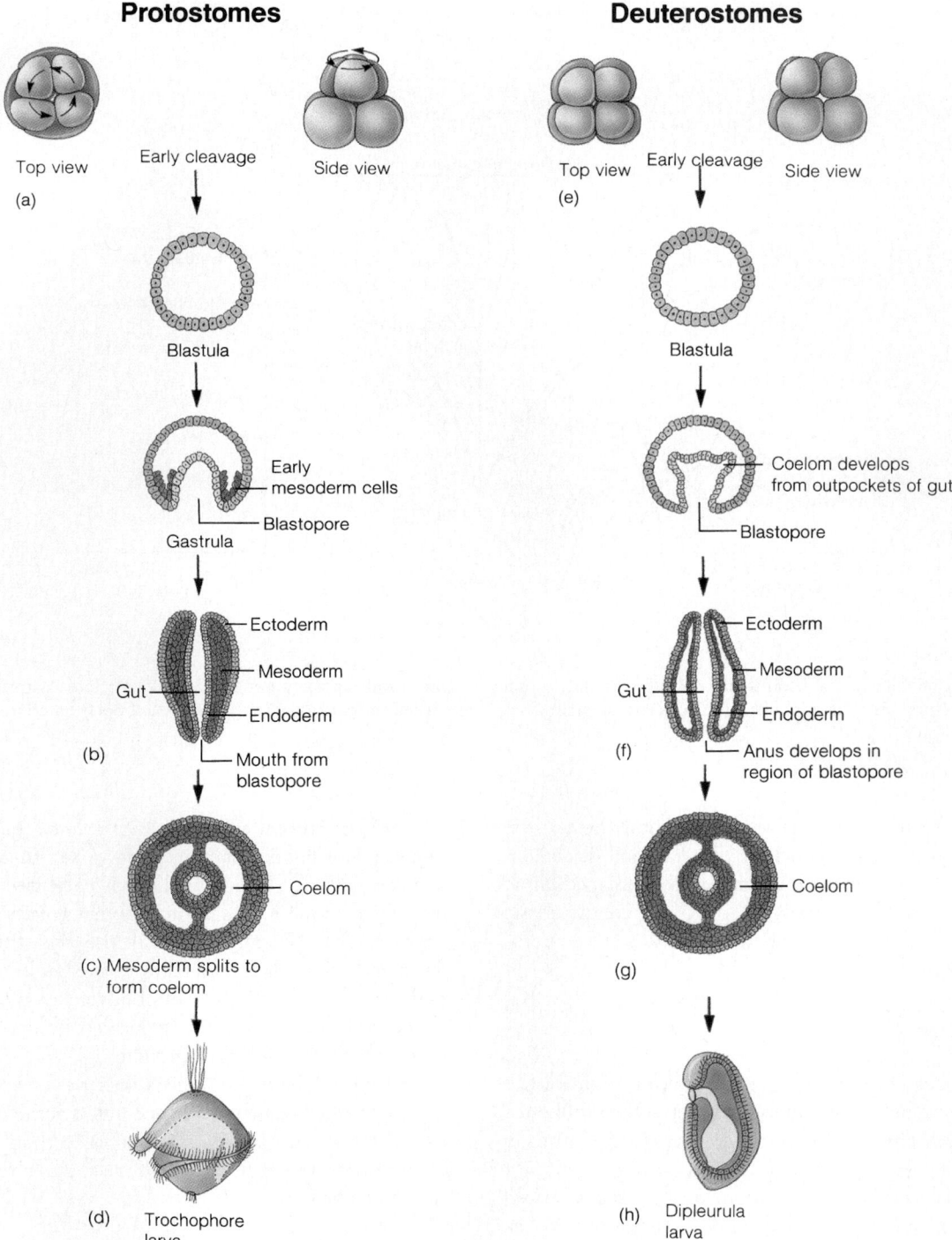

Protostomes

Deuterostomes

FIGURE 21.3

Developmental Characteristics of Protostomes and Deuterostomes. Protostomes are characterized by spiral and determinate cleavage (*a*), a mouth that forms from an embryonic blastopore (*b*), schizocoelous coelom formation (*c*), and a trochophore larva (*d*). Deuterostomes are characterized by radial and indeterminate cleavage (*e*), an anus that forms in the region of the embryonic blastopore (*f*), and enterocoelous coelom formation (*g*). A dipleurula larva is often represented as being characteristic of deuterostomes. Although a dipleurula is present in some echinoderms, there is no characteristic deuterostome larval stage (*h*).

21.4

TABLE 21.1 CLASSIFICATION OF THE MOLLUSCA

Phylum Mollusca (mol-lus'kah)
The coelomate animal phylum whose members possess a head-foot, visceral mass, mantle, and mantle cavity. Most molluscs also possess a radula and a calcareous shell.

Class Caudofoveata (kaw'do-fo've-a'ta)
Wormlike molluscs with a cylindrical, shell-less body and scalelike calcareous spicules; lack eyes, tentacles, statocysts, crystalline style, foot, and nephridia. Deep-water, marine burrowers. *Chaetoderma.*

Class Aplacophora (a'pla-kof"o-rah)
Shell, mantle, and foot lacking; wormlike; head poorly developed; burrowing molluscs. Marine. *Neomenia.*

Class Polyplacophora (pol'e-pla-kof'o-rah)
Elongate, dorsoventrally flattened; head reduced in size; shell consisting of eight dorsal plates. Marine, on rocky intertidal substrates. *Chiton.*

Class Monoplacophora (mon'o-pla-kof"o-rah)
Molluscs with a single arched shell; foot broad and flat; certain structures serially repeated. Marine. *Neopilina.*

Class Scaphopoda (ska-fop'o-dah)
Body enclosed in a tubular shell that is open at both ends; tentacles used for deposit feeding. No head. Marine. *Dentalium.*

Class Bivalvia (bi"val've-ah)
Body enclosed in a shell consisting of two valves, hinged dorsally; no head or radula; wedge-shaped foot. Marine and fresh water. *Anodonta, Mytilus, Venus.*

Class Gastropoda (gas-trop'o-dah)
Shell, when present, usually coiled; body symmetry distorted by torsion; some monoecious species. Marine, fresh water, terrestrial. *Nerita, Orthaliculus, Helix.*

Class Cephalopoda (sef'ah-lop'o-dah)
Foot modified into a circle of tentacles and a siphon; shell reduced or absent; head in line with the elongate visceral mass. Marine. *Octopus, Loligo, Sepia, Nautilus.*

This taxonomic listing reflects a phylogenetic sequence. The discussions that follow, however, begin with molluscs that are familiar to most students.

Characteristics of the phylum Mollusca include the following:

1. Body of two parts: head-foot and visceral mass
2. Mantle that secretes a calcareous shell and covers the visceral mass
3. Mantle cavity functions in excretion, gas exchange, elimination of digestive wastes, and release of reproductive products
4. Bilateral symmetry
5. Protostome characteristics including trochophore larvae, spiral cleavage, and schizocoelous coelom formation

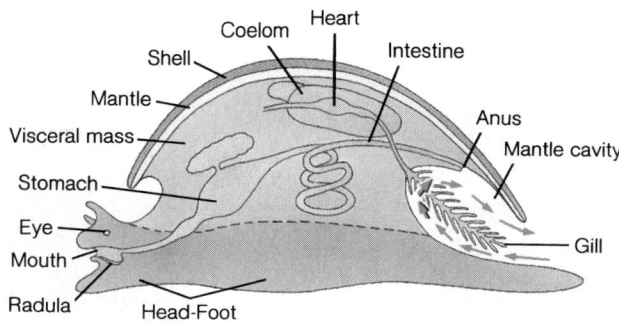

FIGURE 21.4
Molluscan Body Organization. All molluscs possess three features unique to the phylum. The head-foot is a muscular structure usually used for locomotion and sensory perception. The visceral mass contains organs of digestion, circulation, reproduction, and excretion. The mantle is a sheet of tissue that enfolds the rest of the body and secretes the shell. Arrows indicate the flow of water through the mantle cavity.

6. Coelom reduced to cavities surrounding the heart, nephridia, and gonads
7. Open circulatory system in all but one class (Cephalopoda)
8. Radula usually present and used in scraping food

The body of a mollusc is divided into two main regions—the head-foot and the visceral mass (figure 21.4). The **head-foot** is elongate with an anterior head, containing the mouth and certain nervous and sensory structures, and an elongate foot, used for attachment and locomotion. A **visceral mass** contains the organs of digestion, circulation, reproduction, and excretion and is attached at the dorsal aspect of the head-foot.

The **mantle** of a mollusc usually attaches to the visceral mass, enfolds most of the body, and may secrete a shell that overlies the mantle. The shell of a mollusc is secreted in three layers (figure 21.5). The outer layer of the shell is called the periostracum. This protein layer is secreted by mantle cells at the outer margin of the mantle. The middle layer of the shell, called the prismatic layer, is the thickest of the three layers and consists of calcium carbonate mixed with organic materials. It is also secreted by cells at the outer margin of the mantle. The inner layer of the shell, the nacreous layer, forms from thin sheets of calcium carbonate alternating with organic matter. The nacreous layer is secreted by cells along the entire epithelial border of the mantle. Secretion of nacre causes the shell to grow in thickness.

Between the mantle and the foot is a space called the **mantle cavity.** The mantle cavity opens to the outside and functions in gas exchange, excretion, elimination of digestive wastes, and release of reproductive products.

The mouth of most molluscs possesses a rasping structure, called a **radula,** which consists of a chitinous belt and rows of posteriorly curved teeth (figure 21.6). The radula overlies a fleshy, tonguelike structure supported by a cartilaginous

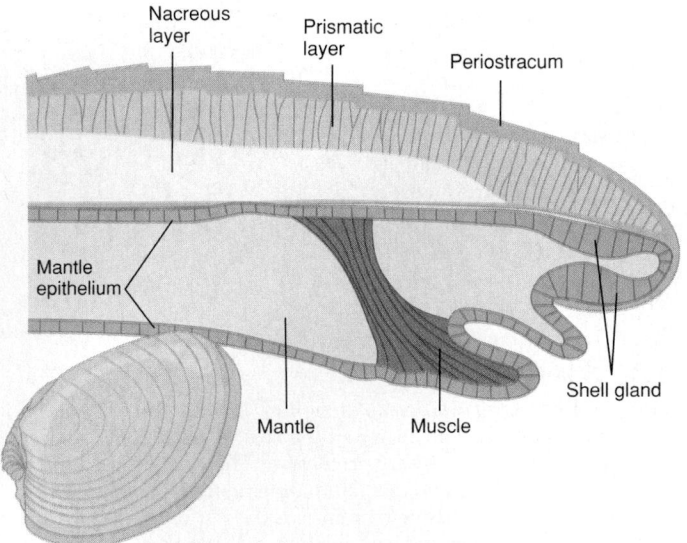

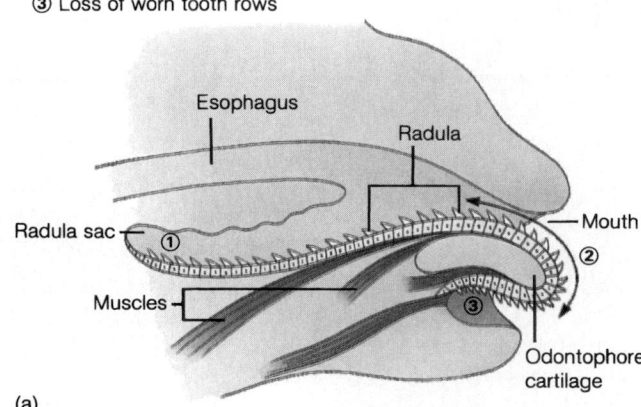

Figure 21.5

The Molluscan Shell and Mantle. A transverse section of a bivalve shell and mantle shows the three layers of the shell and the portions of the mantle responsible for secretion of the shell.

odontophore. Muscles associated with the odontophore permit the radula to be protruded from the mouth. Muscles associated with the radula move the radula back and forth over the odontophore. Food is scraped from a substrate and passed posteriorly to the digestive tract.

Stop and Ask Yourself

1. What characteristics unite the protostomes? The deuterostomes?

2. Why does the schizocoel hypothesis of the origin of the coelom suggest that coelomate animals evolved from triploblastic animals?

3. What are the three regions of the body of a generalized mollusc? What are the functions of these three regions?

4. What are the functions of the mantle cavity of a mollusc?

Class Gastropoda

The class Gastropoda (gas-trop'o-dah) (Gr. *gaster*, gut + *podos*, foot) includes the snails, limpets, and slugs. With over 35,000 living species (*see table 21.1*), Gastropoda is the largest and most varied molluscan class. Its members occupy a wide variety of marine, freshwater, and terrestrial habitats. Most people give gastropods little thought unless they encounter *Helix pomatia* (escargot) in a French restaurant or are

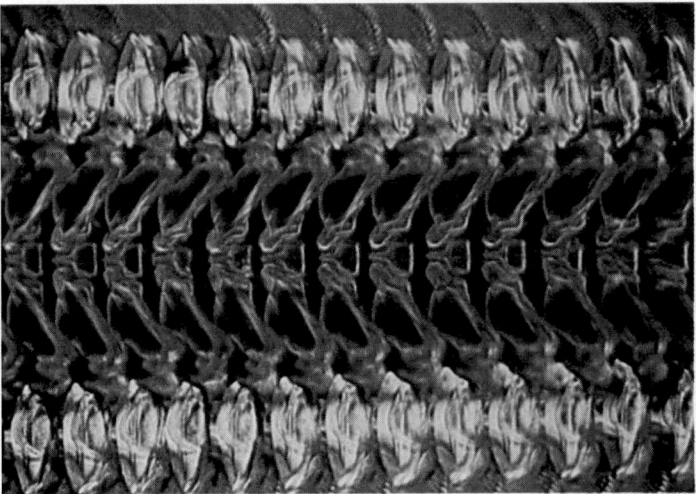

Figure 21.6

Radular Structure. (*a*) The radular apparatus lies over the cartilaginous odontophore. Muscles attached to the radula move the radula back and forth over the odontophore. (*b*) Micrograph of radular teeth arrangement of the marine snail, *Nerita*. Tooth structure is an important taxonomic characteristic for zoologists who study molluscs. (*a*) *From: "A LIFE OF INVERTEBRATES" © 1979 W. D. Russel-Hunter.*

pestered by garden slugs and snails. One important impact of gastropods on the lives of many humans is that gastropods are intermediate hosts for some medically important trematode parasites of humans (*see chapter 19*).

Torsion

One of the most significant modifications of the molluscan body form in the gastropods occurs early in gastropod development. **Torsion** is a 180°, counterclockwise twisting of the visceral mass, the mantle, and the mantle cavity. After torsion, the gills, anus, and openings from the excretory and reproductive systems are positioned just behind the head and

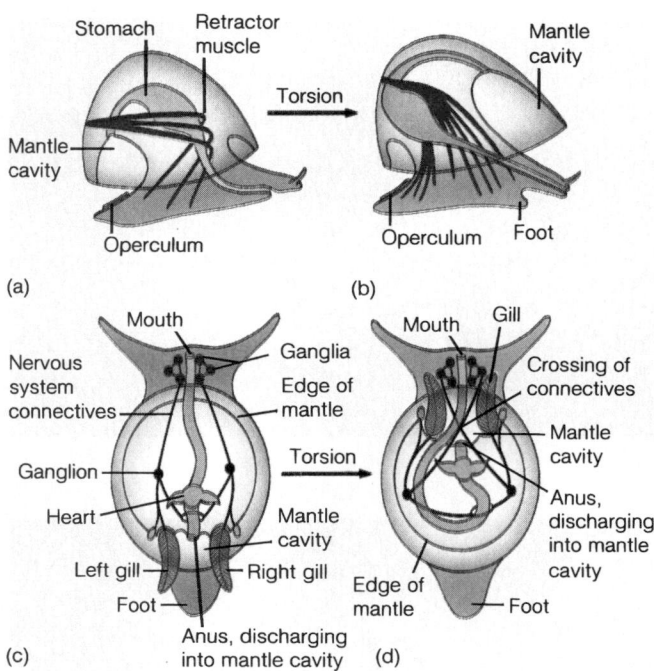

Figure 21.7

Torsion in Gastropods. (*a*) A pretorsion gastropod larva. Note the posterior opening of the mantle cavity and the untwisted digestive tract. (*b*) After torsion, the digestive tract is looped, and the mantle cavity opens near the head. The foot is drawn into the shell last, and the operculum closes the shell opening. (*c*) A hypothetical (adult) ancestor shows the arrangement of internal organs prior to torsion. (*d*) Modern adult gastropods have an anterior opening of the mantle cavity and the looped digestive tract. *Redrawn from L. Hyman,* The Invertebrates, *Volume VI. Copyright © 1967 McGraw-Hill, Inc. Used by permission.*

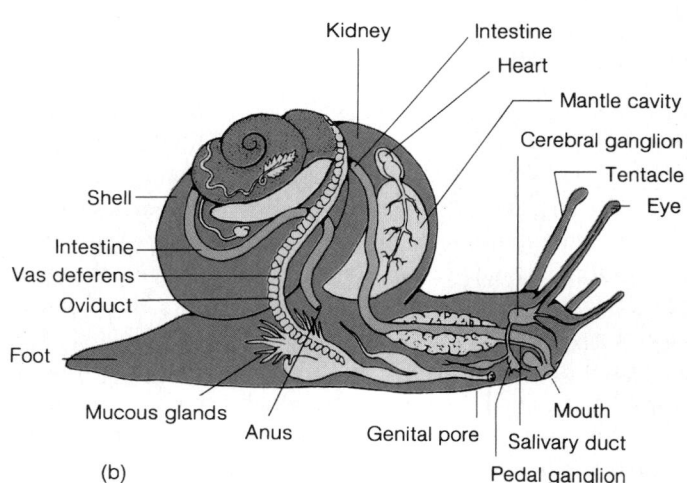

Figure 21.8

Gastropod Structure. (*a*) A land (pulmonate) gastropod (*Orthaliculus*). (*b*) Internal structure of a generalized gastropod.

nerve cords, and the digestive tract is twisted into a U shape (figure 21.7).

The adaptive significance of torsion is speculative; however, three advantages are plausible. First, without torsion, withdrawal into the shell would proceed with the foot entering first, and the more vulnerable head entering last. With torsion, the head enters the shell first and is followed by the foot, leaving the head less exposed to potential predators. In some snails, protection is enhanced by a proteinaceous covering, called an **operculum,** on the dorsal, posterior margin of the foot. When the foot is drawn into the mantle cavity, the operculum closes the opening of the shell, thus preventing desiccation when the snail is in drying habitats. Another advantage of torsion concerns an anterior opening of the mantle cavity that allows clean water from in front of the snail to enter the mantle cavity, rather than water contaminated with silt stirred up by the snail's crawling. An additional advantage to torsion derives from the twist in the mantle's sensory organs around to the head region. This positioning allows a snail greater sensitivity to stimuli coming from the direction in which it moves.

Note in figure 21.7*d* that after torsion the anus and nephridia empty dorsal to the head and create potential fouling problems. However, a number of evolutionary adaptations seem to circumvent this problem. Various modifications allow water and the wastes it carries to exit the mantle cavity through notches or openings in the mantle and shell posterior to the head. Some gastropods undergo detorsion, in which the embryo undergoes a full 180° torsion and then untwists approximately 90°. The mantle cavity thus opens on the right side of the body, behind the head.

Shell Coiling

The earliest fossil gastropods possessed a shell that was coiled in one plane. This arrangement is not common in later fossils, probably because growth resulted in an increasingly cumbersome shell. (Some modern snails, however, have secondarily returned to this shell form.)

Most modern snail shells are asymmetrically coiled into a more compact form, with successive coils or whorls slightly larger than, and ventral to, the preceding whorl (figure 21.8*a*).

(2) This pattern leaves less room on one side of the visceral mass for certain organs, and it is thought that organs that are now single were probably paired ancestrally. This asymmetrical arrangement of internal organs will be described further when particular body systems are described.

LOCOMOTION

Nearly all gastropods have a flattened foot that is often ciliated, covered with gland cells, and used to creep across the substrate (figure 21.8*b*). The smallest gastropods use cilia to propel themselves over a mucous trail. Larger gastropods use waves of muscular contraction that move over the foot. The foot of some gastropods is modified for clinging, as in abalones and limpets, or for swimming, as in sea butterflies and sea hares.

FEEDING AND DIGESTION

Most gastropods feed by scraping algae or other small, attached organisms from their substrate. Others are herbivores that feed on larger plants, scavengers, parasites, or predators (figure 21.9).

The anterior portion of the digestive tract may be modified into an extensible proboscis, which contains the radula. This structure is important for some predatory snails that must extract animal flesh from hard to reach areas. The digestive tract of gastropods, like that of most molluscs, is ciliated. Food is trapped in mucous strings and incorporated into a rotating mucoid mass called the **protostyle,** which extends to the stomach and is rotated by cilia. Enzymes and acid are released into the stomach from a digestive gland located in the visceral mass, and food trapped on the protostyle is freed and digested. Wastes are formed into fecal pellets in the intestine.

OTHER MAINTENANCE FUNCTIONS

Gas exchange always involves the mantle cavity. Primitive gastropods had two gills; modern gastropods have lost one gill because of coiling. Some gastropods have a rolled extension of the mantle, called a **siphon,** that serves as an inhalant tube. Species that burrow extend the siphon to the surface of the substrate to bring in water. Gills are lost or reduced in land snails (pulmonates), but these snails have a richly vascular mantle that is used for gas exchange between blood and air. Contractions of the mantle help circulate air and water through the mantle cavity.

Gastropods, as do most molluscs, have an **open circulatory system.** During part of its circuit around the body, blood leaves the vessels and directly bathes cells in tissue spaces called sinuses. Molluscs typically have a heart consisting of a single, muscular ventricle and two auricles. Most gastropods have lost one member of the pair of auricles because of coiling.

In addition to transporting nutrients, wastes, and gases, the blood of molluscs acts as a hydraulic skeleton. A **hydraulic skeleton**

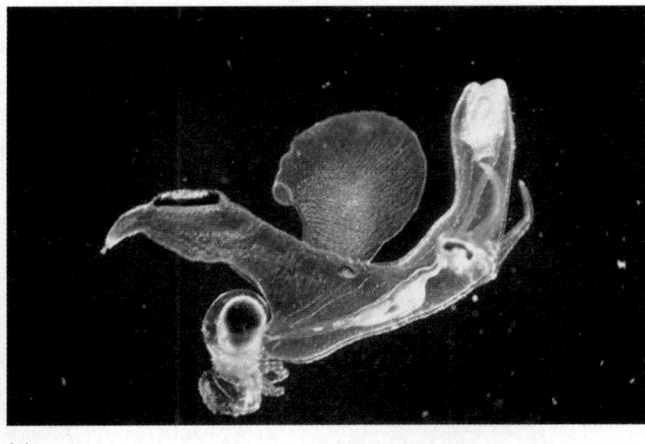

(a)

(b)

FIGURE 21.9

Variations in the Gastropod Body Form. (*a*) This heteropod (*Carinaria*) is a predator that swims upside down in the open ocean. Its body is nearly transparent. The head is at the left, and the shell is below and to the right. (*b*) Colorful nudibranchs have no shell or mantle cavity. The projections on the dorsal surface are used in gas exchange. In some nudibranchs, the dorsal projections are armed with nematocysts that the nudibranchs use for protection. Nudibranchs prey on sessile animals, such as soft corals and sponges.

uses blood confined to tissue spaces for support. A mollusc uses its hydraulic skeleton to extend body structures by contracting muscles distant from the extending structure. (3) For example, snails have sensory tentacles on their heads, and if the tentacle is touched, it can be rapidly withdrawn by retractor muscles. However, no antagonistic muscles exist to extend the tentacle. Extension is accomplished more slowly by contracting distant muscles to squeeze blood into the tentacle from adjacent blood sinuses.

The nervous system of primitive gastropods is characterized by six ganglia located in the head-foot and visceral mass (*see figure 21.8b*). The nerves that link these ganglia are twisted by torsion. The evolution of the gastropod nervous system has resulted in the untwisting of nerves and the concentration of nervous tissues into fewer, larger ganglia, especially in the head.

Gastropods have well-developed sensory structures. Eyes may be at the base or at the end of tentacles, they may be simple pits of photoreceptor cells, or consist of a lens and cornea. Statocysts are in the foot. Osphradia are chemoreceptors in the anterior wall of the mantle cavity that detect sediment and chemicals in inhalant water or air. The osphradia of predatory gastropods help detect prey.

Primitive gastropods possessed two nephridia. In modern species, the right nephridium has disappeared, probably because of shell coiling. The nephridium consists of a sac with highly folded walls and is connected to the reduced coelom, the pericardial cavity. Excretory wastes are derived largely from fluids filtered and secreted into the coelom from the blood. The nephridium modifies this waste by selectively reabsorbing certain ions and organic molecules. The nephridium opens to the mantle cavity or, in land snails, on the right side of the body adjacent to the mantle cavity and anal opening. Ammonia is the primary excretory product for aquatic species, because they have access to water in which toxic ammonia is diluted. Terrestrial snails must convert ammonia to a less toxic form—uric acid. Because uric acid is relatively insoluble in water and less toxic, it can be excreted in a semisolid form, which helps conserve water.

REPRODUCTION AND DEVELOPMENT

Many marine snails are dioecious. Gonads lie in spirals of the visceral mass (*see figure 21.8b*). Ducts discharge gametes into the sea, where external fertilization occurs.

Many other snails are monoecious, and internal, cross-fertilization is the rule. Copulation may result in mutual sperm transfer, or one snail may act as the male and the other as the female. A penis has evolved from a fold of the body wall, and portions of the female reproductive tract have become glandular and secrete a protective jelly or capsule around the fertilized egg. Some monoecious snails are protandric in that testes develop first, and after they degenerate, ovaries mature.

Eggs are shed singly or in masses for external fertilization. Internally fertilized eggs are deposited in gelatinous strings or masses. Eggs of terrestrial snails are large and yolky. These are deposited in moist environments, such as forest-floor leaf litter, and may be encapsulated by a calcareous shell. In marine gastropods, spiral cleavage results in a free-swimming trochophore larva that develops into another free-swimming larva with foot, eyes, tentacles, and shell, called a **veliger larva.** Sometimes, the trochophore is suppressed, and the veliger is the primary larva. Torsion occurs during the veliger stage, followed by settling and metamorphosis to the adult.

CLASS BIVALVIA

With close to 30,000 species, the class Bivalvia (bi″val′ve-ah) (L. *bis*, twice + *valva*, leaf) is the second largest molluscan class. This class includes the clams, oysters, mussels, and scallops (*see table 21.1*). These laterally compressed animals are covered by a

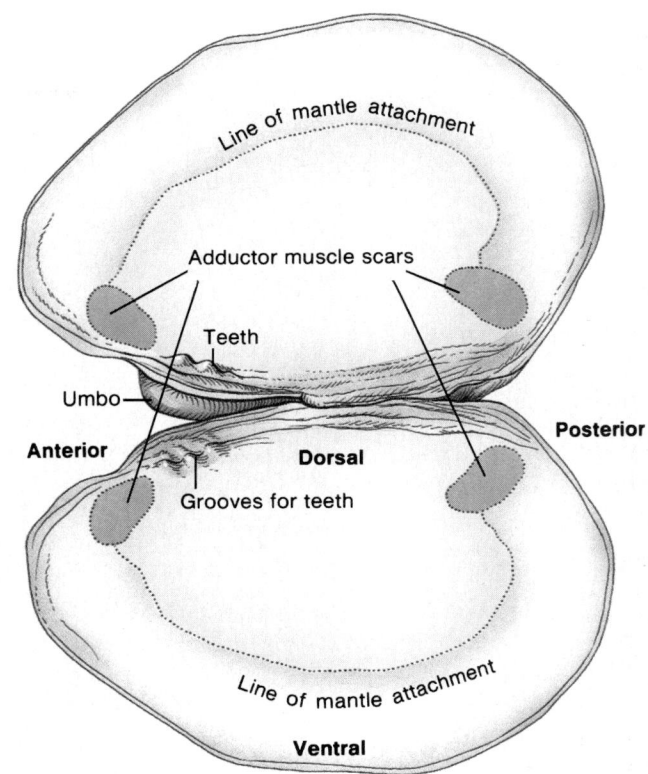

FIGURE 21.10

Inside View of a Bivalve Shell. The umbo is the oldest part of the bivalve shell. As the bivalve grows, the mantle lays down more shell in concentric lines of growth.

sheetlike mantle and a shell consisting of two valves (hence the class name). Many bivalves are edible, and some form pearls. Because most bivalves are filter feeders, another value is in the removal of bacteria from polluted water.

SHELL AND ASSOCIATED STRUCTURES

The two convex halves of the shell are called **valves.** Along the dorsal margin of the shell is a proteinaceous hinge and a series of tongue-and-groove modifications of the shell, called teeth, that prevent the valves from twisting (figure 21.10). The oldest part of the shell is the **umbo,** a swollen area near the anterior margin of the shell. Although bivalves appear to have two shells, embryologically the shell forms as a single structure. The shell is continuous along its dorsal margin, but the mantle, in the region of the hinge, secretes relatively greater quantities of protein and relatively little calcium carbonate. The result is an elastic hinge ligament. The elasticity of the hinge ligament opens the valves when certain muscles are relaxed.

Adductor muscles are located at either end of the dorsal half of the shell and are responsible for closing the shell. Anyone who has tried to force apart the valves of a bivalve mollusc knows the effectiveness of these muscles. This is important for bivalves, because the primary defense of most bivalves against

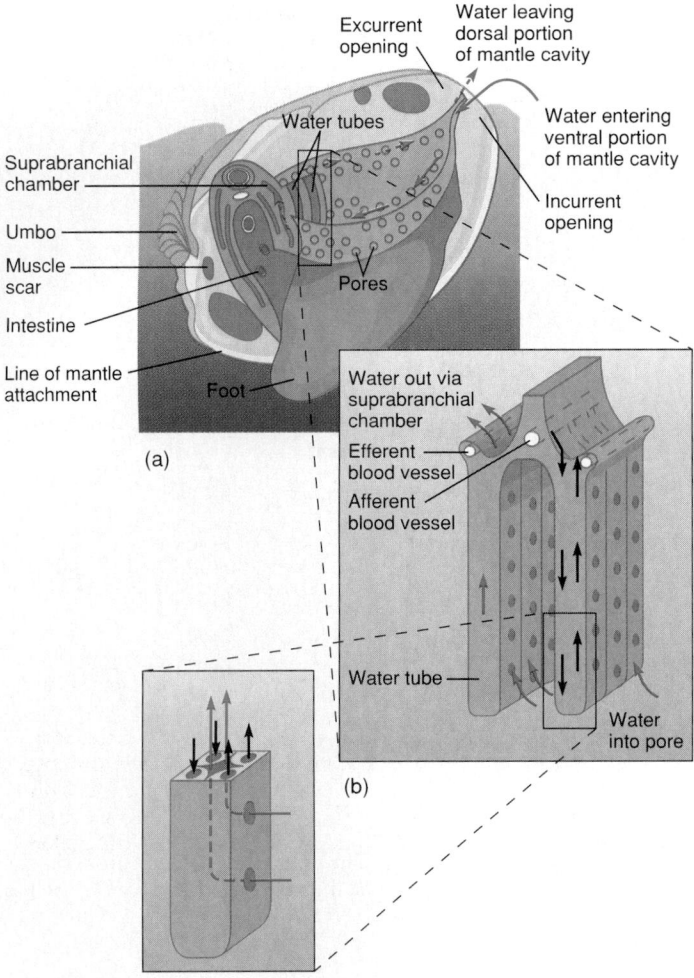

FIGURE 21.11

The Lamellibranch Gill of a Bivalve. (*a*) Blue arrows indicate incurrent and excurrent water currents. Food is filtered as water enters water tubes through pores in the gills. (*b*) Cross section through a portion of a gill. Water passing through a water tube passes in close proximity to blood. Gas exchange occurs between water and blood in the water tubes. Blue arrows show the path of water. Black arrows show the path of blood.

predatory sea stars is to tenaciously refuse to open their shell. In chapter 25, you will see how sea stars are adapted to meet this defense strategy.

The mantle of bivalves is attached to the shell around the adductor muscles and near the margin of the shell.   ④   If a sand grain or a parasite becomes lodged between the shell and the mantle, the mantle secretes nacre around the irritant, gradually forming a pearl. Highest quality pearls are formed by the Pacific pearl oysters *Pinctada margaritifera* and *Pinctada mertensi*.

GAS EXCHANGE, FILTER FEEDING, AND DIGESTION

The adaptation of bivalves to sedentary, filter-feeding life-styles includes the loss of the head and radula and, except for a few bivalves, the gills have become greatly expanded and covered with cilia. Gills form folded sheets (lamellae), with one end attached

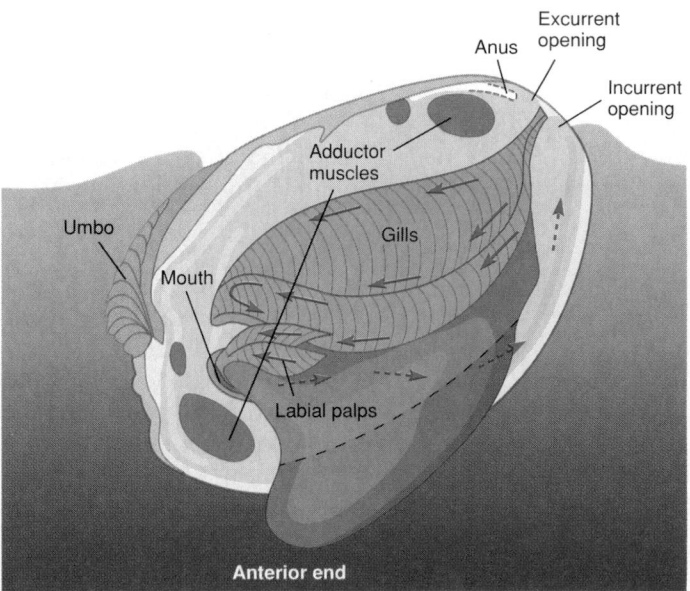

FIGURE 21.12

Bivalve Feeding. Solid blue arrows show the path of food particles after being filtered by the gills. Dashed blue arrows show the path of particles rejected by the gills and the labial palps.

to the foot and the other end attached to the mantle. The mantle cavity ventral to the gills is the inhalant region, and the cavity dorsal to the gills is the exhalant region (figure 21.11*a*). Cilia move water into the mantle cavity through an incurrent opening of the mantle. Sometimes this opening is at the end of a siphon, which is an extension of the mantle. A bivalve buried in the substrate can extend its siphon to the surface and still feed and exchange gases. Water moves from the mantle cavity into small pores in the surface of the gills, and from there, into vertical channels in the gills, called water tubes. In moving through water tubes, blood and water are in close proximity, and gases are exchanged by diffusion (figure 21.11*b*). Water exits the bivalve through a part of the mantle cavity at the dorsal aspect of the gills called the suprabranchial chamber, and through an excurrent opening in the mantle (figure 21.11*a*).

⑤   Cilia covering the gills not only create water currents, but they also filter suspended food from the water, transport food toward the mouth, and sort filtered particles (figure 21.12). Cilia covering leaflike **labial palps,** located on either side of the mouth, also sort filtered particles. Small particles are carried by cilia into the mouth, and larger particles are moved to the edges of the palps and gills. This rejected material, called pseudofeces, falls, or is thrown, onto the mantle and is transported posteriorly by a ciliary tract on the mantle. Pseudofeces are washed from the mantle cavity by water rushing out when the valves are forcefully closed.

The digestive tract of bivalves is similar to that of other molluscs (figure 21.13*a*). Food entering the esophagus is entangled in a mucoid food string, which extends to the stomach and is rotated by cilia lining the digestive tract. A consolidated mucoid

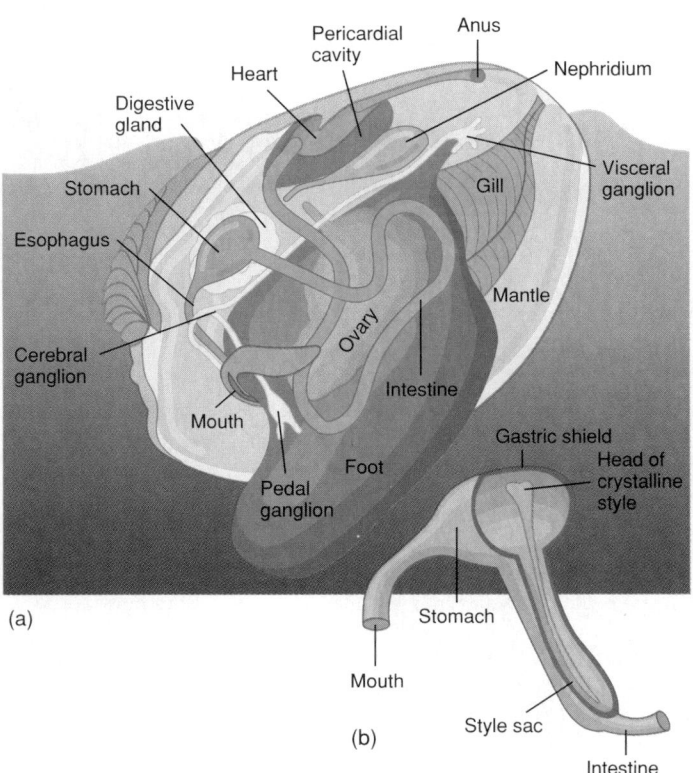

FIGURE 21.13

Bivalve Structure. (*a*) Internal structure of a bivalve. (*b*) The bivalve stomach showing the crystalline style and associated structures.

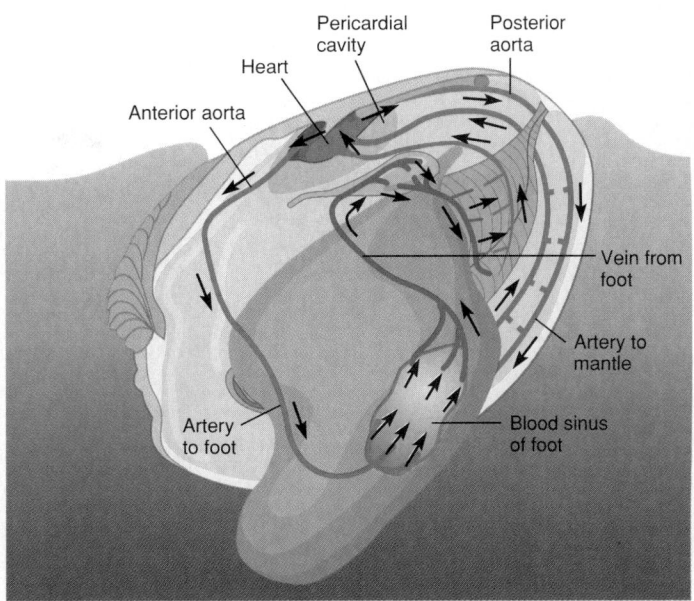

FIGURE 21.14

Bivalve Circulation. Blood flows from the single ventricle to tissue sinuses through anterior and posterior aortae. Blood from tissue sinuses flows to the nephridia, to the gills, and then enters the auricles of the heart. In all bivalves, the mantle is an additional site for oxygenation. In some bivalves, a separate aorta delivers blood to the mantle. This blood returns directly to the heart. The ventricle of bivalves is always folded around the intestine. Thus, the pericardial cavity (the coelom) encloses the heart and a portion of the digestive tract.

mass, the **crystalline style,** projects into the stomach from a diverticulum, called the style sac (figure 21.13*b*). Enzymes for carbohydrate and fat digestion are incorporated into the crystalline style. Cilia of the style sac rotate the style against a chitinized **gastric shield.** Abrasion of the style against the gastric shield and acidic conditions in the stomach dislodge enzymes. As the crystalline style rotates, the mucoid food string winds around the crystalline style, and is pulled farther into the stomach from the esophagus. Food particles in the food string are dislodged by this action and the acidic pH in the stomach. Further sorting separates fine particles from undigestible coarse materials. The latter are sent on to the intestine. Partially digested food from the stomach enters a digestive gland, where intracellular digestion occurs. Undigested wastes in the digestive gland are carried back to the stomach and then to the intestine by cilia. The intestine empties through the anus near the excurrent opening, and feces are carried away by excurrent water.

OTHER MAINTENANCE FUNCTIONS

In bivalves, blood flows from the heart to tissue sinuses, nephridia, gills, and back to the heart (figure 21.14). The mantle is an additional site for oxygenation. In some bivalves, a separate aorta delivers blood directly to the mantle. Two nephridia are located below the pericardial cavity (the coelom). Their

duct system connects to the coelom at one end and opens at nephridiopores in the anterior region of the suprabranchial chamber.

The nervous system of bivalves consists of three pairs of interconnected ganglia associated with the esophagus, the foot, and the posterior adductor muscle. The margin of the mantle is the principal sense organ. It always has sensory cells, and it may have sensory tentacles and photoreceptors. In some species, photoreceptors are in the form of complex eyes with a lens and a cornea (e.g., scallops). Other receptors include statocysts near the pedal ganglion and an osphradium in the mantle, beneath the posterior adductor muscle.

REPRODUCTION AND DEVELOPMENT

Most bivalves are dioecious. A few are monoecious, and some of these species are protandric. Gonads are located in the visceral mass, where they surround the looped intestine. Ducts of these gonads open directly to the mantle cavity or by the nephridiopore to the mantle cavity.

External fertilization occurs in most bivalves. Gametes exit through the suprabranchial chamber of the mantle cavity and the exhalant opening. Development proceeds through trochophore and veliger stages (figure 21.15*a,b*). When the veliger settles, the adult form is assumed.

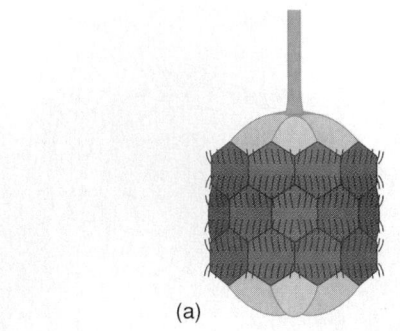

(a)

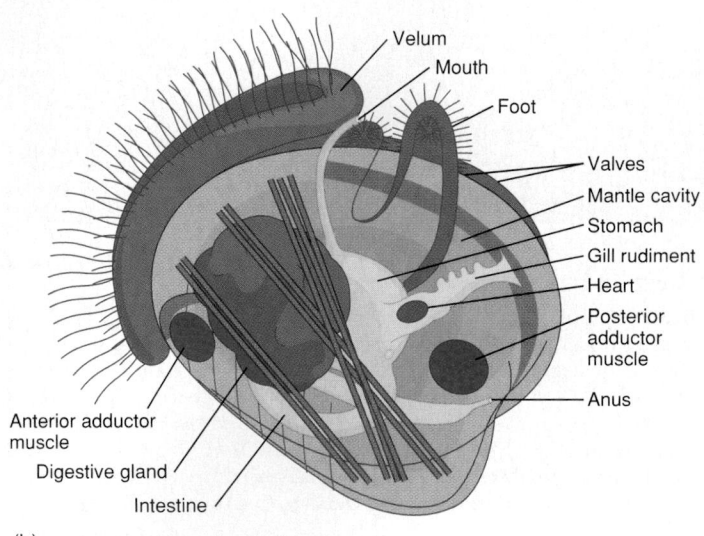

Velum
Mouth
Foot
Valves
Mantle cavity
Stomach
Gill rudiment
Heart
Posterior adductor muscle
Anus
Anterior adductor muscle
Digestive gland
Intestine

(b)

(c)

Figure 21.15

Larval Stages of Bivalves. (*a*) A trochophore larva of *Yoldia limatula*. (*b*) A veliger of an oyster. (*c*) A glochidium of a freshwater clam. Note the tooth used to attach to fish gills.

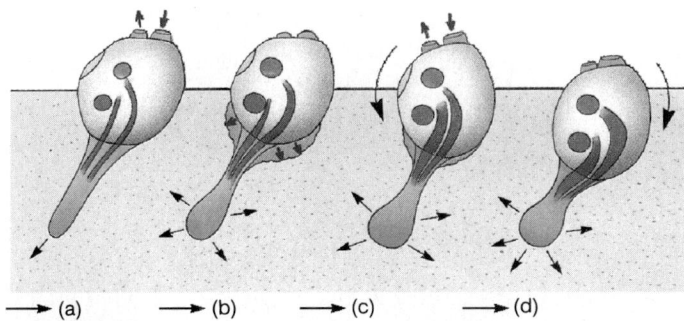

(a) (b) (c) (d)

Figure 21.16

Bivalve Burrowing. (*a*) Adductor muscles relax, and the valves push against the substrate to anchor the bivalve. The foot is extended by hydraulic pressure and pedal protractor muscles, which extend from each side of the foot to each valve. Circular and transverse muscles contract to form the foot into a narrow, probing structure. Blue arrows show movement of water into and out of the mantle cavity. (*b*) The tip of the foot is dilated with blood to form a second anchor, and the valves are closed. Water from the mantle cavity washes substrate away from the bivalve when the valves close (lower blue arrows). (*c,d*) Pedal retractor muscles contract and pull the bivalve downward. The process is repeated as necessary. *From: "A LIFE OF INVERTEBRATES"* © *1979 W. D. Russell-Hunter.*

The largest families of freshwater bivalves brood their young. Fertilization occurs in the mantle cavity by sperm brought in with inhalant water. Some brood their young in maternal gills through reduced trochophore and veliger stages. Young clams are shed from the gills. Others brood their young to a modified veliger stage called a **glochidium,** which is parasitic on fishes (figure 21.15c). These larvae possess two tiny valves, and some species have toothlike hooks. Larvae exit through the exhalant aperture and sink to the substrate. Most of these will die. If a fish contacts a glochidium, however, the larva attaches to the gills, fins, or another body part and begins to feed on host tissue. The fish forms a cyst around the larva. After a period of larval development, during which it begins acquiring its adult structures, the miniature clam falls from its host and takes up its filter-feeding life-style. The glochidium acts as a dispersal stage for an otherwise sedentary animal.

Bivalve Diversity

Bivalves are found in nearly all aquatic habitats. They may live completely or partially buried in sand or mud, attached to solid substrates, or burrowed into submerged wood, coral, or limestone (box 21.1).

The mantle margins of burrowing bivalves are frequently fused to form distinct openings in the mantle cavity (siphons). This fusion helps to direct the water washed from the mantle cavity during burrowing and helps keep sediment from accumulating in the mantle cavity (figure 21.16).

BOX 21.1   THE ZEBRA MUSSEL—ANOTHER BIOLOGICAL INVASION

About 100 years ago, a bird fancier released a few starlings in New York City's Central Park. Today the starling is the most common bird in the United States. In 1866 the gypsy moth was transported from Europe to the New England states. It proliferated at the expense of North American forests. Today, these European invaders are joined by another, the zebra mussel (*Dreissena polymorpha*). This invasion, like the others before it, has been very costly, both economically and ecologically for much of North America.

The zebra mussel is actually one of about 120 exotic invaders of the Great Lakes. The invasion began in 1985 or 1986 when larval mussels were picked up in freshwater ports of Europe when cargo ships filled their ballast tanks with fresh water. The larvae were released when ballast tanks were emptied into the Great Lakes. Within three or four years the mussel spread into Lakes Erie, Ontario, Huron, and southern Lake Michigan. By June 1991, records of the mussels were being made in the Illinois River and the mussel now threatens much of the Mississippi River drainage basin.

Many of the problems associated with the zebra mussels are a result of their high reproductive potential. A single female may release 40,000 eggs. Their veliger larval stages may drift in the plankton for up to five weeks and be carried long distances by water currents. When larvae settle on a hard substrate, they attach by tough byssal threads. They grow to a length of about 2 cm, and densities of 200 individuals/m^2 are common (figure 1).

Economic problems associated with zebra mussels result from their settling on, and clogging, water intake pipes. Detroit Edison officials reported 700,000 mussels/m^2 on a single water intake screen. In December 1988, mussels and ice shards blocked water intake to the Detroit Edison plant, which resulted in power outages throughout Detroit. It cost the company $250,000 to restore electricity to the city. Detroit Edison officials spent six million dollars on a new intake system that they hope will reduce the fouling problems. It is estimated that throughout the Great Lakes, two billion dollars will be spent cleaning and refitting pipes in Great Lakes port cities through the 1990s.

Zebra mussels also threaten the ecology of freshwater ecosystems. They are very efficient filter feeders and are expected to disrupt freshwater food webs. As larvae settle and encrust hard substrates, they may disrupt the spawning ground of game fish such as

FIGURE 1   The zebra mussel (*Dreissena polymorpha*) invaded U.S. fresh waters and is threatening native bivalves and other freshwater species.

walleyed pike. There is particular concern for the Mississippi River drainage basin. The Mississippi River and its tributaries contain the highest diversity of clams in the world. Some of these clams are endangered species. In other places, where native clams have been displaced by the zebra mussel, the valves of a native clam make an excellent substrate for the attachment of the zebra mussel. The native clam can be so densely covered that feeding is impossible.

While research efforts are under way to monitor the spread of the zebra mussel and to search for its "Achilles' heel," a larger question looms in the background: "Are more invaders on the way?" One study of the ballast water of 55 cargo ships revealed that 17 species of animals were still alive in each ship by the time they arrived in fresh waters of North America. Estimates of the number of individuals alive per species ranged between 10,000 and eight billion! A relatively simple, partial solution to the problem of ballast-water invaders has been to require ships to dump ballast water from foreign, freshwater ports into the open ocean. This ballast water is then replaced with seawater. Seawater kills most freshwater organisms, and freshwater kills most marine organisms.

Some surface-dwelling bivalves are attached to the substrate either by proteinaceous strands called byssal threads, which are secreted by a gland in the foot, or by cementation to the substrate. The former method is used by the common marine mussel *Mytilus*, and the latter by oysters.

Boring bivalves live beneath the surface of limestone, clay, coral, wood, and other substrates.   ⑥   Boring begins after the larvae settle to the substrate, and it occurs by mechanical abrasion of the substrate by the anterior margin of the valves. Physical abrasion is sometimes accompanied by acidic secretions from the mantle margin that dissolve limestone. As the bivalve grows, portions of the burrow recently bored are larger in diameter than other, usually external, portions of the burrow. Thus, the bivalve is often imprisoned in its rocky burrow.

(a)

(b)

FIGURE 21.17

Class Cephalopoda. (*a*) A chambered nautilus. (*b*) An octopus.

Stop and Ask Yourself

5. What are three advantages conferred to gastropods by torsion?
6. What is a hydraulic skeleton?
7. How do bivalves discourage predatory sea stars?
8. How do bivalves feed?

CLASS CEPHALOPODA

The class Cephalopoda (sef'ah-lop'o-dah) (L. *cephalic*, head + Gr. *podos*, foot) includes the octopuses, squids, cuttlefish, and nautili (figure 21.17; table 21.1). They are the most complex molluscs and, in many ways, the most complex invertebrates. The anterior portion of their foot has been modified into a circle of tentacles or arms that are used for prey capture, attachment, locomotion, and copulation (figure 21.18). The foot is also incorporated into a funnel that is associated with the mantle cavity and used for jetlike locomotion. The molluscan body plan is further modified in that the cephalopod head is in line with the visceral mass. Cephalopods have a highly muscular mantle that encloses all of the body except the head and tentacles. The mantle acts as a pump for bringing large quantities of water into the mantle cavity.

SHELL

Ancestral cephalopods probably had a conical shell. The only living cephalopods that possess an external shell are the nautili (*see figure 21.17a*). They have a coiled shell that is subdivided by septa. As the nautilus grows, it moves forward, secreting new shell around itself and leaving an empty septum behind. Only

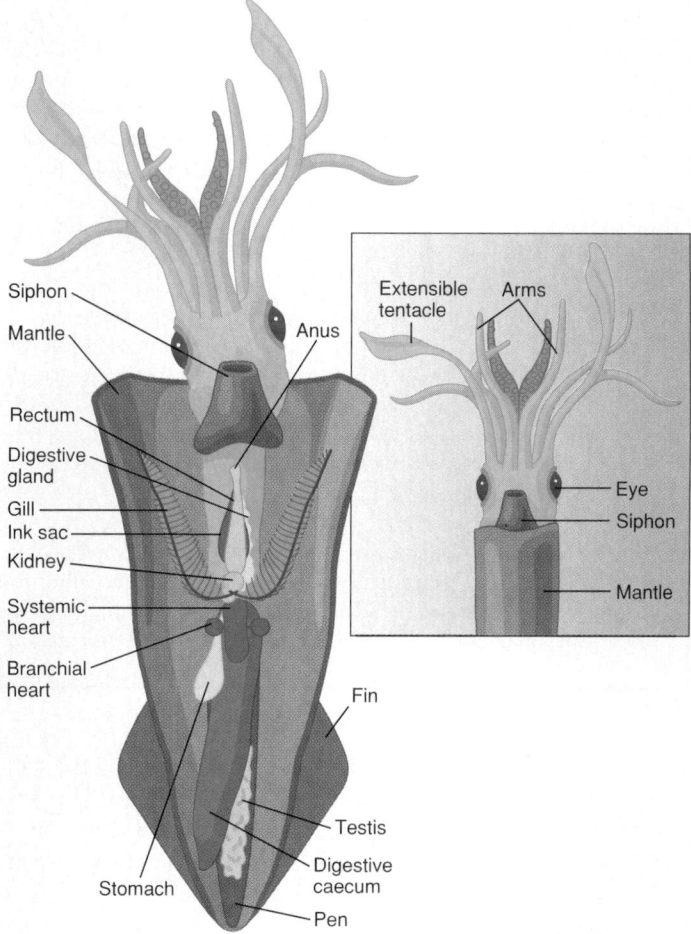

FIGURE 21.18

Internal Structure of the Squid, *Loligo*. The shell of most cephalopods is reduced or absent, and the foot is modified into a circle of tentacles and/or arms that encircle the head and a funnel. The inset shows the undissected anatomy of the squid.

the last chamber is occupied. These chambers are fluid filled when they are formed. Septa are perforated by a cord of tissue called a siphuncle, which absorbs fluids by osmosis and replaces them with metabolic gases. The amount of gas in the chambers is regulated to alter the buoyancy of the animal.

In all other cephalopods, the shell is reduced or absent. In cuttlefish, the shell is internal and laid down in thin layers, leaving small, gas-filled spaces that increase buoyancy. Cuttlefish shell, called cuttlebone, has been used to make powder for polishing and has been fed to pet birds to supplement their diet with calcium. The shell of a squid is reduced to an internal, chitinous structure called the pen. In addition to this reduced shell, squid also have cartilaginous plates in the mantle wall, neck, and head that support the mantle and protect the brain. The shell is absent in octopuses.

LOCOMOTION

As predators, cephalopods depend upon their ability to move quickly using a jet-propulsion system. The mantle of cephalopods contains radial and circular muscles. When circular muscles contract, they decrease the volume of the mantle cavity and close collarlike valves to prevent water from moving out of the mantle cavity between the head and the mantle wall. Water is thus forced out of a narrow funnel. Muscles attached to the funnel control the direction of the animal's movement. Radial mantle muscles bring water into the mantle cavity by increasing the volume of the mantle cavity. Posterior fins act as stabilizers in squid and also aid in propulsion and steering in cuttlefish. "Flying squid" (family Onycoteuthidae) have been clocked at speeds of 20 knots (about 20 mph). Octopuses are more sedentary animals. They may use jet propulsion in an escape response, but normally they crawl over the substrate using their tentacles.

FEEDING AND DIGESTION

Cephalopod prey are located by sight and are captured with tentacles, which bear adhesive cups. In squid, these cups are reinforced with tough protein around their margins and sometimes possess small hooks (figure 21.19).

Jaws and a radula are present in all cephalopods. The jaws are powerful, beaklike structures used for tearing food, and the radula rasps food, forcing it into the mouth cavity.

Cuttlefish and nautili feed on small invertebrates on the ocean floor. Octopuses are nocturnal hunters and feed on snails, fish, and crustaceans. Octopuses have salivary glands that are used to inject venom into their prey. Squid feed on fishes and shrimp, which they kill by biting across the back of the head. ⑦ Giant squid even prey upon the young of sperm whales—just as adult sperm whales prey upon the young of giant squid.

The digestive tract of cephalopods is muscular, and peristalsis (coordinated muscular waves) replaces ciliary action in

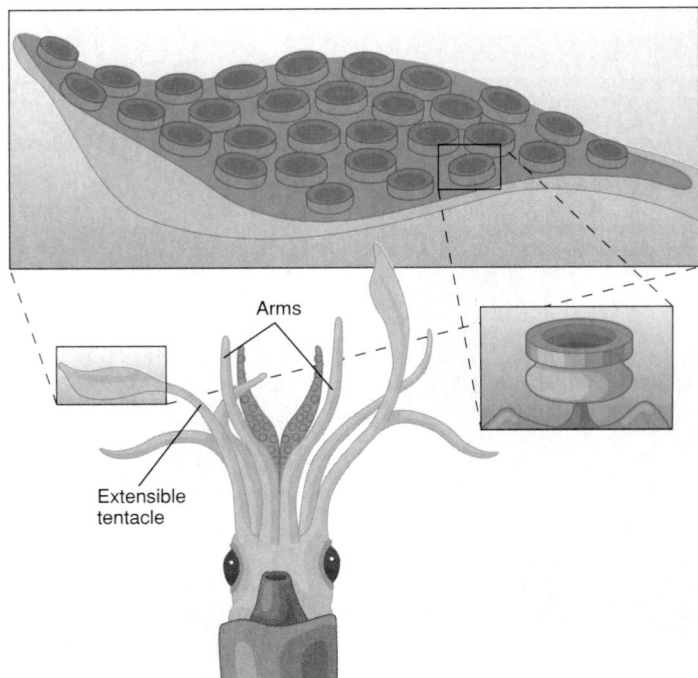

FIGURE 21.19

A Cephalopod Tentacle. Suction cups are used for prey capture and as holdfast structures.

moving food. Most digestion occurs in a stomach and a large cecum. Digestion is primarily extracellular with large digestive glands supplying enzymes. An intestine ends at the anus, near the funnel, and wastes are carried out of the mantle cavity with exhalant water.

OTHER MAINTENANCE FUNCTIONS

Cephalopods, unlike other molluscs, have a **closed circulatory system.** Blood is confined to vessels throughout its circuit around the body. Capillary beds connect arteries and veins, and exchanges of gases, nutrients, and metabolic wastes occur across capillary walls. In addition to having a heart consisting of two auricles and one ventricle, cephalopods have contractile arteries and structures called branchial hearts. The latter are located at the base of each gill and help move blood through the gill. These modifications increase blood pressure and the rate of blood flow—necessary for active animals with relatively high metabolic rates. Large quantities of water circulate over the gills at all times.

Greater excretory efficiency is achieved in the cephalopods because of the closed circulatory system. A close association of blood vessels with nephridia allows both filtration and secretion of wastes directly from the blood into the excretory system.

⑧ The cephalopod nervous system is unparalleled by any other invertebrate. Cephalopod brains are large, and their evolution is directly related to cephalopod predatory habits and dexterity.

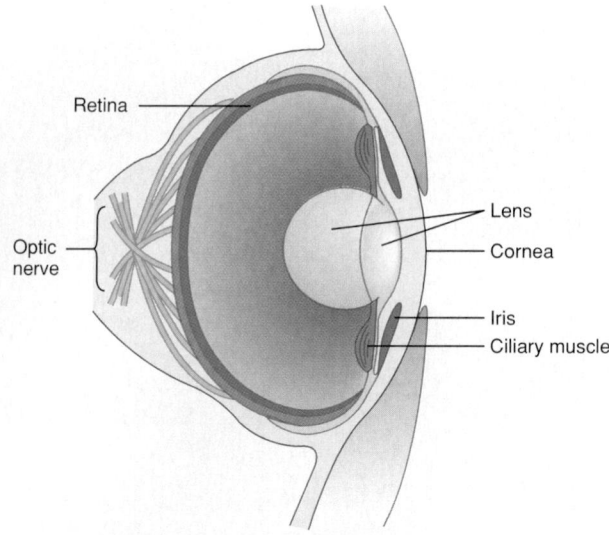

Figure 21.20

The Cephalopod Eye. The eye is immovable in a supportive and protective socket of cartilages. It contains a rigid, spherical lens. An iris in front of the lens forms a slitlike pupil that can open and close in response to varying light conditions. Note that the optic nerve comes off the back of the retina.

The brain is formed by a fusion of ganglia. It has large areas devoted to controlling muscle contraction (e.g., swimming movements and sucker closing), sensory perception, and functions such as memory and decision making. Research on cephalopod brains has provided insight into human brain functions.

The eyes of octopuses, cuttlefish, and squids are similar in structure to vertebrate eyes (figure 21.20). (This similarity is an excellent example of convergent evolution.) In contrast to the vertebrate eye, nerve cells leave the eye from the outside of the eyeball, so that no blind spot exists. Like many aquatic vertebrates, cephalopods focus by moving the lens back and forth. Cephalopods can form images, distinguish shapes, and discriminate some colors. The nautiloid eye is less complex. It lacks a lens, and the interior is open to seawater, thus it acts as a pinhole camera.

Cephalopod statocysts respond to gravity and acceleration and are located in cartilages next to the brain. Osphradia are present only in *Nautilus.* Tactile receptors and additional chemoreceptors are widely distributed over the body.

Cephalopods have pigment cells called **chromatophores.** Tiny muscles attach to these pigment cells and, when these muscles contract, the chromatophores quickly expand and change the color of the animal. Color changes, in combination with ink discharge, function in alarm responses. In defensive displays, color changes may spread in waves over the body to form large, flickering patterns. Color changes may also help cephalopods to blend with their background. The cuttlefish, *Sepia,* can even make a remarkably good impression of a checkerboard background. Color changes are also involved with courtship displays. Some species combine chromatophore displays with bioluminescence.

All cephalopods possess an ink gland that opens just behind the anus. Ink is a brown or black fluid containing melanin and other chemicals. Discharged ink confuses a predator, allowing the cephalopod to escape. For example, *Sepiola* reacts to danger by darkening itself with chromatophore expansion prior to releasing ink. After ink discharge, *Sepiola* changes to a lighter color again to assist its escape.

Reproduction and Development

Cephalopods are dioecious. Gonads are located in the dorsal portion of the visceral mass. The male reproductive tract consists of testes and structures for encasing sperm in packets called **spermatophores.** The female reproductive tract produces large, yolky eggs and is modified with glands that secrete gellike cases around eggs. These cases frequently harden on exposure to seawater.

One tentacle of male cephalopods, called the **hectocotylus,** is modified for spermatophore transfer. In *Loligo* and *Sepia,* the hectocotylus has several rows of smaller suckers capable of picking up spermatophores. During copulation, male and female tentacles intertwine, and the male removes spermatophores from his mantle cavity. The male inserts his hectocotylus into the mantle cavity of the female and deposits a spermatophore near the opening to the oviduct. Spermatophores have an ejaculatory mechanism that frees sperm from the baseball-bat-shaped capsule. Eggs are fertilized as they leave the oviduct and deposited singly or in stringlike masses. They are usually attached to some substrate, such as the ceiling of an octopus' den. Octopuses tend eggs during development by cleaning them of debris with their arms and squirts of water.

Development of cephalopods occurs in the confines of the egg membranes, and the hatchlings are miniatures of adults. Young are never cared for after hatching.

Stop and Ask Yourself

9. How does the jet-propulsion system of a squid work?
10. In what way is the mechanism of movement of food in the cephalopod digestive tract different from that in other molluscs?
11. What is a closed circulatory system?
12. What is a chromatophore? A spermatophore?

Class Polyplacophora

The class Polyplacophora (pol'e-pla-kof"o-rah) (Gr. *polys,* many + *plak,* plate + *phoros,* to bear) contains the chitons. Chitons are common inhabitants of shallow marine waters, wherever hard substrates occur. Chitons were used for food by early Native Americans. They have a fishy flavor but are tough to chew, and difficult to collect.

Chitons are easy to recognize. They have a reduced head, a flattened foot, and a shell that is divided into eight articulating

(a)

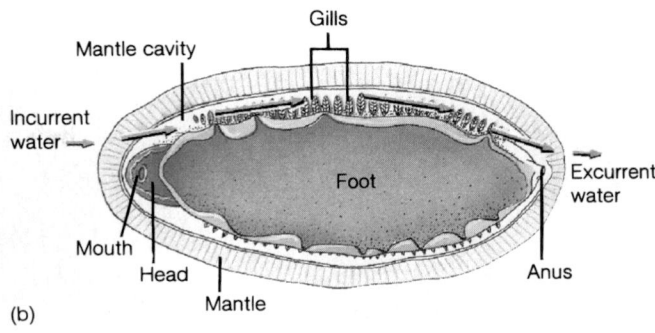

(b)

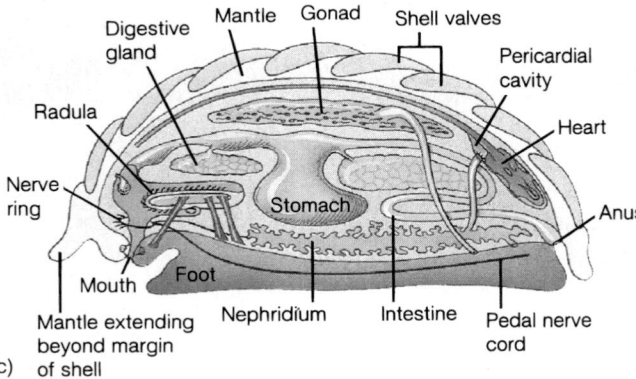

(c)

FIGURE 21.21

Class Polyplacophora. (*a*) Dorsal view of a chiton. Note the shell consisting of eight valves and the mantle extending beyond the margins of the shell. (*b*) A ventral view of a chiton. The mantle cavity is the region between the mantle and the foot. Arrows show the path of water moving across gills in the mantle cavity. (*c*) Internal structure.

dorsal valves (figure 21.21*a*). The broad foot is covered by a muscular mantle that extends beyond the margins of the shell and foot (figure 21.21*b*). The mantle cavity is restricted to the space between the margin of the mantle and the foot. Chitons crawl over their substrate in a manner similar to gastropods. The muscular foot promotes secure attachment to a substrate, which allows chitons to withstand strong waves and tidal currents. When chitons are disturbed, the edges of the mantle are applied tightly to the substrate, and contraction of foot muscles raises the middle of the foot, creating a powerful vacuum that holds the chiton to its substrate. Articulations in the shell allow chitons to roll into a ball when dislodged from the substrate.

A linear series of gills are located in the mantle cavity on each side of the foot. Currents of water, created by cilia on the gills, enter below the anterior mantle margins and exit posteriorly. Openings of the digestive, excretory, and reproductive tracts are located near the exhalant area of the mantle cavity, and products of these systems are carried away with exhalant water.

Most chitons feed on attached algae. A chemoreceptor, the subradular organ, is extended from the mouth to detect food, which the radula rasps from the substrate. Food is trapped in mucus and enters the esophagus by ciliary action. Extracellular digestion occurs in the stomach, and wastes are sent on to the intestine (figure 21.21*c*).

The nervous system is ladderlike, with four anteroposterior nerve cords and numerous transverse nerves. A nerve ring encircles the esophagus. Sensory structures include osphradia, tactile receptors on the mantle margin, chemoreceptors near the mouth, and statocysts in the foot. In some chitons, photoreceptors dot the surface of the shell.

Sexes are separate in chitons. External fertilization and development result in a swimming trochophore that settles and metamorphoses into an adult without passing through a veliger stage.

CLASS SCAPHOPODA

Members of the class Scaphopoda (ska-fop'o-dah) (Gr. *skaphe*, boat + *podos*, foot) are called tooth shells or tusk shells. There are over 300 species, and all are burrowing marine animals that inhabit moderate depths. Their most distinctive characteristic is a conical shell that is open at both ends. The head and foot project from the wider end of the shell, and the rest of the body, including the mantle, is greatly elongate and extends the length of the shell (figure 21.22). Scaphopods live mostly buried in the substrate with head and foot oriented down and with the apex of the shell projecting into the water above. Incurrent and excurrent water enters and leaves the mantle cavity through the opening at the apex of the shell. Functional gills are absent, and gas exchange occurs across mantle folds. Scaphopods have a radula and tentacles, which they use in feeding on foraminiferans. Sexes are separate, and trochophore and veliger larvae are produced.

CLASS MONOPLACOPHORA

Members of the class Monoplacophora (mon'o-pla-kof"o-rah) (Gr. *monos*, one + *plak*, plate + *phoros* to bear) possess an undivided, arched shell; a broad, flat foot; and serially repeated pairs of gills and foot retractor muscles. They are dioecious;

FIGURE 21.22

Class Scaphopoda. This conical shell is open at both ends. In its living state, the animal would be mostly buried with the apex of the shell projecting into the water.

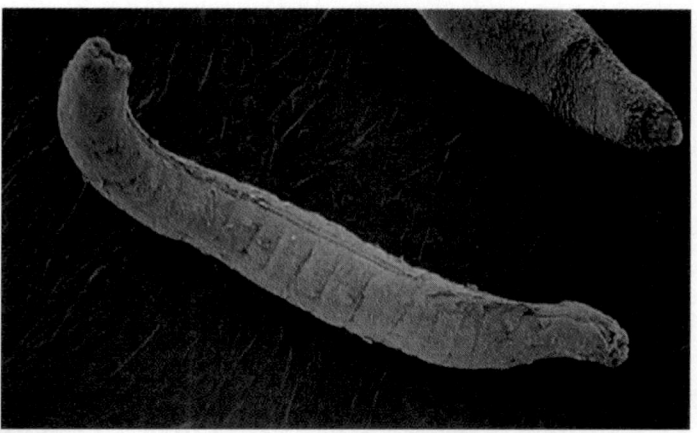

FIGURE 21.24

Class Aplacophora. A scanning electron micrograph of the solenogaster, *Meiomenia*. The body is covered by flattened, spinelike calcareous spicules. The ventral groove shown here may be formed from a rolling of the mantle margins. *Meiomenia* is approximately 2 mm long.

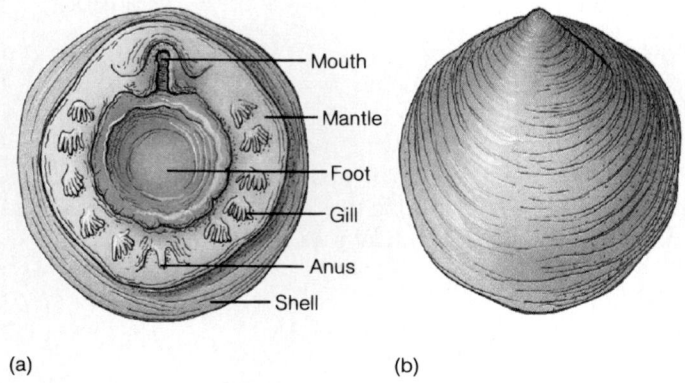

Mouth
Mantle
Foot
Gill
Anus
Shell

(a)   (b)

FIGURE 21.23

Class Monoplacophora. (*a*) Ventral and (*b*) dorsal views of *Neopilina*.

CLASS APLACOPHORA

Members of the class Aplacophora (a′pla-kof″o-rah) (Gr. *a*, without + *plak*, plate + *phoros*, to bear) are called solenogasters (figure 21.24). There are about 250 species of these cylindrical molluscs that lack a shell and crawl on their ventral surface. Their nervous system is ladderlike and reminiscent of the flatworm body form, causing some to suggest that this group may be closely related to the ancestral molluscan stock. One small group of aplacophorans contains burrowing species that feed on microorganisms and detritus and possess a radula and nephridia. The majority of these molluscs, however, lack nephridia and a radula, are mostly surface dwellers on corals and other substrates, and are carnivores, frequently feeding on cnidarian polyps.

FURTHER PHYLOGENETIC CONSIDERATIONS

Fossil records of molluscan classes indicate that the phylum is over 500 million years old. Although molluscs have protostome affinities, zoologists do not know the exact relationship of this phylum to other animal phyla. The discovery of *Neopilina* (class Monoplacophora) in 1952 seemed to revolutionize ideas regarding the position of the molluscs in the animal phyla. The most striking feature of *Neopilina* was a segmental arrangement of gills, excretory structures, and nervous system. Because annelids and arthropods (*see chapters 23 and 24*) also have a segmental arrangement of body parts, monoplacophorans were considered a "missing link" between other molluscs and the annelid-arthropod evolutionary line. This link was further supported by the fact that molluscs, annelids, and arthropods share certain protostome characteristics (*see figure 21.3a*), and chitons also show a repetition of some body parts.

Most zoologists now agree that the segmentation seen in some molluscs is very different from that of annelids and arthro-

however, nothing is known of their embryology. This group of molluscs was known only from fossils until 1952, when a limpetlike monoplacophoran, named *Neopilina*, was dredged up from a depth of 3,520 m off the Pacific coast of Costa Rica (figure 21.23).

CLASS CAUDOFOVEATA

Members of the class Caudofoveata (kaw′do-fo′ve-a′ta) (L. *cauda*, tail + *fovea*, small pit) are wormlike molluscs that range in size from 2 mm to 14 cm and live in vertical burrows on the deep-sea floor. They possess scalelike spicules on the body wall and lack the following typical molluscan characteristics: shell, crystalline style, statocysts, foot, and nephridia. Approximately 70 species have been described but little is known of their ecology.

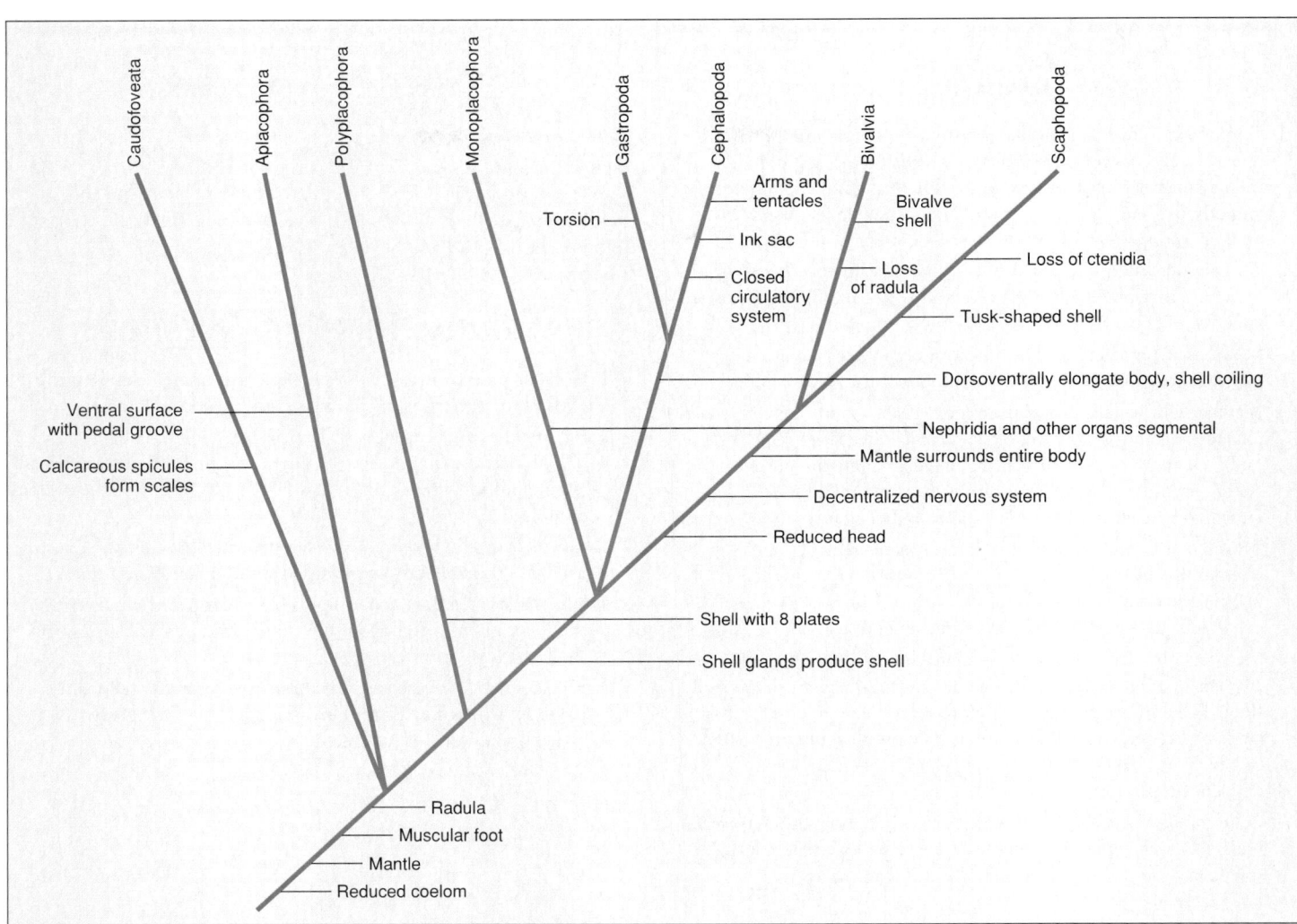

Figure 21.25

Molluscan Phylogeny. A cladogram showing possible evolutionary relationships among the molluscs.

pods. Although information on the development of the serially repeating structures in *Neopilina* is not available, no serially repeating structure in any other mollusc develops in an annelid-arthropod fashion. Segmentation is probably not an ancestral molluscan characteristic. Many zoologists now believe that molluscs diverged from ancient triploblastic stocks independently of any other phylum. Other zoologists maintain that, in spite of the absence of annelidlike segmentation in molluscs, protostomate affinities still tie the molluscs to the annelid-arthropod line. Whichever is the case, the relationship of the molluscs to other animal phyla is distant.

The diversity of body forms and life-styles in the phylum Mollusca is an excellent example of adaptive radiation. Molluscs probably began in Precambrian times as slow-moving, marine, bottom dwellers. The development of unique molluscan features allowed them to diversify relatively quickly. By the end of the Cambrian period, some were filter feeders, some were burrowers, and others were swimming predators. Later, some molluscs became terrestrial and invaded many habitats, from tropical rain forests to arid deserts.

One interpretation of molluscan phylogeny is shown in figure 21.25. The lack of a shell in the classes Caudofoveata and Aplacophora is thought to be a primitive character. All other molluscs have a shell or are derived from shelled ancestors. The multipart shell distinguishes the Polyplacophora from other classes. Other selected synapomorphies, discussed earlier in this chapter, are noted in the cladogram. There are, of course, other interpretations of molluscan phylogeny. The extensive adaptive radiation of this phylum has made higher taxonomic relationships very difficult to discern.

Stop and Ask Yourself

13. What molluscs have eight dorsal, articulating plates?

14. How would you characterize members of the class Scaphopoda?

15. What mollusc has serially repeated pairs of gills and an undivided, arched shell?

16. What is the significance of *Neopilina* in hypotheses concerning molluscan phylogeny?

SUMMARY

1. Triploblastic animals are divided into two groups, which may represent evolutionary assemblages. Protostomes, or spiralians, include members of the phyla Mollusca, Annelida, Arthropoda, and others. Deuterostomes, or radialians, include members of the phyla Echinodermata, Hemichordata, Chordata, and others.

2. Theories regarding the origin of the coelom influence how zoologists interpret evolutionary relationships among triploblastic animals.

3. Molluscs are characterized by a head-foot, a visceral mass, a mantle, and a mantle cavity. Most molluscs also have a radula.

4. Members of the class Gastropoda are the snails and slugs. They are characterized by torsion and often have a coiled shell. Like most molluscs, they use cilia for feeding, have an open circulatory system, well-developed sensory structures, and nephridia. Gastropods may be either monoecious or dioecious.

5. The class Bivalvia includes the clams, oysters, mussels, and scallops. Bivalves lack a head and are covered by a sheetlike mantle and a shell consisting of two valves. Most bivalves use expanded gills for filter feeding and most are dioecious.

6. Members of the class Cephalopoda are the octopuses, squids, cuttlefish, and nautili. Except for the nautili, they have a reduced shell. The anterior portion of their foot has been modified into a circle of tentacles. Cephalopods have a closed circulatory system, highly developed nervous and sensory systems, and they are efficient predators.

7. Other molluscs include tooth shells (class Scaphopoda), *Neopilina* (class Monoplacophora), caudofoveates (class Caudofoveata), solenogasters (class Aplacophora), and chitons (class Polyplacophora).

8. Some zoologists believe that the molluscs are derived from the annelid-arthropod lineage. Others believe that they arose from triploblastic stocks independently of any other phylum. Adaptive radiation in the molluscs has resulted in the invasion of most ecosystems of the earth.

SELECTED KEY TERMS

deuterostomes (*p. 322*)

glochidium (*p. 332*)

head-foot (*p. 325*)

mantle (*p. 325*)

protostomes (*p. 322*)

radula (*p. 325*)

torsion (*p. 326*)

trochophore larva (*p. 322*)

veliger larva (*p. 329*)

visceral mass (*p. 325*)

CRITICAL THINKING QUESTIONS

1. Compare and contrast hydraulic skeletons of molluscs with the hydrostatic skeletons of cnidarians and pseudocoelomates.

2. Review the functions of body cavities presented in chapter 16. Which of those functions would apply to the coelom of molluscs? What additional function(s), if any, are carried out by the coelom of molluscs?

3. Torsion and shell coiling are often confused by students. Describe each and their effects on gastropod structure and function.

4. Why do you think that nautiloids have retained their external shell, but other cephalopods have a reduced internal shell or no shell at all?

5. Bivalves are often used as indicators of environmental quality. Based on your knowledge of bivalves, describe why bivalves are good animals for this purpose.

ANNELIDA:
THE METAMERIC BODY FORM

Outline

Concepts

1. Members of the phylum Annelida are the segmented worms. The relationships of annelids to lower triploblastic animals are debated.
2. Metamerism has important influences on virtually every aspect of annelid structure and function.
3. Members of the class Polychaeta are annelids that have become adapted to a variety of marine habitats. Some live in or on marine substrates; others live in burrows or are free swimming. They are characterized by the presence of parapodia and numerous, long setae.
4. Members of the class Oligochaeta are found in freshwater and terrestrial habitats. They lack parapodia and have fewer, short setae.
5. The class Hirudinea contains the leeches. They are predators in freshwater, marine, and terrestrial environments. Body-wall musculature and the coelom are modified from the pattern found in the other annelid classes. These differences influence locomotor and other functions of leeches.
6. The ancient polychaetes are probably the ancestral stock from which modern polychaetes, oligochaetes, and leeches evolved.

Would You Like to Know:

1. what worm is the basis of a great communal feast? (p. 342)
2. what metamerism is? (p. 342)
3. how the fan of a fanworm is used? (p. 346)
4. why the blood of some marine worms is green? (p. 346)
5. why swarming of epitokes is advantageous for some marine worms? (p. 349)
6. why an earthworm is so difficult to extract from its burrow? (p. 351)
7. why leeches should be referred to as predators rather than parasites? (p. 353)
8. why earthworms are found in soil around deciduous vegetation? (p. 356)

These and other useful questions will be answered in this chapter.

This chapter contains evolutionary concepts, which are set off in this font.

EVOLUTIONARY PERSPECTIVE

At the time of the November full moon, on islands near Samoa in the South Pacific, natives rush about preparing for one of their biggest yearly feasts. In just one week, the sea will yield a harvest that can be scooped up in nets and buckets. Worms by the millions transform the ocean into what one writer called a "vermicelli soup!" Celebrants gorge themselves on worms that have been cooked or wrapped in breadfruit leaves.   ① The Samoan palolo worm (*Eunice viridis*) spends its entire adult life in coral burrows at the sea bottom. Each November, 1 week after the full moon, this worm emerges from its burrow, and specialized body segments devoted to sexual reproduction break free and float to the surface, while the rest of the worm is safe on the ocean floor. The surface water is discolored as gonads release their countless eggs and sperm. The natives' feast is shortlived, however; these reproductive swarms last only 2 days and do not recur for another year.

The Samoan palolo worm is a member of the phylum Annelida (ah-nel'i-dah) (*L. annellus,* ring). Other members of this phylum include countless marine worms (figure 22.1), the soil-building earthworms, and predatory leeches (table 22.1).

Characteristics of the phylum Annelida include the following:

1. Body metameric, bilaterally symmetrical, and wormlike
2. Protostome characteristics include spiral cleavage, trochophore larvae (when larvae are present), and schizocoelous coelom formation
3. Paired, epidermal setae
4. Closed circulatory system
5. Dorsal suprapharyngeal ganglia and ventral nerve cord(s) with ganglia
6. Metanephridia (usually) or protonephridia

RELATIONSHIPS TO OTHER ANIMALS

Annelids are protostomes (*see figure 21.3*). Protostome characteristics, such as spiral cleavage, a mouth derived from an embryonic blastopore, schizocoelous coelom formation, and trochophore larvae are present in most members of the phylum (figure 22.2). (Certain exceptions will be discussed later.) The origin of this diverse phylum, like that of most other phyla, occurred at least as early as Precambrian times, more than 600 million years ago. Unfortunately, there is little evidence documenting the evolutionary pathways that resulted in the first annelids.

There are a number of hypotheses that account for annelid origins. These hypotheses are tied into hypotheses regarding the origin of the coelom (*see chapter 21*). If one assumes a schizocoelous origin of the coelom, as many zoologists believe, then the annelids evolved from ancient flatworm stock. On the other hand, if an enterocoelous coelom origin is correct, then annelids evolved from ancient diploblastic animals, and the triploblastic, acoelomate body may have been derived from a triploblastic, coelomate ancestor. The recent discovery of a worm, *Lobatocerebrum,*

FIGURE 22.1

Phylum Annelida. The phylum Annelida includes about 9,000 species of segmented worms. Most of these are marine members of the class Polychaeta. The fanworm (*Sriro branchus*) is shown here. The fan of this tube-dwelling polychaete is specialized for feeding and gas exchange.

which shares annelid and flatworm characteristics, has lent support to the enterocoelous origin hypothesis. *Lobatocerebrum* is classified as an annelid based on the presence of certain segmentally arranged excretory organs, an annelidlike body covering, a complete digestive tract, and an annelidlike nervous system. As do flatworms, however, it has a ciliated epidermis and is acoelomate. Some zoologists believe that *Lobatocerebrum* illustrates how the triploblastic, acoelomate design could have been derived from the annelid lineage.

METAMERISM AND TAGMATIZATION

When one looks at an earthworm, one of the first characteristics noticed is the organization of the body into a series of ringlike segments. What is not externally obvious, however, is that the body is divided internally as well.   ② Segmental

TABLE 22.1	CLASSIFICATION OF THE PHYLUM ANNELIDA

Phylum Annelida (ah-nel′i-dah)
The phylum of triploblastic, coelomate animals whose members are metameric (segmented), elongate, and cylindrical or oval in cross section. Annelids have a complete digestive tract; paired, epidermal setae; and a ventral nerve cord. The phylum is divided into three classes.

Class Polychaeta (pol″e-ket′ah)
The largest annelid class; mostly marine; head with eyes and tentacles; parapodia bear numerous setae; monoecious or dioecious; development frequently involves a trochophore larval stage. *Nereis, Arenicola, Sabella.*

Class Oligochaeta (ol″i-go-ket′ah)
Few setae and no parapodia; no distinct head; monoecious with direct development; primarily fresh water or terrestrial. *Lumbricus, Tubifex.*

Class Hirudinea (hi′roo-din″eah)
Leeches; bodies with 34 segments; each segment subdivided into annuli; anterior and posterior suckers present; parapodia absent; setae reduced or absent. Fresh water, marine, and terrestrial. *Hirudo.*

arrangement of body parts in an animal is called **metamerism** (Gr. *meta*, after + *mere*, part).

Metamerism has profound influences on virtually every aspect of annelid structure and function, such as the anatomical arrangement of organs that are coincidentally associated with metamerism. For example, the compartmentalization of the body has resulted in each segment having its own excretory, nervous, and circulatory structures. Two related functions are probably the primary adaptive features of metamerism: flexible support and efficient locomotion. These functions depend on the metameric arrangement of the coelom and can be understood by examining the development of the coelom and the arrangement of body-wall muscles.

During embryonic development, the body cavity of annelids arises by a segmental splitting of a solid mass of mesoderm that occupies the region between ectoderm and endoderm on either side of the embryonic gut tract. Enlargement of each cavity forms a double-membraned septum on the anterior and posterior margin of each coelomic space and dorsal and ventral mesenteries associated with the digestive tract (figure 22.3).

Muscles also develop from the mesodermal layers associated with each segment. A layer of circular muscles lies below the epidermis, and a layer of longitudinal muscles, just below

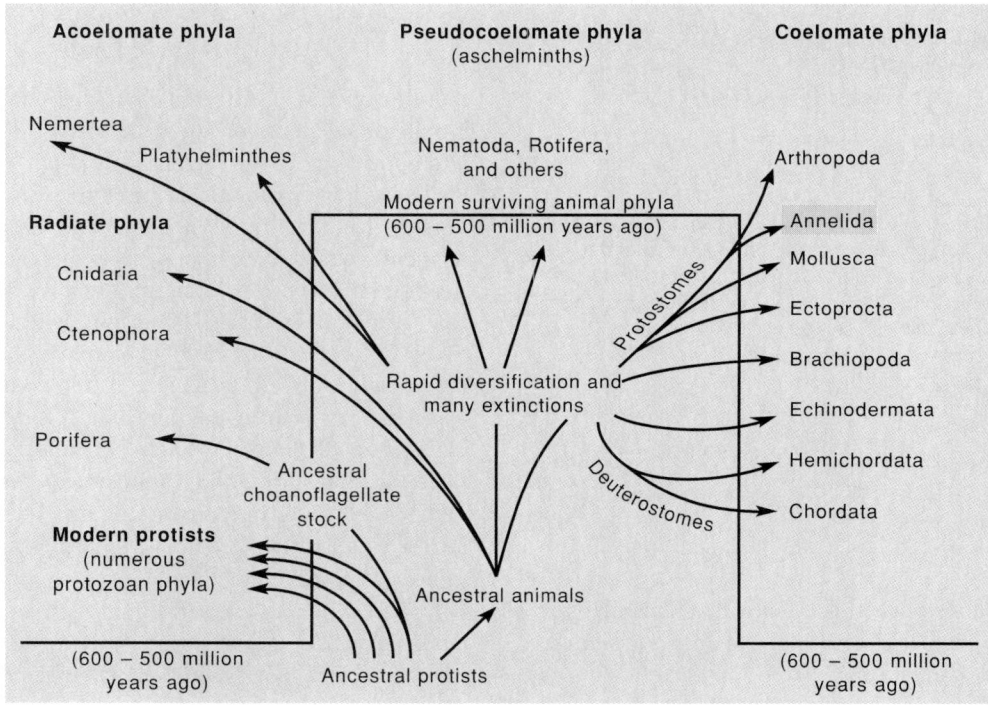

FIGURE 22.2
Evolutionary Relationships of the Annelida. Annelids (shaded in orange) are protostomes with close evolutionary ties to the arthropods.

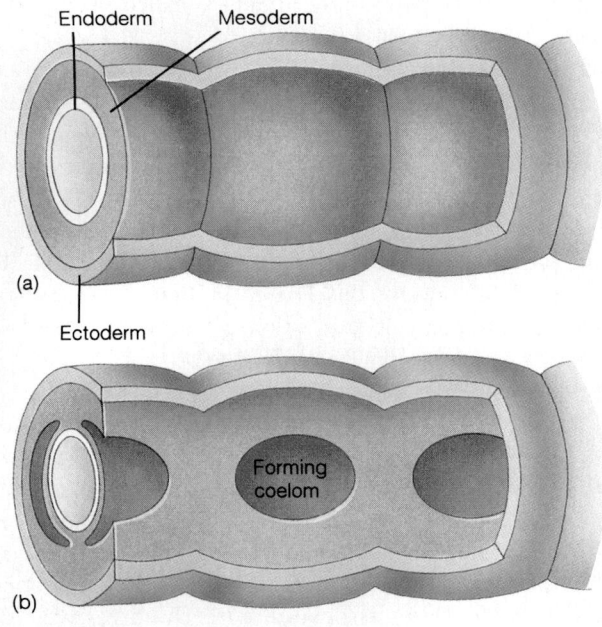

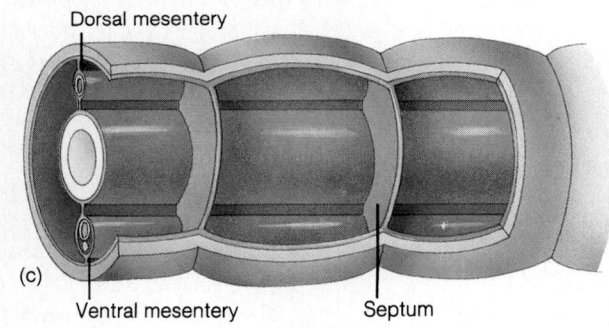

FIGURE 22.3

Development of Metameric, Coelomic Spaces in Annelids. (*a*) A solid mesodermal mass separates ectoderm and endoderm in early embryological stages. (*b*) Two cavities in each segment form from a splitting of the mesoderm on each side of the endoderm (schizocoelous coelom formation). (*c*) These cavities spread in all directions. Enlargement of the coelomic sacs leaves a thin layer of mesoderm applied against the outer body wall (the parietal peritoneum) and the gut tract (the visceral peritoneum), and it forms dorsal and ventral mesenteries. Anterior and posterior expansion of the coelom in adjacent segments results in the formation of the double-membraned septum that separates annelid metameres.

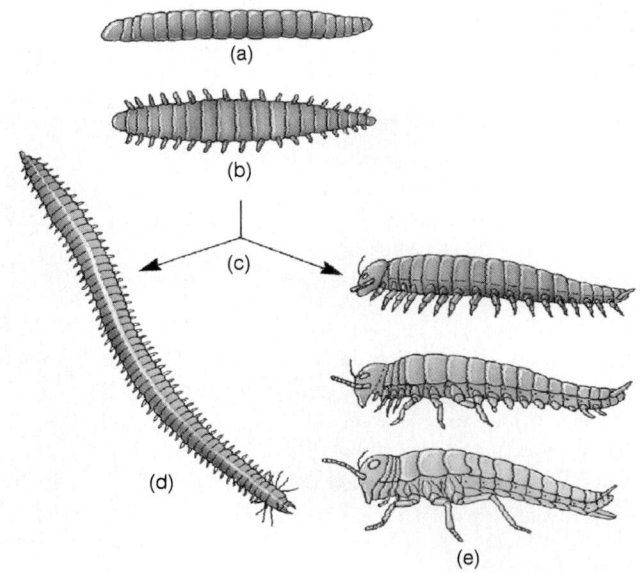

FIGURE 22.4

A Possible Origin of Annelids and Arthropods. A possible sequence in the evolution of the annelid/arthropod line from a hypothetical wormlike ancestor. (*a*) A wormlike prototype. (*b*) Paired, metameric appendages develop. (*c*) Divergence of the annelid and arthropod lines. (*d*) Paired appendages develop into parapodia of ancestral polychaetes. (*e*) Extensive tagmatization results in specializations characteristic of the arthropods. A head is a sensory and feeding tagma, a thorax is a locomotor tagma, and an abdomen contains visceral organs.

the circular muscles, runs between the septa that separate each segment. In addition, some polychaetes have oblique muscles and the leeches have dorsoventral muscles.

One advantage of the segmental arrangement of coelomic spaces and muscles is the creation of hydrostatic compartments, which makes possible a variety of advantageous locomotor and supportive functions not possible in nonmetameric animals that utilize a hydrostatic skeleton. Each segment can be controlled independently of distant segments, and muscles can act as antagonistic pairs within a segment. The constant volume of coelomic fluid provides a hydrostatic skeleton against which

muscles operate. Resultant localized changes in the shape of groups of segments provide the basis for swimming, crawling, and burrowing.

A second advantage of metamerism is that it lessens the impact of injury. If one or a few segments are injured, adjacent segments, set off from injured segments by septa, may be able to maintain nearly normal functions, which increases the likelihood that the worm, or at least a part of it, will survive the trauma.

A third advantage of metamerism is that it permits the modification of certain regions of the body for specialized functions, such as feeding, locomotion, and reproduction. The specialization of body regions in a metameric animal is called **tagmatization** (Gr. *tagma*, arrangement). Although it is best developed in the arthropods, some annelids also display tagmatization. (The arthropods include animals such as insects, spiders, mites, ticks, and crayfish.)

Virtually all zoologists agree that, because of similarities in the development of metamerism in the two groups, annelids and arthropods are closely related. Other common features include triploblastic coelomate organization, bilateral symmetry, a complete digestive tract, and a ventral nerve cord. As usual, there is little fossil evidence documenting ancestral pathways that led from a common ancestor to the earliest representatives of these two phyla. Zoologists are confident that the annelids and arthropods evolved from a marine, wormlike, bilateral ancestor that possessed metameric design. Figure 22.4 depicts a sequence of evolutionary changes that may have given rise to these two phyla.

FIGURE 22.5

Class Polychaeta. External structure of *Nereis virens*. Note the numerous parapodia.

Stop and Ask Yourself

1. What are two hypotheses regarding the origin of the phylum Annelida?
2. What is metamerism? What is tagmatization?
3. What are three advantages of metameric organization?
4. What other phylum is closely related to the annelids?

CLASS POLYCHAETA

Members of the class Polychaeta (pol″-e-ket′ah) (Gr. *polys*, many + *chaite*, hair) are mostly marine, and are usually between 5 and 10 cm long (*see table 22.1*). With more than 5,300 species, Polychaeta is the largest of the annelid classes. Polychaetes have become adapted to a variety of habitats. Many live on the ocean floor, under rocks and shells, and within the crevices of coral reefs. Other polychaetes are burrowers and move through their substrate by peristaltic contractions of the body wall. A bucket of intertidal sand normally yields vast numbers and an amazing variety of these burrowing annelids. Other polychaetes construct tubes of cemented sand grains or secreted organic materials. Mucus-lined tubes serve as protective retreats and feeding stations.

EXTERNAL STRUCTURE AND LOCOMOTION

In addition to metamerism, the most distinctive feature of polychaetes is the presence of lateral extensions called **parapodia** (Gr. *para*, beside + *podion*, little foot) (figure 22.5). Para-

podia are supported by chitinous rods, and numerous setae project from the parapodia, giving them their class name. **Setae** (L. *saeta*, bristle) are bristles that are secreted from invaginations of the distal ends of parapodia. They aid locomotion by digging into the substrate and are also used to hold a worm in its burrow or tube.

The **prostomium** (Gr. *pro*, before + *stoma*, mouth) of a polychaete is a lobe that projects dorsally and anteriorly to the mouth and contains numerous sensory structures, including eyes, antennae, palps, and ciliated pits or grooves, called nuchal organs. The first body segment, the **peristomium** (Gr. *peri*, around), surrounds the mouth and bears sensory tentacles or cirri.

The epidermis of polychaetes consists of a single layer of columnar cells that secrete a protective, nonliving **cuticle.** Some polychaetes have epidermal glands that secrete luminescent compounds.

Various species of polychaetes are capable of walking, fast crawling, or swimming. To do so, the longitudinal muscles on one side of the body act antagonistically to the longitudinal muscles on the other side of the body so that undulatory waves move along the length of the body from the posterior end toward the head. The propulsive force is the result of parapodia and setae acting against the substrate or water. Parapodia on opposite sides of the body are out of phase with one another. When longitudinal muscles on one side of a segment contract, the parapodial muscles on that side also contract, stiffening the parapodium and protruding the setae for the power stroke (figure 22.6*a*). As a polychaete changes from a slow crawl to swimming, the period and amplitude of undulatory waves increase (figure 22.6*b*).

Burrowing polychaetes push their way through sand and mud by contractions of the body wall or by eating their way through the substrate. In the latter, organic matter in the substrate is digested and absorbed and undigestible materials are eliminated via the anus.

FEEDING AND THE DIGESTIVE SYSTEM

The digestive tract of polychaetes is a straight tube and is suspended in the body cavity by mesenteries and septa. The anterior region of the digestive tract is modified into a proboscis, which can be everted through the mouth by special protractor muscles and coelomic pressure. Retractor muscles bring the proboscis back into the peristomium. In some, when the proboscis is everted, paired jaws are opened and may be used for seizing prey. Predatory polychaetes may not leave their burrow or coral crevice. When prey approaches a burrow entrance, the anterior portion of the worm is quickly extended, the proboscis is everted, and the prey is pulled back into the burrow. Some polychaetes have poison glands at the base of the jaw. Other polychaetes are herbivores and scavengers and use jaws for tearing food. Deposit-feeding polychaetes (e.g., *Arenicola*, the lugworm) extract organic matter from the marine sediments they ingest. The digestive tract consists of a pharynx that

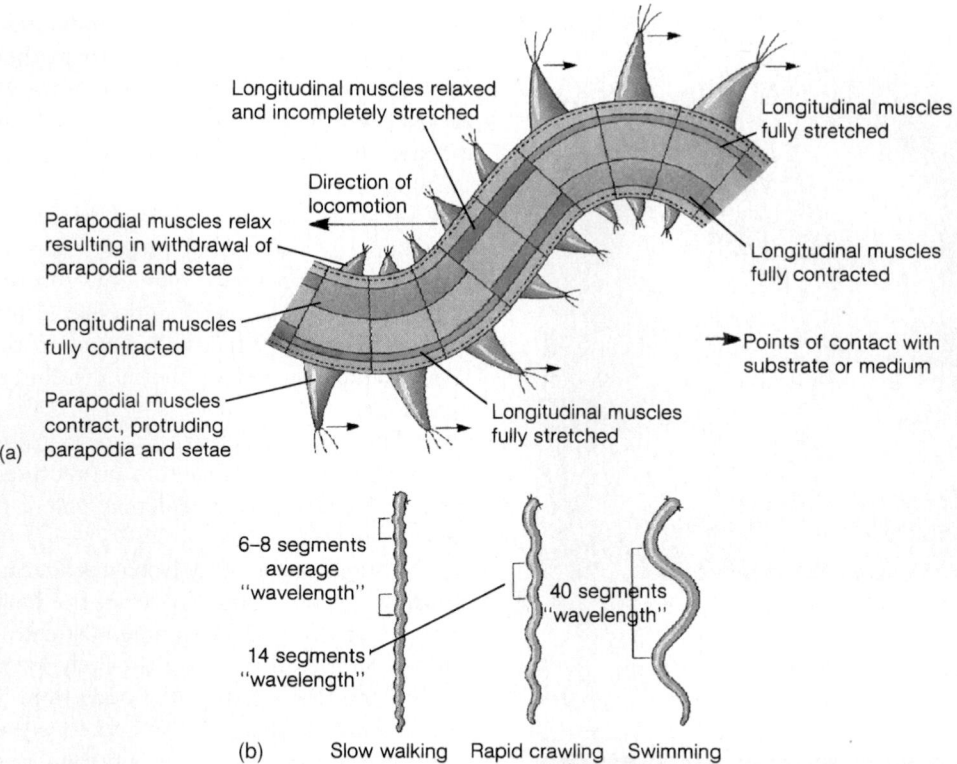

FIGURE 22.6

Polychaete Locomotion. (*a*) Dorsal view of a primitive polychaete showing the antagonism of longitudinal muscles on opposite sides of the body and the resultant protrusion and movement of parapodia. (*b*) Both the period and amplitude of locomotor waves increase as a polychaete changes from a "slow walk" to a swimming mode. *From: "A LIFE OF INVERTEBRATES" © 1979 W. D. Russell-Hunter.*

when everted, forms the proboscis; a storage sac, called a crop; a grinding gizzard; and a long, straight intestine. These are similar to digestive organs of earthworm (*see figure 22.13*). Organic matter is digested extracellularly, and the inorganic particles are passed through the intestine and released as "castings."

Many sedentary and tube-dwelling polychaetes are filter feeders. They usually lack a proboscis but possess other specialized feeding structures. Some tube dwellers, called fanworms, possess radioles that form a funnel-shaped fan. ③ Cilia on the radioles circulate water through the fan, trapping food particles. Trapped particles are carried along a food groove at the axis of the radiole. During transport, a sorting mechanism rejects the largest particles and transports the finest particles to the mouth. Another filter feeder, *Chaetopterus*, lives in a U-shaped tube and secretes a mucous bag that collects food particles, which may be as small as 1 micrometer (μm). The parapodia of segments 14 through 16 are modified into fans that create filtration currents. When full, the entire mucous bag is ingested.

Elimination of digestive waste products can be a problem for tube-dwelling polychaetes. Those that live in tubes that open at both ends simply have wastes carried away by water circulating through the tube. Those that live in tubes that open at one end must turn around in the tube to defecate, or they may use ciliary tracts along the body wall to carry feces to the tube opening.

Polychaetes that inhabit substrates rich in dissolved organic matter can absorb as much as 20 to 40% of their energy requirements across their body wall as sugars and other organic compounds. This method of feeding occurs in other animal phyla too, but rarely accounts for more than 1% of their energy needs.

GAS EXCHANGE AND CIRCULATION

Respiratory gases of most annelids simply diffuse across the body wall, and parapodia increase the surface area for these exchanges. In many polychaetes, the surface area for gas exchange is further increased by parapodial gills.

The circulatory system of polychaetes is a closed system. Oxygen is usually carried in combination with molecules called respiratory pigments, which are usually dissolved in the plasma rather than contained in blood cells. ④ Blood may be

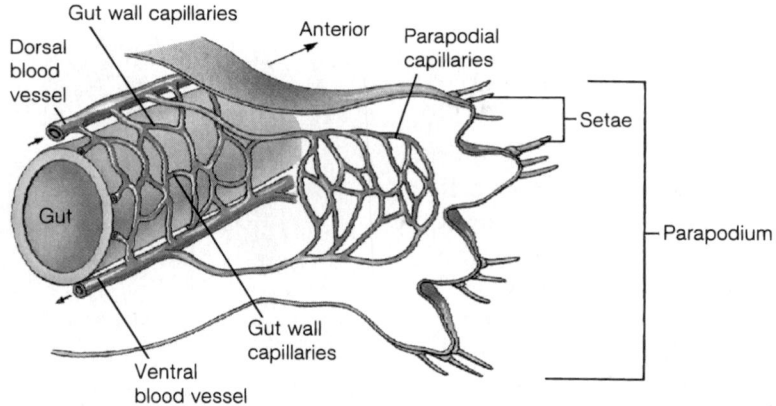

FIGURE 22.7

The Circulatory System of a Polychaete. In the closed circulatory system shown here, blood passes posterior to anterior in the dorsal vessel and anterior to posterior in the ventral vessel. Dorsal and ventral vessels are interconnected by capillary beds.

colorless, green, or red, depending on the presence and/or type of respiratory pigment.

Contractile elements of polychaete circulatory systems consist of a dorsal aorta that lies just above the digestive tract and propels blood from rear to front, and a ventral aorta that lies ventral to the digestive tract and propels blood from front to rear. Running between these two vessels are two or three sets of segmental vessels that receive blood from the ventral aorta and break into capillary beds in the gut and body wall. Capillaries coalesce again into segmental vessels that deliver blood to the dorsal aorta (figure 22.7).

NERVOUS AND SENSORY FUNCTIONS

Nervous systems are similar in all three classes of annelids. The annelid nervous system includes a pair of suprapharyngeal ganglia, which are connected to a pair of subpharyngeal ganglia by circumpharyngeal connectives that run dorsoventrally along either side of the pharynx. A double ventral nerve cord runs the length of the worm along the ventral margin of each coelomic space, and there is a paired segmental ganglion in each segment. The double ventral nerve cord and paired segmental ganglia may be fused to varying extents in different taxonomic groups. Lateral nerves emerge from each segmental ganglion, supplying the body-wall musculature and other structures of that segment (figure 22.8a).

Segmental ganglia are responsible for coordinating swimming and crawling movements in isolated segments. (Anyone who has used portions of worms as live fish bait can confirm that the head end—with the pharyngeal ganglia—is not necessary for coordinated movements.) Each segment acts separately from, but is closely coordinated with, neighboring segments. The subpharyngeal ganglia help mediate locomotor functions requiring coordination of distant segments. The

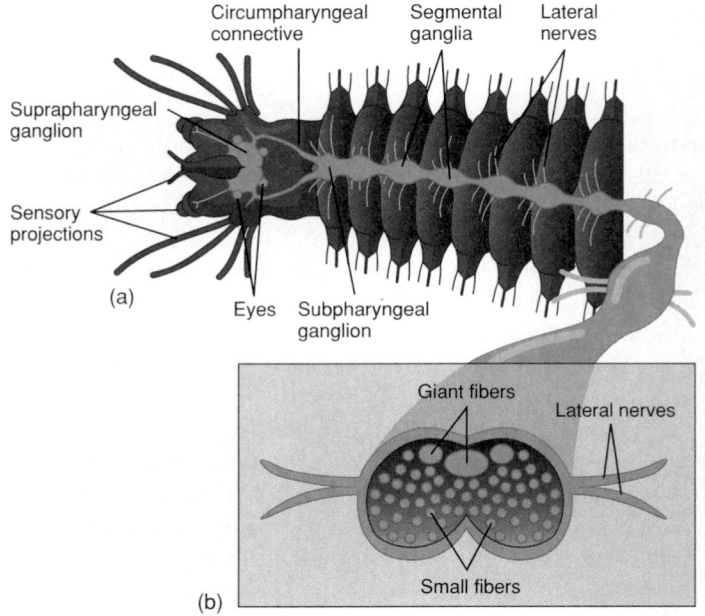

FIGURE 22.8

The Nervous System of a Polychaete. (*a*) Suprapharyngeal and subpharyngeal ganglia are linked by connectives. Segmental ganglia and lateral nerves occur along the length of the worm. (*b*) Cross section of the ventral nerve cord showing giant fibers.

suprapharyngeal ganglia probably control motor and sensory functions involved with feeding, and sensory functions associated with forward locomotion.

In addition to small-diameter fibers that help coordinate locomotion, the ventral nerve cord also contains giant fibers (figure 22.8b). Annelid giant fibers are involved with escape reactions. For example, a harsh stimulus at one end of a worm, such as a fishhook, causes a very rapid withdrawal from the stimulus. Giant fibers are approximately 50 μm in diameter and conduct nerve impulses at 30 m/second (as opposed to 0.5 m/second in the smaller, 4 μm diameter annelid fibers).

Polychaetes have various sensory structures. Two to four pairs of eyes occur on the surface of the prostomium. They vary in complexity from a simple cup of receptor cells to structures made up of a cornea, lens, and vitreous body. Most polychaetes react negatively to increased light intensities. Fanworms, however, react negatively to decreasing light intensities. If shadows cross them, fanworms retreat into their tubes. This response is believed to help protect fanworms from passing predators. Nuchal organs are pairs of ciliated sensory pits or slits in the head region. They are innervated by nerves from the suprapharyngeal ganglia and are thought to be chemoreceptors for food detection. Statocysts are found in the head region of polychaetes, and the body wall is covered by ciliated tubercles, ridges, and bands, all of which contain receptors for tactile senses.

EXCRETION

Annelids excrete ammonia, and because ammonia diffuses readily into the water, most nitrogen excretion probably occurs across the body wall. Excretory organs of annelids are more active in regulating water and ion balances, although these abilities are limited. Most marine polychaetes, if presented with extremely diluted seawater, cannot survive the osmotic influx of water and the loss of ions that results. The evolution of efficient osmoregulatory abilities has allowed only a few polychaetes to invade fresh water.

The excretory organs of annelids, like those of many invertebrates, are called nephridia. Two types of nephridia are found in annelids. A protonephridium consists of a tubule with a closed bulb at one end and a connection to the outside of the body at the other end. Protonephridia have a tuft of flagella in their bulbular end that drives fluids through the tubule (figure 22.9a; see also figure 19.6). Some primitive polychaetes possess paired, segmentally arranged protonephridia that have their bulbular end projecting through the anterior septum into an adjacent segment and the opposite end opening through the body wall at a nephridiopore.

Most polychaetes possess a second kind of nephridium, called a metanephridium. A **metanephridium** consists of an open, ciliated funnel, called a nephrostome, that projects through an anterior septum into the coelom of an adjacent segment. At the opposite end, a tubule opens through the body wall at a nephridiopore or occasionally through the intestine (figure 22.9b,c). There is usually one pair of metanephridia per segment, and tubules may be extensively coiled, with one portion dilated into a bladder. A capillary bed is usually associated with the tubule of a metanephridium

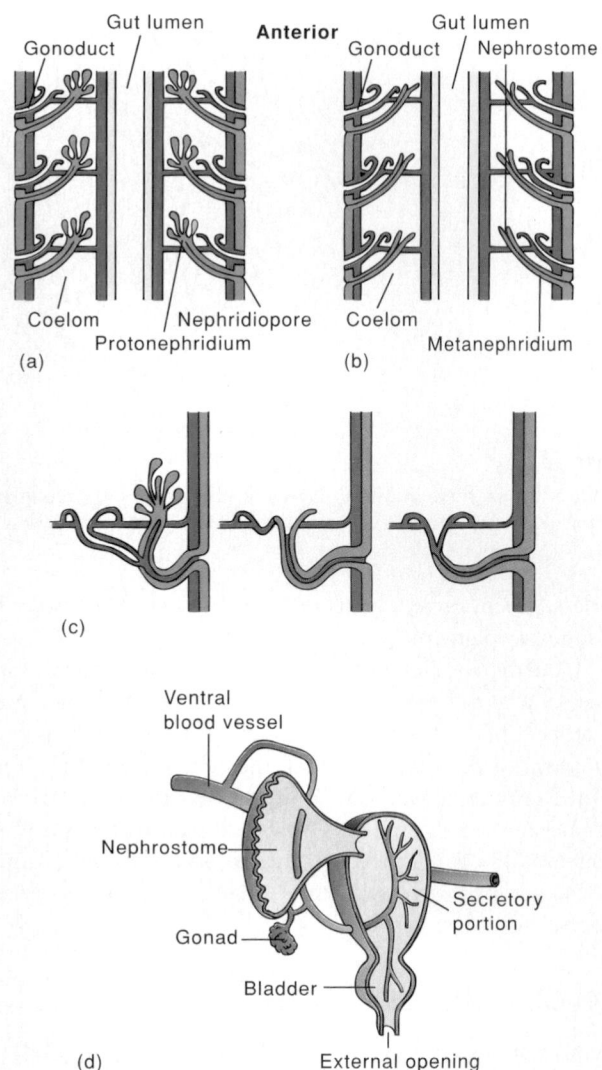

FIGURE 22.9

Annelid Nephridia. (a) The protonephridium. The bulbular ends of this nephridium contain a tuft of flagella that drives wastes to the outside of the body. In primitive polychaetes, a gonoduct (coelomoduct) carries reproductive products to the outside of the body. (b) The metanephridium. An open ciliated funnel (the nephrostome) drives wastes to the outside of the body. (c) In modern annelids, the gonoduct and the nephridial tubules undergo varying degrees of fusion. (d) Nephridia of modern annelids are closely associated with capillary beds for secretion, and nephridial tubules may have an enlarged bladder. *From: "A LIFE OF INVERTEBRATES" © 1979 W. D. Russell-Hunter.*

for active transport of ions between the blood and the nephridium (figure 22.9d).

Some polychaetes also have chloragogen tissue associated with the digestive tract. This tissue functions in amino acid metabolism in all annelids and will be described further in a later section.

REGENERATION, REPRODUCTION, AND DEVELOPMENT

All polychaetes have remarkable powers of regeneration. They can replace lost parts, and some species have break points that allow worms to sever themselves when grabbed by a predator. Lost segments are later regenerated.

Some polychaetes reproduce asexually by budding or by transverse fission; however, sexual reproduction is much more common. Most polychaetes are dioecious. Gonads develop as masses of gametes and project from the coelomic peritoneum. Primitively, gonads occur in every body segment, but most polychaetes have gonads limited to specific segments. Gametes are shed into the coelom where they mature. Mature female worms are often packed with eggs. Gametes may exit worms by entering nephrostomes of metanephridia and exiting through the nephridiopore, or they may be released, in some polychaetes, after the worm ruptures. In these cases, the adult soon dies. Only a few polychaetes have separate gonoducts, a condition that is believed to be primitive (see figure 22.9a–c).

Fertilization is external in most polychaetes, although copulation occurs in a few species. One of the most unique copulatory habits has been reported in *Platynereis megalops* from Woods Hole, Massachusetts. Toward the end of their lives, male and female worms cease feeding, and their intestinal tracts begin to degenerate. At this time, gametes have accumulated in the body cavity. During sperm transfer, male and female worms coil together, and the male inserts his anus into the mouth of the female. Because the digestive tracts of the worms have degenerated, sperm are transferred directly from the male's coelom to the egg-filled coelom of the female. This method ensures fertilization of most eggs, and after fertilization is accomplished, the female sheds eggs from her anus. Both worms die soon after copulation.

Epitoky is the formation of a reproductive individual (an epitoke) that differs from the nonreproductive form of the species (an atoke). Frequently, an epitoke has a body that is modified into two body regions. Anterior segments carry on normal maintenance functions, and posterior segments are enlarged and filled with gametes. The epitoke may have modified parapodia for more efficient swimming.

At the beginning of this chapter, there was an account of the reproductive swarming habits of *Eunice viridis* (the Samoan palolo worm), and one culture's response to those swarms. Similar swarming occurs in other species, usually in response to changing light intensities and lunar periods. The Atlantic palolo worm, for example, swarms at dawn during the first and third quarters of the July lunar cycle.

Swarming of epitokes is believed to accomplish at least three things. First, because nonreproductive individuals remain safe below the surface waters, predators cannot devastate an entire population. Second, external fertilization requires

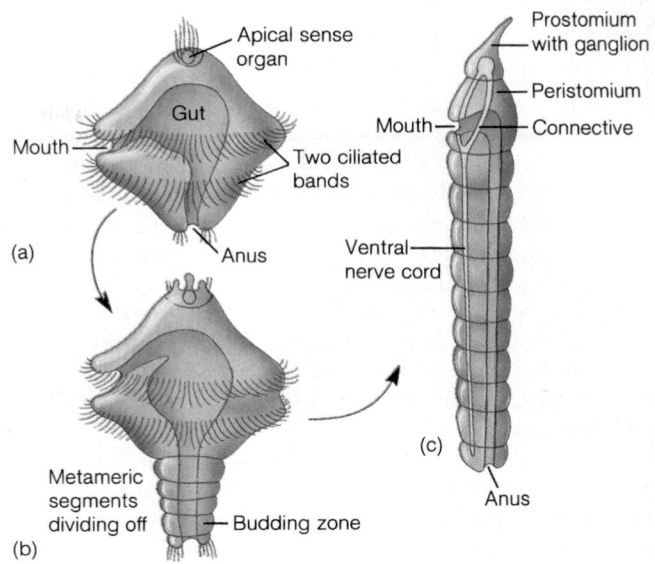

FIGURE 22.10

Polychaete Development. (*a*) A trochophore. (*b*) A later planktonic larva showing the development of body segments. As more segments develop, the larva will settle to the substrate. (*c*) A juvenile worm. *From: "A LIFE OF INVERTEBRATES" © 1979 W. D. Russell-Hunter.*

that individuals become reproductively active at the same time and in close proximity to one another. Swarming ensures that large numbers of individuals will be in the right place at the proper time. Third, swarming of vast numbers of individuals for brief periods provides a banquet for predators. However, because vast numbers of prey are available for only short periods during the year, predator populations cannot increase beyond the limits of their normal diets. Therefore, predators can dine gluttonously and still leave epitokes that will yield the next generation of animals.

Spiral cleavage of fertilized eggs may result in planktonic trochophore larvae that bud segments anterior to the anus. Larvae eventually settle to the substrate (figure 22.10). As growth proceeds, newer segments continue to be added posteriorly. Thus, the anterior end of a polychaete is the oldest end. Many other polychaetes lack a trochophore and display direct development or metamorphosis from another larval stage.

Stop and Ask Yourself

5. How is the body wall of a polychaete involved with crawling movement?
6. What is the function of giant nerve fibers in polychaetes?
7. What is epitoky? Why is it advantageous for some polychaetes?

22.1   SOIL CONDITIONING BY EARTHWORMS

Earthworms have had an inestimable impact on the development of our planet's soil. For the past 100 million years earthworms have evolved with deciduous vegetation. Leaf fall and the death of land plants have provided a massive food source for earthworms and other soil-inhabiting organisms. The excrement, death, and decay of these soil organisms build the organic constituents of our soils, and burrowing by earthworms aerates the soil and improves drainage.

In typical grassland and woodland soils, earthworms reach populations of hundreds of animals per square meter. They often dominate the invertebrate biomass (the total mass of invertebrate animals) in a region. Earthworms ingest soil as they feed on organic matter and as they burrow through the soil. Charles Darwin estimated that 15 tons of soil per acre per year passed through earthworm bodies. Recent, more accurate estimates of earthworm populations, give even more impressive tillage figures of nearly 40 tons per acre per year!

Earthworms are surface feeders that emerge at night to feed on leaf fragments and other plant debris. Some of these fragments are ingested immediately, others are carried into burrows. Of the plant matter ingested by earthworms, less than 10% is incorporated into worm tissues. The rest passes through the digestive tract, is incorporated into castings (fecal material and soil), and released deeper in the soil. Earthworm castings are also rich in ammonia, which is a form of nitrogen usable by some plants.

Earthworms function as vegetation shredders in our soils. Shredding vegetation and incorporating it into fecal material increases the surface area of plant matter by several orders of magnitude and hastens its eventual decomposition by bacteria and fungi. One study demonstrated the role of shredders in the breakdown of plant litter by soil animals. Leaf-filled nylon bags were buried in the soil. Some bags had a 0.5 mm mesh size, which excluded all earthworms and other large invertebrates. Other bags had a mesh size of 7 mm, which allowed all invertebrates to enter. The rate of breakdown of leaf litter was reduced by approximately two-thirds in the small mesh bags.

CLASS OLIGOCHAETA

The class Oligochaeta (ol''i-go-ket'ah) has over 3,000 species that are found throughout the world in freshwater and terrestrial habitats (*see table 22.1*). A few oligochaetes are estuarine, and some are marine. Aquatic species live in shallow water, where they burrow in mud and debris. Terrestrial species are found in soils with high organic content, and these species rarely leave their burrows. In hot, dry weather they may retreat to depths of 3 m below the surface. Soil-conditioning habits of earthworms are well known (box 22.1). *Lumbricus terrestris* is commonly used in zoology laboratories because of its large size. It was introduced to the United States from northern Europe and has flourished. Common native species like *Eisenia foetida* and various species of *Allolobophora* are smaller.

EXTERNAL STRUCTURE AND LOCOMOTION

Oligochaetes (Gr. *oligos,* few + *chaite,* hair) have setae, but fewer than are found in polychaetes (thus the derivation of the class name). Oligochaetes lack parapodia, because parapodia and long setae would interfere with their burrowing life-styles, although they do have short setae on their integument. The prostomium consists of a small lobe or cone in front of the mouth and lacks sensory appendages. A series of segments in the anterior half of an oligochaete is usually swollen into a girdlelike structure called the **clitellum** that is used for mucous secretion during copulation and cocoon formation (figure 22.11). As in the polychaetes, the body is covered by a nonliving, secreted cuticle.

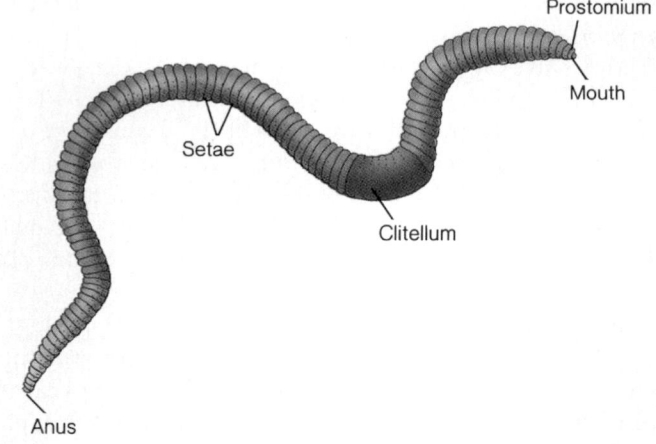

FIGURE 22.11
Class Annelida. External structures of the earthworm, *Lumbricus terrestris.*

Oligochaete locomotion involves the antagonism of circular and longitudinal muscles in groups of segments. Neurally controlled waves of contraction move from rear to front.

Segments bulge and setae protrude when longitudinal muscles are contracted, providing points of contact with the burrow wall. In front of each region of longitudinal muscle contraction, circular muscles contract, causing the setae to retract, and the segments to elongate and push forward. Contraction of longitudinal muscles in segments behind a bulging region causes those segments to be pulled forward. Thus, segments move forward relative to the burrow as waves of muscle contraction move anteriorly on the worm (figure 22.12).

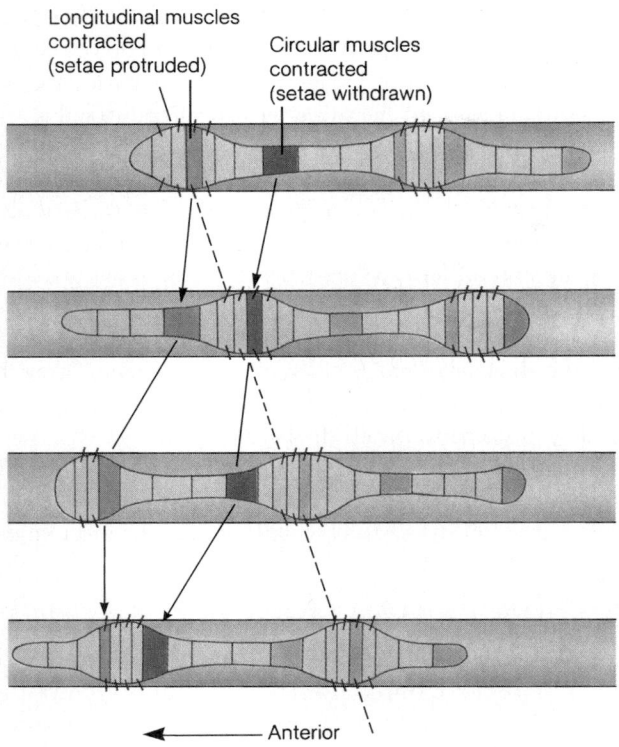

FIGURE 22.12

Earthworm Locomotion. Arrows designate activity in specific segments of the body, and the broken lines indicate regions of contact with the substrate. *From: "A LIFE OF INVERTEBRATES" © 1979 W. D. Russell-Hunter.*

Burrowing is the result of coelomic hydrostatic pressure being transmitted toward the prostomium. As an earthworm pushes its way through the soil, it uses expanded posterior segments and protracted setae to anchor itself to its burrow wall. ⑥ (Any child pursuing fishing worms experiences the effectiveness of this anchor when trying to extract a worm from its burrow.) Contraction of circular muscles transforms the prostomium into a conical wedge, 1 mm in diameter at its tip. Contraction of body-wall muscles generates coelomic pressure that forces the prostomium through the soil. During burrowing, earthworms swallow considerable quantities of soil.

FEEDING AND THE DIGESTIVE SYSTEM

Oligochaetes are scavengers and feed primarily on fallen and decaying vegetation, which they drag into their burrows at night. The digestive tract of oligochaetes is tubular and straight (figure 22.13). The mouth leads to a muscular pharynx. In the earthworm, pharyngeal muscles attach to the body wall. The pharynx acts as a pump for ingesting food. The mouth pushes against food and the pharynx pumps the food into the esophagus. The esophagus is narrow and tubular and frequently is expanded to form a stomach, crop, or gizzard; the latter two are common in terrestrial species. A crop is a thin-walled storage structure, and a gizzard is a muscular, cuticle-lined grinding structure. Calciferous glands are evaginations of the esophageal wall that rid the body of excess calcium absorbed from food. Calciferous glands also have an important function in regulating the pH of body

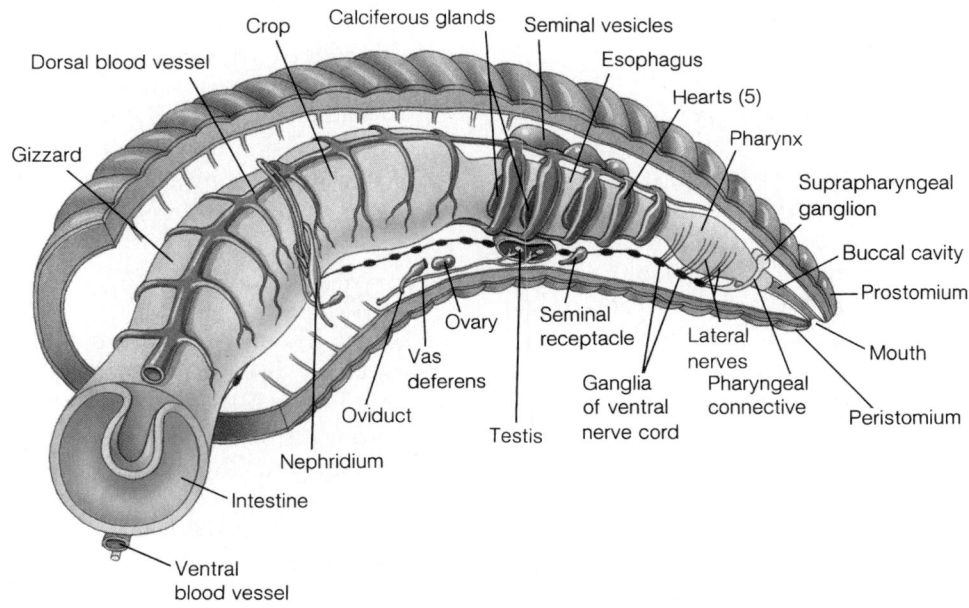

FIGURE 22.13

Earthworm Structure. This diagram shows a lateral view of the internal structures in the anterior ⅓ of an earthworm.

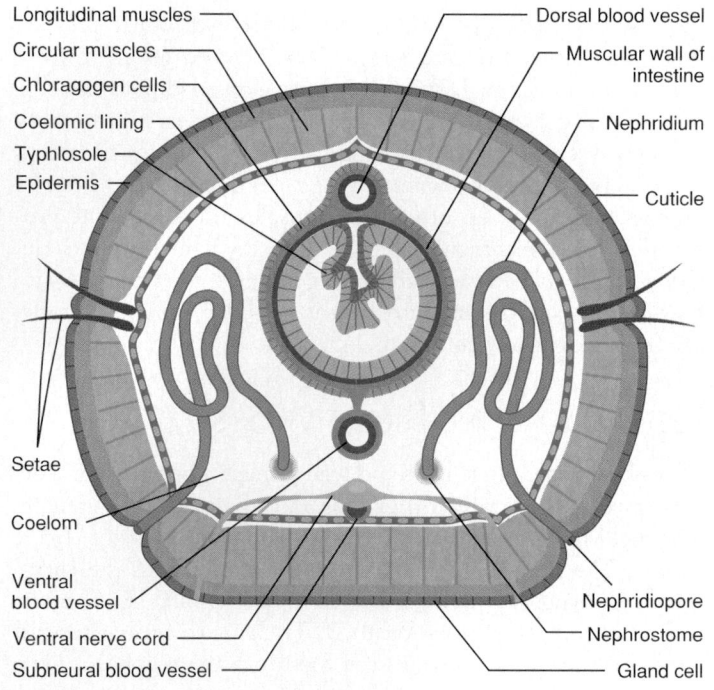

Longitudinal muscles
Circular muscles
Chloragogen cells
Coelomic lining
Typhlosole
Epidermis

Dorsal blood vessel
Muscular wall of intestine
Nephridium
Cuticle

Setae
Coelom
Ventral blood vessel
Ventral nerve cord
Subneural blood vessel

Nephridiopore
Nephrostome
Gland cell

FIGURE 22.14

Earthworm Cross Section. The nephrostomes shown here would actually be associated with the next anterior segment.

fluids. The intestine is a straight tube and is the principal site of digestion and absorption. The surface area of the intestine is increased substantially by a dorsal fold of the lumenal epithelium called the typhlosole (figure 22.14). The intestine ends at the anus.

GAS EXCHANGE AND CIRCULATION

Both respiratory and circulatory functions are as described for polychaetes. Some segmental vessels are expanded and may be contractile. In the earthworm, for example, expanded segmental vessels surrounding the esophagus propel blood between dorsal and ventral blood vessels and anteriorly in the ventral vessel toward the mouth. Even though these are sometimes called "hearts," the main propulsive structures are the dorsal and the ventral vessels (*see figure 22.13*). Branches from the ventral vessel supply the intestine and body wall.

NERVOUS AND SENSORY FUNCTIONS

The ventral nerve cords and all ganglia of oligochaetes have undergone a high degree of fusion. Other aspects of nervous structure and function are essentially the same as those described earlier for polychaetes. As with polychaetes, giant fibers mediate escape responses. An escape response results from the

stimulation of either the anterior or the posterior end of a worm. An impulse conducted to the opposite end of the worm initiates the formation of an anchor, and longitudinal muscles contract to quickly pull the worm away from the stimulus.

Oligochaetes lack well-developed eyes, which should not be surprising given their subterranean life-style. It is not unusual for animals living in perpetual darkness to be without well-developed eyes. Other oligochaetes have simple pigment-cup ocelli, and all have a "dermal light sense" that arises from photoreceptor cells scattered over the dorsal and lateral surfaces of the body. Scattered photoreceptor cells mediate a negative phototaxis in strong light (evidenced by movement away from the light source) and a positive phototaxis in weak light (evidenced by movement toward the light source).

Oligochaetes are sensitive to a wide variety of chemical and mechanical stimuli. Receptors for these stimuli are scattered over the surface of the body, especially around the prostomium.

EXCRETION

Oligochaetes use metanephridia for excretion and for ion and water regulation. As with polychaetes, funnels of metanephridia are associated with the segment just anterior to the segment containing the tubule and the nephridiopore. Nitrogenous wastes include ammonia and urea. Oligochaetes excrete copious amounts of very dilute urine, although they retain vital ions, which is very important for organisms living in environments where water is plentiful but essential ions are limited.

Oligochaetes (as well as other annelids) possess chloragogen tissue that surrounds the dorsal blood vessel and lies over the dorsal surface of the intestine (*see figure 22.14*). **Chloragogen tissue** acts similarly to the vertebrate liver. It is a site of amino acid metabolism. Deamination of amino acids, and the conversion of ammonia to urea occurs there. Chloragogen tissue also converts excess carbohydrates into energy-storage molecules of glycogen and fat.

REPRODUCTION AND DEVELOPMENT

All oligochaetes are monoecious, and mutual sperm exchange occurs during copulation. One or two pairs of testes and one pair of ovaries are located on the anterior septum of certain anterior segments. Both the sperm ducts and the oviducts have ciliated funnels at their proximal ends to draw gametes into their respective tubes.

Testes are closely associated with three pairs of **seminal vesicles,** which are sites for maturation and storage of sperm prior to their release. **Seminal receptacles** receive sperm during copulation. A pair of very small ovisacs, associated with oviducts, are sites for the maturation and storage of eggs prior to egg release (figure 22.15).

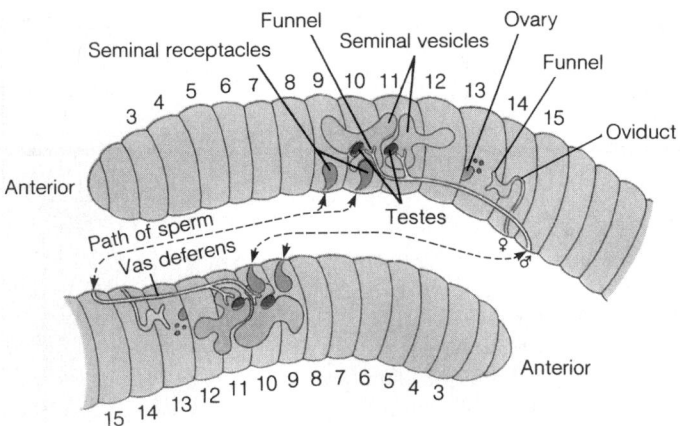

FIGURE 22.15

Earthworm Reproduction. Mating earthworms showing arrangements of reproductive structures and the path taken by sperm during sperm exchange (shown by arrows).

During copulation of *Lumbricus*, two worms line up facing in opposite directions, with the ventral surfaces of their anterior ends in contact with each other. This orientation lines up the clitellum of one worm with the genital segments of the other worm. Worms are held in place by a mucous sheath, secreted by the clitellum, that envelopes the anterior halves of both worms. Some species also have penile structures and genital setae that help maintain contact between worms. In *Lumbricus*, sperm are released from the sperm duct and travel along the external, ventral body wall in sperm grooves formed by the contraction of special muscles. Muscular contractions along this groove help propel sperm toward the openings of the seminal receptacles. In other oligochaetes, copulation results in the alignment of sperm duct and seminal receptacle openings and transfer of sperm is direct. Copulation lasts 2 to 3 hours, during which both worms give and receive sperm.

Following copulation, the clitellum forms a cocoon for the deposition of eggs and sperm. The cocoon consists of mucoid and chitinous materials that encircle the clitellum. A food reserve, albumen, is secreted into the cocoon by the clitellum, and the worm begins to back out of the cocoon. Eggs are deposited in the cocoon as the cocoon passes the openings to the oviducts, and sperm are released as the cocoon passes the openings to the seminal receptacles. Fertilization occurs in the cocoon and, as the worm continues backing out, the ends of the cocoon are sealed, and the cocoon is deposited in moist soil.

Spiral cleavage is modified, and no larva is formed. Hatching occurs in one to a few weeks, depending on the species, when young worms emerge from one end of the cocoon.

Asexual reproduction also occurs in freshwater oligochaetes. It consists of transverse division of a worm, followed by regeneration of missing segments.

Stop and Ask Yourself

8. How does an earthworm move across a substrate? How does an earthworm burrow?

9. What is the function of calciferous glands? The typhlosole? Chloragogen tissue?

10. How would you describe the method of sperm transfer and egg deposition in earthworms?

11. In what way is development of an oligochaete different from that of a polychaete?

CLASS HIRUDINEA

The class Hirudinea (hi'roo-din"eah) (L. *hirudin,* leech) contains approximately 500 species of leeches (*see table 22.1*). Most leeches are fresh water; others are marine, or completely terrestrial. Leeches prey on small invertebrates or feed on body fluids of vertebrates (box 22.2).

EXTERNAL STRUCTURE AND LOCOMOTION

Leeches lack parapodia and head appendages. Setae are absent in most leeches. In a few species, setae occur only on anterior segments. Leeches are dorsoventrally flattened and taper anteriorly. They have 34 segments, but the segments are difficult to distinguish externally because they have become secondarily divided. Several secondary divisions, called **annuli,** are in each true segment. Anterior and posterior segments are usually modified into suckers (figure 22.16).

Modifications of body-wall musculature and the coelom influence patterns of locomotion in the leeches. The musculature of leeches is more complex than that of other annelids. A layer of oblique muscles is present between the circular and longitudinal muscle layers. In addition, dorsoventral muscles are responsible for the typical leech flattening. The coelom of leeches has lost its metameric partitioning. Septa are lost, and the coelom has been invaded by connective tissue, resulting in a series of interconnecting sinuses.

These modifications have resulted in altered patterns of locomotion. Rather than being able to utilize independent coelomic compartments, the leech has a single hydrostatic cavity and uses it in a looping type of locomotion. The mechanics of this locomotion are described in figure 22.17. Leeches also swim using undulations of the body.

FEEDING AND THE DIGESTIVE SYSTEM

Many leeches feed on body fluids or the entire bodies of other invertebrates. Some feed on blood of vertebrates, including human blood.   ⑦   Leeches are sometimes called parasites; however, the association between a leech and its host is relatively brief.

BOX 22.2 LEECHES AND SCIENCE

At first mention of the word leech, most thoughts turn to the medicinal leech, *Hirudo medicinalis* (figure 1), and the practice of bloodletting. In past centuries, various illnesses have been attributed to "bad blood," and the practice of bloodletting was common. Medicinal leeches were used in bloodletting because when they feed, they ingest seven to eight times their weight in blood—one of the biggest meals in the animal kingdom. After such a meal, the leech may not feed again for a year.

The use of leeches in bloodletting during the second century is documented in the writings of Galen, an early Greek physician. The practice remained very common through the early nineteenth century. The medicinal leech and medicine became almost synonymous. Physicians themselves were sometimes (respectfully) referred to as "leeches." During the late nineteenth and early twentieth century, the use of leeches in medicine declined. Now, however, the medicinal leech is again being used in medicine to remove excess blood from tissues after plastic surgery, or after the reattachment of amputated appendages. If the excess blood is not removed, blood accumulating in tissues of postoperative patients often slows the regrowth of capillary beds and can cause tissues to die.

Leeches are also being used to investigate the physiology of nervous systems. The fact that the nervous system of a leech is simpler than that of many other animals that show system-level organization, and the fact that the nerve cells of all animals share similar physiological properties, make leeches ideal subjects for research into animal nervous systems. Certain chemicals, such as serotonin, are secreted from leech nerve cells and have been found to help regulate all aspects of leech feeding—from finding prey to ingesting blood. Organisms such as leeches may hold the keys to discovering the roles of essentially identical chemicals in the nervous systems of other animals.

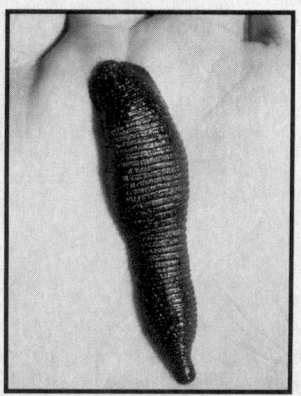

FIGURE 1 The Medicinal Leech, *Hirudo medicinalis.*

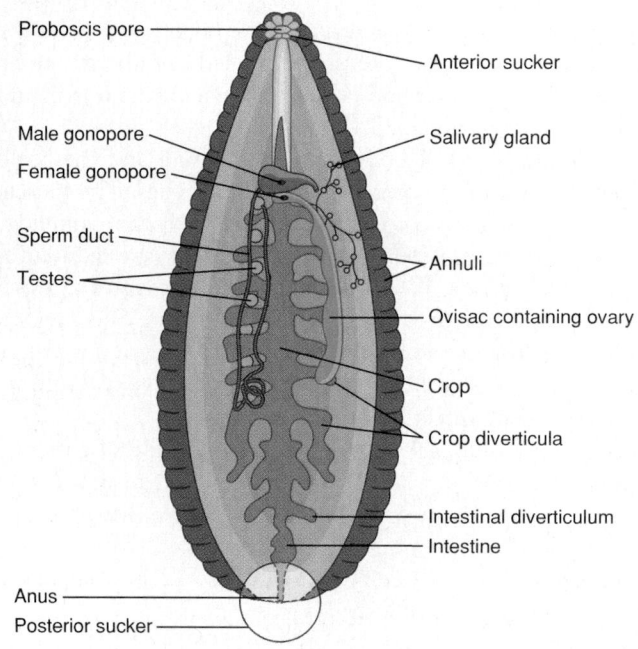

Proboscis pore
Anterior sucker
Male gonopore
Salivary gland
Female gonopore
Sperm duct
Testes
Annuli
Ovisac containing ovary
Crop
Crop diverticula
Intestinal diverticulum
Intestine
Anus
Posterior sucker

FIGURE 22.16

Internal Structure of a Leech. Each true segment is subdivided by annuli and the coelom is not subdivided by septa.

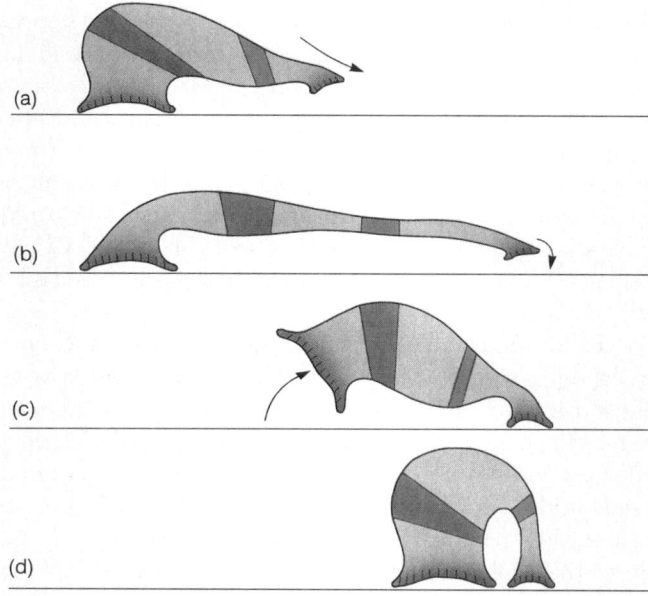

(a)

(b)

(c)

(d)

FIGURE 22.17

Leech Locomotion. (*a,b*) Attachment of the posterior sucker causes reflexive release of the anterior sucker, contraction of circular muscles, and relaxation of longitudinal muscles. This muscular activity compresses fluids in the single hydrostatic compartment, and the leech extends. (*c,d*) Attachment of the anterior sucker causes reflexive release of the posterior sucker, the relaxation of circular muscles, and the contraction of longitudinal muscles, causing body fluids to expand the diameter of the leech. The leech shortens, and the posterior sucker again attaches. *From: "A LIFE OF INVERTEBRATES" © 1979 W. D. Russell-Hunter.*

Therefore, describing leeches as predatory is probably more accurate. Leeches are also not species specific, as are most parasites. (Leeches are, however, class specific. That is, a leech that preys upon a turtle may also prey on an alligator, but probably would not prey on a fish or a frog.)

The mouth of a leech opens in the middle of the anterior sucker. In some leeches, the anterior digestive tract is modified into a protrusible proboscis, lined inside and outside by a cuticle. In others, the mouth is armed with three chitinous jaws. While feeding, a leech attaches to its prey by the anterior sucker and either extends its proboscis into the prey or uses its jaws to slice through host tissues. Salivary glands secrete an anticoagulant called "hirudin" that prevents blood from clotting.

Behind the mouth is a muscular pharynx that pumps body fluids of the prey into the leech. The esophagus follows the pharynx and leads to a large stomach with lateral cecae. Most leeches ingest large quantities of blood or other body fluids and gorge their stomachs and lateral cecae, increasing their body mass 2 to 10 times. After engorgement, a leech can tolerate periods of fasting that may last for months. The digestive tract ends in a short intestine and anus (*see figure 22.16*).

GAS EXCHANGE AND CIRCULATION

Gas exchange occurs across the body wall. The basic annelid circulatory pattern is retained in some leeches, but in most it is highly modified, and vessels are replaced by coelomic sinuses. Coelomic fluid has taken over the function of blood and, except in two orders, respiratory pigments are lacking.

NERVOUS AND SENSORY FUNCTIONS

The nervous system of leeches is similar to that of other annelids. Ventral nerve cords are unfused, except at the ganglia. The suprapharyngeal and subpharyngeal ganglia and the pharyngeal connectives are all fused into a nerve ring that surrounds the pharynx. There is also a similar fusion of ganglia at the posterior end of the animal.

A variety of epidermal sense organs are widely scattered over the body. Most leeches have photoreceptor cells located in pigment cups (2 to 10) along the dorsal surface of the anterior segments. Normally, leeches are negatively phototactic, but when searching for food, the behavior of some leeches changes, and they become positively phototactic, which increases the likelihood of contacting prey that happens to pass by.

Hirudo medicinalis, the medicinal leech, has a well-developed temperature sense. This sense helps the leech detect the higher body temperature of its mammalian prey. Other leeches are attracted to extracts of prey tissues.

All leeches have sensory cells with terminal bristles in a row along the middle annulus of each segment. These sensory cells, called sensory papillae, are of uncertain function but are taxonomically important.

EXCRETION

Leeches have 10 to 17 pairs of metanephridia, 1 per segment in the middle segments of the body. Their metanephridia are highly modified and possess, in addition to the nephrostome and tubule, a capsule that is believed to be involved with the production of coelomic fluid. Chloragogen tissue is proliferated through the body cavity of most leeches.

REPRODUCTION AND DEVELOPMENT

All leeches reproduce sexually and are monoecious. None are capable of asexual reproduction or regeneration. They have a single pair of ovaries and from four to many testes. Leeches have a clitellum that includes three body segments. The clitellum can be seen only in the spring when most leeches breed.

Sperm transfer and egg deposition usually occur in the same manner as described for oligochaetes. A penis assists the transfer of sperm between individuals. A few transfer sperm by expelling a spermatophore from one leech into the integument of another, a form of hypodermic impregnation. Special tissues within the integument connect to the ovaries by short ducts. Cocoons are deposited in the soil or are attached to underwater objects. There are no larval stages, and the offspring are mature by the following spring.

FURTHER PHYLOGENETIC CONSIDERATIONS

Although the origins of the phylum as a whole are speculative and somewhat controversial, the evolutionary relationships among members of the three annelid classes are as clear as those in any other phylum of animals. Polychaetes are the most primitive of the three annelid classes, as evidenced by basic metamerism, spiral cleavage, and trochophore larval stages in some species. (Some zoologists contend that the occurrence of the latter is too variable to be considered a part of the evidence of the ancestral status of the class.) Adaptive radiation of polychaetes has resulted in the great diversity of modern polychaetes.

Some members of the ancient annelid stock invaded fresh waters, which required the ability to regulate the salt and water content of body fluids. It was from this group that the oligochaetes probably evolved. Initially, oligochaetes were strictly fresh water, and many remain in that habitat; however, during the Cretaceous period, approximately 100 million years ago, oligochaetes invaded

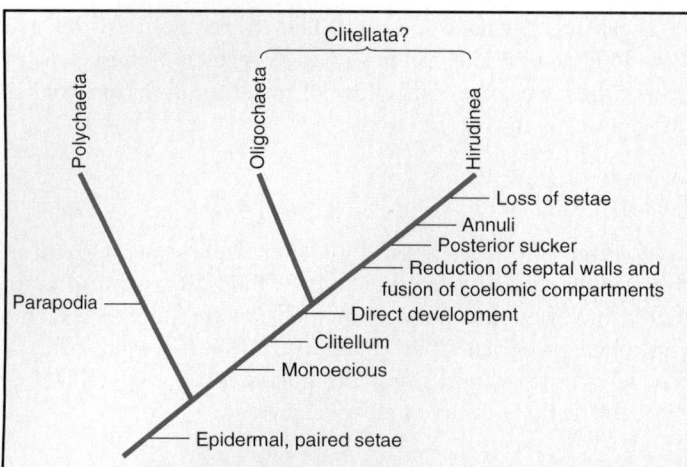

Figure 22.18

Annelid Phylogeny. A cladogram illustrating the evolutionary relationships of the three annelid classes. The ancestors of the annelids and arthropods were metameric coelomate animals in the protostome lineage. Paired epidermal setae are diagnostic of the phylum. The polychaetes were the first modern annelids to be derived from the ancestral annelids. Some zoologists believe that these animals should be grouped into a single class, Clitellata. (Note the question mark in the cladogram.) The oligochaetes and leeches were derived from a second major lineage of annelids. Note that the oligochaetes are distinguished from the leeches by the absence of derived characters.

moist, terrestrial environments. This period saw the climax of the giant land reptiles, but, more importantly, it was a time of proliferation of flowering land plants.   ⑧   The reliance of modern earthworms on deciduous vegetation can be traced

back to the exploitation of this food source by their ancestors. As described earlier, terrestrial oligochaetes deserve a large share of the credit for developing the soils of this planet (*see* box 22.1). A few oligochaetes have secondarily invaded marine environments.

Some of those early freshwater oligochaetes also gave rise to the Hirudinea. As with the oligochaetes, some leeches colonized marine habitats from fresh water.

Figure 22.18 is a cladogram showing the evolutionary relationships among the three annelid classes. The polychaetes are depicted as the first modern annelids. The oligochaetes and leeches are shown as sharing a second major lineage. There are no known derived characteristics (synapomorphies) unique to the oligochaetes. Instead, the oligochaetes are defined by the absence of leech characteristics. This fact supports the idea that the oligochaetes are ancestral to the leeches, and it also leads some taxonomists to believe that the oligochaetes and leeches should be combined into a single class—Clitellata.

Stop and Ask Yourself

12. How is basic annelid metamerism modified in leeches?

13. How are the body-wall musculature and the body cavity of a leech used in locomotion?

14. Why is it more accurate to call leeches predators than parasites?

15. What are the phylogenetic relationships of the annelid classes?

SUMMARY

1. The origin of the Annelida is largely unknown. A diagnostic characteristic of the annelids is metamerism.

2. Metamerism allows efficient utilization of separate coelomic compartments as a hydrostatic skeleton for support and movement. Metamerism also lessens the impact of injury and makes tagmatization possible.

3. Members of the class Polychaeta are mostly marine and possess parapodia with numerous setae. Locomotion of polychaetes involves the antagonism of longitudinal muscles on opposite sides of the body, which creates undulatory waves along the body wall and causes parapodia to act against the substrate.

4. Polychaetes may be predators, herbivores, scavengers, or filter feeders.

5. The nervous system of polychaetes usually consists of a pair of suprapharyngeal ganglia, subpharyngeal ganglia, and double ventral nerve cords that run the length of the worm.

6. Polychaetes have a closed circulatory system. Oxygen is carried by respiratory pigments dissolved in blood plasma.

7. Either protonephridia or metanephridia are used in excretion in polychaetes.

8. Most polychaetes are dioecious, and gonads develop from coelomic epithelium. Fertilization is usually external. Epitoky occurs in some polychaetes.

9. Development of polychaetes usually results in a planktonic trochophore larva that buds off segments near the anus.

10. The class Oligochaeta includes primarily freshwater and terrestrial annelids. Oligochaetes possess few setae and they lack a head and parapodia.

11. Oligochaetes are scavengers that feed on dead and decaying vegetation. Their digestive tract is tubular, straight, and frequently has modifications for storing and grinding food, and increasing the surface area for secretion and absorption.

12. Oligochaetes possess metanephridia. Chloragogen tissue is a site for the formation of urea from protein metabolism and synthesis and storage of glycogen and fat.

13. Oligochaetes are monoecious and exchange sperm during copulation.

14. Members of the class Hirudinea are the leeches. Complex arrangements of body-wall muscles and the loss of septa influence patterns of locomotion.

15. Leeches are predatory and feed on body fluids, the entire bodies of other invertebrates, and the blood of vertebrates.

16. Leeches are monoecious, and reproduction and development occur as in oligochaetes.

17. Ancestral annelids gave rise to three major classes. The earliest lineage gave rise to modern polychaetes. Some members of this ancient annelid stock invaded fresh water and gave rise to early freshwater oligochaetes. These oligochaetes gave rise to modern freshwater oligochaetes, terrestrial oligochaetes, and leeches.

SELECTED KEY TERMS

chloragogen tissue (*p. 352*)   parapodia (*p. 345*)
clitellum (*p. 350*)   peristomium (*p. 345*)
epitoky (*p. 349*)   prostomium (*p. 345*)
metamerism (*p. 343*)   tagmatization (*p. 344*)
metanephridium (*p. 348*)

CRITICAL THINKING QUESTIONS

1. What evidence is there that would link the annelids and arthropods in the same evolutionary line?

2. Distinguish between a protonephridium and a metanephridium. Name a class of annelids whose members may have protonephridia. What other phylum have we studied whose members also had protonephridia? Do you think that metanephridia would be more useful for a coelomate or an acoelomate animal? Explain.

3. In what annelid groups does one see the loss of septa between coelomic compartments? What advantages does this loss give each group?

4. What are the differences in the structure of nephridia that one might expect to see in freshwater and marine annelids?

5. Very few polychaetes have invaded fresh water. Can you think of a reasonable explanation for this?

SOME LESSER KNOWN INVERTEBRATES: POSSIBLE ANNELID RELATIVES

THREE PHYLA OF LIKELY ANNELID RELATIVES: THE ECHIURA, POGONOPHORA, AND SIPUNCULA

The coelomate phyla Echiura, Pogonophora, and Sipuncula comprise fewer than 600 protostome species that may be annelid relatives. They probably branched off from various points along the annelid-arthropod lineage.

PHYLUM ECHIURA: THE SPOON WORMS

The echiurans (ek-ee-yur'ans) (Gr. *echis*, serpent + *oura*, tail) consist of about 130 species of marine animals that have a worldwide distribution. Echiurans usually live in shallow waters, where they either burrow in mud or sand, or live protected in rock crevices. The soft body is covered only by a thin cuticle. As a result, the animals keep to the safety of their burrows or crevices, even when feeding. An echiuran feeds by sweeping organic material into its spatula-shaped proboscis that contains a ciliated gutter (figure 1). The proboscis can be extended for a considerable distance, but it can never be retracted into the body. Echiurans are sometimes called spoon worms because of the spatulate nature of the proboscis. Individual echiurans are from 15 to 50 cm in length, but the extensible proboscis may increase their length up to 2 m.

All echiurans are dioecious, and sexual dimorphism is extreme in some species. The eggs or sperm do not complete their development in the single ventral gonad but are released into the coelom. After they mature, they are collected by special collecting organs and then released into the seawater, where fertilization occurs, giving rise to free-swimming trochophore larvae. The early development of echiurans is similar to that of annelids with spiral cleavage. However, later development diverges from the annelid pattern in that no segmentation occurs.

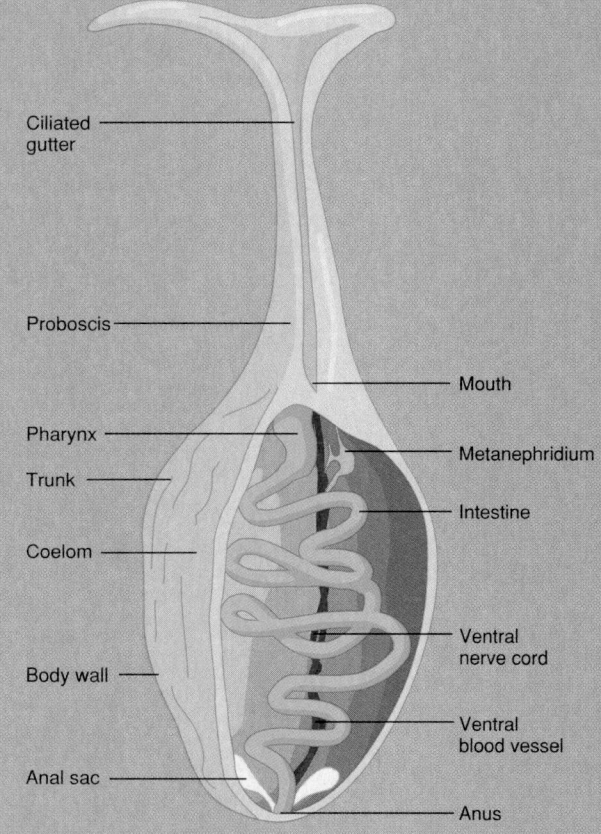

FIGURE 1   Phylum Echiura. Internal structure of an echiuran. The muscular body wall surrounds the large coelom, in which a long, coiled intestine is located. A simple closed circulatory system is present, as well as a ventral nerve cord that extends into the proboscis, several pairs of metanephridia, and a pair of anal sacs that empty into the anus at the end of the worm. The exchange of gases takes place through the body wall and proboscis.

359

FIGURE 2 **Phylum Pogonophora.** Giant red pogonophorans (*Riftia*) inside their tubes.

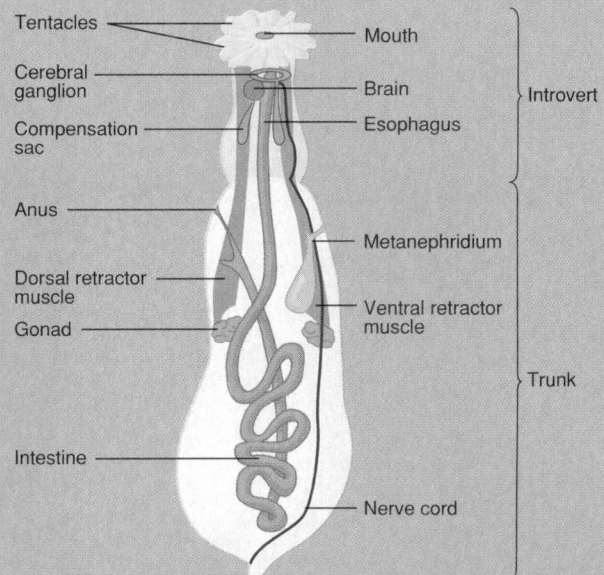

FIGURE 3 **Phylum Sipuncula.** Anatomy of a typical sipunculan. The body is composed of an anterior introvert and a posterior trunk. When the introvert is extended, the anterior portion, with its ciliated tentacles, surrounds the mouth. The long, U-Shaped intestine is arranged in a spiral coil. Anteriorly, the intestine ends at an anus that opens to the outside, near the introvert. A large pair of metanephridia is located in the anterior trunk. The anterior nervous system is annelidlike, with a supraesophageal brain and a ventral nerve cord that runs the length of the trunk.

PHYLUM POGONOPHORA: THE POGONOPHORANS, OR BEARD WORMS

The pogonophorans (po′go-nof′or-ans) (Gr. *pogon*, beard + *phora*, bearing) or beard worms are a group of about 120 species of tube-dwelling marine worms distributed throughout the world's oceans, especially along the continental slopes. They are named for the thick tuft of white or reddish tentacles (*see box 15.1*).

The slender, delicate body is protected in a secreted chitinous tube consisting of a series of rings, to which the worm adds as it grows (figure 2). The tubes are embedded in soft marine sediments in cold, deep (over 100 m), nutrient-poor waters. They range in length from about 10 cm to over 2 m.

Pogonophorans have no mouth or digestive tract. Nutrient uptake is via the outer cuticle and from the endosymbiotic bacteria that they harbor in the posterior part (trophosome) of the body. These bacteria are able to fix carbon dioxide into organic compounds that both the host and symbiont can use.

Very little is known about pogonophoran reproduction and development. In general, there are separate sexes, and sperm are packaged into spermatophores before being released by a male. The mechanism of fertilization is unknown. After fertilization, a solid blastula develops following radial cleavage.

PHYLUM SIPUNCULA: THE SIPUNCULANS, OR PEANUT WORMS

The sipunculans (sigh-pun′kyu-lans) (Gr. L. *sipunculus*, little siphon) or peanut worms (because of their peanut shape when disturbed) consist of about 350 species of unsegmented, coelomate, burrowing worms found in oceans throughout the world. These worms live in mud, sand, or any protected retreat. Their burrows may be mucus lined, but sipunculans do not construct true tubes as do pogonophorans. They range in length from about 2 mm to 75 cm (figure 3).

Sipunculans are dioecious. Gonads are attached to the coelomic wall and liberate their gametes into the coelom. After maturity, the gametes escape into the seawater via the metanephridia. Fertilization is external, cleavage is spiral, and development is either direct (no larva) or it may produce a free-swimming trochophore larva. The larva eventually settles to the bottom and grows into an adult. In a few species, asexual reproduction can also occur by transverse fission—the posterior part of the parent constricts to give rise to a new individual.

THE ARTHROPODS:
BLUEPRINT FOR SUCCESS

Concepts

1. Arthropods have been successful in almost all habitats on the earth. Some ancient arthropods were the first animals to live most of their lives in terrestrial environments.
2. Metamerism with tagmatization, a chitinous exoskeleton, and metamorphosis have contributed to the success of arthropods.
3. Members of the subphylum Trilobitomorpha are extinct arthropods that were a dominant form of life in the oceans between 345 and 600 million years ago.
4. Members of the subphylum Chelicerata have a body divided into two regions and have chelicerae. The class Merostomata contains the horseshoe crabs. The class Arachnida contains the spiders, mites, ticks, and scorpions. Some ancient arachnids were among the earliest terrestrial arthropods, and modern arachnids have numerous adaptations for terrestrial life. The class Pycnogonida contains the sea spiders.
5. Animals in the subphylum Crustacea have biramous appendages and two pairs of antennae. The class Branchiopoda includes the fairy shrimp, brine shrimp, and water fleas. The class Malacostraca includes the crabs, lobsters, crayfish, and shrimp. The classes Copepoda and Cirrepedia include the copepods and barnacles, respectively.

Would You Like to Know:

1. what the most abundant animal is? (*p. 362*)
2. how an arthropod grows within the confines of a rigid exoskeleton? (*p. 364*)
3. how arthropods were preadapted for terrestrialism? (*p. 368*)
4. why some spiders go ballooning? (*p. 370*)
5. what two spiders found in the United States are dangerous to humans? (*p. 370*)
6. what causes the bite of a chigger to itch so badly? (*p. 372*)
7. what mite lives in the hair follicles of most readers of this textbook? (*p. 372*)
8. what crustaceans colonize the hulls of ships? (*p. 378*)

These and other useful questions will be answered in this chapter.

This chapter contains evolutionary concepts, which are set off in this font.

EVOLUTIONARY PERSPECTIVE

What animal species has the greatest number of individuals? The answer can only be an educated guess; however, many zoologists would argue that one of the many species of small (1 to 2 mm) crustaceans, called copepods, that drift in the open oceans must have this honor. Copepods have been very successful, feeding on the vast photosynthetic production of the open oceans (figure 23.1). After only 20 minutes of towing a plankton net behind a slowly moving boat (at the right location and during the right time of year), one can collect over 3 million copepods—enough to solidly pack a 2 gallon pail! Copepods are food for fish, such as herring, sardines, mackerel, as well as for whale sharks and the largest mammals, the blue whale and its relatives. Humans benefit from copepod production by eating fish that·feed on copepods. (Unfortunately, we use a small fraction of the total food energy in these animals. In spite of ½ of the earth's inhabitants lacking protein in their diet, humans process into fish meal most of the herring and sardines caught, which is then fed to poultry and hogs. In eating the poultry and hogs, we lose over 99% of the original energy present in the copepods!)

Copepods are one of many groups of animals belonging to the phylum Arthropoda (ar'thra-po'dah) (Gr. *arthro*, joint + *podos*, foot). Crayfish, lobsters, spiders, mites, scorpions, and insects are also arthropods. About 1 million species of arthropods have been described, and recent studies estimate that there may be 30 to 50 million undescribed species. In this chapter and chapter 24, you will discover the many ways in which some arthropods are considered among the most successful of all animals.

Characteristics of members of the phylum Arthropoda include the following:

1. Metamerism modified by the specialization of body regions for specific functions (tagmatization)
2. Chitinous exoskeleton provides support, protection, and is modified to form sensory structures
3. Paired, jointed appendages
4. Growth accompanied by ecdysis or molting
5. Ventral nervous system
6. Coelom reduced to cavities surrounding gonads and sometimes excretory organs
7. Open circulatory system in which blood is released into tissue spaces (hemocoel) derived from the blastocoel
8. Complete digestive tract
9. Metamorphosis often present; reduces competition between immature and adult stages

CLASSIFICATION AND RELATIONSHIPS TO OTHER ANIMALS

As discussed in chapter 22, arthropods and annelids are closely related to each other. Shared protostome characteristics, such as the development of the mouth from the blastopore and schizocoelous coelom formation, as

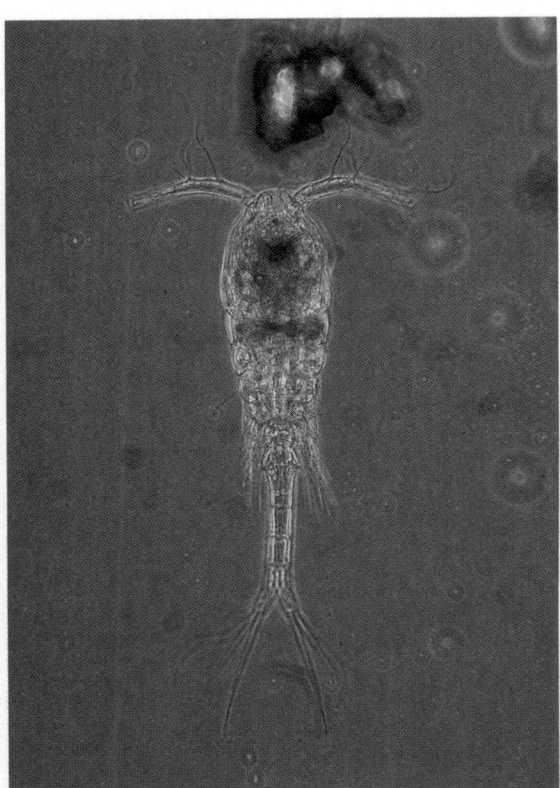

FIGURE 23.1

The Most Abundant Animal? Copepods, such as *Calanus*, are extremely abundant in the oceans of the world and form important links in oceanic food webs.

well as other common characteristics, such as the presence of a paired ventral nerve cord and metamerism, give evidence of a common ancestry (figure 23.2).

Zoologists, however, disagree about the evolutionary relationships among the arthropods. Many zoologists believe that it is not one phylum, but three. These ideas are discussed at the end of chapter 24. The arthropods are treated in this textbook as members of a single phylum. Living arthropods are divided into three subphyla: Chelicerata, Crustacea, and Uniramia. All members of a fourth subphylum, Trilobita, are extinct (table 23.1). Trilobita, Chelicerata, and Crustacea are discussed in this chapter and the Uniramia are discussed in chapter 24.

METAMERISM AND TAGMATIZATION

Three aspects of arthropod biology have been important in contributing to their success. One of these is metamerism. Metamerism of arthropods is most evident externally, because the arthropod body is often composed of a series of similar segments, each bearing a pair of appendages (*see figure 22.4e*). Internally, however, the body cavity of arthropods is not divided by septa, and most organ systems are not metamerically arranged. The reason for the loss of internal metamerism is speculative; however, the presence of

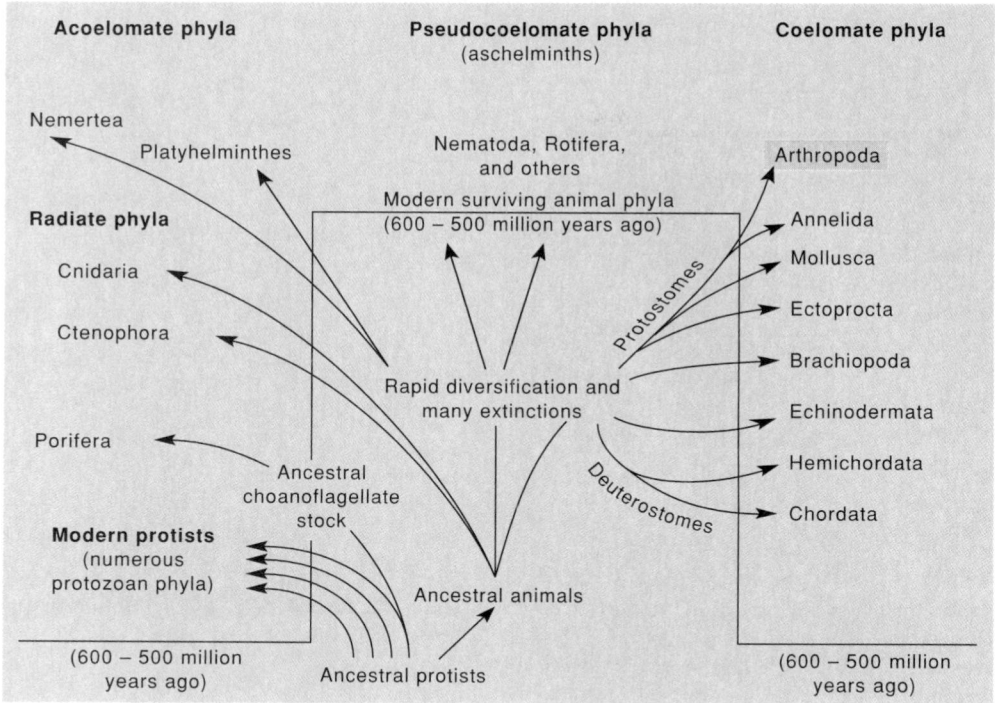

FIGURE 23.2

Evolutionary Relationships of the Arthropods. Arthropods (shaded in orange) are protostomes with close evolutionary ties to the annelids. This is shown by the presence of a paired ventral nerve cord and metamerism in both groups.

metamerically arranged hydrostatic compartments would be of little value in the support or locomotion of animals enclosed by an external skeleton (discussed below).

As discussed in chapter 22, metamerism permits the specialization of regions of the body for specific functions. This regional specialization is called tagmatization. In arthropods, body regions, called tagmata (s., tagma), are specialized for feeding and sensory perception, locomotion, and visceral functions.

THE EXOSKELETON

Arthropods are enclosed by an external, jointed skeleton, called an **exoskeleton** or **cuticle.** The exoskeleton is often cited as the major reason for arthropod success. It provides structural support, protection, impermeable surfaces for prevention of water loss, and a system of levers for muscle attachment and movement.

The exoskeleton covers all body surfaces and invaginations of the body wall, such as the anterior and posterior portions of the gut tract. It is nonliving and is secreted by a single layer of epidermal cells (figure 23.3). The epidermal layer is sometimes called the hypodermis because, unlike other epidermal tissues, it is covered on the outside by exoskeleton rather than being directly exposed to air or water.

The exoskeleton is composed of two layers. The epicuticle is the outermost layer. Because it is made of a waxy lipoprotein, it is impermeable to water and serves as a barrier to microorganisms and pesticides. The bulk of the exoskeleton is below the epicuticle and is called the procuticle. (In crustaceans, the procuticle is sometimes called the endocuticle.) The procuticle is composed of **chitin,** a tough, leathery polysaccharide and several kinds of proteins (*see figure 2.11*). Hardening of the procuticle is accomplished through a process called sclerotization and sometimes by impregnation with calcium carbonate. Sclerotization is a tanning process in which layers of protein are chemically cross-linked with one another—hardening and darkening the exoskeleton. In insects and most other arthropods, this bonding occurs in the outer portion of the procuticle. Hardening of the exoskeleton of crustaceans is accomplished by sclerotization and by the deposition of calcium carbonate in the middle regions of the procuticle. Some proteins give the exoskeleton resiliency. When the exoskeleton is distorted, energy is stored. Stored energy can be used in activities such as flapping wings and jumping. The inner portion of the procuticle is not hardened.

Hardening in the procuticle provides armorlike protection for arthropods, but it also necessitates a variety of adaptations to allow arthropods to live and grow within their confines. Invaginations of the exoskeleton form firm ridges and bars for muscle attachment. Another modification of

TABLE 23.1	CLASSIFICATION OF THE PHYLUM ARTHROPODA

Phylum Arthropoda (ar'thra-po'dah)
Animals that show metamerism with tagmatization, a jointed exoskeleton, and a ventral nervous system.

Subphylum Trilobitomorpha (tri"lo-bit'o-mor'fah)
Marine, all extinct; lived from Cambrian to Carboniferous periods; bodies are divided into three longitudinal lobes; head, thorax, and abdomen present; one pair of antennae and biramous appendages.

Subphylum Chelicerata (ke-lis"e-ra'tah)
Body usually divided into prosoma and opisthosoma; first pair of appendages piercing or pincerlike (chelicerae) and used for feeding.

Class Merostomata (mer'o-sto'mah-tah)
Marine, with book gills on opisthosoma. Two subclasses: Eurypterida, a group of extinct arthropods called giant water scorpions, and Xiphosura, the horseshoe crabs. *Limulus.*

Class Arachnida (ah-rak'ni-dah)
Mostly terrestrial, with book lungs, tracheae, or both; usually four pairs of walking legs in adults. Spiders, scorpions, ticks, mites, harvestmen, and others.

Class Pycnogonida (pik'no-gon"i-dah)
Reduced abdomen; no special respiratory or excretory structures; four to six pairs of walking legs; common in all oceans. Sea spiders.

Subphylum Crustacea (krus-tas'eah)
Most aquatic, head with two pairs of antennae, one pair of mandibles, and two pairs of maxillae; biramous appendages.

Class Remipedia (ri-mi-pe'de-ah)
A single species of cave-dwelling crustaceans from the Bahamas; body with approximately 30 segments that bear uniform, biramous appendages.

Class Cephalocarida (sef'ah-lo-kar'i-dah)
Small (3 mm) marine crustaceans with uniform, leaflike, triramous appendages.

Class Branchiopoda (brang'ke-o-pod'ah)
Flattened, leaflike appendages used in respiration, filter feeding, and locomotion; found mostly in fresh water. Fairy shrimp, brine shrimp, clam shrimp, water fleas.

Class Malacostraca (mal-ah-kos'trah-kah)
Appendages may be modified for crawling, feeding, swimming. Lobsters, crayfish, crabs, shrimp, isopods (terrestrial).

Class Copepoda (ko'pepod'ah)
Maxillipeds modified for feeding. Copepods.

Class Cirripedia (sir'i-ped'eah)
Sessile as adults, marine, and enclosed by calcium carbonate valves. Barnacles.

Subphylum Uniramia (yoo'ne-ram'eah)
Head with one pair of antennae and usually one pair of mandibles; all appendages uniramous. Insects and their relatives. See chapter 24.

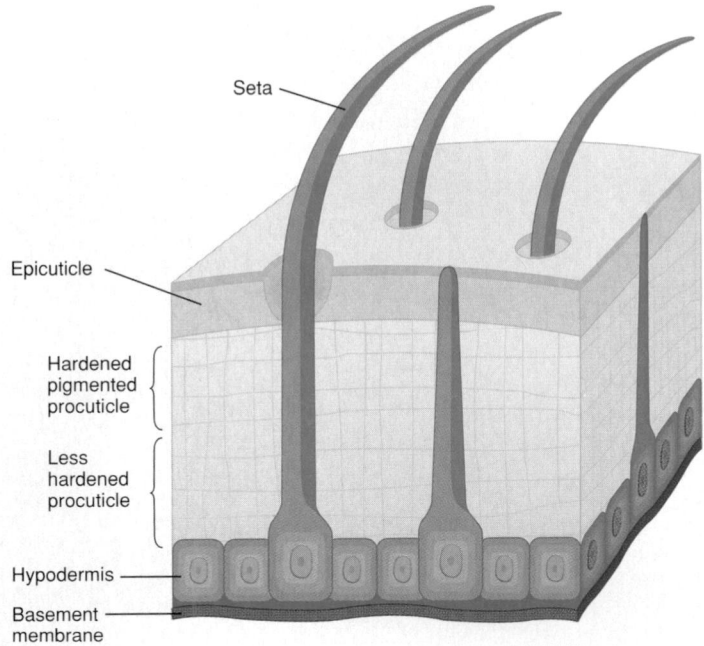

FIGURE 23.3

The Arthropod Exoskeleton. The epicuticle is made of a waxy lipoprotein and is impermeable to water. The outer layer of the procuticle is hardened by calcium carbonate deposition and/or sclerotization. Chitin, a tough, leathery polysaccharide, and several kinds of proteins make up the bulk of the procuticle. The entire exoskeleton is secreted by the hypodermis.

the exoskeleton is the formation of joints. A flexible membrane, called an articular membrane, is present in regions where the procuticle is thinner and less hardened (figure 23.4). Other modifications of the exoskeleton include sensory receptors, called sensilla, that are in the form of pegs, bristles, and lenses, and modifications of the exoskeleton that permit gas exchange.

Growth of an arthropod would be virtually impossible unless the exoskeleton were periodically shed; such as in the molting process called **ecdysis** (Gr. *ekdysis*, getting out). Ecdysis is divided into four stages: (1) enzymes, secreted from hypodermal glands, begin digesting the old endocuticle. This digestion separates the hypodermis and the exoskeleton (figure 23.5*a,b*); (2) digestion of the endocuticle is followed by the secretion of new procuticle and epicuticle (figure 23.5*c,d*); (3) the old exoskeleton is split open along predetermined ecdysal lines when the animal stretches by air or water intake. Additional epicuticle is secreted through pores in the procuticle (figure 23.5*e*); (4) finally, the new exoskeleton is hardened by deposition of calcium carbonate and/or sclerotization (figure 23.5*f*). During the few hours or days of the hardening process, the arthropod is vulnerable to predators and remains hidden. All of these changes are controlled by the nervous and endocrine systems; the controls will be discussed in more detail later.

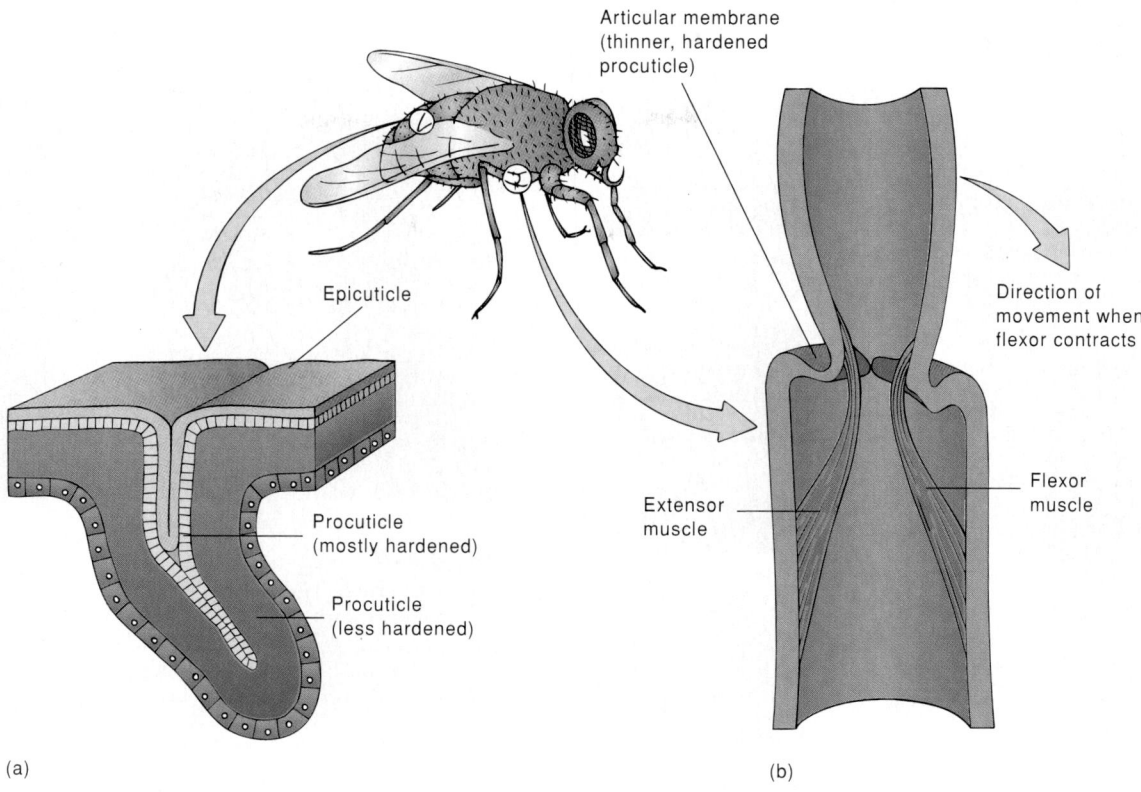

Figure 23.4

Modifications of the Exoskeleton. (*a*) Invaginations of the exoskeleton result in firm ridges and bars when the procuticle in the region of the invagination remains thick and hard. These are used as muscle attachment sites. (*b*) Regions where the procuticle is thinned are flexible and form membranes and joints. *From: "A LIFE OF INVERTEBRATES" © 1979 W. D. Russell-Hunter.*

METAMORPHOSIS

A third characteristic that has contributed to arthropod success is a reduction of competition between adults and immature stages because of metamorphosis. Metamorphosis is a radical change in body form and physiology that occurs as an immature stage, usually called a larva, becomes an adult. The evolution of arthropods has resulted in an increasing divergence of body forms, behaviors, and habitats between immature and adult stages. Adult crabs, for example, are usually found prowling the sandy bottoms of their marine habitats for live prey or decaying organic matter, whereas larval crabs live and feed in the plankton. Similarly, the caterpillar that feeds on leafy vegetation eventually develops into a nectar-feeding adult butterfly or moth. Having different adult and immature stages means that they will not compete with each other for food or living space. In some arthropod and other animal groups, larvae also serve as the dispersal stage.

SUBPHYLUM TRILOBITOMORPHA

Members of the subphylum Trilobitomorpha (tri″lo-bit′o-mor′fah) (Gr. *tri*, three + *lobos*, lobes) were a dominant form of life in the oceans from the Cambrian period (600 million years

ago) to the Carboniferous period (345 million years ago). They crawled along the substrate feeding on annelids, molluscs, and decaying organic matter. The body of trilobites was oval, flattened, and divided into three longitudinal regions (figure 23.6). All body segments articulated so the trilobite could roll into a ball to protect its soft ventral surface. Most fossilized trilobites are found in this position. Trilobite appendages consist of two lobes. The inner lobe served as a walking leg, and the outer lobe bore spikes or teeth that may have been used in digging or swimming or as gills in gas exchange. Because they possessed two lobes or rami, these appendages are called **biramous** (L. *bi*, twice + *ramus*, branch) **appendages.**

Stop and Ask Yourself

1. What are the four subphyla of arthropods?
2. What three aspects of structure and function have been important in arthropod success?
3. How does metamorphosis reduce competition between adult and immature forms?
4. In what way is the name "trilobite" descriptive of that group of animals?

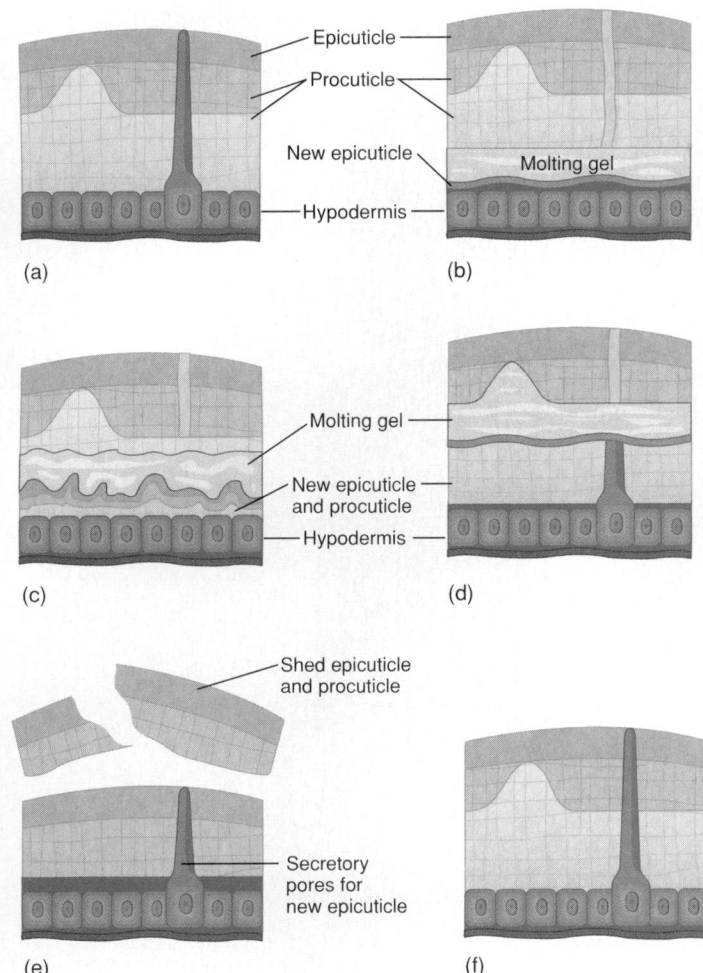

(a)   (b)

(c)   (d)

(e)   (f)

FIGURE 23.5

Events of Ecdysis. (*a,b*) During preecdysis, the hypodermis detaches from the exoskeleton and the space between the old exoskeleton and the hypodermis is filled with a fluid called molting gel. (*c,d*) The hypodermis begins secreting a new epicuticle and a new procuticle is formed as the old procuticle is digested. The products of digestion are incorporated into the new procuticle. Note that the new epicuticle and procuticle are wrinkled beneath the old exoskeleton to allow for increased body size after ecdysis. (*e*) Ecdysis occurs when the animal swallows air or water, and the exoskeleton splits along predetermined ecdysal lines. The animal pulls out of the old exoskeleton. (*f*) After ecdysis, the new exoskeleton hardens by calcium carbonate deposition, and/or sclerotization, and pigments are deposited in the outer layers of the procuticle. Additional material is added to the epicuticle.

SUBPHYLUM CHELICERATA

One arthropod lineage, the subphylum Chelicerata (ke-lis"e-ra'tah) (Gr. *chele*, claw + *ata*, plural suffix) includes familiar animals, such as spiders, mites, and ticks, and less familiar animals, such as horseshoe crabs and sea spiders. These animals have two tagmata. The **prosoma** or **cephalothorax** is a sensory, feeding, and locomotor tagma. It usually bears eyes, but unlike other arthropods, never has antennae. Paired appendages attach to the prosoma. The first pair, called **chelicerae,** are often pincerlike or chelate and are most often used in feeding. They

FIGURE 23.6

Trilobite Structure. The body of a trilobite was divided into three longitudinal sections (thus the subphylum name). It was also divided into three tagmata. A head, or cephalon, bore a pair of antennae and eyes. The trunk, or thorax, bore appendages used in swimming or walking. A series of posterior segments formed the pygidium, or tail.

may also be specialized as hollow fangs or for a variety of other functions. The second pair, called **pedipalps,** are usually sensory but may also be used in feeding, locomotion, or reproduction. Pedipalps are followed by paired walking legs. Posterior to the prosoma is the **opisthosoma,** which contains digestive, reproductive, excretory, and respiratory organs.

CLASS MEROSTOMATA

Members of the class Merostomata (mer'o-sto'mah-tah) are divided into two subclasses. The Xiphosura are the horseshoe crabs, and the Eurypterida are the giant water scorpions (figure 23.7). The latter are extinct, having lived from the Cambrian period (600 million years ago) to the Permian period (280 million years ago).

There are only four species of horseshoe crabs living today; one species, *Limulus polyphemus*, is widely distributed in the Atlantic Ocean and the Gulf of Mexico (figure 23.8a). Horseshoe crabs scavenge sandy and muddy substrates for annelids, small molluscs, and other invertebrates. Their body form has remained virtually unchanged for over 200 million years, and they were cited in chapter 12 as an example of stabilizing selection.

The cephalothorax of horseshoe crabs is covered with a hard, horseshoe-shaped carapace. The chelicerae, pedipalps, and first three pairs of walking legs are chelate and are used for walking and food handling. The last pair of appendages has leaflike plates at their tips and are used for locomotion and digging (figure 23.8b).

The opisthosoma of a horseshoe crab includes a long, unsegmented telson. If a horseshoe crab is flipped over by wave action, it arches its opisthosoma dorsally, causing the animal to

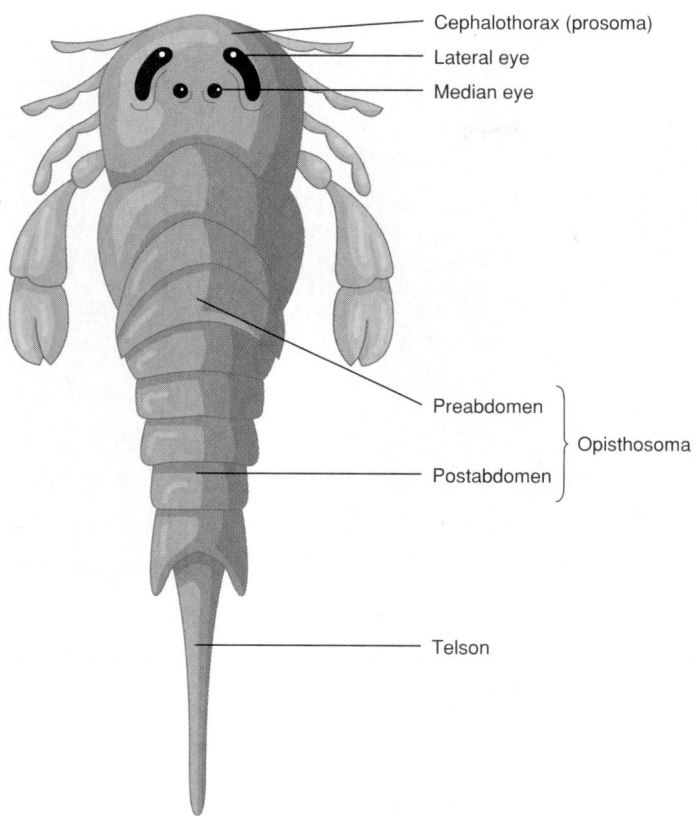

FIGURE 23.7

Class Merostomata. A eurypterid, *Euripterus remipes*.

(a)

roll to its side and flip right side up again. The first pair of
opisthosomal appendages cover genital pores and are called
genital opercula. The remaining five pairs of appendages are
book gills. The name is derived from the resemblance of these
platelike gills to the pages of a closed book. Gas exchange between the blood and water occurs as blood circulates through
the book gills. Horseshoe crabs have an open circulatory system, as do all arthropods. Blood circulation in horseshoe crabs
is similar to that described later in this chapter for arachnids
and crustaceans.

Horseshoe crabs are dioecious. During reproductive periods, males and females congregate in intertidal areas. The male
mounts the female and grasps her with his pedipalps. The female excavates shallow depressions in the sand, and eggs are
fertilized by the male as they are shed from the female into depressions. Fertilized eggs are covered with sand and develop unattended.

CLASS ARACHNIDA

Members of the class Arachnida (ah-rak′ni-dah) (Gr. *arachne*,
spider) are some of the most misrepresented members of the animal kingdom. Their reputation as fearsome and grotesque crea-
tures is vastly exaggerated. The majority of spiders, mites, ticks,
scorpions, and related forms are either harmless or very beneficial to humans.

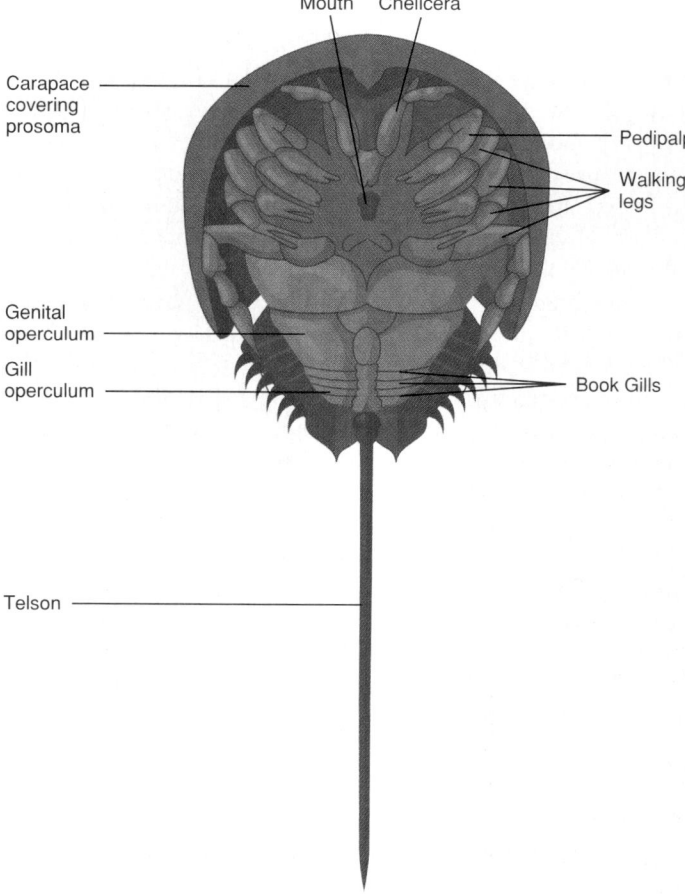

(b)

FIGURE 23.8

Class Merostomata. (*a*) Dorsal view of the horseshoe crab, *Limulus
polyphemus*. (*b*) Ventral view.

23.7

Most zoologists believe that arachnids arose from the eurypterids and were very early terrestrial inhabitants. The earliest fossils of aquatic scorpions date back to the Silurian period (405 to 425 million years ago), fossils of terrestrial scorpions date from the Devonian period (350 to 400 million years ago), and fossils of all other arachnid groups are present by the Carboniferous period (280 to 345 million years ago).

3 Water conservation is a major concern for any terrestrial organism, and ancestral arachnids were preadapted for terrestrialism by their relatively impermeable exoskeleton. **Preadaptation** occurs when a structure present in members of a species proves useful in promoting reproductive success when an individual encounters new environmental situations. Later adaptations included evolution of efficient excretory structures, internal surfaces for gas exchange, appendages modified for locomotion on land, and greater deposition of wax in the epicuticle.

Form and Function

Most arachnids are carnivores. Small arthropods are usually held by the chelicerae while enzymes from the gut tract pour over the prey. Partially digested food is then taken into the mouth. The gut tract of arachnids is divided into three regions. The anterior portion is called the foregut, and the posterior portion is called the hindgut. Both develop as infoldings of the body wall and are lined with cuticle. A portion of the foregut is frequently modified into a pumping pharynx, and the hindgut is frequently a site of water reabsorption. The midgut is between the foregut and hindgut. It is noncuticular and lined with secretory and absorptive cells. Lateral diverticula increase the area available for absorption and storage.

Arachnids use coxal glands and/or malpighian tubules for excreting nitrogenous wastes. **Coxal glands** are paired, thin-walled, spherical sacs bathed in the blood of body sinuses. Nitrogenous wastes are absorbed across the wall of the sacs, transported into a long, convoluted tubule, and excreted through excretory pores at the base of the posterior appendages. Arachnids that are adapted to dry environments possess blind-ending diverticula of the gut tract that arise at the juncture of the midgut and hindgut. These tubules are called **malpighian tubules.** They absorb waste materials from the blood, and empty them into the gut tract. Excretory wastes are then eliminated with digestive wastes. The major excretory product of arachnids is uric acid. As discussed in chapter 38, uric acid excretion is advantageous for terrestrial animals because it is excreted as a semisolid with little water loss.

Gas exchange also occurs with minimal water loss because arachnids have few exposed respiratory surfaces. Some arachnids possess structures, called **book lungs,** that are assumed to be modifications of the book gills found in the Merostomata. Book lungs are paired invaginations of the ventral body wall that are folded into a series of leaflike lamellae (figure 23.9). Air enters the book lung through a slitlike opening and circulates between lamellae. Diffusion of respiratory gases occurs between the blood moving among the lamellae

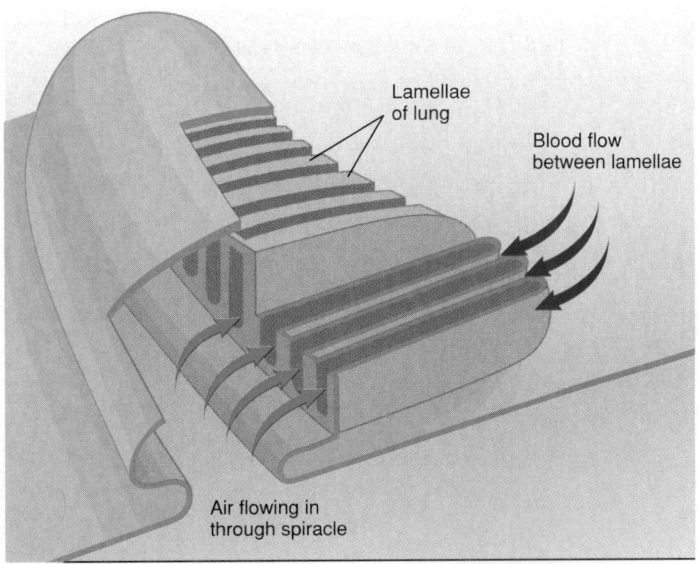

FIGURE 23.9

An Arachnid Book Lung. Air and blood moving on opposite sides of a lamella of the lung exchange respiratory gases by diffusion. Figure 23.12 shows the location of book lungs in spiders.

and the air in the lung chamber. Other arachnids possess a series of branched, chitin-lined tubules that deliver air directly to body tissues. These tubule systems, called **tracheae** (s., trachea), open to the outside through openings called **spiracles** that are located along the ventral or lateral aspects of the abdomen. (Tracheae are also present in insects but had a separate evolutionary origin. Aspects of their physiology will be described in chapter 24.)

The circulatory system of arachnids, like that of most arthropods, is an open system in which blood is pumped by a dorsal contractile vessel (usually called the dorsal aorta or "heart") and is released into tissue spaces. In arthropods, the coelom is reduced to cavities surrounding the gonads and sometimes the coxal glands. Large tissue spaces, or sinuses, are derived from the blastocoel and are called the **hemocoel.** Blood bathes the tissues and then returns to the dorsal aorta through openings in the aorta called ostia. Arachnid blood contains the dissolved respiratory pigment hemocyanin and has amoeboid cells that aid in clotting and body defenses.

The nervous system of all arthropods is ventral and, in ancestral arthropods, must have been laid out in a pattern similar to that of the annelids (see figure 22.8a). With the exception of scorpions, the nervous system of arachnids is greatly concentrated by fusion of ganglia.

The body of an arachnid is supplied with a variety of sensory structures. Most mechanoreceptors and chemoreceptors are modifications of the exoskeleton, such as projections, pores, and slits together with sensory and accessory cells. Collectively, these receptors are called **sensilla.** For example, setae are hairlike, cuticular modifications that may be set into membranous sockets. Displacement of a seta initiates a nerve im-

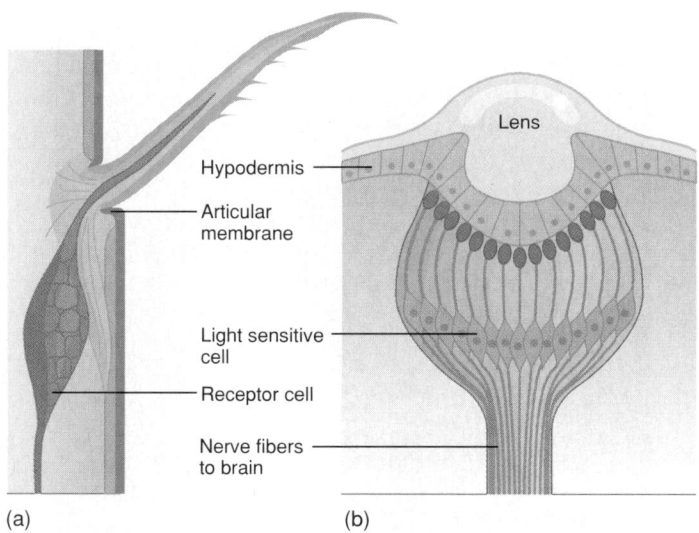

(a)   (b)

FIGURE 23.10

Arthropod Seta and Eye (Ocellus). (*a*) A seta is a hairlike modification of the cuticle set in a membranous socket. Displacement of the seta initiates a nerve impulse in a receptor cell (sensillum) associated with the base of the seta. (*b*) The lens of this spider eye is a thickened, transparent modification of the cuticle. Below the lens and hypodermis are light-sensitive sensillae that contain pigments that convert light energy into nerve impulses.

pulse in an associated nerve cell (figure 23.10*a*). Vibration receptors are very important to some arachnids. Spiders that use webs to capture prey, for example, determine both the size of the insect and its position on the web by the vibrations the insect makes while struggling to free itself. The chemical sense of arachnids is comparable to taste and smell in vertebrates. Small pores in the exoskeleton are frequently associated with peglike, or other, modifications of the exoskeleton, and allow chemicals to stimulate nerve cells. Arachnids possess one or more pairs of eyes (figure 23.10*b*). These eyes are used primarily for detecting movement and changes in light intensity. The eyes of some hunting spiders probably form images.

Arachnids are dioecious. Paired genital openings are on the ventral side of the second abdominal segment. Sperm transfer is usually indirect. The male often packages sperm in a spermatophore, after which it is transferred to the female. Courtship rituals confirm that individuals are of the same species, attract a female to the spermatophore, and position the female to receive the spermatophore. In some taxa (e.g., spiders), copulation occurs, and sperm transfer is accomplished via a modified pedipalp of the male. Development is direct, and the young hatch from eggs as miniature adults. Many arachnids tend their developing eggs and young during and after development.

Order Scorpionida

Members of the order Scorpionida (skor″pe-ah-ni′dah) are the scorpions (figure 23.11*a*). They are common from tropical to warm temperate climates. Scorpions are secretive and nocturnal, spending most of the daylight hours hidden under logs and stones.

(a)

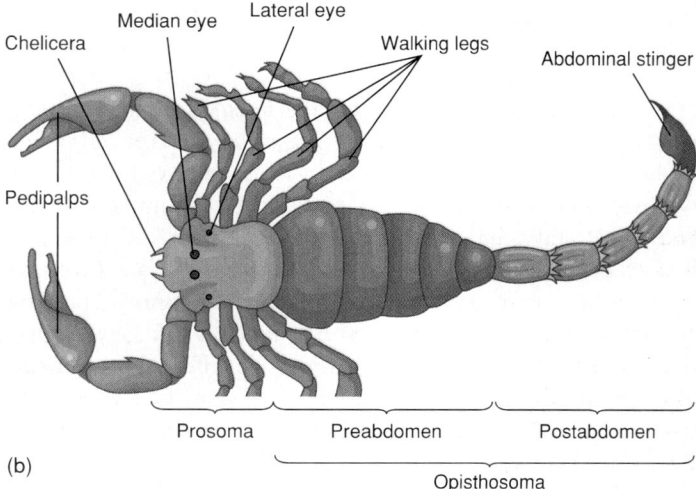

(b)

FIGURE 23.11

Order Scorpionida. (*a*) A scorpion captures its prey using chelate pedipalps. Venom from its sting paralyzes the prey prior to feeding. This Kenyan scorpion (*Pardinus*) is shown eating a cricket. (*b*) External anatomy of a scorpion.

Scorpions have small chelicerae that project anteriorly from the front of the carapace (figure 23.11*b*). A pair of enlarged, chelate pedipalps are posterior to the chelicerae. The opisthoma is divided. An anterior preabdomen contains the slitlike openings to book lungs, comblike tactile and chemical receptors called pectines, and genital openings. The postabdomen (commonly called the tail) is narrower than the preabdomen and is curved dorsally and anteriorly over the body when aroused. At the tip of the postabdomen is a sting. The sting has a bulbular base that contains venom-producing glands and a hollow, sharp, barbed point. Smooth muscles eject venom during stinging. Only a few scorpions have venom that is highly toxic to humans. Species in the genera *Androctonus* (northern Africa) and *Centuroides* (Mexico, Arizona, and New Mexico) have been responsible for human deaths. Other scorpions from the southern and southwestern areas of North America give stings comparable to wasp stings.

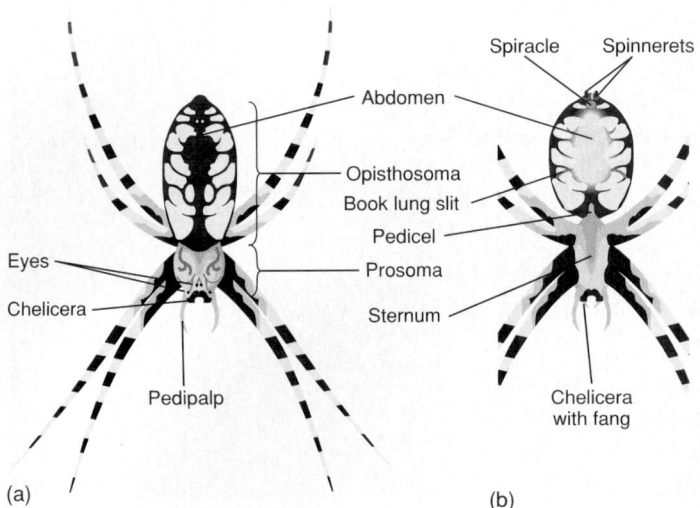

(a)

(b)

FIGURE 23.12

External Structure of a Spider. (*a*) Dorsal view. (*b*) Ventral view.

Sources: (a) After Sherman and Sherman. (b) After the Kastons.

Prior to reproduction, male and female scorpions have a period of courtship that lasts from five minutes to several hours. Male and female scorpions face each other and extend their abdomens high into the air. The male seizes the female with his pedipalps, and they repeatedly walk backward and then forward. The lower portion of the male reproductive tract forms a spermatophore that is deposited on the ground. During courtship, the male positions the female so that the genital opening on her abdomen is positioned over the spermatophore. Downward pressure of the female's abdomen on a triggerlike structure of the spermatophore causes sperm to be released into the female's genital chamber.

Most arthropods are **oviparous;** females lay eggs that develop outside the body. Many scorpions and some arthropods are **ovoviviparous;** internal development occurs, although large, yolky eggs provide all the nourishment for development. Some scorpions, however, are **viviparous** meaning the embryos are nourished by nutrients provided by the mother. Eggs develop in diverticula of the ovary that are closely associated with diverticula of the digestive tract. Nutrients pass from the digestive tract diverticula to the developing embryos. Development requires up to 1.5 years and 20 to 40 young are brooded. After birth, the young crawl onto the mother's back, where they remain for up to 1 month.

Order Araneae

With about 34,000 species, the order Araneae (ah-ran'a-e) is the largest group of arachnids (figure 23.12). The prosoma of spiders bears chelicerae with poison glands and fangs. Pedipalps are leglike, and in males, are modified for sperm transfer. There are usually eight eyes on the dorsal, anterior margin of the carapace.

The prosoma is attached to the opisthosoma by a slender, waistlike pedicel. The abdomen is swollen or elongate

FIGURE 23.13

Order Araneae. Some of the most beautiful and intricate spider webs are produced by members of the family Araneidae, the orb weavers. Many species are relatively large, like this garden spider—*Argiope*. A web is not a permanent construction. When webs become wet with rain or dew, or when they age, they lose their stickiness. The entire web, or at least the spiraled portion, is eaten and replaced.

and contains openings to the reproductive tract, book lungs, and tracheae. It also has six to eight conical projections, called spinnerets, that are associated with silk glands. The protein that forms silk is emitted as a liquid, but hardens as it is drawn out. Several kinds of silk are formed, each with its own use. In addition to being formed into webs for capturing prey, (figure 23.13) silk is used to line retreats, to lay a safety line that is fastened to the substrate to interrupt a fall, and to wrap eggs into a case for development. Silk lines produced by young spiders are caught by air currents and serve as a dispersal mechanism. ④ Silk lines have been known to carry spiders at great altitudes for hundreds of miles. This behavior is called ballooning.

Most spiders feed on insects and other arthropods. A few (e.g., tarantulas or "bird spiders") feed on small vertebrates. Once captured in webs or by hunting, prey are paralyzed by the spider's bite and sometimes wrapped in silk. Enzymes are introduced through a puncture in the body wall, and predigested products are sucked into the spider's digestive tract by a pumping stomach. The venom of most spiders is harmless to humans. ⑤ Black widow spiders (*Lactrodectus*) and brown recluse spiders (*Loxosceles*) are exceptions since their venom is toxic to humans (box 23.1).

BOX 23.1   A FEARSOME TWOSOME

The fearsome reputation of spiders is vastly exaggerated. All spiders have poison glands and fangs (modifications of chelicerae) that are used in immobilizing prey. The venom of most spiders, however, is not dangerous to humans. There are only about 20 species of spiders whose bite is considered dangerous to humans. Of these dangerous species, only two are found in North America.

The black widow spider (*Latrodectus mactans*) is found throughout the United States and southern Canada (figure 1*a*). The black widow's venom is a neurotoxin. The bite of a black widow is not particularly painful, but symptoms of the bite can be very severe. Symptoms include abdominal and leg pain, high cerebrospinal fluid pressure, nausea, muscular spasms, and respiratory paralysis. Since an antivenom is available, human deaths are rare.

The brown recluse spider (*Loxosceles reclusa*) is common in the midwestern United States (figure 1*b*). The venom of a brown recluse is a hemolytic toxin. The effects of a brown recluse's bite are initially confined to the site of the bite and consist of localized tissue death and ulceration. The ulceration, however, quickly spreads to adjacent tissues and creates a large ulcer that heals very slowly. Human deaths from brown recluse bites are likewise also rare since an antivenom is available.

Of these two species of spiders, one is probably more likely to encounter the brown recluse. The black widow is usually found in the wild—under rocks and logs, in brush piles, and in other natural areas. Its distinctive marking—a ventral red hourglass pattern on a shiny black body—is very easy to recognize. The brown recluse, on the other hand, lives closely with humans and domestic animals. It is nocturnal, secretive, and may go unnoticed. During the winter months, the brown recluse is relatively inactive. Unlike the black widow, the brown recluse is a drab-looking spider. It is brown, but if one looks closely, a distinctive violin-shaped mark on the dorsal aspect of the prosoma is clearly visible. An encounter with the brown recluse is fairly likely. In the midwestern United States, most human dwellings have had or will have brown recluse spiders in residence. Controlling these spiders by spraying with pesticides is possible; but because of their reclusive habits and inactive periods, the sprays will not always reach their intended targets.

The best advice concerning these two species of spiders is to learn to recognize them, and to shake out shoes, boots, and other articles of clothing that have not been recently worn. These spiders, like all of their relatives, have exaggerated reputations—but the key to a peaceful coexistence is to respect the spiders' venomous bites.

(a)

(b)

FIGURE 1   **Two Venomous Spiders.** (*a*) A black widow spider (*Lactrodectus mactans*) is recognized by its shiny black body with a red hourglass pattern on the ventral surface of its opisthosoma. (*b*) A brown recluse spider (*Loxosceles reclusa*) is recognized by the dark brown, violin-shaped mark on the dorsal aspect of its prosoma.

Mating of spiders involves complex behaviors that include chemical, tactile, and/or visual signals. Chemicals called pheromones are deposited by a female on her web or on her body to attract a male. (Pheromones are chemicals released into the environment by one individual to create a behavioral change in another member of the same species.) A male may attract a female by plucking the strands of a female's web. The pattern of plucking is species specific and helps identify and locate a potential mate. The tips of a male's pedipalps possess a bulblike reservoir with an ejaculatory duct and a penislike structure called an embolus. Prior to mating, the male fills the reservoir of his pedipalps by depositing sperm on a small web and then collecting sperm with his pedipalps. During mating, a pedipalp is engorged with blood, the embolus is inserted into the female's reproductive opening, and sperm are discharged. The female deposits up to 3,000 eggs in a silken egg case, which is sealed and attached to webbing, placed in a retreat, or carried about by the female.

Order Opiliones

Members of the order Opiliones (o'pi-le"on-es) are the harvestmen or daddy longlegs. The prosoma is broadly joined to the opisthosoma, and thus the body appears ovoid. Legs are very long and slender. Many harvestmen are omnivores (they feed on a variety of plant and animal material), and others are strictly predators. Prey are seized by pedipalps and ingested as described for other arachnids. Digestion is both external and internal. Sperm transfer is direct, as males have a penislike structure. Females have a tubular ovipositor that is projected from a sheath at the time of egg laying. Hundreds of eggs are deposited in damp locations on the ground.

Order Acarina

Members of the order Acarina (ak'ar-i"nah) are the mites and ticks. Many are ectoparasites (parasites on the outside of the body) on humans and domestic animals. Others are free living in both terrestrial and aquatic habitats. Of all arachnids, acarines have had the greatest impact on human health and welfare.

Mites are 1 mm or less in length. The prosoma and opisthosoma are fused and covered by a single carapace. Mouthparts are carried on an anterior projection called the capitulum. Chelicerae and pedipalps are variously modified for piercing, biting, anchoring, and sucking, and adults have four pairs of walking legs.

Free-living mites may be herbivores or scavengers. Herbivorous mites, such as spider mites, cause damage to ornamental and agricultural plants. Scavenging mites are among the most common animals in soil and in leaf litter. These mites include some pest species that feed on flour, dried fruit, hay, cheese, and animal fur (figure 23.14).

Parasitic mites usually do not remain permanently attached to their hosts, but feed for a few hours or days and then drop to the ground. One mite, the notorious chigger or red bug (*Trombicula*), is a parasite during one of its larval stages on all groups of terrestrial vertebrates.   ⑥   Host skin is enzymatically broken down and sucked by a larva, causing local inflammation and intense itching at the site of the bite. The chigger larva drops from the host and then molts to the next immature stage, called a nymph. Nymphs eventually molt to adults, and both nymphs and adults feed on insect eggs.

A few mites are permanent ectoparasites.   ⑦   The follicle mite, *Demodex folliculorum*, is very common (but harmless) in hair follicles of most of the readers of this text. Itch mites cause scabies in humans and other animals. *Sarcoptes scabei* is the human itch mite. It tunnels in the epidermis of human skin, where females lay about 20 eggs each day. Secre-

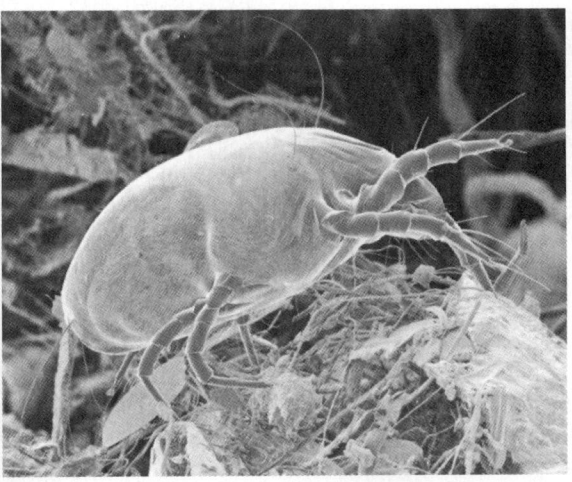

FIGURE 23.14

Order Acarina. *Dermatophagoides farinae* is common in homes and grain storage areas. It is believed to be a major cause of dust allergies (×200).

tions of the mites cause skin irritation, and infections are acquired by contact with an infected individual.

Ticks are ectoparasites during their entire life history. They may be up to 3 cm in length, but are otherwise similar to mites. Hooked mouthparts are used to attach to their hosts and to feed on blood. The female ticks, whose bodies are less sclerotized than those of males, expand when engorged with blood. Copulation occurs on the host, and after feeding, females drop to the ground to lay eggs. Eggs hatch into six-legged immatures called seed ticks. Immatures feed on host blood and drop to the ground for each molt. Some ticks transmit diseases to humans and domestic animals. For example, *Dermacentor andersoni* transmits the bacteria that cause Rocky Mountain spotted fever and tularemia, and *Ixodes scapularis* transmits the bacterium that causes Lyme disease (figure 23.15). Other orders of arachnids include whip scorpions, whip spiders, pseudoscorpions, and others.

CLASS PYCNOGONIDA

Members of the class Pycnogonida (pik'no-gon"i-dah) are the sea spiders. All are marine and are most common in cold waters (figure 23.16). Pycnogonids live on the ocean floor and are frequently found feeding on cnidarian polyps and ectoprocts. Some sea spiders feed by sucking up prey tissues through a proboscis. Others tear at prey with their chelicerae.

Pycnogonids are dioecious. Gonads are U-shaped, and branches of the gonads extend into each leg. Gonopores are located on one of the pairs of legs. Eggs are released by the female, and as the male fertilizes the eggs, they are cemented into spherical masses and attached to a pair of elongate appendages of their male, called ovigers, where they are brooded until hatching.

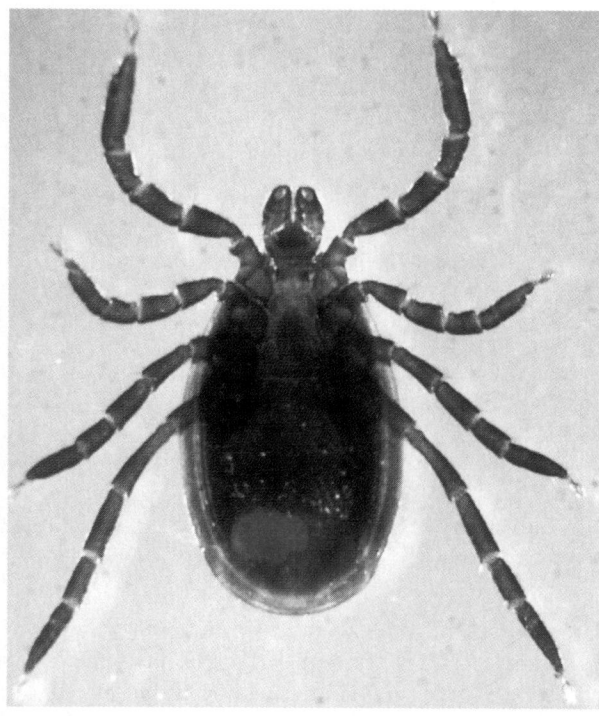

(a)

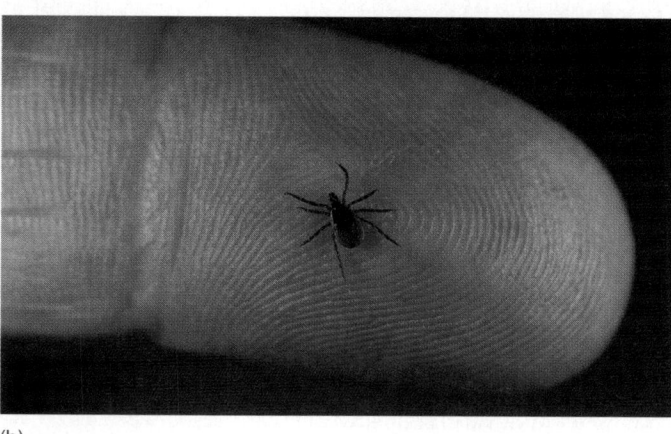

(b)

Figure 23.15

Order Acarina. *Ixodes scapularis*, the tick that transmits the bacterium that causes Lyme disease is shown here (*a*). The adult is about the size of a sesame seed (*b*), and the nymph is the size of a poppy seed. People walking in tick-infested regions should examine themselves regularly and remove any ticks found on their skin, because ticks can transmit diseases, such as Rocky Mountain spotted fever, tularemia, and Lyme disease.

Stop and Ask Yourself

5. How are the members of the subphylum Chelicerata characterized?

6. What are book lungs? What animals have them?

7. What characteristic of arachnids preadapted them for terrestrial environments?

8. What are three ways that spiders use silk?

Figure 23.16

Class Pycnogonida. Sea spiders, such as *Pycnogonum*, are often found in intertidal regions feeding on cnidarian polyps.

Subphylum Crustacea

Some of the members of subphylum Crustacea (krus-tas'eah) (L. *crustaceus*, hard shelled), such as crayfish, shrimp, lobsters, and crabs, are familiar to nearly everyone. In addition, there are many lesser-known, but very common, taxa. These include copepods, cladocerans, fairy shrimp, isopods, amphipods, and barnacles. Except for some isopods and crabs, crustaceans are all aquatic.

Crustaceans differ from other living arthropods in two ways. They have two pairs of antennae, whereas all other arthropods have one pair or none. In addition, crustaceans possess biramous appendages, each of which consists of a basal segment, called the **protopodite,** with two rami (distal processes that give the appendage a Y shape) attached. The medial ramus is the **endopodite** and the lateral ramus is the **ex-opodite** (figure 23.17). A similar condition was described for the trilobites and may be evidence that the trilobites were ancestral to the crustaceans.

Class Malacostraca

Malacostraca (mal-ah-kos'trah-kah) (Gr. *malakos*, soft + *os-treion*, shell) is the largest class of crustaceans. It includes crabs, lobsters, crayfish, shrimp, mysids, shrimplike krill, isopods, and amphipods.

The order Decapoda (dek-i-pod'ah) is the largest order of crustaceans and includes shrimp, crayfish, lobsters, and crabs. Shrimp have a laterally compressed, muscular abdomen and pleopods that are used for swimming. Lobsters, crabs, and crayfish are adapted to crawling on the surface of the substrate (figure 23.18). The abdomen of crabs is greatly reduced and is held flexed beneath the cephalothorax.

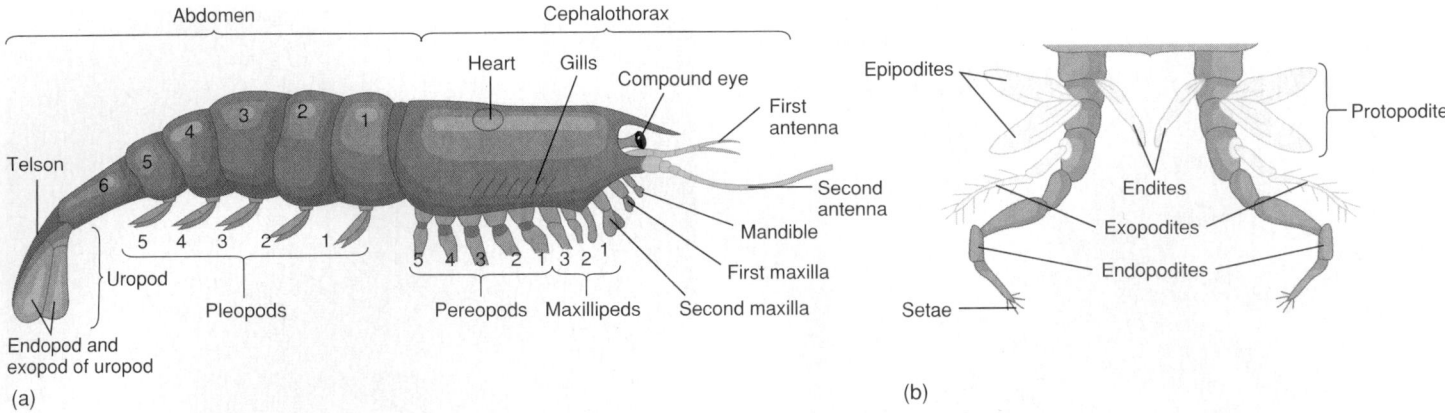

(a)

(b)

FIGURE 23.17

The Crustacean Body Form. (*a*) The external anatomy of a crustacean. (*b*) A pair of appendages showing the generalized biramous structure. A protopodite attaches to the body wall. An exopodite (a lateral ramus) and an endopodite (a medial ramus) attach at the end of the protopodite. In modern crustaceans, both the distribution of appendages along the length of the body and the structure of appendages are modified for specialized functions.

FIGURE 23.18

Order Decapoda. The lobsters, shrimp, crayfish, and crabs comprise the largest crustacean order. The lobster, *Homarus americanus*, is shown here.

Crayfish are often used to illustrate general crustacean structure and function. They are convenient to study because of their relative abundance and large size. The body of a crayfish is divided into two regions. A cephalothorax is derived from developmental fusion of a sensory and feeding tagma (the head) with a locomotor tagma (the thorax). The exoskeleton of the cephalothorax extends laterally and ventrally to form a shield-like carapace. The abdomen is posterior to the cephalothorax, has locomotor and visceral functions, and in crayfish, takes the form of a muscular "tail."

Paired appendages are present in both body regions (figure 23.19). The first two pairs of cephalothoracic appendages are the first and second antennae. The third through the fifth pairs of appendages are associated with the mouth. During crustacean evolution, the third pair of appendages became modified into chewing or grinding structures called **mandibles.** The fourth and fifth pairs of appendages, called **maxillae,** are used for food handling. The second maxilla bears a gill and a thin, bladelike structure, called a

scaphognathite (gill bailer), used to circulate water over the gills. The sixth through the eighth cephalothoracic appendages are called maxillipeds and are derived from the thoracic tagma. They are accessory sensory and food handling appendages. Each also bears a gill. Appendages 9 to 13 are thoracic appendages called periopods (walking legs). The first periopod, known as the cheliped, is enlarged and chelate (pincherlike) and used in defense and capturing food. All but the last pair of appendages of the abdomen are called pleopods (swimmerets) and used for swimming. In females, developing eggs are attached to pleopods, and the embryos are brooded until after hatching. In males, the first two pairs of pleopods are modified into gonopods (claspers) that are used for sperm transfer during copulation. The abdomen ends in a median extension called the telson. The telson bears the anus and is flanked on either side by flattened, biramous appendages of the last segment, called uropods. The telson and uropods make an effective flipperlike structure used in swimming and in escape responses.

All crustacean appendages, except the first antennae, have presumably evolved from an ancestral biramous form, as evidenced by their embryological development, in which they arise as simple two-branched structures. (First antennae develop as uniramous appendages and later acquire the branched form. The crayfish and their close relatives are unique in having branched first antennae.) Structures, such as the biramous appendages of a crayfish, whose form is based upon a common ancestral pattern and that have similar development in the segments of an animal, are said to be **serially homologous.**

Crayfish prey upon other invertebrates, eat plant matter, and scavenge dead and dying animals. The foregut includes an enlarged stomach, part of which is specialized for grinding. A digestive gland secretes digestive enzymes and absorbs products of digestion. The midgut extends from the stomach and is often called the intestine. A short hindgut ends in an anus and is important in water and salt regulation (figure 23.20a).

As described above, the gills of a crayfish are attached to the bases of some cephalothoracic appendages. Gills are located

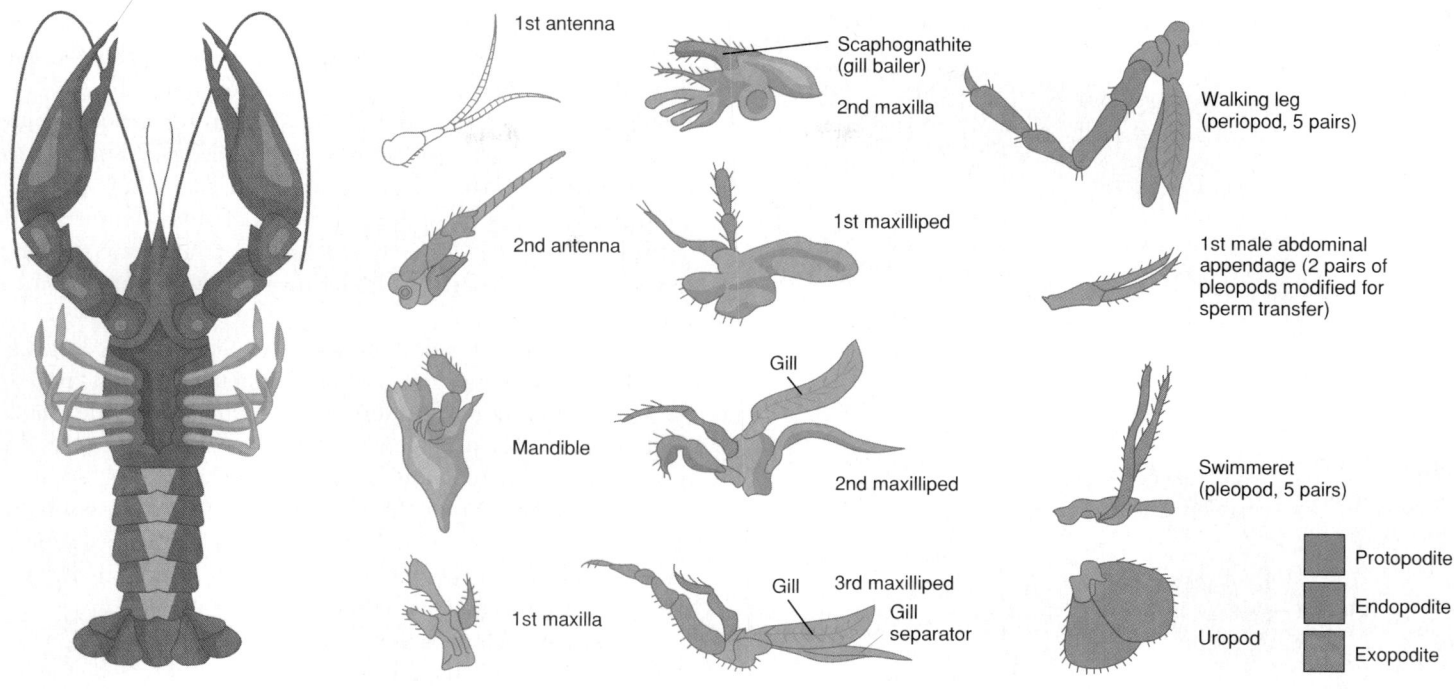

FIGURE 23.19

Crayfish Appendages. Ventral view of a crayfish. Appendages removed and arranged in sequence. Homologies regarding the structure of appendages are color coded. The origin and homology of the first antennae are uncertain.

in a branchial (gill) chamber, the space between the carapace and the lateral body wall (figure 23.20*b*). Water is driven anteriorly through the branchial chamber by the beating of the scaphognathite of the second maxilla. Oxygen and carbon dioxide are exchanged between blood and water across the gill surfaces, and oxygen is carried in blood plasma by a respiratory pigment, hemocyanin.

Circulation in crayfish is similar to that of most arthropods. Dorsal, anterior, and posterior arteries lead away from a muscular heart. Branches of these vessels empty into sinuses of the hemocoel. Blood returning to the heart collects in a ventral sinus and enters the gills before returning to the pericardial sinus, which surrounds the heart (figure 23.20*b*).

Crustacean nervous systems show trends similar to those in annelids and arachnids. Primitively, the ventral nervous system is ladderlike. Higher crustaceans show a tendency toward centralization and cephalization. In crayfish, there are supraesophageal and subesophageal ganglia that receive sensory input from receptors in the head and control the head appendages. There is a fusion of the ventral nerves and segmental ganglia, and giant neurons in the ventral nerve cord function in escape responses (figure 23.20*a*). When nerve impulses are conducted posteriorly along giant nerve fibers of a crayfish, powerful abdominal flexor muscles of the abdomen contract alternately with weaker extensor muscles, causing the abdomen to flex (the propulsive stroke) and then extend (the recovery stroke). The telson and uropods form a paddlelike "tail" that propels the crayfish posteriorly.

In addition to antennae, the sensory structures of crayfish include compound eyes, simple eyes, statocysts, chemoreceptors, proprioceptors, and tactile setae. Chemical receptors are widely distributed over the appendages and the head. Many of the setae covering the mouthparts and antennae are chemoreceptors that are used in sampling food and detecting pheromones. A single pair of statocysts is located at the bases of the first antennae. A statocyst is a pitlike invagination of the exoskeleton that contains setae and a group of cemented sand grains called a statolith. Movements of the crayfish cause the statolith to move and displace setae. Statocysts provide information regarding movement, orientation with respect to the pull of gravity, and vibrations of the substrate. Because the statocyst is cuticular, it is replaced with each molt. Sand is incorporated into the statocyst when the crustacean is buried in sand. Other receptors involved with equilibrium, balance, and position senses are tactile receptors on the appendages and at joints. When a crustacean is crawling or resting, stretch receptors at the joints are stimulated. Tilting is detected by changing patterns of stimulation. These widely distributed receptors are very important to most crustaceans, because many lack statocysts.

Crayfish have compound eyes that are mounted on movable eyestalks. The lens system consists of 25 to 14,000 individual receptors called ommatidia. Compound eyes also occur in insects, and their physiology is discussed in chapter 24. Larval crustaceans have a single, median photoreceptor consisting of a few sensilla. These simple eyes, called ocelli, allow larval crustaceans to orient

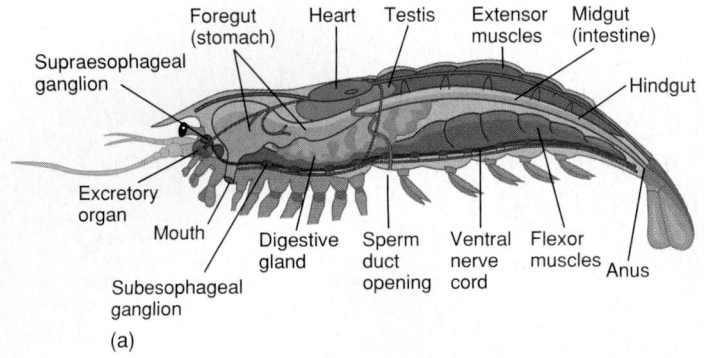

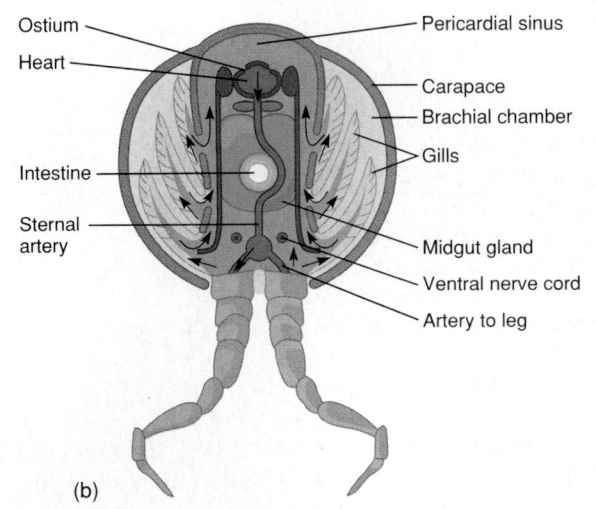

FIGURE 23.20

Internal Structure of a Crayfish. (*a*) Lateral view of a male. In the female, the ovary is located in the same place as the testis of the male, but the gonoducts open at the base of the third periopods. (*b*) Cross section of the thorax in the region of the heart. In this diagram, gills are shown attached higher on the body wall than they actually occur in order to show the path of blood flow (arrows) through them.

toward or away from the light but do not form images. Many larvae are planktonic and use their ocelli to orient toward surface waters.

The endocrine system of a crayfish controls functions such as ecdysis, sex determination, and color change. Endocrine glands release chemicals called hormones into the blood, where they circulate and cause responses at certain target tissues. In crustaceans, endocrine functions are closely tied to nervous functions. Nervous tissues that produce and release hormones are called neurosecretory tissues. X-organs are neurosecretory tissues located in eyestalks of crayfish. Associated with each X-organ is a sinus gland that accumulates and releases the secretions of the X-organ. Other glands, called Y-organs, are not directly associated with nervous tissues. They are located near the bases of the maxillae. Both the X-organ and the Y-organ control ecdysis. The X-organ produces molt-inhibiting hormone, and the sinus

gland releases it. The target of this hormone is the Y-organ. As long as molt-inhibiting hormone is present, the Y-organ is inactive. Under certain conditions, molt-inhibiting hormone release is prevented and the Y-organ releases ecdysone hormone, leading to molting (*see figure 35.5*). (These "certain conditions" are often complex and species specific. They include factors such as nutritional state, temperature, and photoperiod.) Other hormones that facilitate molting have also been described, including, among others, a molt-accelerating factor.

Another endocrine function is mediated by androgenic glands, located in the cephalothorax of males. (Females possess rudiments of these glands during development, but the glands never mature.) Normally, androgenic hormone(s) promotes the development of testes and male characteristics, such as gonopods. Removal of androgenic glands from males results in the development of female sex characteristics, and if androgenic glands are experimentally implanted into a female, she will develop testes and gonopods.

Many other crustacean functions are probably regulated by hormones. Some that have been investigated include the development of brooding structures of females in response to ovarian hormones, the seasonal regulation of ovarian functions, the regulation of heart rate by eyestalk hormones, and the regulation of body color changes by eyestalk hormones.

The excretory organs of crayfish are called antennal glands (green glands) because they are located at the bases of the second antennae and are green in living crayfish. In other crustaceans, they are called maxillary glands because they are located at the base of the second maxillae. In spite of their name, they are not glands. They are structurally similar to the coxal glands of arachnids, and they presumably had a common evolutionary origin. Excretory products are formed by filtration of blood. Ions, sugars, and amino acids are reabsorbed in the tubule before the diluted urine is excreted. As with most aquatic animals, ammonia is the primary excretory product. However, crayfish do not rely solely on the antennal glands to excrete ammonia. Diffusion of ammonia across thin parts of the exoskeleton is very important. Even though it is toxic, ammonia is water soluble and rapidly diluted by water. All freshwater crustaceans face a continual influx of fresh water and loss of ions. Thus, the elimination of excess water and the reabsorption of ions become extremely important functions. Gill surfaces are also important in ammonia excretion and water and ion regulation (osmoregulation).

Crayfish, and all other crustaceans except the barnacles, are dioecious. Gonads are located in the dorsal portion of the thorax, and gonoducts open at the base of the third (females) or fifth (males) periopods. Mating occurs just after a female has molted. The male turns the female onto her back and deposits nonflagellated sperm near the openings of the female's gonoducts. Fertilization occurs after copulation, as the eggs are shed. The eggs are sticky and become securely fastened to the female's pleopods. Fanning movements of the pleopods over the eggs keeps them aerated. The development of crayfish embryos

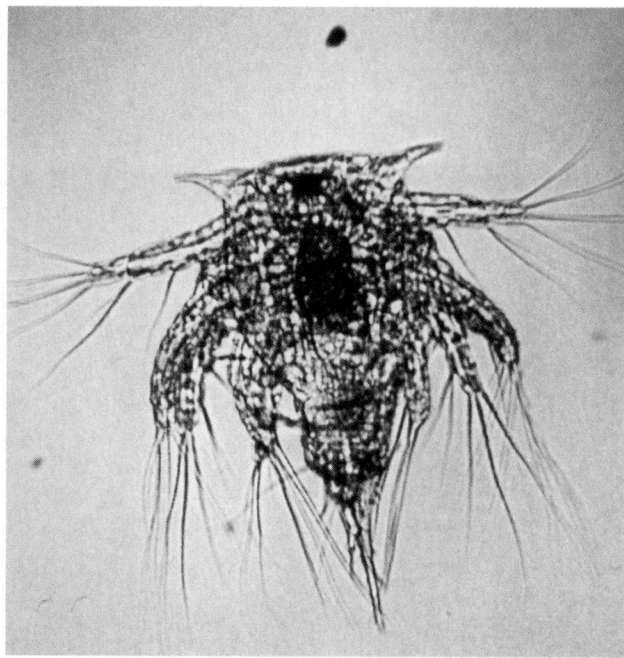

(a)

(b)

Figure **23.21**

Crustacean Larvae. (*a*) Nauplius larva of a barnacle. (*b*) Zoea larvae of a crab.

(a)

(b)

Figure **23.22**

Orders Isopoda and Amphipoda. (*a*) Some isopods roll into a ball when disturbed or threatened with drying—thus, the name "pillbug." (*b*) This amphipod (*Orchestoidea californiana*) spends some time out of the water hopping along beach sands—thus, the name "beachhopper."

is direct, with young hatching as miniature adults. In many other crustaceans, a planktonic, free-swimming larva called a nauplius is present (figure 23.21*a*). In some, the nauplius develops into a miniature adult. In crabs and their relatives, a second larval stage called a zoea is present (figure 23.21*b*). When all adult features are present, except sexual maturity, the immature is called the postlarva.

Two other orders of malacostracans have members that are encountered by many students. Members of the order Isopoda (i'so'pod'ah) include "pillbugs." Isopods are dorsoventrally flattened, and may be either aquatic or terrestrial, and scavenge decaying plant and animal material. Some have become modified for clinging to and feeding on other animals. Terrestrial isopods live under rocks and logs and in leaf litter (figure 23.22*a*). Members of the order Amphipoda (am-fi-pod'ah) have a laterally compressed body that gives them a shrimplike appearance. Amphipods move by crawling or swimming on their sides along the substrate. Some species are modified for burrowing, climbing, or jumping (figure 23.22*b*). Amphipods are scavengers, and a few species are parasites.

CLASS BRANCHIOPODA

Members of the class Branchiopoda (bran'ke-o-pod'ah) (Gr. *branchio*, gill + *podos*, foot) are primarily found in fresh water. All branchiopods possess flattened, leaflike appendages that are used in respiration, filter feeding, and locomotion.

Fairy shrimp and brine shrimp comprise the order Anostraca (an-ost'ra-kah). Fairy shrimp are usually found in temporary ponds formed by spring thaws and rains. Eggs are brooded, and when the female dies, and the temporary pond begins to dry, the embryos become dormant in a resistant capsule. Embryos lay on the forest floor until the pond fills again the following spring, at which time they hatch into nauplius larvae. Dispersal may occur if embryos are carried to other locations by animals, wind, or water currents. Their short and uncertain life cycle is an adaptation to living in ponds that dry up. The vulnerability of these slowly swimming and defenseless crustaceans probably explains why they live primarily in temporary ponds, a habitat that contains few larger predators. Brine shrimp also form resistant embryos. They live in salt lakes and ponds (e.g., the Great Salt Lake in Utah).

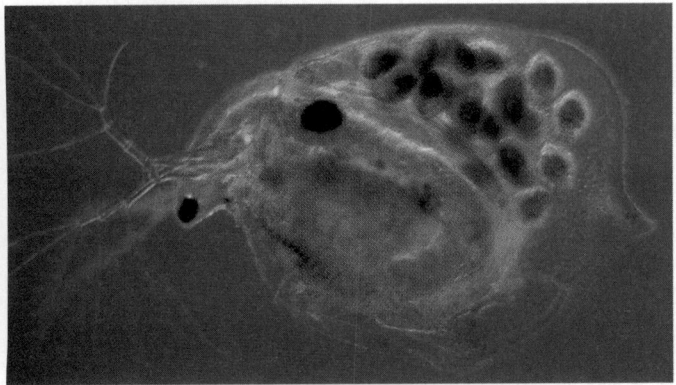

FIGURE 23.23

Class Branchiopoda. This cladoceran water flea (*Vetulus*) is carrying young under its carapace.

Members of the order Cladocera (kla-dos'er-ah) are called water fleas (figure 23.23). Their bodies are covered by a large carapace, and they swim using their second antennae, which they repeatedly thrust downward to create a jerky, upward locomotion. Females reproduce parthenogenetically (without fertilization) in spring and summer and can rapidly populate a pond or lake. Eggs are brooded in an egg case beneath the carapace. At the next molt, the egg case is released and either floats or sinks to the bottom of the pond or lake. In response to decreasing temperature, changing photoperiod, or decreasing food supply, females produce eggs that develop parthenogenetically into males. Sexual reproduction then occurs and produces resistant "winter eggs" that overwinter and hatch in the spring.

CLASS COPEPODA

Members of the class Copepoda (ko'pe-pod'ah) (Gr. *kope*, oar + *podos*, foot) include some of the most abundant crustaceans. There are both marine and freshwater species. Copepods possess a cylindrical body and a median ocellus that develops in the nauplius stage and persists into the adult stage. The first antennae (and the thoracic appendages in some) are modified for swimming, and the abdomen is free of appendages. Most copepods are planktonic and use their second maxillae for filter feeding. Their importance in marine food webs was noted in the introduction to this chapter. A few copepods live on the substrate, a few are predatory, and others are commensals or parasites of marine invertebrates, fishes, or marine mammals.

CLASS CIRRIPEDIA

Members of the class Cirripedia (sir'i-ped'eah), the barnacles, are sessile and highly modified as adults (figure 23.24*a*). They are exclusively marine and include about 1,000 species. Most barnacles are monoecious (figure 23.24*a*). The planktonic nauplius of barnacles is followed by a planktonic larval stage, called a cypris larva, which has a bivalved carapace. Cypris larvae attach to the

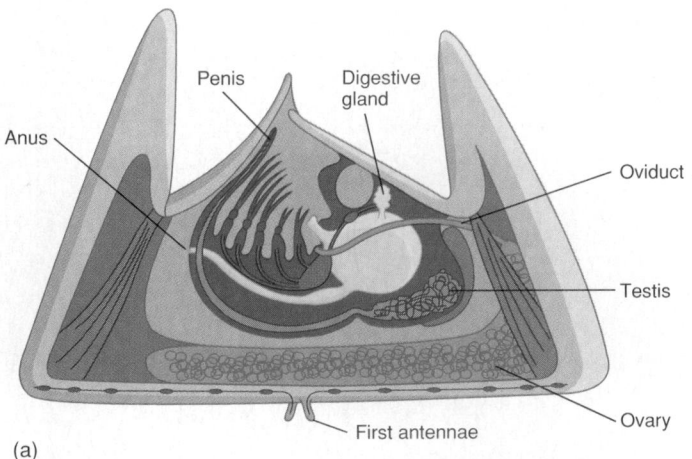

FIGURE 23.24

Class Cirripedia. (*a*) Internal structure of a stalkless (acorn) barnacle. (*b*) Stalked (gooseneck) barnacles (*Lepas*).

substrate by their first antennae and metamorphose to adults. In the process of metamorphosis, the abdomen is reduced, and the gut tract becomes U-shaped. Thoracic appendages are modified for filtering and moving food into the mouth. The larval carapace is covered by calcareous plates in the adult stage.

⑧ Barnacles attach to a variety of substrates, including rock outcroppings, the bottom of ships, whales, and other animals. Some barnacles attach to their substrate by a stalk (figure 23.24*b*). Others are nonstalked and are called acorn

23.2   *SACCULINA*: A HIGHLY MODIFIED PARASITE

Barnacles of the order Rhizocephala are parasites. Many are very similar to free-living barnacles but others, such as *Sacculina,* are some of the most highly modified of all animal parasites. Not only do adults not look like barnacles, they are difficult to recognize as animals and more closely resemble a fungus. Larval stages, however, disclose the true identity of this parasite.

The life cycle of *Sacculina* begins when a cypris larva attaches by its first antennae to a seta on a limb of a crab. The larva moves to a membranous area and bores through the crab exoskeleton. Once inside the body, the larva loses its exoskeleton, and dedifferentiated cells move through the blood to the midgut. The parasite then grows throughout the hemocoel and branches into a myceliumlike mass of parasite tissue. When the crab molts, a brood sac containing the parasite's eggs is formed in the flexed abdomen of the crab—in the same position that the female crabs normally brood their own young.

Early research indicated that all crabs parasitized by *Sacculina* were apparently females. It was later discovered that in fact males were parasitized and transformed into females by the parasite! It was once thought that the destruction of the testes caused the sex change, but it is now known that the parasite destroys the androgenic gland. Just as experimental removal of the androgenic glands transforms males to females, so does parasitization.

The crab cares for the parasite's brood sac as if it were its own. Fertilization occurs when a male cypris larva introduces sperm-forming tissue into the parasite's brood sac. Nauplius larvae are released from the brood sac, and they metamorphose into cypris larvae. Parasitism prevents further molting by the crab, results in sterility, and usually causes the crab's death.

---

barnacles. Barnacles that colonize the bottom of ships reduce both ship speed and fuel efficiency. Much time, effort, and money has been devoted to research on how to keep ships free of barnacles.

Some barnacles have become highly modified parasites (box 23.2). The evolution of parasitism in barnacles is probably a logical consequence of living attached to other animals.

FURTHER PHYLOGENETIC CONSIDERATIONS

After studying this chapter, it should be clear that the arthropods have been very successful. This is evidenced by diverse body forms and life-styles of copepods, crabs, lobsters, crayfish, and barnacles, which are an example of adaptive radiation. Few aquatic environments are without some crustaceans.

The subphylum Chelicerata is a very important group of animals from an evolutionary standpoint even though they are less numerous in terms of numbers of species and individuals than are many of the crustacean groups. Their arthropod exoskeleton and the evolution of excretory and respiratory systems that minimize water loss, resulted in ancestral members of this subphylum becoming some of the first terrestrial animals. Chelicerates, however, are not the only terrestrial arthropods. In terms of numbers of species and numbers of individuals, chelicerates are dwarfed in terrestrial environments by the fourth arthropod lineage—the insects and their relatives. This lineage and the evolutionary relationships within the entire phylum are the subject of the next chapter.

Stop and Ask Yourself

9. What evidence supports the hypothesis that trilobites were ancestral to the crustaceans?

10. What structures of a crayfish are serially homologous? What does this mean?

11. What are neurosecretory tissues? How are they involved in regulating crustacean metamorphosis?

12. What crustaceans belong to the class Branchiopoda and reproduce by parthenogenesis?

SUMMARY

1. Arthropods and annelids are closely related animals. Living arthropods are divided into three subphyla: Chelicerata, Crustacea, and Uniramia. All members of a fourth subphylum, Trilobitomorpha, are extinct.

2. Arthropods have three distinctive characteristics: they are metameric and display tagmatization, they possess an exoskeleton, and many undergo metamorphosis during development.

3. Members of the extinct subphylum Trilobitomorpha had bodies that were oval and flattened and consisted of three tagmata and three longitudinal lobes. Appendages were biramous.

4. The subphylum Chelicerata has members whose bodies are divided into a prosoma and an opisthosoma. They also possess a pair of feeding appendages called chelicerae.

5. The horseshoe crabs and the giant water scorpions belong to the class Merostomata.

6. The class Arachnida includes spiders, mites, ticks, scorpions, and others. Their exoskeleton partially preadapted the arachnids for their terrestrial habitats.

7. The sea spiders are the only members of the class Pycnogonida.

8. The subphylum Crustacea contains animals characterized by two pairs of antennae and biramous appendages. All crustaceans, except for some isopods, are primarily aquatic.

9. Members of the class Branchiopoda have flattened, leaflike appendages. Examples are fairy shrimp, brine shrimp, and water fleas.

10. The class Malacostraca includes the crabs, lobsters, crayfish, shrimp, isopods, and amphipods. This is the largest crustacean class in terms of numbers of species and contains the largest crustaceans.

11. Members of the class Copepoda include the copepods.

12. The class Cirrepedia contains the barnacles, which are sessile filter feeders.

SELECTED KEY TERMS

biramous appendages (*p. 365*)
chelicerae (*p. 366*)
ecdysis (*p. 364*)
exoskeleton or cuticle (*p. 363*)
hemocoel (*p. 368*)

mandibles (*p. 374*)
oviparous (*p. 370*)
ovoviviparous (*p. 370*)
serially homologous (*p. 374*)
viviparous (*p. 370*)

CRITICAL THINKING QUESTIONS

1. What is tagmatization, and why is it advantageous for metameric animals?

2. In spite of being an armorlike covering, the exoskeleton permits movement and growth. Explain how this is accomplished.

3. Why is the arthropod exoskeleton often cited as the major reason for arthropod success?

4. Explain why excretory and respiratory systems of ancestral arachnids probably preadapted these organisms for terrestrial habitats.

5. Barnacles are obviously very successful arthropods. What factors do you think are responsible for the evolution of their highly modified body form?

THE HEXAPODS AND MYRIAPODS: TERRESTRIAL TRIUMPHS

Outline

Concepts

1. Flight, along with other arthropod characteristics, has resulted in insects becoming the most abundant and diverse group of terrestrial animals.
2. The myriapods include members of the classes Diplopoda, Chilopoda, Pauropoda, and Symphyla.
3. Members of the class Hexapoda (Insecta) are characterized by three pairs of legs, and they usually have wings.
4. Adaptations for living on land are reflected in many aspects of insect structure and function.
5. Insects have important effects on human health and welfare.
6. Some zoologists believe that the arthropods should be divided into three phyla: the Chelicerata, Crustacea, and Uniramia.

Would You Like to Know:

1. why insects have been so successful on land? (*p. 382*)
2. what animals were the first to invade terrestrial habitats? (*p. 383*)
3. how fast the wings of a midge beat? (*p. 387*)
4. how far a human could leap if one could jump, relative to body size, the same distance a flea can jump? (*p. 387*)
5. what an insect sees? (*p. 389*)
6. how insects communicate over long distances? (*p. 391*)
7. how the social organization in a honeybee hive is regulated? (*p. 394*)

These and other useful questions will be answered in this chapter.

This chapter contains evolutionary concepts, which are set off in this font.

Evolutionary Perspective

By almost any criterion, the insects have been enormously successful. There are approximately 750,000 described species, and some zoologists estimate that there may be as many as 30 million species of insects! Most of the undescribed species are found in tropical rain forests. The described species of insects comprise ¾ of all living species. Obviously, the total number of described and undescribed insects dwarfs all other kinds of living organisms. Although there are numerous freshwater and parasitic species, the success of insects has largely been due to their ability to exploit terrestrial habitats (figure 24.1).

During the late Silurian and early Devonian periods (about 400 million years ago), terrestrial environments were largely uninhabited by animals. Low-growing herbaceous plants and the first forests were beginning to flourish, and enough ozone had accumulated in the upper atmosphere to filter ultraviolet radiation from the sun. Animals with adaptations that permitted life on land had a wealth of photosynthetic production available, and unlike in marine habitats, had little competition with other animals for resources. However, the problems associated with terrestrial life were substantial. Support and movement outside of a watery environment were difficult on land, as were water, ion, and temperature regulation.

What factors have permitted the insect dominance of terrestrial habitats? ① A number of factors contributed to their success. The exoskeleton preadapted the insects for life on land. Not only is the exoskeleton supportive, but also the evolution of a waxy epicuticle enhanced the exoskeleton's water-conserving properties. The evolution of flight has also played a big role in insect success. The ability to fly has allowed insects to use widely scattered food resources, to invade new habitats, and to escape unfavorable environments. These factors—along with desiccation resistant eggs, metamorphosis, high reproductive potential, and diversification of mouthparts and feeding habits—have permitted insects to become the dominant class of organisms on the earth.

The insects make up one of five classes in the subphylum Uniramia (table 24.1; figure 24.2). The four noninsect classes

Figure 24.1

Class Hexopoda. Insects were early inhabitants of terrestrial environments. The exoskeleton and the evolution of flight have contributed to the enormous success of this group of arthropods.

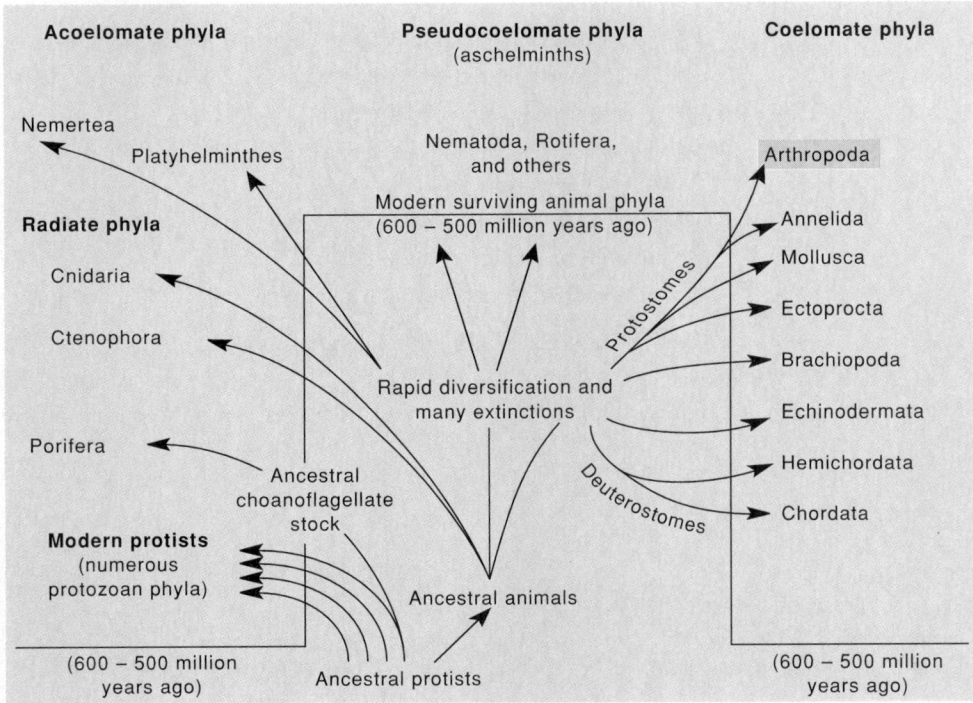

Figure 24.2

Evolutionary Relationships of the Arthropods. The arthropods (shaded in orange) are protostomes that are closely related to the annelids. Members of the subphylum Uniramia are the subject of this chapter.

(a)

(b)

FIGURE **24.3**
The Myriapods. (*a*) A woodland millipede (*Ophyiulus pilosus*). (*b*) A centipede (*Scolopendra heros*).

(discussed next) are grouped into a convenient, nontaxonomic grouping called the **myriapods** (Gr. *myriad*, ten thousand + *podus*, foot).

CLASS DIPLOPODA

The class Diplopoda (dip'lah-pod'ah) (Gr. *diploos*, twofold + *podus*, foot) contains the millipedes. ❷ Ancestors of this group appeared on land during the Devonian period and were among the first terrestrial animals. Millipedes have 11 to 100 trunk segments that have been derived from an embryological and evolutionary fusion of primitive metameres. An obvious result of this fusion is the occurrence of two pairs of appendages on each apparent trunk segment. Each segment is actually the fusion of two segments. Fusion is also reflected internally by two ganglia, two pairs of ostia, and two pairs of tracheal trunks per apparent segment. Most millipedes are round in cross section, although some are more flattened (figure 24.3a).

Millipedes are worldwide in distribution and are nearly always found in or under leaf litter, humus, or decaying logs. Their epicuticle does not contain much wax; therefore, their choice of habitat is important to prevent desiccation. Their many legs, simultaneously pushing against the substrate, help millipedes bulldoze through the habitat. Millipedes feed on decaying plant matter using their mandibles in a chewing or scraping fashion. A few millipedes have mouthparts modified for sucking plant juices.

Millipedes roll into a ball when faced with desiccation or when they are disturbed. Many also possess repugnatorial glands that produce hydrogen cyanide, which is repellant to other animals. Hydrogen cyanide is not synthesized and stored as hydrogen cyanide because it is very caustic and would destroy millipede tissues. Instead, a precursor com-

pound and an enzyme are mixed as they are released from separate glandular compartments. Repellants increase the likelihood that the millipede will be dropped unharmed and decrease the chances that the same predator will try to feed on another millipede.

Sperm are transferred to the female millipede with modified trunk appendages of the male, called gonopods, or in spermatophores. Eggs are fertilized as they are laid, and hatch in several weeks. Immatures acquire more legs and segments with each molt until they reach adulthood.

CLASS CHILOPODA

Members of the class Chilopoda (ki'lah-pod'ah) (Gr. *cheilos*, lip + *podus*, foot) are the centipedes. Most centipedes are nocturnal and spend their time scurrying about the surfaces of logs, rocks, or other forest-floor debris. As do millipedes, most centipedes lack a waxy epicuticle, and therefore are found in moist habitats. Their bodies are flattened in cross section, and they have a single pair of long legs on each of their 15 or more trunk segments. The last pair of legs is usually modified into long sensory appendages.

Centipedes are fast-moving predators. Food usually consists of small arthropods, earthworms, and snails; however, some feed on frogs and rodents (figure 24.3b). Poison claws (modified first trunk appendages called maxillipeds) are used to kill or immobilize prey. Maxillipeds, along with mouth appendages, hold the prey as mandibles chew and ingest the food. The venom of most centipedes is essentially harmless to humans, although many centipedes have bites that are comparable to wasp stings; a few human deaths have been reported from large, tropical species.

TABLE 24.1	CLASSIFICATION OF THE SUBPHYLUM UNIRAMIA*

Phylum Arthropoda (ar'thra-po'dah)
Animals with metamerism and tagmatization, a jointed exoskeleton, and a ventral nervous system.
  Subphylum Uniramia (yoo'ne-ram'eah) (L. *unis*, one + *ramis*, branch)
  Head with one pair of antennae and usually one pair of mandibles; all appendages uniramous.
   Class Diplopoda (dip'le-pod'ah)
   Two pairs of legs per apparent segment; body usually round in cross section. Millipedes.
   Class Chilopoda (ki'le-pod'ah)
   One pair of legs per segment; body oval in cross section; poison claws. Centipedes.
   Class Pauropoda (por'e-pod'ah)
   Small (0.5 to 2 mm), soft-bodied animals; 11 segments; nine pairs of legs; live in leaf mold. Pauropods.
   Class Symphyla (sim-fi'lah)
   Small (2 to 10 mm); long antennae; centipedelike; 10 to 12 pairs of legs; live in soil and leaf mold. Symphylans.
   Class Hexapoda (hex'sah-pod'ah)**
   Three pairs of legs; usually two pairs of wings; body with head, thorax, and abdomen; mandibulate mouthparts variously adapted. Insects.
    Subclass Apterygota (ap-ter-i-go'tah)
    Primitively wingless insects; pregenital abdominal appendages; ametabolous metamorphosis; indirect sperm transfer.
     Order Collembola (col-lem'bo-lah)
     Antennae with four to six segments; compound eyes absent; abdomen with six segments, most with springing appendage on fourth segment; inhabit soil and leaf litter. Springtails.
     Order Protura (pro-tu'rah)
     Minute, with cone-shaped head; antennae, compound eyes, and ocelli absent; abdominal appendages on first three segments; inhabit soil and leaf litter. Proturans.
     Order Diplura (dip-lu'rah)
     Head with many segmented antennae; compound eyes and ocelli absent; cerci multisegmented or forcepslike; inhabit soil and leaf litter. Diplurans.
     Order Thysanura (thi-sa-nu'rah)
     Tapering abdomen; flattened; scales on body; terminal cerci; long antennae. Silverfish.
    Subclass Pterygota (ter-i-go'tah)
    Insects descendant from winged ancestors. No pregenital abdominal appendages; direct sperm transfer.
     Superorder Exopterygota (eks-op-ter-i-go'tah)
     Paurometabolous (or hemimetabolous) metamorphosis; wings develop as external wing pads.
      Order Ephemeroptera (e-fem-er-op'ter-ah)
      Elongate, abdomen with two or three tail filaments; two pairs of membranous wings with many veins; forewings triangular; short bristlelike antennae. Mayflies.
      Order Odonata (o-do-nat'ah)
      Elongate, membranous wings with netlike venation; abdomen long and slender; compound eyes occupy most of head. Dragonflies, damselflies.
      Order Phasmida (fas'mi-dah)
      Body elongate and sticklike; wings reduced or absent; some tropical forms are flattened and leaflike. Walking sticks, leaf insects.
      Order Orthoptera (or-thop'ter-ah)
      Forewing long, narrow, and leathery; hindwing broad and membranous; chewing mouthparts. Grasshoppers, crickets, katydids.

*Selected orders of insects are described.
**Most entomologists now use the term "Hexapoda" as the inclusive class name. The term "Insecta" is used in a more restricted sense to refer to ectognathous hexapods (those whose mouthparts are more or less exposed). The common use of the term "insect" to refer to hexapods in general is followed in this textbook.

Centipede reproduction may involve courtship displays in which the male lays down a silk web using glands at the posterior tip of the body. A spermatophore is placed in the web and picked up by the female who introduces the spermatophore into her genital opening. Eggs are fertilized as they are laid. A female may brood and guard eggs by wrapping her body around the eggs, or they may be deposited in the soil. Young are similar to adults except that they have fewer legs and segments. Legs and segments are added with each molt.

CLASSES PAUROPODA AND SYMPHYLA

Members of the class Pauropoda (por'o-pod'ah) (Gr. *pauros*, small + *podus*, foot) are soft-bodied animals with 11 segments. These animals live in forest-floor litter, where they feed on fungi, humus, and other decaying organic matter. Their very small size and thin, moist exoskeleton allow gas exchange across the body surface and diffusion of nutrients and wastes in the body cavity.

Order Mantodea (man-to'deah)
Prothorax long; prothoracic legs long and armed with strong spines for grasping prey; predators. Mantids.
Order Blattaria (blat-tar'eah)
Body oval and flattened; head concealed from above by a shieldlike extension of the prothorax. Cockroaches.
Order Isoptera (i-sop'ter-ah)
Workers white and wingless; front and hind wings of reproductives of equal size; reproductives and some soldiers may be sclerotized; abdomen broadly joins thorax; social. Termites.
Order Dermaptera (der-map'ter-ah)
Elongate; chewing mouthparts; threadlike antennae; abdomen with unsegmented forcepslike cerci. Earwigs.
Order Phthiraptera (fthi-rap'ter-ah)
Small, wingless ectoparasites of birds and mammals; body dorsoventrally flattened; white. Sucking and chewing lice.
Order Hemiptera (hem-ip'ter-ah)
Proximal portion of forewing sclerotized, distal portion membranous; sucking mouthparts arise ventrally on anterior margin of head. True bugs.
Order Homoptera (ho-mop'ter-ah)
Wings entirely membranous; mouthparts arise ventrally on posterior margin of head (hypognathous). Cicadas, leafhoppers, aphids, whiteflies, scale insects.
Order Thysanoptera (thi-sa-nop'ter-ah)
Small bodied; sucking mouthparts; wings narrow and fringed with long setae; plant pests. Thrips.
Superorder Endopterygota (en-dop-ter-i-go'tah)
Holometabolous metamorphosis; wings develop internally during the pupal stage.
Order Neuroptera (neu-rop'ter-ah)
Wings membranous; hind wings held rooflike over body at rest. Lacewings, snakeflies, antlions, dobsonflies.
Order Coleoptera (ko-le-op'ter-ah)
Forewings sclerotized, forming covers (elytra) over the abdomen; hindwings membranous; chewing mouthparts; the largest insect order. Beetles.
Order Trichoptera (tri-kop'ter-ah)
Mothlike with setae-covered antennae; chewing mouthparts; wings covered with setae and held rooflike over abdomen at rest; larvae aquatic and often dwell in cases that they construct. Caddis flies.
Order Lepidoptera (lep-i-dop'ter-ah)
Wings broad and covered with scales; mouthparts formed into a sucking tube. Moths, butterflies.
Order Diptera (dip'ter-ah)
Mesothoracic wings well developed; metathoracic wings reduced to knoblike halteres; variously modified but never chewing mouthparts. Flies.
Order Siphonaptera (si-fon-ap'ter-ah)
Laterally flattened, sucking mouthparts; jumping legs; parasites of birds and mammals. Fleas.
Order Hymenoptera (hi-men-op'ter-ah)
Wings membranous with few veins; well-developed ovipositor, sometimes modified into a sting; mouthparts modified for biting and lapping; social and solitary species. Ants, bees, wasps.

Members of the class Symphyla (sim-fil'ah) (Gr. *sym*, same + *phyllos*, leaf) are small arthropods (2 to 10 mm in length) that occupy soil and leaf mold, superficially resemble centipedes, and are often called garden centipedes. They lack eyes and have 12 leg-bearing trunk segments. The posterior segment may have one pair of spinnerets or long sensory bristles. Symphylans normally feed on decaying vegetation; however, some species are pests of vegetables and flowers.

Stop and Ask Yourself

1. What probably accounts for the dominance of insects on land over other animals?
2. What classes of arthropods are collectively called the myriapods?
3. How would you characterize members of the following classes: Diplopoda? Chilopoda? Pauropoda? Symphyla?
4. How do millipedes discourage predators?

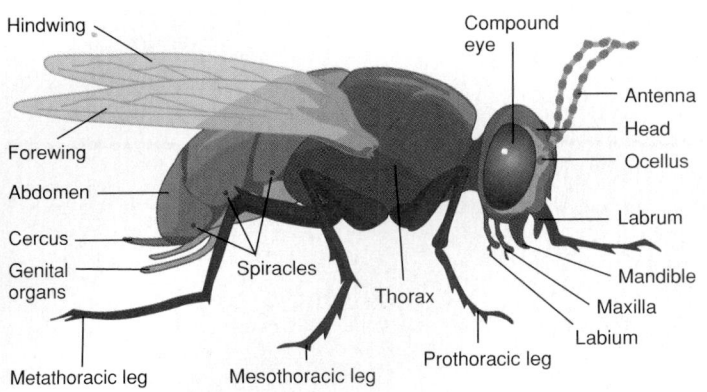

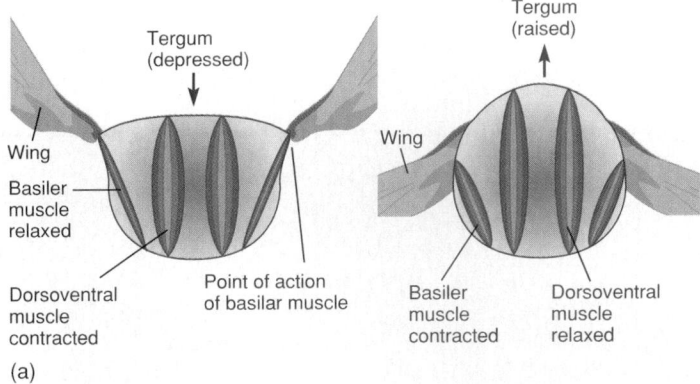

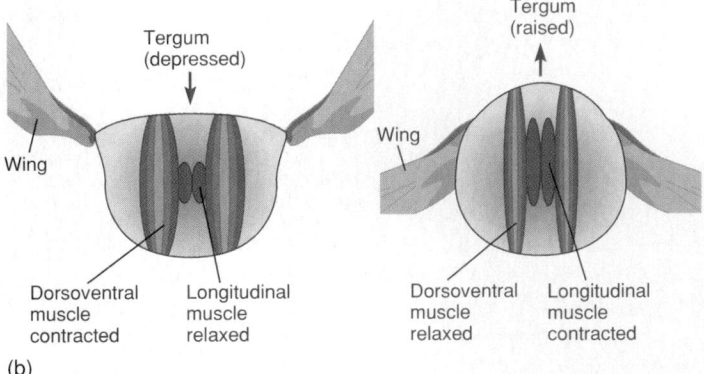

Figure 24.4

The External Structure of a Generalized Insect. Insects are characterized by a body divided into head, thorax, and abdomen; three pairs of legs; and two pairs of wings.

Class Hexapoda

Members of the class Hexapoda (Gr. *hexa*, six + *podus*, feet) are, in terms of numbers of species and individuals, the most successful land animals. Order-level classification varies depending on the authority consulted. One system is shown in table 24.1. In spite of obvious diversity, there are common features that make insects easy to recognize. Many insects have wings and one pair of antennae, and virtually all adults have three pairs of legs.

External Structure and Locomotion

The body of an insect is divided into three tagmata: head, thorax, and **abdomen** (figure 24.4). The head bears a single pair of antennae, mouthparts, compound eyes, and zero, two, or three ocelli. The thorax consists of three segments. They are, from anterior to posterior, the **prothorax,** the **mesothorax,** and the **metathorax.** One pair of legs attaches along the ventral margin of each thoracic segment, and a pair of wings, when present, attaches at the dorsolateral margin of the mesothorax and metathorax. Wings have thickened, hollow veins for increased strength. The thorax also contains two pairs of spiracles, which are openings to the tracheal system. Most insects have 10 or 11 abdominal segments, each of which has a lateral fold in the exoskeleton that allows the abdomen to expand when the insect has gorged itself or when it is full of mature eggs. Each abdominal segment has a pair of spiracles. Also present are genital structures used during copulation and egg deposition, and sensory structures called cerci. Gills are present on abdominal segments of certain immature aquatic insects.

Insect Flight

The great diversity of insects and insect habitats is accompanied by diversity in how insects move. From an evolutionary perspective, however, flight is the most important form of insect locomotion. Insects were the first animals to fly. One of the most

Figure 24.5

Insect Flight. (*a*) Muscle arrangements for the direct or synchronous flight mechanism. Note that muscles responsible for the downstroke attach at the base of the wings. (*b*) Muscle arrangements for an indirect or asynchronous flight mechanism. Wings move up and down as a result of muscles changing the shape of the thorax.

popular hypotheses on the origin of flight states that wings may have evolved from rigid, lateral outgrowths of the thorax that probably served as protection for the legs or spiracles. Later, these fixed lobes could have been used in gliding from the top of tall plants to the forest floor. The ability of the wing to flap, tilt, and fold back over the body probably came later.

Another requirement for flight was the evolution of limited thermoregulatory abilities. Thermoregulation is the ability to maintain body temperatures at a level different from environmental temperatures. Achieving relatively high body temperatures, perhaps 25° C or greater, is needed for flight muscles to contract rapidly enough for flight.

Some insects use a **direct** or **synchronous flight** mechanism, in which a downward thrust of the wings results from the contraction of muscles acting on the bases of the wings. The upward thrust of the wings is accomplished by the contraction of muscles attaching dorsally and ventrally on the exoskeleton (figure 24.5a). The synchrony of direct flight mechanisms comes from the fact that each wingbeat must be preceded by a nerve impulse to the flight muscles.

Other insects use an **indirect** or **asynchronous flight** mechanism. Muscles act to change the shape of the exoskeleton for both upward and downward strokes of the wings. The upward thrust of the wing is produced by dorsoventral muscles pulling the dorsal exoskeleton downward. The downward thrust occurs when longitudinal muscles contract and cause the exoskeleton to arch upward (figure 24.5b). The power and velocity of these strokes are enhanced by the resilient properties of the exoskeleton. During a wingbeat, the thorax is deformed, and in the process, energy is stored in the exoskeleton. At a critical point midway into the downstroke, stored energy reaches a maximum, and at the same time, resistance to wing movement suddenly decreases. The wing then "clicks" through the rest of the cycle using energy stored in the exoskeleton. Asynchrony of this flight mechanism arises from the fact that there is no one-to-one correspondence between nerve impulses and wingbeats. ③ A single nerve impulse can result in approximately 50 cycles of the wing, and frequencies of 1,000 cycles per second (cps) have been recorded in some midges! The asynchrony between wingbeat and nerve impulses is dependent on flight muscles being stretched during the "click" of the thorax. The stretching of longitudinal flight muscles during the upward beat of the wing initiates the subsequent contraction of these muscles. Similarly, stretching during the downward beat of the wing initiates subsequent contraction of dorsoventral flight muscles. Indirect flight muscles are frequently called **fibrillar flight muscles.**

Simple flapping of wings is not enough for flight. The tilt of the wing must be controlled to provide lift and horizontal propulsion. In most insects, muscles that control wing tilting attach to sclerotized plates at the base of the wing.

Other Forms of Locomotion

Locomotion across the ground or other substrate is accomplished by walking, running, jumping, or swimming. When walking, insects have three or more legs on the ground at all times, creating a very stable stance. When running, fewer than three legs may be in contact with the ground. A fleeing cockroach (order Blattaria) reaches speeds of about 5 km/hour, although it seems much faster when trying to catch one. The apparent speed is the result of their small size and ability to quickly change directions. Jumping insects, such as grasshoppers (order Orthoptera), usually have long metathoracic legs in which leg musculature is enlarged to generate large, propulsive forces. Energy for a flea's (order Siphonaptera) jump is stored as elastic energy of the exoskeleton. Muscles that flex the legs distort the exoskeleton. A catch mechanism holds the legs in this "cocked" position until special muscles release the catches and allow the stored energy to quickly extend the legs. This action hurls the flea for distances that exceed 100 times its body length. ④ A comparable distance for a human long jumper would be the length of two football fields (*see figure 32.23*)!

Nutrition and the Digestive System

The diversity of insect feeding habits parallels the diversity of insects themselves. Figure 24.6 shows the head and mouthparts of an insect such as a grasshopper or cockroach. An upper, liplike

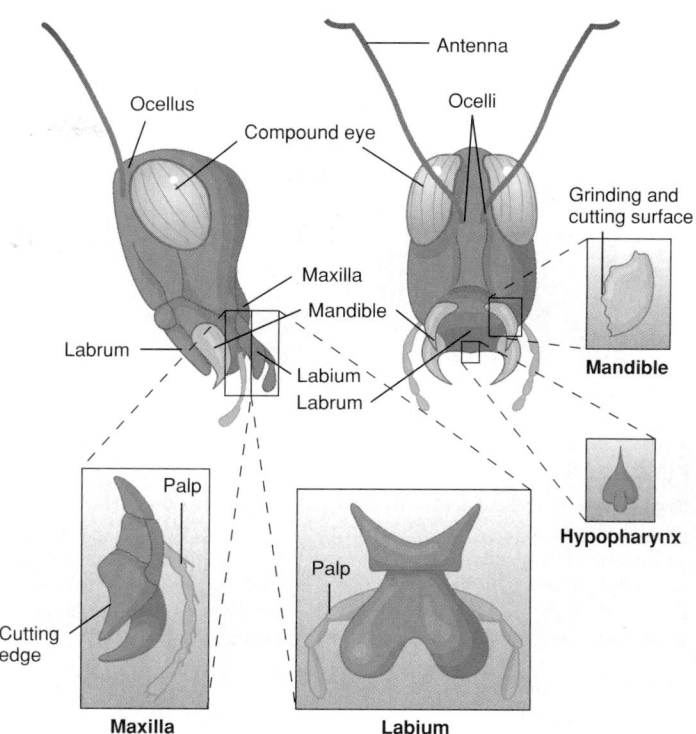

Figure 24.6

The Head and Mouthparts of a Grasshopper. All mouthparts except the labrum are derived from segmental appendages. The labrum is a sensory upper lip. The mandibles are heavily sclerotized and used for tearing and chewing. The maxillae have cutting edges and a sensory palp. The labium forms a sensory lower lip. The hypopharynx is a sensory, tonguelike structure.

structure is called the labrum. It is sensory, and unlike the remaining mouthparts, is not derived from segmental, paired appendages. Mandibles are sclerotized, chewing mouthparts. The maxillae often have cutting surfaces and bear a sensory palp. The **labium** is a sensory lower lip. All of these aid in food handling. Variations on this plan are specializations for sucking or siphoning plant or animal fluids (figure 24.7). The digestive tract, as in all arthropods, consists of a foregut, a midgut, and a hindgut (figure 24.8). Enlargements for storage and diverticula that secrete digestive enzymes are common.

Gas Exchange

Gas exchange with air requires a large surface area for the diffusion of gases. In terrestrial environments, these surfaces are also avenues for water loss. Respiratory water loss in insects, as in some arachnids, is reduced through the invagination of respiratory surfaces to form highly branched systems of chitin-lined tubes, called tracheae.

Tracheae open to the outside of the body through spiracles, which are usually provided with some kind of closure device to prevent excessive water loss. Spiracles lead to tracheal trunks that branch, eventually giving rise to smaller branches, the tracheoles. Tracheoles end intracellularly and

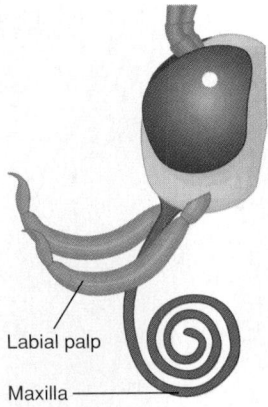

Figure 24.7

Specialization of Insect Mouthparts. The mouthparts of insects are often highly specialized for specific feeding habits. For example, the sucking mouthparts of a butterfly consist of modified maxillae that coil when not in use. Mandibles, labia, and the labrum are reduced in size. A portion of the anterior digestive tract is modified as a muscular pump for drawing liquids through the mouthparts.

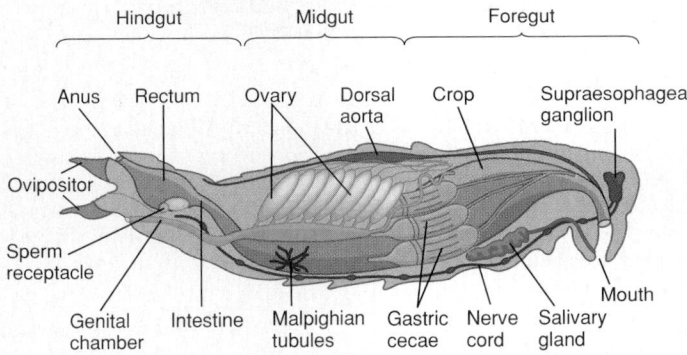

Figure 24.8

Internal Structure of a Generalized Insect. Salivary glands produce enzymes, but may be modified for the secretion of silk, anticoagulants, or pheromones. The crop is an enlargement of the foregut that is used for storing food. The proventriculus is a grinding and/or straining structure at the junction of the midgut and hindgut. Gastric cecae secrete digestive enzymes. The intestine and the rectum are modifications of the hindgut that function in absorbing water and the products of digestion.

are especially abundant in metabolically active tissues, such as flight muscles. No cells are more than 2 or 3 μm from a tracheole (figure 24.9).

Most insects have ventilating mechanisms that move air into and out of the tracheal system. For example, alternate compression and expansion of the larger tracheal trunks by contracting flight muscles ventilates the tracheae. In some insects, carbon dioxide produced by metabolically active cells is sequestered in the hemocoel as bicarbonate ions (HCO_3^-). As oxygen diffuses from the tracheae to the body tissues, and is not replaced by carbon dioxide, a vacuum is created that

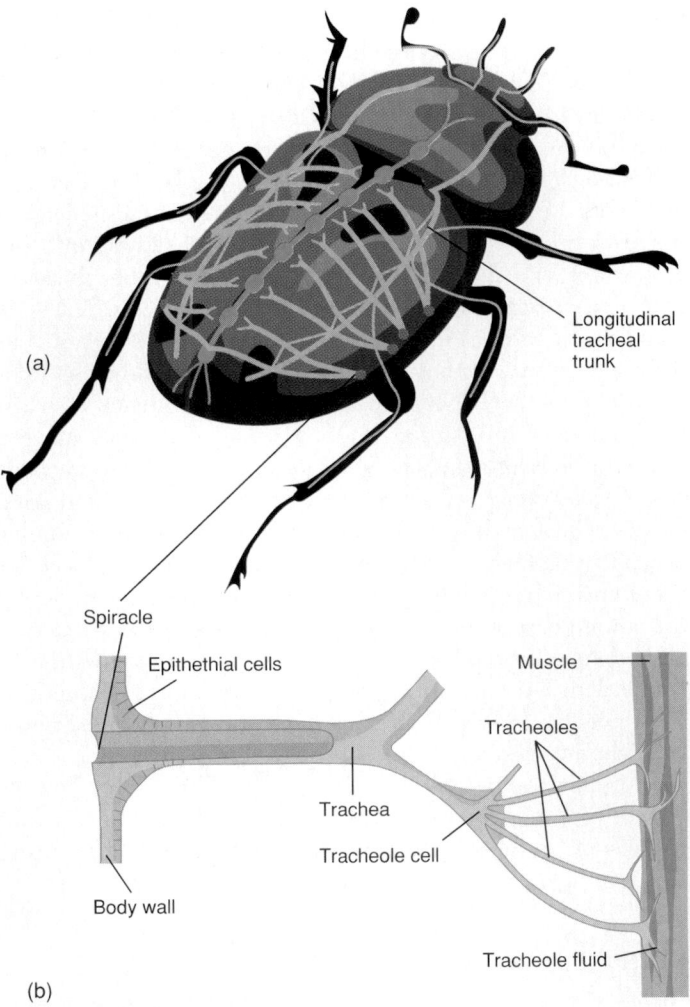

Figure 24.9

The Tracheal System of an Insect. (*a*) Major tracheal trunks. (*b*) Tracheoles end in cells, and the terminal portions of tracheoles are fluid filled.

draws more air into the spiracles. This process is called passive suction. Periodically, the sequestered bicarbonate ions are converted back into carbon dioxide, which escapes through the tracheal system. Other insects move air in and out of their tracheal systems by contracting abdominal muscles in a pump-like fashion.

Circulation and Temperature Regulation

The circulatory system of insects is similar to that described for other arthropods, although the blood vessels are less well developed. Blood distributes nutrients, hormones, and wastes, and amoeboid blood cells participate in body defense and repair mechanisms. Blood is not important in gas transport.

As described earlier, thermoregulation is a requirement for flying insects. Virtually all insects warm themselves by basking in the sun or resting on warm surfaces. Because they use external heat sources in temperature regulation, insects are generally considered to be ectotherms. Other insects (e.g., some moths, alpine bumblebees, and beetles) can generate heat by rapid contraction of flight muscles, a process called shivering thermogenesis. Metabolic heat generated in this way can raise the temperature of thoracic muscles from near 0 to 30° C. Because some insects rely to a limited extent on metabolic heat sources, they have a variable body temperature and are sometimes called heterotherms. Insects are also able to cool themselves by seeking cool, moist habitats. Honeybees can cool a hive by beating their wings at the entrance of the hive, thus circulating cooler outside air through the hive.

Stop and Ask Yourself

5. How can you recognize an arthropod as being an insect?

6. Why was the evolution of thermoregulatory abilities an important step in the evolution of flight?

7. What is indirect or asynchronous flight?

8. What are the functions of the circulatory system of insects?

NERVOUS AND SENSORY FUNCTIONS

The nervous system of insects is similar to the pattern described for annelids and other arthropods (see figure 24.8). The supraesophageal ganglion is associated with sensory structures of the head. It is joined by connectives to the subesophageal ganglion, which innervates the mouthparts and salivary glands and has a general excitatory influence on other body parts. Segmental ganglia of the thorax and abdomen undergo various degrees of fusion in different taxa. Insects also possess a well-developed visceral nervous system that innervates the gut tract, reproductive organs, and heart.

Research has demonstrated that insects are capable of some learning and have a memory. For example, bees (order Hymenoptera) instinctively recognize flowerlike objects by their shape and ability to absorb ultraviolet light, which makes the center of the flower appear dark. If a bee is rewarded with nectar and pollen, it learns the odor of the flower. Bees that feed once at artificially scented feeders choose that odor in 90% of subsequent feeding trials. Odor is a very reliable cue for bees because it is more constant than color and shape. The latter may be damaged by wind, rain, and herbivores.

Sense organs of insects are similar to those found in other arthropods, although they are usually specialized for functioning on land. Mechanoreceptors perceive physical displacement of the body or one of its parts. Setae are distributed over the mouthparts, antennae, and legs (see figure 23.10a). Displacement of setae may occur as a result of touch, air movements,

and vibrations of the substrate. Stretch receptors at the joints, on other parts of the cuticle, and on muscles monitor posture and position.

Hearing is a mechanoreceptive sense in which airborne pressure waves displace certain receptors. All insects can respond to pressure waves with generally distributed setae; others have specialized receptors. For example, **Johnston's organs** are found in the base of the antennae of most insects, including mosquitoes and midges (order Diptera). Antennae of these insects are covered with long setae that vibrate when struck by certain frequencies of sound. The vibrating setae cause the antenna to move in its socket, stimulating sensory cells. Sound waves in the frequency range of 500 to 550 cycles per second (cps) attract and elicit mating behavior of male mosquitoes (*Aedes aegypti*). These waves are in the range of the sounds produced by the wings of females. **Tympanal (tympanic) organs** are found in the legs of crickets and katydids (order Orthoptera), in the abdomen of grasshoppers (order Orthoptera) and some moths (order Lepidoptera), and in the thorax of other moths. Tympanal organs consist of a thin, cuticular membrane covering a large air sac. The air sac acts as a resonating chamber. Just under the membrane are sensory cells that detect pressure waves. Grasshopper tympanal organs can detect sounds in the range of 1,000 to 50,000 cps. (The human ear can detect sounds between 20 and 20,000 cps.) Bilateral placement of tympanal organs allows insects to discriminate the direction and origin of a sound (box 24.1).

Chemoreception is used in feeding, selection of egg-laying sites, mate location, and in some insects, social organization. Chemoreceptors are usually abundant on the mouthparts, antennae, legs, and ovipositors and take the form of hairs, pegs, pits, and plates that have one or more pores leading to internal nerve endings. Chemicals diffuse through these pores and bind to and excite nerve endings.

All insects are capable of detecting light and may use light in orientation, navigation, feeding, or other functions. **Compound eyes** are well developed in most adult insects. They are similar in structure and function to those of other arthropods, although their possible homology (of common ancestry) with those of crustaceans, horseshoe crabs, and trilobites is debated. Compound eyes consist of a few to 28,000 receptors, called **ommatidia**, that are fused into a multifaceted eye. The outer surface of each ommatidium is a lens and is one facet of the eye. Below the lens is a crystalline cone. The lens and the crystalline cone serve as light-gathering structures. Certain cells of an ommatidium, called retinula cells, have special light-collecting areas, called the rhabdom. The cells of the rhabdom convert light energy into nerve impulses. Pigment cells surround the crystalline cone, and sometimes the rhabdom, and prevent the light that strikes one rhabdom from reflecting into an adjacent ommatidium (figure 24.10).

Although many insects form an image of sorts, the concept of an image has no real significance for most species.

BOX 24.1 BAT ECHOLOCATION AND MOTH RESPONSES

Bats, some of the most successful nighttime hunters, feed on flying insects and rely on **echolocation** for finding their prey. During echolocation, bats emit ultrasonic sounds (sound at frequencies too high to be heard by humans) that reflect from flying insects back to the bats' unusually large external ears. Using this information, bats can determine the exact location of an insect and can even distinguish the kind of insect.

Noctuid moths, a prey item of these bats, possess an effective escape behavior. The tympanal organs of noctuid moths are sensitive to sounds in the 3,000 to 150,000 cps frequency range, which encompasses frequencies characteristic of a bat's cries. A weak stimulus from a bat a long distance away results in a moth flying away from the source of the sound. A stronger stimulus results in the moth's flight becoming very erratic. Often, strong stimuli result in the moth diving straight for the ground, a reflexive behavior advantageous for the moth, because sound echoing off the insect becomes indistinguishable from sound echoing off objects on the ground.

The stereotyped nature of a moth's response is explained by the structure and placement of its tympanal organs. They are located on either side of the metathoracic segment, and their bilat-

eral placement helps a moth determine the direction of incoming sound. Sound arriving from a moth's right side strikes the right tympanal organ more strongly, because the moth's body shades the left tympanal organ from sound. Thus, the moth can determine the approximate location of the predator. In addition, each receptor consists of a cuticular membrane overlying an air-filled cavity. Nerve impulses are initiated when sound waves displace the cuticular membrane and one of two sensory cells associated with the inside of the membrane. One cell, called the A_1 cell, is stimulated by relatively low-energy sound waves. These sounds are made by a bat so far away that sounds echoing off the moth would be undetectable by the bat. In this situation, a moth turns away from the source of the sound. A second cell, called the A_2 cell, is stimulated by high-energy sound waves. These sounds are made by a bat near enough to detect the moth. The response of the moth to the activity of the A_2 cell is erratic flight and/or a dive toward the ground.

The apparent complexity of some insect behavior is deceptive. It may seem as if insects make conscious decisions in their actions; however, this is seldom the case. As with a noctuid moth's evasive responses to a bat's cries, most insect behavior patterns are reflexes programmed by specific interconnections of nerve cells.

The compound eye is better suited for detecting movement. Movement of a point of light less than 0.1° can be detected as light successively strikes adjacent ommatidia. For this reason, bees are attracted to flowers blowing in the wind, and predatory insects select moving prey. Compound eyes detect wavelengths of light that the human eye cannot detect, especially in the ultraviolet end of the spectrum. In some insects, compound eyes also detect polarized light, which may be used for navigation and orientation.

Ocelli consist of 500 to 1,000 receptor cells beneath a single cuticular lens (see figure 23.10b). Ocelli are sensitive to changes in light intensity and may be important in the regulation of daily rhythms.

EXCRETION

The primary insect excretory structures are the malpighian tubules and the rectum. Malpighian tubules end blindly in the hemocoel and open to the gut tract at the junction of the midgut and the hindgut. The inner surface of their cells is covered with microvilli. Various ions are actively transported into the tubules, and water passively follows. Uric acid is secreted into the tubules and then into the gut tract, as are amino acids and ions (figure 24.11). In the rectum, water, certain ions, and other materials are reabsorbed, and the uric acid is eliminated.

As described in chapter 23, excretion of uric acid is advantageous for terrestrial animals because it is accompanied by little water loss. There is, however, an evolutionary trade-off to consider. The conversion of primary nitrogenous wastes (ammonia) to uric acid is energetically costly. It has been estimated that nearly ½ of the food energy consumed by a terrestrial insect is used to process metabolic wastes! In aquatic insects, ammonia simply diffuses out of the body into the surrounding water.

CHEMICAL REGULATION

Many physiological functions of insects, such as cuticular sclerotization, osmoregulation, egg maturation, cellular metabolism, gut peristalsis, and heart rate, are controlled by the endocrine system. As in all arthropods, ecdysis is under neuroendocrine control. In insects, the subesophageal ganglion and two endocrine glands, the corpora allata and the prothoracic glands, control these activities.

Neurosecretory cells of the subesophageal ganglion manufacture ecdysiotropin. This hormone travels in neurosecretory cells to a structure called the corpora cardiaca. The corpora cardiaca then releases thoracotropic hormone, which stimulates the prothoracic gland to secrete ecdysone. Ecdysone initiates the reabsorption of the inner portions of the procuticle and the formation of the new exoskeleton. These events are discussed further in chapter 35 (see figure 35.6). Other hormones are also in-

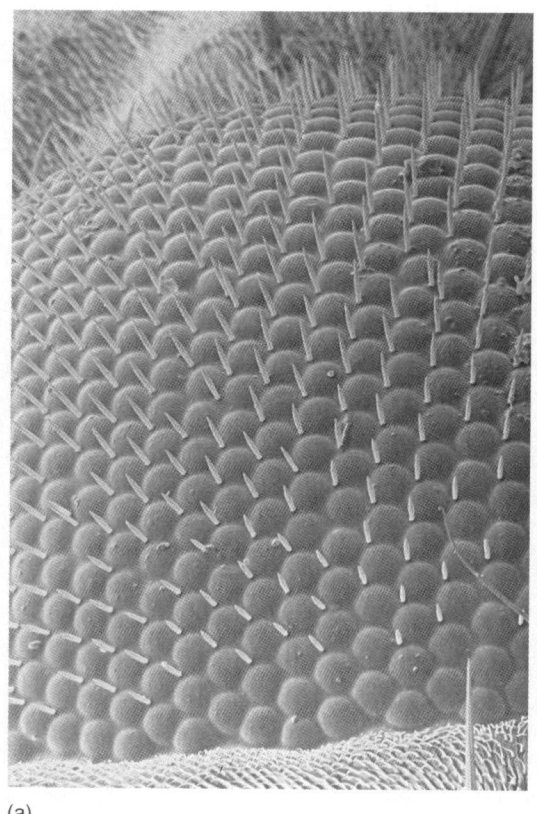

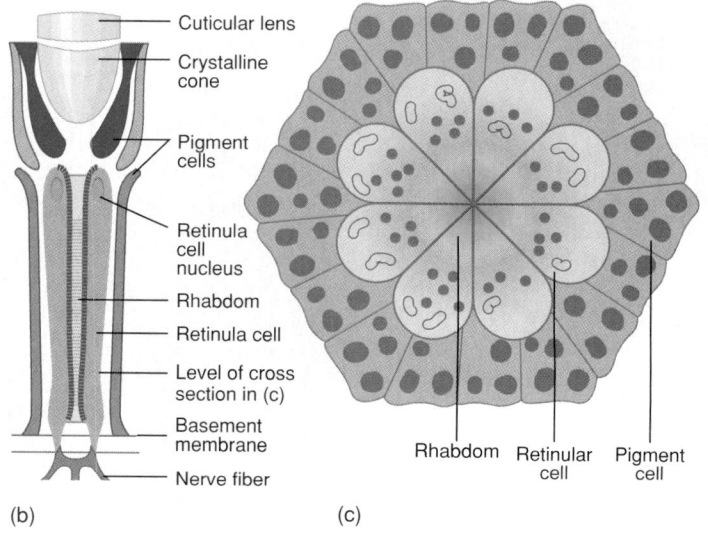

(a)   (b)   (c)

Figure 24.10

The Compound Eye of an Insect. (*a*) Scanning electron micrograph of the compound eye of *Drosophila* (×300). Each facet of the eye is the lens of a single sensory unit called an ommatidium. (*b*) The structure of an ommatidium. The lens and the crystalline cone serve as light-gathering structures. Retinula cells have light-gathering areas, called the rhabdom. Pigment cells prevent light in one ommatidium from reflecting into adjacent ommatidia. In insects that are active at night, the pigment cells are often migratory, and pigment can be concentrated around the crystalline cone. In these insects, low levels of light from widely scattered points can excite an ommatidium. (*c*) Cross section through the rhabdom region of an ommatidium.

volved in ecdysis. The recycling of materials absorbed from the procuticle, changes in metabolic rates, and pigment deposition are a few of probably many functions controlled by hormones.

In immature stages, the corpora allata produces and releases small amounts of juvenile hormone. The amount of juvenile hormone circulating in the hemocoel determines the nature of the next molt. Large concentrations of juvenile hormone result in a molt to a second immature stage. Intermediate concentrations of juvenile hormone result in a molt to a third immature stage. Low concentrations of juvenile hormone result in a molt to the adult stage. Decreases in the level of circulating juvenile hormone also lead to the degeneration of the prothoracic gland so that in most insects, no further molts occur once adulthood is reached. Interestingly, once the final molt has been accomplished, the level of juvenile hormone increases again, but now it promotes the development of accessory sexual organs, the synthesis of yolk, and the maturation of eggs.

Pheromones are chemicals released by an animal that cause behavioral or physiological changes in another member of the same species. Many different uses of pheromones by insects have

been described (table 24.2). Pheromones are often so specific that the stereoisomer (chemical mirror image) of the pheromone may be ineffective in initiating a response.   ⑥   They may be carried several kilometers by wind or water, and a few molecules falling on a chemoreceptor of another individual may be enough to elicit a response.

Stop and Ask Yourself

9. What evidence indicates that bees are capable of learning?

10. Compound eyes are particularly well suited for what visual function?

11. What are the endocrine functions that regulate ecdysis in insects?

12. What are pheromones? What are three kinds of functions they serve in insects?

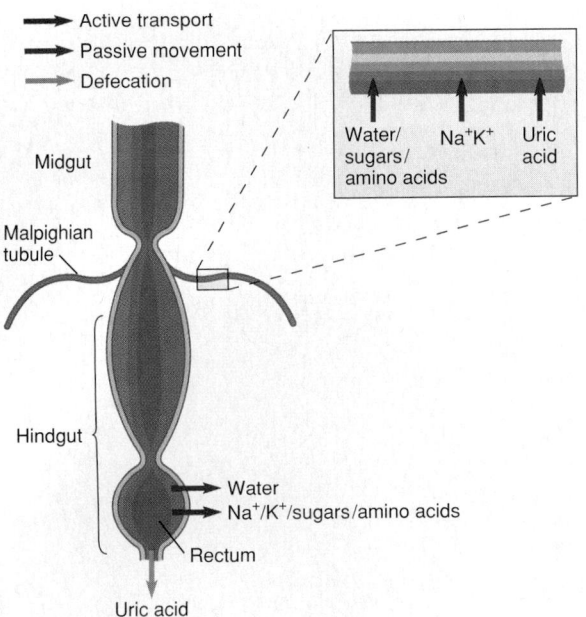

Figure 24.11

Insect Excretion. Malpighian tubules remove nitrogenous wastes from the hemocoel. Various ions are actively transported across the outer membrane of the tubule. Water follows these ions into the tubule and carries amino acids, sugars, and some nitrogenous wastes along passively. Some water, ions, and organic compounds are reabsorbed in the basal portion of the malpighian tubules and the hindgut; the rest are reabsorbed in the rectum. Uric acid moves into the hindgut and is excreted.

Reproduction and Development

One of the reasons for the success of insects is their high reproductive potential. Reproduction in terrestrial environments, however, has its risks. Temperature, moisture, and food supplies vary with the season. Internal fertilization requires highly evolved copulatory structures because gametes will dry quickly on exposure to air. In addition, mechanisms are required to bring males and females together at appropriate times.

Sexual maturity is regulated by complex interactions between internal and external environmental factors. Internal regulation includes interactions between endocrine glands (primarily the corpora allata) and reproductive organs. External regulating factors may include the quantity and quality of food. For example, the eggs of mosquitoes (order Diptera) do not mature until after the female takes a meal of blood, and the number of eggs produced is proportional to the quantity of blood ingested. The photoperiod (the relative length of daylight and darkness in a 24-hour period) is used by many insects for timing reproductive activities, because it can be used to anticipate seasonal changes. Population density, temperature, and humidity also influence reproductive activities.

A few insects, including silverfish (order Thysanura) and springtails (order Collembola) have indirect fertilization. The male deposits a spermatophore that is picked up later by the female. Most insects have a complex mating behavior that is used to locate and recognize a potential mate, to position a mate for copulation, or to pacify an aggressive mate. Mating behavior

Table 24.2 Functions of Insect Pheromones

Sex pheromones—Excite or attract members of the opposite sex; accelerate or retard sexual maturation. Example: female moths produce and release pheromones that attract males.

Caste regulating pheromones—Used by social insects to control the development of individuals in a colony. Example: the amount of "royal jelly" fed a female bee larva will determine whether the larva will become a worker or a queen.

Aggregation pheromones—Produced to attract individuals to feeding or mating sites. Example: certain bark beetles aggregate on pine trees during an attack on a tree.

Alarm pheromones—Warn other individuals of danger; may cause orientation toward the pheromone source and elicit a subsequent attack or flight from the source. Example: when one is stung by one bee, other bees in the area are alarmed and are likely to attack.

Trailing pheromones—Laid down by foraging insects to help other members of a colony identify the location and quantity of food found by one member of the colony. Example: ants can often be observed trailing on a pheromone path to and from a food source. The pheromone trail is reinforced each time an ant travels over it.

may involve the use of pheromones (moths, order Lepidoptera), visual signals (fireflies, order Coleoptera), and auditory signals (cicadas, order Homoptera; and grasshoppers, crickets, and katydids, order Orthoptera). Once other stimuli have brought the male and female together, tactile stimuli from the antennae and other appendages help position the insects for mating.

Sperm transfer is usually accomplished by abdominal copulatory appendages of the male, and sperm are stored in an outpocketing of the female reproductive tract, the sperm receptacle (see figure 24.6). Eggs are fertilized as they leave the female and are usually laid near the larval food supply. Females may use an **ovipositor** to deposit eggs in or on some substrate.

Insect Development and Metamorphosis

Insect evolution has resulted in the divergence of immature and adult body forms and habits. For insects in the superorder Endopterygota (see table 24.1), immature stages, called **larval instars,** have become a time of growth and accumulation of reserves for the transition to adulthood. The adult stage is associated with reproduction and dispersal. In these orders, there is a tendency for insects to spend a greater part of their lives in juvenile stages. The developmental patterns of insects reflect degrees of divergence between immatures and adults and are classified into three (or sometimes four) categories.

In insects that display **ametabolous** (Gr. *a*, without + *metabolos*, change) **metamorphosis,** the primary differences between adults and larvae are body size and sexual maturity.

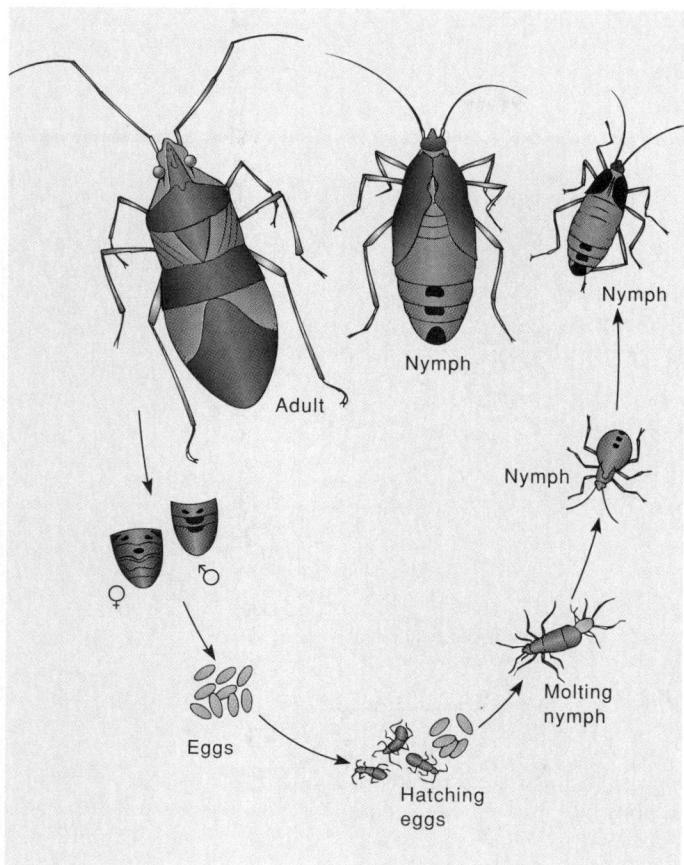

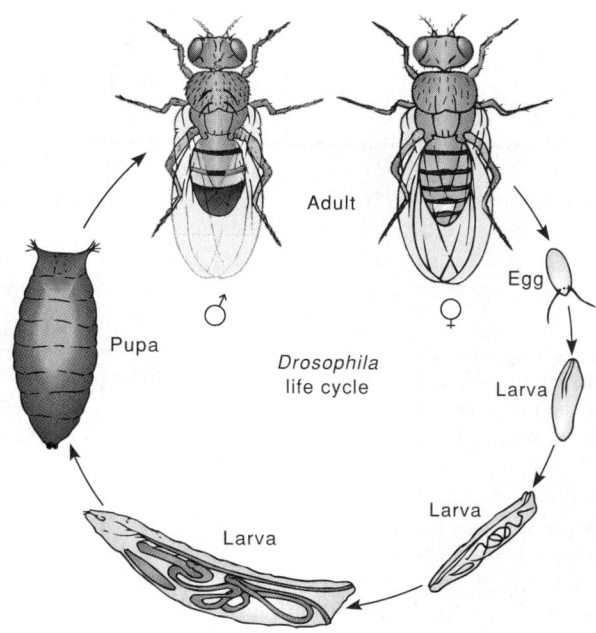

Figure 24.13

Holometabolous Development of the Fruit Fly, *Drosophila melanogaster* **(Order Diptera).** The egg hatches into a larva that is very different in form and habitat from the adult. After a certain number of larval instars, the insect pupates. During the pupal stage all characteristics of the adult are formed.

Figure 24.12

Paurometabolous Development of the Milkweed Bug, *Oncopeltus fasciatus* **(Order Hemiptera).** Eggs hatch into nymphs. Note the gradual increase in size of the nymphs and the development of external wing pads. In the adult stage, the wings are fully developed, and the insect is sexually mature.

Both adults and larvae are wingless. The number of molts in the ametabolous development of a species is variable and, unlike most other insects, molting continues after sexual maturity is reached. Silverfish (order Thysanura) have ametabolous metamorphosis.

Paurometabolous (Gr. *pauros*, small) **metamorphosis** involves a species-specific number of molts between egg and adult stages, during which immatures gradually take on the adult form. The external development of wings (except in those insects, such as lice, that have secondarily lost wings), the attainment of adult body size and proportions, and the development of genitalia occur during this time. Immatures are called **nymphs.** Grasshoppers (order Orthoptera) and milkweed bugs (order Hemiptera) show paurometabolous metamorphosis (figure 24.12).

Some authors use an additional classification for insects that have a series of gradual changes in their development, but whose immature form is much different from the adult form usually due to the presence of gills (e.g., mayflies, order Ephemeroptera; dragonflies, order Odonata). This kind

of development is called **hemimetabolous** (Gr. *hemi*, half) **metamorphosis,** and the immatures are aquatic and called **naiads** (L. *naiad*, water nymph).

In **holometabolous** (Gr. *holos*, whole) **metamorphosis,** immatures are called larvae because they are very different from the adult in body form, behavior, and habitat (figure 24.13). There is a species-specific number of larval instars, and the last larval molt forms the **pupa.** The pupa is a time of apparent inactivity but is actually a time of radical cellular change, during which all characteristics of the adult insect take form. The pupal stage may be enclosed in a protective case. A **cocoon** is constructed partially or entirely from silk by the last larval instar (e.g., moths, order Lepidoptera). The **chrysalis** (e.g., butterflies, order Lepidoptera) and **puparium** (e.g., flies, order Diptera) are the last larval exoskeletons and are retained through the pupal stage. Other insects (e.g., mosquitoes, order Diptera) have pupae that are unenclosed by a larval exoskeleton, and the pupa may be active. The final molt to the adult stage usually occurs within the cocoon, chrysalis, or puparium, and the adult then exits, frequently using its mandibles to open the cocoon or other enclosure. This final process is called emergence or eclosion.

Insect Behavior

Insects have many complex behavior patterns (*see box 24.1*). Most of these are innate (genetically programmed). For example, a newly emerged queen in a honeybee hive will search out and try to destroy other queen larvae and pupae in the hive.

BOX 24.2   COMMUNICATION IN HONEYBEES

The exploitation of food sources by honeybees has been studied for decades, but its study still offers important challenges for zoologists. One of these areas of research concerns the extent to which honeybees communicate the location of food to other bees. A worker bee that returns to a hive laden with nectar and pollen stimulates other experienced workers to leave the hive and visit productive pollen and nectar sources. Inexperienced workers are also recruited to leave the hive and search for nectar and pollen, but stronger stimuli are needed to elicit their searching behavior. In the darkness of the hive, the incoming bee performs what researchers have described as a round dance and a waggle dance. Throughout the dancing, other workers contact the dancing bee with their antennae and mouthparts, picking up the odors associated with pollen, nectar, and other objects in the vicinity of the incoming bee's food source. During the dance, the incoming bee moves first in a semicircle to the left, then in a straight course to the starting point. Next, she follows a semicircle to the right, and then another straight course to the starting point. During the linear parts of the dance, the abdomen of the bee moves in a waggling fashion (figure 1). These stimuli apparently encourage inexperienced workers to leave the hive and begin searching for food. As described in the text, their search relies heavily on olfaction, and workers tend to be attracted to pollen and nectar similar to that brought back to the hive by the dancing bee.

The round and waggle dances may also convey information on location of a food source. Biologists have found that information regarding the direction and distance of a food source from the hive are contained in the dance. The angle that the waggle dance makes with the vertical of the comb approximates the angle between the

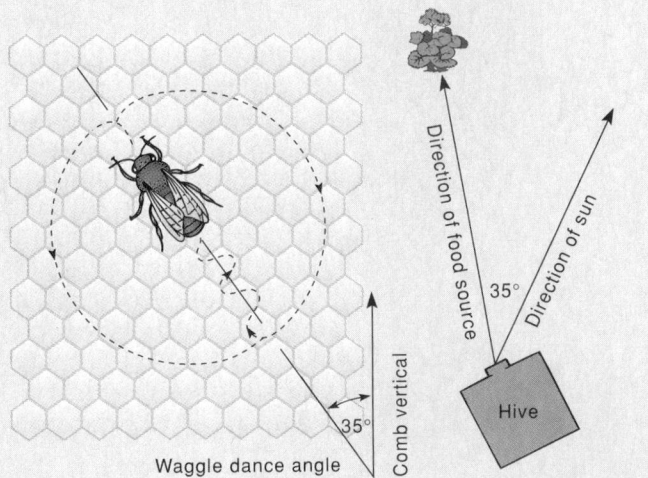

FIGURE 1   Insect Communication. The waggle dance of the honeybee. *From: "A LIFE OF INVERTEBRATES" © 1979 W. D. Russell-Hunter.*

sun and the food source (figure 1). Similarly, the number of straight line runs per unit time, the duration of sounds made during the dance, and the number of waggles during the dance vary with the distance of the food source from the hive.

These observations indicate that bees communicate information regarding distance, direction, and kind of food to other bees when returning from a foraging trip. Thus, the exploitation of pollen and nectar is a very efficient process and is one source of evidence of the highly evolved nature of the honeybee colony.

This behavior is innate because no experiences taught the potential queen that her survival in the hive required the death or dispersal of all other potential queens. Similarly, no experience taught her how queen-rearing cells differ from the cells containing worker larvae and pupae. Some insects are capable of learning and remembering and these abilities play important roles in insect behavior.

Social Insects

The evolution of social behavior has occurred in many insects, and is particularly evident in those insects that live in colonies (box 24.2). Usually, different members of the colony are specialized, often structurally as well as behaviorally, for performing different tasks. Social behavior is most highly evolved in the bees, wasps, and ants (order Hymenoptera) and termites (order Isoptera). Each kind of individual in an insect colony is called a **caste.** Often, three or four castes are present in a colony. Reproductive females are referred to as queens. Workers may be sterile males and females (termites) or sterile females

(Hymenoptera) and are involved with support, protection, and maintenance of the colony. Their reproductive organs are often degenerate. Reproductive males inseminate the queen(s) and are called kings or drones. Soldiers are usually sterile and may possess large mandibles to defend the colony.

Honeybees (order Hymenoptera) have three of the above castes in their colonies (figure 24.14). A single queen lays all the eggs. Workers are female and they construct the comb out of wax that they produce. They also gather nectar and pollen, feed the queen and drones, care for the larvae, and guard and clean the hive. These tasks are divided among workers according to age. Younger workers take care of jobs around the hive, and older workers forage for nectar and pollen. Except for those that overwinter, workers live for about 1 month. Drones develop from unfertilized eggs, do not work, and are fed by workers until they leave the hive to attempt mating with a queen.

⑦   The honeybee caste system is controlled by a pheromone released by the queen. Workers lick and groom the queen and other workers. In so doing, they pick up and pass to

(a)   (b)   (c)

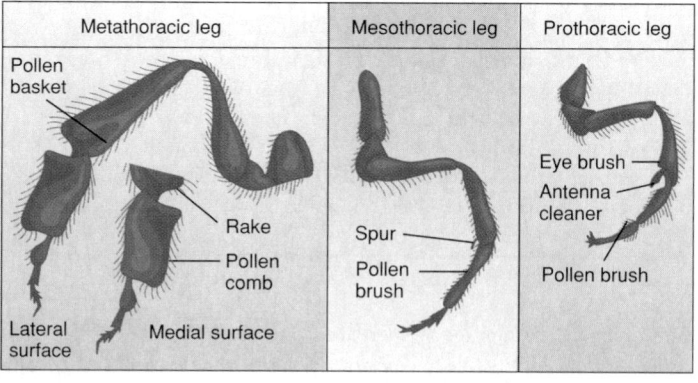

(d)

Figure 24.14

Honeybees (Order Hymenoptera). Honeybees have a social organization consisting of three castes. The castes are distinguished by overall body size, as well as the size of their eyes. (*a*) A worker bee. (*b*) A drone bee. (*c*) A queen bee. (*d*) The inner surface of metathoracic legs have setae, called the pollen comb, that remove pollen from the mesothoracic legs and the abdomen. Pollen is then compressed into a solid mass by being squeezed in a pollen press and moved to a pollen basket on the outer surface of the leg, where the pollen is carried. The mesothoracic legs are used for gathering pollen from body parts. The prothoracic legs of a worker bee are used to clean pollen from the antennae and body.

other workers a caste-regulating pheromone. This pheromone inhibits the rearing of new queens by workers. As the queen ages, or if she dies, the amount of caste-regulating pheromone in the hive decreases. As the pheromone decreases, workers begin to feed the food for queens ("royal jelly"), to several female larvae that are developing in the hive. This food contains chemicals that promote development of queen characteristics. The larvae that receive royal jelly develop into queens, and as they emerge, the new queens begin to eliminate each other until only one remains. The queen that remains goes on a mating flight and returns to the colony, where she will live for several years.

The evolution of social behavior with many individuals leaving no offspring and where individuals are sacrificed for the perpetuation of the colony has puzzled evolutionists for many

years. It may be explained by the concepts of kin selection and altruism, which were discussed in chapter 13.

Insects and Humans

Only about 0.5% of insect species adversely affect human health and welfare (box 24.3). Many others have provided valuable services throughout human history. Commercially valuable insect products, such as wax, honey, and silk have been utilized by humans for thousands of years. Insects are responsible for the pollination of approximately 65% of all plant species. Insects and flowering plants have coevolutionary relationships that directly benefit humans. The annual value of insect-pollinated crops is estimated at 19 billion dollars per year in the United States.

Insects also serve as agents of biological control. The classic example of the regulation of a potentially harmful insect by another insect is the control of cottony-cushion scale by vedalia (lady bird) beetles. The scale insect, *Icerya purchasi*, was introduced into California in the 1860s. Within 20 years, the citrus industry in California was virtually destroyed. The vedalia beetle (*Vedalia cardinalis*) was brought to the United States in 1888 and 1889 and cultured on trees infested with scale. In just a few years, the scale was under control, and the citrus industry began to recover.

There are many other beneficial insects. Soil-dwelling insects play important roles in aeration, drainage, and turnover of soil, and they promote decay processes. Other insects serve important roles in food webs. Insects are used in teaching and research and have contributed to advances in genetics, population ecology, and physiology. Insects have also given endless hours of pleasure to those who collect them and enjoy their beauty.

Some insects, however, are parasites and vectors of disease. Parasitic insects include head, body, and pubic lice (order Anoplura); bed bugs (order Hemiptera); and fleas (order Siphonaptera). Other insects transmit disease-causing microorganisms, nematodes, and flatworms. The impact of insect-transmitted diseases, such as malaria, yellow fever, bubonic plague, encephalitis, leishmaniasis, and typhus, has changed the course of history (*see box 17.2*).

Other insects are pests of domestic animals and plants. Some reduce the health of domestic animals and the quality of animal products. Insects feed on crops and transmit diseases of plants, such as Dutch elm disease, potato virus, and asters yellow. Annual lost revenue from insect damage to crops or insect-transmitted diseases in the United States is approximately 5 billion dollars.

Further Phylogenetic Considerations

A fundamental question regarding arthropod evolution concerns whether or not the arthropod taxa represent fundamentally different evolutionary lineages. Many zoologists believe that the living arthropods should be divided into three separate

<table>
<tr><td>

BOX 24.3   "KILLER BEES?"

</td></tr>
</table>

The "African bee," *Apis mellifera scutellata*, is common in most parts of Africa. It is a small bee and is adapted to warm climates with extended dry seasons. In its home range, it has many enemies, including humans and birds. Aggressive behavior and frequent swarming have allowed colonies to escape predation and survive drought.

In 1956, a few *Apis mellifera scutellata* queens were imported to Brazil in hopes of breeding these queens with local stocks to create bees better adapted to tropical climates than were the local bees. (Bees of the Americas were imported from Europe in the 1600s.) A few of these queens escaped captivity and hybridized with local bees. (It is really not accurate to refer to the hybridized bees as "African bees," "Africanized bees," or "killer bees." Their reputation as "killers" has been exaggerated. Most authorities now refer to hybridized bees as Brazilian bees.) Many of the qualities that allowed the African bee to succeed in Africa allowed these Brazilian bees to spread 100 to 200 mi/year. Their frequent swarming and their ability to nest in relatively open shelters gives a

distinct selective advantage over the bees imported from Europe many years earlier. By 1969, Brazilian bees had spread to Argentina; by 1973, to Venezuela; and by early 1980, they had crossed the Panama Canal. Mexico presented few barriers to their spread toward the southern United States, and they have now crossed the border into the southwestern United States. How far will Brazilian bees ultimately spread? An educated guess may be made by looking at the distribution of the African bee in Africa. African bees cannot overwinter outside of tropical regions. Similarly, the Brazilian bee will likely be limited in America to the warmer latitudes.

The primary implications of the spread of Brazilian bees has less to do with threats to human health than to the health of the beekeeping industry. The unpleasant temperament of these bees can be dealt with by wearing protective clothing. More formidable problems associated with the culture of these bees include their tendency to swarm and their lower productivity. Swarming for a beekeeper means the loss of bees and a lowered honey production. Frequent swarming makes profitable beekeeping almost impossible.

phyla: Chelicerata, Crustacea, and Uniramia. A polyphyletic origin of these groups implies convergent evolution of remarkably similar arthropodan features in all three (or at least two of three) phyla. Although there is evidence for dual origins of tracheae, mandibles, and compound eyes, convergence in all other arthropod traits seems unlikely to many zoologists.

This textbook assumes a monophyletic origin of the arthropods. Given this assumption, the phylogenetic relationships within the Arthropoda are also debated. Members of all four subphyla are present in the fossil record from the early Paleozoic era, and there currently are no known fossils of arthropods from Precambrian times. The fossil record, therefore, is of little help in discovering the evolutionary relationships among the arthropod subphyla. Zoologists must rely on comparative anatomy, comparative embryology, and molecular studies to investigate these relationships.

Central to the questions surrounding arthropod phylogeny are two important issues. One issue is whether or not the biramous limbs of crustaceans and trilobites are homologous. Homology of these appendages would imply that the trilobites were closely related to the crustaceans; therefore, many zoologists view the trilobites as an important ancestral group. It is possible to envision crustaceans, and possibly the arachnids, arising from the trilobites, but it is more difficult to envision a similar origin for the myriapods and insects. A second important issue is whether or not the

mandibles of uniramians and crustaceans are homologous. Superficially, the mandibles of members of these groups are structurally similar and have similar functions. Muscle arrangements and methods of articulation, however, are different enough that many zoologists doubt that these appendages are homologous. Discussions of arthropod phylogeny also center around the origins and possible homologies of arthropod compound eyes, tracheal systems, and malpighian tubules.

Depending on how these issues have been interpreted, a number of hypotheses regarding the relationships of the arthropod subphyla have been presented. Two of these hypotheses are shown in figure 24.15. In figure 24.15a, the Uniramia and the Crustacea are depicted as being closely related. This hypothesis emphasizes possible homologies between the mandibles, compound eyes, and other structures of these two groups. In figure 24.15b, the Uniramia are shown diverging independently of the Chelicerata and Crustacea. The latter two subphyla are depicted as being closely related to the trilobites. This figure implies that the mandibles of the crustaceans and uniramians are not homologous and that the biramous appendages of the crustaceans and trilobites are homologous.

Questions regarding the evolutionary relationships within the arthropods are difficult to answer. These questions will probably remain unanswered until new fossils are discovered or data from molecular studies provide more information on ancestral arthropods.

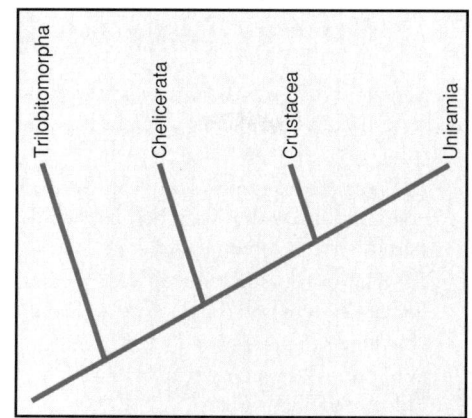

(a)

(b)

Figure 24.15

Two Interpretations of Arthropod Phylogeny. A number of interpretations of arthropod phylogeny are possible. (*a*) Some zoologists think that the crustaceans and uniramians are closely related. Evidence for this hypothesis comes from possible homologies of mandibles, compound eyes, and other characters within the groups. (*b*) Other zoologists prefer to think of the uniramians as being more distantly related to other arthropods. Note that the trilobites are depicted here as an important ancestral group of arthropods. The many characters used in establishing these cladograms are not shown in these figures in order to simplify the presentation.

Stop and Ask Yourself

13. What is the sequence of changes that occurs in the life history of a holometabolous insect?

14. What are three castes in a honeybee hive and how is the caste system regulated?

15. What is the nature of the debate regarding arthropod phylogeny?

SUMMARY

1. During the Devonian period, insects began to exploit terrestrial environments. Flight, the exoskeleton, and metamorphosis are probably keys to insect success.

2. Myriapods include four classes of arthropods. Members of the class Diplopoda are the millipedes and are characterized by apparent segments bearing two pairs of legs. The centipedes are in the class Chilopoda. They are characterized by a single pair of legs on each of their 15 segments and a body that is flattened in cross section. The class Pauropoda contains soft-bodied animals that feed on fungi and decaying organic matter in forest-floor litter. Members of the class Symphyla are centipedelike arthropods that live in soil and leaf mold, where they feed on decaying vegetation.

3. Animals in the class Hexapoda are characterized by a head with one pair of antennae, compound eyes, and ocelli; a thorax with three pairs of legs and usually two pairs of wings; and an abdomen that is free of appendages except terminal sensory (cerci) and reproductive (ovipositor) structures.

4. Insect flight involves either a direct (synchronous) flight mechanism or an indirect (asynchronous) flight mechanism.

5. Mouthparts of insects are adapted for chewing, piercing, and/or sucking, and the gut tract may be modified for pumping, storage, digestion, and water conservation.

6. Gas exchange occurs through a tracheal system.

7. The insect nervous system is similar to that of other arthropods. Sensory structures include tympanal organs, compound eyes, and ocelli.

8. Malpighian tubules transport uric acid to the digestive tract. Conversion of nitrogenous wastes to uric acid conserves water but is energetically expensive.

9. Hormones regulate many insect functions, including ecdysis and metamorphosis. Pheromones are chemicals emitted by one individual that alter the behavior of another member of the same species.

10. Insect adaptations for reproduction on land include resistant eggs, external genitalia, and behavioral mechanisms that bring males and females together at appropriate times.

11. Metamorphosis of an insect may be ametabolous, paurometabolous, hemimetabolous, or holometabolous. Metamorphosis is controlled by neuroendocrine and endocrine secretions.

12. Insects show both innate and learned behavior.

13. Many insects are beneficial to humans, and a few are parasites and/or transmit diseases of humans or agricultural products. Others attack cultivated plants and stored products.

14. Whether the arthropods represent a monophyletic group or a polyphyletic group is a question that is still being debated.

SELECTED KEY TERMS

ametabolous metamorphosis
  (*p. 392*)
caste (*p. 394*)
direct or synchronous flight
  (*p. 386*)
hemimetabolous metamorphosis
  (*p. 393*)
holometabolous metamorphosis
  (*p. 393*)

indirect or asynchronous flight
  (*p. 386*)
larval instars (*p. 392*)
nymphs (*p. 393*)
paurometabolous metamorphosis
  (*p. 393*)
pupa (*p. 393*)

CRITICAL THINKING QUESTIONS

1. What are the problems associated with living and reproducing in terrestrial environments? Explain how insects overcome these problems.
2. List as many examples as you can think of how insects communicate with each other. In each case, what is the form and purpose of the communication?
3. In what way does holometabolous metamorphosis reduce competition between immature and adult stages? Give specific examples.
4. What role does each stage play in the life history of holometabolous insects?
5. Some biologists think that the arthropods are a polyphyletic group. What does that mean? What would polyphyletic origins require in terms of the origin of the exoskeleton and its derivatives?

Some Lesser Known Invertebrates: Possible Arthropod Relatives

Three Phyla of Uncertain Affiliation: The Onychophora, Pentastomida, and Tardigrada

Animals in the phyla Onychophora, Pentastomida, and Tardigrada show a combination of arthropod and nonarthropod characteristics.

Phylum Onychophora: The Onychophorans, Velvet Worms or Walking Worms

The onychophorans (on-y-kof'o-rans) (Gr. *onyx*, claw + *pherein*, to bear), also known as velvet or walking worms, are free-living terrestrial animals that live in certain humid, tropical regions. Their ancestors have been considered an evolutionary transition between annelids and arthropods because of their many similarities to both phyla. These interesting worms may live up to 6 years. More than 100 species have been described, with *Peripatus* being the best-known genus.

Onychophorans usually come out at night and move by using their unjointed legs to crawl (figure 1). Most species are predaceous and feed on small invertebrates. In order to capture fast-moving prey, onychophorans secrete an adhesive slime (produced in their adhesive gland) from their oral papillae. Some species can eject a stream of slime with enough force to strike a prey animal 50 cm away. The slime hardens immediately, entangling the prey which is then masticated with the mandibles and sucked into the mouth.

The sexes are separate and fertilization is internal. Onychophorans are either oviparous or viviparous. The oviparous species lay large, yolky eggs, each enclosed in a shell, in moist places; cleavage is spiral. The viviparous species retain the embryos in the uterus.

(a)

(b)

Figure 1 **Phylum Onychophora.** (*a*) *Peripatus.* (*b*) Lateral view of the internal anatomy of a female. The anterior end consists of two large antennae and ventral mouth. The mouth is surrounded by oral papillae and clawlike mandibles analogous to those of arthropods. The legs vary in number from 14 to 43 pairs; each leg has a pair of terminal claws. The entire surface of the body is covered by large and small tubercles that are covered by small scales and arranged in rings or bands.

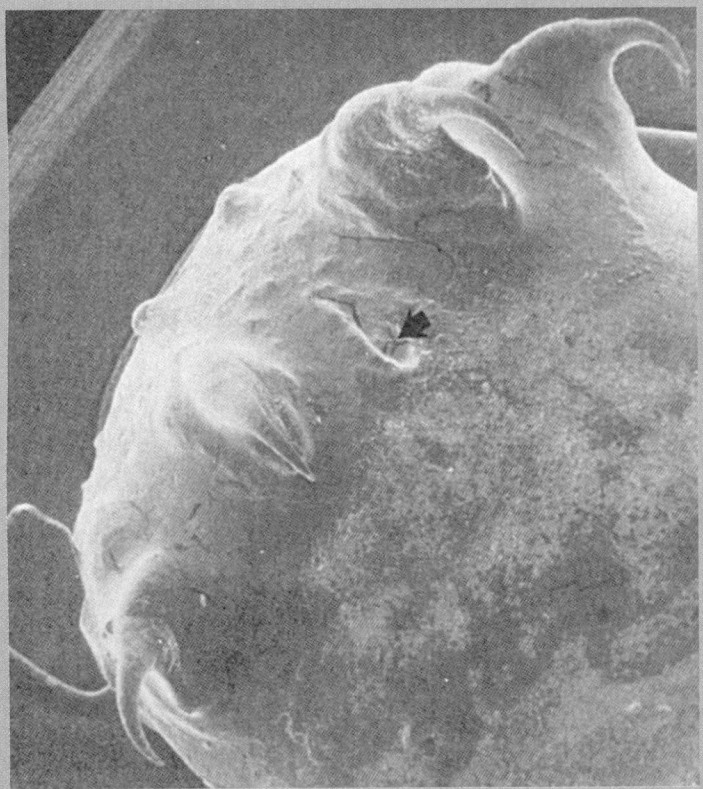

FIGURE 3   **Phylum Tardigrada.** Scanning electron micrograph of the tardigrade, *Macrobiotus tonolli.* The body is elongate, cylindrical, unsegmented, and has four pairs of unsegmented legs with claws. The entire body is covered with a proteinaceous cuticle that is periodically molted (×1,080).

FIGURE 2   **Phylum Pentastomida.** Close-up view of the hooks used by pentastomids to attach to their hosts. Note the mouth between the middle hooks (arrow). When feeding, a pentastomid grasps the host tissue with its clawed legs, inflicting a wound. The mouth is applied to the wound, and blood and tissue fluid are sucked into the worm.

PHYLUM PENTASTOMIDA: THE PENTASTOMIDS, OR TONGUE WORMS

The pentastomids (pent-ta-stom'ids) (Gr. *pente*, five + *stoma*, mouth) or tongue worms are all endoparasitic in the lungs or nasal passageways of carnivorous vertebrates (figure 2). Ninety percent of pentastomids' hosts are reptiles (e.g., snakes, lizards, crocodiles). There are about 90 species; two of the more well-known genera are *Linguatula* and *Raillietiella.*

Pentastomids are dioecious, and females are larger than males. Gonads are unpaired, and gonopores open to the outside. Male and female pentastomids mate in the final host. Following internal fertilization, females lay millions of shelled eggs, which pass out in the host's nasal secretions, saliva, or feces. If the eggs are eaten by one of a variety of vertebrate intermediate hosts, the larvae develop. The larva is characterized by having four to six arthropodlike jointed appendages. When the intermediate host is eaten by a final host, the larva is freed by the digestive enzymes and it migrates up the esophagus to the lungs, trachea, or nasal sinuses. Just as in the arthropods, pentastomids possess a brain and ventral nerve cord with ganglia and a hemocoel.

PHYLUM TARDIGRADA: THE TARDIGRADES, OR WATER BEARS

The tardigrades (tar-di-gray'ds) (L. *tardus*, slow + *gradus*, step) are commonly called water bears because of their body shape and legs and the way they lumber over aquatic vegetation (figure 3). These small animals (less than 1 mm in length) live in marine interstitial areas, in freshwater detritus, and in the water film on terrestrial lichens, liverworts, and mosses. There are about 500 species; the most common genera are *Echiniscus, Echiniscoides,* and *Macrobiotus.*

Tardigrades are dioecious with a single gonad dorsal to the midgut. A single oviduct or sperm duct empties into a gonopore. Fertilization is internal. Several dozen ornate eggs are laid by the female. After about 2 weeks, a juvenile hatches from the egg, molts, and develops into an adult. In some moss-dwelling species, males are rare or have never been observed, and parthenogenic reproduction presumably occurs.

Tardigrades (as well as nematodes and many rotifers) are able to enter a period of suspended animation termed cryptobiosis (Gr. *kryptos*, hidden + *bios*, life). This ability offers great survival benefit to these animals that live in habitats where conditions can suddenly become adverse. If a tardigrade begins to dry out (desiccate), it contracts into a shape that produces an ordered packing of organs and tissues to minimize mechanical damage caused by the desiccation. Overall metabolism slows. When rehydration occurs, the above events are reversed. Interestingly, repeated periods of cryptobiosis can extend a life span of approximately 1 year to 60 to 70 years.

chapter 25

THE ECHINODERMS

Concepts

1. Echinoderms are a part of the deuterostome evolutionary lineage. They are characterized by pentaradial symmetry, a calcium carbonate internal skeleton, and a water-vascular system.
2. Although there are many classes of extinct echinoderms, living echinoderms are divided into six classes. These are Asteroidea—the sea stars, Ophiuroidea—brittle stars and basket stars, Echinoidea—sea urchins and sand dollars, Holothuroidea—sea cucumbers, Crinoidea—sea lilies and feather stars, and Concentricycloidea—sea daisies.
3. Pentaradial symmetry of echinoderms probably developed during the evolution of sedentary life-styles, in which the water-vascular system was used in suspension feeding. Later, evolution resulted in some echinoderms becoming more mobile, and the water-vascular system came to be used primarily in locomotion.

Would You Like to Know:

1. what evidence links echinoderms and chordates to a common evolutionary pathway? (*p. 402*)
2. why most sea stars have five arms, rather than four or six? (*p. 403*)
3. how a sea star can open the shell of a clam? (*p. 405*)
4. how brittle stars use their snakelike arms? (*p. 407*)
5. what sea urchins use to chew through rock and coral? (*p. 410*)
6. how sea cucumbers "spill their insides" for a predator or a collector? (*p. 411*)
7. what the most recently discovered class of living echinoderms is? (*p. 413*)
8. what the original function of the water-vascular system was? (*p. 413*)

These and other useful questions will be answered in this chapter.

This chapter contains evolutionary concepts, which are set off in this font.

Evolutionary Perspective

If one could visit 400-million-year-old Paleozoic seas, one would see representatives of nearly every phylum studied in the previous eight chapters of this textbook. In addition, one would observe many representatives of the phylum Echinodermata (i-ki'na-dur"ma-tah) (Gr. *echinos*, spiny + *derma*, skin + *ata*, to bear). Many ancient echinoderms were attached to their substrate and probably lived as filter feeders—a feature found in only one class of modern echinoderms (figure 25.1). Today, we know this phylum by the relatively common sea stars, sea urchins, sand dollars, and sea cucumbers. In terms of numbers of species, echinoderms may seem to be a declining phylum. Studies of fossil records indicate that about 12 of 18 classes of echinoderms have become extinct. That does not mean, however, that living echinoderms are of minor importance. Members of three classes of echinoderms have flourished and often make up a major component of the biota of marine ecosystems (table 25.1).

Characteristics of the phylum Echinodermata include the following:

1. Calcareous endoskeleton in the form of ossicles that arise from mesodermal tissue
2. Adults with pentaradial symmetry and larvae with bilateral symmetry
3. Water-vascular system composed of water-filled canals used in locomotion, attachment, and/or feeding
4. Complete digestive tract that may be secondarily reduced
5. Hemal system derived from coelomic cavities
6. Nervous system consisting of a nerve net, nerve ring, and radial nerves

Relationships to Other Animals

Most zoologists believe that echinoderms share a common ancestry with hemichordates and chordates. ① Evidence of these evolutionary ties is seen in the deuterostome characteristics that they share (*see figure 21.3*): an anus that develops in the region of the blastopore, a coelom that forms from outpockets of the embryonic gut tract (vertebrate chordates are an exception), and radial, indeterminate cleavage. Unfortunately, no fossils have been discovered that document a common ancestor for these phyla or that demonstrate how the deuterostome lineage was derived from ancestral diploblastic or triploblastic stocks (figure 25.2).

Although adults are radially symmetrical, it is generally accepted that echinoderms evolved from bilaterally symmetrical ancestors. Evidence for this relationship includes bilaterally symmetrical echinoderm larval stages and extinct forms which were not radially symmetrical.

Echinoderm Characteristics

There are approximately 7,000 species of living echinoderms. They are exclusively marine and occur at all depths in all oceans. Modern echinoderms have a form of radial symmetry, called **pentaradial symmetry,** in which body parts are arranged

Figure 25.1

Phylum Echinodermata. This feather star (*Comanthina*) uses its highly branched arms in filter feeding. Although this probably reflects the original use of echinoderm appendages, most modern echinoderms use arms for locomotion, capturing prey, and scavenging the substrate for food.

TABLE 25.1	CLASSIFICATION OF THE PHYLUM ECHINODERMATA

Phylum Echinodermata (i-ki'na-dur"ma-tah).
The phylum of triploblastic, coelomate animals whose members are pentaradially symmetrical as adults, possess an endoskeleton covered by epithelium, and possess a water-vascular system. Pedicellaria often present.

Class Crinoidea (kri-noi'de-ah)
Free-living or attached by an aboral stalk of ossicles; flourished in the Paleozoic era; approximately 230 living species. Sea lilies, feather stars.

Class Asteroidea (as'te-roi"de-ah)
Rays not sharply set off from central disk; ambulacral grooves with tube feet; suction disks on tube feet; pedicellariae present. Sea stars.

Class Ophiuroidea (o-fe-u-roi"de-ah)
Arms sharply marked off from the central disk; tube feet without suction disks. Brittle stars.

Class Concentricycloidea (kon-sen'tri-si-kloi"de-ah)
Two concentric water-vascular rings encircle a disklike body; no digestive system; digest and absorb nutrients across their lower surface; internal brood pouches; no free-swimming larval stage. Sea daisies.

Class Echinoidea (ek'i-noi"de-ah)
Globular or disk shaped; no rays; movable spines; skeleton (test) of closely fitting plates. Sea urchins, sand dollars.

Class Holothuroidea (hol'o-thu-roi"de-ah)
No rays; elongate along the oral-aboral axis; microscopic ossicles embedded in a muscular body wall; circumoral tentacles. Sea cucumbers.

This listing reflects a phylogenetic sequence; however, the discussion that follows begins with the echinoderms that are familiar to most students.

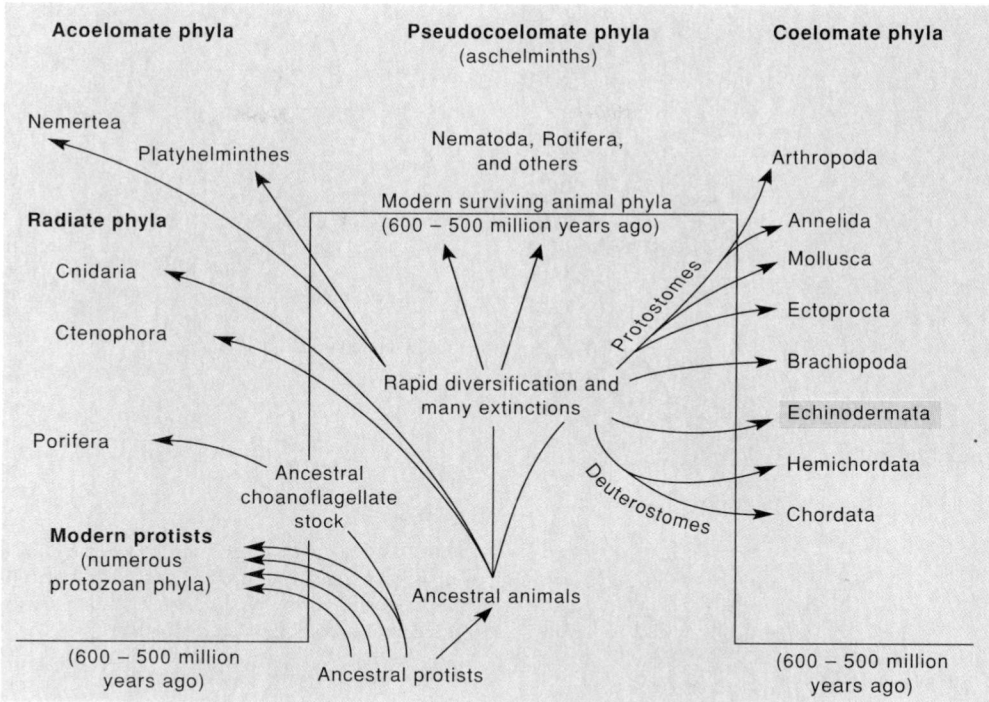

FIGURE 25.2

Evolutionary Relationships of the Echinoderms. The echinoderms (shaded in orange) diverged from the deuterostomate lineage at least 600 million years ago. Although modern echinoderms are pentaradially symmetrical, the earliest echinoderms were probably bilaterally symmetrical.

in fives, or a multiple of five, around an oral-aboral axis (figure 25.3a). Radial symmetry is adaptive for sedentary or slowly moving animals because it allows a uniform distribution of sensory, feeding, and other structures around the animal. Some modern mobile echinoderms, however, have secondarily returned to a basically bilateral form.

The skeleton of echinoderms consists of a series of calcium carbonate plates called ossicles. These plates are derived from mesoderm, held in place by connective tissues, and covered by an epidermal layer. If the epidermal layer is abraded away, the skeleton may be exposed in some body regions. The skeleton is frequently modified into fixed or articulated spines that project from the body surface.

② The evolution of the skeleton may be responsible for the pentaradial body form of echinoderms. The joints between two skeletal plates represent a weak point in the skeleton (figure 25.3b). By not having weak joints directly opposite one another, the skeleton is made stronger than if the joints were arranged opposite each other.

The **water-vascular system** of echinoderms is a series of water-filled canals, and their extensions are called tube feet. It originates embryologically as a modification of the coelom and is ciliated internally. The water-vascular system includes a ring canal that surrounds the mouth (figure 25.4). The ring canal usually opens to the outside or to the body cavity through a stone canal and a sievelike plate, called the madreporite. The

madreporite may serve as an inlet to replace water lost from the water-vascular system and may help equalize pressure differences between the water-vascular system and the outside. Tiedemann bodies are swellings that are often associated with the ring canal. They are believed to be the site for production of phagocytic cells, called coelomocytes, whose functions will be described later in this chapter. Polian vesicles are sacs that are also associated with the ring canal and function in fluid storage for the water-vascular system.

Five (or a multiple of five) radial canals branch from the ring canal. Radial canals are associated with arms of star-shaped echinoderms. In other echinoderms, they may be associated with the body wall and arch toward the aboral pole. Many lateral canals branch off each radial canal and end at the tube feet.

Tube feet are extensions of the canal system and usually emerge through openings in skeletal ossicles (*see figure 25.3a*). Internally, tube feet usually terminate in a bulblike, muscular ampulla. When an ampulla contracts, it forces water into a tube foot, which then extends. Valves prevent the backflow of water from the tube foot into the lateral canal. A tube foot often has a suction cup at its distal end. When the foot is extended and comes into contact with solid substrate, muscles of the suction cup contract and create a vacuum. In some taxa, the tube feet have a pointed or blunt distal end. These echinoderms may extend their tube feet into a soft substrate to secure contact during locomotion or to sift sediment during feeding.

(a)

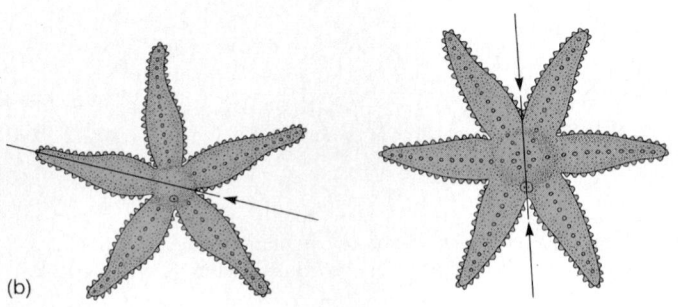

(b)

FIGURE 25.3

Pentaradial Symmetry. (*a*) Echinoderms possess a form of radial symmetry, called pentaradial symmetry, in which body parts are arranged in fives around an oral/aboral axis. Note the madreporite between the bases of the two arms in the foreground and the tube feet on the tips of the upturned arm. (*b*) Comparison of hypothetical penta- and hexaradial echinoderms. The five-part organization may be advantageous because joints between skeletal ossicles are never directly opposite one another, as they would be if an even number of parts were present. Having joints on opposite sides of the body in line with each other (arrows) could make the skeleton weaker.

The water-vascular system has other functions in addition to locomotion. As will be discussed at the end of this chapter, the original function of water-vascular systems was probably feeding, not locomotion. In addition, the soft membranes of the water-vascular system permit diffusion of respiratory gases and nitrogenous wastes across the body wall.

A **hemal system** consists of strands of tissue that encircle an echinoderm near the ring canal of the water-vascular system and run into each arm near the radial canals (*see figure 25.4*). The hemal system has been likened to a vestigial circulatory system; however, its function is largely unknown. It may aid in the transport of large molecules, hormones, or coelomocytes, which are cells that engulf and transport waste particles within the body.

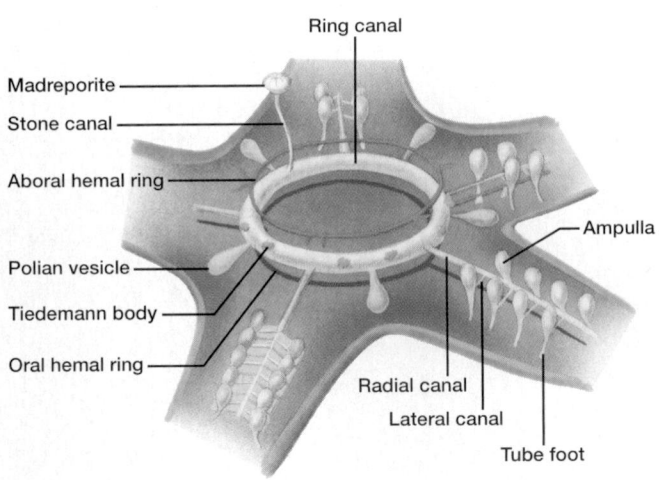

FIGURE 25.4

The Water-Vascular System of a Sea Star. The ring canal gives rise to radial canals that lead into each arm, a stone canal that ends at a madreporite on the aboral surface, and often has Polian vesicles and Tiedemann bodies associated with it.

CLASS ASTEROIDEA

The sea stars make up the class Asteroidea (as'te-roi"de-ah) (Gr. *aster*, star + *oeides*, in the form of) and include about 1,500 species (box 25.1). They are often found on hard substrata in marine environments, although some species are also found in sandy or muddy substrates. Sea stars may be brightly colored with red, orange, blue, or gray. *Asterias* is an orange sea star common along the Atlantic coast of North America and is frequently studied in introductory zoology laboratories.

Sea stars have five arms that radiate from a central disk. The oral opening, or mouth, is in the middle of one side of the central disk. It is normally oriented downward and is surrounded by movable oral spines. The aboral surface is roughened by movable and fixed spines that project from the skeleton. Thin folds of the body wall, called **dermal branchiae,** extend between ossicles and function in gas exchange (figure 25.5). In some sea stars, the aboral surface has numerous pincherlike structures called **pedicellariae,** which are used for cleaning the body surface of debris and for protection. Pedicellariae may be attached on a movable spine, or they may be immovably fused to skeletal ossicles.

An **ambulacral groove** runs the length of the oral surface of each arm and is formed by a series of ossicles in the arm. It houses the radial canal, and paired rows of tube feet protrude through the body wall on either side of the ambulacral groove. Tube feet of sea stars move in a stepping motion. Alternate extension, attachment, and contraction of tube feet move sea stars across their substrate. Tube feet are coordinated by the nervous system so that all feet move the sea star in the same direction; however, the tube feet do not move in unison. The

BOX 25.1   A THORNY PROBLEM FOR AUSTRALIA'S BARRIER REEF

The crown-of-thorns sea star (*Acanthaster planci*) is a common inhabitant of the South Pacific. Adults have a diameter of about 0.5 m and 13 to 16 arms (figure 1). Their common name is derived from their large venomous spines that can cause swelling, pain, and nausea in humans.

The crown-of-thorns sea star has become a problem in the waters off Australia and other South Pacific coasts. It feeds on coral polyps, and in one day, a single individual can extract polyps from 0.1 m² of reef. Over the last 20 years, the crown-of-thorns sea star has experienced a dramatic population increase. Thousands of sea stars have been observed moving slowly along a reef, leaving a white, almost sterile, limestone coral skeleton in their trail. They have seriously damaged over 500 km² of Australia's Great Barrier Reef.

One or more hypotheses may explain why there is a problem now, when these sea stars and coral polyps have coexisted for millions of years. Some believe that a part of the increase in sea stars may be due to the destruction of sea star predators, in particular, the giant triton gastropods. Tritons are valued for their beautiful shells, and their habitat has been disrupted by blasting to create shipping channels. Pesticides and other pollutants are also believed to be responsible for the destruction of predators of crown-of-thorns larvae. Another hypothesis suggests that the apparent increase in the sea star population may be a natural fluctuation in population size.

The reefs of the South Pacific are a source of economic wealth in the form of fisheries and tourism; therefore, the proliferation of crown-of-thorns sea stars has been the subject of intense study and control efforts. The Australian government has spent in excess of $3,000,000 and has not yet achieved satisfactory control. Control measures have included the injection of formaldehyde into adults by SCUBA divers, the erection of wire fences to divert populations

FIGURE 1   **The Crown-of-Thorns Sea Star (*Acanthaster*).** This sea star is shown here feeding on coral (*Pocillopora*).

away from reefs, and the use of computers to predict movements of colonies and local population explosions. One of the difficulties in these control efforts stems from the fact that sea star larvae are planktonic and are widely dispersed by oceanic currents.

The original relationship between the crown-of-thorns sea star, coral polyps, and possibly sea star predators is an interesting example of a balanced predator-prey relationship. What is unfortunate is that humans often do not appreciate such balances until they have been altered.

---

suction disks of tube feet are effective attachment structures, allowing sea stars to maintain their position, or move from place to place, in spite of strong wave action.

MAINTENANCE FUNCTIONS

Sea stars feed on snails, bivalves, crustaceans, polychaetes, corals, detritus, and a variety of other food items. The mouth opens to a short esophagus and then to a large stomach that fills most of the coelom of the central disk. The stomach is divided into two regions. The larger, oral stomach, sometimes called the cardiac stomach, receives ingested food (figure 25.6). It joins the smaller, aboral stomach, sometimes called the pyloric stomach. The pyloric stomach gives rise to ducts that connect to secretory and absorptive structures called pyloric ceca.

Two pyloric ceca extend into each arm. A short intestine leads to rectal ceca (uncertain functions) and to a nearly nonfunctional anus, which opens on the aboral surface of the central disk.

Some sea stars ingest whole prey, which are digested extracellularly within the stomach. Undigested material is expelled through the mouth. Many sea stars feed on bivalves by forcing the valves apart. (Anyone who has tried to pull apart the valves of a bivalve shell can appreciate that this is a remarkable accomplishment.)   (3)   When a sea star feeds on a bivalve, it wraps itself around the ventral margin of a bivalve. Tube feet attach to the outside of the shell, and the body-wall musculature forces the valves apart. (This is possible because the sea star changes tube feet when the muscles of engaged tube feet begin to tire.) When the valves are opened about 0.1 mm,

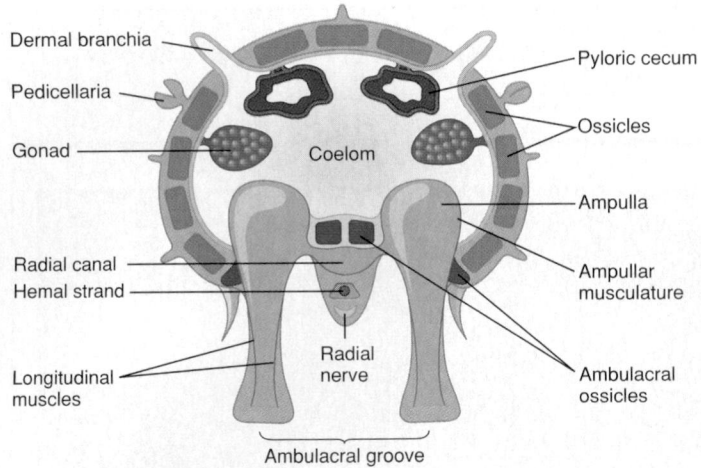

Figure 25.5

Body Wall and Internal Anatomy of a Sea Star. A cross section through one arm of a sea star shows the structures of the water-vascular system and the tube feet extending through the ambulacral groove.

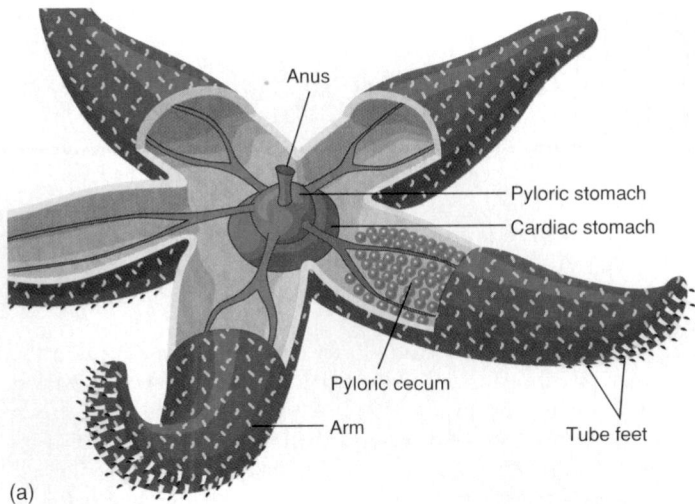

(a)

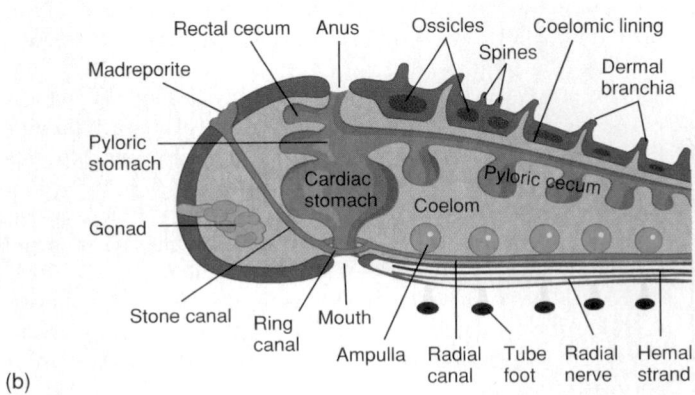

(b)

Figure 25.6

Digestive Structures in a Sea Star. A mouth leads to a large cardiac stomach and a pyloric stomach. Pyloric ceca extend into each arm. (*a*) Aboral view. (*b*) Lateral view through central disk and one arm.

the oral (cardiac) portion of the stomach is everted through the mouth and into the bivalve shell by increased coelomic pressure. Digestive enzymes are released, and partial digestion occurs in the bivalve shell. This digestion further weakens the bivalve's adductor muscles, and the shell eventually opens completely. Partially digested tissues are taken into the aboral (pyloric) portion of the stomach, and into the pyloric ceca for further digestion and absorption. After feeding and initial digestion, the stomach is retracted using stomach retractor muscles.

Transport of gases, nutrients, and metabolic wastes in the coelom occurs by diffusion and by the action of ciliated cells lining the body cavity. Gas exchange and excretion of metabolic wastes (principally ammonia) occur by diffusion across dermal branchiae, tube feet, and other membranous structures. A sea star's hemal system consists of strands of tissue that encircle the mouth near the ring canal, extend aborally near the stone canal, and run into the arms near radial canals (*see figure 25.4*).

The nervous system of sea stars consists of a nerve ring that encircles the mouth and radial nerves that extend into each arm. Radial nerves lie within the ambulacral groove, just oral to the radial canal of the water-vascular system and the radial strands of the hemal system (*see figure 25.5*). Radial nerves are essential for coordinating the functions of tube feet. Other nervous elements are in the form of a nerve net that is associated with the body wall.

Most sensory receptors are distributed over the surface of the body and tube feet. Sea stars respond to light, chemicals, and various mechanical stimuli. They often have specialized

photoreceptors at the tips of their arms. These are actually tube feet that lack suction cups but have a pigment spot surrounding a group of ocelli.

Regeneration, Reproduction, and Development

Sea stars are well known for their powers of regeneration. Any part of a broken arm can be regenerated. In a few species, an entire starfish can be regenerated from a broken arm if the arm contains a portion of the central disk. Regeneration is a slow process, taking up to 1 year for complete regeneration. Asexual reproduction involves dividing the central disk, followed by regeneration of each half.

Sea stars are dioecious, but sexes are indistinguishable externally. Two gonads are present in each arm and increase in size to nearly fill an arm during the reproductive periods. Gonopores open between the bases of each arm.

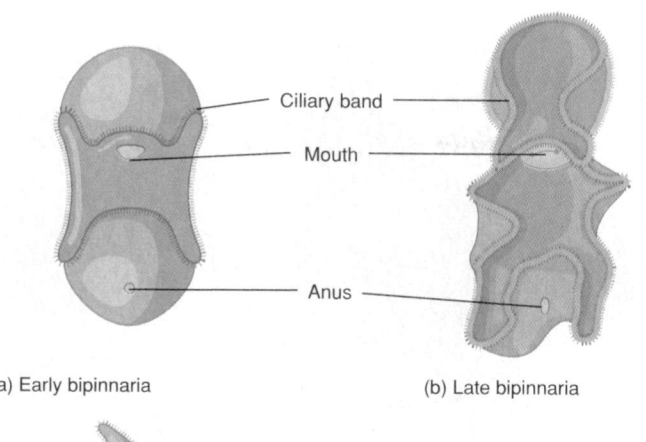

(a) Early bipinnaria

Ciliary band

Mouth

Anus

(b) Late bipinnaria

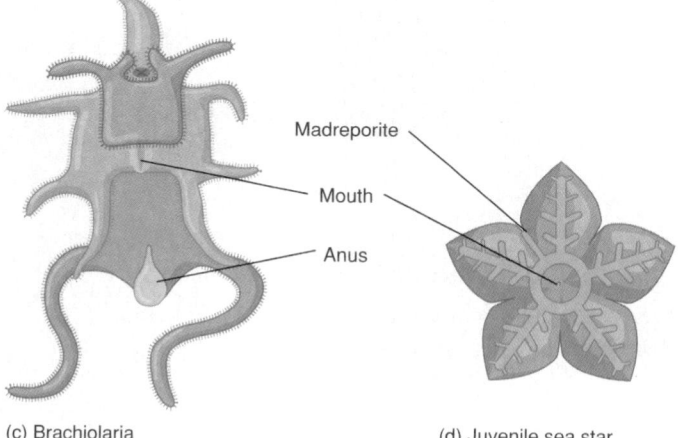

Madreporite

Mouth

Anus

(c) Brachiolaria

(d) Juvenile sea star

FIGURE 25.7

Development of a Sea Star. Later embryonic stages are ciliated and swim and feed in the plankton. In a few species, embryos develop from yolk stored in the egg during gamete formation. Following blastula and gastrula stages, larvae develop. (*a*) Early bipinnaria larva. (*b*) Late bipinnaria larva. (*c*) Brachiolaria larva. (*d*) Juvenile sea star.

The embryology of echinoderms has been studied extensively because of the relative ease of inducing spawning and maintaining embryos in the laboratory. External fertilization is the rule. Because gametes cannot survive long in the ocean, maturation of gametes and spawning must be coordinated if fertilization is to take place. The photoperiod (the relative length of light and dark in a 24-hour period) and temperature are environmental factors that are used to coordinate sexual activity. In addition, the release of gametes by one individual is accompanied by the release of spawning pheromones, which induce other sea stars in the area to spawn, increasing the likelihood of fertilization.

The early stages of echinoderm embryology are covered in detail in chapter 10. Embryos are planktonic, and cilia are used in swimming (figure 25.7). After gastrulation, bands of cilia differentiate, and a bilaterally symmetrical larva, called a bipinnaria larva, is formed. The larva usually feeds on planktonic protists. The development of larval arms results in a brachiolaria larva. Settling to the substrate is followed by attachment and metamorphosis to a juvenile sea star.

1. Why do many zoologists believe that ancestral echinoderms were bilaterally symmetrical?
2. What are the functions of the water-vascular system?
3. How does a sea star feed on a clam?
4. How is the nervous tissue arranged in a sea star?

CLASS OPHIUROIDEA

The class Ophiuroidea (o′fe-u-roi′de-ah) (Gr. *ophis*, snake + *oura*, tail + *oeides*, in the form of) includes the basket stars and the brittle stars. With over 2,000 species, this is the most diverse group of echinoderms. Ophiuroids, however, are often overlooked because of their small size and their tendency to occupy crevices in rocks and coral or to cling to algae.

The arms of ophiuroids are long and, unlike those of asteroids, are sharply set off from the central disk, giving the central disk a pentagonal shape. Brittle stars have unbranched arms and most range in size from 1 to 3 cm (figure 25.8*a*). Basket stars have arms that branch repeatedly (figure 25.8*b*). Neither dermal branchiae nor pedicellariae are present in ophiuroids. The tube feet of ophiuroids lack suction disks and ampullae, and contraction of muscles associated with the base of a tube foot causes the tube foot to be extended. Unlike the sea stars, the madreporite of ophiuroids is located on the oral surface.

The water-vascular system of ophiuroids is not used for locomotion. Instead, the skeleton is modified to permit a unique form of grasping and movement. Superficial ossicles, which originate on the aboral surface, cover the lateral and oral surfaces of each arm. The ambulacral groove—containing the radial nerve, hemal strand, and radial canal—is thus said to be "closed." Ambulacral ossicles are in the arm, forming a central supportive axis. ④ Successive ambulacral ossicles articulate with one another and are acted upon by relatively large muscles to produce snakelike movements, allowing the arms to be curled around a stalk of algae or hooked into a coral crevice. During locomotion, the central disk is held above the substrate and two arms are used to pull the animal along, while other arms extend forward and/or trail behind the animal.

MAINTENANCE FUNCTIONS

Ophiuroids are predators and scavengers. They use their arms and tube feet in sweeping motions to collect prey and particulate matter, which are then transferred to the mouth. Some ophiuroids are filter feeders that wave their arms and trap plankton on mucus-covered tube feet. Trapped plankton is passed from tube foot to tube foot along the length of an arm until it reaches the mouth.

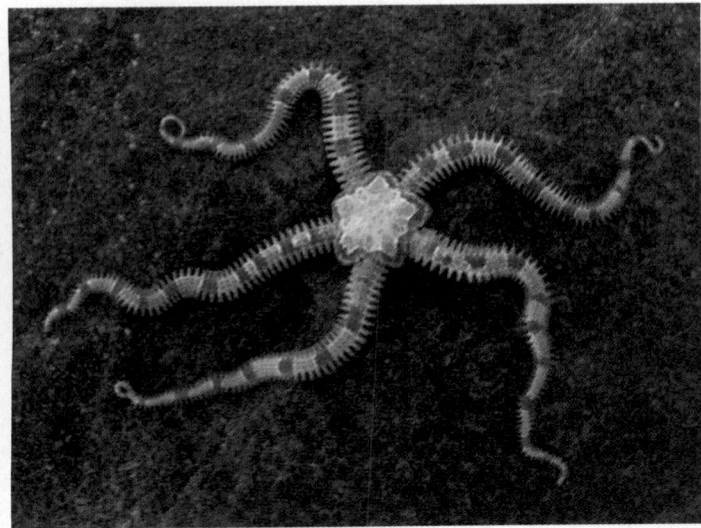

(a)

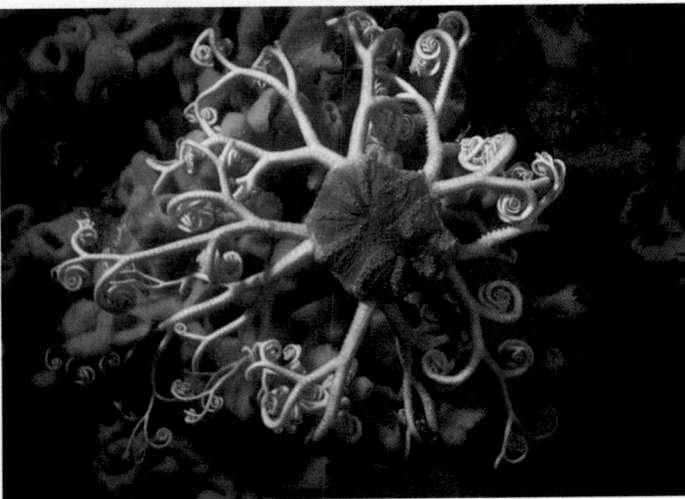

(b)

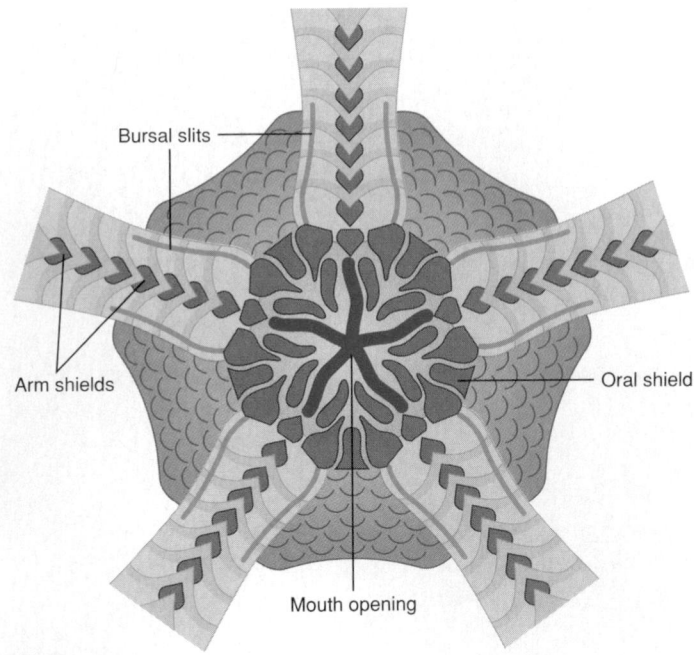

FIGURE 25.9

Class Ophiuroidea. Oral view of the disk of the brittle star, *Ophiomusium*. *Redrawn from L. Hyman, The Invertebrates, Volume IV. Copyright © 1959 McGraw-Hill, Inc. Used by permission.*

FIGURE 25.8

Class Ophiuroidea. (*a*) This brittle star (*Ophiopholis aculeata*) uses its long, snakelike arms for crawling along its substrate and curling around objects in its environment. (*b*) Basket stars have five highly branched arms. The arms are waved in the water to capture planktonic organisms on mucous-covered tube feet.

The mouth of ophiuroids is in the center of the central disk, and five triangular jaws form a chewing apparatus. The mouth leads to a saclike stomach. There is no intestine, and no part of the digestive tract extends into the arms.

The coelom of ophiuroids is reduced and is mainly confined to the central disk, but it still serves as the primary means for the distribution of nutrients, wastes, and gases. Coelomocytes aid in the distribution of nutrients and the expulsion of particulate wastes. Ammonia is the primary nitrogenous waste product and it is lost by diffusion. Diffusion occurs across tube

feet and membranous sacs, called **bursae,** that invaginate from the oral surface of the central disk. Slits in the oral disk, near the base of each arm, allow cilia to move water into and out of the bursae (figure 25.9).

REGENERATION, REPRODUCTION, AND DEVELOPMENT

Ophiuroids, as sea stars, are able to regenerate lost arms. If a brittle star is grasped by an arm, the contraction of certain muscles may sever and cast off the arm—hence the common name brittle star. This process is called autotomy (Gr. *autos*, self + *tomos*, to cut) and is used in escape reactions. The arm is later regenerated. Some species also have a fission line across their central disk. When split into halves along this line, two ophiuroids will be regenerated.

Ophiuroids are dioecious. Males are usually smaller than females and often are carried about by females. The gonads are associated with each bursa, and gametes are released into the bursa. Eggs may be shed to the outside, or retained in the bursa, where they are fertilized and held through early development. Embryos are protected in the bursa and are sometimes nourished by the parent. A larval stage, called an ophiopluteus, is planktonic. Its long arms bear ciliary bands that are used to feed on plankton, and it undergoes metamorphosis before sinking to the substrate.

(a)

(b)

FIGURE 25.10

Class Echinoidea. (*a*) A sea urchin (*Strongylocentrotus*). (*b*) Sand dollars are specialized for living in soft substrates, where they often occur partially buried.

CLASS ECHINOIDEA

The sea urchins, sand dollars, and heart urchins make up the class Echinoidea (ek'i-noi-de-ah) (Gr. *echinos,* spiny + *oeides,* in the form of). There are about 1,000 species widely distributed in nearly all marine environments. Sea urchins are specialized for living on hard substrates, often wedging themselves into crevices and holes in rock or coral (figure 25.10*a*). Sand dollars and heart urchins usually live in sand or mud and burrow just below the surface (figure 25.10*b*). They use tube feet to catch organic matter settling on them or passing over them. Sand dollars often occur in very dense beds, which favors efficient reproduction and feeding.

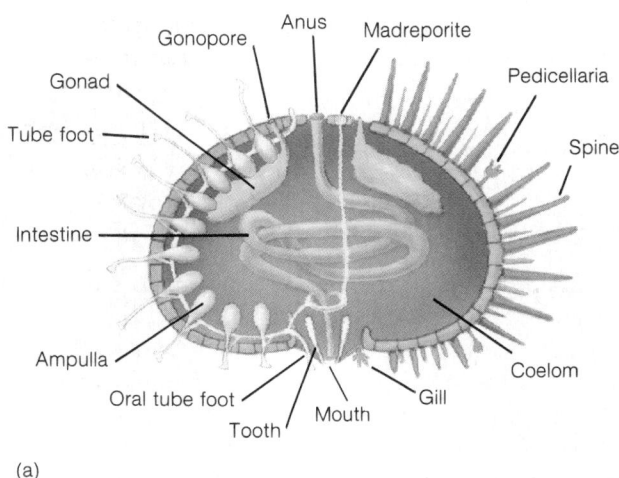

(a)

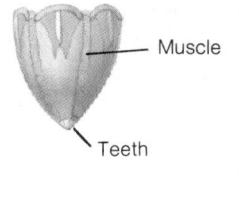

(b)

FIGURE 25.11

Internal Anatomy of a Sea Urchin. (*a*) Sectional view.
(*b*) Aristotle's lantern is a chewing structure consisting of about 35 ossicles and associated muscles.

Sea urchins are rounded and have their oral end oriented toward the substrate. Their skeleton, called a test, consists of 10 closely fitting plates that arch between oral and aboral ends. Five ambulacral plates have openings for tube feet, and alternate with five interambulacral plates, which have tubercles for the articulation of spines. The base of each spine is a concave socket, and muscles at its base move the spine. Spines are often sharp and sometimes hollow and contain venom that is dangerous to swimmers. The pedicellariae of sea urchins have either two or three jaws and are connected to the body wall by a relatively long stalk (figure 25.11*a*). They are used for cleaning the body of debris and capturing planktonic larvae, which provide an extra source of food. Pedicellariae of some sea urchins contain venom sacs and are grooved or hollow to inject venom into a predator, such as a sea star.

The water-vascular system is similar to that of other echinoderms. Radial canals run along the inner body wall between the oral and the aboral poles. Tube feet possess ampullae and suction cups, and the water-vascular system opens to the outside through many pores in one aboral ossicle that serves as a madreporite.

Echinoids move by using spines for pushing against the substrate and tube feet for pulling. Sand dollars and heart urchins use spines to help burrow in soft substrates. ⑤ Some sea urchins burrow into rock and coral to escape the action of waves and strong currents. They form cup-shaped depressions and deeper burrows using the action of their chewing Aristotle's lantern, which is described next.

MAINTENANCE FUNCTIONS

Echinoids feed on algae, bryozoans, coral polyps, and dead animal remains. Food is manipulated by oral tube feet surrounding the mouth. A chewing apparatus, called **Aristotle's lantern,** projects from the mouth (figure 25.11b). It consists of about 35 ossicles and attached muscles and cuts food into small pieces for ingestion. The mouth cavity leads to a pharynx, an esophagus, and a long, coiled intestine that ends aborally at the anus.

Echinoids have a large coelom, and coelomic fluids are the primary circulatory medium. Small gills, found in a thin membrane surrounding the mouth, are outpockets of the body wall and are lined by ciliated epithelium. Gas exchange occurs by diffusion across this epithelium and across the tube feet. Ciliary currents, changes in coelomic pressure, and the contraction of muscles associated with Aristotle's lantern move coelomic fluids into and out of gills. Excretory and nervous functions are similar to those described for asteroids.

REPRODUCTION AND DEVELOPMENT

Echinoids are dioecious. Gonads are located on the internal body wall of the interambulacral plates. During breeding season, they nearly fill the spacious coelom. One gonopore is located in each of five ossicles, called genital plates, at the aboral end of the echinoid, although the sand dollars usually have only four gonads and gonopores. Gametes are shed into the water, and fertilization is external. Development eventually results in a pluteus larva that spends several months in the plankton and eventually undergoes metamorphosis to the adult (*see figure 10.6*).

Stop and Ask Yourself

5. How is a sea star distinguished from a brittle star?
6. What is autotomy?
7. What is Aristotle's lantern?
8. What structures of echinoids are used for gas exchange?

CLASS HOLOTHUROIDEA

There are approximately 1,500 species in the class Holothuroidea (hol'o-thu-roi'de-ah) (Gr. *holothourion,* sea cucumber + *oeides,* in the form of), and they are commonly called sea cucumbers. Sea cucumbers are found at all depths in all oceans, where they crawl over hard substrates or burrow through soft substrates (figure 25.12).

FIGURE 25.12
Class Holothuroidea. A sea cucumber (*Parastichopus californicus*).

Sea cucumbers have no arms, and they are elongate along the oral-aboral axis. They lie on one side, which is usually flattened as a permanent ventral side, giving them a secondary bilateral symmetry. Tube feet surrounding the mouth are elongate and referred to as tentacles. Most adults range in length between 10 and 30 cm. Their body wall is thick and muscular and lacks protruding spines or pedicellariae. Beneath the epidermis is the dermis, a thick layer of connective tissue in which ossicles are embedded. Ossicles of sea cucumbers are microscopic in size and do not function in determining body shape. A circle of larger ossicles forms a calcareous ring and encircles the oral end of the digestive tract, serving as a point of attachment for body wall muscles (figure 25.13). Beneath the dermis is a layer of circular muscles overlying longitudinal muscles. The body wall of sea cucumbers, when boiled and dried, is known as trepang in the Orient. It may be eaten as a main course item or be added to soups as flavoring and a source of protein.

The madreporite of sea cucumbers is internal, and the water-vascular system is filled with coelomic fluid. The ring canal encircles the oral end of the digestive tract and gives rise to one to ten Polian vesicles. Five radial canals and the canals to the tentacles branch from the ring canal. Radial canals and tube feet, with suction cups and ampullae, run between the oral and aboral poles. The side of a sea cucumber resting on the substrate contains three of the five rows of tube feet, which are primarily used for attachment. The two rows of tube feet on the upper surface may be reduced in size, or they may be absent.

Sea cucumbers are mostly sluggish burrowers and creepers, although some swim by undulating their body from side to side. Locomotion using tube feet is inefficient because the tube feet are not anchored by body wall ossicles. Locomotion more commonly results from contractions of body wall muscles, producing wormlike, locomotor waves that pass along the length of the body.

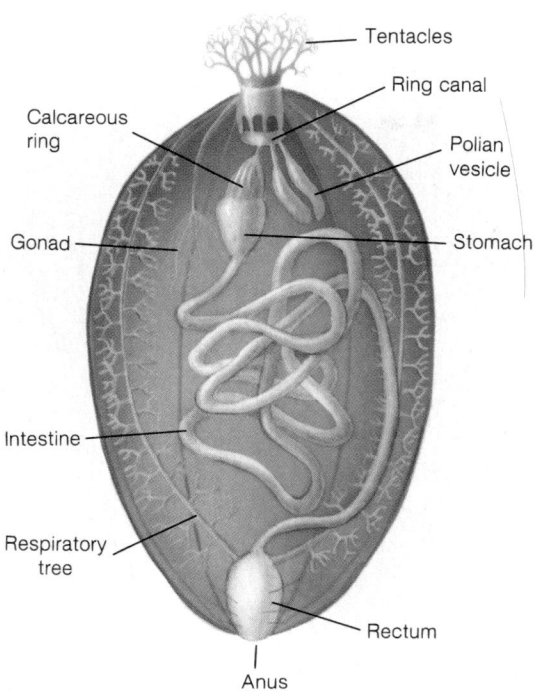

Figure 25.13

Internal Structure of a Sea Cucumber, *Thyone*. The mouth leads to a stomach that is supported by a calcareous ring. The calcareous ring is also the attachment site for longitudinal retractor muscles of the body. Contractions of these muscles pull the tentacles into the anterior end of the body. The stomach leads to a looped intestine. The intestine continues to the rectum and anus. (The anterior portion of the digestive tract is displaced aborally in this illustration.)

Maintenance Functions

Most sea cucumbers ingest particulate organic matter using their tentacles. Food is trapped in mucus covering the tentacles, either as the tentacles sweep across the substrate or while tentacles are held out in seawater. The digestive tract consists of a stomach; a long, looped intestine; a rectum; and an anus (figure 25.13). Tentacles are thrust into the mouth to wipe off trapped food. During digestion, coelomocytes move across the intestinal wall, secrete enzymes to aid in digestion, and engulf and distribute the products of digestion.

The coelom of sea cucumbers is large, and the cilia of the coelomic lining circulate fluids throughout the body cavity, distributing respiratory gases, wastes, and nutrients. The hemal system of sea cucumbers is well developed, with relatively large sinuses and a network of channels containing coelomic fluids. Its primary role is food distribution.

Respiratory trees are a pair of tubes that attach at the rectum and branch throughout the body cavity of sea cucumbers. Water circulates into these tubes by the pumping action of the rectum. When the rectum dilates, water moves through the anus into the rectum. Contraction of the rectum, along with contraction of an anal sphincter, forces water into the respiratory tree. Water exits the respiratory tree when tubules of the tree contract. Respiratory gases and nitrogenous wastes move between the coelom and seawater across these tubules.

The nervous system of sea cucumbers is similar to that of other echinoderms, but has additional nerves supplying the tentacles and pharynx. Some sea cucumbers have statocysts, and others have relatively complex photoreceptors.

Casual examination would lead one to believe that sea cucumbers are defenseless against predators. Many sea cucumbers, however, produce toxins in their body walls that act to discourage predators. In other sea cucumbers, tubules of the respiratory tree, called Cuverian tubules, can be everted through the anus. They contain sticky secretions and toxins capable of entangling and immobilizing predators.   ⑥   In addition, contractions of the body wall may result in expulsion of one or both respiratory trees, the digestive tract, and the gonads through the anus. This process is called evisceration and is a defensive adaptation that may discourage predators. It is followed by regeneration of lost parts.

Reproduction and Development

Sea cucumbers are dioecious. They possess a single gonad, located anteriorly in the coelom, and a single gonopore near the base of the tentacles. Fertilization is usually external, and embryos develop into planktonic larvae. Metamorphosis precedes settling to the substrate. In some species, eggs are trapped by a female's tentacles as they are released. After fertilization, eggs are transferred to the body surface, where they are brooded. Although it is rare, coelomic brooding also occurs. Eggs are released into the body cavity where fertilization (by an unknown mechanism) and early development occur. The young leave by a rupture in the body wall. Sea cucumbers can also reproduce by transverse fission, followed by regeneration of lost parts.

Stop and Ask Yourself

9. What structural features of sea cucumbers result in their having a secondary bilateral symmetry?
10. How is the water-vascular system of sea cucumbers modified for feeding?
11. What is a respiratory tree?
12. How does a sea cucumber defend itself against predators?

Class Crinoidea

Members of the class Crinoidea (krin-oi′de-ah) (Gr. *krinon*, lily + *oeides*, in the form of) include the sea lilies and the feather stars. They are the most primitive of all living echinoderms and are very different from any covered thus far. There are approximately

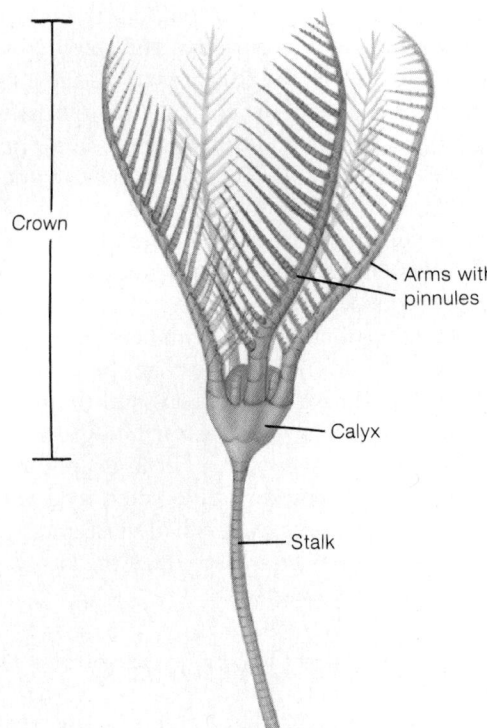

FIGURE 25.14
Class Crinoidea. A sea lily (*Ptilocrinus*).

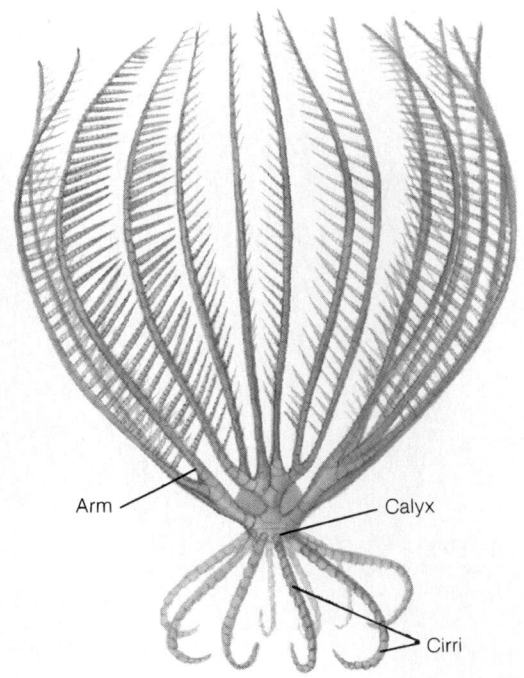

FIGURE 25.15
Class Crinoidea. A feather star (*Neometra*).

630 species living today; however, an extensive fossil record indicates that many more were present during the Paleozoic era, 200 to 600 million years ago.

Sea lilies are attached permanently to their substrate by a stalk (figure 25.14). The attached end of the stalk bears a flattened disk or rootlike extensions that are fixed to the substrate. Disklike ossicles of the stalk appear to be stacked on top of one another and are held together by connective tissues, giving a jointed appearance. The stalk usually bears projections, or cirri that are arranged in whorls around the stalk. The unattached end of a sea lily is called the crown. The aboral end of the crown is attached to the stalk and is supported by a set of ossicles, called the **calyx.** Five arms also attach at the calyx. They are branched, supported by ossicles, and bear smaller branches—giving them a featherlike appearance. Tube feet are located in a double row along each arm. Ambulacral grooves on the arms lead toward the mouth. The mouth and anus open onto the upper (oral) surface.

Feather stars are similar to sea lilies, except they lack a stalk and are swimming and crawling animals (figure 25.15). The aboral end of the crown bears a ring of rootlike cirri, which are used for clinging when the animal is resting on a substrate. Swimming is accomplished by raising and lowering the arms, and crawling results from using the tips of the arms to pull the animal over the substrate.

MAINTENANCE FUNCTIONS

Circulation, gas exchange, and excretion in crinoids are similar to these functions in other echinoderms. In feeding, however, crinoids differ from other living echinoderms. They use outstretched arms for suspension feeding. When a planktonic organism contacts a tube foot, it is trapped and carried to the mouth by cilia in ambulacral grooves. Although this method of feeding is different from the way other modern echinoderms feed, it probably reflects the original function of the water-vascular system.

Crinoids lack the nerve ring found in most echinoderms. Instead, a cup-shaped nerve mass below the calyx gives rise to radial nerves that extend through each arm and control the tube feet and arm musculature.

REPRODUCTION AND DEVELOPMENT

Crinoids, as other echinoderms, are dioecious. Gametes form from germinal epithelium in the coelom and are released by rupturing the walls of the arms. Some species spawn into seawater, where fertilization and development occur. Other species brood embryos on the outer surface of the arms. Metamorphosis occurs after larvae have attached to the substrate. As with other echinoderms, crinoids can regenerate lost parts.

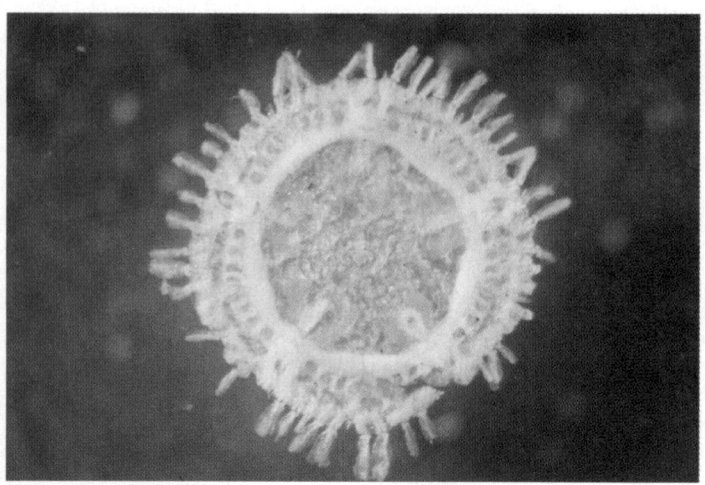

Figure 25.16

Class Concentricycloidea. Photograph of a preserved sea daisy (*Xyloplax medusiformis*). This specimen is 3 mm in diameter.

Class Concentricycloidea

The class Concentricycloidea (kon-sen'tri-si-kloi''de-ah) (ME *consentrik*, having a common center + Gr. *kykloeides*, like a circle) contains a single described species, known as the sea daisy. ⑦ Sea daisies have been recently discovered on debris in deep oceans (figure 25.16). They lack arms and are less than 1 cm in diameter. The most distinctive feature of this species is two circular water-vascular rings that encircle the disklike body. The inner of the two rings probably corresponds to the ring canal of members of other classes because it has Polian vesicles attached. The outer ring contains tube feet and ampullae and probably corresponds to the radial canals of members of other classes. In addition, this animal lacks an internal digestive system. Instead, the surface of the animal that is applied to the substrate (e.g., decomposing wood) is covered by a thin membrane, called a velum, that digests and absorbs nutrients. Internally, there are five pairs of brood pouches where embryos are held during development. There are apparently no free-swimming larval stages. The mechanism for fertilization is unknown.

Further Phylogenetic Considerations

As described earlier, most zoologists believe that echinoderms evolved from bilaterally symmetrical ancestors. Radial symmetry probably evolved during the transition from active to more sedentary life-styles; however, the oldest echinoderm fossils, about 600 million years old, give little direct evidence of how this transition occurred.

Ancient fossils do give clues regarding the origin of the water-vascular system and the calcareous endoskeleton. Of all living echinoderms, the crinoids most closely resemble the oldest fossils. ⑧ Because crinoids use their water-vascular system for suspension feeding, it is believed that filter feeding, not locomotion, was probably the original function of the water-vascular system. As do crinoids, early echinoderms probably assumed a mouth-up position and were attached aborally. Arms and tube feet could have been used to capture food and move it to the mouth. The calcium carbonate endoskeleton may have evolved for support of extended filtering arms and for protection of these sessile animals.

Many modern echinoderms are more mobile. This free-living life-style is probably secondarily derived, as is the mouth-down orientation of most echinoderms. The mouth-down position would be advantageous for predatory and scavenging life-styles. Similarly, changes in the water-vascular system, such as the evolution of ampullae, suction disks, and feeding tentacles, can be interpreted as adaptations for locomotion and feeding in a more mobile life-style. The idea that the free-living life-style is secondary is reinforced by the observation that some echinoderms, such as the irregular echinoids and the holothuroids, have bilateral symmetry imposed upon a pentaradial body form.

The evolutionary relationships among the echinoderms are not clear. There are numerous fossils dating into the Cambrian period, but there is no definitive interpretation of the evolutionary relationships among living and extinct echinoderms. One interpretation of the evolutionary relationships among extant (with living members) echinoderm classes is shown in figure 25.17. Most taxonomists agree that the echinoids and holothuroids are closely related. Whether the ophiuroids are more closely related to the echinoid/holothuroid lineage or the asteroid lineage is debated. The position of the Concentricycloidea in echinoderm phylogeny is highly speculative and is not shown in the figure.

Stop and Ask Yourself

13. What is the function of the stalk, calyx, and cirri in crinoids?

14. How is the function of the crinoid water-vascular system different from that of other echinoderms?

15. How do the water-vascular systems and feeding mechanisms of sea daisies differ from those of other echinoderms?

16. What could account for the evolution of the calcium carbonate endoskeleton of echinoderms?

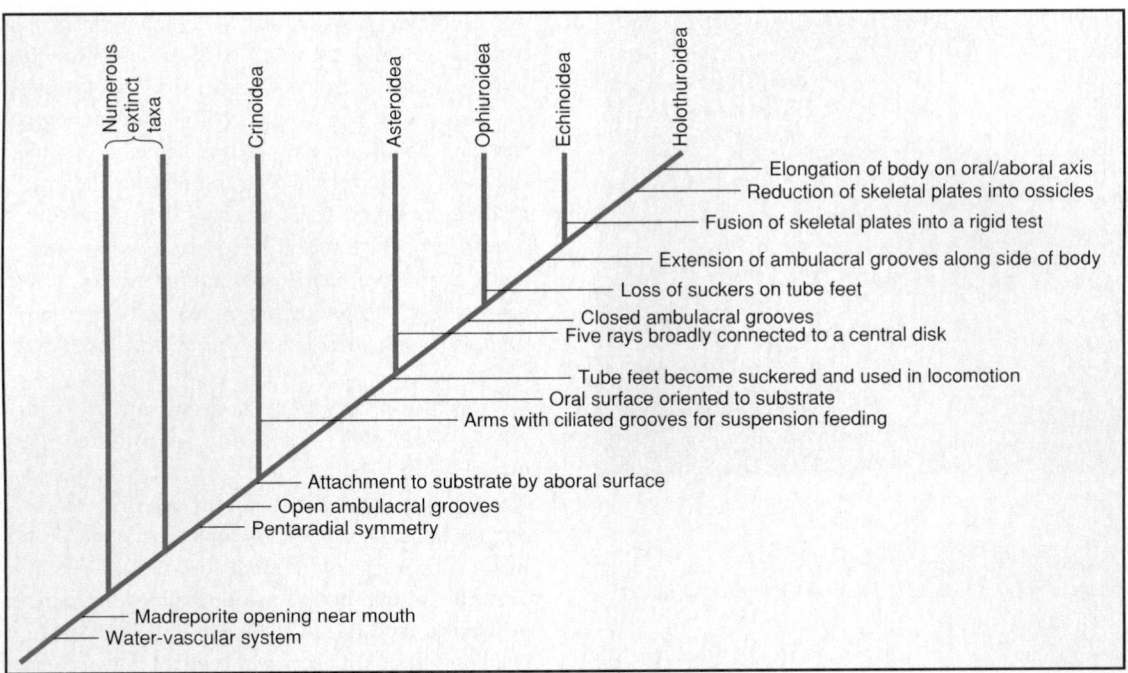

Figure 25.17

Echinoderm Phylogeny. The evolutionary relationships among echinoderms are not clear. The interpretation shown here depicts a relatively distant relationship between the Asteroidea and Ophiuroidea. Some taxonomists interpret the five-rayed body form as synapomorphy that links these two groups to a single ancestral lineage. The position of the Concentricycloidea is highly speculative and is not shown here.

Summary

1. Echinoderms, chordates, and other deuterostomes share a common, but remote, ancestry. Modern echinoderms were probably derived from bilaterally symmetrical ancestors.

2. Echinoderms are pentaradially symmetrical, have an endoskeleton of interlocking calcium carbonate ossicles, and have a water-vascular system that is used for locomotion, food gathering, attachment, and exchanges with the environment.

3. Members of the class Asteroidea are the sea stars. They are predators and scavengers, and their arms are broadly joined to the central disk. Sea stars are dioecious, and external fertilization results in the formation of planktonic bipinaria and brachiolaria larvae. Sea stars also have remarkable powers of regeneration.

4. The brittle stars and basket stars make up the class Ophiuroidea. Arms are sharply set off from the central disk. Ophiuroids are dioecious. Externally fertilized eggs may either develop in the plankton, or they may be brooded.

5. The class Echinoidea includes the sea urchins, heart urchins, and sand dollars. They have a specialized chewing structure, called Aristotle's lantern. External fertilization results in a planktonic pluteus larva.

6. Members of the class Holothuroidea include the sea cucumbers. They rest on one side, are elongate along their oral-aboral axis, and their body wall contains microscopic ossicles. Many sea cucumbers eviscerate themselves when disturbed. Sea cucumbers are dioecious, and fertilization and development are external.

7. The class Crinoidea contains the sea lilies and feather stars. They are oriented oral side up and use arms and tube feet in suspension feeding. Crinoids are dioecious, and fertilization and development are external.

8. The class Concentricycloidea contains one recently discovered species that lives on wood and other debris in deep water.

9. Radial symmetry of echinoderms probably evolved during a transition to a sedentary, filter-feeding life-style. The water-vascular system and the calcareous endoskeleton are probably adaptations for that life-style. The evolution of a more mobile life-style has resulted in the use of the water-vascular system for locomotion and the assumption of a mouth-down position.

Selected Key Terms

ambulacral groove (*p. 404*)
Aristotle's lantern (*p. 410*)
dermal branchiae (*p. 404*)
pedicellariae (*p. 404*)

pentaradial symmetry (*p. 402*)
respiratory trees (*p. 411*)
tube feet (*p. 403*)
water-vascular system (*p. 403*)

Critical Thinking Questions

1. What is pentaradial symmetry and why is it adaptive for echinoderms?

2. Why do zoologists think that pentaradial symmetry was not present in the ancestors of echinoderms?

3. Compare and contrast the structure and function of the water-vascular systems of asteroids, ophiuroids, echinoids, holothuroids, and crinoids.

4. In which of the above groups is the water-vascular system probably most similar in form and function to an ancestral condition? Explain your answer.

5. What physical process is responsible for gas exchange and excretion in all echinoderms? What structures facilitate these exchanges in each echinoderm class?

endpaper FOUR

SOME LESSER KNOWN INVERTEBRATES: THE LOPHOPHORATES

THE LOPHOPHORATES: BRACHIOPODA, ECTOPROCTA (BRYOZOA), AND PHORONIDA

The three phyla (Brachiopoda, Ectoprocta [Bryozoa], and Phoronida) discussed in this endpaper share one major anatomical feature—the **lophophore** (Gr. *lophos*, crest or tuft + *phorein*, to bear). The lophophore is a circumoral (around the mouth) body region characterized by a circular or U-shaped ridge, with either one or two rows of ciliated, hollow tentacles (figure 1). The lophophore functions as a food-collecting organ and as a surface for gas exchange. It also has sensory cells receptive to chemicals and touch that are concentrated on its tentacles. The lophophore can usually be extended for feeding or withdrawn for protection.

All lophophorates are sessile or sedentary filter feeders that possess a U-shaped digestive tract and live in a secreted chitinous or calcareous tube. As in deuterostomes, these phyla have radial cleavage in embryonic stages and a coelom that is divided into compartments. As in protostomes, however, the embryonic mouth forms in the region of the blastopore. Although it has been debated, most zoologists have considered the lophophorates to be deuterostomes. Recent molecular biological studies involving the sequencing of ribosomal DNA, however, suggest that the lophophorates are protostomes.

The evolutionary relationships between the lophophorate phyla are very distant. The presence of a lophophore in all three phyla indicates common evolutionary ties. Other similarities—such as a reduced head, U-shaped digestive tract, and secreted protective covering—are correlated with adaptations for a sessile, filter-feeding existence. These common features may represent evolutionary convergence rather than close evolutionary relationships.

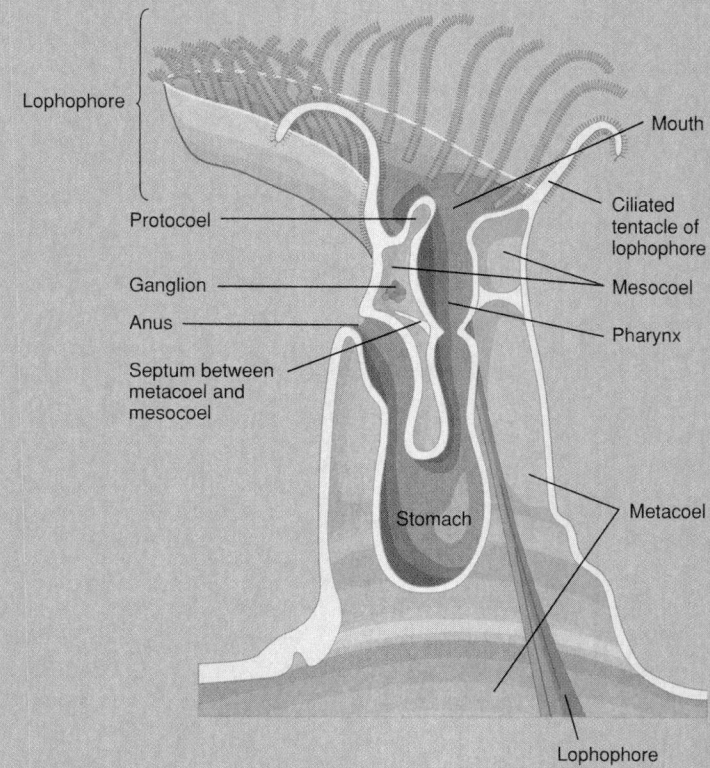

FIGURE 1   **Lophophorates.** Longitudinal section through the body of a lophophorate with the lophophore extended.

PHYLUM BRACHIOPODA: THE BRACHIOPODS, OR LAMPSHELLS

The brachiopods (brak-i-op′ods) (Gr. *brachion*, arm + *podos*, foot) bear a superficial resemblance to the bivalve molluscs because they have a bivalved, calcareous and/or chitinous shell that is secreted by a mantle that encloses nearly all of the body. However, unlike

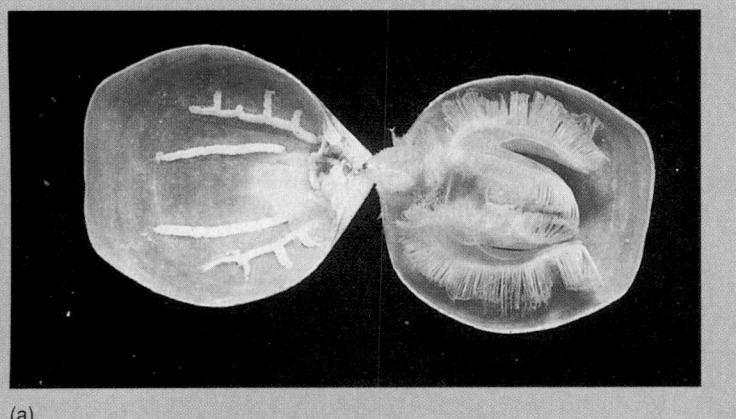

(a)

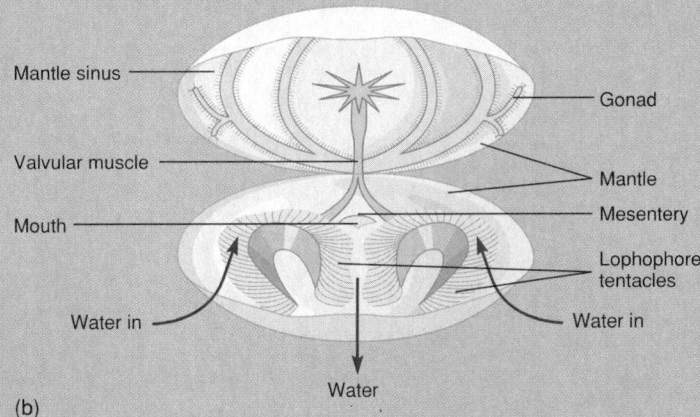

(b)

FIGURE 2 **Phylum Brachiopoda.** (*a*) Articulata brachiopod opened to show the two attached valves. (*b*) The internal anatomy of an articulate brachiopod.

the left and right valves in molluscs, the brachiopods have dorsal and ventral valves. In addition, molluscs filter with their gills, whereas brachiopods use a lophophore. Brachiopods are commonly called lampshells because they resemble ancient Roman oil lamps.

Brachiopods are exclusively marine; most species live from the tidal zone to the edge of the continental shelves (about 200 m deep). There are about 300 living species in the phylum. In the Articulata, the valves are composed primarily of calcium carbonate and have a hinge with interlocking teeth (figure 2a). The Inarticulata have unhinged valves that are composed primarily of calcium phosphate. The Inarticulata valves are held together only by muscles. Most members of both classes have a stalked pedicel that is usually attached to a hard surface. Some, such as *Lingula*, have a muscular pedicel used for burrowing and anchoring in mud or sand.

The large horseshoe-shaped lophophore in the anterior mantle cavity bears long, ciliated tentacles used in respiration and feeding (figure 2b). The cilia set up water currents that carry food particles (mainly organic detritus and algae) between the valves and over the lophophore into the mouth.

A solitary, dioecious brachiopod reproduces sexually by releasing gametes from multiple gonads into the metacoel and discharging them into the water by the nephridia. Fertilization is usually external, and the nonfeeding, ciliated, free-swimming larva is planktonic before settling and developing into an adult. Development is similar to deuterostomes, with radial, mostly equal, holoblastic cleavage, and enterocoelous coelom formation. In the Inarticulata, the juvenile resembles a small brachiopod with a coiled pedicel in the mantle cavity. There is no metamorphosis; when the juvenile settles to the bottom, the pedicel attaches to a solid object, and adult existence begins.

PHYLUM ECTOPROCTA (BRYOZOA): MOSS ANIMALS

The ectoprocts (ek-to-proks) (Gr. *ektos*, outside + *proktos*, anus) or bryozoans superficially resemble hydroids or corals. Bryozoa (Gr. *bryon*, moss + *zoon*, animal) means moss animals and refers to the mosslike appearance of the colonies. The name ectoprocta is used to distinguish this group of coelomate animals, with the anus located outside the ring of tentacles,

from the entoprocts in which the anus is within the ring of tentacles (*see figure 20.21*). There are about 4,000 living species of pseudocoelomate ectoprocts belonging to three classes. All species are aquatic (both fresh water and marine) and less than 1.5 mm in length.

Each body, or zooid, has a circular or horseshoe-shaped lophophore and is covered with a thin cuticle that encloses a calcified exoskeleton (*see figure 1 on page 415*). The feeding body (lophophore, digestive tract, muscles, nerves) is called the polypide, the exoskeleton plus body wall (epidermis) is the cystid, and the secreted, nonliving part (exoskeleton) is the zooecium (Gr. *zoo*, animal + *oceus*, house). Ectoprocts have an eversible lophophore that can be withdrawn into the body. Contraction of the retractor muscle rapidly withdraws the lophophore, whereas contraction of the muscles encircling the body wall exert pressure on the coelomic fluid, everting the lophophore.

Ectoprocts grow by budding. Thin portions of the body wall grow out as small vesicles or tubes and contain a complete zooid. The different budding patterns reflect the genetics of the individual animal and factors such as current flow and substrate. These factors determine the colony shape (e.g., thin sheets, convoluted folds, massive corallike heads, upright tangles) (figure 3a). Each colony can contain about 2 million zooids.

Most ectoprocts are monoecious. In some species, heterozooids produce either eggs or sperm in different colonies. In others, both sperm and eggs are produced in the same autozooid in simple gonads. Sperm are released into the coelomic cavity, exit through pores in the tips of the tentacles, and are caught by the tentacles of other colonies. Eggs are fertilized as they are released and brooded in the coelom; some species have a modified ovicell in which the embryo develops. Marine species have radial cleavage and a free-swimming, ciliated larva. This larva swims for a variable period of time, depending on the species, and then sinks and attaches to a rock or other substrate and grows into a zooid. A colony is formed by budding.

Some freshwater ectoprocts produce a dormant stage called a statoblast (figure 3b). A statoblast is a hard, resistant capsule containing a mass of germinative cells. Statoblasts are asexually produced and accumulate in the metacoel. They can survive long periods of freezing and drying, enabling a colony to survive many years in seasonally variable lakes and ponds. Some

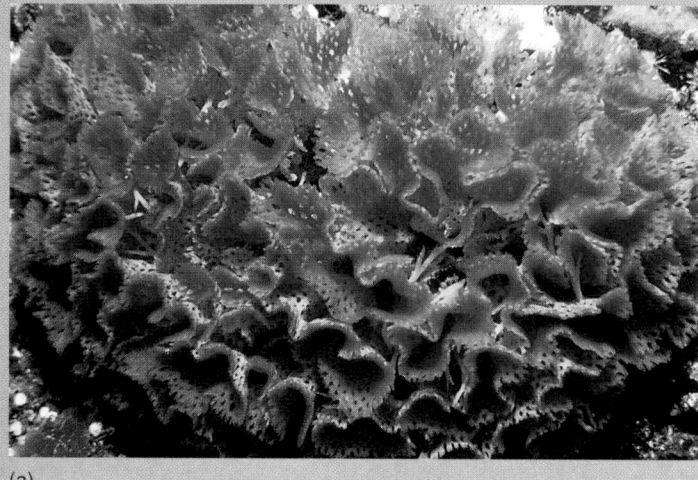

(a)

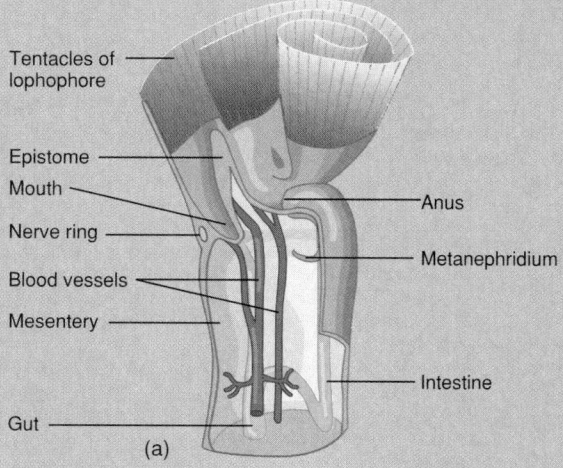

(a)

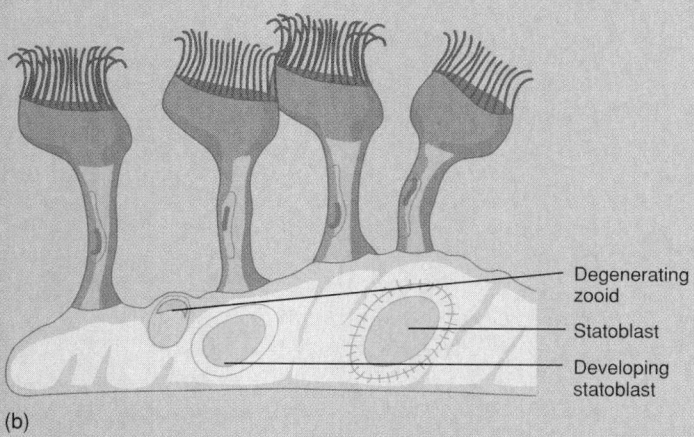

(b)

FIGURE 3   **Phylum Ectoprocta.** (*a*) Ectoprocts have a wide variety of shapes. *Philolopora* has lacy, delicate folds. (*b*) An ectoproct colony forming statoblasts.

float and are carried downstream, or are blown or carried from pond to pond, spreading ectoprocts over a large area. When environmental conditions become favorable, the statoblasts hatch and give rise to new polypides and eventually new colonies.

PHYLUM PHORONIDA: THE PHORONIDS

The phoronids (fo-ron-ids) consist of about one dozen marine species divided between two genera: *Phoronis* and *Phoronopsis*. These animals live in permanent, chitinous tubes either buried in muddy or sandy sediments, or attached to solid surfaces. A few species bore into mollusc shells or calcareous rock. Generally, only the tentacles extend into the overlying water. Most phoronids are small—less than 20 cm long.

The adult phoronid body consists of an anterior lophophore with two parallel rings of long tentacles (figure 4). The tentacles of the lophophore are filled with coelomic fluid that serves as a hydrostatic skeleton to hold them upright. The cilia on the tentacles drive water into the ring of tentacles from the top of the lophophore and out through the narrow spaces between the tentacles. Suspended food particles are directed toward the mouth. A flap of tissue called the epistome (Gr. *epi*, around + *stome*, mouth) covers the mouth.

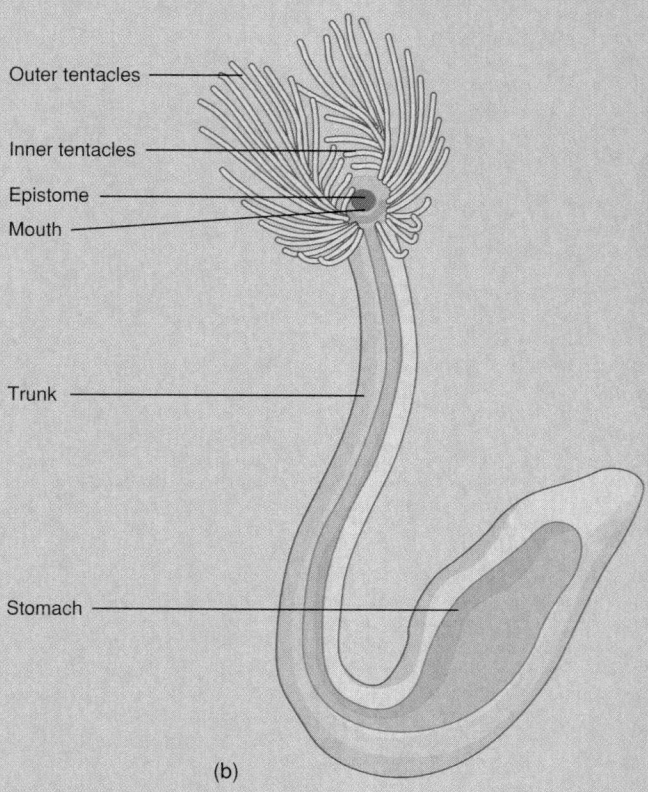

(b)

FIGURE 4   **Phylum Phoronida.** (*a*) A longitudinal view of the internal anatomy of the anterior portion of a phoronid. (*b*) A phoronid removed from its tube.

Some phoronids reproduce asexually by budding and transverse fission; however, the majority are hermaphroditic. The gonads are located in the coelom. Gametes pass from the coelom through the nephridiopore to the tentacles. Cross-fertilization is the rule, and the zygotes are either protected among the coils of the lophophore or released into the sea. Cleavage is radial, and a free-swimming larva called the actinotroch develops and feeds on plankton while drifting in the sea. It eventually settles to the bottom, metamorphoses, and begins to grow ventrally to form the body of the sedentary adult. As the animal grows, it burrows into the substrate. The body wall contains gland cells that eventually secrete the chitinous tube.

HEMICHORDATA AND INVERTEBRATE CHORDATES

Outline

Concepts

1. Members of the phyla Echinodermata, Hemichordata, and Chordata are probably derived from a common diploblastic or triploblastic ancestor.
2. The phylum Hemichordata includes the acorn worms (class Enteropneusta) and the pterobranchs (class Pterobranchia). Hemichordates live in or on marine substrates and feed on sediment or suspended organic matter.
3. Animals in the phylum Chordata are characterized by a notochord, pharyngeal gill slits or pouches, a tubular nerve cord, and a postanal tail.
4. The urochordates are marine, and are called tunicates. They are attached or planktonic, and solitary or colonial as adults. All are filter feeders.
5. Members of the subphylum Cephalochordata are called lancelets. They are filter feeders that spend most of their time partly buried in marine substrates.
6. Motile, fishlike chordates may have evolved from sedentary, filter-feeding ancestors as a result of paedomorphosis in a motile larval stage.

Would You Like to Know:

1. what acorn worms are? (p. 420)
2. what characteristics are shared by all chordates at some time in their life history? (p. 424)
3. what animals deposit cellulose in their body walls? (p. 425)
4. why sea squirts are classified in the same phylum (Chordata) as humans? (p. 427)
5. why cephalochordates, such as amphioxus, are studied in introductory zoology laboratories? (p. 427)
6. how fishlike chordates could have evolved from filter-feeding ancestors? (p. 428)

These and other useful questions will be answered in this chapter.

This chapter contains evolutionary concepts, which are set off in this font.

EVOLUTIONARY PERSPECTIVE

Some members of one of the phyla discussed in this chapter are more familiar to beginning students of zoology than members of any other group of animals. This familiarity is not without good reason, for zoologists themselves are members of one of these phyla—Chordata. Other members of these phyla, however, are much less familiar. Observations during a walk along a seashore at low tide may reveal coiled castings (sand, mud, and excrement) at the openings of U-shaped burrows, and excavating these burrows may reveal a wormlike animal that is one of the members of a small phylum—Hemichordata. Other members of this phylum include equally unfamiliar filter feeders called pterobranchs.

While at the seashore, one could also see animals clinging to rocks exposed by low tide. At first glance, they might be described as jellylike masses with two openings at their unattached end. Some are found as solitary individuals, others live in colonies. Handling these animals may be rewarded with a stream of water squirted from their openings. Casual observations provide little evidence that these small filter feeders, called sea squirts or tunicates, are chordates. However, detailed studies have made that conclusion certain. Tunicates and a small group of fishlike cephalochordates are often called the invertebrate chordates because they lack a vertebral column (figure 26.1).

PHYLOGENETIC RELATIONSHIPS

Animals in the phyla Hemichordata and Chordata share deuterostome characteristics with echinoderms (figure 26.2). Most zoologists, therefore, believe that ancestral representatives of these phyla were derived from a common, as yet undiscovered, triploblastic ancestor. The chordates are characterized by a dorsal, tubular nerve cord, a notochord, pharyngeal gill slits, and a postanal tail. The only characteristics that they share with the hemichordates are gill slits and, in some species, a dorsal, tubular nerve cord. Therefore, most zoologists agree that the evolutionary ties between the chordates and hemichordates are closer than those between echinoderms and either phylum. Chordates and hemichordates, however, probably diverged from widely separated points along the deuterostome lineage. This generalization is supported by the diverse body forms and life-styles present in these phyla.

PHYLUM HEMICHORDATA

The phylum Hemichordata (hem′i-kor-da′tah) (Gr. hemi, half + L. chorda, cord) includes the acorn worms (class Enteropneusta) and the pterobranchs (class Pterobranchia) (table 26.1). Members of both classes live in or on marine sediments.

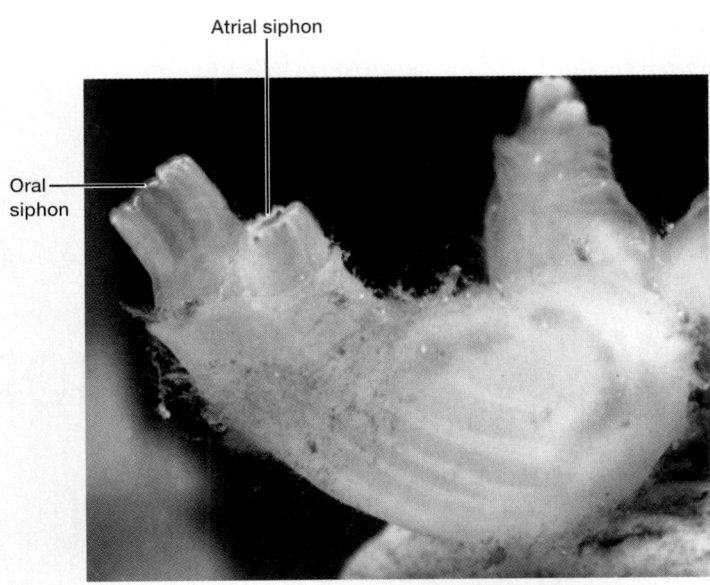

FIGURE 26.1

Phylum Chordata. This tunicate, or sea squirt (*Ciona intestinalis*), is an invertebrate chordate that is found attached to substrates in marine environments. Note the two siphons used in circulating water through a filter-feeding apparatus.

Characteristics of the phylum Hemichordata include the following:

1. Marine, deuterostomate animals with a body divided into three regions: proboscis, collar, and trunk; coelom divided into three cavities
2. Ciliated, pharyngeal gill slits
3. Open circulatory system
4. Complete digestive tract
5. Dorsal, sometimes hollow, nerve cord

CLASS ENTEROPNEUSTA

Members of the class Enteropneusta (ent′er-op-nus″tah) (Gr. *entero*, intestine + *pneustikos*, for breathing) are marine worms that usually range in size between 10 and 40 cm, although some can be as long as 2 m. There are about 70 described species, and most occupy U-shaped burrows in sandy and muddy substrates between the limits of high and low tides. ❶ The common name of the enteropneusts—acorn worms—is derived from the appearance of the proboscis, which is a short, conical projection at the anterior end of the worm. A ringlike collar is posterior to the proboscis, and an elongate trunk is the third division of the body (figure 26.3). Acorn worms are covered by a ciliated epidermis and gland cells. The mouth is located ventrally between the proboscis and the collar. A variable number of gill slits, from a few to several hundred, are positioned laterally on the trunk. Gill slits are openings between the anterior region of the digestive tract, called the pharynx, and the outside of the body.

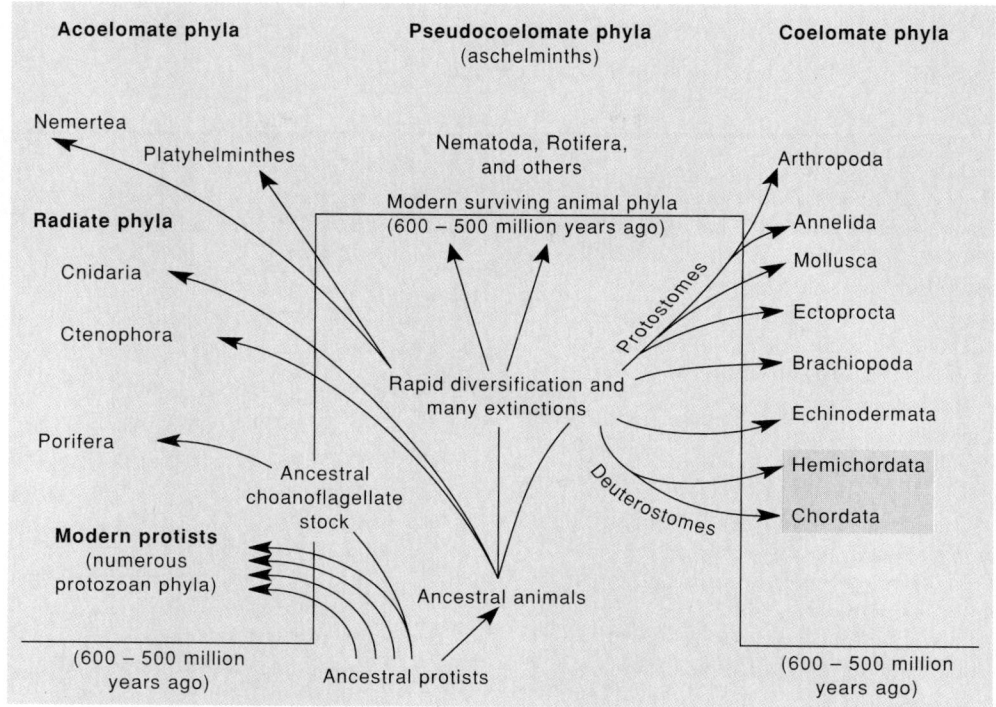

Figure 26.2

Phylogenetic Relationships among the Hemichordata and Chordata. Hemichordates and chordates (shaded in orange) are distantly related deuterostomes derived from a common, as yet undiscovered, diploblastic or triploblastic ancestor.

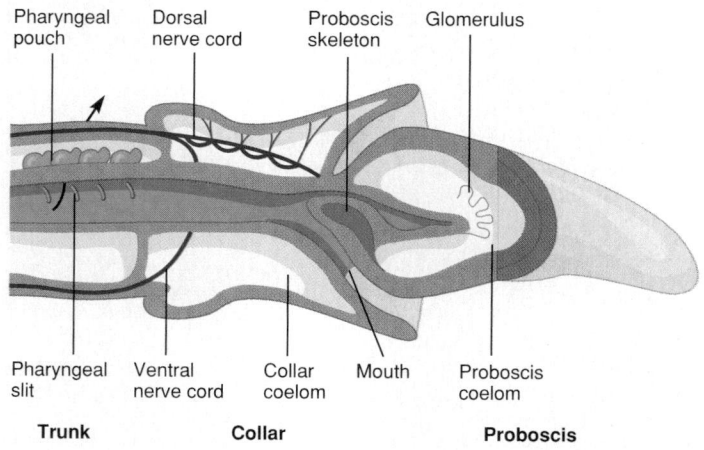

Figure 26.3

Class Enteropneusta. Longitudinal section showing the proboscis, collar, pharyngeal regions, and the internal structures. The arrow shows the path of water through a gill slit.

Maintenance Functions

Feeding of acorn worms is assisted by cilia and mucus. Detritus and other particles adhere to the mucus-covered proboscis. Tracts of cilia transport food and mucus posteriorly and ventrally. Ciliary tracts converge near the mouth and form a mucoid string that enters the mouth. Acorn worms may reject some substances trapped in the mucoid string by pulling the proboscis against the collar. Material to be rejected is transported along ciliary tracts of the collar and trunk and discarded posteriorly.

The digestive tract of enteropneusts is a simple tube. Digestion of food occurs as enzymes are released from diverticula of the gut, called hepatic sacs. The posterior end of the worm is extended out of the burrow during defecation. At low tide, one may see coils of fecal material, called castings, lying on the substrate at an opening of a burrow.

The nervous system of enteropneusts is ectodermal in origin and lies at the base of the ciliated epidermis. It consists of dorsal and ventral nerve tracts and a network of epidermal nerve cells, called a nerve plexus. In some species, the dorsal nerve is tubular and usually contains giant nerve fibers that rapidly transmit impulses. There are no major ganglia. Sensory receptors are unspecialized and widely distributed over the body.

Because acorn worms are small, exchanges of respiratory gases and metabolic waste products (principally ammonia) probably occur by diffusion across the body wall. In addition, respiratory gases are exchanged at the pharyngeal gill slits. Cilia associated with pharyngeal gill slits circulate water into the mouth and out of the body through gill slits. As water passes through gill slits, gases are exchanged by diffusion between water and blood sinuses surrounding the pharynx.

TABLE 26.1	CLASSIFICATION OF THE HEMICHORDATA AND CHORDATA

Phylum Hemichordata (hem'i-kor-da'tah)
Widely distributed in shallow, marine, tropical waters and deep, cold waters; soft bodied and wormlike; epidermal nervous system; most with pharyngeal gill slits.

   Class Enteropneusta (ent'er-op-nus''tah)
   Shallow water, wormlike animals; inhabit burrows on sandy shorelines; body divided into three regions: proboscis, collar, and trunk. Acorn worms (*Balanoglossus, Saccoglossus*).

   Class Pterobranchia (ter'o-brang''ke-ah)
   With or without gill slits; two or more arms; often colonial, living in an externally secreted encasement. *Rhabdopleura*.

   Class Planctosphaeroidea (plank'to-sfer-roi'de-ah)
   Body spherical with ciliary bands covering the surface; U-shaped digestive tract; coelom poorly developed; planktonic. Only one species is known to exist (*Planctosphaera pelagica*).

Phylum Chordata (kor-dat'ah) (L. *chorda*, cord)
Occupy a wide variety of marine, freshwater, and terrestrial habitats. A notochord, pharyngeal gill slits, a dorsal tubular nerve cord, and a postanal tail all present at some time in chordate life histories.

   Subphylum Urochordata (u'ro-kor-dat'ah)
   Notochord, nerve cord, and postanal tail present only in free-swimming larvae; adults sessile, or occasionally planktonic, and enclosed in a tunic that contains some cellulose; marine. Sea squirts or tunicates.

      Class Ascidiacea (as-id'e-as''e-ah)
      All sessile as adults; solitary or colonial; colony members interconnected by stolons.

      Class Appendicularia (a-pen'di-ku-lar'e-ah)
      (Larvacea) (lar-vas'e-ah)
      Planktonic; adults retain tail and notochord; lack a cellulose tunic; epithelium secretes a gelatinous covering of the body.

      Class Sorberacea (sor'ber-as''e-ah)
      Ascidianlike urochordates possessing dorsal nerve cords as adults; deep water, benthic; carnivorous. *Octacnemus*.

      Class Thaliacea (tal'e-as''e-ah)
      Planktonic; adults are tailless and barrel shaped; oral and atrial openings are at opposite ends of the tunicate; water currents produced by muscular contractions of the body wall.

   Subphylum Cephalochordata (sef'a-lo-kor-dat'ah)
   Body laterally compressed and transparent; fishlike; all four chordate characteristics persist throughout life. Amphioxus (*Branchiostoma*).

   Subphylum Vertebrata (ver'te-bra'tah)
   Notochord, nerve cord, postanal tail, and gill slits present at least in embryonic stages; vertebrae surround nerve cord and serve as primary axial support; skeleton modified anteriorly into a skull for protection of the brain.

      Class Cephalaspidomorphi (sef-ah-las'pe-do-morf'e)
      Fishlike; jawless; no paired appendages; cartilaginous skeleton; sucking mouth with teeth and rasping tongue. Lampreys.

      Class Myxini (mik-sy-ny)
      Fishlike; jawless; no paired appendages; mouth with four pairs of tentacles; olfactory sacs open to mouth cavity; 5 to 15 pairs of gill slits. Hagfishes.

      Class Chondrichthyes (kon-drik'thi-es)
      Fishlike; jawed; paired appendages and cartilaginous skeleton; no swim bladder. Skates, rays, sharks.

      Class Osteichthyes (os'te-ik'thee-ez)
      Bony skeleton; swim bladder and operculum present. Bony fishes.

      Class Amphibia (am-fib'e-ah)
      Skin with mucoid secretions; possess lungs and/or gills; moist skin serves as respiratory organ, aquatic developmental stages usually followed by metamorphosis to an adult. Frogs, toads, salamanders.

      Class Reptilia (rep-til'e-ah)
      Dry skin with epidermal scales; amniotic eggs; terrestrial embryonic development. Snakes, lizards, alligators.

      Class Aves (a'vez)
      Scales modified into feathers for flight; efficiently regulate body temperature (endothermic); amniotic eggs. Birds.

      Class Mammalia (ma-may'le-ah)
      Bodies at least partially covered by hair; endothermic; young nursed from mammary glands; amniotic eggs. Mammals.

The circulatory system of acorn worms consists of one dorsal and one ventral contractile vessel. Blood moves anteriorly in the dorsal vessel and posteriorly in the ventral vessel. Branches from these vessels lead to open sinuses. All blood flowing anteriorly passes into a series of blood sinuses, called the glomerulus, at the base of the proboscis. Excretory wastes may be filtered through the glomerulus, into the coelom of the proboscis, and released to the outside through one or two pores in the wall of the proboscis. The blood of acorn worms is colorless, lacks cellular elements, and distributes nutrients and wastes.

Reproduction and Development

Enteropneusts are dioecious. Two rows of gonads lie in the body wall in the anterior region of the trunk, and each gonad opens separately to the outside. Fertilization is external. Spawning by one worm induces others in the area to spawn—behavior that suggests the presence of spawning pheromones. Ciliated larvae, called **tornaria**, swim in the plankton for several days to a few weeks. The larvae settle to the substrate and are gradually transformed into the adult form (figure 26.4).

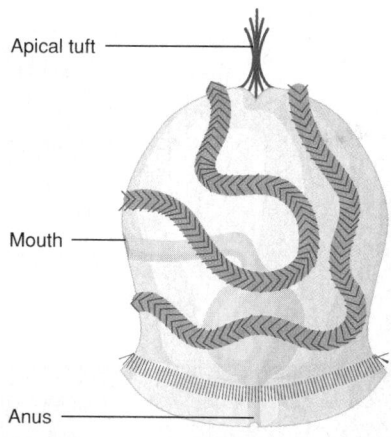

FIGURE 26.4

The Tornaria Larva (*Balanoglossus*). When larval development is complete, a tornaria locates a suitable substrate, settles, and begins to burrow and elongate.

CLASS PTEROBRANCHIA

Pterobranchia (ter'o-brang"ke-ah) (Gk. *pteron*, wing or feather + *branchia*, gills) is a small class of hemichordates found mostly in deep, oceanic waters of the Southern Hemisphere. A few are found in European coastal waters and in shallow waters near Bermuda. There are about 20 described species of pterobranchs.

Pterobranchs are small, ranging in size from 0.1 to 5 mm. Most live in secreted tubes in asexually produced colonies. As in enteropneusts, the pterobranch body is divided into three regions. The proboscis is expanded and shieldlike (figure 26.5). It secretes the tube and aids in movement in the tube. The collar possesses two to nine arms with numerous ciliated tentacles. The trunk is U-shaped.

Maintenance Functions

Pterobranchs use water currents generated by cilia on their arms and tentacles to filter feed. Food particles are trapped and transported by cilia toward the mouth. Although there is a single pair of pharyngeal gill slits in one genus, there is little need for either respiratory or excretory structures in animals as small as pterobranchs, because exchanges of gases and wastes occur by diffusion.

Reproduction and Development

Asexual budding is common in pterobranchs and is responsible for colony formation. Pterobranchs also possess one or two gonads in the anterior trunk. Most species are dioecious, and external fertilization results in the development of a planulalike larva that lives for a time in the tube of the female. This non-feeding larva eventually leaves the female's tube, settles to the substrate, forms a cocoon, and metamorphoses into an adult.

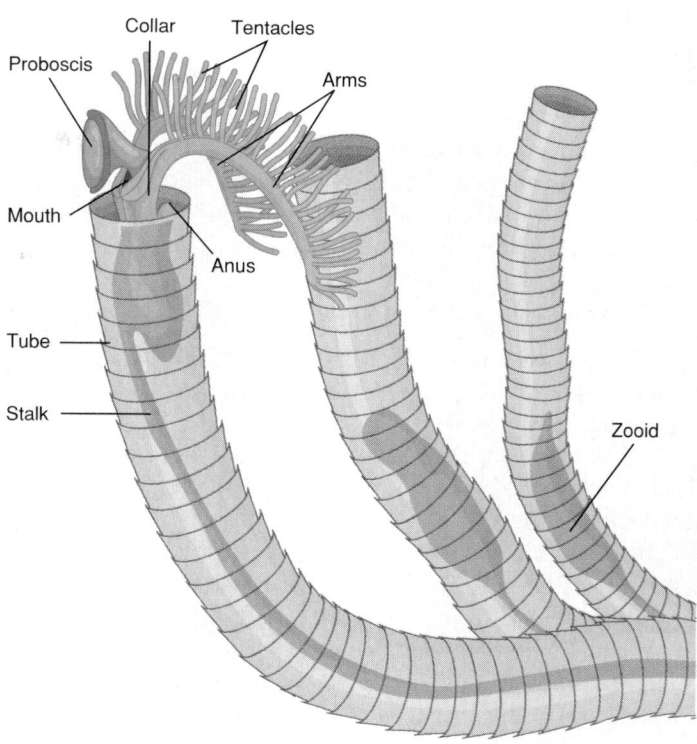

FIGURE 26.5

External Structure of *Rhabdopleura*. Ciliated tracts on tentacles and arms direct food particles toward the mouth.

Stop and Ask Yourself

1. What are the three body regions of a hemichordate? What is the function of these regions in acorn worms? In pterobranchs?

2. How are the feeding mechanisms of acorn worms and pterobranchs similar?

3. How do respiratory and excretory functions occur in hemichordates?

PHYLUM CHORDATA

Although the phylum Chordata (kor-dat'ah) (L. *chorda*, cord) does not have an inordinately large number of species (about 45,000), its members have been very successful at adapting to aquatic and terrestrial environments throughout the world. Sea squirts, members of the subphylum Urochordata, were briefly described in the introduction to this chapter. Other chordates include lancelets (subphylum Cephalochordata) and the vertebrates (subphylum Vertebrata) (*see table 26.1*). Characteristics of the phylum Chordata include the following:

1. Bilaterally symmetrical, deuterostomate animals
2. Four unique characteristics present at some stage in development: notochord, pharyngeal gill slits, dorsal tubular nerve cord, and postanal tail
3. Presence of an endostyle or thyroid gland
4. Complete digestive tract
5. Ventral, contractile blood vessel (heart)

② Four of the characteristics listed above (no. 2) are unique to all chordates. They are discussed further in the following paragraphs (*see figure 10.7a,b*).

The phylum is named after the **notochord** (Gr. *noton*, the back + L. *chorda*, cord), a supportive rod that extends most of the length of the animal dorsal to the body cavity and into the tail. It consists of a connective-tissue sheath that encloses cells, each of which contains a large, fluid-filled vacuole. This arrangement gives the notochord some turgidity, which prevents compression along the anteroposterior axis. At the same time, it is flexible enough to allow some freedom for lateral bending, as in the lateral undulations of a fish during swimming. In most adult vertebrates, the notochord is partly or entirely replaced by cartilage or bone.

Pharyngeal gill slits are a series of openings in the pharyngeal region between the digestive tract and the outside of the body. In some chordates, diverticula from the gut in the pharyngeal region never break through to form an open passageway to the outside. These diverticula are then called pharyngeal gill pouches. The earliest chordates used the gill slits for filter feeding; some living chordates still use them for feeding. Other chordates have developed gills in the pharyngeal pouches for gas exchange. The pharyngeal gill slits of terrestrial vertebrates are mainly embryonic features and may be incomplete.

The **tubular nerve cord** and its associated structures are largely responsible for the success of the chordates. The nerve cord runs along the longitudinal axis of the body, just dorsal to the notochord, and is usually expanded anteriorly as a brain. This central nervous system is associated with the development of complex systems for sensory perception, integration, and motor responses.

The fourth chordate characteristic is a **postanal tail.** (A postanal tail extends posteriorly beyond the anal opening.) The tail is either supported by the notochord or vertebral column.

SUBPHYLUM UROCHORDATA

Members of the subphylum Urochordata (u'ro-kor-dat'ah) (Gr. *uro*, tail + L. *chorda*, cord) are the tunicates or sea squirts. The ascidians comprise the largest class of tunicates (table 26.1). They are sessile as adults and are either solitary or colonial. The

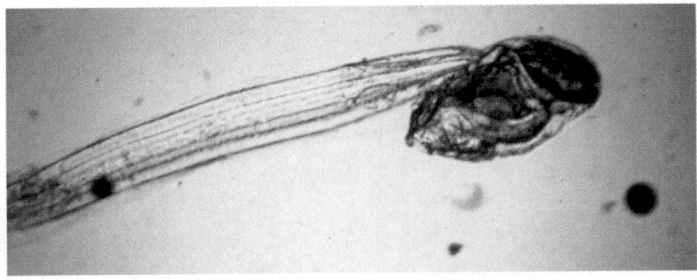

(a)

(b)

FIGURE 26.6

Subphylum Urochordata. (*a*) Members of the class Appendicularia are planktonic and have a tail and notochord that persist into the adult stage. (*b*) The thaliaceans are barrel-shaped, planktonic urochordates. Oral and atrial siphons are at opposite ends of the body, and muscles of the body wall contract to create a form of weak jet propulsion.

appendicularians and thaliaceans are planktonic as adults (figure 26.6; box 26.1). In some localities, tunicates occur in large enough numbers to be considered a dominant life form.

Sessile urochordates attach their saclike bodies to rocks, pilings, hulls of ships, and other solid substrates. The unattached

BOX 26.1 | PLANKTONIC TUNICATES

Although the description of urochordates in this textbook is based primarily upon attached ascidian tunicates, planktonic species are numerous and important in marine food webs. Dense swarms of tunicates, hundreds of kilometers wide and many meters deep, are common in the open ocean. Swarms of larvaceans (*see figure 26.6a*) have been estimated to contain up to 25,000 animals per cubic meter! Larvaceans filter organisms as small as bacteria (0.1 μm in diameter), and in turn, are fed on by other plankton feeders, such as sardines and herring.

Thaliacean tunicates also occur in large, dense swarms in the open ocean (*see figure 26.6b*). Most are aggregations of solitary individuals; however, some form spectacular luminescent colonies. Pyrosome colonies, such as the one shown in figure 1, are found in many oceans. Colonies 10 m long and 1 m in diameter are common. Individuals are oriented with oral siphons pointed outward and atrial siphons directed toward the center of the colony. Ciliary currents and contractions of body-wall muscles direct water toward a central cavity of the colony and slowly move the entire colony through the water. When a part of the colony is stimulated by chemical or mechanical stimuli, it luminesces and ceases ciliary beating. The luminescence spreads over

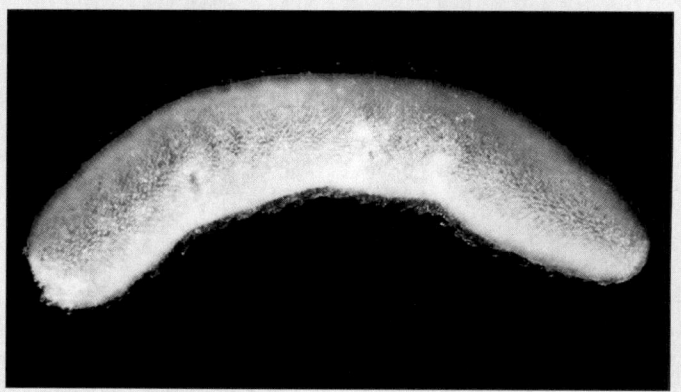

FIGURE 1 **Planktonic Tunicates.** A pyrosome colony (*Pyrosoma spinosum*).

the entire colony, and the colony stops moving. This behavior may help the colony avoid unfavorable environments or confuse or frighten predators.

---

end of urochordates contains two siphons that permit seawater to circulate through the body. One siphon is the oral siphon, which is the inlet for water circulating through the body and is usually directly opposite the attached end of the ascidian (figure 26.7). It also serves as the mouth opening. The second siphon, the atrial siphon, is the opening for excurrent water.

3 The body wall of most tunicates (L. *tunicatus*, to wear a tunic or gown) is a connective-tissuelike covering, called the tunic, that appears gellike, but is often quite tough. It is secreted by the epidermis and is composed of proteins, various salts, and cellulose. Some mesodermally derived tissues are incorporated into the tunic, including blood vessels and blood cells. Rootlike extensions of the tunic, called stolons, help anchor a tunicate to the substrate and may connect individuals of a colony.

Maintenance Functions

Longitudinal and circular muscles are present below the body wall epithelium and help to change the shape of the adult tunicate. They act against the elasticity of the tunic and the hydrostatic skeleton created by seawater confined to internal chambers.

The nervous system of tunicates is largely confined to the body wall. It forms a nerve plexus with a single ganglion located on the wall of the pharynx between the oral and atrial openings (figure 26.8a). This ganglion is not vital for coordinating bodily functions. Tunicates are sensitive to many kinds of mechanical and chemical stimuli, and receptors for these senses are distributed over the body wall, especially around the siphons. There are no complex sensory organs.

The most obvious internal structures of the urochordates are a very large pharynx and a cavity, called the atrium, that surrounds the pharynx laterally and dorsally (figure 26.8b). The pharynx of tunicates originates at the oral siphon and is continuous with the remainder of the digestive tract. The oral margin of the pharynx has tentacles that prevent large objects from entering the pharynx. The pharynx is perforated by numerous gill slits called stigmas. Cilia associated with the stigmas cause water to circulate into the pharynx, through the stigmas, and into the surrounding atrium. Water leaves the tunicate through the atrial siphon.

The digestive tract of adult tunicates continues from the pharynx and ends at the anus near the atrial siphon. During feeding, a mucous sheet is formed by cells of a ventral, ciliated

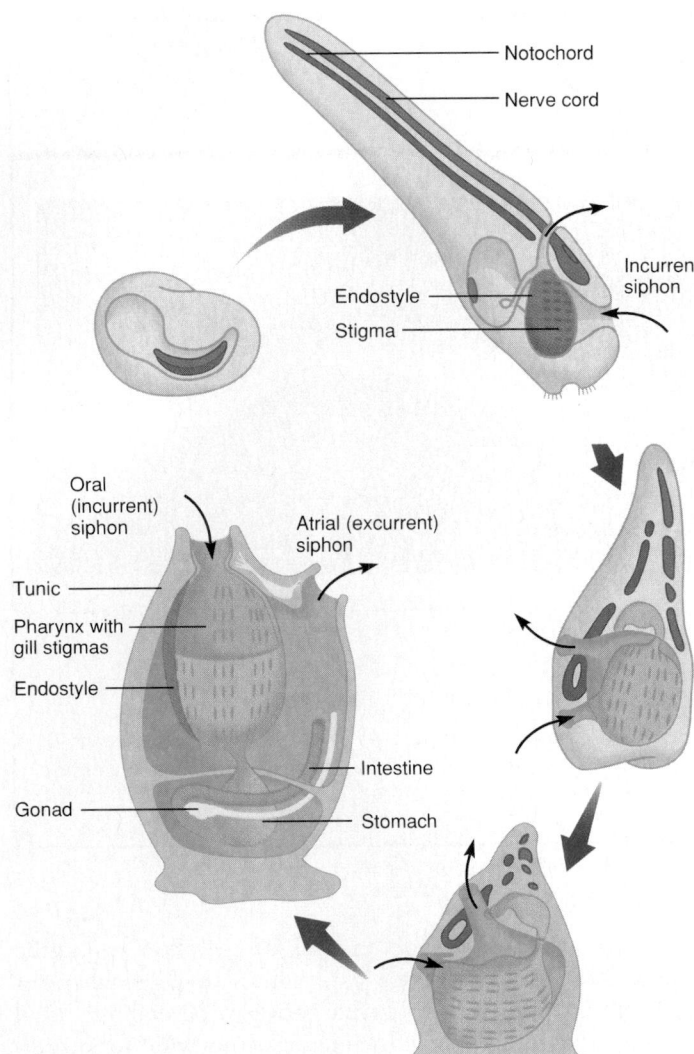

FIGURE 26.7

Tunicate Metamorphosis. Small arrows show the path of water through the body.

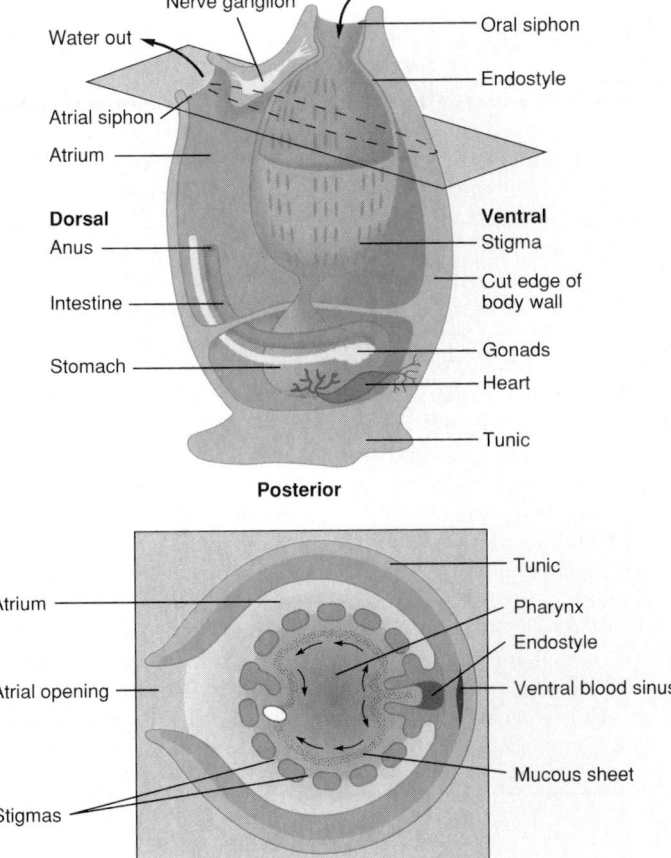

FIGURE 26.8

Internal Structure of a Tunicate. (*a*) Longitudinal section. Arrows show the path of water. (*b*) Cross section at the level of the atrial siphon. Arrows show movement of food trapped in mucus, which is produced by the endostyle.

groove, called the **endostyle** (figure 26.8*b*; box 26.2). Cilia move the mucous sheet dorsally across the pharynx. Food particles, brought into the oral siphon with incurrent water, are trapped in the mucous sheet and passed dorsally. Food is incorporated into a string of mucus that is moved by ciliary action into the next region of the gut tract. Digestive enzymes are secreted in the stomach, and most absorption occurs across the walls of the intestine. Digestive wastes are carried from the anus out of the atrial siphon with excurrent water.

In addition to its role in feeding, the pharynx also functions in gas exchange. Gases are exchanged between water circulating through the tunicate.

The tunicate heart lies at the base of the pharynx. One vessel from the heart runs anteriorly under the endostyle and another runs posteriorly to the digestive organs and gonads. Blood flow through the heart is not unidirectional. Peristaltic contractions of the heart may propel blood in one direction for a few beats, then the direction is reversed. The significance of this reversal is not understood. Tunicate blood plasma is colorless and contains various kinds of amoeboid cells.

Excretion is accomplished by the diffusion of ammonia into water that passes through the pharynx. In addition, amoeboid cells of the circulatory system accumulate uric acid and sequester it in the intestinal loop. Pyloric glands on the outside of the intestine are also thought to have excretory functions.

| BOX | 26.2 | THE ENDOSTYLE AND THE VERTEBRATE THYROID GLAND |

Neither the structure nor the function of the urochordate or cephalochordate endostyle give any clue to its fate in the vertebrates. Similarly, when examining adult vertebrates, one never sees a ciliated groove that once functioned to produce a sticky, mucous trap for filter-feeding ancestors. The study of the development of one group of vertebrates, the lampreys, has provided insight into the endostyle's evolutionary fate.

An endostyle is present in larval lampreys, where it produces a mucous filter, just as in the invertebrate chordates. In addition, it has the ability to bind iodine to the amino acid tyrosine. The significance of this second function is revealed in observing what happens to the endostyle when the larval lamprey metamorphoses to the adult and becomes a predator. Mucus-secreting functions of the endostyle become secondary, and the secretion of iodine-bound tyrosine derivatives becomes its primary function. During larval metamorphosis, the endostyle is transformed into an endocrine gland common to all vertebrates, the thyroid gland. The iodine-containing secretions of the thyroid gland of vertebrates regulate metamorphosis and metabolic rate.

The development of the thyroid gland of lampreys may reflect evolutionary events leading to the vertebrate thyroid gland. The endostyle of vertebrate ancestors may have had both mucus-secreting and endocrine functions. With the evolution of jaws and a more active, predatory life-style, endocrine functions were probably favored.

Reproduction and Development

both ♀ + ♂

Urochordates are monoecious. Gonads are located near the loop of the intestine, and genital ducts open near the atrial siphon. Gametes may be shed through the atrial siphon for external fertilization, or eggs may be retained in the atrium for fertilization and early development. Although self-fertilization occurs in some species, cross-fertilization is the rule. ④ Development results in the formation of a tadpolelike larva that possesses all four chordate characteristics. Metamorphosis begins after a brief free-swimming larval existence, during which the larva does not feed. The larva settles to a firm substrate and attaches by adhesive papillae located below the mouth. During metamorphosis, the tail is reduced by a shrinking of the outer epidermis that pulls the notochord and other tail structures internally for reorganization into adult tissues. The internal structures rotate 180°, resulting in the positioning of the oral siphon opposite the adhesive papillae and the bending of the digestive tract into a U shape (*see figure 26.7*).

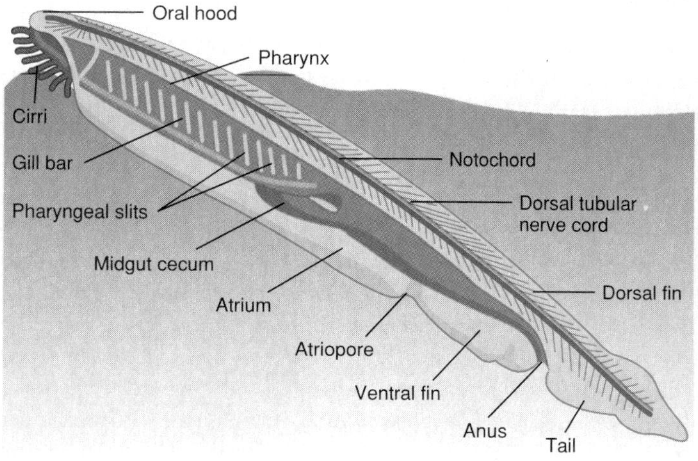

SUBPHYLUM CEPHALOCHORDATA

Members of the subphylum Cephalochordata (sef´a-lo-kordat″ah) (Gr. *kephalo*, head + L. *chorda*, cord) are called lancelets. ⑤ They are almost universally studied in introductory zoology courses during introductions to chordate structure and function because they so clearly demonstrate the four chordate characteristics.

There are two genera, *Branchiostoma* (amphioxus) and *Asymmetron*, and about 45 species of cephalochordates. They

FIGURE **26.9**
Subphylum Cephalochordata. Internal structure of *Branchiostoma* (amphioxus) shown in its partially buried feeding position.

are distributed throughout the world's oceans in shallow waters that have clean sand substrates.

Cephalochordates are small (up to 5 cm long), tadpolelike animals. They are elongate, laterally flattened, and nearly transparent. In spite of their streamlined shape, cephalochordates are relatively weak swimmers and spend most of their time in a filter-feeding position—partly to mostly buried with their anterior end sticking out of the sand (figure 26.9).

The notochord of cephalochordates extends from the tail to the head, giving them their name. Unlike the notochord of other chordates, most of the cells are muscle cells, making the notochord somewhat contractile. Both of these characteristics are probably adaptations to burrowing. Contraction of the muscle cells increases the rigidity of the notochord by compressing the fluids within, giving additional support when pushing into sandy substrates. Relaxation of these muscle cells allows increased flexibility for swimming.

Muscle cells are arranged on either side of the notochord and cause undulations that propel the cephalochordate through the water. Longitudinal, ventrolateral folds of the body wall help stabilize cephalochordates during swimming, and a median dorsal fin and a caudal fin also aid in swimming.

An oral hood projects from the anterior end of cephalochordates. Ciliated, fingerlike projections, called cirri, hang from the ventral aspect of the oral hood and are used in feeding. The posterior wall of the oral hood bears the mouth opening that leads to a large pharynx. Numerous pairs of gill slits perforate the pharynx and are supported by cartilaginous gill bars. Large folds of the body wall extend ventrally around the pharynx and fuse at the ventral midline of the body, creating the atrium, which is a chamber that surrounds the pharyngeal region of the body. It may protect the delicate, filtering surfaces of the pharynx from bottom sediments. The opening from the atrium to the outside is called the atriopore (figure 26.9).

Maintenance Functions

Cephalochordates are filter feeders. During feeding, they are partially or mostly buried in sandy substrates with their mouths pointed upwards. Water is brought into the mouth by the action of cilia on the lateral surfaces of gill bars. Water passes from the pharynx, through gill slits to the atrium, and out of the body through the atriopore. Initial sorting of food occurs at the cirri. Larger materials are caught on cilia of the cirri. As these larger particles accumulate, they are thrown off by contractions of the cirri. Smaller, edible particles are pulled into the mouth with water and are collected by cilia on the gill bars and in mucus secreted by the endostyle. As in tunicates, the endostyle is a ciliated groove that extends longitudinally along the midventral aspect of the pharynx. Cilia move food and mucus dorsally, forming a food cord that is moved by cilia to the gut. A ring of cilia rotates the food cord, and in the process, food is dislodged. Digestion is both extracellular and intracellular. A diverticulum off the gut, called the midgut cecum, extends anteriorly. It ends blindly along the right side of the pharynx and secretes digestive enzymes. An anus is on the left side of the ventral fin.

Cephalochordates do not possess a true heart. Blood is propelled by contractile waves in the walls of major vessels. Blood contains amoeboid cells and bathes tissues in open spaces.

Excretory tubules are modified coelomic cells that are closely associated with blood vessels. This arrangement suggests active transport of materials between the blood and excretory tubules.

The coelom of cephalochordates is reduced as compared to most other chordates. It is restricted to canals near the gill bars, the endostyle, and the gonads.

Reproduction and Development

Cephalochordates are dioecious. Gonads bulge into the atrium from the lateral body wall. Gametes are shed into the atrium and leave the body through the atriopore. External fertilization leads to a bilaterally symmetrical larva. Larvae are free swimming, but they eventually settle to the substrate before metamorphosing into adults.

FURTHER PHYLOGENETIC CONSIDERATIONS

The evolutionary relationships between the hemichordates and chordates are difficult to document with certainty. The dorsal, tubular nerve cord and pharyngeal gill slits of hemichordates are evidence of evolutionary ties between these phyla (figure 26.10). There are, however, questions regarding the homologies of these structures. Synapomorphies that distinguish chordates from hemichordates include tadpole larvae, notochord, postanal tail, and an endostyle.

Evolutionary relationships between members of the three chordate subphyla are also shown in figure 26.10. As discussed in chapter 25, the earliest echinoderms were probably sessile filter feeders.

The life-style of adult urochordates suggests a similar ancestry (perhaps from a common ancestor with echinoderms) for chordates. The evolution of motile chordates from attached ancestors may have involved the development of a tadpolelike larva. Increased larval mobility is often adaptive for species with sedentary adults because it promotes dispersal.   ⑥   The evolution of motile adults could have resulted from paedomorphosis, which is the development of sexual maturity in the larval body form. (The occurrence of paedomorphosis is well documented in the animal kingdom, especially among amphibians.) Paedomorphosis could have led to a small, sexually reproducing, fishlike chordate that could have been the ancestor of higher chordates.

The largest and most successful chordates belong to the subphylum Vertebrata. They are characterized by bony or cartilaginous vertebrae that completely or partially replace the notochord. A high degree of cephalization is evidenced by the development of the anterior end of the nerve cord into a brain and the development of specialized sense organs

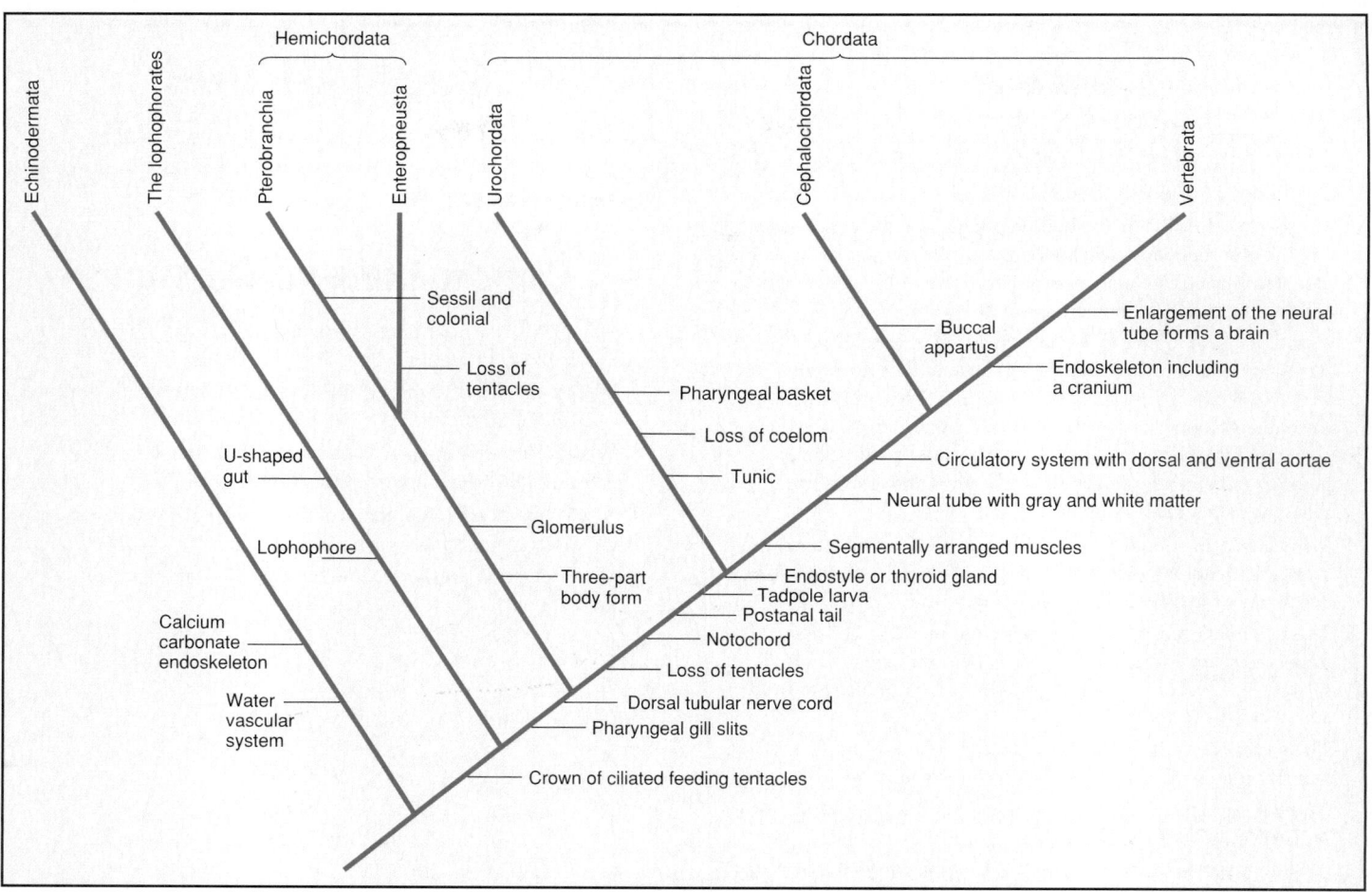

FIGURE 26.10

One Interpretation of Deuterostomate Phylogeny. The dorsal tubular nerve cord and pharyngeal gill slits are possible synapomorphies that link the Hemichordata and the Chordata. The notochord, postanal tail, and endostyle or thyroid gland are important characters that distinguish the Hemichordata and Chordata. Some of the synapomorphies that distinguish the chordate subphyla are shown.

on the head. The skeleton is modified anteriorly into a skull or cranium. There are eight classes of vertebrates (*see table 26.1*). Because of their cartilaginous and bony endoskeletons, vertebrates have left an abundant fossil record. Ancient jawless fishes were common in the Ordovician period, approximately 500 million years ago. Over a period of approximately 100 million years, fishes became the dominant vertebrates. Near the end of the Devonian period, approximately 400 million years ago, terrestrial vertebrates made their appearance. Since that time, vertebrates have radiated into most of the earth's habitats. Chapters 27 to 31 give an account of these events.

Stop and Ask Yourself

4. What are four characteristics shared by all chordates at some time in their life history?

5. What group of chordates deposit cellulose in their body wall?

6. What is an endostyle? What functions does it have in urochordates? In cephalochordates?

7. What is the function of the midgut cecum of cephalochordates?

SUMMARY

1. Echinoderms, hemichordates, and chordates share deuterostome characteristics and are believed to have evolved from a common diploblastic or triploblastic ancestor.

2. Members of the phylum Hemichordata include the acorn worms and the pterobranchs. Acorn worms are burrowing, marine worms, and pterobranchs are marine hemichordates whose collar possesses arms with numerous ciliated tentacles.

3. Chordates have four unique characteristics. A notochord is a supportive rod that extends most of the length of the animal. Pharyngeal gill slits are a series of openings between the digestive tract and the outside of the body. The tubular nerve cord lies just above the notochord and is expanded anteriorly into a brain. A postanal tail extends posteriorly to the anus and is supported by the notochord or the vertebral column.

4. Members of the subphylum Urochordata are the tunicates or sea squirts. Urochordates are sessile or planktonic filter feeders. Their development involves a tadpolelike larva.

5. The subphylum Cephalochordata includes small, tadpolelike filter feeders that live in shallow, marine waters with clean sandy substrates. Their notochord extends from the tail into the head and is somewhat contractile.

6. The presence of gill slits and a tubular nerve cord link hemichordates and chordates to the same evolutionary lineage.

7. Chordates probably evolved from a sessile, filter-feeding ancestor. A larval stage of this sedentary ancestor may have undergone paedomorphosis to produce a small, sexually reproducing fishlike chordate.

SELECTED KEY TERMS

endostyle (*p. 426*)
notochord (*p. 424*)
pharyngeal gill slits (*p. 424*)

postanal tail (*p. 424*)
tubular nerve cord (*p. 424*)

CRITICAL THINKING QUESTIONS

1. What evidence links hemichordates and chordates to the same evolutionary lineage?

2. What evidence of chordate affinities is present in adult tunicates? In larval tunicates?

3. What is paedomorphosis? What is a possible role for paedomorphosis in chordate evolution?

4. Discuss the possible influence of filter-feeding life-styles on early chordate evolution.

5. What selection pressures could have favored a foraging or predatory life-style for later chordates?

THE FISHES: VERTEBRATE SUCCESS IN WATER

Concepts

1. The earliest fossil vertebrates are 510-million-year-old ostracoderms.
2. Members of the superclass Agnatha include extinct ostracoderms, the lampreys, and the hagfishes. Agnathans lack jaws and paired appendages.
3. The superclass Gnathostomata includes the cartilaginous (class Chondrichthyes) and bony (class Osteichthyes) fishes.
4. Aquatic environments have selected for certain adaptations in fishes. These include the ability to move in a relatively dense medium, exchange gases with water or air, regulate buoyancy, detect environmental changes, regulate salt and water in their tissues, and successfully reproduce.
5. Adaptive radiation resulted in the large variety of fishes present today. Evolution of some fishes led to the terrestrial vertebrates.

Would You Like to Know:

1. what group of fishes probably gave rise to all other fishes? (*p. 432*)
2. how a shark's teeth are replaced? (*p. 438*)
3. what fishes have lungs and breathe air? (*p. 439*)
4. what fish living today is the closest relative of terrestrial vertebrates? (*p. 440*)
5. why some sharks never stop moving? (*p. 443*)
6. how a shark can find a flounder completely covered by sand? (*p. 445*)
7. what environmental conditions selected for adaptations in fishes that eventually led to terrestrial vertebrates? (*p. 449*)

These and other useful questions will be answered in this chapter.

This chapter contains evolutionary concepts, which are set off in this font.

EVOLUTIONARY PERSPECTIVE

Over 70% of the earth's surface is covered by water, a medium that is buoyant and resistant to rapid fluctuations in temperature. Because life began in water, and living tissues are made mostly of water, it might seem that nowhere else would life be easier to sustain. This chapter describes why that is not entirely true.

You do not need to wear SCUBA gear to appreciate the fact that fishes are adapted to aquatic environments in a fashion unsurpassed by any other group of animals. If you spend recreational hours with hook and line, visit a marine theme park, or simply glance into a pet store when walking through a shopping mall, you can attest to the variety and beauty of fishes. This variety is evidence of adaptive radiation that began 500 million years ago and shows no sign of ceasing. Fishes not only dominate many watery environments, they are also the ancestors of all other members of the subphylum Vertebrata.

PHYLOGENETIC RELATIONSHIPS

Fishes are members of the chordate subphylum Vertebrata; thus, they have vertebrae that surround their spinal cord and provide the primary axial support. They also have a skull that protects the brain (*see table 26.1*; figure 27.1).

Zoologists do not know what animals were the first vertebrates. Recent cladistic analysis of vertebrate evolution indicates that a group of fishes, called hagfishes, are the most primitive vertebrates known (living or extinct). Fossilized bony fragments indicate that bone was present at least 510 million years ago. These fossils are from bony armor that covered animals called ostracoderms. Ostracoderms were relatively inactive filter feeders that lived on the bottom of prehistoric lakes and seas. They possessed neither jaws nor paired appendages; however, the evolution of fishes resulted in both jaws and paired appendages as well as many other structures. The results of this adaptive radiation are described in this chapter.

Did ancestral fishes live in fresh water or in the sea? The answer to this question is not simple. The first vertebrates were probably marine because ancient stocks of other deuterostome phyla were all marine. Vertebrates, however, adapted to fresh water very early, and much of the evolution of fishes occurred there. Apparently, early vertebrate evolution involved the movement of fishes back and forth between marine and freshwater environments. The majority of the evolutionary history of some fishes took place in ancient seas, and most of the evolutionary history of others occurred in fresh water. The importance of fresh water in the evolution of fishes is evidenced by the fact that over 41% of all fish species are found in fresh water, even though freshwater habitats represent only a small percentage (0.0093% by volume) of the earth's water resources.

FIGURE 27.1

The Fishes. Five hundred million years of evolution have resulted in unsurpassed diversity in the fishes. The spines of this beautiful marine lionfish (*Pterois*) are extremely venomous.

SURVEY OF FISHES

The taxonomy of fishes has been the subject of debate for many years. Modern cladistic analysis has resulted in complex revisions in the taxonomy of this group of vertebrates (figure 27.2). The system used in this textbook divides fishes into two superclasses based on whether they lack jaws and paired appendages (superclass Agnatha) or possess those structures (superclass Gnathostomata) (table 27.1).

SUPERCLASS AGNATHA

Members of the superclass Agnatha (ag-nath'ah) (Gr. *a*, without + *gnathos*, jaw), in addition to lacking jaws and paired appendages, possess a cartilaginous skeleton and a notochord that persists into the adult stage.   Ancient agnathans are believed to be ancestral to all other fishes (*see figure 27.2*).

Ostracoderms are extinct agnathans that belonged to several classes. The fossils of predatory water scorpions (phylum Arthropoda [*see figure 23.7*]) are often found with fossil ostracoderms. As sluggish as ostracoderms apparently were, bony armor was probably their only defense. Ostracoderms were bottom dwellers, often about 15 cm long (figure 27.3). Most are believed to have been filter feeders, either filtering suspended organic matter from the water or extracting annelids and other animals from muddy sediments. Bony plates around the mouths of some ostracoderms may have been used in a jawlike fashion to crack gastropod shells or the exoskeletons of arthropods.

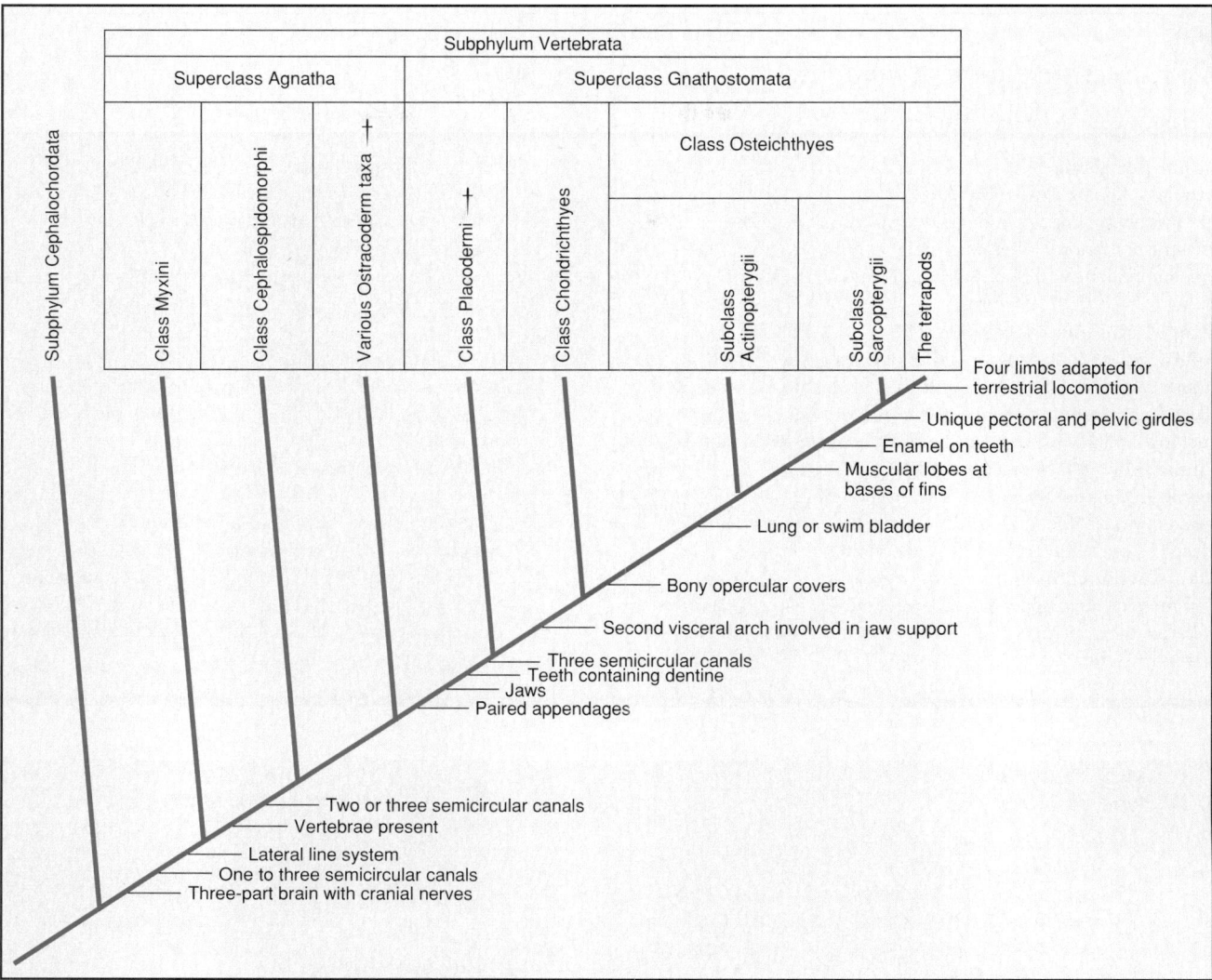

FIGURE **27.2**

One Interpretation of the Phylogeny of the Fishes. The evolutionary relationships among the fishes are unsettled. A few selected ancestral and derived characters are shown in this cladogram. Each lower taxon has numerous synapomorphies that are not shown. The position of the lampreys in fish phylogeny is debated. Recent evidence indicates that both lampreys and ostracoderms are more closely related to jawed vertebrates than to hagfishes. The ostracoderms are considered a paraphyletic group (having multiple lineages) by most zoologists. Their representation as a monophyletic group is an attempt to simplify this presentation. Groups whose members are extinct are indicated with daggers (†).

Class Myxini

Hagfishes are members of the class Myxini (mik-sy′ny) (Gr. *myxa*, slime). Hagfishes live buried in the sand and mud of marine environments, where they feed on soft-bodied invertebrates and scavenge dead and dying fish (figure 27.4). When hagfishes find a suitable fish, they enter the fish through the mouth and eat the contents of the body, leaving only a sack of skin and bones. Anglers must contend with hagfishes because they will bite at a baited hook. Hagfishes have the annoying habit of swallowing a hook so deeply that the hook is frequently lodged near the anus. The excessively slimy bodies of hagfishes

make all but the grittiest fishermen cut their lines and tie on a new hook. Most zoologists now consider the hagfishes to be the most primitive group of vertebrates.

Class Cephalaspidomorphi

Lampreys are agnathans in the class Cephalaspidomorphi (sef-ah-las′pe-do-morf′e) (Gr. *kephale*, head + *aspidos*, shield + *morphe*, form). They are common inhabitants of marine and freshwater environments in temperate regions. Most adult lampreys prey on other fishes, and the larvae are filter feeders. The mouth of an adult is suckerlike and surrounded by lips that

TABLE 27.1	CLASSIFICATION OF LIVING FISHES

Subphylum Vertebrata

 Superclass Agnatha (ag-nath´ah)
 Lack jaws and paired appendages; cartilaginous skeleton; persistent notochord; two semicircular canals. (Hagfishes have one semicircular canal that may represent a fusion of two canals.)

  Class Myxini (mik-sy´ny)
  Mouth with four pairs of tentacles; olfactory sacs open to mouth cavity; 5 to 15 pairs of gill slits. Hagfishes.

  Class Cephalaspidomorphi (sef-ah-las´pe-do-morf´e)
  Sucking mouth with teeth and rasping tongue; seven pairs of gill slits; blind olfactory sacs. Lampreys.

 Superclass Gnathostomata (na´tho-sto´ma-tah)
 Hinged jaws and paired appendages present; notochord may be replaced by vertebral column; three semicircular canals.

  Class Chondrichthyes (kon-drik´thi-es)
  Tail fin with large upper lobe (heterocercal tail); cartilaginous skeleton; lack opercula and a swim bladder or lungs. Sharks, skates, rays, ratfishes.

   Subclass Elasmobranchii (e-laz-mo´bran´ke-i)
   Cartilaginous skeleton may be partially ossified; placoid scales or no scales. Sharks, skates, rays.

   Subclass Holocephali (hol´o-sef´a-li)
   Operculum covers gill slits; lack scales; teeth modified into crushing plates; lateral-line receptors in an open groove. Ratfishes.

  Class Osteichthyes (os´te-ik´´the-es)
  Most with bony skeleton; single gill opening covered by operculum; pneumatic sacs function as lungs or swim bladders. Bony fishes.

   Subclass Sarcopterygii (sar-kop-te-rij´e-i)
   Paired fins with muscular lobes; pneumatic sacs funtion as lungs. Lungfishes and coelacanths (lobe-finned fishes).

   Subclass Actinopterygii (ak´tin-op´´te-rig-e-i)
   Paired fins supported by dermal rays; basal portions of paired fins not especially muscular; tail fin with approximately equal upper and lower lobes (homocercal tail); blind olfactory sacs. Ray-finned fishes.

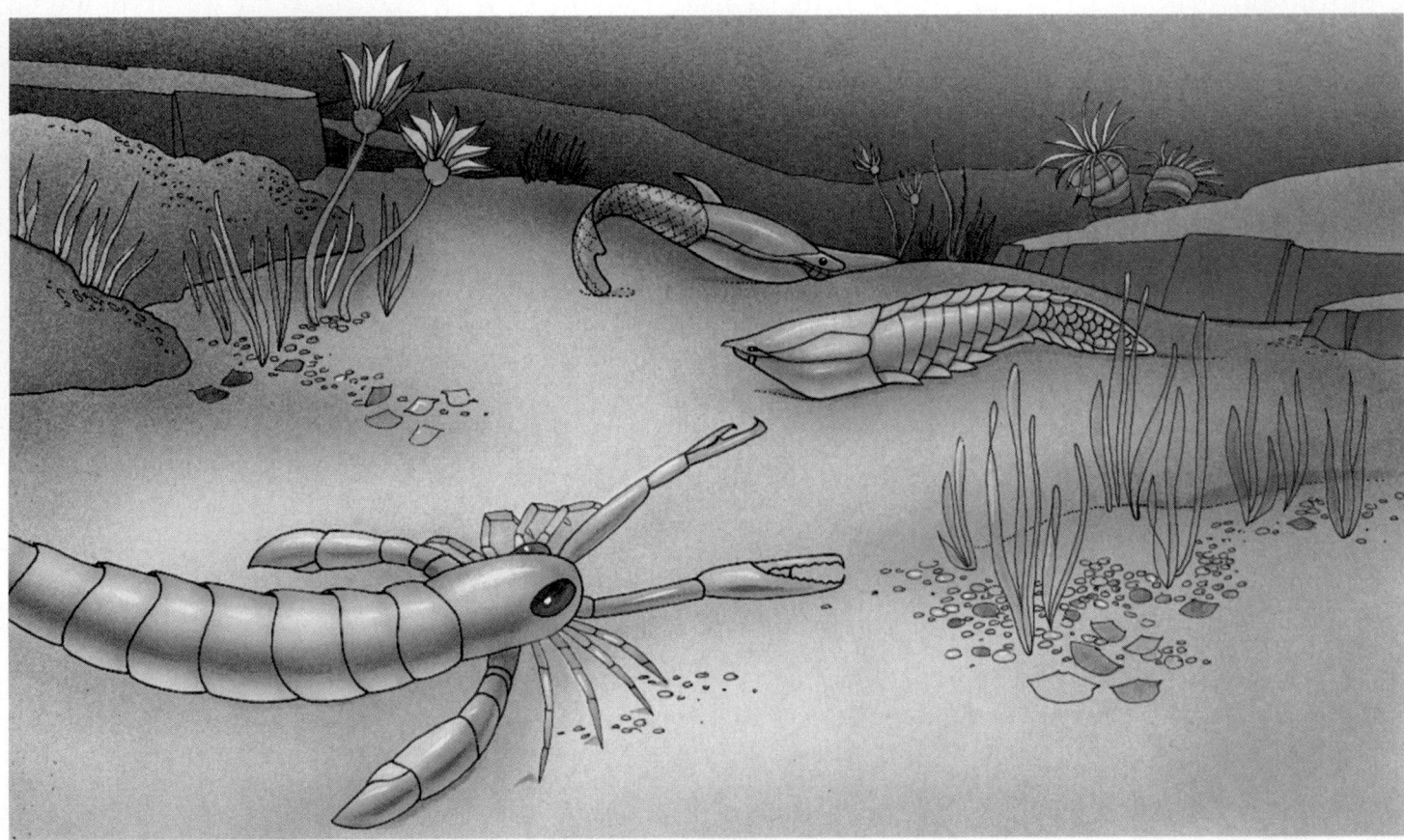

FIGURE 27.3

Artist's Rendering of an Ancient Silurian Seafloor. Two ostracoderms, *Pteraspis* and *Anglaspis*, are shown in the background and a predatory water scorpion (phylum Arthropoda, class Merostomata) is shown in the foreground.

27.4

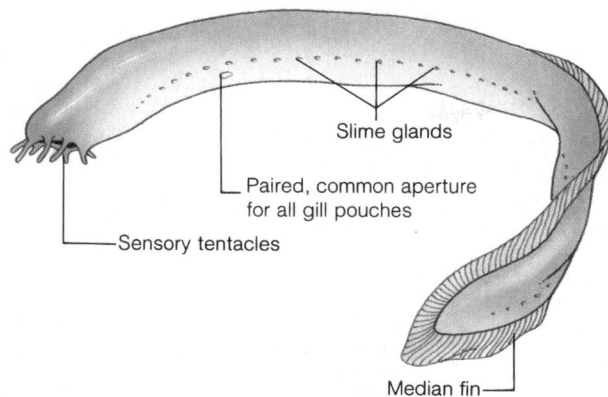

FIGURE 27.4

Class Myxini. Hagfish external structure.

FIGURE 27.5

Class Agnatha. A lamprey (*Petromyzon marinus*). Note the sucking mouth and teeth used to feed on other fish.

have sensory and attachment functions. Numerous epidermal teeth line the mouth and cover a movable tonguelike structure (figure 27.5). Adults attach to prey with their lips and teeth and use their tongue to rasp away scales. Lampreys have salivary glands with anticoagulant secretions and feed mainly on the blood of their prey (box 27.1). Some lampreys, however, are

BOX 27.1   LAMPREYS AND GREAT LAKES FISHERIES

Along with many other European immigrants to the United States in the nineteenth century came many Scandinavians. Many of these Scandinavian immigrants fished for a living, and they were understandably attracted to the Great Lakes Region. Through the early part of the twentieth century, fishing was very good. Catches included a variety of smaller fishes that inhabited the shoals and bays of the Great Lakes, but the prize catches were two deep water predators—lake trout (*Salvelinus namaycush*) and whitefish (*Corygonus clupeaformis*). The yearly catch of lake trout in each of the Great Lakes in the 1930s exceeded 2,000 metric tons.

These commercial fisheries, however, were doomed. Their fate was sealed years before many immigrants even left their homes in Scandinavia. In 1829, the Welland Canal was completed. It provided a shipping route around Niagara Falls between Lakes Ontario and Erie. Niagara Falls, however, had not only been a barrier to shipping, it had also been a barrier to the sea lamprey. After the Welland Canal was completed, sea lampreys slowly worked their way from Lake Ontario to the other Great Lakes. By 1937, spawning lampreys were recorded in Lake Michigan, and by the early 1940s Great Lakes fishermen had to work very hard to bring home a single lake trout with a day's catch of predominately smaller fishes. The lamprey, like humans, had a decided preference for the larger, cold-water fish species. In 1944, the annual catch of lake trout from Lake Michigan had been reduced to less than 100 metric tons. In 1953, the annual catch of lake trout in Lake Michigan was reduced to a few hundred kilograms!

Although the invasion of lampreys into the Great Lakes brought severe economic hardship to many fishermen, it also resulted in an important success story in fishery management. In the 1950s, an intensive lamprey control program was instituted by the states bordering the Great Lakes and by Canada. Control measures involved the use of mechanical weirs that prevented spawning migrations of lampreys into the tributaries of the Great Lakes. Electrical shocking devices were employed in an attempt to kill lampreys in spawning streams. Finally, chemical control measures were employed. Lamprey populations began to decline, and by the mid-1960s lamprey control measures were considered a success.

The void left by the decline of lake trout has been filled by a sport fishery. In the late 1960s, Coho (*Concorhynchus kisutch*) and Chinook (*Oncorhynchus tshawytscha*) salmon were stocked in the Great Lakes to create a sport fishery. Survival and growth of these salmon have been remarkable, and fewer than 5% of the salmon caught are marked by lamprey wounds. Whitefish and lake trout are again being caught. To preserve this fishery, lamprey control measures will be maintained in the future to prevent large-scale growth of lamprey populations.

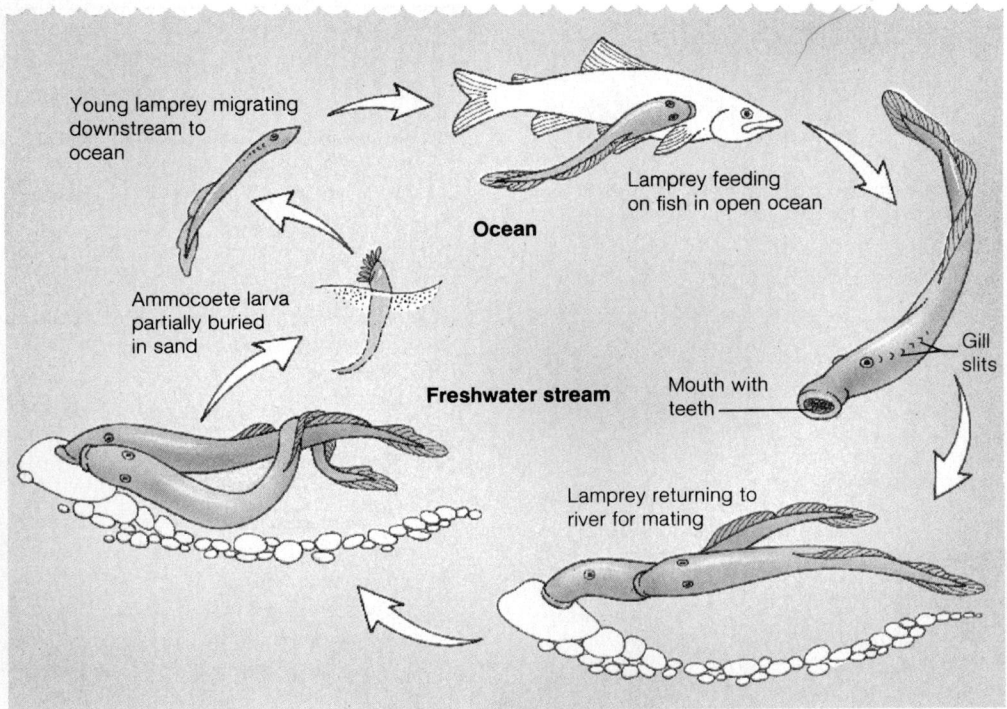

FIGURE 27.6

External Structure and Life History of a Sea Lamprey. Sea lampreys feed in the open ocean and near the end of their lives, migrate into freshwater streams where mating occurs. Eggs are deposited in nests on the stream bottom, and young ammocoete larvae hatch in about 3 weeks. Ammocoete larvae live as filter feeders until they attain sexual maturity.

not predatory. Members of the genus *Lampetra* are called brook lampreys. The larval stages of brook lampreys last for about 3 years, and the adults neither feed nor leave their stream. They reproduce soon after metamorphosis and then die.

Adult sea lampreys live in the ocean or the Great Lakes. Near the end of their lives, they undertake a migration that may take them hundreds of miles to a spawning bed in a freshwater stream. Once lampreys reach their spawning site, usually in relatively shallow water with swift currents, nest building begins. Lampreys make small depressions in the substrate. When the nest is prepared, a female usually attaches to a stone with her mouth. A male attaches to the female's head using his mouth, and wraps his body around the female (figure 27.6). Eggs are shed in small batches over a period of several hours, and fertilization is external. The relatively sticky eggs are then covered with sand.

Eggs hatch in approximately 3 weeks into ammocoete larvae. The larvae drift downstream to softer substrates, where they bury themselves in sand and mud and filter feed in a fashion similar to amphioxus (*see figure 26.9*).

Ammocoete larvae grow from 7 mm to about 17 cm over 3 years. During later developmental stages, the larvae metamorphose to the adult over a period of several months. The mouth becomes suckerlike, and the teeth, tongue, and feeding musculature develop. Lampreys eventually leave the mud permanently and begin a journey to the sea to begin life as predators. Adults will return only once to the headwaters of their stream to spawn and die.

Stop and Ask Yourself

1. What superclass of vertebrates contains the probable ancestors of all other vertebrates?
2. How are members of the superclass Agnatha characterized?
3. What animals make up the class Myxini?
4. How are the life-styles of adult and larval lampreys different?

SUPERCLASS GNATHOSTOMATA

Two major developments in vertebrate evolution were the appearance of jaws and paired appendages. These structures are first seen in members of the superclass Gnathostomata (na'tho-sto'ma-tah) (Gr. *gnathos*, jaw + *stoma*, mouth). Jaws are used in feeding and are partly responsible for a transition to more active, predatory life-styles. Pectoral fins of fishes are appendages that are usually located just behind the head, and

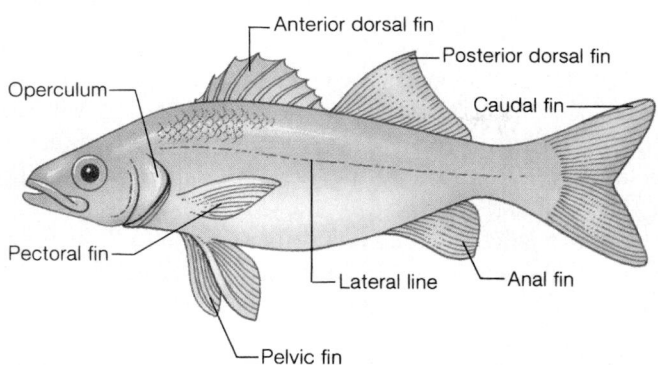
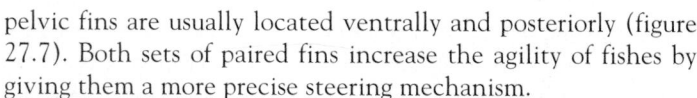

FIGURE 27.7

Paired Appendages. Appendages of a member of the superclass Gnathostomata. These appendages are secondarily reduced in some species.

(a)

(b)

pelvic fins are usually located ventrally and posteriorly (figure 27.7). Both sets of paired fins increase the agility of fishes by giving them a more precise steering mechanism.

Two classes of gnathostomes still have living members: the cartilaginous fishes (class Chondrichthyes) and the bony fishes (class Osteichthyes). Another class, the armored fishes, or placoderms, contained the earliest jawed fishes. They are now extinct and apparently left no descendants. A fourth group of ancient, extinct fishes, the acanthodians, may be more closely related to the bony fishes (*see figure 27.1*).

Class Chondrichthyes

Members of the class Chondrichthyes (kon-drik′thi-es) (Gr. *chondros*, cartilage + *ichthyos*, fish) include the sharks, skates, rays, and ratfishes (*see table 27.1*). Most chondrichthians are carnivores or scavengers, and most are marine species. In addition to their biting mouthparts and paired appendages, chondrichthians possess epidermal placoid scales and a cartilaginous endoskeleton.

There are about 700 species in the subclass Elasmobranchii (e-laz′mo-bran′ke-i) (Gr. *elasmos*, plate metal + *branchia*, gills), which includes the sharks, skates, and rays (figure 27.8a–c). Sharks arose from early jawed fishes midway through the Devonian period, about 375 million years ago. The absence of certain features characteristic of bony fishes (e.g., a swim bladder to regulate buoyancy, a gill cover, and a bony skeleton) is sometimes interpreted as evidence of the primitiveness of elasmobranchs. This interpretation is mistaken, as these characteristics simply resulted from different adaptations in the two groups to similar selection pressures. Some of these adaptations are described later in this chapter.

(c)

FIGURE 27.8

Class Chondrichthyes. (*a*) A gray reef shark (*Carcharhinus*). (*b*) A manta ray (*Manta hamiltoni*) with two remoras (*Remora remora*) attached to its ventral surface. (*c*) A bullseye stingray (*Urolophus concentricus*).

(a)

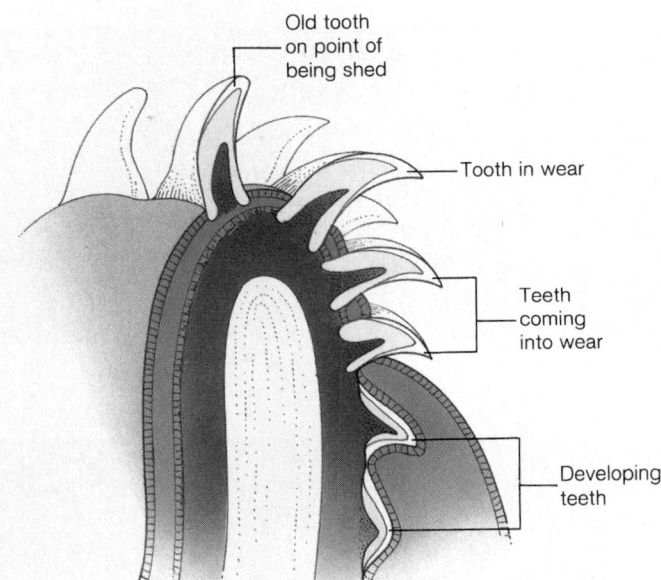

Old tooth
on point of
being shed

Tooth in wear

Teeth
coming
into wear

Developing
teeth

(b)   **Inside of jaw**

FIGURE 27.9

Scales and Teeth of Sharks. (*a*) A section of shark skin magnified to show posteriorly pointing placoid scales (scanning electron micrograph × 500). (*b*) The teeth of sharks develop as modified placoid scales. Older teeth are continuously replaced by newer teeth that move from the inside to the outside of the jaw.

Sharks are covered by tough skin with dermal, placoid scales (figure 27.9*a*). These scales project posteriorly and give the skin a tough, sandpaper texture. (In fact, dried sharkskin has been used for sandpaper.) Posteriorly pointed scales also reduce friction with the water when a shark is swimming.

The teeth of sharks are actually modified placoid scales. The row of teeth on the outer edge of the jaw is backed up by rows of teeth attached to a ligamentous band that covers the jaw cartilage inside the mouth. ② As the outer teeth wear and become useless, they are replaced by newer teeth moving into position from inside the jaw. In young sharks, this replacement is rapid, with a new row of teeth developing every 7 or 8 days (figure 27.9*b*). Crowns of teeth in different species may be adapted for shearing prey or for crushing the shells of molluscs.

Sharks range in size from less than 1 m (e.g., *Squalus,* the laboratory dissection specimen) to greater than 10 m (e.g., basking sharks and whale sharks). The largest sharks are not predatory but are filter feeders. They have gill-arch modifications that strain plankton. The fiercest and most feared sharks are the great white shark (*Carcharodon*) and the mako (*Isurus*). Extinct specimens may have reached lengths of 25 m or more (box 27.2)!

Skates and rays are specialized for life on the ocean floor. They usually inhabit shallow water, where they use their blunt teeth to feed on invertebrates. Their most obvious modification for life on the ocean floor is a lateral expansion of the pectoral fins into winglike appendages. Locomotion results from dorsoventral muscular waves that pass posteriorly along the fins. Frequently, elaborate color patterns on the dorsal surface of these animals provide effective camouflage (*see figure 27.8c*). The sting ray (*Raja*) has a tail modified into a defensive lash— the dorsal fin persists as a venomous spine. Also included in this group are the electric rays (*Narcine*) and manta rays (*Aetobatus*) (*see figure 27.8b*).

A second major group of chondrichthians, in the subclass Holocephali (hol'o-sef'a-li) (Gr. *holos,* whole + *kephalidos,* head), contains about 30 species. A frequently studied example, *Chimaera,* has a large head with a small mouth that is surrounded by large lips. A narrow tapering tail has resulted in the common name "ratfish." Holocephalans diverged from other chondrichthians nearly 300 million years ago. During this time, specializations not found in other elasmobranchs have evolved. These include a gill cover, called an **operculum,** and teeth modified into large plates that are used for crushing the shells of molluscs. Holocephalans lack scales.

Class Osteichthyes

Members of the class Osteichthyes (os'te-ik''the-es) (Gr. *osteon,* bone + *ichthyos,* fish) are characterized by having at least some bone in their skeleton and/or scales, an operculum covering the gill openings, and lungs or a swim bladder. Any group that has 20,000 species and is a major life-form in most of the earth's vast aquatic habitats must be judged very successful from an evolutionary perspective.

The first fossils of bony fishes are from late Silurian deposits (approximately 405 million years old). By the Devonian period (350 million years ago), the two subclasses were in the midst of their adaptive radiations (table 27.1; *see also figure 27.2*).

BOX 27.2   JAWS FROM THE PAST

Paleontological records can tell scientists much about life-forms from the past. We know most about ancient animals whose bodies contained hard parts that were resistant to decay and that were more likely to fossilize. The fossil record for fishes that contained substantial quantities of bone is fairly complete. Records of fishes that lack bone are usually harder to find.

In spite of the cartilaginous skeletons of sharks, our knowledge of ancient sharks, although not perfect, is more complete than might be expected. Much of what we know of ancient sharks comes from discoveries made in Ohio. Sharks in Ohio may seem surprising at first, but during the upper Devonian (about 350 million years ago), the sea extended southwest from the St. Lawrence River region, across the Great Lakes, and down to Arkansas. The floor of this ocean, in the region now occupied by Ohio, was made of soft, deep sediments—ideal for fossilization. Some elasmobranch specimens are so well preserved that not only are cartilaginous skeletons preserved, but details of gill structures, details of muscle organization, and even remains of a last meal are sometimes found intact.

Discoveries such as these provide a wealth of information about ancient sharks. The body form of ancient sharks allowed them to become efficient predators, and that basic form is retained in most modern sharks. The shape of fossilized teeth can sometimes be used to identify the kind of shark they came from. Mineral deposits build up on teeth as they rest on the ocean floor. Assuming mineral deposits accumulate at a constant rate, it is possible to determine how long teeth have been resting on the ocean floor. Assuming that a ratio between tooth size and body size is constant for a given species, estimates of the length of a shark can be obtained from a fossilized tooth.

Reconstruction of ancient sharks from all available evidence is the job of some museum scientists. The reconstruction shown in figure 1 is of an ancient shark that was found in a North Carolina

FIGURE 1   **Ancient Jaws.** These reconstructed jaws of *Carcharodon megalodon* measure 1 m wide by 2 m high.

quarry. (Because too few teeth were found to fill out the entire jaw, false teeth were constructed from hard rubber.) They are the teeth of a 30-million-year-old *Carcharodon megalodon*, that was the ancestor of the great white shark. The largest tooth of this specimen was about 15 cm (6 in.) long. Because 2.5 cm (1 in.) of tooth equals about 3 m (10 ft) of shark, it is estimated that this specimen was 18.5 m (60 ft) long! The model shown in figure 1 is on display in the Smithsonian's National Museum of Natural History.

Members of the subclass Sarcopterygii (sar-kop-te-rij′e-i) (Gr. *sark*, flesh + *pteryx*, fin) have muscular lobes associated with their fins and usually use lungs in gas exchange. One group of sarcopterygians are the lungfishes. Only three genera survive today, and all are found in regions where seasonal droughts are common.   ③   When freshwater lakes and rivers begin to stagnate and dry, these fishes use lungs to breathe air (figure 27.10). Some (*Neoceratodus*) inhabit the fresh waters of Queensland, Australia. They survive stagnation by breathing air, but normally use gills and cannot withstand total drying. Others are found in freshwater rivers and lakes in tropical Africa (*Protopterus*) and tropical South America (*Lepidosiren*). They have completely lost the use of gills for gas exchange and can survive when rivers or lakes completely dry. When a lake or river has nearly dried, these lungfishes burrow into the mud. They keep a

FIGURE 27.10

Subclass Sarcopterygii. The lungfish, *Lepidosiren paradoxa*, has lungs that allow it to withstand stagnation and drying of its habitat.

(a)

(b)

FIGURE 27.11

A Sarcopterygian, the Coelacanth. *Latimeria* is the only known surviving coelacanth.

FIGURE 27.12

Subclass Actinopterygii, the Chondrosteans. (*a*) A shovelnose sturgeon (*Scaphirhynchus platorynchus*). Sturgeons are covered anteriorly by heavy bony plates and posteriorly by scales. (*b*) The distinctive rostrum of a paddlefish (*Polydon spathula*) is densely innervated with sensory structures that are probably used to detect minute electric fields. Note the mouth in its open, filter-feeding position.

narrow air pathway open by bubbling air to the surface. After the substrate dries, the only evidence of a lungfish burrow is a small opening in the earth. Lungfishes may remain in aestivation for 6 months or more. (Aestivation is a dormant state that helps an animal withstand hot, dry periods.) When rain again fills the lake or riverbed, lungfishes emerge from their burrows to feed and reproduce.

A second group of sarcopterygians are the coelacanths. The most recent fossils of coelacanths are over 70 million years old. In 1938, however, people fishing in deep water off the coast of South Africa brought up fishes that were identified as coelacanths (figure 27.11). Since then, numerous other specimens have been caught in deep water around the Comoro Islands off Madagascar. ❹ The discovery of this fish, *Latimeria chalumnae*, was a milestone event because *Latimeria* is probably the closest living fish relative of terrestrial vertebrates. It is large—up to 80 kg—and has heavy scales. Ancient coelacanths lived in freshwater lakes and rivers; thus, the ancestors of *Latimeria* must have moved from freshwater habitats to the deep sea.

A third group of sarcopterygians are entirely extinct. These fish, called rhipidistians, became extinct before the close of the Paleozoic period and are believed to have been the ancestors of ancient amphibians.

The subclass Actinopterygii (ak′tin-op″te-rig-e-i) (Gr. *aktis*, ray + *pteryx*, fin) contains fishes that are sometimes called the ray-finned fishes because their fins lack muscular lobes. They usually possess **swim bladders,** which are gas-filled sacs located along the dorsal wall of the body cavity and used to regulate buoyancy. Zoologists now realize that there have been many points of divergence in the evolution of the Actinopterygii. One modern classification system divides the Actinopterygii into two infraclasses.

One group of actinopterygians, the chondrosteans, contains many species that lived during the Permian, Triassic, and Jurassic periods (215 to 120 million years ago), but only 25 species remain today. Ancestral chondrosteans had a bony skeleton, but living members, the sturgeons and paddlefishes, have cartilaginous skeletons. Chondrosteans also have a tail with a large upper lobe.

Most sturgeons live in the sea and migrate into rivers to breed (figure 27.12*a*). (Some sturgeons live in fresh water but maintain the migratory habits of their marine relatives.) They are very large (up to 1,000 kg) and have bony plates covering the anterior portion of the body. Heavy scales cover the tail. The mouth of a sturgeon is small, and its jaws are weak. Sturgeons feed on invertebrates that they stir up from the sea or riverbed using their snout. Because sturgeons are valued for their caviar (eggs), they have been severely overfished.

Paddlefishes are large, freshwater chondrosteans. They have a large, paddlelike rostrum that is innervated with sensory organs believed to detect weak electric fields (figure 27.12*b*). They swim through the water with their large mouths open, filtering crustaceans and small fishes. They are found mainly in lakes and large rivers of the Mississippi River basin and are also known from western North America.

The second group of actinopterygians flourished in the Jurassic period and succeeded most chondrosteans. Two very primitive genera occur in temperate to warm fresh waters of North America. *Lepisosteus*, the garpike, has thick scales and long jaws that it uses to catch fishes. *Amia* is commonly referred to as the dogfish or bowfin. Most living fishes are members of this group and are referred to as teleosts or modern bony fishes. They have a symmetrical caudal fin and a swim bladder that has lost its connection to the digestive tract. After their divergence from ancient marine actinopterygians in the late Triassic period, a remarkable evolutionary diversification occurred. Teleosts adapted to nearly every available aquatic habitat (figure 27.13*a–c*). There are in excess of 20,000 species of teleosts.

(a)

Stop and Ask Yourself

5. What are characteristics of the superclass Gnathostomata? In what ways are members of this superclass considered more advanced than agnathans?
6. What class of fishes is characterized by jaws, paired appendages, a cartilaginous skeleton, and placoid scales?
7. What class of fishes is characterized by some bone in their skeleton, an operculum, and usually lungs or a swim bladder?
8. What is aestivation? What is the role of aestivation in the life of some lungfishes?

(b)

Evolutionary Pressures

Why is a fish fishlike? This apparently redundant question is unanswerable in some respects because some traits of animals are selectively neutral and, thus, neither improve nor detract from overall fitness. On the other hand, aquatic environments have physical characteristics that are important selective forces for aquatic animals. Although animals have adapted to aquatic environments in different ways, one can understand many aspects of the structure and function of a fish by studying the fish's habitat. The material presented in this section will help you appreciate the many ways that a fish is adapted for life in water.

(c)

Figure 27.13

Subclass Actinopterygii, the Teleosts. (*a*) Bottom fish, such as this winter flounder (*Pseudopleuronectes americanus*), have both eyes on one side of the head, and they often rest on their side fully or partially buried on the substrate. (*b*) Freshwater teleosts, such as this speckled darter (*Etheostoma stigmaeum*), are common in temperate streams. (*c*) Cichlid fish, including this harlequin cichlid (*Cichlasoma festae*), are common in tropical fresh waters.

LOCOMOTION

Picture a young girl running full speed down the beach and into the ocean. She hits the water and begins to splash. At first, she lifts her feet high in the air between steps, but as she goes deeper, her legs encounter more and more resistance. The momentum of her upper body causes her to fall forward and she resorts to labored and awkward swimming strokes. The density of the water makes movement through it difficult and costly. For a fish, however, swimming is less energetically costly than running is for a terrestrial organism. Friction between a fish and the water is reduced by the streamlined shape of a fish and the mucoid secretions that lubricate the body surface. The buoyant properties of water also contribute to the efficiency of a fish's movement through the water. A fish needs to expend little energy in support against the pull of gravity.

Fishes move through the water using their fins and body wall to push against the incompressible surrounding water. Anyone who has eaten a fish filet probably realizes that muscle bundles of most fishes are arranged in a ≤ pattern. Because these muscles extend posteriorly and anteriorly in a zig-zag fashion, contraction of each muscle bundle can affect a relatively large portion of the body wall. Very efficient, fast-swimming fishes, such as tuna and mackerel, supplement body movements with a vertical caudal (tail) fin that is tall and forked. The forked shape of the caudal fin reduces surface area that could cause turbulence and interfere with forward movement.

NUTRITION AND THE DIGESTIVE SYSTEM

The earliest fishes were probably filter feeders and scavengers that sifted through the mud of ancient sea floors for decaying organic matter, annelids, molluscs, or other bottom-dwelling invertebrates. Dramatic changes in the nutrition of fishes came about when the evolution of jaws transformed early fishes into efficient predators.

Most modern fishes are predators and spend much of their life searching for food. The prey that different fishes eat vary tremendously. Some fishes feed on invertebrate animals floating or swimming in the plankton or living in or on the substrate. Many feed on other vertebrates. Similarly, the kinds of food that one fish eats at different times in its life varies. For example, a fish may feed on plankton as a larva but switch to larger prey, such as annelids or smaller fish, as an adult. Prey are usually swallowed whole. Teeth are often used to capture and hold prey, and some fishes have teeth that are modified for crushing the shells of molluscs or the exoskeletons of arthropods. Prey capture often utilizes the suction created by closing the opercula and rapidly opening the mouth, which develops a negative pressure that sweeps water and prey inside the mouth.

Other feeding strategies have also evolved in fishes. Herring, paddlefishes, and whale sharks are filter feeders. Long gill processes, called **gill rakers,** trap plankton while the fish is swimming through the water with its mouth open (*see figure 27.12b*). Other fishes, such as carp, feed on a variety of plants and small animals. A few, such as the lamprey, are external parasites for at least a portion of their life. A few are primarily herbivores, feeding on plants.

The digestive tract of a fish is similar to that of other vertebrates. An enlargement, called the stomach, is primarily used for storing large, often infrequent, meals. The small intestine, however, is the primary site for enzyme secretion and food digestion. Sharks and other elasmobranchs have a spiral valve in their intestine, and bony fishes possess outpockets of the intestine, called pyloric ceca, which increase absorptive and secretory surfaces.

CIRCULATION AND GAS EXCHANGE

All vertebrates have a closed circulatory system in which blood, with red blood cells containing hemoglobin, is pumped by a heart through a series of arteries, capillaries, and veins. The evolution of lungs in fishes was paralleled by changes in vertebrate circulatory systems. These changes are associated with the loss of gills, delivery of blood to the lungs, and separation of oxygenated and unoxygenated blood in the heart.

The vertebrate heart develops from four embryological enlargements of a ventral aorta. In fishes, blood flows from the venous system through the sinus venosus, the atrium, the ventricle, the conus arteriosus, and into the ventral aorta (figure 27.14a). Five afferent vessels carry blood to the gills, where the vessels branch into capillaries. Blood is collected by efferent vessels, delivered to the dorsal aorta, and distributed to the body.

Even though lungfishes are not a transitional group, they provide a good example of how the presence of lungs alters the circulatory pattern. There is still circulation to gills, but a vessel to the lungs has developed as a branch off aortic arch VI (figure 27.14b). This vessel is now called the pulmonary artery. Blood returns to the heart through pulmonary veins and enters the left side of the heart. The atrium and ventricle of the lungfish heart are partially divided. These partial divisions help keep unoxygenated blood from the body separate from the oxygenated blood from the lungs. A spiral valve in the conus arteriosus helps direct blood from the right side of the heart to the pulmonary artery and blood from the left side of the heart to the remaining aortic arches. Thus, in the lungfishes, we see a distinction between a pulmonary circuit and a systemic circuit.

Gas Exchange

Fishes live in an environment that contains less than 2.5% of the oxygen present in air. To maintain adequate levels of oxygen in their bloodstream, fishes must pass large quantities of water across gill surfaces and extract the small amount of oxygen present in the water.

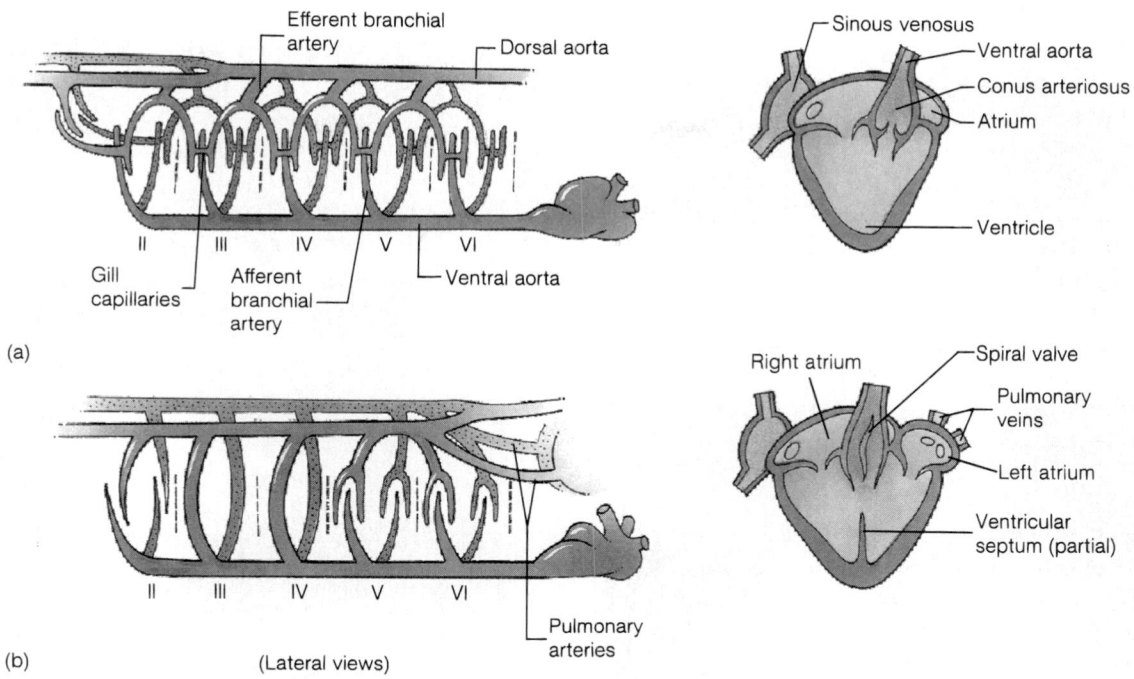

FIGURE 27.14

Circulatory System of Fishes. Diagrammatic representation of the circulatory systems of (*a*) bony fishes and (*b*) lungfishes. Hearts are drawn from a ventral view. Major branches of arteries carrying blood to and from the gills are called branchial arteries (or embryologically, aortic arches) and are numbered with Roman numerals. They begin with II because aortic arch I is lost during embryological development.

Most fishes use a muscular pumping mechanism to move the water into the mouth and pharynx, over the gills, and out of the fish through gill openings. This pump is powered by muscles surrounding the pharynx and the opercular cavity, which is between the gills and the operculum.

Some elasmobranchs and open-ocean bony fishes, such as the tuna, maintain water flow by holding their mouth open while swimming. This method is called **ram ventilation.** Elasmobranchs do not have opercula to help pump water, and therefore, some sharks must keep moving to survive. Others can move water over their gills by a pumping mechanism similar to that described above. Rather than using an operculum in the pumping process, however, their gill bars have external flaps that close and form a cavity functionally similar to the opercular cavity of other fishes. Spiracles are modified gill slits that open just behind the eyes of elasmobranchs and are used as an alternate route for water entering the pharynx.

Gas exchange across gill surfaces is very efficient. Gills are supported by **gill (visceral) arches. Gill filaments** extend from each gill arch and include vascular folds of epithelium, called **gill lamellae** (figure 27.15*a,b*). Blood is carried to the gills and into gill filaments in branchial arteries. The arteries break into capillary beds in gill lamellae. Gas exchange occurs as blood and water move in opposite directions on either side of the lamellar epithelium. This **countercurrent exchange mechanism** provides very ef-ficient gas exchange by maintaining a concentration gradient between the blood and the water over the entire length of the capillary bed (figure 27.15*c,d*).

Swim Bladders and Lungs

The Indian climbing perch spends its life almost entirely on land. These fishes, as most bony fishes, have gas chambers called **pneumatic sacs.** In nonteleost fishes, the pneumatic sacs connect to the esophagus or another part of the digestive tract by a pneumatic duct. Swallowed air enters these sacs, and gas exchange occurs across vascular surfaces. Thus, in the Indian climbing perch, lungfishes, and ancient rhipidistians, pneumatic sacs function(ed) as lungs. In other bony fishes, pneumatic sacs act as swim bladders.

Most zoologists believe that lungs are more primitive than swim bladders. Much of the early evolution of bony fishes occurred in warm, freshwater lakes and streams during the Devonian period. These bodies of water frequently became stagnant and periodically dried. Having lungs in these habitats could have meant the difference between life and death. On the other hand, later evolution of modern bony fishes occurred in marine and freshwater environments where stagnation was not a problem. In these environments, the use of pneumatic sacs in buoyancy regulation would have been adaptive (figure 27.16).

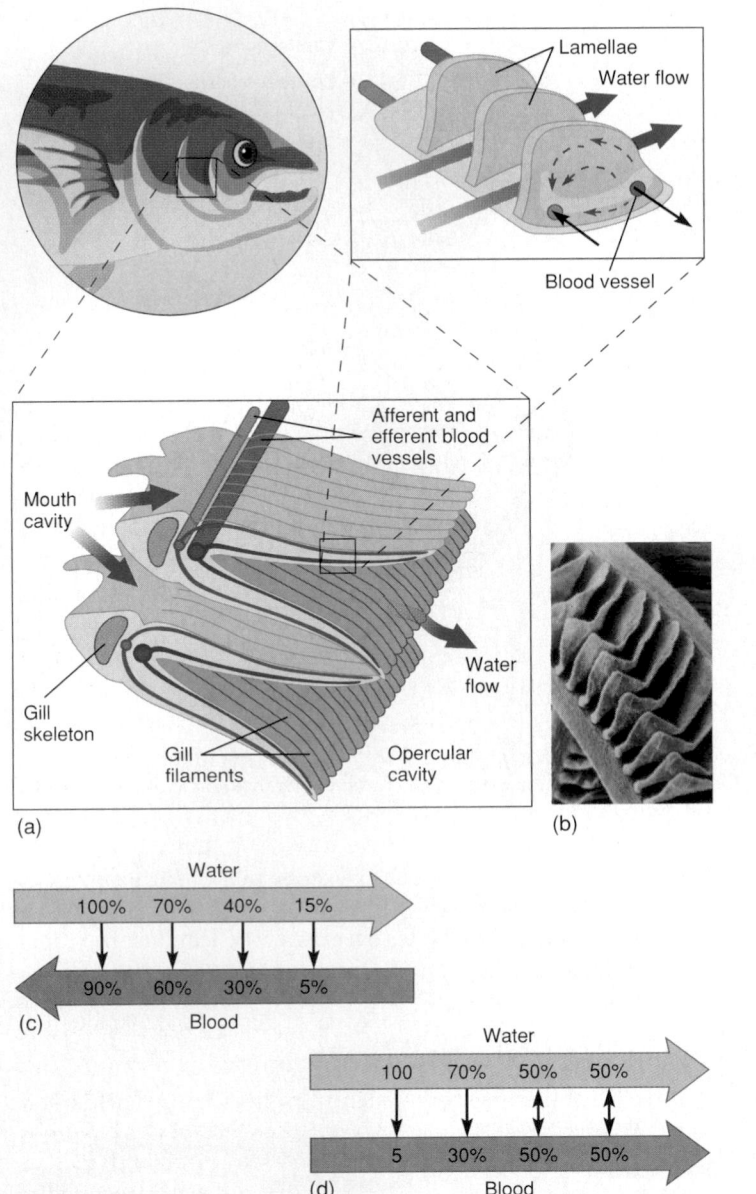

FIGURE 27.15

Gas Exchange at the Gill Lamellae. (*a*) The gill arches under the operculum support two rows of gill filaments. Blood flows into gill filaments through afferent branchial arteries, and these arteries break into capillary beds in the gill lamellae. Water and blood flow in opposite directions on either side of the lamellae. (*b*) Electron micrograph of the tip of a trout gill filament showing numerous lamellae. A comparison of countercurrent (*c*) and parallel (*d*) exchanges. Water entering the spaces between gill lamellae is saturated with oxygen in both cases. In countercurrent exchange, this water encounters blood that is almost completely oxygenated, but a diffusion gradient still favors the movement of more oxygen from the water to the blood. As water continues to move between lamellae, it loses oxygen to the blood, because it is continually encountering blood that has a lower oxygen concentration than is present in the water. Thus, a diffusion gradient is maintained along the length of the lamellae. If blood and water were to move in parallel fashion, diffusion of oxygen from water to blood would occur only until the concentration of oxygen in blood equalled the concentration of oxygen in water, and the exchange would be much less efficient.

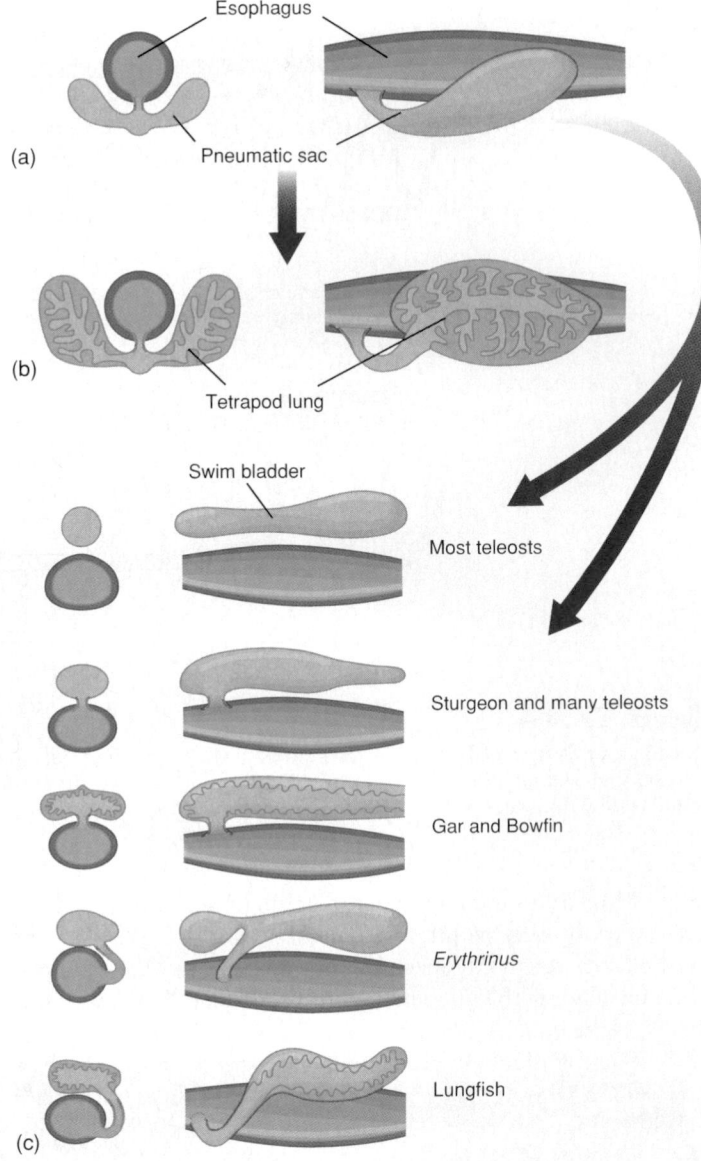

FIGURE 27.16

A Possible Sequence in the Evolution of Pneumatic Sacs. (*a*) Pneumatic sacs may have originally developed from ventral outgrowths of the esophagus. Many ancient fishes probably used pneumatic sacs as lungs. (*b*) Primitive lungs developed further during the evolution of land vertebrates. Internal compartmentalization increases surface area for gas exchange in land vertebrates. (*c*) In most bony fishes, pneumatic sacs are called swim bladders, and they are modified for buoyancy regulation. Swim bladders are in a dorsal position to prevent a tendency for the fish to "belly up" in the water. Pneumatic duct connections to the esophagus are frequently lost, and gases are transferred from the blood to the swim bladder.

Buoyancy Regulation

Did you ever consider why it is possible for you to float in water? Water is a supportive medium, but that is not sufficient to prevent you from sinking. Even though you are made mostly of water, other constituents of tissues are more dense than water. Bone, for example, has a specific gravity twice that of water. Why is it then that you can float? Largely because of two large, air-filled organs called lungs that allow you to float to the surface.

Fishes maintain their vertical position in a column of water in four ways. One way is to incorporate low-density compounds into their tissues. Fishes (especially their livers) are saturated with buoyant oils. A second way fishes maintain vertical position is to use fins to provide lift. The pectoral fins of a shark serve as planing devices that help to create lift as the shark moves through the water. Also, the large upper lobe of a shark's caudal fin provides upward thrust for the posterior end of the body (see figure 27.8a). A third adaptation is the reduction of heavy tissues in fishes. The bones of fishes are generally less dense than those of terrestrial vertebrates. One of the adaptive features of the elasmobranch cartilaginous skeleton probably results from cartilage being only slightly heavier than water. The fourth adaptation is the swim bladder. Using a swim bladder, buoyancy can be regulated to meet the day-to-day needs of a fish by precisely regulating the volume of gas in it. (You can mimic this adaptation while floating in water. How well do you float after forcefully exhaling as much air as possible?)

The swim bladders of garpike, sturgeons, and other primitive bony fishes connect to the esophagus or another part of the digestive tract by the pneumatic duct. These fishes gulp air at the surface to force air into their swim bladders.

Most teleosts have swim bladders that have lost a functional connection to the digestive tract. Gases (various mixtures of nitrogen and oxygen) are secreted into the swim bladder from the blood using a countercurrent exchange mechanism in a vascular network called the rete mirabile ("miraculous net"). Gases may be reabsorbed into the blood at the posterior end of the bladder.

NERVOUS AND SENSORY FUNCTIONS

The central nervous system of fishes, as in other vertebrates, consists of a brain and a spinal cord. Sensory receptors are widely distributed over the body. In addition to generally distributed receptors for touch and temperature, fishes possess specialized receptors for olfaction, vision, hearing, equilibrium and balance, and for detecting water movements.

Openings in the snout of fishes, called external nares, lead to olfactory receptors. In most fishes, receptors are located in blind-ending olfactory sacs. In a few fishes, the external nares open to nasal passages that lead to the mouth cavity. Recent research has revealed that some fishes rely heavily on their sense of smell. For example, salmon and lampreys return to spawn in the streams in which they hatched years earlier. Their migrations to these streams often involve distances of hundreds of miles and are guided by the fishes' perception of the characteristic odors of their spawning stream.

The eyes of fishes are similar in most aspects of structure to those found in other vertebrates. They are lidless, however, and the lenses are round. Focusing is accomplished by moving the lens forward or backward in the eye. (Most other vertebrates focus by changing the shape of the lens.)

Receptors for equilibrium, balance, and hearing are located in the inner ears of fishes, and their functions are similar to those of other vertebrates. Semicircular canals detect rotational movements, and other sensory patches help with equilibrium and balance by detecting the direction of the gravitational pull. Fishes lack the outer and/or middle ear, which conducts sound waves to the inner ear in other vertebrates. As anyone who enjoys fishing knows, however, most fishes can hear. Vibrations may be passed from the water through the bones of the skull to the middle ear, and a few fishes have chains of bony ossicles (modifications of vertebrae) that connect the swim bladder to the back of the skull. Vibrations strike the fish, are amplified by the swim bladder, and sent through the ossicles to the skull.

Running along each side and branching over the head of most fishes is a lateral-line system. The **lateral-line system** consists of sensory pits in the epidermis of the skin that connect to canals that run just below the epidermis. In these pits are receptors that are stimulated by water moving against them. Lateral lines are used either to detect water currents or for detecting a predator or a prey that may be causing water movements in the vicinity of the fish. Low-frequency sound may also be detected.

Electric Fishes

A U.S. Navy pilot has just ejected from his troubled aircraft over shark-infested water! What measures can the pilot take to ensure survival under these hostile conditions? The Navy has considered this scenario. One of the solutions to the problem is a polyvinyl bag suspended from an inflatable collar. The polyvinyl bag helps conceal the downed flyer from a shark's vision and keen sense of smell. But is that all that is required to ensure protection?

All organisms produce weak electrical fields from the activities of nerves and muscles. **Electroreception** is the detection of electrical fields generated by the fish or another organism in the environment. Electroreception and/or electrogeneration has been demonstrated in over 500 species of fishes in seven families of Chondrichthyes and Osteichthyes. These fishes use their electroceptive sense for detecting prey and for orienting toward or away from objects in the environment.

Nowhere is prey detection with this sense better developed than in the rays and sharks. Spiny dogfish sharks, the common laboratory specimens, locate prey by electroreception. 6 A shark can find and eat a flounder that is buried in sand and it will try to find and eat electrodes that are creating electrical signals similar to those emitted by the flounder. On the other hand, a shark cannot find a dead flounder buried in the sand or a live flounder covered by an insulating polyvinyl sheet.

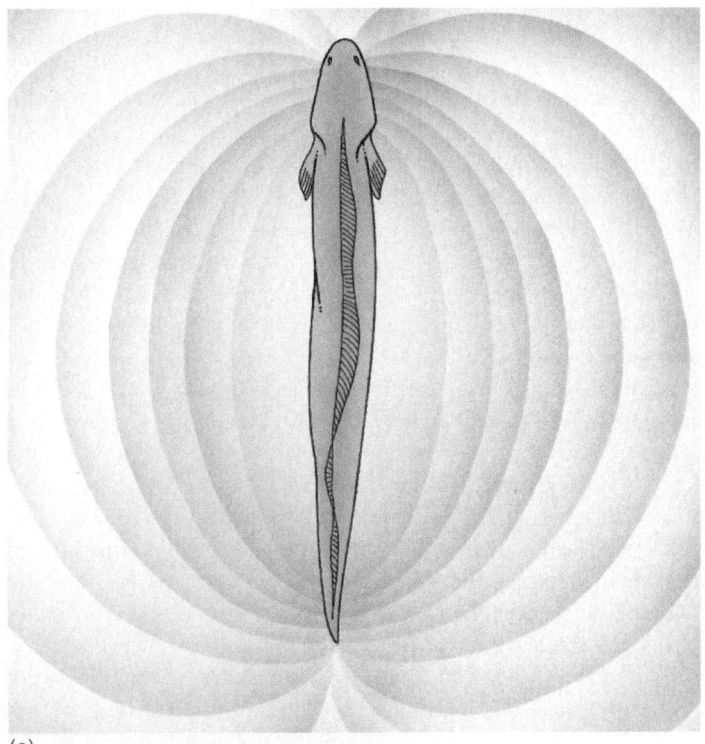

(a)

(b)

Figure 27.17

Electric Fishes. (*a*) The electric field of *Gymnarchus niloticus* is used to detect the presence of prey and other objects in the fish's murky environment. Currents circulate from electric organs in its tail to electroreceptors near its head. An object in this electrical field changes the pattern of stimulation of electroreceptors. (*b*) The electric fish (*Gymnarchus niloticus*).

Some fishes are not only capable of electroreception, but are also capable of generating electrical currents. An electric fish (*Gymnarchus niloticus*) lives in freshwater systems of Africa. Muscles near its caudal fin are modified into organs that produce a continuous electrical discharge. This current spreads between the tail and the head. Porelike perforations near the head contain electroreceptors. The electrical waves

Figure 27.18

Electric Fishes. A lesser electric ray (*Narcine brasiliensis*).

circulating between the tail and the head are distorted by objects in their field. This distortion is detected in changing patterns of stimulation of receptors (figure 27.17). The electrical sense of *Gymnarchus* is an adaptation to living in murky freshwater habitats where eyes are of limited value.

The fishes best known for producing strong electric currents are the electric eel (a bony fish) and the electric ray (an elasmobranch). The electric eel (*Electrophorus*) occurs in rivers of the Amazon basin in South America. The organs used for producing electric currents are located in the trunk of the electric eel and can deliver shocks in excess of 500 volts. The electric ray (*Narcine*) (figure 27.18), has electric organs in its fins that are capable of producing pulses of 50 amperes at about 50 volts. Shocks produced by these fishes are sufficiently strong to stun or kill prey, discourage large predators, and teach unwary humans a lesson that will never need to be repeated.

Stop and Ask Yourself

9. What are two methods of gill ventilation used by fishes?
10. What is a countercurrent exchange mechanism, and why does it occur in fish gills?
11. Why do some fishes, such as lungfishes, need lungs?
12. What are four mechanisms used by fishes to improve their buoyancy?

EXCRETION AND OSMOREGULATION

Fishes, as all animals, must maintain a proper balance of ions and water in their tissues. The regulation of these balances is called osmoregulation and is a major function of the kidneys and gills of fishes. Kidneys are located near the midline of the body, just dorsal to the peritoneal membrane that lines the body cavity. As with all vertebrates, the excretory structures in the kidneys are called **nephrons.** Nephrons filter bloodborne nitrogenous wastes, ions, water, and small organic compounds across a network of capillaries called a **glomerulus.** The filtrate then passes into a tubule system, where essential components may be reabsorbed into the blood. The filtrate remaining in the tubule system is then excreted.

Freshwater fishes live in an environment containing few dissolved substances. Osmotic uptake of water across gill, oral, and intestinal surfaces, and the loss of essential ions by excretion and defecation are constant. To control the excess buildup of water and loss of ions, freshwater fishes never drink, and only take in water when feeding. Also, the nephrons of freshwater fishes are numerous and frequently possess large glomeruli and relatively short tubule systems. Filtration is followed by reabsorption of some ions and organic compounds. Because the tubule system is relatively short, little water is reabsorbed. Thus, large quantities of very dilute urine are produced. Even though the urine of freshwater fishes is dilute, ions are still lost through the urine and by diffusion across gill and oral surfaces. Loss of ions is compensated for by active transport of ions into the blood at the gills. Freshwater fishes also get some salts in their food (figure 27.19a).

Marine fishes face the opposite problems. Their environment contains 3.5% ions, and their tissues contain approximately 0.65% ions. Marine fishes, therefore, must combat water loss and accumulation of excess ions. They drink water and eliminate excess ions by excretion, defecation, and active transport across gill surfaces. The nephrons of marine fishes frequently possess small glomeruli and long tubule systems. Much less blood is filtered than in freshwater fishes, and water is efficiently, although not entirely, reabsorbed from the nephron (figure 27.19b).

Elasmobranchs have a unique osmoregulatory mechanism. They convert some of their nitrogenous wastes into urea in the liver. This in itself is somewhat unusual, because most fishes excrete ammonia rather than urea. Even more unusual, however, is that urea is sequestered in tissues all over the body. Enough urea is stored to make body tissues isosmotic with seawater. (That is, the concentration of solutes in a shark's tissues is essentially the same as the concentration of ions in seawater.) Therefore, the problem most marine fishes have of losing water to their environment is much less severe for elasmobranchs. Energy that does not have to be devoted to water conservation can now be used in other ways. This adaptation required the development of tolerance to high levels of urea, because urea disrupts important enzyme systems in the tissues of most other animals.

In spite of this unique adaptation, elasmobranchs must still regulate the concentrations of ions in their tissues. In addition to

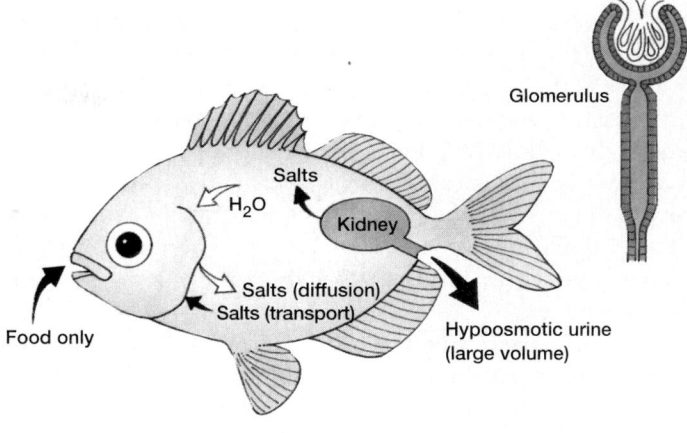

(a) Freshwater teleosts (hypertonic blood)

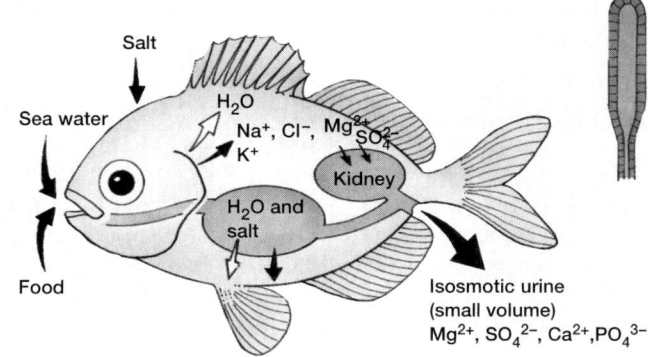

(b) Marine teleosts (hypotonic blood)

FIGURE 27.19

Osmoregulation by (a) Freshwater and (b) Marine Fishes. Large arrows indicate passive uptake or loss of water or ions through ingestion and excretion. Small solid arrows indicate active transport processes occurring at gill membranes and kidney tubules. Small open arrows indicate passive uptake or loss by diffusion through permeable surfaces. Insets of kidney nephrons depict adaptations within the kidney. Water, ions, and small organic molecules are filtered from the blood at the glomerulus of the nephron. Essential components of the filtrate can be reabsorbed within the tubule system of the nephron. Marine fishes conserve water by reducing the size of the glomerulus of the nephron, and thus reducing the quantity of water and ions filtered from the blood. Salts can be secreted from the blood into the kidney tubules. Marine fishes can produce urine that is isoosmotic with the blood. Freshwater fishes have enlarged glomeruli and short tubule systems. They filter large quantities of water from the blood, and tubules reabsorb some ions from the filtrate. Freshwater fishes produce a hypoosmotic urine.

having ion-absorbing and secreting tissues in their gills and kidneys, elasmobranchs possess a rectal gland that removes excess sodium chloride from the blood and excretes it into the cloaca. (A **cloaca** is a common opening for excretory, digestive, and reproductive products.)

Diadromous fishes migrate between freshwater and marine environments. Salmon (e.g., *Oncorhynchus*) and marine lampreys (*Petromyzon*) migrate from the sea to fresh water to spawn, and the freshwater eel (*Anguilla*) migrates from freshwater to marine environments to spawn. Diadromous migrations require that gills are capable of coping with both uptake and secretion of ions. Osmoregulatory powers needed for migration between marine and freshwater environments may not be developed in all life-history stages. Young salmon, for example, cannot enter the sea until certain cells on the gills develop ion-secreting powers.

Fishes have few problems getting rid of the nitrogenous by-products of protein metabolism. Up to 90% of nitrogenous wastes are eliminated as ammonia by diffusion across gill surfaces. Even though ammonia is very toxic, its use as an excretory product is possible in aquatic organisms because ammonia can diffuse into the surrounding water. The remaining 10% of nitrogenous wastes are excreted as urea, creatine, or creatinine. These wastes are produced in the liver and are excreted via the kidneys.

REPRODUCTION AND DEVELOPMENT

Imagine, 45 kg of caviar from a single, 450 kg sturgeon! Admittedly, a 450 kg sturgeon is a very large fish (even for a sturgeon), but it is not unusual for a fish to produce millions of eggs in a single season. These numbers simply reflect the hazards of developing in aquatic habitats unattended by a parent. The vast majority of these millions of potential adults will never survive to reproduce. Many eggs will never be fertilized, many fertilized eggs may wash ashore and dry, many eggs and embryos may be smashed by currents and tides, and others will fall victim to predation. In spite of all of these hazards, if only four of the millions of embryos of each breeding pair survive and reproduce, the population will double.

Producing overwhelming numbers of eggs, however, is not the only way that fishes increase the chances that a few of their offspring will survive. Some fishes show mating behavior that helps ensure fertilization, or nesting behavior that protects eggs from predation, sedimentation, and fouling.

Mating may occur in large schools, and the release of eggs or sperm by one individual often releases spawning pheromones that induce many other adults to spawn. Huge masses of eggs and sperm released into the open ocean help to ensure fertilization of as many eggs as possible.

The vast majority of fishes are oviparous, meaning that eggs develop outside the female from stored yolk. Some elasmobranchs are ovoviviparous, and their embryos develop in a modified oviduct of the female. Nutrients are supplied from yolk stored in the egg. Other elasmobranchs, including gray reef sharks and hammerheads, are viviparous. A placentalike outgrowth of a modified oviduct diverts nutrients from the female

FIGURE 27.20

A Male Garibaldi (*Hypsypops rubicundus*) Guarding Eggs. The male cultivates a nest of filamentous red algae and then entices a female to lay eggs in the nest. This male is carrying off a bat star that came too close to the nest.

to the yolksacs of developing embryos. Internal development of viviparous bony fishes usually occurs in ovarian follicles, rather than in the oviduct. In guppies (*Lebistes*), eggs are retained in the ovary, and fertilization and early development occur there. Embryos are then released into a cavity within the ovary and development continues, with nourishment coming partly from yolk and partly from secretions of the ovary.

Some fishes have specialized structures that aid in sperm transfer. Male elasmobranchs, for example, have modified pelvic fins called claspers. During copulation, a clasper is inserted into the cloaca of a female. Sperm travel along grooves of the clasper. Fertilization occurs in the reproductive tract of the female and usually results in a higher proportion of eggs being fertilized than in external fertilization. Thus, internal fertilization is usually accompanied by the production of fewer eggs.

In many fishes, care of the embryos is limited or nonexistent. Some fishes, however, construct and tend nests (figure 27.20), and some carry embryos during development. Clusters of embryos may be brooded by being attached to some part of the body in special pouches, or they may be brooded in the mouth. Some of the best-known brooders include the seahorses (*Hippocampus*) and pipefishes (e.g., *Syngnathus*). Males of these closely related fishes carry embryos throughout development in ventral pouches. The male Brazilian catfish (*Loricaria typhys*) broods embryos in an enlarged lower lip.

Most fishes do little, if any, caring for young after they have hatched. There are exceptions, however. Short-term care of posthatching young occurs in sunfishes and sticklebacks. Male sticklebacks collect fresh plant material and accumulate it into a mass. Young take refuge in this mass. If one wanders too far from the nest, the male will snap it up in its mouth and spit it back into the nest. Sunfish males do the same for young that wander from schools of recently hatched fish. Longer-term care occurs in the Chichlidae (*see figure 27.13c*). In some species, young are mouth brooded, and other species tend young in a nest. After hatching, the young venture from the parent's mouth or nest, but the young return quickly when the parent signals danger with a flicking of the pelvic fins.

FURTHER PHYLOGENETIC CONSIDERATIONS

Two important series of evolutionary events occurred during the evolution of the Osteichthyes. One of these was an evolutionary explosion that began about 150 million years ago and resulted in the vast diversity of teleosts that we see today. The last half of this chapter should have helped you appreciate some of these events.

To appreciate the second series of events, let us again consider the lungfishes. The lungfishes' life-style represents a survival strategy that must have been important for some early Devonian fishes. The current seasonal droughts of tropical South America and Africa must be similar to, but much less geographically extensive than, those in the Devonian period. As in the lungfishes, the ability to breathe air and aestivate must have been present in many freshwater Devonian fishes. Distinctive characteristics of the lungfish skeleton lead most zoologists to

conclude that the lungfish evolutionary line gave rise to no other vertebrate taxa. Instead, the rhipidistians are thought to be a part of the evolutionary lineage that led to terrestrial vertebrates. Rhipidistians, like lungfishes, had lungs, could breathe air, and may have used their muscular fins to crawl across land looking for water when their own stream dried.

7   Adaptations that favored survival in Devonian streams and lakes may have preadapted some rhipidistians for life that would become increasingly terrestrial. While millions of years would elapse before any vertebrate could be considered terrestrial, brief excursions onto land allowed some vertebrates to exploit resources that for the previous 50 million years were available only to terrestrial arthropods.

Stop and Ask Yourself

13. Why is osmoregulation, not excretion, the major function of the kidneys of fishes?
14. What osmoregulatory problems are faced by a diadromous fish?
15. What is viviparity? How does viviparity of some elasmobranchs differ from that of some teleosts?
16. What adaptations to climatic conditions may have preadapted rhipidistian fishes for a partially terrestrial existence?

SUMMARY

1. Ancient members of the vertebrate superclass Agnatha were probably the ancestors of all other vertebrates.
2. Agnathans lack jaws and paired appendages and include the extinct ostracoderms, lampreys, and hagfishes. Hagfishes are scavengers in marine environments. Lampreys have a life history involving migrations from the open ocean, or large body of fresh water, to freshwater spawning streams.
3. The superclass Gnathostomata includes fishes with jaws and paired appendages. The class Chondrichthyes includes the sharks, skates, rays, and ratfishes. The class Osteichthyes includes the bony fishes.
4. There are two subclasses of Osteichthyes. The subclass Sarcopterygii includes the lungfishes, the coelacanths, and the rhipidistians; and the subclass Actinopterygii includes the ray-finned fishes. In the Actinopterygii, the teleosts are the modern bony fishes. Members of this very large group have adapted to virtually every available aquatic habitat.
5. Fishes show numerous adaptations to living in aquatic environments. These adaptations include an arrangement of body-wall muscles that creates locomotor waves in the body wall; mechanisms that provide constant movement of water across gill

surfaces; a countercurrent exchange mechanism to promote efficient gas exchange; buoyancy regulation; well-developed sensory receptors, including eyes, inner ears, and lateral line receptors; mechanisms of osmoregulation; and mechanisms that help ensure successful reproduction.
6. Two evolutionary lineages in the Actinopterygii are very important. One of these resulted in the adaptive radiation of modern bony fishes, the teleosts. The second evolutionary line probably diverged from the rhipidistians. Adaptations that favored the survival of rhipidistians in early Devonian streams preadapted some rhipidistians for terrestrial habitats.

SELECTED KEY TERMS

cloaca (*p. 447*)
countercurrent exchange mechanism (*p. 443*)
gill (visceral) arches (*p. 443*)
gill filaments (*p. 443*)
gill lamellae (*p. 443*)

lateral-line system (*p. 445*)
operculum (*p. 438*)
pneumatic sacs (*p. 443*)
ram ventilation (*p. 443*)
swim bladders (*p. 440*)

CRITICAL THINKING QUESTIONS

1. What characteristic of water makes it difficult to move through, but also makes support against gravity a minor consideration? How is a fish adapted for moving through water?

2. Would it be possible for a fish to drown? Explain. Would it make a difference if the fish was an open-ocean fish, such as a tuna, or a fish such as a freshwater perch?

3. Why is it a mistake to consider the cartilaginous skeleton of chondrichthians a primitive characteristic?

4. Would swim bladders with functional pneumatic ducts work well for a fish that lives at great depths? Why or why not?

5. What would happen to a deep-sea fish that was rapidly brought to the surface? Explain your answer in light of the fact that gas pressure in the swim bladders of some deep-sea fishes is increased up to about 300 atmospheres.

chapter

28

AMPHIBIANS:
THE FIRST TERRESTRIAL VERTEBRATES

Concepts

1. Adaptations that favored survival of fishes during periodic droughts preadapted vertebrates to life on land. There were two lineages of ancient amphibians: one gave rise to modern amphibians, and the other lineage resulted in amniote vertebrates.
2. Modern amphibians belong to three orders. Caudata contains the salamanders, Gymnophiona contains the caecilians, and Anura contains the frogs and toads.
3. Although amphibians are restricted to moist habitats, most spend much of their adult life on land. Virtually all amphibian body systems show adaptations for living on land.
4. Evolution of eggs and developmental stages that were resistant to drying probably occurred in some ancient amphibians. This development was a major step in vertebrate evolution as it weakened vertebrate ties to moist environments.

Would You Like to Know:

1. how the skeleton of an amphibian is adapted for life on land? (p. 457)
2. how frogs, toads, and some salamanders catch prey with their tongues? (p. 458)
3. why an amphibian's skin is moist? (p. 459)
4. what terrestrial animals lack lungs? (p. 459)
5. how a frog's ear can filter out certain frequencies of sound? (p. 461)
6. what the functions of a frog's calls are? (p. 463)
7. what adaptations permitted life on land? (p. 465)

These and other useful questions will be answered in this chapter.

This chapter contains evolutionary concepts, which are set off in this font.

EVOLUTIONARY PERSPECTIVE

Who, while walking along the edge of a pond or stream, has not been startled by the "plop" of an equally startled frog jumping to the safety of its watery retreat? Or who has not marveled at the sounds of a chorus of frogs breaking through an otherwise silent spring evening? These experiences and others like them have led some to spend their lives studying members of the class Amphibia (am-fib′e-ah) (L. *amphibia*, living a double life): frogs, toads, salamanders, and caecilians (figure 28.1). The class name implies that amphibians either move back and forth between water and land, or live one stage of their life in water and another on land. One or both of these descriptions is accurate for most amphibians.

Amphibians are the first vertebrates we have encountered that are called **tetrapods** (Gr. *tetra*, four + *podos*, foot). It is a nontaxonomic designation that applies to all vertebrates other than fishes, and adaptations for life on land are found in most tetrapods.

PHYLOGENETIC RELATIONSHIPS

During the first 250 million years of vertebrate history, adaptive radiation resulted in vertebrates filling most aquatic habitats. There were many active, powerful predators in the prehistoric waters. Land, however, was free of vertebrates and except for some arthropods, was free of predators. Animals that moved around the water's edge were not likely to be prey for other animals. With lungs for breathing air and muscular fins to scurry across mud, these animals probably found ample food in the arthropods that lived there. It is no surprise that the major component of the diet of most modern amphibians is arthropods.

The origin of amphibians from ancient sarcopterygians was described in chapter 27. Adaptive radiation of amphibians resulted in a much greater variety of forms than exists today. Later convergent and parallel evolution and widespread extinction have clouded our perceptions of evolutionary pathways. No one knows, therefore, what animal was the first amphibian, but the structure of limbs, skulls, and teeth suggests that *Ichthyostega* is probably similar to the earliest amphibians (figure 28.2). During the late Devonian and early Carboniferous periods, two lineages of early amphibians can be distinguished by details of the way the roof and the posterior portion of the skull are attached to each other. One lineage of amphibians became extinct late in the Carboniferous period. The development of an egg that was resistant to drying, an amniotic egg (*see figure 10.13*), occurred in this group. This lineage, called the **amniote lineage,** left as its descendants the reptiles, birds, and mammals (figure 28.3). A second lineage, flourished into the Jurassic period. Most of this lineage became extinct, but not before giving rise to the three orders of living amphibians. This lineage is called the **nonamniote lineage.**

FIGURE 28.1

Class Amphibia. Amphibians, like this tree frog (*Hyla andersoni*) are common vertebrates in most terrestrial and freshwater habitats. Their ancestors were the first terrestrial vertebrates.

SURVEY OF AMPHIBIANS

Amphibians occur on all continents except Antarctica, but are absent from many oceanic islands. The 3,000 modern species are a mere remnant of this once-diverse group. Modern amphibians are divided into three orders: Caudata or Urodela, the salamanders; Anura, the frogs and toads; and Gymnophiona, the caecilians (table 28.1).

ORDER CAUDATA

Members of the order Caudata (kaw′dat-ah) (L. *cauda*, tail + Gr. *ata*, to bear) are the salamanders. They possess a tail throughout life, and both pairs of legs, when present, are relatively unspecialized (figure 28.4).

Approximately 115 of the 350 described species of salamanders occur in North America. Most terrestrial salamanders live in moist forest-floor litter and have aquatic larvae. A number of families are found in caves, where constant temperature and moisture conditions create a nearly ideal environment. Salamanders in the family Plethodontidae are the most fully terrestrial salamanders in that their eggs are laid on land, and the young hatch as miniatures of the adult. Members of the

FIGURE 28.2

Ichthyostega: **An Early Amphibian.** Fossils of this early amphibian were discovered in eastern Greenland in late Devonian deposits. The total length of the restored specimen is about 65 cm. Terrestrial adaptations are heavy pectoral and pelvic girdles and sturdy limbs that probably aided in lifting the body off the ground. Strong jaws suggest that it was a predator in shallow water, perhaps venturing onto shore. Other features include a skull that is similar in structure to ancient sarcopterygian fishes and a finlike tail. Note that the tail fin is supported by bony rays dorsal to the spines of the vertebrae. This pattern is similar to the structure of the dorsal fins of fishes and is unknown in any other tetrapod.

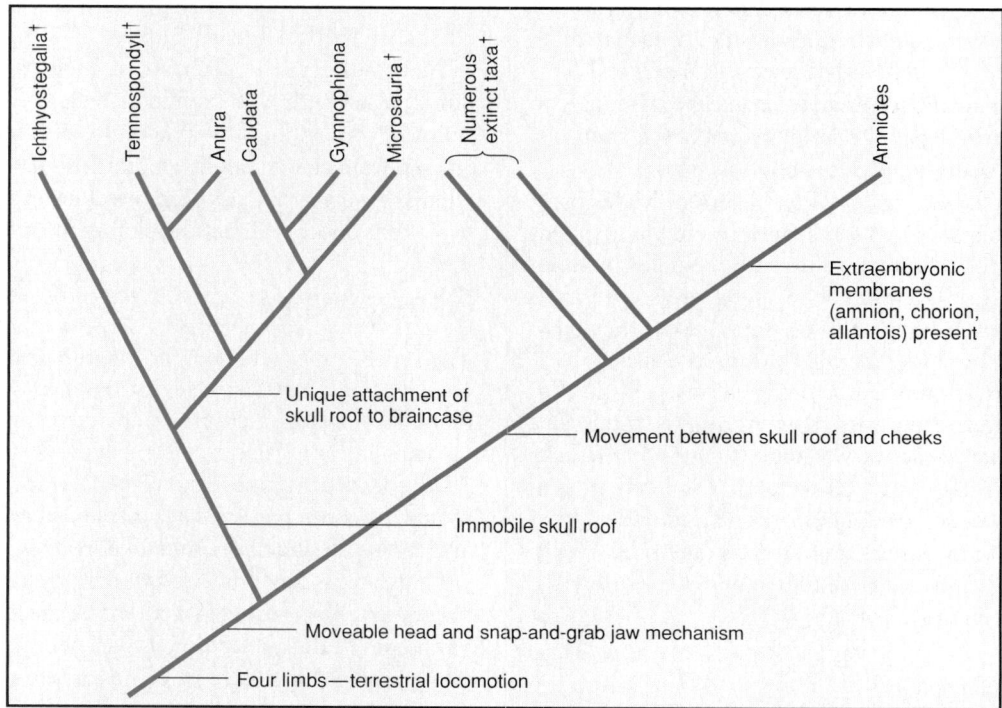

FIGURE 28.3

Evolutionary Relationships among the Amphibians. Earliest amphibians arose during the Devonian period. A nonamniotic lineage gave rise to three classes of modern amphibians and numerous extinct taxa. Some zoologists think that the class Amphibia is a paraphyletic group. If this is true, the three modern classes should be represented as monophyletic taxa. The amniotic lineage of early tetrapods gave rise to reptiles, birds, mammals, and other extinct taxa. Extinct taxa are indicated with a dagger (†). Synapomorphic characters for lower taxonomic groups are not indicated.

TABLE 28.1	CLASSIFICATION OF LIVING AMPHIBIANS

Class Amphibia (am-fib′e-ah)
Skin with mucoid secretions and lacks epidermal scales, feathers, or hair; larvae usually aquatic and undergo metamorphosis to the adult; two atrial chambers in the heart. One cervical and one sacral vertebra.

   Order Caudata (kaw′dat-ah)
   Long tail, two pairs of limbs; lack middle ear. Salamanders, newts.

   Order Gymnophiona (jim′no-fy″o-nah)
   Elongate, limbless; segmented by annular grooves; specialized for burrowing; tail short and pointed; rudimentary left lung. Caecilians.

   Order Anura (ah-noor′ah)
   Tailless; elongate hind limbs modified for jumping and swimming; five to nine presacral vertebrae with transverse processes (except the first); postsacral vertebrae fused into rodlike urostyle; tympanum and larynx well developed. Frogs, toads.

FIGURE 28.4
Order Caudata. Blue Ridge Spring salamander (*Gyrinophilus danielsi*).

family Salimandridae are commonly called newts. They spend most of their lives in water and frequently retain caudal fins. Salamanders range in length from only a few centimeters to 1.5 m (the Japanese giant salamander, *Andrias japonicus*). The largest North American salamander is the hellbender (*Cryptobranchus alleganiensis*), which reaches lengths of about 65 cm.

Most salamanders have internal fertilization. Males produce a pyramidal, gelatinous spermatophore that is capped with sperm and is deposited on the substrate. Females pick up the sperm cap with the cloaca, and the sperm are stored in a special pouch, the spermatheca. Eggs are fertilized as they pass through the cloaca and are usually deposited singly, in clumps, or in strings (figure 28.5a). Larvae are similar to adults but smaller. They often possess external gills, a tail fin, larval dentition, and a rudimentary tongue (figure 28.5b). The aquatic larval stage usually undergoes metamorphosis into a terrestrial adult (figure 28.5c). Many other salamanders undergo incomplete metamorphosis and are paedomorphic (e.g., *Necturus*); that is, they become sexually mature while still showing larval characteristics.

ORDER GYMNOPHIONA

Members of the order Gymnophiona (jim′no-fy″o-nah) (Gr. *gymnos*, naked + *ophineos*, like a snake) are the caecilians (figure 28.6). There are about 160 described species, which are confined to tropical regions. Caecilians are wormlike burrowers that feed on worms and other invertebrates in the soil. Caecilians appear segmented because of folds in the skin that overlie separations between muscle bundles. They have a retractile tentacle between their eyes and nostrils. The tentacle may transport chemicals from the environment to olfactory cells in

the roof of the mouth. The eyes are covered by skin; thus, caecilians are probably nearly blind.

Fertilization is internal in caecilians. Larval stages are often passed within the oviducts, where they feed on the inner lining of the oviducts by scraping it with fetal teeth. The young emerge from the female as miniatures of the adults. Other caecilians lay eggs that develop into either aquatic larvae or embryos that undergo direct development on land.

ORDER ANURA

The order Anura (ah-noor″ah) (Gr. *a*, without + *oura*, tail) includes about 3,500 species of frogs and toads. Anurans are found in most moist environments, except in high latitudes and on some oceanic islands. A few even occur in very dry deserts. Adults lack tails, and caudal (tail) vertebrae are fused into a rodlike structure called the urostyle. Hind limbs are very long and muscular, and they end in webbed feet.

Anurans have diverse life histories. Fertilization is almost always external, and eggs and larvae are typically aquatic. Larval stages, called tadpoles, have well-developed tails. Their plump bodies lack limbs until near the end of their larval existence. Unlike adults, the larvae are herbivores and possess a proteinaceous, beaklike structure used in feeding. Anuran larvae undergo a drastic and rapid metamorphosis from the larval to the adult body form.

The distinction between "frog" and "toad" is more vernacular than scientific. "Toad" usually refers to anurans with relatively dry and warty skin, and they are more terrestrial than other members of the order. These characteristics are found in a number of distantly related taxa. True toads belong to the family Bufonidae (figure 28.7).

(a)

(b)

(c)

Figure 28.5

Order Caudata. (*a*) Eggs, (*b*) larva, and (*c*) adult of the spotted salamander, *Ambystoma maculatum*. Larvae are herbivores, and adults feed on worms and small arthropods.

Figure 28.6

Order Gymnophiona. A caecilian (*Ichthyophis glutinosus*).

Figure 28.7

Order Anura. American toad (*Bufo americanus*).

BOX 28.1 POISON FROGS OF SOUTH AMERICA

A South American native stalks quietly through the jungle, peering into the tree branches overhead. A monkey's slight movements divulge its presence, and the hunter takes careful aim with what appears to be an almost toylike bow and arrow. The arrow sails true, and the monkey is hit. The arrow seems ineffectual at first, however, after a few moments, the monkey tumbles from the tree. Thousands of years of cultural evolution have taught these natives a deadly secret that makes effective hunting tools out of seemingly innocuous instruments.

All amphibians possess glandular secretions that are noxious or toxic to varying degrees. These glands are distributed throughout the skin and exude milky toxins that help ward off potential predators. Toxic secretions are frequently accompanied by warning (aposematic) coloration that signals to predators the presence of noxious secretions (figure 1).

Four genera of frogs (*Atopophryhnus, Colostethus, Dendrobates,* and *Phyllobates*) in the family Dendrobatidae live in tropical forests from Costa Rica to southern Brazil. South American natives use toxins from these frogs to tip their arrows. Frogs are killed with a stick and held over a fire. Granular glands in the skin release their venom, which is collected and allowed to ferment. Poisons collected in this manner are neurotoxins that prevent the transmission of nerve impulses between nerves and between nerves and muscles. Arrow tips dipped in this poison and allowed to dry contain sufficient toxin to paralyze a bird or small mammal.

Members of this family of frogs, in addition to being exploited by South American natives, have interesting reproductive

FIGURE 1 **A Poison Arrow Frog (*Dendrobates pumilo*).** The striking coloration shown here is an example of aposematic coloration.

habits. A female lays one to six large eggs in moist, terrestrial habitats. The female promptly abandons the eggs, but the male visits the clutch regularly and guards the eggs. The eggs hatch after approximately 2 weeks, and the tadpoles wiggle onto the male's back. The male then transports the tadpoles from the egg-laying site to water, where they are left to develop. The tadpoles metamorphose to the adult body form after approximately 6 weeks.

Stop and Ask Yourself

1. What were two ancient lineages of amphibians? What groups of animals are the modern descendants of each lineage?

2. What animals are members of the order Caudata?

3. What order of amphibians is characterized by wormlike burrowing?

4. What order of amphibians is characterized by tail vertebrae fused into a urostyle?

EVOLUTIONARY PRESSURES

Most amphibians divide their lives between fresh water and land. This divided life is shown by adaptations to both environments that can be observed in virtually every body system. In the water, amphibians are supported by water's buoyant properties, they exchange gases with the water, and face the same osmoregulatory problems as freshwater fishes. On land, amphibians support themselves against gravity, exchange gases with the air, and tend to lose water to the air.

EXTERNAL STRUCTURE AND LOCOMOTION

Vertebrate skin protects against infective microorganisms, ultraviolet light, desiccation, and mechanical injury. As discussed later in this chapter, the skin of amphibians also functions in gas exchange, temperature regulation, and absorption and storage of water.

The skin of amphibians lacks a covering of scales, feathers, or hair. It is, however, highly glandular and its secretions aid in protection. These glands keep the skin moist to prevent drying. They also produce sticky secretions that help a male cling to a female during mating and produce toxic chemicals that discourage potential predators (box 28.1). The skin of many amphibians is smooth, although epidermal thickenings may produce warts, claws, or sandpapery textures, which are usually the result of keratin deposits or the formation of hard, bony areas.

Chromatophores are specialized cells in the epidermis and dermis of the skin and are responsible for skin color and color changes. Cryptic coloration, aposematic coloration (box 28.1), and mimicry are all common in amphibians.

Support and Movement

Water buoys and supports aquatic animals. The skeletons of fishes function primarily in protecting internal organs, providing

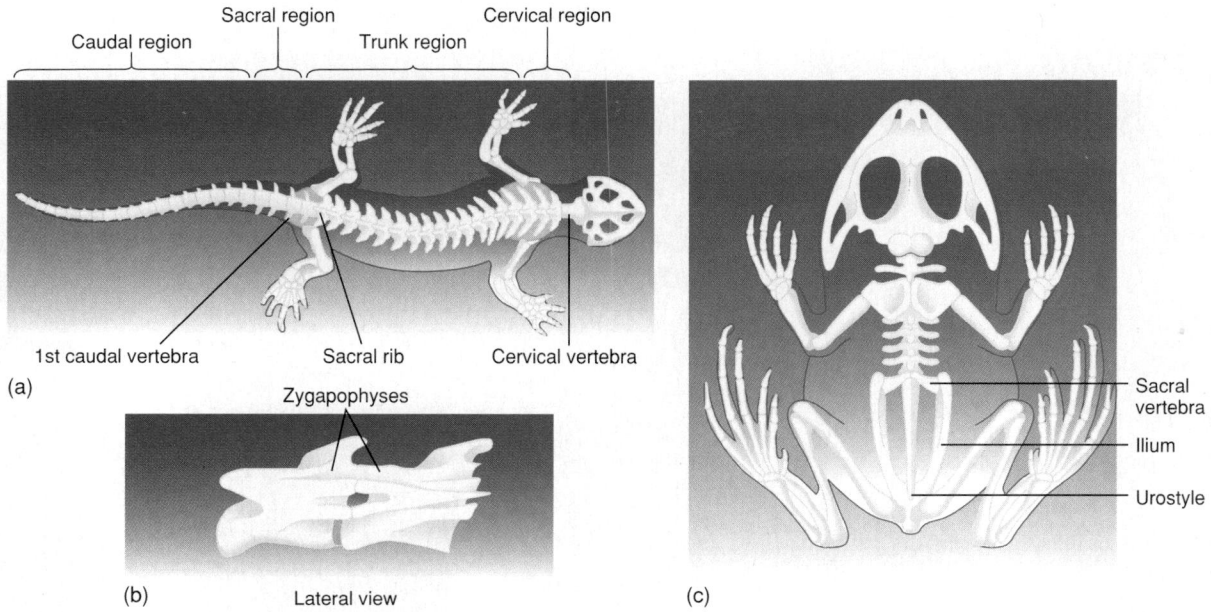

FIGURE 28.8

The Skeletons of Amphibians. (*a*) The salamander skeleton is divided into four regions: cervical, trunk, sacral, and caudal. (*b*) Interlocking processes, called zygapophyses prevent twisting between vertebrae. (*c*) The skeleton of a frog shows adaptations for jumping. Note the long back legs and the firm attachment of the back legs to the vertebral column through the ilium and urostyle.

points of attachment for muscles, and keeping the body from collapsing during movement. In terrestrial vertebrates, however, the skeleton is modified to provide support against gravity and must be strong enough to support the relatively powerful muscles that propel terrestrial vertebrates across land. ① The skull of amphibians is flattened, is relatively smaller, and has fewer bony elements than the skull of fishes. These changes lighten the skull so it can be supported out of the water. Changes in jaw structure and musculature allow a crushing force to be applied to prey held in the mouth.

The vertebral column of amphibians is modified to provide support and flexibility on land (figure 28.8). It acts somewhat like the arch of a suspension bridge by supporting the weight of the body between anterior and posterior paired appendages. Supportive processes called zygapophyses on each vertebra prevent twisting. Unlike fishes, amphibians have a neck. The first vertebra is a cervical vertebra, which moves against the back of the skull and allows the head to nod vertically. The last trunk vertebra is a sacral vertebra. This vertebra is used to anchor the pelvic girdle to the vertebral column to provide increased support. A ventral plate of bone, called the sternum, is present in the anterior, ventral trunk region and provides support for the forelimbs and protection for internal organs. It is reduced or absent in the Anura.

The origin of the bones of vertebrate appendages is not precisely known; however, similarities in the structures of the bones of the amphibian appendages and the bones of the fins of ancient rhipidistian fishes suggest possible homologies (figure 28.9). The presence of joints at the shoulder, hip, elbow, knee, wrist, and ankle allows freedom of movement and better contact with the substrate. The pelvic girdle of amphibians consists of three

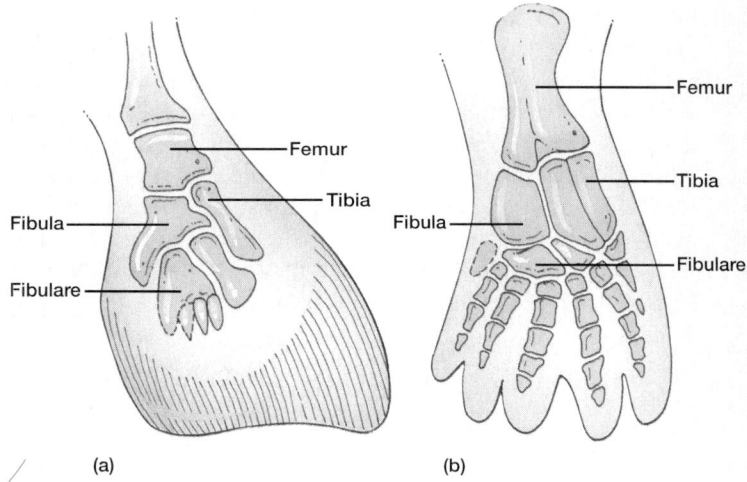

FIGURE 28.9

The Origin of Tetrapod Appendages. A comparison between the fin bones of a rhipidistian (*a*) and the limb bones of a tetrapod (*b*). This comparison suggests that the basic arrangements of bones seen in tetrapod limbs was already present in primitive fishes.

bones (the ilium, ischium, and pubis) that attach pelvic appendages firmly to the vertebral column. These bones, which are present in all tetrapods, but not fishes, are important for support on land.

Tetrapods depend more on appendages than the body wall for locomotion. Thus, body-wall musculature is reduced, and appendicular musculature predominates. (Contrast, for example, what one eats in a fish dinner as compared to a plate of frog legs.)

Figure 28.10

Salamander Locomotion. The pattern of leg movement in salamander locomotion. Arrows show leg movements.

Salamanders employ a relatively unspecialized form of locomotion that is reminiscent of the undulatory waves that pass along the body of a fish. Terrestrial salamanders also move by a pattern of limb and body movements in which the alternate movement of appendages results from muscle contractions that throw the body into a curve to advance the stride of a limb (figure 28.10). Caecilians move in an accordionlike movement in which adjacent parts of the body are pushed or pulled forward at the same time. The long hindlimbs and the pelvic girdle of anurans are modified for jumping. The dorsal bone of the pelvis (the ilium) extends anteriorly and is securely attached to the vertebral column, and the urostyle extends posteriorly and attaches to the pelvis (*see figure 28.8*). These skeletal modifications stiffen the posterior half of the anuran. Long hindlimbs and powerful muscles form an efficient lever system for jumping. Elastic connective tissues and muscles attach the pectoral girdle to the skull and vertebral column and function as shock absorbers for landing on the forelimbs.

Nutrition and the Digestive System

Most adult amphibians are carnivores that feed on a wide variety of invertebrates. The diets of some anurans, however, are more diverse. For example, a bullfrog will prey on small mammals, birds, and other anurans. The main factors that determine what amphibians will eat are prey size and availability. Larvae are herbivorous and feed on algae and other plant matter. Most amphibians locate their prey by sight and simply wait for prey to pass by. Olfaction plays an important role in prey detection by aquatic salamanders and caecilians.

Many salamanders are relatively unspecialized in their feeding methods, using only their jaws to capture prey. Anurans and plethodontid salamanders, however, use their tongue and jaws in a flip-and-grab feeding mechanism (figure 28.11). A true tongue is first seen in amphibians. (The "tongue" of fishes is simply a fleshy fold on the floor of the mouth. Fish food is swallowed whole and not manipulated by the "tongue.") ② The tongue of amphibians is attached at the anterior margin of the jaw and lies folded back over

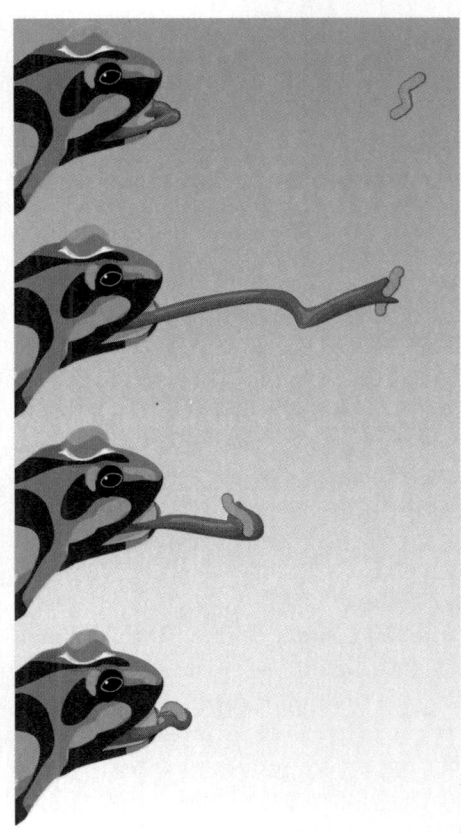

Figure 28.11

Flip-and-Grab Feeding in a Toad. The tongue is attached at the anterior margin of the toad's jaw and is flipped out to capture a prey on its sticky secretions.

the floor of the mouth. Mucous and buccal glands on the tip of the tongue exude sticky secretions. When a prey comes within range, an amphibian lunges forward and flicks out its tongue. The tongue turns over, and the lower jaw is depressed. The fact that the head can tilt on its single cervical vertebra aids in aiming the strike. The tip of the tongue entraps the prey, and the tongue and prey are flicked back inside the mouth. All of this may happen in 0.05 to

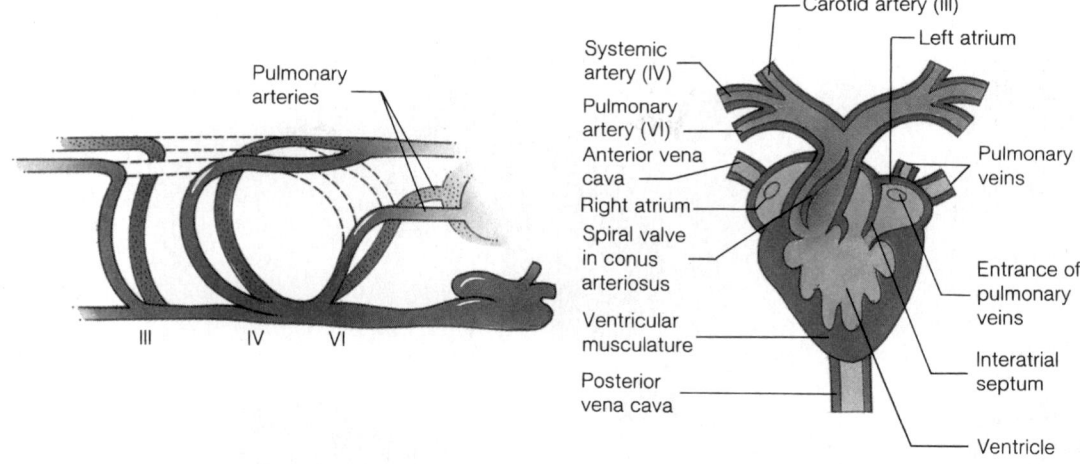

FIGURE 28.12

Diagrammatic Representation of an Anuran Circulatory System. (*a*) The Roman numerals indicate the various aortic arches. Vessels shown in dashed outline are lost during embryological development. (*b*) The heart is drawn in a ventral view.

0.15 second! The prey is held by pressing it against teeth on the roof of the mouth, and the tongue and other muscles of the mouth push food toward the esophagus. The eyes sink downward during swallowing, and help force food toward the esophagus.

CIRCULATION, GAS EXCHANGE, AND TEMPERATURE REGULATION

The circulatory system of amphibians shows remarkable adaptations for a life that is divided between aquatic and terrestrial habitats. The separation of pulmonary and systemic circuits is less efficient in amphibians than in lungfishes (figure 28.12; *see also figure 27.14b*). The atrium is partially divided in urodeles and completely divided in anurans. The ventricle has no septum. A spiral valve is present in the conus arteriosus or ventral aorta and helps direct blood into pulmonary and systemic circuits. As discussed later, gas exchange occurs across the skin of amphibians, as well as in the lungs. Therefore, blood entering the right side of the heart is nearly as well oxygenated as blood entering the heart from the lungs! When an amphibian is completely submerged, all gas exchange occurs across the skin and other moist surfaces; therefore, blood coming into the right atrium has a higher oxygen concentration than blood returning to the left atrium from the lungs. Under these circumstances, blood vessels leading to the lungs constrict, reducing blood flow to the lungs and conserving energy. This adaptation is especially valuable for those frogs and salamanders that overwinter in the mud at the bottom of a pond.

Fewer aortic arches are present in adult amphibians than in fishes. After leaving the conus arteriosus, blood may enter the carotid artery (aortic arch III), which takes blood to the head; the systemic artery (aortic arch IV), which takes blood to the body; or the pulmonary artery (aortic arch VI).

In addition to a vascular system that circulates blood, amphibians have a well-developed lymphatic system of blind-ending vessels that returns fluids, proteins, and ions filtered from capillary beds in tissue spaces to the circulatory system. Water absorbed across the skin is also transported by the lymphatic system. Unlike other vertebrates, amphibians have contractile vessels, called lymphatic hearts, that pump fluid through the lymphatic system. Lymphatic spaces are present between body-wall muscles and the skin. These spaces transport and store water absorbed across the skin.

Gas Exchange

Terrestrial animals need to expend much less energy moving air across gas-exchange surfaces than do aquatic organisms because air contains 20 times more oxygen per unit volume than does water. On the other hand, exchanges of oxygen and carbon dioxide require moist surfaces, and exposure of respiratory surfaces to air may result in rapid water loss.

Anyone who has searched pond and stream banks for frogs knows that the skin of amphibians is moist.   ③ Amphibian skin is also richly supplied with capillary beds. These two factors permit the skin to function as a respiratory organ. Gas exchange across the skin is called **cutaneous respiration** and can occur either in water or on land. This ability allows a frog to spend the winter in the mud at the bottom of a pond. In salamanders, 30 to 90% of gas exchange occurs across the skin. Gas exchange also occurs across the moist surfaces of the mouth and pharynx. This is called **buccopharyngeal respiration** and accounts for 1 to 7% of total gas exchange.

④ Most amphibians, except for plethodontid salamanders, possess lungs (figure 28.13a). The lungs of salamanders are relatively simple sacs. The lungs of anurans are subdivided, increasing the surface area for gas exchange. Pulmonary (lung) ventilation occurs by a **buccal pump** mechanism. Muscles of the mouth and pharynx create a positive pressure to force air into the lungs (figure 28.13b–e).

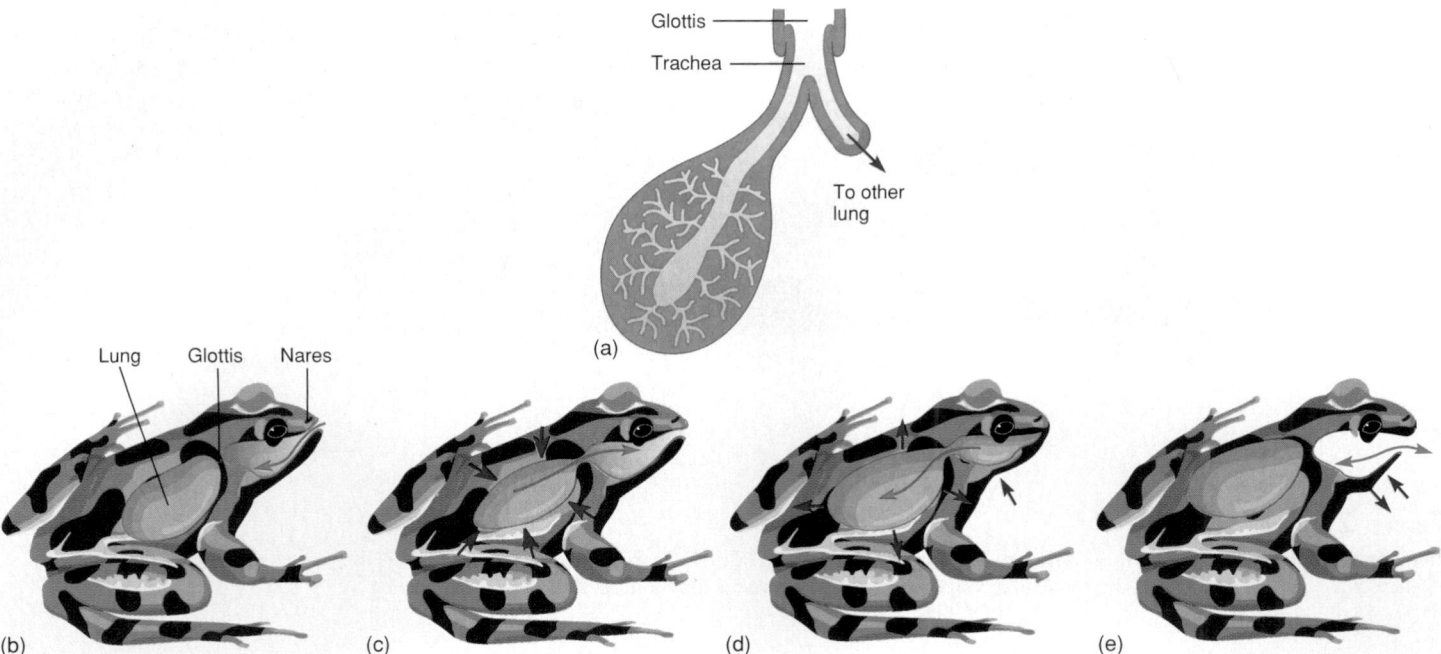

FIGURE 28.13

Amphibian Lung Structure, Buccal Pump, and Buccopharyngeal Ventilation. (*a*) Lung structure of a frog. (*b*) With the opening of the respiratory tract (the glottis) closed, the floor of the mouth is lowered, and air enters the mouth cavity. (*c*) The glottis opens, and the elasticity of the lungs and contraction of the body wall forces air out of the lungs, over the top of air just brought into the mouth. (*d*) The mouth and nares are closed, and the floor of the mouth is raised, forcing air into the lungs. (*e*) With the glottis closed, oscillations of the floor of the mouth exchange air in the mouth cavity to facilitate buccopharyngeal respiration. Blue arrows show air movements. Red arrows show movements of the lungs and body wall.

Cutaneous and buccopharyngeal respiration have a disadvantage in that the absolute contribution of these exchange mechanisms to total gas exchange is relatively constant. There is no way to increase the quantity of gas exchanged across these surfaces when the metabolic rate increases. Lungs, however, compensate for this shortcoming. As environmental temperature and activity increase, lungs contribute more to total gas exchange. At 5° C, approximately 70% of gas exchange occurs across the skin and mouth lining of a frog. At 25° C, the absolute quantity of oxygen exchanged across external body surfaces does not change significantly, but because pulmonary respiration is increased, exchange across skin and mouth surfaces accounts for only about 30% of total oxygen exchange.

Amphibian larvae and some adults respire using external gills. Three pairs of gills are supported by cartilaginous rods that are formed between embryonic gill slits. At metamorphosis, the gills are usually reabsorbed, gill slits close, and lungs become functional.

Temperature Regulation

Amphibians are ectothermic. (They depend upon external sources of heat to maintain body temperature [*see chapter 38*].) Any poorly insulated aquatic animal, regardless of how much metabolic heat is produced, will lose heat as quickly as it is produced because of the powerful heat-absorbing properties of water. Therefore, when amphibians are in water, they take on the temperature of their environment. On land, however, their body temperatures can differ from that of the environment.

Temperature regulation is mainly behavioral. Some cooling results from evaporative heat loss. In addition, many amphibians are nocturnal and remain in cooler burrows or under moist leaf litter during the hottest part of the day. Amphibians may warm themselves by basking in the sun or on warm surfaces. Body temperatures may be raised 10° C above the air temperature. Basking after a meal is common, because increased body temperature increases the rate of all metabolic reactions—including digestive functions, growth, and the deposition of fats necessary to survive periods of dormancy.

Amphibians often experience wide daily and seasonal temperature fluctuations, and therefore have correspondingly wide temperature tolerances. Critical temperature extremes for some salamanders lie between −2 and 27° C, and for some anurans between 3 and 41° C.

Stop and Ask Yourself

5. What are the functions of amphibian skin?
6. What chambers are present in a frog's heart?
7. Why is the incomplete separation of atria and ventricles believed to be adaptive for an amphibian?
8. What are four forms of gas exchange in amphibians?

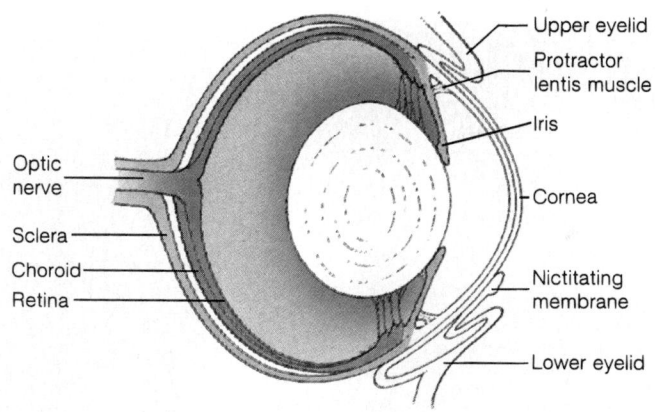

FIGURE 28.14

The Amphibian Eye. Longitudinal section of the eye of the leopard frog, *Rana pipiens*.

NERVOUS AND SENSORY FUNCTIONS

The nervous system of amphibians is similar to that of other vertebrates. The brain of adult vertebrates develops from three embryological subdivisions. In amphibians, the forebrain contains olfactory centers and regions that regulate color change and visceral functions. The midbrain contains a region called the optic tectum, in which sensory information is assimilated and motor responses are initiated. Visual sensory information is also processed in the midbrain. The hindbrain functions in motor coordination and in regulating heart rate and mechanics of respiration.

Many amphibian sensory receptors are widely distributed over the skin. Some of these are simply bare nerve endings that respond to heat, cold, and pain. The lateral-line system is similar in structure to that found in fishes, and it is present in all aquatic larvae, aquatic adult salamanders, and some adult anurans. Lateral-line organs are distributed singly or in small groups along the lateral and dorsolateral surfaces of the body, especially the head. These receptors respond to low-frequency vibrations in the water and movements of the water relative to the animal. On land, however, lateral-line receptors are less important.

Chemoreception is an important sense for many amphibians. Chemoreceptors are located in the nasal epithelium, the lining of the mouth, on the tongue, and over the skin. Olfaction is used in mate recognition, as well as detecting noxious chemicals and in locating food.

Vision is one of the most important senses in amphibians because they are primarily sight feeders. (Caecilians are an obvious exception.) A number of adaptations allow the eyes of amphibians to function in terrestrial environments (figure 28.14). The fact that the eyes of some amphibians (i.e., anurans and some salamanders) are located on the front of the head provides the binocular vision and well-developed depth perception necessary for capturing prey. Other amphibians with smaller lateral eyes (some salamanders) lack binocular vision.

The lower eyelid is movable and functions to clean and protect the eye. Much of it is transparent and is called the **nictitating membrane.** When the eyeball is retracted into the orbit of the skull, the nictitating membrane is drawn up over the cornea. In addition, orbital glands lubricate and wash the eye. Together, eyelids and glands keep the eye free of dust and other debris. The lens is large and nearly round. It is set back from the cornea and is surrounded by a fold of epithelium called the iris. The iris can dilate or constrict to control the size of the pupil.

Focusing, or accommodation, involves bending (refracting) light rays to a focal point on the retina. Light waves moving from air across the cornea are refracted because of the change in density between the two media. Further refraction is accomplished by the lens. As are the eyes of most tetrapods, the amphibian eye is focused on distant objects when the eye is at rest. To focus on near objects, the lens must be moved forward by the protractor lentis muscle (figure 28.14). Receptors called rods and cones are found in the retina. Because cones are associated with color vision in some other vertebrates, their occurrence suggests that amphibians are capable of distinguishing between some wavelengths of light. The extent to which color vision is developed is unknown. The neuronal interconnections in the retina are very complex and allow an amphibian to distinguish between flying insect prey, shadows that may warn of an approaching predator, and background movements, such as blades of grass moving with the wind.

The auditory system of amphibians is clearly an evolutionary adaptation to life on land. It transmits both substrateborne vibrations and, in anurans, airborne vibrations. The ears of anurans consist of a tympanic membrane, a middle ear, and an inner ear. The tympanic membrane is a piece of integument stretched over a cartilaginous ring that receives airborne vibrations and transmits these vibrations to the middle ear, which is a chamber beneath the tympanic membrane. Abutting the tympanic membrane is a middle-ear ossicle (bone) called the stapes (columella), which transmits vibrations of the tympanic membrane into the inner ear (*see figure 34.9*). High-frequency (1,000 to 5,000 Hz) airborne vibrations are transmitted to the inner ear through the tympanic membrane. Low-frequency (100 to 1,000 Hz) substrateborne vibrations are transmitted through the front appendages and the pectoral girdle to the inner ear through a second ossicle called the operculum.

5 Muscles attached to the operculum and stapes can lock either or both of these ossicles, allowing an anuran to screen out either high- or low-frequency sounds. This mechanism is adaptive because low-and high-frequency sounds are used in different situations by anurans. Mating calls are high-frequency sounds that are of primary importance for only a part of the year (breeding season). At other times, low-frequency sounds may warn of approaching predators.

Salamanders lack a tympanic membrane and middle ear. They live in streams, ponds, caves, and beneath leaf litter. They have no mating calls, and the only sounds they hear are probably low-frequency vibrations transmitted through the substrate and skull to the stapes and inner ear.

(a)

(b)

FIGURE **28.15**

Water Conservation by Anurans. (*a*) The daytime sleeping posture of the green tree frog, *Hyla cinerea*. Exposed surface area is reduced by the closely tucked appendages. (*b*) The Australian burrowing frog, *Cyclorana alboguttatus*, in its burrow and water-retaining skin.

The sense of equilibrium and balance is similar to that described for fishes in the previous chapter. The inner ear of amphibians has semicircular canals that help detect rotational movements and other sensory patches that respond to gravity. The latter detect linear acceleration and deceleration.

EXCRETION AND OSMOREGULATION

The kidneys of amphibians lie on either side of the dorsal aorta on the dorsal wall of the body cavity. A duct leads to the cloaca, and a storage structure, the urinary bladder, is a ventral outgrowth of the cloaca.

The nitrogenous waste product excreted by amphibians is either ammonia or urea. Amphibians that live in fresh water excrete ammonia. It is the immediate end product of protein metabolism; therefore, no energy is expended converting it into other products. The toxic effects of ammonia are avoided by its rapid diffusion into the surrounding water. Amphibians that spend more time on land excrete urea that is produced from ammonia in the liver. Although urea is less toxic than ammonia, it still requires relatively large quantities of water for its excretion. Unlike ammonia, urea can be stored in the urinary bladder. Some amphibians excrete ammonia when in water and urea when on land.

One of the biggest problems faced by amphibians is osmoregulation. In water, amphibians face the same osmoregulatory problems as freshwater fishes. They must rid the body of excess water and conserve essential ions. Amphibian kidneys produce large quantities of hypotonic urine, and the skin and walls of the urinary bladder transport Na$^+$, Cl$^-$, and other ions into the blood.

On land, amphibians must conserve water. Adult amphibians do not replace water by intentional drinking, nor do they have the impermeable skin characteristic of other tetrapods or kidneys capable of producing a hypertonic urine. Instead, amphibians limit water loss by behavior that reduces exposure to desiccating conditions. Many terrestrial amphibians are nocturnal. During daylight hours, they retreat to areas of high humidity, such as under stones, in logs, in leaf mulch, or in burrows. Water loss on nighttime foraging trips must be compensated for by water uptake across the skin while in the retreat. Diurnal amphibians usually live in areas of high humidity and rehydrate themselves by entering the water. Many amphibians reduce evaporative water loss by reducing the amount of body surface exposed to air. They may curl their bodies and tails into tight coils and tuck their limbs close to their bodies (figure 28.15a). Individuals may form closely packed aggregations to reduce overall surface area.

Some amphibians have protective coverings that reduce water loss. Hardened regions of skin are resistant to water loss and may be used to plug entrances to burrows or other retreat openings to maintain high humidity in the retreat. Other amphibians prevent water loss by forming cocoons that encase the body during long periods of dormancy. Cocoons are made from outer layers of the skin that detach and become parchmentlike. These cocoons open only at the nares or the mouth and have been found to reduce water loss 20 to 50% over noncocooned individuals (figure 28.15b).

Paradoxically, the skin—the most important source of water loss—is also the most important structure for rehydration. When an amphibian flattens its body on moist surfaces, the skin, especially in the ventral pelvic region, absorbs water. The permeability and vascularization of the skin and its epidermal sculpturing are all factors that promote water reabsorption. Minute channels increase surface area and spread water over surfaces not necessarily in direct contact with water.

Amphibians can also temporarily store water. Water accumulated in the urinary bladder and lymph sacs can be selectively reabsorbed to replace evaporative water loss. Amphibians living in very dry environments can store volumes of water equivalent to 35% of their total body weight.

REPRODUCTION, DEVELOPMENT, AND METAMORPHOSIS

Amphibians are dioecious, and ovaries and testes are located near the dorsal body wall. Fertilization is usually external, and because the developing eggs lack any resistant coverings, development is tied to moist habitats, usually water. A few anurans have terrestrial nests that are kept moist by being enveloped in foam or by being located near the water and subjected to flooding. In a few species, larval stages are passed in the egg membranes, and the immatures hatch into an adultlike body. The main exception to external fertilization in amphibians is the salamanders. Only about 10% of all salamanders have external fertilization. All others use spermatophores, and fertilization is internal. Eggs may be deposited in soil or water or retained in the oviduct during development. All caecilians have internal fertilization and 75% have internal development. Amphibian development has been studied extensively and usually includes the formation of larval stages called tadpoles. Amphibian tadpoles often differ from the adults in mode of respiration, form of locomotion, and diet. These differences reduce competition between adults and larvae.

The timing of reproductive activities is determined by interactions between internal (largely hormonal) controls and extrinsic factors. In temperate regions, breeding periods are seasonal and occur during spring and summer. In temperate areas, temperature seems to be the most important environmental factor that induces physiological changes associated with breeding. In tropical regions, breeding of amphibians is correlated with rainy seasons.

Courtship behavior helps individuals locate breeding sites, identify potential mates, prepare individuals for reproduction, and ensure that eggs are fertilized and deposited in locations that promote successful development.

Salamanders rely primarily on olfactory and visual cues in courtship and mating, whereas in anurans, vocalizations by the male and tactile cues are important. Many species congregate in one location during times of intense breeding activity. Calls by males are usually species specific, and they function in the initial attraction between mates. Once initial contact has been made, tactile cues become more important. The male grasps the female—his forelimbs around her waist—so that they are oriented in the same direction, and the male is dorsal to the female (see figure 10.8a). This positioning is called **amplexus** and may last from 1 to 24 hours. During amplexus, the male releases sperm as the female releases eggs.

Little is known of caecilian breeding behavior. Males possess an intromittent organ that is a modification of the cloacal wall, and fertilization is internal.

Vocalization

6 Sound production is primarily a reproductive function of male anurans. Advertisement calls attract females to breeding areas, and announce to other males that a given territory is occupied. Advertisement calls are species specific, and any one species has a very limited repertoire of calls. They may also help induce psychological and physiological readiness to breed. Reciprocation calls are given by females in response to male calls to indicate receptiveness of a female. Release calls inform a partner that a frog is incapable of reproducing. They are given by unresponsive females during attempts at amplexus by a male, or by males that have been mistakenly identified as female by another male. Distress calls are not associated with reproduction, but are given by either sex in response to pain or being seized by a predator. These calls may be loud enough to cause a predator to release the frog. The distress call of the South American jungle frog, *Leptodactylus pentadactylus*, is a loud scream similar to the call of a cat in distress.

The sound-production apparatus of frogs consists of the larynx and its vocal cords. This laryngeal apparatus is well developed in males, who also possess a vocal sac. In the majority of frogs, vocal sacs develop as a diverticulum from the lining of the buccal cavity (figure 28.16). Air from the lungs is forced over the vocal cords and cartilages of the larynx, causing them to vibrate. Muscles control the tension of the vocal cords and are responsible for regulating the frequency of the sound. Vocal sacs act as resonating structures and increase the volume of the sound.

The use of sound to attract mates is especially useful in organisms that occupy widely dispersed habitats and must come together for breeding. Because many species of frogs often converge at the same pond for breeding, finding a mate of the proper species could be chaotic. Vocalizations help to reduce the chaos.

Parental Care

Parental care increases the chances of any one egg developing, but it requires large energy expenditures on the part of the parent. The most common form of parental care in amphibians is attendance of the egg clutch by either parent. Maternal care occurs in species with internal fertilization (predominantly salamanders and caecilians), and paternal care may occur in species with external fertilization (predominantly anurans). It may involve aeration of aquatic eggs, cleaning and/or moistening of terrestrial eggs, protection of eggs from predators, or removal of dead and infected eggs.

Transport of eggs may occur when development occurs on land. Females of the genus *Pipa* carry eggs on their back.

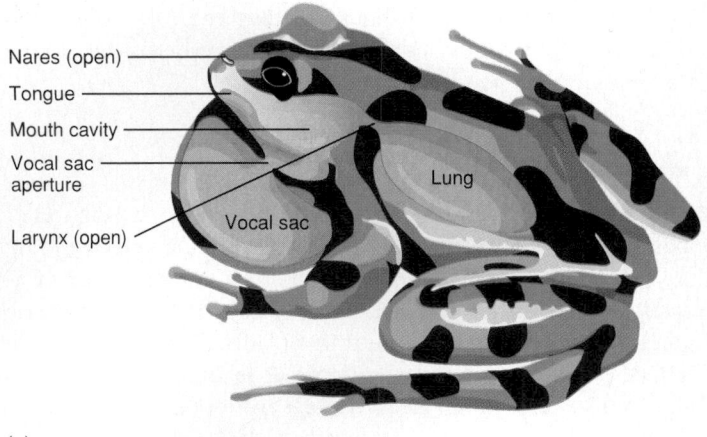

(a)

(b)

FIGURE 28.16

Anuran Vocalization. (*a*) Generalized vocal apparatus of anurans. (*b*) Inflated vocal sac of the Great Plains toad, *Bufo cognatus*.

Rheobatrachus females carry developing eggs and tadpoles in their stomach, and the young emerge from the female's mouth (figure 28.17)! Viviparity and ovoviviparity occur primarily in salamanders and caecilians.

Metamorphosis

Metamorphosis is a series of abrupt structural, physiological, and behavioral changes that transform a larva into an adult. The time required for metamorphosis is influenced by a variety of environmental conditions, including crowding and food availability. Most directly, however, metamorphosis is under the control of neurosecretions of the hypothalamus, hormones of the anterior lobe of the pituitary gland (the adenohypophysis), and the thyroid gland (*see figure 35.10*).

Morphological changes associated with metamorphosis of caecilians and salamanders are relatively minor. Reproductive structures develop, gills are lost, and a caudal fin (when present)

FIGURE 28.17

Parental Care of Young. Female *Rheobatrachus* with young emerging from her mouth.

is lost. In the Anura, however, changes from the tadpole into the small frog are more dramatic (figure 28.18). Limbs and lungs develop, the tail is reabsorbed, the skin thickens, and marked changes in the head and digestive tract (associated with a new mode of nutrition) occur.

Paedomorphosis in amphibians can be explained based on the mechanisms of metamorphosis. Some salamanders are paedomorphic because of a failure of cells to respond to thyroid hormones, whereas others are paedomorphic because of a failure to produce the hormones associated with metamorphosis. Should environmental conditions change, they are able to metamorphose into the adult form.

FURTHER PHYLOGENETIC CONSIDERATIONS

One unresolved controversy concerning amphibian phylogeny is the relationship among the three orders of modern amphibians. Some zoologists place anurans, urodeles, and caecilians into a single subclass, Lissamphibia. This placement implies a common ancestry for modern amphibians and suggests that they are more closely related to each other than to any other group. Supporters of this classification point to common characteristics, such as the stapes/operculum complex, the importance of the skin in gas exchange, and aspects of the structure of the skull and teeth, as evidence of this close relationship. This interpretation is depicted in figure 28.3. Other zoologists think that modern amphibians were derived from at least two nonamniotic lineages. They note that fine details of other structures, such as the vertebral column, are different enough in the three orders to suggest separate origins. If this is true, the class Amphibia

(a)

(b)

(c)

(d)

Figure 28.18

Events of Metamorphosis in the Frog, *Rana temporaria*. (*a*) Before metamorphosis. Prolactin secretion, controlled by the hypothalamus and the adenohypophysis, promotes the growth of larval structures. (*b*–*d*) Metamorphosis. The median eminence of the hypothalamus develops and initiates the secretion of thyroid-stimulating hormone (TSH). TSH begins to inhibit prolactin release. TSH causes the release of large quantities of T_4 and T_3, which promote the growth of limbs, reabsorption of the tail, and other changes of metamorphosis, resulting eventually in a young, adult frog.

would be a paraphyletic group and should be divided into multiple monophyletic taxa. This controversy is not likely to be settled soon.

In the next three chapters, our attention will turn to descendants of the amniote lineage (*see figure 28.3*). A group called anthracosaurs are often cited as amphibian ancestors of these animals, but support for this conclusion is weak.

7 Three sets of evolutionary changes occurred in amphibian lineages that allowed movement onto land. Two of these occurred early enough that they are found in all amphibians. One was the set of changes in the skeleton and muscles that allowed greater mobility on land. A second change involved a jaw mechanism and moveable head that permitted effective exploitation of insect resources on land. A jaw-muscle arrangement that permitted rhipidistian fishes to snap, grab, and hold prey was adaptive when early tetrapods began feeding on insects in terrestrial environments. The third set of changes occurred in the amniote lineage—the development of an egg that was resistant to drying. Although the **amniotic egg** is not completely independent of water, a series of extraembryonic membranes form during development that protect the embryo from desiccation,

store wastes, and promote gas exchange. In addition, this egg has a leathery or calcified shell that is protective, yet porous enough to allow exchange of gases with the environment (*see figure 10.13*). These evolutionary events eventually resulted in the remaining three vertebrate groups: reptiles, birds, and mammals.

Stop and Ask Yourself

9. What region of the amphibian brain integrates sensory information and initiates motor responses?

10. What respiratory and excretory adaptations do amphibians possess that promote life in terrestrial environments?

11. What are four functions of anuran vocalizations?

12. In what ways are amniotic eggs adaptive for life on land?

SUMMARY

1. Terrestrial vertebrates are called tetrapods and probably arose from sarcopterygians. Two lineages of ancient amphibians diverged. The nonamniote lineage gave rise to the three orders of modern amphibians. The amniote lineage gave rise to reptiles, birds, and mammals.

2. Members of the order Caudata are the salamanders. Salamanders are widely distributed, usually have internal fertilization, and may have aquatic larvae or direct development.

3. The order Gymnophiona contains the caecilians. Caecilians are tropical, wormlike burrowers. They have internal fertilization and many are viviparous.

4. Frogs and toads comprise the order Anura. Anurans lack tails and possess adaptations for jumping and swimming. External fertilization results in tadpole larvae, which metamorphose to adults.

5. The skin of amphibians is moist and functions in gas exchange, water regulation, and protection.

6. Skeletal and muscular systems of amphibians are adapted for movement on land.

7. Amphibians are carnivores that capture prey in their jaws or by using their tongue.

8. The circulatory system of amphibians is modified to accommodate the presence of lungs, gas exchange at the skin, and loss of gills in most adults.

9. Gas exchange is cutaneous, buccopharyngeal, and pulmonary. Pulmonary ventilation is accomplished by a buccal pump. A few amphibians retain gills as adults.

10. Sensory receptors of amphibians, especially the eye and ear, are adapted for functioning on land.

11. Amphibians excrete ammonia or urea. Ridding the body of excess water when in water and conserving water when on land are functions of the kidneys, the skin, and behavior.

12. Reproductive habits of amphibians are diverse. Many have external fertilization and development. Others have internal fertilization and development. Courtship, vocalizations, and parental care are common in some amphibians. Metamorphosis is under the control of the nervous and endocrine systems.

13. The evolution of an egg that is resistant to drying occurred in the amniote lineage, which is represented today by reptiles, birds, and mammals.

SELECTED KEY TERMS

amniote lineage (p. 452)
amplexus (p. 463)
buccal pump (p. 459)
buccopharyngeal respiration (p. 459)
cutaneous respiration (p. 459)
nictitating membrane (p. 461)
nonamniote lineage (p. 452)
tetrapods (p. 452)

CRITICAL THINKING QUESTIONS

1. How are skeletal and muscular systems of amphibians adapted for life on land?

2. Would the buccal pump be more important for an active amphibian or for one that is becoming inactive for the winter? Explain your answer.

3. Why is the separation of oxygenated and nonoxygenated blood in the heart not very important for amphibians?

4. Explain how the skin of amphibians is used in temperature regulation, protection, gas exchange, and water regulation. Under what circumstances might cooling interfere with water regulation?

5. In what ways could anuran vocalizations have influenced the evolution of that order?

chapter

REPTILES:
THE FIRST AMNIOTES

Concepts

1. Adaptive radiation of primitive amniotes resulted in the three or four lineages of reptiles. These lineages have given rise to four orders of modern reptiles, the birds, and the mammals.
2. The class Reptilia is divided into four orders: Testudines includes the turtles; Squamata includes the lizards, the snakes, and the worm lizards; Rhynchocephalia includes a single species, *Sphenodon punctatus*; and Crocodilia includes the alligators and crocodiles.
3. Reptiles possess adaptations that allow many members of the class to spend most of their lives apart from standing or flowing water. These include adaptations for support and movement, feeding, gas exchange, temperature regulation, excretion, osmoregulation, and reproduction.
4. Two reptilian evolutionary lineages gave rise to other vertebrate classes: Aves and Mammalia.

Would You Like to Know:

1. what living animals are most closely related to dinosaurs? (*p.* 468)
2. why turtles are vulnerable to extinction? (*p.* 472)
3. what animal "walks at both ends"? (*p.* 474)
4. why a lizard's tail breaks easily? (*p.* 475)
5. how a chameleon captures prey? (*p.* 476)
6. why reptiles divert blood away from their lungs? (*p.* 477)
7. what a median eye is? (*p.* 479)

These and other useful questions will be answered in this chapter.

This chapter contains evolutionary concepts, which are set off in this font.

EVOLUTIONARY PERSPECTIVE

The earliest members of the class Reptilia (rep-til'e-ah) (L. *reptus*, to creep) were the first vertebrates to possess **amniotic eggs** (figure 29.1). Amniotic eggs have a series of extraembryonic membranes that protect the embryo from desiccation, cushion the embryo, promote gas transfer, and store waste materials (*see figures 10.11 and 10.13*). The amniotic eggs of reptiles and birds also have hard or leathery shells that protect the developing embryo, albumen that cushions and provides moisture and nutrients for the embryo, and yolk to supply food to the embryo. All of these features are adaptations for development on land. (The amniotic egg is not, however, the only kind of land egg—some arthropods, amphibians, and even a few fishes have eggs that develop on land.) The amniotic egg is the major synapomorphy that distinguishes the reptiles, birds, and mammals from vertebrates in the nonamniote lineage. Even though the amniotic egg has played an important role in the successful invasion of terrestrial habitats by vertebrates, it is one of many reptilian adaptations that have allowed members of this class to flourish on land. Living representatives of the class Reptilia include the turtles, lizards, snakes, worm lizards, crocodilians, and the tuatara (table 29.1).

Even though there are abundant fossil records of many reptiles, there is much to be learned of reptilian origins. As indicated by the circle at the base of the cladogram in figure 29.2, the ancestral amniote has not yet been discovered. The adaptive radiation of the early amniotes began in the late Carboniferous and early Permian periods. This time coincided with the adaptive radiation of terrestrial insects, the major prey of early amniotes. The adaptive radiation of the amniotes resulted in the lineages described below. One of the ways that these lineages are distinguished is by the structure of the skull, particularly the modifications in jaw muscle attachment (figure 29.3).

Reptiles in the subclass Anapsida (Gr. *an*, without + *hapsis*, arch) lack openings or fenestrae in the temporal (posterolateral) region of the skull. This lineage is represented today by the turtles. Recent evidence suggests that the anapsid lineage probably does not share close evolutionary ties to other reptiles. Changes have occurred in their long evolutionary history, but the fundamental form of their skull and shell is recognizable in 200-million-year-old fossils. Evidence of the anapsid lineage has been found in 245-million-year-old rocks from South Africa.

A second group of reptiles are diapsid (Gr. *di*, two). They have upper and lower openings in the temporal region of the skull. It is debated whether or not this condition reflects a single lineage (*see figure 29.2*). Some taxonomists prefer to divide this group into two subclasses. One subclass, the Lepidosauria, includes modern snakes, lizards, and tuataras. A second subclass, Archosauria, underwent extensive evolutionary radiation in the Mesozoic era and includes the dinosaurs. Most archosaurs are now extinct (box 29.1). ① Living archosaurs include the crocodilians and the dinosaurs' closest living relatives—the birds.

Another group of reptiles are synapsid (Gr. *syn*, with). They possess a single dorsal opening in the temporal region of the skull. Although there are no living reptilian descendants of this group, they are important because a group of synapsids, called therapsids, gave rise to the mammals.

FIGURE 29.1

Class Reptilia. Members of the class Reptilia were the first vertebrates to possess amniotic eggs, which develop free from standing or flowing water. Numerous other adaptations have allowed members of this class to flourish on land. A Nile crocodile (*Crocodylus niloticus*) is shown here.

TABLE 29.1	CLASSIFICATION OF LIVING REPTILES

Class Reptilia (rep-til´e-ah)
Skin dry, with epidermal scales; skull with one point of articulation with the vertebral column (occipital condyle); respiration via lungs; metanephric kidneys; internal fertilization; amniotic eggs.

   Order Testudines (tes-tu´din-ez) or Chelonia (ki-lo´ne-ah)
   Teeth absent in adults and replaced by a horny beak; body short and broad; shell consisting of a dorsal carapace and ventral plastron. Turtles.

   Order Rhynchocephalia (rin´ko-se-fay´le-ah)
   Contains very primitive, lizardlike reptiles; well-developed parietal eye. A single species, *Sphenodon punctatus*, survives in New Zealand. Tuataras.

   Order Squamata (skwa-ma´tah)
   Recognized by specific characteristics of the skull and jaws (temporal arch reduced or absent and quadrate movable or secondarily fixed); the most successful and diverse group of living reptiles. Snakes, lizards, worm lizards.

   Order Crocodilia (krok´o-dil´e-ah)
   Elongate, muscular, and laterally compressed; tongue not protrusible; complete ventricular septum. Crocodiles, alligators, caimans, gavials.

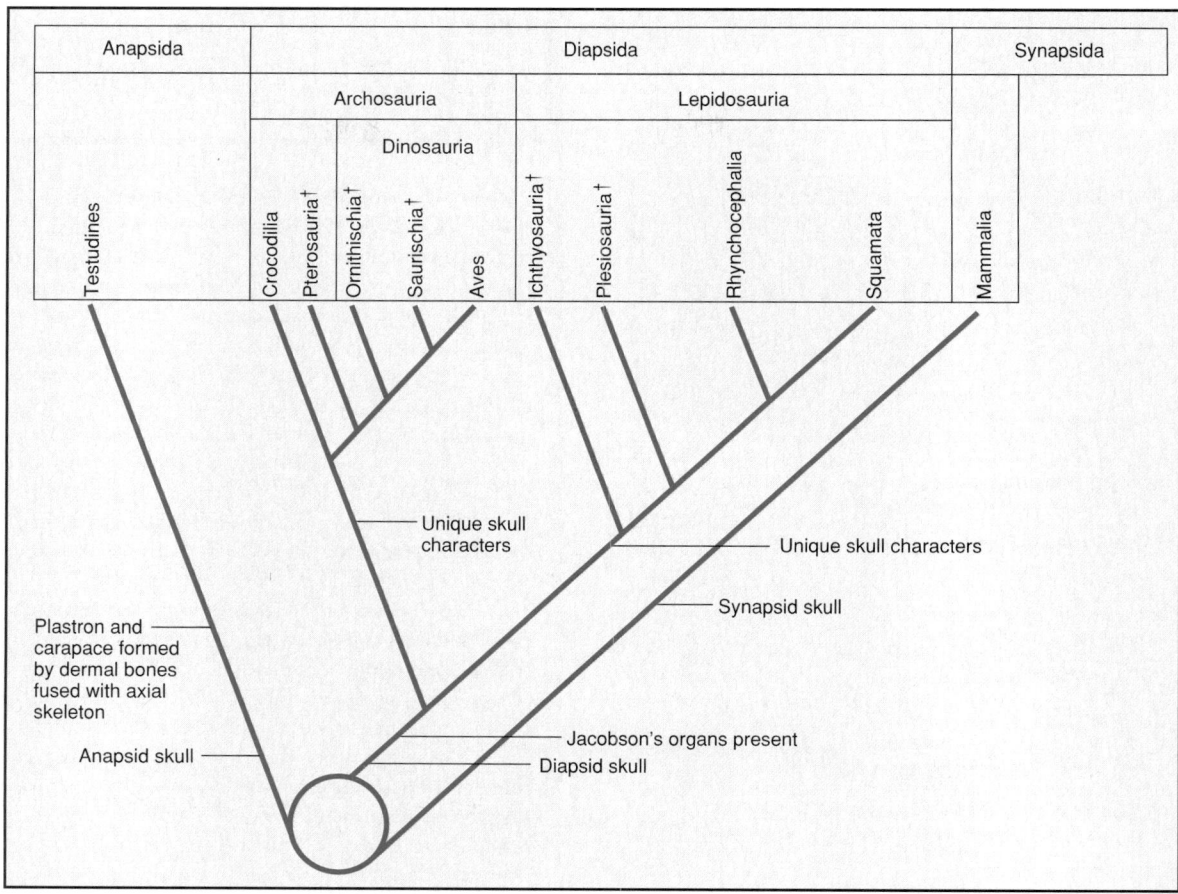

Figure 29.2

Amniote Phylogeny. This cladogram shows one interpretation of the phylogeny of the amniotes. The circle at the base of the cladogram indicates that the ancestral amniotes have not been described. Some researchers believe that the Diapsida is not a single lineage and that the Archosauria and Lepidosauria should be elevated to subclass status. Synapomorphies used to distinguish lower taxa are not shown. Some extinct taxa are indicated with a dagger (†). Numerous extinct other taxa are not shown.

CLADISTIC INTERPRETATION OF THE AMNIOTIC LINEAGE

Cladistic taxonomic methods have resulted in a reexamination and reinterpretation of the amniotic lineage. As shown in figure 28.3, the amniotic lineage is monophyletic. Figure 29.2 shows that the birds (traditionally the class Aves) and the mammals (traditionally the class Mammalia) share a common ancestor with the reptiles. The rules of cladistic analysis state that all descendants of a most recent common ancestor must be included in a particular taxon. Clearly that is not the case with the traditional class Reptilia—the birds and mammals are excluded even though they share a common ancestry with reptiles. According to cladistic interpretations, birds should be classified as "reptiles" with their closest relatives, the dinosaurs. Similarly, cladistic interpretations take into account the close relationships of the mammals and a group of ancient reptiles, the mammal-like reptiles.

Evolutionary systematists disagree with cladists' interpretations. They contend that both the birds and the mammals

have important morphological, behavioral, and ecological characteristics (e.g., feathers and endothermy in the birds; hair, mammary glands, and endothermy in mammals) that make their assignment to separate classes warranted. In effect, evolutionary systematists weigh these characters and conclude that they are of overriding importance in the taxonomy of these groups.

The classification of the amniotes presented in this textbook follows the traditional interpretation. Students should realize, however, that the presentation of amniote systematics may change in future editions of this textbook since the disagreements between cladists and evolutionary systematists will probably continue.

SURVEY OF THE REPTILES

Reptiles are characterized by a skull with one surface (condyle) for articulation with the first neck vertebra, respiration by lungs, metanephric kidneys, internal fertilization, and amniotic eggs. Reptiles also have dry skin with keratinized

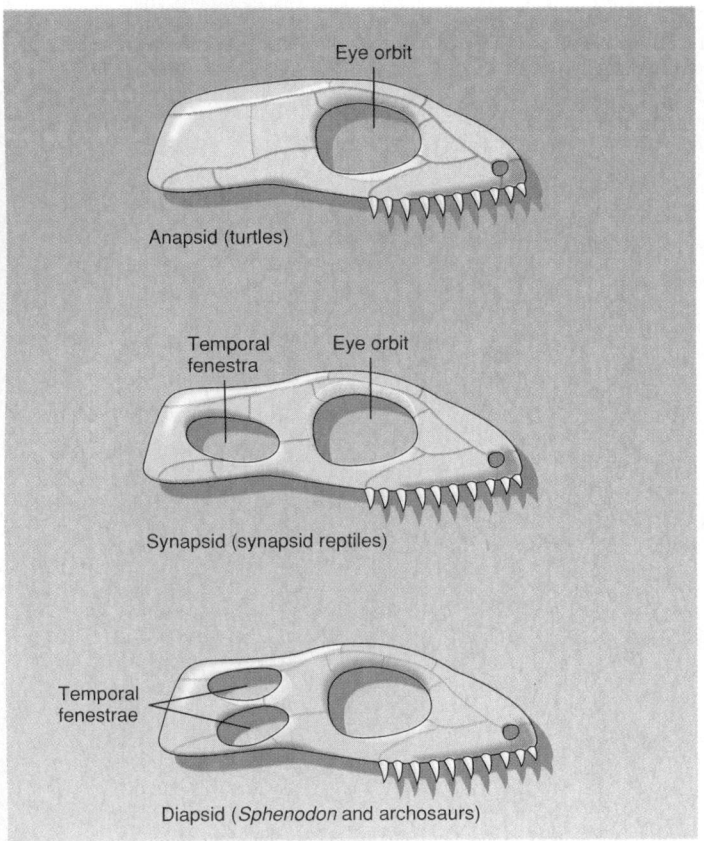

Anapsid (turtles)

Temporal fenestra   Eye orbit

Synapsid (synapsid reptiles)

Temporal fenestrae

Diapsid (*Sphenodon* and archosaurs)

FIGURE 29.3

Amniote Skull Characteristics. Amniotes are classified based upon skull characteristics and the attachment of jaw muscles. (*a*) Anapsid skulls lack openings in the temporal region of the skull. This kind of skull is characteristic of turtles. (*b*) Synapsid skulls have a single temporal opening and are characteristic of the lineage of amniotes leading to mammals. (*c*) Diapsid skulls have two temporal openings. This kind of skull is characteristic of lizards, snakes, worm lizards, the tuatara, and birds.

epidermal scales. **Keratin** is a resistant protein found in epidermally derived structures of amniotes. It is protective, and when it is chemically bonded to phospholipids, it prevents water loss across body surfaces. Members of three of the four orders described on the following pages are found on all continents except Antarctica. However, reptiles are a dominant part of any major ecosystem only in tropical and subtropical environments. There are 17 orders of reptiles, but members of most orders are extinct. The four orders containing living representatives are described next (*see table 29.1*).

ORDER TESTUDINES OR CHELONIA

Members of the order Testudines (tes-tu'din-ez) (L. *tes-tudo*, tortise), or Chelonia (ki-lo'ne-ah) (Gr. *chelone*, tortise) are the turtles. There are about 225 species of turtles in the world, and they are characterized by a bony shell with limbs articulating

 **29.1**   COLLISION OR COINCIDENCE?

Extinction is the eventual fate of all species. Indeed, 99% of all species ever on the earth are now extinct. Often, the rate of extinction is low; however, on several occasions in the history of the earth, rates of extinction have increased dramatically, resulting in the total extinction of many formerly successful taxa. For example, at the Permian/Triassic boundary, a mass extinction resulted in the loss of 80 to 90% of all animal species. About 65 million years ago, the dinosaurs, along with 50% of all other animal species became extinct. This Cretaceous/Tertiary extinction occurred over a period of tens of thousands to several million years. From a geological perspective, these extinctions are "sudden." How the age of the reptiles ended has been the subject of speculation for many years. Various hypotheses involving catastrophic or gradual change have been proposed.

The impact of asteroids or periods of intense volcanic activity are catastrophic events that have been suggested as causes of mass extinctions. Both events may have injected large quantities of dust into the air that shaded the earth's surface, reducing photosynthetic production, and thus food for animals.

The presence of the element iridium in rock strata from the Cretaceous/Tertiary boundary and other periods of mass extinction is the primary evidence supporting the catastrophic hypotheses. Iridium is a primarily extraterrestrial element that is deposited during asteroid impacts with the earth. Some deposits may also result from volcanic activity. Opponents of the catastrophic hypotheses do not deny that asteroid impacts or periods of volcanic activity resulted in iridium deposits on the earth. They question, however, whether the catastrophes are responsible for mass extinctions. They point out that the paleontological record indicates that extinctions are not as abrupt as implied in catastrophic hypotheses. Extinctions apparently occurred over tens of thousands of years, not tens of years. In addition, catastrophic events would be expected to affect all animal groups more or less equally, which was not the case with the Cretaceous/Tertiary extinction. For example, dinosaurs became extinct, but crocodiles, turtles, birds, and early mammals did not.

Numerous hypotheses propose gradual, selective changes as explanations for mass extinction. Some of these involve climatic changes that could have been induced by continental drift. In the Cretaceous period, 70% of the present land area was covered by warm, shallow seas. By the end of the Cretaceous period, these seas were reduced to 15% of the present land area, resulting in the reduction of habitat for shallow-water marine organisms, a decrease in atmospheric temperatures, and dissection of land areas by newly formed rivers. Climatic and habitat changes such as these could have resulted in extinctions over periods of tens of thousands of years.

Regardless of what hypothesis (or hypotheses) of mass extinction is correct, this question is a good example of how interest fueled by controversy stimulates scientific inquiry. The gradualism/catastrophism debate has led to new, innovative ideas on the origin, evolution, and extinction of taxa.

BOX 29.2 | BONE AND SCALES

Bone is the primary skeletal tissue of vertebrates. In addition to making up the skeleton, it also is present in the scales of some vertebrates.

Developmentally, bone is derived from two sources. Dermal or membrane bone forms many of the superficial, flat bones of the top (dorsal) portion of the skull and some bones in the pectoral girdle. These bones were especially numerous in the roof of the skull of early vertebrates. Dermal bone is formed in the connective tissues of the dermis of the skin. During its formation, bone-forming cells called osteoblasts line up along connective-tissue fibers and begin depositing bone. Bony fibers coalesce into the latticework that makes up a flat bone.

Endochondral bone forms many of the long bones and the ventral and posterior bones of the skull. It develops by replacing the cartilage that formed early in development (figure 1a). The cartilage-based bone grows during development. As it does, osteoblasts lay down a collar of bone around the middle region, the diaphysis. Cartilage cells in the diaphysis begin to break down, beginning the formation of cavity called the marrow cavity. Eventually, this cavity will be filled with bone marrow, in which blood cells are formed. Bone formation proceeds toward the ends of a bone. The cartilage near the end of the bone, however, continues to grow and results in further bone elongation. Each end of the bone is an epiphysis. In mammals, a secondary ossification center occurs in each epiphysis and forms bony caps on the ends of the bone. However, a cartilaginous plate, the epiphyseal plate, remains between the epiphysis and the diaphysis and is the site of cartilage growth and bone elongation. Bone growth continues until maturity. Except for thin cartilages at the ends of bones that provide gliding surfaces for joints, all cartilage is replaced by bone at maturity, and growth stops.

The scales of fishes are composed, in part, of dermal bone. Osteoblasts in the dermis of the skin lay down a core of bone. Other dermal cells lay down a layer of dentine, which is similar to bone, around the bony core. Then, epidermal cells lay down a covering of enamel (figure 1b). Enamel is one of the hardest tissues in the vertebrate body and also occurs on teeth.

The scales of the skin of reptiles and the legs of birds are formed entirely in the epidermis of the skin and do not contain bone. These scales are composed of many layers of epidermal cells (figure 1c). Keratin and phospholipids are incorporated into the outer, horny layers of a scale to reduce water loss across the skin. As you will see in chapter 30, the feathers of birds are modified epidermal scales.

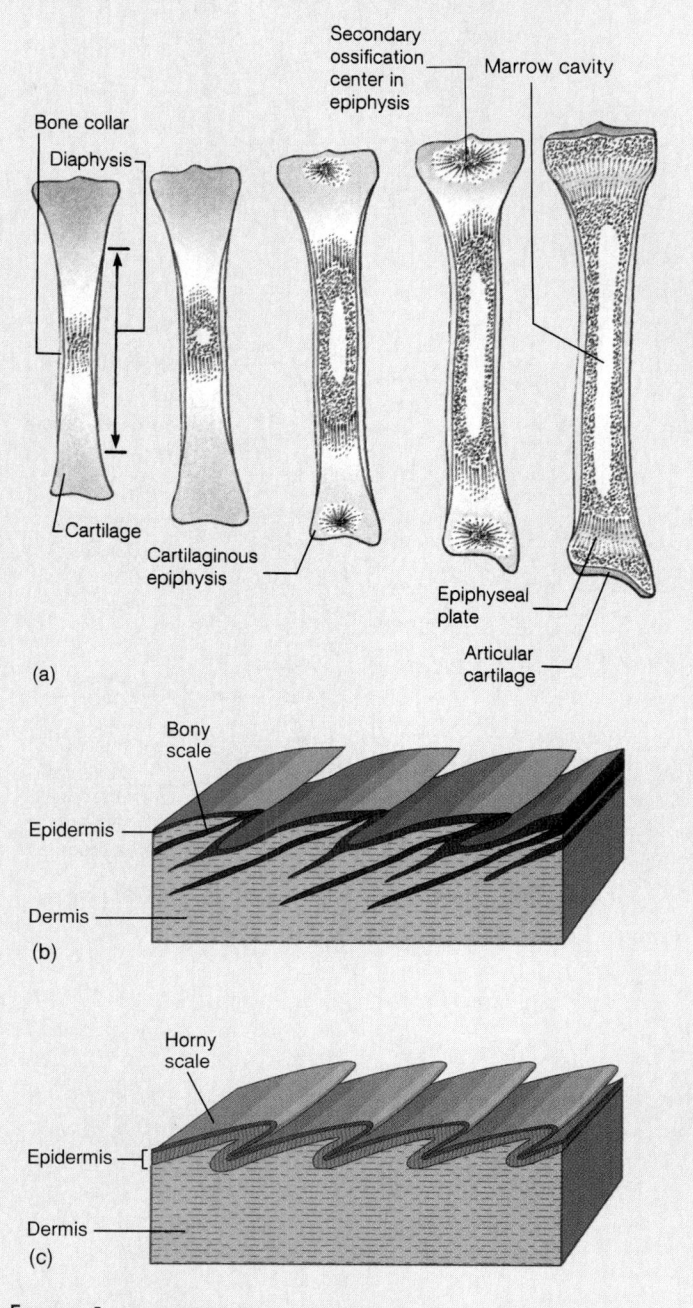

FIGURE 1 **Bone and Scales.** (a) The formation of endochondral bone. (b) Dermal scales of a fish. (c) Epidermal scales of a reptile.

internally to the ribs and a keratinized beak rather than teeth. The dorsal portion of the shell is the **carapace,** which is formed from a fusion of vertebrae, expanded ribs, and bones formed in the dermis of the skin (box 29.2). The bone of the carapace is covered by keratin. The ventral portion of the shell is the **plastron.** It is formed from bones of the pectoral girdle and dermal bone, and is

also covered by keratin (figure 29.4). In some turtles, such as the North American box turtle (*Terrapene*), the shell has flexible areas, or hinges, that allow the anterior and posterior edges of the plastron to be raised. The hinge allows the shell openings to close when the turtle is withdrawn into the shell. Turtles have eight cervical vertebrae that can be articulated into an

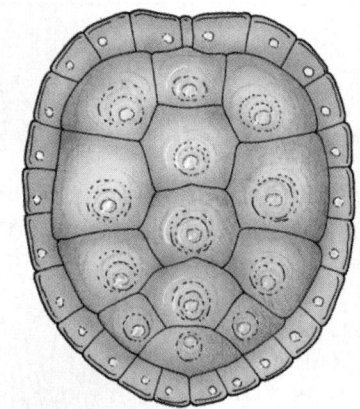

(a)

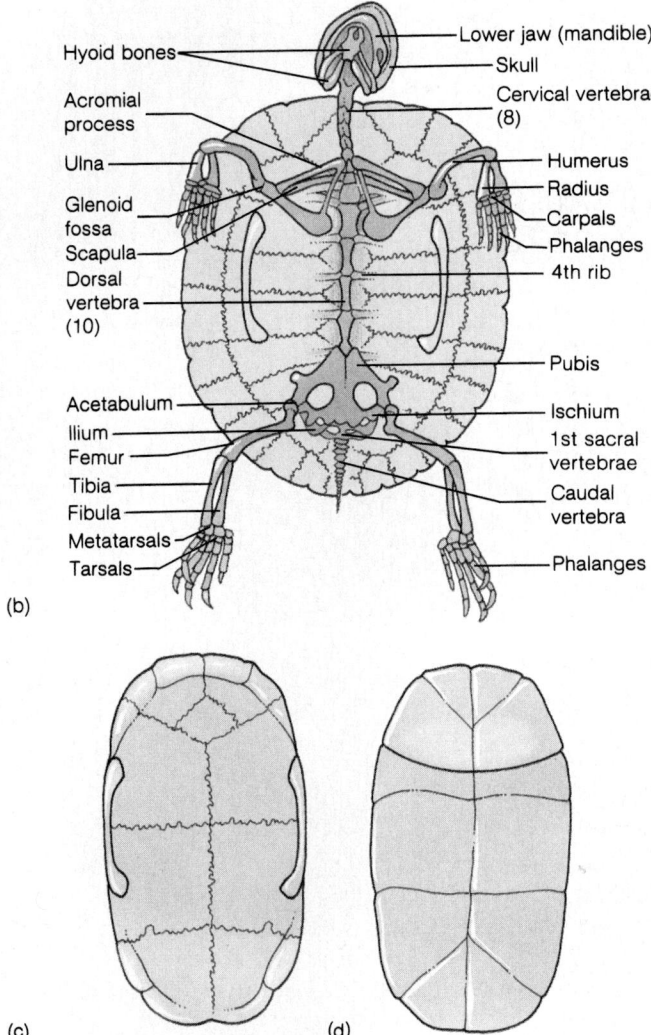

(b)

(c)   (d)

Figure 29.4

The Skeleton of a Turtle. (*a*) Dorsal view of the carapace.
(*b*) Ventral view of the carapace and appendicular skeleton. The
carapace is composed of fused vertebrae, expanded ribs, and dermal
bone and is covered by keratin. (*c*) Dorsal view of the plastron.
(*d*) Ventral view of the plastron. The plastron is formed from dermal
bone and bone of the pectoral girdle. It is also covered by keratin.

"S-shaped" configuration, which allows the head to be drawn
into the shell.

Turtles have long life spans. Most reach sexual maturity
after 7 or 8 years and live 14 or more years. Large tortoises of
the Galápagos Islands may live in excess of 100 years (*see figure
11.2*). All turtles are oviparous. Females use their hind limbs to
excavate nests in the soil. Clutches of 5 to 100 eggs are laid and
covered with soil. Development takes from 4 weeks to 1 year,
and eggs are not attended by the parent during development.
The young are independent of the parent at hatching.

In recent years, turtle conservation programs have been
enacted. ② Slow rates of growth and long juvenile periods make turtles vulnerable to extinction in the face of high
mortality rates. Turtle hunting and predation on young turtles
and turtle nests by dogs and other animals has severely threatened some species. Predation on nests and young is made
more serious by the fact that certain beaches are used year
after year by nesting sea turtles. Conservation of sea turtles is
complicated by the fact that they have ranges of thousands of
square kilometers of ocean, so that protective areas must include waters under the jurisdiction of many different nations
(figure 29.5).

Order Rhynchocephalia

The one surviving species of the order Rhynchocephalia
(rin′ko-se-fay′le-ah) (Gr. *rhynchos*, snout + *kephale*, head) is
the tuatara (*Sphenodon punctatus*) (figure 29.6). This superficially lizardlike reptile is virtually unchanged from extinct relatives that were present at the beginning of the Mesozoic era,
nearly 200 million years ago. It is distinguished from other reptiles by tooth attachment and structure. Two rows of teeth on
the upper jaw and a single row of teeth in the lower jaw produce a shearing bite that can decapitate a small bird. Formerly
more widely distributed in New Zealand, the tuatara fell prey
to human influences and domestic animals. It is now present
only on remote offshore islands and is protected by New
Zealand law. It is oviparous and shares underground burrows
with ground-nesting seabirds. Tuataras venture out of their
burrows at dusk and dawn to feed on insects or occasionally
small vertebrates.

Order Squamata

The order Squamata (skwa-ma′tah) (L. *squama*, scale + *ata*, to
bear) is divided into three suborders. Ancestral members of
these suborders originated in the lepidosaur lineage about 150
million years ago and diverged into numerous modern forms.

Suborder Sauria—The Lizards

There are about 3,300 species of lizards in the suborder Sauria
(sawr′e-ah) (Gr. *sauro*, lizard). In contrast to snakes, lizards usually have two pairs of legs. The few that are legless retain remnants of a pectoral girdle and sternum. Lizards vary in length

FIGURE 29.5

Order Testudines. Green sea turtles (*Chelonia mydas*) nest every 2 to 4 years and migrate many miles to nesting beaches in the Caribbean and South Atlantic Oceans.

FIGURE 29.6

Order Rhynchocephalia. The tuatara (*Sphenodon punctatus*).

from only a few centimeters to as large as 3 m. Many lizards live on surface substrates and retreat under rocks or logs when necessary. Others are burrowers or tree dwellers. Most lizards are oviparous; some are ovoviviparous or viviparous. Eggs are usually deposited under rocks, debris, or in burrows.

Geckos, commonly found on the walls of human dwellings, are short and stout. They are nocturnal, and unlike most lizards, are capable of clicking vocalizations. Their large eyes, with pupils that contract to a narrow slit during the day and dilate widely at night, are adapted for night vision. Adhesive disks on their digits aid in clinging to trees and walls.

Iguanas have robust bodies, short necks, and distinct heads. This group includes the marine iguanas of the Galápagos Islands and the flying dragons (*Draco*) of Southeast Asia. The

FIGURE 29.7

Order Squamata. The gila monster (*Heloderma suspectum*) is a poisonous lizard of southwestern North America.

latter have lateral folds of skin that are supported by ribs. Like the ribs of an umbrella, the ribs of *Draco* can be expanded to form a gliding surface. When this lizard launches itself from a tree it can glide 30 m or more!

Another group of iguanas, the chameleons, is found mainly in Africa and India. They are adapted to arboreal lifestyles and use a long, sticky tongue to capture insects. *Anolis*, or the "pet-store chameleon," is also an iguanid, but is not a true chameleon. Chameleons and *Anolis* are well known for their ability to change color in response to illumination, temperature, or their behavioral state.

The only venomous lizards are the gila monster (*Heloderma suspectum*) (figure 29.7) and the Mexican beaded lizard (*Heloderma horridum*). These heavy-bodied lizards are native to southwestern North America. Venom is released into grooves on the surface of teeth and introduced into prey as the lizard chews. Lizard bites are seldom fatal to humans.

Suborder Serpentes—The Snakes

There are about 2,300 species in the suborder Serpentes (ser-pen'tez) (L. *serpere*, to crawl). Although the vast majority of snakes are not dangerous to humans, about 300 species are venomous. Worldwide, about 30,000 to 40,000 people die from snake bites each year. Most of these deaths are in Southeast Asia. In the United States, fewer than 100 people die each year from snake bites.

Snakes are elongate and lack limbs, although vestigial pelvic girdles and appendages are sometimes present. The skeleton may contain more than 200 vertebrae and pairs of ribs. Joints between vertebrae make the body very flexible. Snakes possess skull adaptations that facilitate swallowing large prey. Other differences between lizards and snakes include the mechanism for focusing the eyes and the morphology of the retina. Elongation and narrowing of the body has

FIGURE 29.8

Order Squamata. An amphisbaenian "worm lizard" (*Amphisbaenia alba*), sometimes called a two-headed snake.

resulted in the reduction or loss of the left lung and displacement of the gallbladder, the right kidney, and often the gonads. Most snakes are oviparous, although a few, such as the New World boas, give birth to live young.

The evolutionary origin of the snakes is debated. The earliest fossils are from 135-million-year-old Cretaceous deposits. Some zoologists believe that the earliest snakes were burrowers. Loss of appendages and changes in eye structure could be adaptations similar to those seen in caecilians (*see figure 28.6*). The loss of legs could also be adaptive if early snakes were aquatic or lived where densely tangled vegetation was common.

Suborder Amphisbaenia—Worm Lizards

There are about 135 species in the suborder Amphisbaenia (am'fis-be'ne-ah) (Gr. *amphi*, double + *baen*, to walk). They are specialized burrowers that live in soils of Africa, South America, the Caribbean, and the Mideast (figure 29.8). Most are legless, and their skulls are wedge or shovel shaped. They are distinguished from all other vertebrates by the presence of a single median tooth in the upper jaw. The skin of amphisbaenians has ringlike folds called annuli and is loosely attached to the body wall. Muscles of the skin cause it to telescope and bulge outward, forming an anchor against a burrow wall. ③ Amphisbaenians move easily forward or backward, thus the suborder name. They feed on worms and small insects and are oviparous.

ORDER CROCODILIA

There are 21 species in the order Crocodilia (krok'o-dil'e-ah) (Gr. *krokodeilos*, lizard). Along with dinosaurs, crocodilians are derived from the archosaurs and distinguished from other reptiles by certain skull characteristics: openings in the skull in front of the eye, triangular rather than circular eye orbits, and

laterally compressed teeth. Living crocodilians include the alligators, crocodiles, gavials, and caimans.

Crocodilians have not changed much over their 170-million-year history. The snout is elongate and often used to capture food by a sideways sweep of the head. The nostrils are at the tips of the snout, so the animal can breathe while mostly submerged. Air passageways of the head lead to the rear of the mouth and throat, and a flap of tissue near the back of the tongue forms a watertight seal that allows breathing without inhaling water in the mouth. A plate of bone, called the secondary palate, evolved in the archosaurs and separates the nasal and mouth passageways. The tail is muscular, elongate, and laterally compressed. It is used to swim, in offensive and defensive maneuvers, and to attack prey. Teeth are used only for seizing prey. Food is swallowed whole, but if a prey item is too large, crocodilians tear apart prey by holding onto a limb and rotating their bodies wildly until the prey is dismembered. The stomach is gizzardlike, and crocodilians swallow rocks and other objects as abrasives for breaking apart ingested food. Crocodilians are oviparous and display parental care of hatchlings that parallels that of birds. Nesting behavior and parental care may be traced back to the common ancestor of both groups.

Stop and Ask Yourself

1. What are the evolutionary lineages that diverged from the earliest amniotes?
2. What order of reptiles has members that lack teeth, have ribs and vertebrae incorporated into a bony shell, and are oviparous?
3. What adaptations for burrowing are shown by worm lizards?
4. What is a secondary palate? Why is it adaptive for crocodilians?

EVOLUTIONARY PRESSURES

The life-styles of most reptiles reveal striking adaptations for terrestrialism. To appreciate this, one might consider a lizard common to deserts of southwestern United States, the chuckwalla (*Sauromalus obesus*) (figure 29.9). Chuckwallas survive during late summer when temperatures exceed 40° C (104° F) and when arid conditions result in the withering of plants and blossoms upon which chuckwallas browse. To withstand these hot and dry conditions, chuckwallas disappear below ground and aestivate. Temperatures moderate during the winter, but little rain falls, so life on the desert surface is still not possible for the chuckwalla. The summer's sleep, therefore, merges into a winter's sleep. The chuckwalla will not emerge until March when rain falls, and the desert explodes with greenery and flowers. The chuckwalla browses and drinks, storing water in large

FIGURE 29.11

Order Squamata. A chameleon (*Chameleo chameleon*) using its tongue to capture prey. Note the prehensile tail.

appendages, which extend laterally and move in the horizontal plane. The limbs of other reptiles are more elongate and slender. Limbs are held closer to the body, the knee and elbow joints are rotated posteriorly, so the body is thus higher off the ground and weight is supported vertically. Many prehistoric reptiles were bipedal, meaning that they walked on hind limbs. They had a narrow pelvis and a heavy outstretched tail for balance. Bipedal locomotion freed the front appendages, which became adapted for prey capture or flight in some animals.

NUTRITION AND THE DIGESTIVE SYSTEM

Most reptiles are carnivores, although turtles will eat almost anything organic. The tongues of turtles and crocodilians are nonprotrusible and aid in swallowing. 5 The sticky tongues of some lizards and the tuatara are used to capture prey as do some anurans. The extension of the tongue of chameleons exceeds their body length (figure 29.11).

Probably the most remarkable adaptations of snakes involve modifications of the skull for feeding. The bones of the skull and jaws are loosely joined to each other and may spread apart to ingest prey much larger than a snake's normal head size (figure 29.12a). The bones of the upper jaw are movable on the skull, and the halves of both of the upper and lower jaws are loosely joined anteriorly by ligaments. Therefore, each half of the upper and lower jaws can be moved independently of one another. After a prey is captured, opposite sides of the upper and lower jaws are alternately thrust forward and retracted. Posteriorly pointing teeth prevent the escape of the prey and help force the food into the esophagus. The glottis, the respiratory opening, is far forward so that the snake can breathe while slowly swallowing its prey.

Vipers (family Viperidae) possess hollow fangs on the maxillary bone at the anterior margin of the upper jaw (figure 29.12b). These fangs connect to venom glands that inject venom when the viper bites. The maxillary bone (upper jaw bone) of vipers is hinged so that when the snake's mouth is closed, the fangs fold back and lie along the upper jaw. When the mouth opens, the maxillary bone rotates and causes the fangs to swing down (figure 29.12c). Because the fangs project outward from the mouth, vipers may strike at objects of any size. Rear-fanged snakes (family Colubridae) possess grooved rear teeth. In those that are venomous, venom is channeled along these grooves and worked into prey to quiet them during swallowing. These snakes usually do not strike and most are harmless; however, the African boomslang (*Dispholidus typus*) has caused human fatalities. Coral snakes, sea snakes, and cobras have fangs that are rigidly attached to the upper jaw in an erect position. When the mouth is closed, the fangs fit into a pocket in the outer gum of the lower jaw. Fangs are grooved or hollow, and venom is injected by contraction of muscles associated with venom glands. Some cobras can "spit" venom at their prey and, if not washed from the eyes, may cause blindness.

Venom glands are modified salivary glands. Most snake venoms are mixtures of neurotoxins and hemotoxins. The venoms of coral snakes, cobras, and sea snakes are primarily neurotoxins that attack nerve centers and cause respiratory paralysis. The venoms of vipers are primarily hemotoxins. They break up blood cells and attack blood vessel linings.

(a)

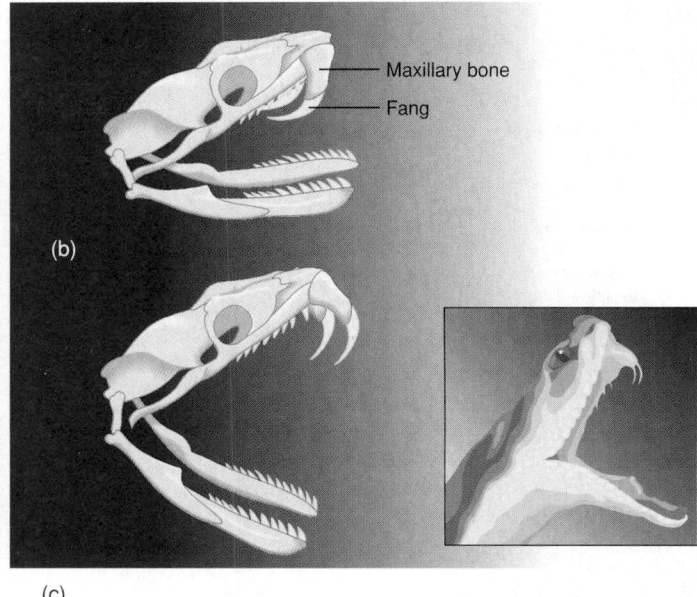

(b)

(c)

Figure 29.12

Feeding Adaptations of Snakes. (*a*) A copperhead (*Ankistrodon*) ingesting a prey. The bones of the skull are joined by flexible joints that allow them to separate during feeding. Note the pit organ located just anterior to the eye. (*b*) The skull of a viper. The hinge mechanism of the jaw allows upper and lower bones on one side of the jaw to slide forward and backward alternately with bones of the other side. Posteriorly curved teeth hold prey as it is worked toward the esophagus. (*c*) Note that the maxillary bone, into which the fang is embedded, swings forward when the mouth is opened.

CIRCULATION, GAS EXCHANGE, AND TEMPERATURE REGULATION

The circulatory system of reptiles is based on that of amphibians. Because reptiles are, on average, larger than amphibians, their blood must travel under higher pressures to reach distant body parts. To take an extreme example, the blood of *Brachiosaurus* had to be pumped a distance of about 6 m from the heart to the head—mostly uphill! (The blood pressure of a giraffe is about double that of a human to move blood the 2 m from heart to head.)

Like amphibians, reptiles possess two atria that are completely separated in the adult and have veins from the body and lungs emptying into them. Except for turtles, the sinus venosus is no longer a chamber but has become a patch of cells that acts as a pacemaker. The ventricle of most reptiles is incompletely divided (figure 29.13). (Only in crocodilians is the ventricular septum complete.) The ventral aorta and the conus arteriosus divide during development and become three major arteries that leave the heart. A pulmonary artery leaves the ventral side of the ventricle and takes blood to the lungs. Two systemic arteries, one from the ventral side of the heart and the other from the dorsal side of the heart, take blood to the lower body and the head.

Blood low in oxygen enters the ventricle from the right atrium and leaves the heart through the pulmonary artery and moves to the lungs. Blood high in oxygen enters the ventricle from the lungs via pulmonary veins and the left atrium, and leaves the heart through left and right systemic arteries.

6   The incomplete separation of the ventricle permits shunting of some blood away from the pulmonary circuit to the systemic circuit by constriction of muscles associated with the pulmonary artery. This is advantageous because virtually all reptiles breathe intermittently. When turtles are withdrawn into their shell, their method of lung ventilation cannot function. They also stop breathing during diving. During periods of apnea ("no breathing"), the flow of blood to the lungs is limited, conserving energy and permitting more efficient use of the pulmonary oxygen supply.

Gas Exchange

Reptiles exchange respiratory gases across internal respiratory surfaces to prevent the loss of large quantities of water. A larynx is present; however, vocal cords are usually absent. The respiratory passages of reptiles are supported by cartilages, and lungs are partitioned into spongelike, interconnected chambers. Lung chambers provide a large surface area for gas exchange.

Lung ventilation occurs in most reptiles by a negative pressure mechanism. Expanding the body cavity by a posterior movement of the ribs and the body wall decreases pressure in the lungs and draws air into the lungs. Air is expelled by elastic recoil of the lungs and forward movements of the ribs and body wall, which compress the lungs. The ribs of turtles are a part of their shell; thus, movements of the body wall to which they are attached are impossible. Turtles exhale by contracting muscles that force the viscera upward, compressing the lungs.

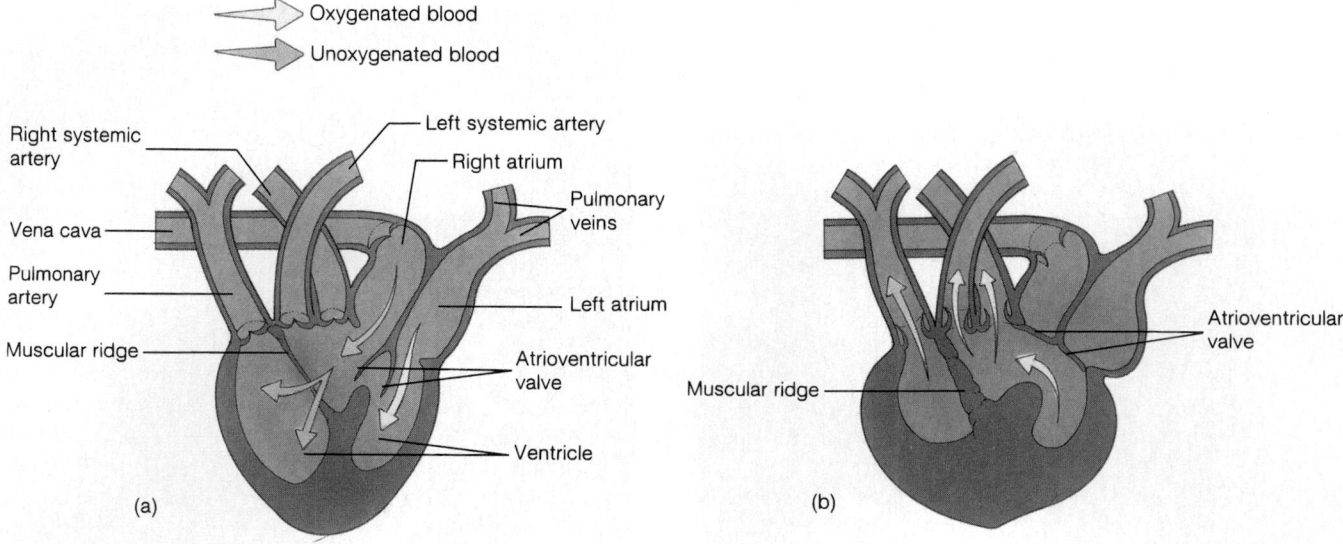

Figure **29.13**

The Heart and Major Arteries of a Lizard. (*a*) When the atria contract, blood enters the ventricle. An atrioventricular valve prevents the mixing of oxygenated and unoxygenated blood across the incompletely separated ventricle. (*b*) When the ventricle contracts, a muscular ridge closes to direct oxygenated blood to the systemic arteries and unoxygenated blood to the pulmonary artery.

They inhale by contracting muscles that increase the volume of the visceral cavity, creating negative pressure to draw air into the lungs.

Temperature Regulation

Unlike aquatic animals, terrestrial animals may be faced with temperature extremes (−65 to 70° C) that are incompatible with life. Temperature regulation, therefore, is important for animals that spend their entire lives out of water. Most reptiles use external heat sources for thermoregulation and are, therefore, ectotherms. Exceptions include monitor lizards and brooding Indian pythons. Female pythons coil around their eggs and elevate their body temperature as much as 7.3° C above the air temperature using metabolic heat sources (box 29.3).

Some reptiles can survive wide temperature fluctuations (e.g., −2 to 41° C for some turtles). To sustain activity, however, body temperatures are regulated within a narrow range, between 25 and 37° C. If that is not possible, the reptile usually seeks a retreat where body temperatures are likely to remain within the range compatible with life.

Most thermoregulatory activities of reptiles are behavioral, and they are best known in the lizards. To warm itself, a lizard may orient itself at right angles to the sun's rays, often on a surface inclined toward the sun, and may press its body tightly to a warm surface to absorb heat by conduction. To cool itself, a lizard will orient its body parallel to the sun's rays, seek shade or burrows, or assume an erect posture (legs extended and tail arched) to reduce conduction from warm surfaces. In hot climates, many reptiles are nocturnal.

Various physiological mechanisms are also used to regulate body temperature. As temperatures rise, some reptiles begin panting, which releases heat through evaporative cooling. (Because their skin is dry, little evaporative cooling occurs across the skin of reptiles.) Marine iguanas divert blood to the skin while basking in the sun and warm up quickly. On diving into the cool ocean, however, heart rate and blood flow to the skin are reduced, which slow heat loss. Chromatophores also aid in temperature regulation. Dispersed chromatophores (thus a darker body) increase the rate of heat absorption.

In temperate regions, many reptiles withstand cold temperatures of winter by entering torpor when body temperatures and metabolic rates decrease. Individuals that are usually solitary may migrate to a common site to spend the winter. Heat loss from these groups, called hibernacula, is reduced because of a reduction in total surface area of many individuals clumped together compared to widely separated animals. Unlike true hibernators, body temperatures of reptiles in torpor are not regulated, and if the winter is too cold or the retreat is too exposed, the animals can freeze and die. Cold death is an important source of mortality for temperate reptiles.

NERVOUS AND SENSORY FUNCTIONS

The brain of reptiles is similar to the brains of other vertebrates. The cerebral hemispheres are somewhat enlarged compared to those of amphibians. This increased size is associated with an improved sense of smell. The optic lobes and the cerebellum are also enlarged, which reflects increased reliance on vision and more refined coordination of muscle functions.

BOX 29.3   CHANGING PERCEPTIONS OF ANCIENT LIFE-STYLES

In the years prior to 1960, paleontologists worked on assembling ancient lineages from fossil remains based on gross anatomical features. Now, it is possible to derive information about the life-styles of extinct animals from markings of blood vessels, muscles, and tendons present on fossils. In the 1970s, Robert T. Bakker began challenging previous perceptions of dinosaurs as lumbering giants and overgrown lizards. Bakker contended that that view of dinosaurs is difficult to reconcile with fossils, indicating that many dinosaurs were bipedal, or at least held their bodies well off the ground. Reptiles achieved many locomotor advancements long before similar advancements ever appeared in mammals. Unlike modern reptiles, dinosaurs had highly vascular bones, a condition typical of endothermic animals. Finally, many believe it unlikely that very large, strictly ectothermic animals could warm up rapidly enough to maintain high activity levels. Bakker proposed that many, if not all dinosaurs were endothermic.

Other scientists discount ideas that dinosaurs were endothermic. They maintain that dinosaurs may have been able to maintain active life-styles, not in spite of their large size, but because of it. As ectotherms increase in size, they resemble endotherms. Large body mass results in slower warming, but it also results in slower heat loss. Further, the climate during the Mesozoic era was considerably warmer than it is now. Even though dinosaurs may have been ectotherms, they could have had stable body temperatures and an active life-style. Opponents of the endothermy hypothesis point out that some ectotherms have highly vascular bones. They also note that large endotherms usually have obvious cooling devices (e.g., the ears of an elephant), and these were not found on most large dinosaurs.

There are no clear winners in this debate. There may not have been a single thermoregulatory strategy for the dinosaurs. The largest dinosaurs could have been ectothermic and, although not swift and agile, they would still have been able to find food and avoid predators. On the other hand, maintenance of speed and agility in smaller dinosaurs that lived in cool climates may have required endothermy.

The complexity of reptilian sensory systems is evidenced by a chameleon's method of feeding. Its protruding eyes that swivel independently each have a different field of view. Initially, the brain keeps both images separate, but when an insect is spotted, both eyes converge on the prey. Binocular vision then provides the depth perception used to determine whether or not the insect is within range of the chameleon's tongue (*see figure 29.11*).

Vision is the dominant sense in most reptiles, and their eyes are similar to those of amphibians (*see figure 28.14*). Snakes focus on nearby objects by moving the lens forward. Contraction of the iris places pressure on the gellike vitreous body in the posterior region of the eye, and displacement of this gel pushes the lens forward. In all other reptiles, focusing on nearby objects occurs when the normally elliptical lens is made more spherical, as a result of ciliary muscles pressing the ciliary body against the lens. Reptiles have a greater number of cones than do amphibians and probably have well-developed color vision.

Upper and lower eyelids, a nictitating membrane, and a blood sinus protect and cleanse the surface of the eye. In snakes and some lizards, the upper and lower eyelids become fused in the embryo to form a protective window of clear skin, called the spectacle. (During ecdysis, the outer layers of the spectacle become clouded and impair the vision of snakes.) The blood sinus, which is at the base of the nictitating membrane, swells with blood to help force debris to the corner of the eye, where it may be rubbed out. Horned lizards squirt blood from their eyes by rupturing this sinus in a defensive maneuver to startle predators.

Some reptiles possess a **median (parietal) eye** that develops from outgrowths of the roof of the forebrain. In the tuatara, it is an eye with a lens, a nerve, and a retina. In other reptiles, the parietal eye is less developed. Parietal eyes are covered by skin and probably cannot form images. They can, however, differentiate light and dark periods and are used in orientation to the sun.

There is variation in the structure of reptilian ears. The ears of snakes detect substrate vibrations. They lack a middle-ear cavity, a eustachian tube, and a tympanic membrane. A bone of the jaw articulates with the stapes and receives substrate vibrations. Snakes can also detect airborne vibrations. In other reptiles, a tympanic membrane may be on the surface or in a small depression in the head. The inner ear of reptiles is similar to that of amphibians.

Olfactory senses are better developed in reptiles than in amphibians. In addition to the partial secondary palate providing more surface for olfactory epithelium, many reptiles possess blind-ending pouches that open through the secondary palate into the mouth cavity. These pouches, called **Jacobson's (vomeronasal) organs,** are found in diapsid reptiles, however, they are best developed in the squamates. Jacobson's organs develop in embryonic crocodilians but are not present in adults of this group. Anapsids (turtles) lack these olfactory organs. The protrusible, forked tongues of snakes and lizards are accessory olfactory organs that are used to sample airborne chemicals. A snake's tongue is flicked out and then moved to the Jacobson's organs where odor molecules are perceived. In the tuatara, Jacobson's organs are used to taste objects held in the mouth.

Rattlesnakes and other pit vipers have heat-sensitive **pit organs** on each side of the face between the eye and nostril (*see figure 29.12a*). These depressions are lined with sensory epithelium and are used to detect objects with temperatures different from the snake's surroundings. Pit vipers are usually nocturnal, and their pits are used to locate small, warm-blooded prey.

5. How is the skin of a reptile adapted for preventing water loss?

6. What is a secondary palate? How is a secondary palate adaptive for reptiles?

7. How are the tongues of reptiles used in feeding? In sensory perception?

8. How is the heart of a reptile adapted for shunting blood away from the pulmonary circulation? Under what circumstances does this shunting occur?

EXCRETION AND OSMOREGULATION

The kidneys of embryonic reptiles are similar to those of fishes and amphibians. Life on land, increased body size, and higher metabolic rates require kidneys capable of processing wastes with little water loss. The embryonic kidney is replaced during development by a kidney with many more blood-filtering units, called nephrons. The functional kidneys of adult reptiles are called metanephric kidneys. Their function depends on a circulatory system that delivers more blood at greater pressures to filter large quantities of blood.

Uric acid is the principal excretory product of most reptiles. It is nontoxic, and being relatively insoluble in water, it will precipitate in the excretory system. Water is reabsorbed by the urinary bladder or the cloacal walls, and the uric acid can be stored in a pastelike form. Utilization of uric acid as an excretory product also made possible the development of embryos in terrestrial environments because nontoxic uric acid can be concentrated in egg membranes.

In addition to water reabsorption by the excretory system, internal respiratory surfaces and relatively impermeable exposed surfaces reduce evaporative water loss. The behaviors that help regulate temperature also help conserve water. Nocturnal habits and avoiding hot surface temperatures during the day by burrowing reduce water loss. When water is available, many reptiles (e.g., chuckwallas) store large quantities of water in lymphatic spaces under the skin or in the urinary bladder. Many lizards possess salt glands below the eyes that are used to rid the body of excess salt.

REPRODUCTION AND DEVELOPMENT

Vertebrates could never be truly terrestrial until their reproduction and embryonic development became separate from standing or running water. For vertebrates, internal fertilization and the amniotic egg (see figure 10.13) made complete movement to land possible. The amniotic egg, however, is not completely independent of water. Pores in the eggshell that permit gas exchange also allow water to evaporate. Amniotic eggs require significant energy expenditures by parents. Parental care occurs in some reptiles and may involve maintaining relatively high humidity around the eggs. These eggs are often supplied with large quantities of yolk for long developmental periods, and parental energy and time is sometimes invested in posthatching care of dependent young.

Accompanying the development of amniotic eggs is the necessity for internal fertilization. Fertilization must occur in the reproductive tract of the female before protective egg membranes are laid down around an egg. All male reptiles, except tuataras, possess an intromittent organ for introducing sperm into the reproductive tract of a female. Lizards and snakes possess paired hemipenes that are located at the base of the tail and are erected by being turned inside out, like the finger of a glove.

Gonads lie in the abdominal cavity. In males, a pair of ducts delivers sperm to the cloaca. After copulation, sperm may be stored in a seminal receptacle in the reproductive tract of the female. Secretions of the seminal receptacle nourish and arrest the activity of the sperm. Sperm may be stored for up to 4 years in some turtles, and up to 6 years in some snakes! In temperate latitudes, sperm can be stored over winter. Copulation may take place in the fall when individuals congregate in hibernacula, and fertilization and development occur in the spring when temperatures favor successful development. Fertilization occurs in the upper regions of the oviduct, which leads from the ovary to the cloaca. Glandular regions of the oviduct are responsible for secreting albumen and the eggshell. The shell is usually tough yet flexible. In some crocodilians, the eggshell is calcareous and rigid, like the eggshells of birds.

Parthenogenesis has been described in six families of lizards and one species of snakes. In these species, no males have been found. Populations of parthenogenetic females have higher reproductive potential than bisexual populations. A population that suffers high mortality over a cold winter can repopulate its habitat rapidly because all surviving individuals can produce offspring. This apparently offsets disadvantages of genetic uniformity resulting from parthenogenesis.

Reptiles often have complex reproductive behaviors that may involve males actively seeking out females. As in other animals, courtship functions in sexual recognition and behavioral and physiological preparation for reproduction. Head-bobbing displays by some male lizards reveal bright patches of color on the throat and enlarged folds of skin. Courtship in snakes is based primarily on tactile stimulation. Tail-waving displays are followed by the male running his chin along the female, entwining his body around her, and creating wavelike contractions that pass posteriorly to anteriorly along his body. Recent research indicates that sex pheromones are also used by lizards and snakes. Vocalizations are important only in crocodilians. During the breeding season, males are hostile and may bark or cough as territorial warnings to other males. Roaring vocalizations also attract females, and mating occurs in the water.

After they are laid, reptilian eggs are usually abandoned (figure 29.14). Virtually all turtles bury their eggs in the ground or in plant debris. Other reptiles lay their eggs under rocks, in debris, or in burrows. About 100 species of reptiles have some degree of parental care of eggs. One example is the American al-

FIGURE **29.14**

Reptile Eggs and Young. These fence lizards (*Sceloporus undulatus*) are hatching from their leathery eggs.

FIGURE **29.15**

Parental Care in Reptiles. A female American alligator (*Alligator mississippiensis*) tending to her nest.

ligator, *Alligator mississippiensis* (figure 29.15). The female builds a mound of mud and vegetation about 1 m high and 2 m in diameter. The center of the mound is hollowed out and filled with mud and debris. Eggs are deposited in a cavity in the center of the mound and covered. The female remains in the vicinity of the nest throughout development to protect the eggs from predation. She frees hatchlings from the nest in response to their high-pitched calls and picks them up in her mouth to transport them to water. She may scoop shallow pools for the young and remain with them for up to 2 years. Young feed on scraps of food dropped by the female when she feeds and on small vertebrates and invertebrates that they catch on their own.

FURTHER PHYLOGENETIC CONSIDERATIONS

The archosaur and synapsid lineages of ancient reptiles diverged from ancient amniotes about 280 million years ago and are ancestral to animals described in the next two chapters (*see figure 29.2*). The archosaur lineage not only included the dinosaurs and gave rise to crocodilians, but also gave rise to two groups of fliers. The pterosaurs (Gr. *pteros*, wing + *sauros*, lizard) ranged from sparrow size to animals with wing spans of 13 m. Their membranous wings were supported by an elongation of the fourth finger, their sternum was adapted for the attachment of flight muscles, and their bones were hollow to lighten the skeleton for flight. As presented in chapter 30, these adaptations are paralleled by,

though not identical to, adaptations in the birds—the descendants of the second lineage of flying archosaurs.

The synapsid lineage eventually gave rise to the mammals. The legs of synapsids were relatively long and held their body off the ground. Teeth and jaws were adapted for effective chewing and tearing. Additional bones were incorporated into the middle ear. These and other mammal-like characteristics developed between the Carboniferous and Triassic periods. The "Evolutionary Perspective" of chapter 31 describes more about the nature of this transition.

Stop and Ask Yourself

9. Why is uric acid an adaptive excretory product for reptiles?
10. What groups of reptiles contain parthenogenetic species?
11. In what group of reptiles are vocalizations an important part of reproductive activities?
12. What reptilian lineage gave rise to the birds? To the mammals?

SUMMARY

1. The earliest amniotes are classified as reptiles. The evolution of the amniotes resulted in lineages leading to the turtles; birds and dinosaurs; squamates (snakes, lizards, and worm lizards) and tuataras; and mammals.

2. The order Testudines contains the turtles. Turtles have a bony shell and lack teeth. All are oviparous.

3. The order Squamata contains the lizards, snakes, and worm lizards. Lizards usually have two pairs of legs and most are oviparous. Snakes lack developed limbs and have skull adaptations for swallowing large prey. Worm lizards are specialized burrowers. They have a single median tooth in the upper jaw and most are oviparous.

4. The order Rhynchocephalia contains one species, the tuatara. It is found only on remote islands of New Zealand.

5. The order Crocodilia contains alligators, crocodiles, caimans, and gavials. They have a well-developed secondary palate and display nesting behaviors and parental care.

6. The skin of reptiles is dry and keratinized, and provides a barrier to water loss. It also has epidermal scales and chromatophores.

7. The reptilian skeleton is modified for support and movement on land. Loss of appendages in snakes is accompanied by greater use of the body wall in locomotion.

8. Reptiles have a tongue that may be used in feeding. Bones of the skull of snakes are loosely joined and spread apart during feeding.

9. The circulatory system of reptiles is divided into pulmonary and systemic circuits and functions under relatively high blood pressures. Blood may be shunted away from the pulmonary circuit during periods of apnea.

10. Gas exchange occurs across convoluted lung surfaces. Ventilation of lungs occurs by a negative-pressure mechanism.

11. Reptiles are ectotherms and mainly use behavioral mechanisms to thermoregulate.

12. Vision is the dominant sense in most reptiles. Parietal eyes, ears, Jacobson's organs, and pit organs are important receptors in some reptiles.

13. Because uric acid is nontoxic and relatively insoluble in water, it can be stored and excreted as a semisolid. Internal respiratory surfaces and dry skin also promote conservation of water.

14. The amniotic egg and internal fertilization permit development on land. They are accompanied by significant energy expenditure on the part of the parent.

15. Some reptiles use visual, olfactory, and auditory cues for reproduction. Parental care is important in crocodilians.

16. Descendants of the diapsid evolutionary lineage include the birds. Descendants of the synapsid lineage are the mammals.

SELECTED KEY TERMS

amniotic eggs (*p.* 468)
Jacobson's organs (*p.* 479)
keratin (*p.* 470)
median (parietal) eye (*p.* 479)
pit organs (*p.* 479)

CRITICAL THINKING QUESTIONS

1. Explain the nature of the controversy between cladists and evolutionary systematists regarding the higher taxonomy of the amniotes. Do you think that the Reptilia should be retained as a formal class designation? If so, what groups of animals should it contain?

2. What characteristics of the life history of turtles make them vulnerable to extinction? What steps do you think should be taken to protect endangered turtle species?

3. What might explain the fact that parental care is common in crocodilians and birds?

4. Make a list of the adaptations that make life on land possible for a reptile. Explain why each is adaptive.

5. The incompletely divided ventricle of reptiles is sometimes portrayed as an evolutionary transition between the heart of primitive amphibians and the completely divided ventricles of birds and mammals. Do you agree with this portrayal? Why or why not?

BIRDS:
FEATHERS, FLIGHT, AND ENDOTHERMY

Outline

Concepts

1. Fossils of the earliest birds clearly show reptilian features. Fossils of *Archaeopteryx* and *Sinornis* give clues to the origin of flight in birds.
2. Integumentary, skeletal, muscular, and gas exchange systems of birds are adapted for flight and endothermic temperature regulation.
3. Large regions of the brain of birds are devoted to integrating sensory information.
4. Complex mating systems and behavior patterns increase the chances of offspring survival.
5. Migration and navigation allow birds to live, feed, and reproduce in environments that are favorable to survival of adults and young.

Would You Like to Know:

1. how flight evolved in birds? (*p. 485*)
2. what ancient animal is the earliest known bird? (*p. 485*)
3. how a bird can sleep without falling from its perch? (*p. 489*)
4. how wings create enough lift to get a bird off the ground? (*p. 489*)
5. how an osprey diving for a fish keeps the fish in focus throughout the dive? (*p. 494*)
6. how birds navigate during migration? (*p. 498*)

These and other useful questions will be answered in this chapter.

This chapter contains evolutionary concepts, which are set off in this font.

EVOLUTIONARY PERSPECTIVE

Drawings of birds on the walls of caves in southern France and Spain, bird images of ancient Egyptian and ancient American cultures, and the bird images in Biblical writings are evidence that humans have marveled at birds and bird flight for thousands of years. From the early drawings of flying machines by Leonardo da Vinci (1490) to the first successful powered flight by Orville Wright on December 17, 1903, humans have tried to take to the sky and experience what it would be like to soar like a bird.

The ability of birds to navigate long distances between breeding and wintering grounds is just as impressive as flight. For example, Arctic terns have a migratory route that takes them from the Arctic to the Antarctic and back again each year, a distance of approximately 35,000 km (22,000 mi) (figure 30.1). Their rather circuitous route takes them across the northern Atlantic Ocean, to the coast of Europe and Africa, and then across vast stretches of the southern Atlantic Ocean before reaching their wintering grounds.

PHYLOGENETIC RELATIONSHIPS

Birds are traditionally classified as members of the class Aves (a′ves) (L. *avis*, bird). Cladistic interpretations of the relationship of birds to other amniotes were discussed in chapter 29 (*see figure 29.2*). The major characteristics of this class concern adaptations for flight, including appendages modified as wings, feathers, endothermy, a high metabolic rate, a vertebral column modified for flight, and bones that are lightened by numerous air spaces. In addition, modern birds possess a horny bill and lack teeth.

The similarities between birds and reptiles are so striking that birds are often referred to as "glorified reptiles." Like the crocodilians, birds have descended from ancient archosaurs (*see figure 29.2*). Other flying reptiles in this evolutionary lineage (e.g., pterosaurs and pterodactyls) are ruled out of bird ancestry because these reptiles lost an important avian feature, the clavicles, long before birds appeared. (The clavicles, or "wishbone" serves as one of the attachment points for flight muscles. Thus, these reptiles could not have been as strong fliers as modern birds.) Rather than having feathered wings, the flight surfaces of the wings of these primitive reptiles were membranous folds of skin.

ANCIENT BIRDS AND THE EVOLUTION OF FLIGHT

In 1861, one of the most important vertebrate fossils was found in a slate quarry in Bavaria, Germany (figure 30.2). It was a fossil of a pigeon-sized animal that lived during the Jurassic period, about 150 million years ago. It had a long, reptilian tail and clawed fingers. The complete head of this specimen was not

(a)

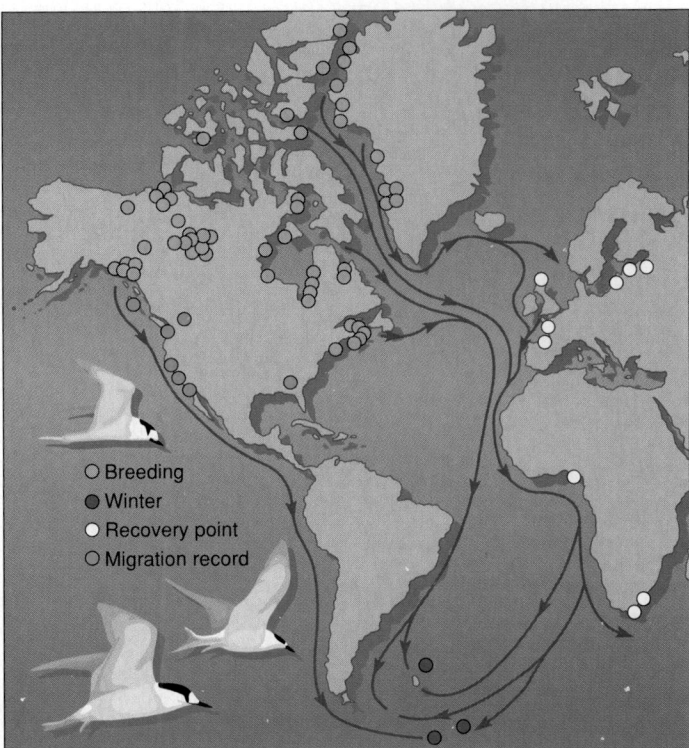
(b)

FIGURE 30.1

Class Aves. (*a*) The birds were derived from the archosaur lineage of ancient reptiles. Adaptations for flight include appendages modified as wings, feathers, endothermy, a high metabolic rate, a vertebral column modified for flight, and bones that are lightened by numerous airspaces. Flight has given birds, like this Arctic tern (*Sterna arctica*), the ability to exploit resources that are unavailable to other vertebrates. (*b*) The migration route of the Arctic tern is shown here. Arctic terns breed in northern North America, Greenland, and the Arctic. Migrating birds cross the Atlantic Ocean on their trip to wintering grounds in Antarctica. In the process, they fly about 22,000 miles each year.

Within figure (b) legend:
○ Breeding
● Winter
○ Recovery point
○ Migration record

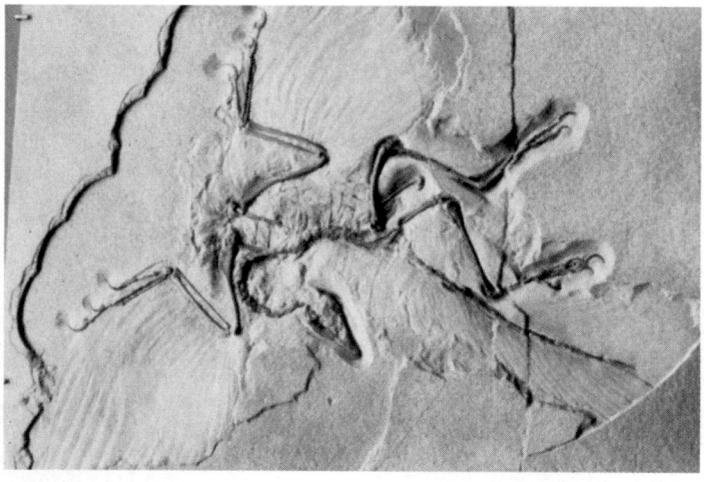

(a)

(b)

FIGURE 30.2

Archaeopteryx, An Ancient Bird. (*a*) *Archaeopteryx* fossil. (*b*) Artist's representation. Some zoologists think that *Archaeopteryx* was a ground dweller rather than the tree dweller depicted here.

preserved, but imprints of feathers on the tail and on short rounded wings were the main evidence that this was the fossil of an ancient bird. It was named *Archaeopteryx* (Gr. *archaios,* ancient + *pteron,* wing). Sixteen years later, a more complete fossil was discovered, revealing teeth in beaklike jaws. Four later discoveries of *Archaeopteryx* fossils have reinforced the ideas of reptilian ancestry for birds.

Interpretations of the life-style of *Archaeopteryx* have been important in the development of hypotheses on the origin of flight. The clavicles (wishbone) of *Archaeopteryx* are well developed and probably provided points of attachment for wing muscles. The sternum, another site for attachment of flight muscles in modern birds, is less developed. These observations indicate that *Archaeopteryx* may have primarily been a glider that was capable of flapping flight over short distances.

① Some zoologists think that the clawed digits of the wings may have been used to climb trees and cling to branches. A sequence in the evolution of flight may have involved jumping from branch to branch or branch to ground. At some later point, gliding evolved. Still later, weak flapping, supplemented gliding and finally wing-powered flight evolved.

Other zoologists note that the structure of the hindlimbs of the earliest birds suggests that they may have been bipedal, running and hopping along the ground. Their wings may have functioned in batting flying insects out of the air or in trapping insects and other prey against the ground. The teeth and claws, which resemble talons of modern predatory birds, may have been used to grasp prey. Wings would have been useful in providing stability during horizontal jumps when pursuing prey, and they would also have allowed flight over short distances. The benefits of such flight may have led eventually to wing-powered flight.

Other ancient fossil birds have been found. One fossil, named *Protoavis,* has been discovered in Texas and dates back 225 million years. This fossil, therefore, predates *Archaeopteryx* by 75 million years. This description has caused considerable controversy. Many paleontologists doubt that *Protoavis* is really a fossil of a bird. They consider it to be a fossilized ancient reptile. Other paleontologists insist that *Protoavis* was a bird, and that its antiquity means that the origin of birds was much earlier than previously assumed. If this is true, *Archaeopteryx* would simply represent an ancient offshoot of the bird lineage. ② At least for now, *Archaeopteryx* is considered by most zoologists to be the oldest bird yet discovered and very close to the main line of evolution between reptiles and birds.

A third ancient bird (*Sinornis*), which was recently discovered in China, fits well with the view that *Archaeopteryx* was closely related to ancestral bird stocks. *Sinornis* fossils are 135 million years old—only 15 million years younger than *Archaeopteryx.* In addition to having has some very primitive dinosaurlike characteristics, *Sinornis* had characteristics similar to modern birds. These characteristics included a shortened body and tail and a sternum with a large surface area for flight muscles. The claws were reduced, and the forelimbs were modified to permit the folding of wings at rest. These characteristics all indicate that powered flight was well developed in birds 135 million years ago.

DIVERSITY OF MODERN BIRDS

Archaeopteryx and *Sinornis* provide the only evidence of the transition between reptiles and birds. We do not know, however, whether or not either bird is the direct ancestor of modern birds. There are a variety of fossil birds found for the period between 100 million and 70 million years ago. Some of these birds were large, flightless birds; others were adapted for swimming and diving, and some were fliers. Most, like *Archaeopteryx,* had reptilelike teeth. Most of the lineages represented by these fossils became extinct, along with the dinosaurs, at the end of the Mesozoic era.

Some of the few birds that survived into the Tertiary period were the ancestors of modern, toothless birds. The phylogeny of

TABLE 30.1	CLASSIFICATION OF THE BIRDS

Class Aves (a′ves) (L. *avis*, bird)*
Adaptations for flight include: foreappendages modified as feathered wings, endothermic, high metabolic rate, neck flexible, posterior vertebrae fused, and bones lightened by numerous air spaces. The skull is lightened by a reduction in bone and the presence of a horny bill that lacks teeth. The birds.

    Order Sphenisciformes (sfe-nis′i-for′mez)
Heavy bodied; flightless, flipperlike wings for swimming; well insulated with fat. Penguins.

    Order Struthioniformes (stroo′the-oni-for′mez)
Large, flightless birds; wings with numerous fluffy plumes. Ostriches.

    Order Rheiformes (re′i-for′mez)
Large, flightless birds; degenerate wings with soft, loose plumes. Rheas.

    Order Casuariiformes (kaz′u-ar′e-i-for′mez)
Wings reduced; plumage coarse and hairlike. Cassowaries, emus.

    Order Gaviiformes (ga′ve-i-for′mez)
Strong, straight bill; diving adaptations include legs far back on body, bladelike tarsus, webbed feet, and heavy bones. Loons.

    Order Podicipediformes (pod′i-si-ped′i-for′mez)
Wings short; plumage soft and dense; feet webbed with flattened nails. Grebes.

    Order Procellariiformes (pro-sel-lar-e-i-for′mez)
Tubular nostrils, large nasal glands; wings long and narrow. Albatrosses, shearwaters, petrels.

    Order Pelecaniformes (pel′e-can-i-for′mez)
Four toes joined in common web; nostrils rudimentary or absent; large gular sac. Pelicans, boobies, cormorants, anhingas, frigatebirds.

    Order Ciconiiformes (si-ko′ne-i-for′mez)
Neck long, often folded in flight; long-legged waders. Herons, egrets, storks, wood ibises, flamingos.

    Order Anseriformes (an′ser-i-for′mez)
South American screamers, ducks, geese and swans. The latter possess a wide flat bill and an undercoat of dense down. Webbed feet. Worldwide.

    Order Falconiformes (fal′ko-ni-for′mez)
Strong, hooked beak; wings large; raptorial feet. Vultures, secretarybirds, hawks, eagles, ospreys, falcons.

Order Galliformes (gal′li-for′mez)
Short beak; short, concave wings; feet and claws strong. Curassows, grouse, quail, pheasants, turkeys.

Order Gruiformes (gru′i-for′mez)
Order characteristics variable and not diagnostic. Marsh birds including cranes, limpkins, rails, coots.

Order Charadriiformes (ka-rad′re-i-for′mez)
Order characteristics variable. Shorebirds, gulls, terns, auks.

Order Columbiformes (co-lum′bi-for′mez)
Dense feathers loosely set in skin; well-developed crop. Pigeons, doves, sandgrouse.

Order Psittaciformes (sit′ta-si-for′mez)
Maxilla hinged to skull; tongue thick; fourth toe reversible; usually brightly colored. Parrots, lories, macaws.

Order Cuculiformes (ku-koo′li-for′mez)
Fourth toe reversible; skin soft and tender; Plantaineaters, roadrunners, cuckoos.

Order Strigiformes (strij′i-for′mez)
Large head with fixed eyes directed forward; raptorial foot. Owls.

Order Caprimulgiformes (kap′ri-mul′ji-for′mez)
Owllike head and plumage, but weak bill and feet; beak with wide gape; insectivorous. Whippoorwills, other goatsuckers.

Order Apodiformes (a-pod′i-for′mez)
Long wings; weak feet. Swifts, hummingbirds.

Order Coraciiformes (kor′ah-si′ah-for′mez)
Large head; large beak; metallic plumage. Kingfishers, todies, bee eaters, rollers.

Order Piciformes (pis′i-for′mez)
Beak usually long and strong; legs and feet strong with fourth toe permanently reversed in woodpeckers. Woodpeckers, toucans, honeyguides, barbets.

Order Passeriformes (pas′er-i-for′mez)
Largest avian order; 69 families of perching birds; perching foot; variable external features. Swallows, larks, crows, titmice, nuthatches, and many others.

*Selected bird orders are described.

modern birds is very controversial. It is sufficient to say that adaptive radiation has resulted in about 9,100 species of living birds, which are divided into about 27 orders (table 30.1). (The number of orders varies depending on the classification system used.) The orders are distinguished from one another by characteristic behaviors, songs, anatomical differences, and ecological niches.

Stop and Ask Yourself

1. What are characteristics of the class Aves?
2. What characteristics of *Archaeopteryx* are reptilelike?
3. What are two hypotheses for the origin of flight in birds? What aspects of the structure of *Archaeopteryx* are used to support each hypothesis?

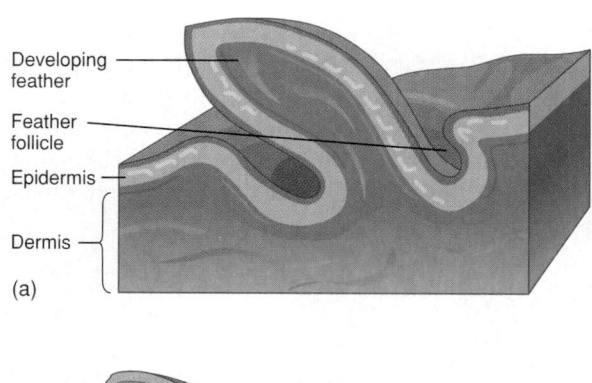

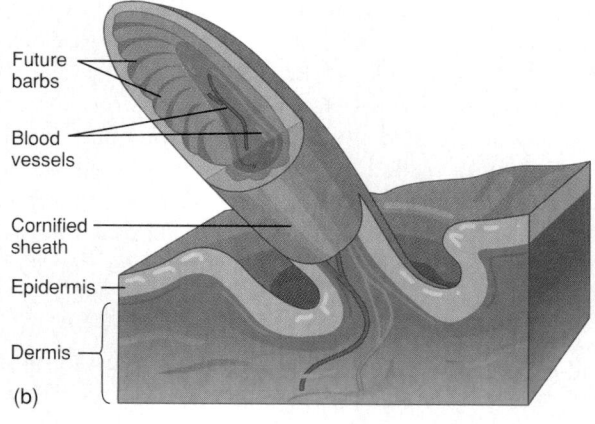

FIGURE 30.3

The Formation of Bird Feathers during Embryonic Development.
(*a*) Feathers form from epidermal evaginations. (*b*) Later in
development, the blood supply to the feather is cut off and the feather
becomes a dead, keratinized epidermal structure seated in a feather
follicle.

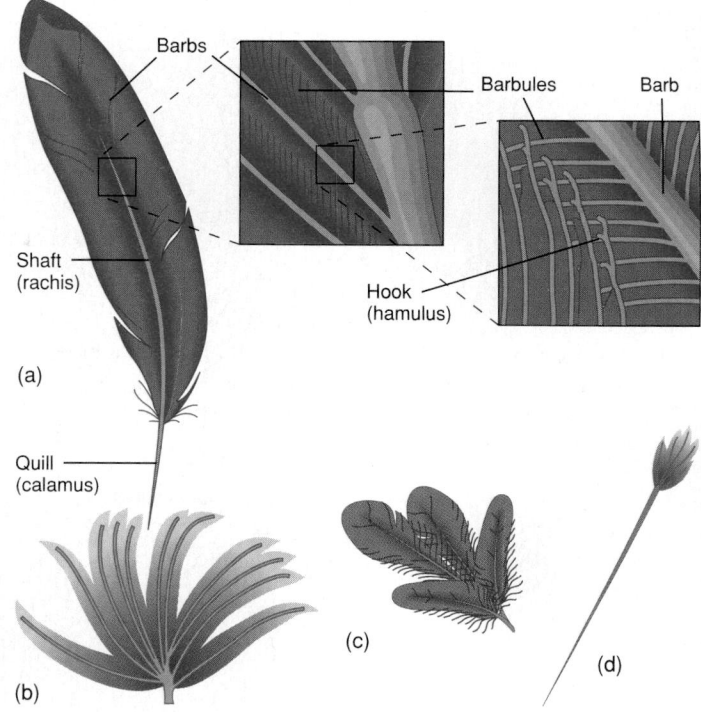

FIGURE 30.4

Anatomy of Selected Feather Types. (*a*) Anatomy of a contour
feather showing enlargements of barbs and barbules. (*b*) A down
feather. Various types of down feathers provide insulation for adult
and immature birds. (*c*) A contour feather with an aftershaft. (*d*) A
filoplume. Filoplume feathers are usually covered by contour feathers
and are associated with nerve endings in the skin, thus serving as
sensory structures.

EVOLUTIONARY PRESSURES

Virtually every body system of a bird shows some adaptation for
flight. Endothermy, feathers, acute senses, long flexible necks, and
lightweight bones are a few of the many adaptations described in
this section.

EXTERNAL STRUCTURE AND LOCOMOTION

The covering of feathers on a bird is called the plumage. Feathers have two primary functions essential for flight. They form
the flight surfaces that provide lift and aid steering, and they
prevent excessive heat loss, permitting the endothermic maintenance of high metabolic rates. Feathers also have roles in
courtship, incubation, and waterproofing.

Feathers develop in a fashion similar to epidermal scales of
reptiles, and this similarity is one source of evidence that demon-
strates the evolutionary ties between reptiles and birds (figure 30.3;
see box 29.2). Only the inner pulp of feathers contains dermal
elements, such as blood vessels, which supply nutrients and pigments for the growing feather. As feathers mature, their blood
supply is cut off, and the feathers become dead, keratinized, epidermal structures seated in epidermal invaginations of the skin
called feather follicles.

The most obvious feathers are **contour feathers,** which
cover the body, wings, and tail (figure 30.4*a*, *c*). Contour feathers consist of a vane with its inner and outer webs, and a supportive shaft. Feather barbs branch off the shaft, and barbules
branch off the barbs. Barbules of adjacent barbs overlap one another. The ends of barbules are locked together with hooklike
hamuli (s., hamulus). Interlocking barbs keep contour feathers
firm and smooth. Other types of feathers include **down feathers,**
which function as insulating feathers, and **filoplume feathers**
(pinfeather), which have sensory functions (figure 30.4*b*, *d*).

Birds maintain a clean plumage to rid the feathers and
skin of parasites. Preening, which is done by rubbing the bill
over the feathers, keeps the feathers smooth, clean, and in
place. Hamuli that become dislodged can be rehooked by running a feather through the bill. Secretions from an oil gland at
the base of the tail of many birds are spread over the feathers
during preening to keep the plumage water repellant and sup-
ple. The secretions also lubricate the bill and legs to prevent
chafing. Anting is a maintenance behavior common to many
songbirds and involves picking up ants in the bill and rubbing
them over the feathers. The formic acid secreted by ants is apparently toxic to feather mites.

Most colors in a bird's plumage are produced by feather
pigments deposited during feather formation. Other colors,

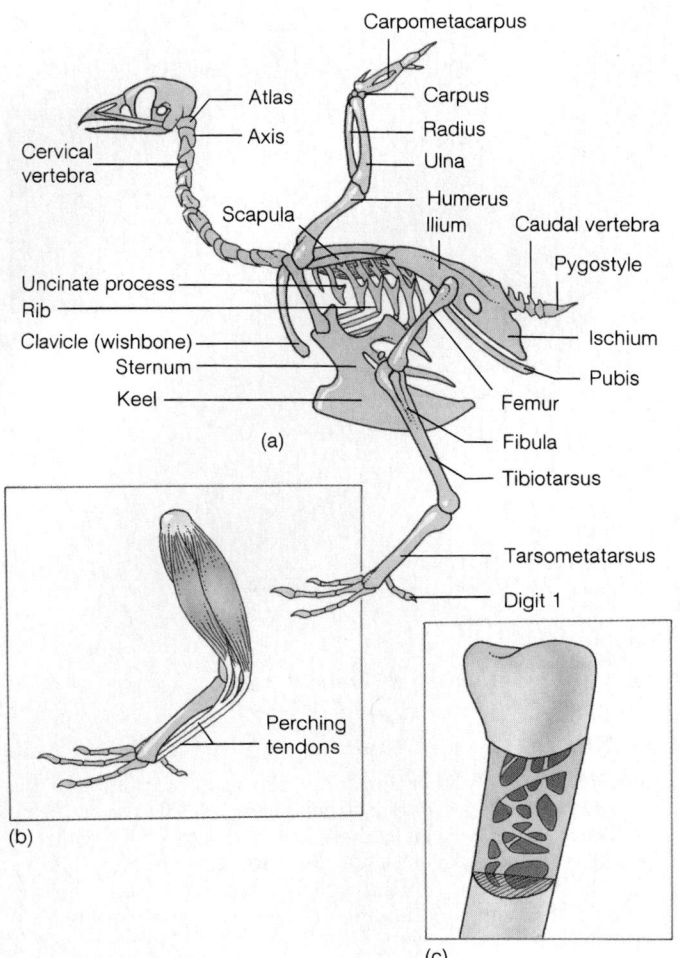

Figure **30.5**

The Bird Skeleton. (*a*) The skeleton of a pigeon. (*b*) Perching tendons run from the toes across the back of the ankle joint, which cause the foot to grip a perch. (*c*) The internal structure of the humerus.

termed structural colors, arise from irregularities on the surface of the feather that diffract white light. For example, blue feathers are never blue because of the presence of blue pigment. A porous, nonpigmented outer layer on a barb reflects blue wavelengths of light. The other wavelengths pass into the barb and are absorbed by the dark pigment melanin. Iridescence results from the interference of light waves caused by a flattening and twisting of barbules. An example of iridescence is the perception of interchanging colors on the neck and back of hummingbirds and grackles. Color patterns are involved in cryptic coloration, species and sex recognition, and sexual attraction.

Mature feathers receive constant wear; thus, all birds undergo a periodic renewal of their feathers by shedding and replacing them in a process called **molting.** The timing of molt periods varies in different taxa. The following is a typical molting pattern for songbirds. After hatching, a chick is covered with down. Down is replaced with juvenile feathers at the postnatal molt. A postjuvenile molt usually occurs in the fall and results in plumage

similar to that of the adult. Once sexual maturity is attained, a prenuptial molt occurs in later winter or early spring, prior to the breeding season. A postnuptial molt usually occurs between July and October. Flight feathers are frequently lost in a particular sequence so that birds are not wholly deprived of flight during molt periods. However, many ducks, coots, and rails cannot fly during molt periods and hide in thick marsh grasses.

The Skeleton

The bones of most birds are lightweight yet strong. Some bones, such as the humerus (forearm bone), have large air spaces and internal strutting (reinforcing bony bars), which increase strength (figure 30.5*c*). (Engineers take advantage of this same principle. They have discovered that a strutted girder is stronger than a solid girder of the same weight.) Birds also have a reduced number of skull bones, and teeth are replaced with a lighter, keratinized sheath called a bill. The demand for lightweight bones for flight is countered in some birds with other requirements. For example, some aquatic birds (e.g., loons) have dense bones, which help reduce buoyancy during diving.

The appendages involved in flight cannot manipulate nesting materials or feed young. These activities are possible because of the bill and very flexible neck. The cervical vertebrae have saddle-shaped articular surfaces that permit great freedom of movement. In addition, the first cervical vertebra (the atlas) has a single point of articulation with the skull (the occipital condyle), which permits a high degree of rotational movement between the skull and the neck. (The single occipital condyle is another characteristic shared with reptiles.) This flexibility allows the bill and neck to function as a fifth appendage.

The pelvic girdle, vertebral column, and ribs are strengthened for flight. The thoracic region of the vertebral column contains ribs, which attach to thoracic vertebrae. The ribs have posteriorly directed uncinate processes that overlap the next rib to strengthen the rib cage (figure 30.5*a*). (Uncinate processes are also present on the ribs of most reptiles and are additional evidence of their common ancestry.) Posterior to the thoracic region is the lumbar region. The **synsacrum** is formed by the fusion of the posterior thoracic vertebrae, all the lumbar and sacral vertebrae, and the anterior caudal vertebrae. Fusion of these bones helps maintain the proper flight posture and supports the hind appendages during landing, hopping, and walking. The posterior caudal vertebrae are fused into a **pygostyle,** which helps support the tail feathers that are important in steering.

The sternum of most birds bears a large, median keel for the attachment of flight muscles. (Exceptions to this include some flightless birds, such as ostriches.) It attaches firmly to the rest of the axial skeleton by the ribs. Paired clavicles are fused medially and ventrally into a furcula (wishbone).

The appendages of birds have also been modified. Some bones of the front appendages have been lost or fused and serve as points of attachment of flight feathers. The rear appendages are used for hopping, walking, running, and perching. Perching tendons run from the toes across the back of the ankle joint to muscles of the lower leg. When the ankle joint is flexed, as in landing on a perch, tension on the perching tendons is increased, and the foot grips the perch (figure 30.5b). ③ This automatic grasp helps a bird perch even while sleeping. The muscles of the lower leg can increase the tension on these tendons, for example, when an eagle grasps a fish in its talons.

Muscles

The largest, strongest muscles of most birds are the flight muscles. They attach to the sternum and clavicles and run to the humerus. The muscles of most birds are adapted physiologically for flight. Flight muscles must contract quickly and fatigue very slowly. These muscles have many mitochondria and produce large quantities of ATP to provide the energy required for flight, especially long-distance migrations. Domestic fowl have been selectively bred for massive amounts of muscle that is well liked by humans as food, but is poorly adapted for flight because it contains rapidly contracting fibers with few mitochondria and poor vascularization.

Flight

The wings of birds are adapted for different kinds of flight. However, regardless of whether a bird soars, glides, or has a rapid flapping flight, the mechanics of staying aloft are similar. Bird wings form an **airfoil.** The anterior margin of the wing is thicker than the posterior margin. The upper surface of the wing is slightly convex, and the lower surface is flat or slightly concave. ④ Air passing over the wing travels farther and faster than air passing under the wing, decreasing air pressure on the upper surface of the wing and creating lift (figure 30.6a). The lift created by the wings must overcome the bird's weight, and the forces that propel the bird forward must overcome the drag created by the friction of the bird moving through the air. Lift can be increased by increasing the angle the leading edge of the wing makes with the oncoming air (the angle of attack). As the angle of attack increases, however, the flow of air over the upper surface becomes turbulent, reducing lift (figure 30.6b). Turbulence can be reduced by forming slots at the leading edge of the wing through which air can flow rapidly, thus smoothing air flow once again. Slotting the feathers at the wing tips and the presence of an alula on the anterior margin of the wing reduce turbulence. The **alula** is a group of small feathers supported by bones of the medial digit. During takeoff, landing, and hovering flight, the angle of attack is increased, and the alula is elevated (figure 30.6c,e). During soaring and fast flight, the angle of attack is decreased, and slotting is reduced.

Most of the propulsive force of flight is generated by the distal part of the wing. Because it is farther from the shoulder joint, the distal part of the wing moves farther and faster than the proximal part of the wing. During the downstroke (the powerstroke), the leading edge of the distal part of the wing is oriented slightly downward and creates a thrust somewhat analogous to the thrust created by a propeller on an airplane (figure 30.6d). During the upstroke (the recovery stroke), the distal part of the wing is oriented upward to decrease resistance. Feathers on a wing overlap so that on the downstroke, air presses the feathers at the wing margins together, allowing little air to pass

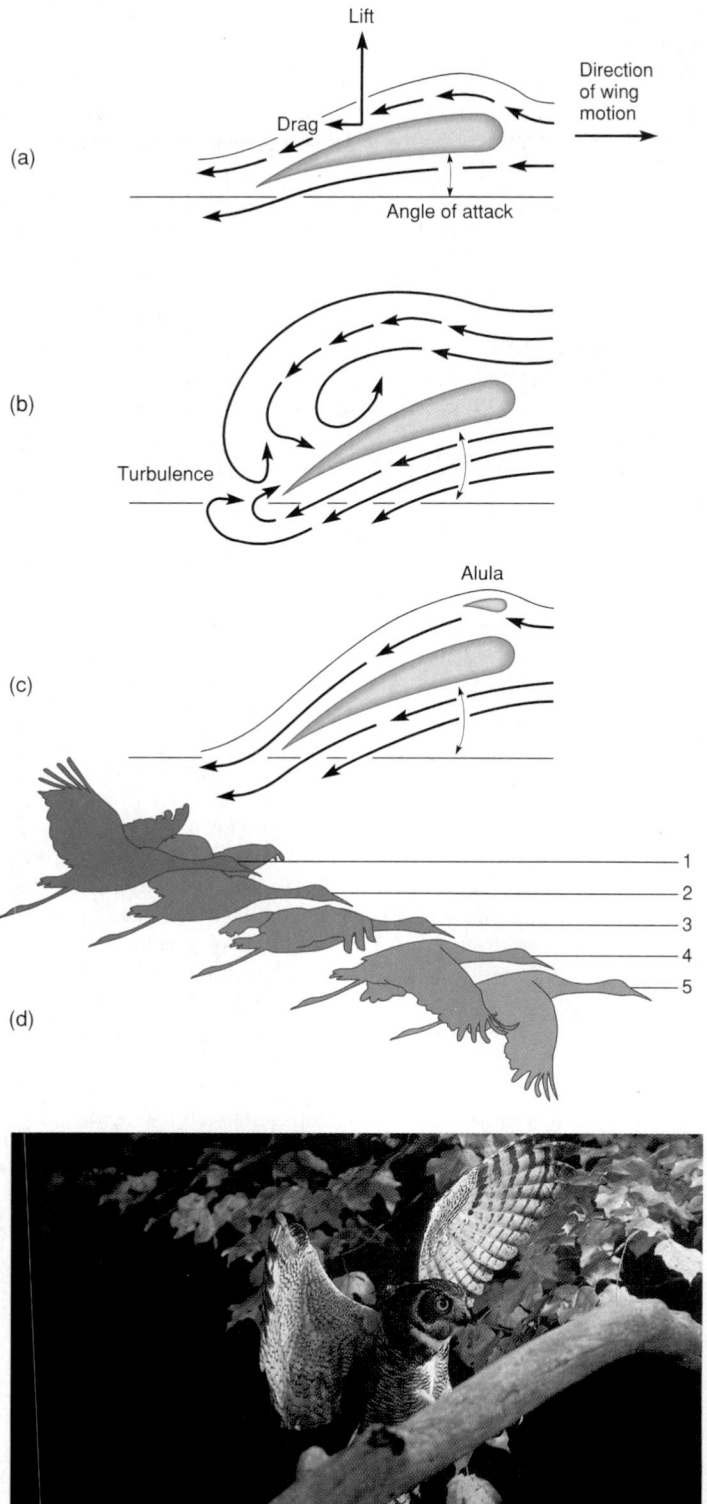

Figure 30.6

Mechanics of Bird Flight. (a) A bird's wing acts as an airfoil. Air passing over the top of the wing travels farther and faster than air passing under the wing, creating lift. (b) Increasing the angle of attack increases lift but also increases turbulence. (c) Turbulence is reduced by the alula. (d) The orientation of the wing during a downstroke. (e) Note the alula on the wings of the great horned owl (*Bubo virginianus*).

BOX 30.1 SAILORS' CURSE—GLIDERS' ENVY

They are known by many, not very complimentary names. Dutch sailors called them mollymawks ("stupid gull"), the English call them goonies (another reference to stupidity), and the Japanese call them bakadori ("foul birds"). The names of albatrosses are probably the result of inexpressive facial features and awkward movements on land. The albatross's reputation for stupidity is accompanied by another reputation. Their appearance alongside a ship was believed to be a sure sign of changing winds. As the old sailor with "a long grey beard and glittering eye" discovered, to kill an albatross brought extremely bad luck. (*The Rime of the Ancient Mariner* by Samuel Coleridge, 1798.) His deadly aim with a crossbow caused the winds to die, and all sailors on the becalmed ship, except the mariner, died of thirst. The mariner was forced to sail on alone with the albatross hung around his neck.

> *And I had done an hellish thing*
> *And it would work 'em woe:*
> *For all averr'd, I had kill'd the Bird*
> *That made the Breeze to blow.*
> *Ah wretch! said they, the bird to slay,*
> *That made the breeze to blow!*

The origin of the superstition that associated the albatross with breezes is not difficult to understand. The albatross has relatively poorly developed flight muscles and relies primarily on soaring flight and wind to keep aloft (figure 1). Most species of albatross are found around the Antarctic where breezes are almost constant, and they can launch themselves from cliffs into the air with minimal flapping flight. They soar swiftly downwind, picking up speed and losing altitude. Just above the water's surface, they turn sharply into the wind and use the oncoming wind to soar higher. When air speed drops, they turn again to move downwind. Under favorable winds, an albatross can follow a ship for many

FIGURE 1   **An Albatross in Flight.** An albatross (*Diomedea irrorata*) uses wind currents to soar around the Southern Hemisphere.

miles, zig-zagging upwind and downwind, without flapping their long, narrow wings. The sight of a soaring albatross usually does mean a favorable sailing breeze!

When grounded in calm winds, an albatross experiences great difficulty becoming airborne again. They must run along the ground, flapping their wings, until air speed adequate for takeoff has been achieved.

Albatrosses feed on fishes and invertebrates near the ocean's surface and on refuse tossed from ships. After a courtship dance and mating, a single egg is laid in a mud nest. Incubation may last as long as 85 days, and parental care another 3 to 9 months. After leaving the nest, young albatrosses depart the nesting grounds and circle their newly discovered world many times. (For most albatrosses "their world" is the entire Southern Hemisphere!) Sexual maturity is reached after about 7 years, and some may live for up to 30 years.

between them, enhancing both lift and propulsive forces. Feathers part slightly on the upstroke, allowing air to pass between them, which reduces resistance during the recovery stroke.

The tail of a bird serves a variety of balancing, steering, and braking functions during flight. During horizontal flight, spreading the tail feathers increases lift at the rear of the bird and causes the head to dip for descent. Closing the tail feathers has the opposite effect. Tilting the tail sideways causes the bird to turn. When a bird lands, its tail is deflected downward, serving as an air brake.

Different kinds of flight are used by different birds or by the same bird at different times. During gliding flight, the wing is stationary, and a bird loses altitude. Waterfowl coming in for a landing use gliding flight. Flapping flight generates the power for flight and is the most common type of flying. Many variations in wing shape and flapping patterns result in species-specific speed and

maneuverability. Soaring flight allows some birds to remain airborne with little energy expenditure. During soaring, wings are essentially stationary, and the bird utilizes updrafts and air currents to gain altitude. Hawks, vultures, and other soaring birds are frequently observed circling along mountain valleys, soaring downwind to pick up speed and then turning upwind to gain altitude. As the bird slows and begins to lose altitude, it turns downwind again. The wings of many soarers are wide and slotted to provide maximum maneuverability at relatively low speeds. Oceanic soarers, such as albatrosses and frigate birds, have long, narrow wings that provide maximum lift at high speeds, but they compromise maneuverability and ease of takeoff and landing (box 30.1). Hummingbirds perform hovering flight. They hover in still air by fanning their wings back and forth (50 to 80 beats per second) to remain suspended in front of a flower or feeding station.

Stop and Ask Yourself

4. Describe feather maintenance behavior.
5. What adaptations of the bird skeleton promote flight?
6. How do bird wings provide lift and forward propulsion during flight?
7. What function is served by the alula?

Figure 30.7

Bird Flight and Feeding Adaptations. This ruby-throated hummingbird (*Archilochus colubris*) hovers while feeding on flower nectar. The beak of hummingbirds often matches the length and curvature of the flower from which it extracts nectar.

NUTRITION AND THE DIGESTIVE SYSTEM

Most birds have ravenous appetites! This appetite supports a high metabolic rate that makes endothermy and flight possible. For example, hummingbirds feed almost constantly during the day. In spite of high rates of food consumption, their rapid metabolism often cannot be sustained overnight and they may become torpid, with reduced body temperature and respiratory rate, until they can feed again in the morning.

Bird bills and tongues are modified for a variety of feeding habits and food sources (figures 30.7 and 30.8). For example, the tongue of a woodpecker is barbed for extracting grubs from the bark of trees (*see figure 37.6d*). Sapsuckers excavate holes in trees and use a brushlike tongue for licking the sap that accumulates in these holes. The tongues of hummingbirds and other nectar feeders are rolled into a tube and used for extracting nectar from flowers.

In many birds, a diverticulum of the esophagus, called the crop, is a storage structure that allows birds to quickly ingest large quantities of locally abundant food and then seek safety while digesting their meal. The crop of pigeons produces "pigeon's milk," a cheesy secretion formed by the proliferation and sloughing of cells lining the crop. Young pigeons (squabs) are fed pigeon's milk until they are able to eat grain. Cedar waxwings, vultures, and birds of prey use their esophagus for similar storage functions. Crops are less well developed in insect-eating birds because insectivorous birds feed throughout the day on sparsely distributed food.

The stomach of birds is modified into two regions. The proventriculus secretes gastric juices that initiate digestion (figure 30.9). The ventriculus (gizzard) has muscular walls to abrade

(a)   (b)   (c)

Figure 30.8

Some Specializations of Bird Bills. (*a*) The bill of a bald eagle (*Haliacetus leucocephalus*) is specialized for tearing prey. (*b*) The thick, powerful bill of this cardinal (*Cardinalis cardinalis*) is used to crack through tough seeds. (*c*) The bill of a flamingo (*Phoenicopterus ruber*) is used for straining food from the water in a head-down feeding posture. The upper and lower mandibles are fringed with large bristles. As water is sucked into the bill, larger particles are filtered and left outside. Inside the bill, smaller algae and animals are filtered on tiny inner bristles. The tongue is used to remove food from the bristles.

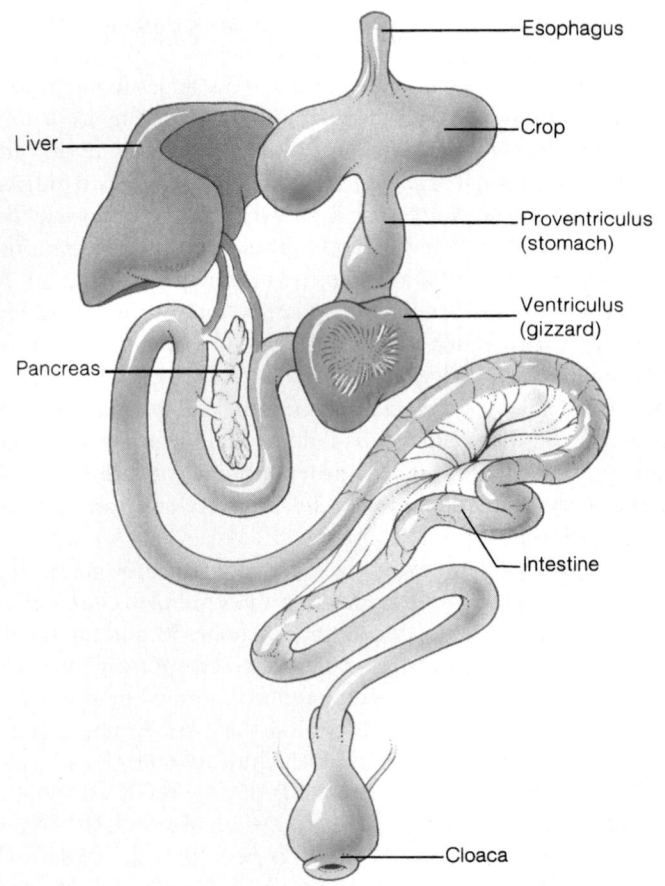

Liver

Pancreas

Esophagus

Crop

Proventriculus
(stomach)

Ventriculus
(gizzard)

Intestine

Cloaca

Figure 30.9

The Digestive System of a Pigeon. Birds have very high metabolic rates that require a nearly constant supply of nutrients.

and crush seeds or other hard materials. Sand and other abrasives may be swallowed to aid digestion. The bulk of enzymatic digestion and absorption occurs in the small intestine, aided by secretions from the pancreas and liver. Paired ceca may be located at the union of the large and small intestine. These blind-ending sacs contain bacteria that aid in the digestion of cellulose. Undigested food is usually eliminated through the cloaca; however, owls form pellets of bone, fur, and feathers that are ejected from the ventriculus through the mouth. Owl pellets accumulate in and around owl nests and are useful in studying their food habits.

It is common practice to group birds by their feeding habits. It is somewhat artificial, however, because birds may eat different kinds of food at different stages in their life history, or they may change diets simply because of changes in food availability. Robins, for example, feed largely on worms and other invertebrates when these foods are available. In the winter, however, robins may feed on berries.

In some of their feeding habits, birds have come into direct conflict with human interests. Bird damage to orchard and grain crops is tallied in the millions of dollars each year. Flocking and roosting habits of some birds, such as European starlings

and redwing blackbirds, concentrate millions of birds in local habitats, and fields of grain can be devastated. Recent monocultural practices tend to aggravate problems with grain-feeding birds by encouraging the formation of very large flocks.

In spite of commonly held beliefs, the impact of birds of prey on poultry, game birds, and commercial fisheries is minimal. Unfortunately, birds of prey have been killed with guns and poisons because of the mistaken impression that they are responsible for significant losses.

CIRCULATION, GAS EXCHANGE, AND TEMPERATURE REGULATION

The circulatory system of birds is similar to that of reptiles, except that the heart has completely separated atria and ventricles, resulting in separate pulmonary and systemic circuits. In vertebrate evolution, the sinus venosus has undergone a gradual reduction in size. It is a separate chamber in fishes, amphibians, and turtles and receives blood from the venous system. In other reptiles, it is a group of cells in the right atrium that serves as the pacemaker for the heart. In birds, the sinus venosus also persists only as a patch of pacemaker tissue in the right atrium. The bird heart is relatively large (up to 2.4% of total body weight), and its rate of beating is rapid. Rates in excess of 1,000 beats per minute have been recorded for hummingbirds under stress. Larger birds have relatively smaller hearts and slower heart rates. The heart rate of an ostrich, for example, varies between 38 and 176 beats per minute. A large heart, rapid heart rate, and complete separation of oxygenated from unoxygenated blood are important adaptations for delivering the large quantities of blood required for endothermy and flight.

Gas Exchange

Because of high metabolic rates associated with flight, birds have a greater rate of oxygen consumption than any other vertebrate. When other vertebrates inspire and expire, air passes into and out of respiratory passageways in a simple back and forth cycle. Ventilation is interrupted during expiration and there is a considerable quantity of "dead air" in the lungs because not all air is forced out during expiration. Because of their unique structure, bird lungs provide a nearly continuous movement of fresh air over respiratory surfaces during inspiratory and expiratory cycles. The quantity of "dead air" in the lungs is sharply reduced compared with other vertebrates.

Most air is taken in through external nares, which lead to nasal passageways and the pharynx. The trachea is supported by bone and cartilage. A larynx is undifferentiated, but a special voicebox, called the syrinx, is located where the trachea divides into bronchi. The muscles of the syrinx and bronchi, as well as characteristics of the trachea are responsible for bird vocalizations.

The lungs of birds are made of small air tubes called **parabronchi** (figure 30.10). Air capillaries about 10 μm in diameter branch from the parabronchi and provide gas-exchange

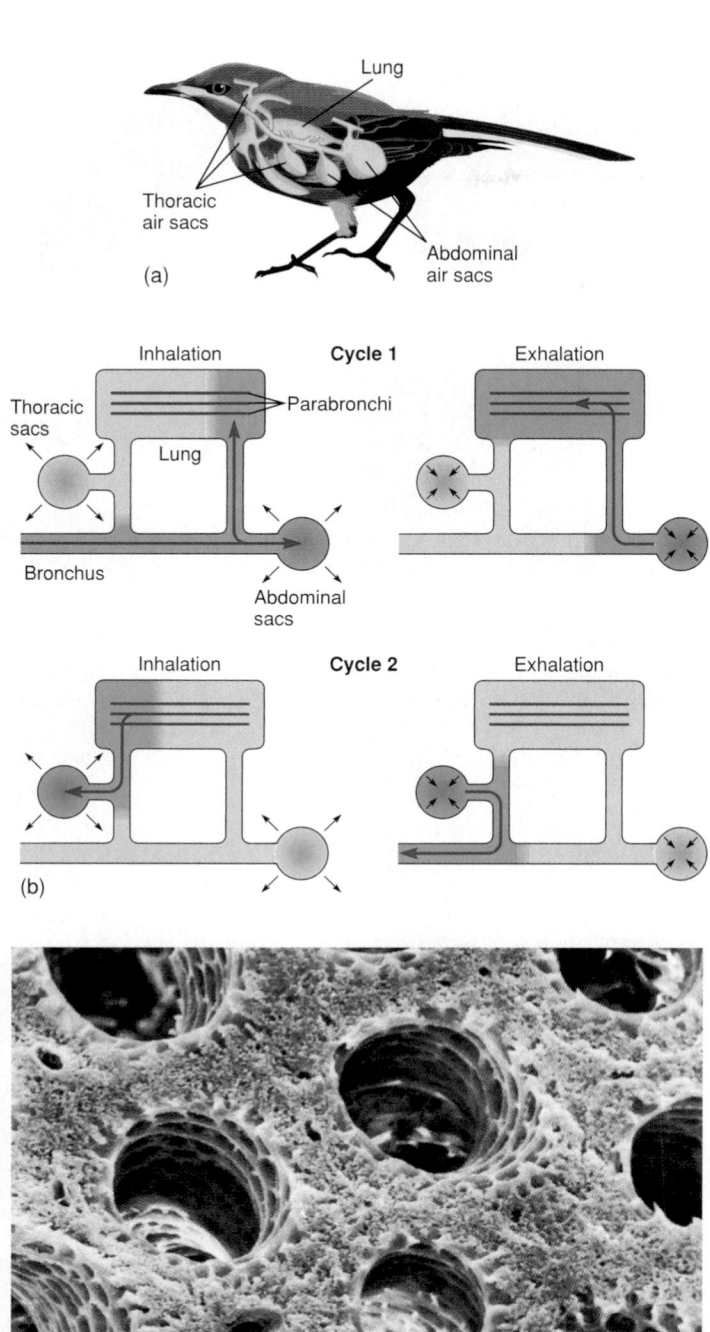

Figure 30.10

The Respiratory System of a Bird. (*a*) Air sacs branch from the respiratory tree. (*b*) Air flow during inspiration and expiration. Air flows through the parabronchi during both inspiration and expiration. The shading represents the movement through the lungs of one inspiration. (*c*) Scanning electron micrograph showing parabronchi.

surfaces. Inspiration and expiration are accomplished by the expansion and compression of thin-walled air sacs that ramify throughout the body cavity and even penetrate some bones, such as the humerus of the wing.

Ventilation occurs by alternate compression and expansion of the air sacs during flight and other activities. When breathing, the movement of the sternum and the posterior ribs compresses the thoracic air sacs. X-ray movies of European starlings in a wind tunnel show that the wishbone is distorted when flight muscles contract. Alternate distortion and recoiling helps compress and expand the air sacs located between the bone's two shafts. During inspiration, air moves into the abdominal air sacs. At the same time, air already in the lungs moves through parabronchi to the thoracic air sacs. During expiration, the air in the thoracic air sacs moves out of the respiratory system, and the air in the abdominal air sacs moves into parabronchi. At the next inspiration, the air moves into the thoracic air sacs, and is expelled during the next expiration. It takes two ventilatory cycles to move a particular volume of air through the respiratory system of a bird.

Thermoregulation

Birds regulate their body temperatures between 38 and 45° C. Lethal extremes are lower than 32 and higher than 47° C. On a cold day, resting birds fluff their feathers to increase their insulating properties, as well as the dead air space within them. They also tuck their bills into their feathers to reduce heat loss from the respiratory tract. The most exposed parts of a bird are the feet and tarsi which have neither fleshy muscles nor a rich blood supply. Temperatures in these extremities are allowed to drop near freezing to prevent heat loss. Countercurrent heat exchange between the warm blood flowing to the legs and feet, and the cooler blood flowing to the body core from the legs and feet, prevent excessive heat loss at the feet by returning heat to the body core before it goes to the extremities and is lost to the environment (*see figure 38.5b*). Shivering is also used to generate heat in extreme cold. Increases in metabolism during winter months require additional food.

Some birds become torpid and allow their body temperatures to drop on cool nights. For example, whippoorwills allow their body temperatures to drop from about 40° C to near 16° C, and respiratory rates become very slow.

Muscular activity during flight produces large quantities of heat. Excess heat can be dissipated by panting. Evaporative heat loss from the floor of the mouth, is enhanced by fluttering vascular membranes of this region.

NERVOUS AND SENSORY SYSTEMS

A mouse skitters across the floor of a barn enveloped in the darkness of night. An owl in the loft overhead turns in the direction of the faint sounds made by tiny feet. As the mouse reaches a

FIGURE 30.11

A Barn Owl (*Tyto alba*). A keen sense of hearing allows barn owls to find prey in spite of the darkness of night.

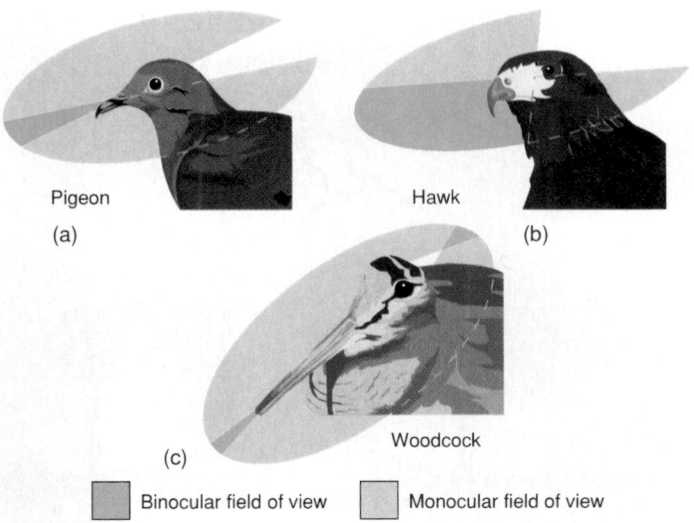

FIGURE 30.12

Avian Vision. The fields of view of a pigeon (*a*), a hawk (*b*), and a woodcock (*c*). Woodcocks have eyes located far posteriorly and have a narrow field of binocular vision in front and behind. They can focus on predators that might be circling above them while probing mud with their long beaks.

sack of grain, and the sounds made by hurrying feet change to a scratchy gnawing of teeth on the sack of feed, the barn owl dives for its prey (figure 30.11). Fluted tips of flight feathers make the owl's approach imperceptible to the mouse, and the owl's ears, not its eyes, provide information to guide the owl to its prey. Under similar circumstances, barn owls will successfully locate and capture prey in over 75% of attempts! This ability is just one example of the many sensory adaptations found in birds.

The forebrain of birds is much larger than that of reptiles due to the enlargement of the cerebral hemispheres, including a region of gray matter, the corpus striatum. The corpus striatum functions in visual learning, feeding, courtship, and nesting. A pineal body is located on the roof of the forebrain. It appears to play a role in stimulating ovarian development and in regulating other functions influenced by light and dark periods. The optic tectum (the roof of the midbrain), along with the corpus striatum, plays an important role in integrating sensory functions. The midbrain also receives sensory input from the eyes. As in reptiles, the hindbrain includes the cerebellum and the medulla oblongata, which coordinate motor activities and regulate heart and respiratory rates, respectively.

Vision is an important sense for most birds. The structure of bird eyes is similar to that of other vertebrates, but they are much larger in proportion to body size than in other vertebrates (*see figure 28.13*). The eyes are usually somewhat flattened in an anteroposterior direction; however, the eyes of birds of prey protrude anteriorly because of a bulging cornea. Birds have a unique, double-focusing mechanism. Padlike structures (similar to those of reptiles) control the curvature of

the lens, and ciliary muscles change the curvature of the cornea.   ⑤   Double, nearly instantaneous focusing allows an osprey, or other bird of prey, to remain focused on a fish throughout a brief, but breathtakingly fast, descent.

The retina of a bird's eye is thick and contains both rods and cones. Rods are active under low light intensities and cones under high light intensities. Cones are especially concentrated ($1,000,000/mm^2$) at a focal point called the fovea. Unlike other vertebrates, some birds have two foveae per eye. The one at the center of the retina is sometimes called the "search fovea" because it gives the bird a wide angle of monocular vision. The other fovea is at the posterior margin of the retina. It functions with the posterior fovea of the other eye to allow binocular vision. The posterior fovea is called the "pursuit fovea," because binocular vision is necessary for depth perception, which is necessary to capture prey. "Search" and "pursuit" are not meant to imply that the two foveae are found only in predatory birds. Other birds use the "search fovea" to observe the landscape below them during flight and the "pursuit" fovea when depth perception is needed, as in landing on a branch of a tree.

The position of the eyes on the head also influences the degree of binocular vision (figure 30.12). Pigeons have eyes located well back on the sides of their head, giving them a nearly 360° monocular field, but a narrow binocular field. They do not have to pursue their food (grain), and a wide monocular field of view helps them stay alert to predators while feeding on the ground. Hawks and owls have eyes farther forward on the head. Their binocular field of view is increased, and their monocular field of view is correspondingly decreased.

Like reptiles, birds have a nictitating membrane that is drawn over the surface of the eye to cleanse and protect the eye.

Olfaction apparently plays a minor role in the lives of most birds. External nares open near the base of the beak, but the olfactory epithelium is poorly developed. Exceptions include turkey vultures, which locate their dead and dying prey largely by smell.

In contrast, hearing is well developed in most birds. The external ear opening is covered by loose, delicate feathers called auriculars. Middle- and inner-ear structures are similar to those of reptiles. The sensitivity of the avian ear (100 to 15,000 Hz) is similar to that of the human ear (16 to 20,000 Hz).

EXCRETION AND OSMOREGULATION

Birds and reptiles face essentially identical excretory and osmoregulatory demands. Like reptiles, birds excrete uric acid, which is temporarily stored in the cloaca. Water reabsorption also occurs in the cloaca. As with reptiles, the excretion of uric acid conserves water and promotes development of embryos in terrestrial environments. In addition, some birds have supraorbital salt glands that drain excess sodium chloride through the nasal openings to the outside of the body (*see box 38.3*). These are especially important in marine birds that drink seawater and feed on invertebrates containing large quantities of salt in their tissues. Salt glands can secrete salt in a solution that is about two to three times more concentrated than other body fluids. Salt glands, therefore, compensate for the kidney's inability to concentrate salts in the urine.

Stop and Ask Yourself

8. What evolutionary remnant of the vertebrate sinus venosus is found in the heart of a bird? What is the function of this remnant?
9. How are the lungs of birds adapted to provide continuous, one-way movement of air across gas exchange surfaces?
10. How does a bird cool itself?
11. What is the value of separate "search" and "pursuit" foveae for a bird of prey?

REPRODUCTION AND DEVELOPMENT

Sexual activities of birds have been observed more closely than those of any other group of animals. These activities include establishing territories, finding mates, constructing nests, incubating eggs, and feeding young.

All birds are oviparous. Gonads are located in the dorsal abdominal region, next to the kidneys. Testes are paired, and coiled tubules (vasa deferentia) conduct sperm to the cloaca.

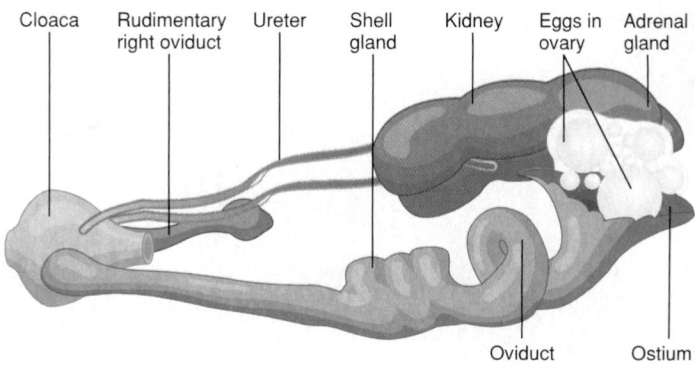

FIGURE 30.13

The Urogenital System of a Female Pigeon. The right ovary and oviduct are rudimentary in most female birds.

An enlargement of the vasa deferentia, the seminal vesicle, is a site for temporary storage and maturation of sperm prior to mating. Testes enlarge during the breeding season. Except for certain waterfowl and ostriches, birds have no intromittent organ, and sperm transfer occurs by cloacal contact during brief mounts by the male on the female.

In females, two ovaries form during development, but usually only the left ovary fully develops (figure 30.13). A large, funnel-shaped opening of the oviduct envelopes the ovary and receives eggs after ovulation. Fertilization of the egg occurs in the upper portions of the oviduct, and the zygote is gradually surrounded by albumen secreted from glandular regions of the oviduct wall as the egg completes its passage. A shell is added by a shell gland in the lower region of the oviduct. The oviduct opens into the cloaca.

Territories are established by many birds prior to mating. Although size and function vary greatly among species, territories generally allow birds to mate without interference. They provide nest locations and sometimes food resources for adults and offspring. Breeding birds defend their territories and expel intruders of the same sex and species. Threats are common, but actual fighting is minimized.

Mating may follow the attraction of a mate to a territory. For example, female woodpeckers are attracted to the drumming by males on trees. Male ruffed grouse fan their wings on logs and create sounds that can be heard for many miles. Cranes have a courtship dance that includes stepping, bowing, stretching, and jumping displays. Mating occurs when a mate's call or posture signals readiness. It is accomplished quickly, but occurs repeatedly to assure fertilization of all the eggs that will be laid.

Over 90% of birds are **monogamous:** a single male pairs with a single female during the breeding season. Some birds (swans, geese, eagles) pair for life. Frequent mating apparently strengthens the pair bonds that develop. Monogamy is common when resources are widely and evenly distributed, and one bird cannot control access to resources. Monogamy is also

Figure 30.14

Courtship Displays. A male, greater prairie chicken (*Tympanuchus cupido*) displaying in a lek.

advantageous because both parents usually participate in nest building and care of the young. One parent can incubate and protect the eggs or chicks while the other searches for food.

Some birds are **polygynous.** Males mate with more than one female, and the females care for the eggs and chicks. Polygyny tends to occur in species whose young are less dependent at hatching and in situations where patchy resource distribution may attract many females to a relatively small breeding area. Prairie chickens are polygynous, and males display in groups called leks. In prairie chicken leks, the males in the center positions are preferred and attract the majority of females (figure 30.14).

A few bird species are **polyandrous,** and the females mate with more than one male. Polyandry occurs in spotted sandpipers. Females are larger than males and establish and defend their territories from other females. They lay a clutch of eggs for each male that is attracted to and builds a nest in her territory. If a males loses his eggs to a predator, the female replaces those eggs. Polyandry results in the production of more eggs than monogamous matings. It is thought to be advantageous when food is plentiful but, because of predation or other threats, the chances of successfully rearing young are low.

Nest construction usually begins after pair formation. It is an instinctive behavior and is usually initiated by the female. A few birds do not make nests. Emperor penguins, for example, breed on the snow and ice of Antarctica where no nest materials are available. Their single egg is incubated on the web of the foot (mostly the male's foot) tucked within a fold of abdominal skin.

Nesting Activities

The nesting behavior of birds is often species specific. Some birds choose nest sites away from other members of their species, and other birds nest in very large flocks. Unfortunately,

predictable nesting behavior has led to the extinction of some species of birds (box 30.2).

The number of eggs laid by a female is usually variable. Most birds incubate their eggs, and some birds have a featherless, vascularized incubation or brood patch (*see figure 35.13*) that helps keep the eggs at temperatures between 33 and 37° C. Eggs are turned to prevent the adherence of egg membranes in the egg and deformation of the embryo. Adults of some species sprinkle the eggs with water to cool and humidify them. The Egyptian plover carries water from distant sites in the breast feathers. The incubation period lasts between 10 and 80 days and is correlated with egg size and degree of development at hatching. One or two days before hatching, the young bird penetrates an air sac at the blunt end of its egg, inflates it lungs, and begins breathing. Hatching occurs as the young bird pecks the shell with a keratinized egg tooth on the tip of the upper jaw and struggles to free itself.

Some birds are helpless at hatching, others are more independent. Those that are entirely dependent on their parents are said to be **altricial** (L. *altricialis,* to nourish), and they are often naked at hatching (figure 30.15a). Altricial young must be brooded constantly at first because endothermy is not developed. They grow rapidly, and when they leave the nest they are nearly as large as their parents. (For example, American robins weigh 4 to 6 g at hatching and leave the nest 13 days later weighing 57 g.) **Precocial** (L. *praecoci,* early ripe) young are alert and lively at hatching (figure 30.15b). They are usually covered by down and can walk, run, swim, and feed themselves—although one parent is usually present to lead the young to food and shelter.

Young altricial birds have huge appetites and keep one or both parents continually searching for food. They may consume a mass of food that equals their own weight each day. Adults bring food to the nest or regurgitate food stored in the crop or esophagus. Vocal signals or color patterns on the bills or throats of adults initiate feeding responses in the young. Parents instinctively feed gaping mouths, and many hatchlings have brightly colored mouth linings that attract a parent's attention. The first-hatched young is fed first and most often because it is usually the largest and can stretch its neck higher than can its nestmates.

Life is usually brief for birds. About 50% of eggs laid yield birds that leave the nest. Most birds, if kept in captivity, have a potential life span of 10 to 20 years. Natural longevity is much shorter. The average American robin lives 1.3 years, and the average black-capped chickadee lives less than 1 year. Mortality is high in the first year from predators and inclement weather.

Migration and Navigation

Over twenty centuries ago, Aristotle described birds migrating to escape the winter cold and summer heat. He had the mistaken impression that some birds disappear during winter because they hibernate, and that others transmutate to another species. It is now known that some birds migrate long distances. Modern zoologists study the timing of migration, the stimuli for

BOX 30.2 | BRIGHT SKIES AND SILENT THUNDER

There is no sadder tale in the history of human interactions with wildlife than that of *Ectopistes migratorius*, the passenger pigeon. Although the full story of the extinction of this bird may never be known, humans will never be able to escape the responsibility for the excessive slaughter that led to the decline of a vulnerable species.

In the nineteenth century, flocks of passenger pigeons were so vast in eastern North America that their numbers were estimated at up to 2 billion birds. In 1813, the famed naturalist John Audubon watched a flock of passenger pigeons pass overhead for 3 days. The flock was said to completely darken the sky by day, and their wings sounded like thunder.

How could a species so abundant become extinct in just a few decades? What made these birds so vulnerable was their social behavior. Passenger pigeons nested, roosted in the evening, and foraged for food in huge aggregations that covered thousands of acres. It is said that trees became so laden with birds that their branches often broke under the weight. One nest site in Wisconsin was said to be 100 miles long! On feeding forays, flocks would travel hundreds of miles and strip trees of acorns, beechnuts, and other nuts. These colonies were apparently not just convenient associations, but were essential for survival. Highly organized flocks were also an important social stimulus for breeding.

Unfortunately, this behavior made the birds vulnerable. Nesting sites were predictable and hunters came to them year after year. Professional hunters are said to have traveled from nest site to nest site during the nesting season. Birds were blinded at night with lights and knocked out of trees. They were captured in huge nets or choked by burning sulfur. Their trees were felled and birds harvested. They were shot by the thousands with guns. In 1861, 14,850,000 passenger pigeons were shipped to big city markets from a single nesting site near Petoskey, Michigan.

How could any bird be expected to successfully produce and rear their young under this onslaught? The single egg tended by a pair of passenger pigeons had little chance for survival during these unfortunate years. Flocks gradually dwindled. By the late 1890s people began to realize that the passenger pigeons were in trouble. In addition to rampant killing and the resultant breakup of the social organization needed for successful mating, deforestation was contributing to the passenger pigeon's decline. Laws that prohibited further killing were too late. After 1900, no passenger pigeons were seen in the wild. "Martha," the last passenger pigeon in captivity (Cincinnati Zoological Gardens), died on September 1, 1914, after living for 29 years.

(a)

(b)

FIGURE 30.15

Altricial and Precocial Chicks. (*a*) An American robin (*Turdus migratorius*) feeding nestlings. Robins have altricial chicks that are helpless at hatching. (*b*) Killdeer (*Charadrius vociferus*) have precocial chicks that are down covered and can move about.

migration, and the physiological changes that occur during migration, as well as migration routes and how birds navigate over huge expanses of land or water.

Migration (as used here) refers to periodic round trips between breeding and nonbreeding areas. Most migrations are annual, with nesting areas in northern regions and wintering grounds in the south. (Migration is more pronounced for species found in the Northern Hemisphere because about 70% of the earth's land is in the Northern Hemisphere.) Migrations occasionally involve east/west movements or altitude changes. Migration allows birds to avoid climatic extremes, and to secure adequate food, shelter, and space throughout the year.

Birds migrate in response to species-specific physiological conditions. Innate (genetic) clocks and environmental factors influence preparation for migration. The photoperiod is often cited as an important migratory cue for many birds, particularly for birds in temperate zones. The changing photoperiod initiates seasonal changes in gonadal development that often serve as migratory stimuli. Increasing day length in the spring promotes gonadal development, and decreasing day length in the fall promotes regression of gonads. In many birds, the changing photoperiod also appears to promote fat deposition, which acts as an energy reserve for migration. The anterior lobe of the pituitary gland and the pineal body have been implicated in mediating photoperiod responses.

The mechanics of migration are species specific. Some long-distance migrants may store fat equal to 50% of their body weight and make nonstop journeys. Other species that take a more leisurely approach to migration begin their journeys early and stop frequently to feed and rest. In clear weather, many birds fly at altitudes greater than 1,000 m, which reduces the likelihood of hitting tall obstacles. Many birds have very specific migration routes (*see figure 30.1*).

Navigation

Homing pigeons have served for many years as a pigeon postal service. As long ago as the ancient Egyptian times, and as recently as World War II, pigeons were used to return messages from the battlefield.

⑥ Two forms of navigation are used by birds. Route-based navigation involves keeping track of landmarks (visual or auditory) on an outward journey so that those landmarks can be used in a reverse sequence on the return trip. Location-based navigation involves establishing the direction of the destination from information available at the journey's site of origin. It involves the use of sun compasses, other celestial cues, and/or the earth's magnetic field.

Birds' lenses are transparent to ultraviolet light, and their photoreceptors respond to it, allowing them to orient using the sun, or even on cloudy days. This orientation cue is referred to as a sun compass. Because the sun moves through the sky between sunrise and sunset, birds use internal clocks to perceive that the sun rises in the east, is approximately overhead at noon, and sets in the west. The biological clocks of migratory birds can be altered. For example, birds ready for northward migration can be held in a laboratory in which the "laboratory sunrise" occurs later than the natural sunrise. When released to natural light conditions, they fly in a direction they perceive to be north, but which is really northwest. Night migrators can also orient using the sun by flying in the proper direction from the sunset.

Celestial cues other than the sun can be used to navigate. Humans recognize that in the Northern Hemisphere, the north star lines up with the axis of rotation of the earth. The angle between the north star and the horizon decreases as one moves toward the equator. Birds may use a similar information to determine latitude. Experimental rotations of the night sky in a planetarium have altered the orientation of birds in test cages.

There has long been speculation that birds employ magnetic compasses to detect the earth's magnetic field, and thus determine direction. Typically, these ideas have been met with skepticism, but direct evidence of their existence has been uncovered. Magnets strapped to the heads of pigeons severely disorient them. European robins and a night migrator, the garden warbler, orient using the earth's magnetic field. However, no discrete magnetic receptors have been found in either birds or other animals. Early reports of finding a magnetic iron, magnetite, in the head and necks of pigeons did not lead to a greater understanding of magnetic compasses. Further experiments failed to demonstrate magnetic properties in these regions. Magnetic iron has been found in bacteria and a variety of animal tissues. None is clearly associated with a magnetic sense, although the pineal body of pigeons has been implicated in the use of a sun compass and in responses to magnetic fields.

There is redundancy in bird navigational mechanisms, which suggests that under different circumstances, different sources of information are probably used.

Stop and Ask Yourself

12. Why is monogamy advantageous for most birds?
13. Why are birds with precocial young more likely to be polygynous than birds with altricial young?
14. What environmental cue is important in preparing birds for migration?
15. What is route-based navigation?

SUMMARY

1. Birds are members of the archosaur lineage. Fossils of ancient birds, *Archaeopteryx* and *Sinornis*, show reptilian affinities and give clues into the origin of flight.

2. Feathers evolved from reptilian scales and function in flight, insulation, sex recognition, and waterproofing. Feathers are maintained and periodically molted.

3. The bird skeleton is light and made more rigid by fusion of bones. The neck and bill are used as a fifth appendage.

4. Bird wings form airfoils that provide lift. Propulsive force is generated by tilting the wing during flapping. Gliding, flapping, soaring, and hovering flight are used by different birds or by the same bird at different times.

5. Birds feed on a variety of foods as reflected in the structure of the bill and other parts of the digestive tract.

6. The heart of birds consists of two atria and two ventricles. A very rapid heart rate, and rapid blood flow, support the high metabolic rate of birds.

7. The respiratory system of birds provides one-way, nearly constant, air movement across respiratory surfaces.

8. Birds are able to maintain high body temperatures endothermically because of insulating fat deposits and feathers.

9. Cerebral hemispheres of a bird are enlarged by the development of the corpus striatum. Vision is the most important avian sense.

10. Birds are oviparous. Reproductive activities include the establishment and defense of territories, courtship, and nest building.

11. Eggs are usually incubated by either or both parents, and one or both parents feed the young. Altricial chicks are helpless at hatching, and precocial chicks are alert and lively shortly after hatching.

12. Migration allows some birds to avoid climatic extremes, and to secure adequate food, shelter, and space throughout the year. The photoperiod is the most important migratory cue for birds.

13. Birds use both route-based navigation and location-based navigation.

SELECTED KEY TERMS

airfoil (*p.* 489)
altricial (*p.* 496)
molting (*p.* 488)
monogamous (*p.* 495)

polyandrous (*p.* 496)
polygynous (*p.* 496)
precocial (*p.* 496)

CRITICAL THINKING QUESTIONS

1. Birds are sometimes called "glorified reptiles." Discuss why this description is appropriate.

2. What adaptations of birds promote endothermy and flight? Why is endothermy important for birds?

3. Birds are, without exception, oviparous. Why do you think that is true?

4. What are the advantages that offset the great energy expenditure required by migration?

5. Compare and contrast the advantages of monogamy, polygyny, and polyandry for birds. In what ways are the advantages and disadvantages of each related to the abundance and utilization of food and other resources?

MAMMALS:
SPECIALIZED TEETH, ENDOTHERMY, HAIR, AND VIVIPARITY

Outline

Concepts

1. Mammalian characteristics evolved gradually over a 200-million-year period in the synapsid lineage.
2. Two subclasses of mammals evolved during the Mesozoic era—Prototheria and Theria. Modern mammals include monotremes, marsupial mammals, and placental mammals.
3. The skin of mammals is thick and protective and has an insulating covering of hair.
4. Adaptations of teeth and the digestive tract allow mammals to exploit a wide variety of food resources.
5. Efficient systems for circulation and gas exchange support the high metabolic rate associated with endothermy.
6. The brain of mammals has an expanded cerebral cortex that processes information from various sensory structures.
7. Metanephric kidneys permit mammals to excrete urea without excessive water loss.
8. Complex behavior patterns enhance survival.
9. Most mammals are viviparous and have reproductive cycles that help ensure internal fertilization and successful development.

Would You Like to Know:

1. what group of ancient reptiles is most closely related to mammals? (p. 502)
2. what group of mammals is oviparous? (p. 503)
3. why mammal hair stands on end when a mammal is frightened? (p. 506)
4. how teeth of mammals are specialized for different feeding habits? (p. 509)
5. why the four-chambered hearts of mammals and birds are an example of convergent evolution? (p. 511)
6. why salt glands are not found in mammals? (p. 514)
7. why a domestic cat rubs its face on furniture around the house? (p. 516)

These and other useful questions will be answered in this chapter.

This chapter contains evolutionary concepts, which are set off in this font.

EVOLUTIONARY PERSPECTIVE

The beginning of the Tertiary period, about 70 million years ago, was the start of the "age of mammals." It coincided with the extinction of many reptilian lineages, which led to the adaptive radiation of the mammals. To trace the roots of the mammals, however, we must go back to the Carboniferous period, when the synapsid lineage diverged from other amniote lineages (*see figure 29.2*).

Mammalian characteristics evolved gradually over a period of 200 million years (figure 31.1). The early synapsids were the pelycosaurs. Some were herbivores; others showed skeletal adaptations that reflect increased effectiveness as predators (figure 31.2*a*). The anterior teeth of their upper jaw were large and were separated from the posterior teeth by a gap that accommodated the enlarged anterior teeth of the lower jaw when the jaw was closed. The palate was arched, which gave additional strength to the upper jaw and allowed air to pass over prey held in the mouth. Their legs were longer and slimmer than those of earlier amniotes.

By the middle of the Permian period, other successful mammallike reptiles had arisen from the pelycosaurs. They were a diverse group known as the therapsids. Some were predators and others were herbivores. In the predatory therapsids, teeth were concentrated at the front of the mouth and enlarged for holding and tearing prey. The posterior teeth were reduced in size and number. The jaws of some therapsids were elongate and generated a large biting force when they snapped closed. The teeth of the herbivorous therapsids were also mammallike. Some had a large space, called the diastema, separating the anterior and posterior teeth. The posterior teeth had ridges (cusps) and cutting edges that were probably used to shred plant material. Unlike other reptiles, the hind limbs of therapsids were held directly beneath the body and moved parallel to the long axis of the body. Changes in the size and shape of the ribs suggest the separation of the trunk into thoracic and abdominal regions and a breathing mechanism similar to that of mammals. The last therapsids were a group called the cynodonts (figure 31.2*b*). Some of these were as large as a big dog, but most were small and little different from the earliest mammals.

FIGURE 31.1

Class Mammalia. The decline of the ruling reptiles about 70 million years ago permitted mammals to radiate into diurnal habitats previously occupied by dinosaurs and other reptiles. Mammals are characterized by hair, endothermy, and mammary glands. The lowland gorilla (*Gorilla gorilla graueri*, order Primates) is shown here.

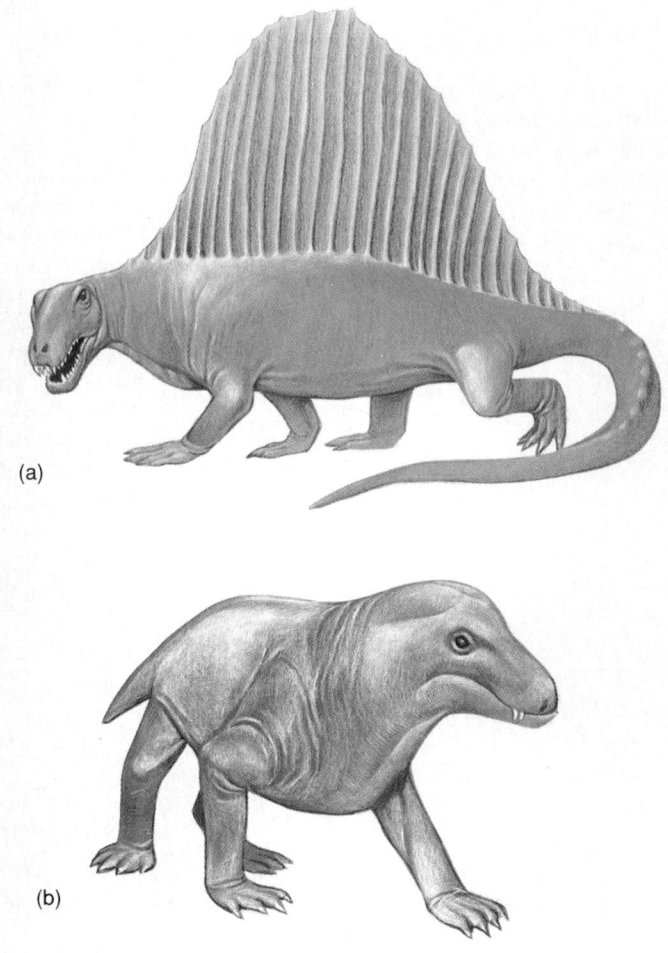

FIGURE 31.2

Members of the Subclass Synapsidia. (*a*) *Dimetrodon* was a 3 m long pelycosaur. It probably fed on other reptiles and amphibians. The large sail may have served as a recognition signal and a thermoregulatory device. (*b*) *Cynognathus* was a mammallike reptile that probably foraged for small animals, much like a badger does today. The badger-sized animal was a cyncodont with the order of Therapsida, the stock from which mammals arose during the mid-Triassic period.

The first mammals were small (less than 10 cm long) with delicate skeletons. Most of our knowledge of early mammalian phylogeny comes from the study of their fossilized teeth and skull fragments. These studies suggest that the mammals of the Jurassic and Cretaceous periods were mostly predators that fed on other vertebrates and arthropods. A few were herbivores, and others combined predatory and herbivorous feeding habits. Changes in the structure of the middle ear and the regions of the brain devoted to hearing and olfaction indicate that these senses were important during the early evolution of mammals.

Although it is somewhat speculative, some zoologists think that the small size, well-developed olfactory and auditory abilities, and the lack of color vision in most mammals suggest that early mammals were nocturnal. This habit may have allowed them to avoid competition with the much larger dinosaurs and the smaller diurnal (day-active [L. *diurnalis,* daily]) reptiles living at the same time. Again it is speculative, but nocturnal habits could have led to endothermy. Endothermy would have allowed small mammals to maintain body temperatures above that of their surroundings after the sun had set and the air temperature began to fall.

DIVERSITY OF MAMMALS

Modern members of the class Mammalia (ma-ma'le-ah) (L. *mamma,* breast) are characterized by hair, mammary glands, specialized teeth, three middle-ear ossicles, and other characteristics listed in table 31.1. It is currently not possible to determine the extent to which all of these characteristics were developed in the earliest mammals. Although there is some disagreement among zoologists regarding subclass-level classification, most zoologists consider mid-Cretaceous (about 130 million years ago) mammals to have diverged into two subclasses (figure 31.3). Until recently, monotremes (the duckbilled platypus and the echidna) were classified in the subclass Prototheria (Gr. *protos,* first + *therion,* wild beast). Recent fossil evidence showing monotreme dentition that is characteristic of the subclass Theria has resulted in this group being reassigned to the latter subclass. The Prototheria, therefore, contains only extinct forms.

The subclass Theria diverged into three infraclasses by the late Cretaceous period. The infraclass Ornithodelphia (Gr. *ornis,* bird + *delphia,* birthplace) contains the monotremes (Gr. *monos,* one + *trema,* opening). This name refers to the fact that, unlike other mammals, monotremes possess a cloaca. Monotremes are distinguished from all other mammals by the fact that they are oviparous (figure 31.4a,b). There are six species of monotremes found in Australia and New Guinea.

The infraclass Metatheria (Gr. *meta,* after) contains the marsupial mammals. They are viviparous, but have very short gestation periods. A protective pouch, called the marsupium, covers the mammary glands of the female. The young crawl into the marsupium after birth, where they feed and complete development. There are about 250 species of marsupials that live in the Australian region and the Americas (figure 31.4c; *see also figure 31.17*).

The other therian infraclass, Eutheria (Gr. *eu,* true), contains the placental mammals. They are usually born at an advanced stage of development, having been nourished within the uterus. Exchanges between maternal and fetal circulatory systems occur by diffusion across an organ called the **placenta,** which is composed of both maternal and fetal tissue. There are about 3,800 species of eutherians that are classified into 17 orders (figures 31.5 and 31.6; *see also figures 31.11 and 31.15–31.17*).

Stop and Ask Yourself

1. What characteristics of synapsid reptiles are mammallike?
2. What source has provided the most information about early mammals?
3. Why do some zoologists think that early mammals were nocturnal?
4. What are two subclasses of mammals?

EVOLUTIONARY PRESSURES

Mammals are naturally distributed on all continents except Antarctica and in all oceans. The many adaptations that have accompanied their adaptive radiation are discussed in this section.

EXTERNAL STRUCTURE AND LOCOMOTION

The skin of a mammal, like that of other vertebrates, consists of epidermal and dermal layers. It protects from mechanical injury, invasion by microorganisms, and the sun's ultraviolet light. Skin is also important in temperature regulation, sensory perception, excretion, and water regulation (*see figure 32.9*).

Hair is a keratinized derivative of the epidermis of the skin and is uniquely mammalian. It is seated in an invagination of the epidermis, called a hair follicle. A coat of hair, called pelage, usually consists of two kinds of hair. Long guard hairs protect a dense coat of smaller, insulating underhairs.

Because hair is composed largely of dead cells, it must be periodically molted. In some mammals (e.g., humans), molting occurs gradually and may not be noticed. In others, hair loss occurs rapidly and may result in altered pelage characteristics. In the fall, many mammals acquire a thick coat of insulating underhair, and the pelage color may change. For example, the Arctic fox takes on a white or cream color with its autumn molt, which helps conceal the fox in a snowy environment. With its spring molt, the Arctic fox acquires a gray and yellow pelage (*see figure 31.6*).

Hair is also important for the sense of touch. Mechanical displacement of a hair stimulates nerve cells associated with the hair root. Guard hairs may sometimes be modified into thick-

31.3

TABLE 31.1	CLASSIFICATION OF MAMMALS

Class Mammalia (ma-ma'le-ah)
Mammary glands; hair; diaphragm; three middle-ear ossicles; heterodont dentition; sweat, sebaceous, and scent glands; four-chambered heart; large cerebral cortex.

    Subclass Prototheria (pro'to-ther'e-ah)
    This subclass formerly contained the monotremes. Monotremes have recently been reclassified and now this subclass contains only extinct species.

    Subclass Theria (ther'e-ah)
    Members of this subclass are distinguished by very technical characteristics of the skull.

        Infraclass Ornithodelphia (or'ne-tho-del'fe-ah)
        Members of this infraclass are distinguished by very technical characteristics of the skull. Monotremes.

        Infraclass Metatheria (met'ah-ther'e-ah)
        Viviparous, primitive placenta; young are born very early and often are carried in a marsupial pouch on the belly of the female. Marsupials.

        Infraclass Eutheria (u-ther'-e-ah)*
        Complex placenta. Young develop to advanced stage prior to birth. Placentals.

            Order Insectivora (in-sec-tiv'or-ah)
            Diverse group of small, primitive mammals; third largest mammalian order. Hedgehogs, tenrecs, moles, shrews.

            Order Chiroptera (ki-rop'ter-ah)
            Cosmopolitan, but especially abundant in the tropics. Bones of the arm and hand are elongate and slender. Flight membranes extend from the body, between digits of forelimbs, to the hindlimbs. Most are insectivorous, but some are fruit eaters, fish eaters, and blood feeders. Bats.

            Order Primates (pri-ma'tez)
            Adaptations of primates reflect adaptations for increased agility in arboreal (tree-dwelling) habitats. Omnivorous diets, unspecialized teeth, grasping digits, freely movable limbs, nails on digits, reduced nasal cavity, enlarged eyes and cerebral hemispheres. Lemurs (Madagascar and the Comoro Islands), tasiers (jungles of Sumatra and the East Indies), monkeys, gibbons, great apes (apes and humans).

            Order Edentata (e'den-ta'tah)
            Incisors and canines absent; cheek teeth, when present, lack enamel. Braincase is long and cylindrical. Hind foot is four toed; forefoot with two or three prominent toes with large claws. Limbs specialized for climbing or digging. Anteaters, tree sloths, armadillos.

            Order Lagamorpha (lag'o-mor'fah)
            Two pairs of upper incisors, one pair of lower incisors. Incisors are ever-growing and slowly worn down by feeding on vegetation. Rabbits, pikas.

            Order Rodentia (ro-den'che-ah)
            Largest mammalian order. Upper and lower jaws bear a single pair of ever-growing incisors. Squirrels, chipmunks, rats, mice, beavers, porcupines, woodchucks, lemmings.

            Order Cetacea (se-ta'she-ah)
            Streamlined, nearly hairless, and insulated by thick layers of fat (blubber). Sebaceous glands are absent. Forelimbs modified into paddlelike flippers for swimming; hindlimbs reduced and not visible externally. Tail fins (flukes) are flattened horizontally. External nares (blowhole) are located on the top of the skull. Toothed whales (beaked whales, narwhals, sperm whales, dolphins, porpoises, killer whales); toothless, filter-feeding whales (right whales, gray whales, blue whales, and humpback whales).

            Order Carnivora (kar-niv'o-rah)
            Predatory mammals; usually have a highly developed sense of smell and a large braincase. Premolars and molars modified into carnassial apparatus; three pairs of upper and lower incisors usually present, and canines are well developed. Dogs, cats, bears, raccoons, minks, sea lions, seals, walruses, otters.

            Order Proboscidea (pro'bah-sid'e-ah)
            Long, muscular proboscis (trunk) with one or two fingerlike processes at the tip. Skull is short, with the second incisor on each side of the upper jaw modified into tusks. Six cheek teeth are present in each half of each jaw. Teeth erupt (grow into place) in sequence from front to rear, so that one tooth in each jaw is functional. African and Indian elephants.

            Order Sirenia (si-re'ne-ah)
            Large, aquatic herbivores that weigh in excess of 600 kg. Nearly hairless, with thick, wrinkled skin. Heavy skeleton. Forelimb is flipperlike, and hindlimb is vestigial. Horizontal tail fluke is present. Teeth lack enamel. Manatees (coastal rivers of the Americas and Africa), dugongs (western Pacific and Indian Oceans).

            Order Perissodactyla (pe-ris'so-dak'ti-lah)
            Skull usually elongate. Large molars and premolars. (The Artiodactyla also have hoofs. Artiodactyls and perissodactyls are, therefore, called *ungulates*. "Ungula" is from the Latin, for hoof.) Primarily grazers. Horses, rhinoceroses, zebras, tapirs.

            Order Artiodactyla (ar'te-o-dak'ti-lah)
            Hoofed. Axis of support passes between third and fourth digits. Digits one, two, and five reduced or lost. Primarily grazing and browsing animals. (Pigs are an obvious exception.) Pigs, hippopotamuses, camels, antelope, deer, sheep, giraffes, cattle.

*Selected eutherian orders are described.

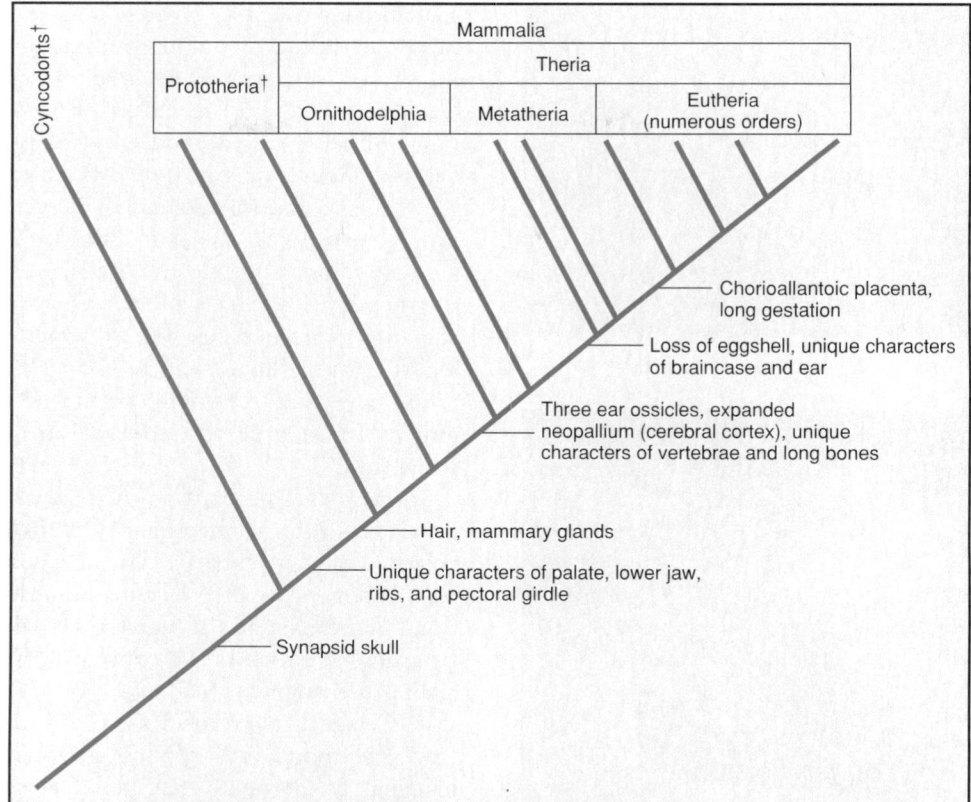

FIGURE 31.3

Mammalian Phylogeny. A cladogram showing the evolutionary relationships among the mammals. Selected characters are shown. Some extinct taxa are indicated with a dagger (†), however, numerous extinct groups have been omitted from the cladogram. The names of the 17 orders of eutherians have also been omitted (*see table 31.1*).

FIGURE 31.4

Representatives of the Mammalian Infraclasses Ornithodelphia and Metatheria. The infraclass Ornithodelphia. (*a*) A duckbilled platypus (*Ornithorhychus anatinus*). (*b*) An echidna or spiny anteater (*Tachyglossus aculeatus*). The infraclass Metatheria. (*c*) The koala (*Phascolarctos cinereus*) feeds on *Eucalyptus* leaves in Australia.

(a)

(b)

FIGURE 31.5

Order Edentata. (*a*) A giant anteater (*Myrmecophaga tridactyla*). Anteaters lack teeth. They use powerful forelimbs to tear into an insect nest and a long tongue covered with sticky saliva to capture prey. (*b*) An armadillo (*Dasypus novemcinctus*).

FIGURE 31.6

Order Carnivora. An Arctic fox (*Alopex lagopus*) with its spring and summer pelage. With its autumn molt, the Arctic fox acquires a white or cream color coat.

shafted hairs called vibrissae. Vibrissae occur around the legs, nose, mouth, and eyes of many mammals. Their roots are richly innervated and very sensitive to displacement.

Air spaces in the hair shaft and air trapped between hair and the skin provide an effective insulating layer. A band of smooth muscle, called the arrector pili muscle, runs between the hair follicle and the lower epidermis. When the muscle contracts, the hairs stand upright, increasing the amount of air trapped in the pelage and improving its insulating properties. Arrector pili muscles are under the control of the autonomic nervous system, which also controls a mammal's "fight-or-flight" response. **3** In threatening situations, the hair (especially on the neck and tail) stands on end and may give the perception of increased size and strength.

Hair color depends on the amount of pigment (melanin) deposited in it and the quantity of air in the hair shaft. The pelage of most mammals is dark above and lighter underneath. This pattern makes them less conspicuous under most conditions. Some mammals advertise their defenses using aposematic (warning) coloration. The contrasting markings of a skunk are a familiar example.

Pelage is reduced in large mammals from hot climates (e.g., elephants and hippopotamuses) and in some aquatic mammals (e.g., whales) that often have fatty insulation.

Claws are present in all amniote classes. They are used for locomotion and offensive and defensive behavior. Claws are formed from accumulations of keratin that cover the terminal phalanx (bone) of the digits. In some mammals, they are specialized to form nails or hooves (figure 31.7).

Glands develop from the epidermis of the skin. **Sebaceous (oil) glands** are associated with hair follicles, and their oily secretion lubricates and waterproofs the skin and hair. Most mammals also possess **sudoriferous (sweat) glands.** Small sudoriferous glands (eccrine glands) release watery secretions used in evaporative cooling. Larger sudoriferous glands (apocrine glands) secrete a mixture of salt, urea, and water, which are converted to odorous products by microorganisms on the skin.

Scent or **musk glands** are located around the face, feet, or anus of many mammals. These glands secrete pheromones, which may be involved with defense, species and sex recognition, and territorial behavior.

Mammary glands are functional in female mammals and are present, but nonfunctional, in males. The milk that they secrete contains water, carbohydrates (especially the sugar lactose), fat, protein, minerals, and antibodies. Mammary glands are probably derived evolutionarily from apocrine glands and usually contain substantial fatty deposits.

Monotremes have mammary glands that lack nipples. The glands discharge milk into depressions on the belly, where it is lapped up by the young. In other mammals, mammary glands open via nipples or teats, and the young suckle for their nourishment (figure 31.8).

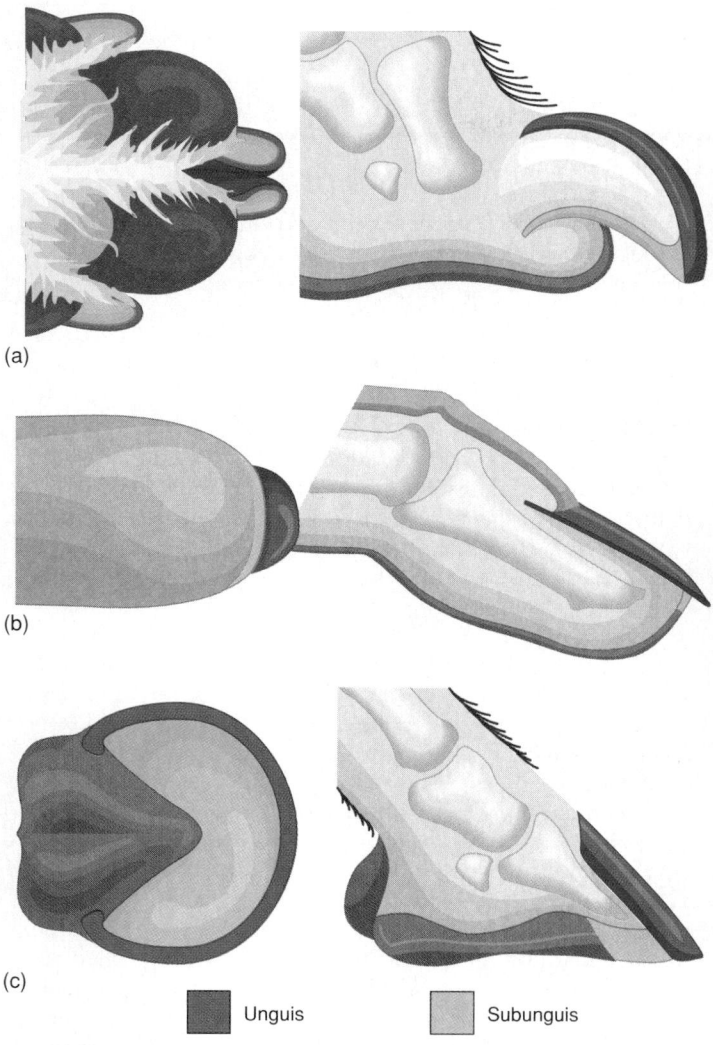

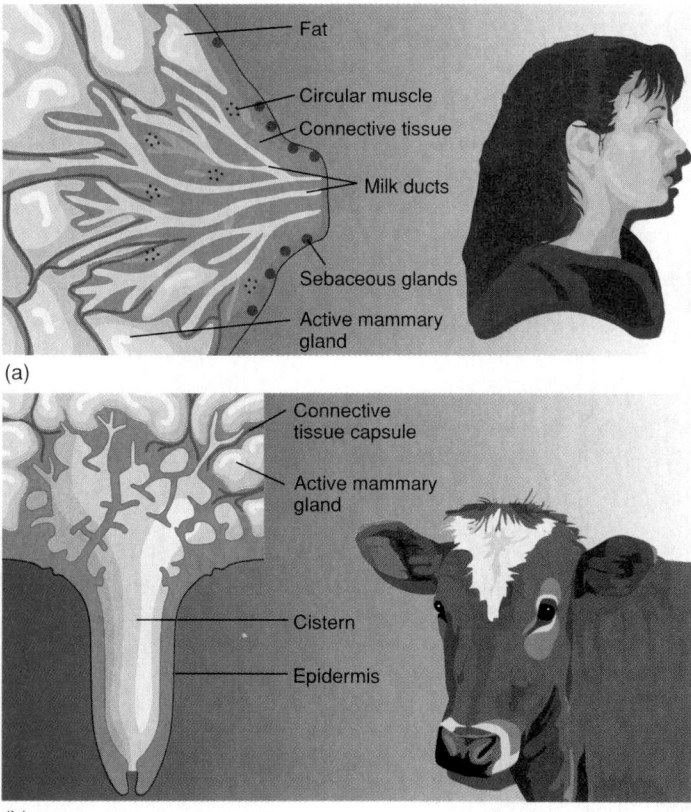

Figure 31.8

Mammary Glands. Mammary glands are specialized to secrete milk following the birth of young. (*a*) Many ducts lead from the glands to a nipple. Parts of the duct system are enlarged to store milk. Suckling by an infant initiates a hormonal response that causes the mammary glands to release milk. (*b*) Some mammals (e.g., cattle) have teats that are formed by the extension of a collar of skin around the opening of mammary ducts. Milk collects in a large cistern prior to its release. The number of nipples or teats varies with the number of young produced.

Figure 31.7

The Structure of Claws, Nails, and Hooves. (*a*) Claws. (*b*) Nails are flat, broad claws found on the hands and feet of primates and are an adaptation for arboreal habits, where grasping is essential. (*c*) Hooves are characteristic of ungulate mammals. The number of toes is reduced, and the animals walk or run on the tips of the remaining digits. The unguis is a hard, keratinized dorsal plate, and the subunguis is a softer ventral plate.

The Skull and Teeth

The skulls of mammals show important modifications of the reptilian pattern (box 31.1). One feature used by zoologists to distinguish reptilian from mammalian skulls is the method of jaw articulation. In reptiles, the jaw articulates at two small bones at the rear of the jaw. In mammals, these bones have moved into the middle ear, and along with the stapes, form the middle-ear ossicles. Jaw articulation in mammals is by a single bone of the lower jaw.

A secondary palate evolved twice in vertebrates—in the archosaur lineage (*see figure 29.2*) and in the synapsid lineage.

In some therapsids, small, shelflike extensions of bone (the hard palate) partially separated the nasal and oral passageways (*see figure 29.10*). In mammals, the secondary palate is extended posteriorly by a fold of skin, called the soft palate, which almost completely separates the nasal passages from the mouth cavity. Unlike other vertebrates that swallow food whole or in small pieces, some mammals chew their food. The more extensive secondary palate allows mammals to breathe while chewing. Breathing needs to stop only briefly during swallowing (figure 31.9).

The structure and arrangement of teeth are important indicators of mammalian life-styles. In reptiles, the teeth are uniformly conical. This condition is referred to as **homodont.** In mammals, the teeth are often specialized for different functions, a condition called **heterodont.** Reptilian teeth are attached along the top or inside of the jaw, whereas in mammals, the teeth are set into sockets of the jaw. Most mammals have two sets of teeth during their life. The first teeth emerge before or shortly after birth and are called deciduous or milk teeth. These teeth are lost and replaced by permanent teeth.

BOX 31.1   HORNS AND ANTLERS

Horns were surely a familiar sight in prehistoric landscapes, 100 million years before they became common in mammals. *Triceratops* had three horns, one nasal horn and two above the eyes. It also had a horny shield along the posterior margin of the head. *Styracosaurus* had a 0.7 m nasal spike. These early reptilian horns probably provided a very effective defense against fierce prehistoric carnivores.

Mammalian horns are a carryover from their reptilian heritage. They are most common in a group of hoofed mammals, the artiodactyls (e.g., cattle, sheep, and goats). A horn is a spike of bone that arises from the frontal bone of the skull and is covered with the protein keratin (figure 1a,b). This bony spike, the "os cornu," grows slowly from youth to adulthood, and its marrow core is highly vascularized. Filaments of keratin arise from folliclelike structures in the skin. Keratin filaments are cemented together and completely cover the os cornu. There is no blood supply to the outer horn layers.

Horns are defensive structures. They exist in symmetrical pairs and are present in both sexes. As any farmer or rancher knows, horns are not regenerated if they are cut off. Horns are usually not shed. One exception is the prong-horn antelope (*Antilocapra americana*). Every year, a new horn grows on the os cornu beneath the old horn, and the latter is eventually pushed off.

Another kind of head ornamentation, the antler, is common in deer, elk, moose, and caribou. Antlers are highly branched structures made of bone, but are not covered by keratin. Unlike horns, they are usually present only in males and are shed and reformed every year (figure 1c). Caribou are an exception because antlers are present in both sexes. Antlers are more recent than horns; the earliest records of antlered animals are from the Miocene epoch (mid-Tertiary period), and by the Pleistocene epoch, they had become common.

Antler development is regulated by seasonal changes in the level of the male hormone testosterone. Antlers of male elk begin to form in April as skin-covered buds from the frontal bone. The primordial cells that initiate antler growth are left behind from the previous year when the antlers were lost. Antlers begin to branch after only 2 weeks. By May, they are well formed, and by August, they are mature. Each year, antlers become more complexly branched. Throughout the spring and summer, they are covered with delicate, vascular tissue called velvet. In August, the bone at the base of the antler becomes progressively more dense and cuts off blood flow to the center of the antler. Later, blood flow to the velvet is cut off, and the velvet begins to dry. It is shed in strips as the antlers are rubbed against the ground or tree branches. Breeding activities commence after the velvet is shed, and the antlers are used in jousting matches as rival males compete for groups of females. (Rarely do these jousting matches lead to severe injury.) Selection by females of males with large antlers may explain why they can get so large in some species. (Although now extinct, the Giant Stag, *Cervis megaceros*, had antlers with a 3 m spread and a mass of 70 kg.) Later in the fall, or in early winter, the base of the antler is weakened as bone is reabsorbed at the pedicels of the frontal bone. Antlers are painlessly cast off when an antler strikes a tree branch or other object.

Other hornlike structures are present in some mammals. Rhinos are the only perissodactyls (e.g., horses, rhinos, and tapirs) to have hornlike structures (*see figure 31.11*). Their "horns" consist of filamentous secretions of keratin cemented together and mounted to the skin of the head. There is no bony core, and thus they are not true horns. Rhino "horns" are prized in the Orient for their presumed aphrodisiac and medicinal properties and as dagger handles in certain mideastern cultures. These demands have led to very serious overhunting of rhinos; in many regions they are almost extinct (*see figure 31.11*).

The horns of giraffes are skin-covered bony knobs. Zoologists do not understand their function.

There are up to four kinds of teeth in adult mammals. Incisors are the most anterior teeth in the jaw. They are usually chisellike and used for gnawing or nipping. Canines are often long, stout, and conical, and are usually used for catching, killing, and tearing prey. Canines and incisors have single roots. Premolars are positioned next to canines, have one or two roots, and truncated surfaces for chewing. Molars have broad chewing surfaces and two (upper molars) or three (lower molars) roots.

Mammalian species have characteristic numbers of each kind of adult tooth. A **dental formula** is an important tool used by zoologists to characterize taxa. It is an expression of the number of teeth of each kind in one-half of the upper and lower jaws. The teeth of the upper jaw are listed above those of the lower jaw and they are indicated in following order: incisors, canine, premolars, and molars. For example:

Human	Beaver
2•1•2•3	1•0•1•3
2•1•2•3	1•0•1•3

Mammalian teeth (dentition) may be specialized for particular diets. In some mammals, the dentition is reduced, sometimes to the point of having no teeth. For example, armadillos and the giant anteater (order Edentata) feed on termites and ants, and their teeth are reduced.

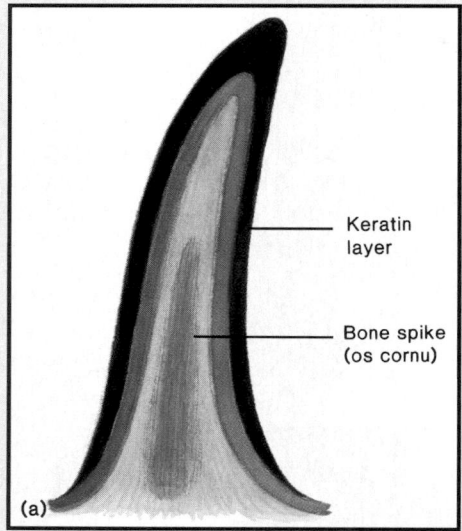

FIGURE 1 **Horns and Antlers.** (*a*) The structure of a horn. (*b*) The horn of a male bighorn sheep (*Orvis canadensis*) (order Artiodactyla). (*c*) Development of deer antlers.

④ Some mammals (e.g., humans, order Primates; and pigs, order Artiodactyla) are omnivorous; they feed on a variety of plant and animal materials. They have anterior teeth with sharp ripping and piercing surfaces, and posterior teeth with flattened grinding surfaces for rupturing plant cell walls (figure 31.10*a*).

Mammals that eat plant material often have flat, grinding posterior teeth and incisors, and sometimes canines, that are modified for nipping plant matter (e.g., horses, order Perissodactyla; deer, order Artiodactyla) or gnawing (e.g., rabbits, order Lagamorpha; beavers, order Rodentia) (figure 31.10*b,c*). In rodents, the incisors grow throughout life. Although most mammals have enamel covering the entire tooth, rodents have enamel only on the front surfaces of their incisors. They are kept sharp by slower wear in front than in back. The anterior food-procuring teeth are separated from the posterior grinding teeth by a gap, called the diastema. The diastema results from elongation of the snout that allows the anterior teeth to reach close to the ground or into narrow openings to procure food. The posterior teeth have a high, exposed surface (crown) and continuous growth, which allows these teeth to withstand years of grinding tough vegetation.

Canines and incisors of predatory mammals are used for catching, killing, and tearing prey. In members of the order Carnivora (e.g., coyotes, dogs, and cats), the fourth upper premolars and first lower molars form a scissorlike shearing surface, called the carnassial apparatus, that is used for cutting flesh from prey (figure 31.10*d*).

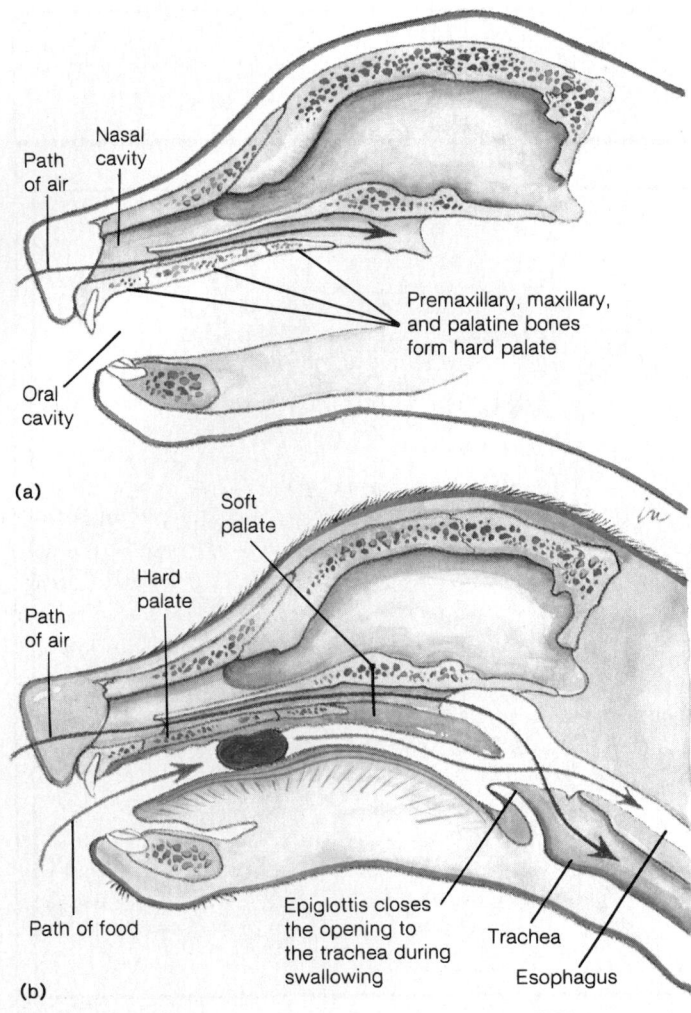

Figure 31.9

The Secondary Palate. (*a*) The secondary palate of a mammal provides a nearly complete separation between nasal and oral cavities. (*b*) Breathing stops only momentarily during swallowing.

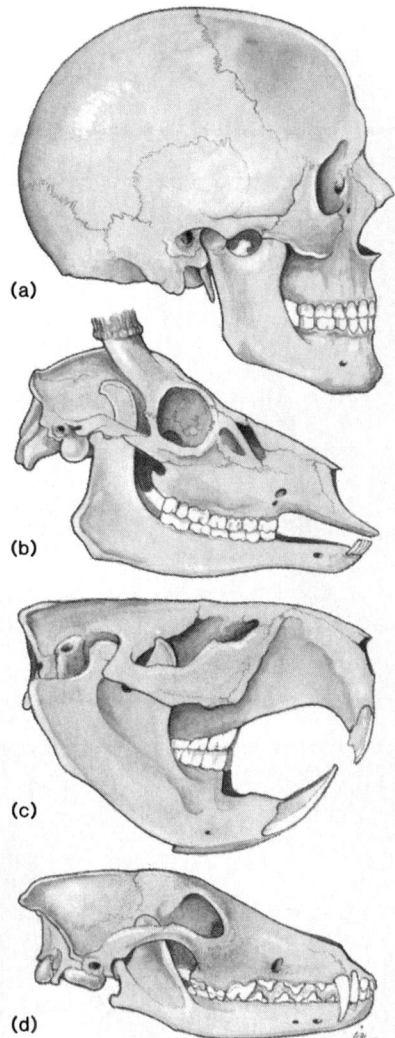

Figure 31.10

Specializations of Teeth. (*a*) An omnivore (*Homo sapiens*). (*b*) An herbivore, the male fallow deer (*Dama dama*). (*c*) A rodent, the beaver (*Castor canadensis*). (*d*) A carnivore, the coyote (*Canis latrans*).

The Vertebral Column and Appendicular Skeleton

The vertebral column of mammals is divided into five regions. As with reptiles and birds, the first two cervical vertebrae are the atlas and axis. These are usually followed by five other cervical vertebrae. Even the giraffe and the whale have seven neck vertebrae, which are greatly elongate or compressed, respectively.

The trunk is divided into thoracic and lumbar regions, as is the case for birds. In mammals, the division is correlated with their method of breathing. The thoracic region contains the ribs, which connect to the sternum via costal cartilage and protect the heart and lungs. The articulation between the thoracic vertebrae provides the flexibility needed in turning, climbing, and lying on the side to suckle young. Lumbar vertebrae have interlocking processes that give support, but little freedom of movement.

The appendicular skeleton of mammals is rotated under the body so that the appendages are usually directly beneath the body. Joints usually limit the movement of appendages to a single anteroposterior plane, causing the tips of the appendages to move in long arcs. The bones of the pelvic girdle are highly fused in the adult, a condition that is advantageous for locomotion, but presents problems during the birth of offspring. In a pregnant female, the ventral joint between the halves of the pelvis—the pubic symphysis—loosens before birth, allowing the pelvis to spread apart during birth.

Muscles

Because the appendages are directly beneath the body of most mammals, the weight of the body is borne by the skeleton. Muscle mass is concentrated in the upper appendages

Figure 31.11

Order Perissodactyla. The black rhino (*Diceros bicornis*) is an endangered herbivore that roams the plains of Africa. There are fewer than 4,000 living in Africa today.

and girdles. Many running mammals (e.g., deer, order Artiodactyla) have little muscle in their lower leg that would slow leg movement. Instead, tendons run from muscles high in the leg to cause movement at the lower joints.

Nutrition and the Digestive System

The digestive tract of mammals is similar to that of other vertebrates. There are, however, many specializations for different feeding habits. Some specializations of teeth have already been described.

It is difficult to make accurate generalizations regarding the feeding habits of mammals. Feeding habits are reflections of the ecological specializations that have evolved. For example, most members of the order Carnivora feed on animal flesh and are, therefore, carnivores. Other members of the order, such as bears, feed on a variety of plant and animal products and are omnivores. Some carnivorous mammals are specialized for feeding on arthropods or soft-bodied invertebrates and are often referred to (rather loosely) as insectivores. These include animals in the orders Insectivora (e.g., shrews), Chiroptera (bats), and Edentata (anteaters) (*see figure 31.5*a). Herbivores such as deer (order Artiodactyla) and rhinos (order Perissodactyla) (figure 31.11) feed mostly on vegetation, but their diet also includes invertebrates inadvertently ingested while feeding.

Specializations in the digestive tract of most herbivores reflect the difficulty of digesting food rich in cellulose. Horses, rabbits, and many rodents have an enlarged **cecum** at the junction of large and small intestines. A cecum serves as a fermentation pouch where microorganisms aid in the digestion of cellulose. Sheep, cattle, and deer are called ruminants (L. *ruminare*, to chew the cud). Their stomachs are modified into four chambers. The first three chambers are storage and fermentation chambers and contain microorganisms that synthesize a cellulose-digesting enzyme (cellulase). Gases produced by fermentation are periodically belched, and some plant matter (cud) is regurgitated and rechewed. Other microorganisms convert nitrogenous compounds in the food into new proteins.

Circulation, Gas Exchange, and Temperature Regulation

The hearts of birds and mammals are superficially similar. Both are four-chambered pumps that keep blood in the systemic and pulmonary circuits separate and both evolved from the hearts of ancient reptiles. Their similarities, however, are a result of adaptations to active life-styles. ⑤ The evolution of similar structures in different lineages is called convergent evolution. The evolution of the mammalian heart occurred in the synapsid reptilian lineage, whereas the avian heart evolved in the archosaur lineage (figure 31.12).

One of the most important adaptations in the circulatory system of eutherian mammals concerns the distribution of respiratory gases and nutrients in the fetus (figure 31.13a). Exchanges between maternal and fetal blood occur across the placenta. Although there is intimate association between maternal and fetal blood vessels, no actual mixing of blood occurs. Nutrients, gases, and wastes simply diffuse between fetal and maternal blood supplies.

Blood entering the right atrium of the fetus is returning from the placenta and is highly oxygenated. Because fetal lungs are not inflated, resistance to blood flow through the pulmonary arteries is high. Therefore, most of the blood entering the right atrium bypasses the right ventricle and passes instead into the left atrium through a valved opening between the atria (the foramen ovale). Some blood from the right atrium, however, does enter the right ventricle and the pulmonary artery. Because of the resistance at the uninflated lungs, most of this blood is shunted to the aorta through a vessel connecting the aorta and pulmonary artery (the ductus arteriosus). At birth, the placenta is lost, and the lungs are inflated. Resistance to blood flow through the lungs is reduced, and blood flow to them increases. Flow through the ductus arteriosus decreases, and the vessel is gradually reduced to a ligament. Blood flow back to the left atrium from the lungs correspondingly increases, and the valve of foramen ovale closes and gradually fuses with the tissue separating the right and left atria.

Gas Exchange

High metabolic rates are accompanied by adaptations for efficient gas exchange. The separate nasal and oral cavities and lengthening of the snout of most mammals provide an increased surface area for warming and moistening inspired air.

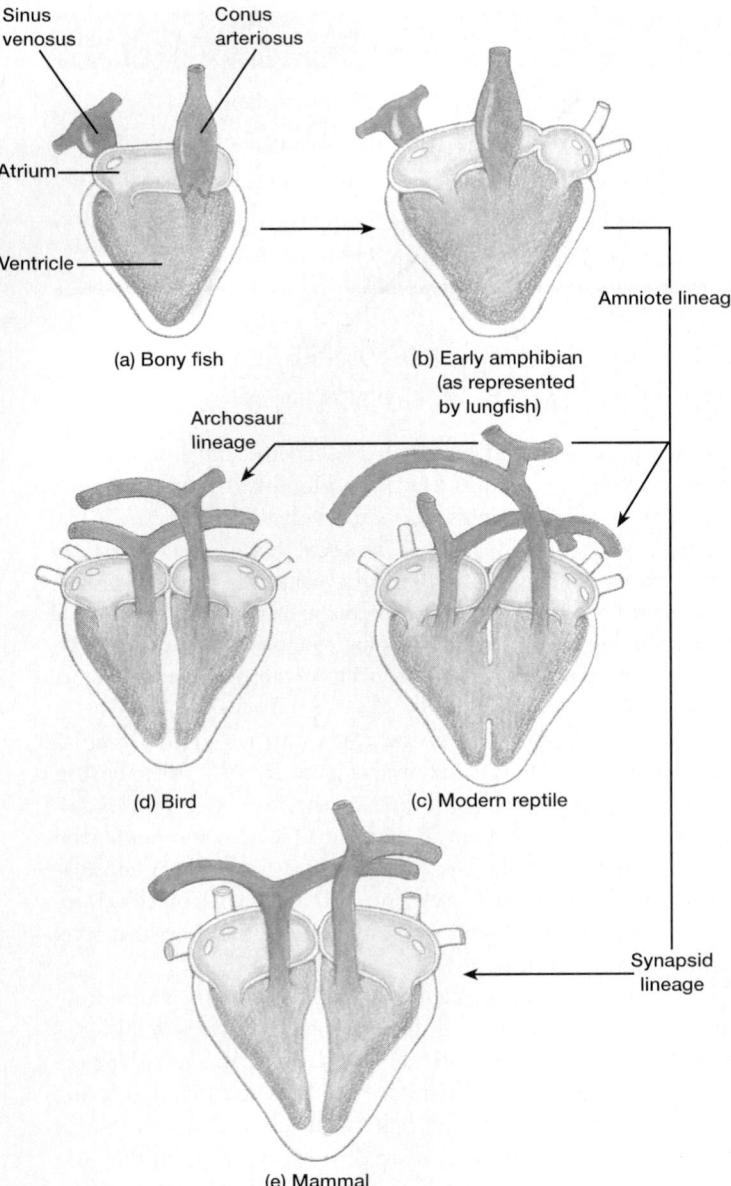

Sinus venosus
Conus arteriosus
Atrium
Ventricle

(a) Bony fish

(b) Early amphibian
(as represented by lungfish)

Amniote lineage

Archosaur lineage

(d) Bird

(c) Modern reptile

Synapsid lineage

(e) Mammal

FIGURE 31.12

A Possible Sequence in the Evolution of the Vertebrate Heart.
(*a*) Diagrammatic representation of a bony fish heart. (*b*) In lungfish, partially divided atria and ventricles separate pulmonary and systemic circuits. This heart was probably similar to that in primitive amphibians and early amniotes. (*c*) The hearts of modern reptiles were derived from the pattern shown in (*b*). (*d*) The archosaur and (*e*) synapsid lineages resulted in completely separated, four-chambered hearts.

Respiratory passageways are highly branched, and large surface areas exist for gas exchange. Mammalian lungs resemble a highly vascular sponge, rather than the saclike structures of amphibians and a few reptiles.

The lungs, like those of reptiles, are inflated using a negative-pressure mechanism. Unlike reptiles and birds, however, mammals possess a muscular **diaphragm** that separates thoracic and abdominal cavities. Inspiration results from contraction of the diaphragm and expansion of the rib cage, both of which decrease the intrathoracic pressure and allow air to enter the lungs. Expiration is by elastic recoil of the lungs. Forceful exhalation can be accomplished by contraction of thoracic and abdominal muscles.

Temperature Regulation

Mammals are widely distributed over the earth, and some face harsh environmental temperatures. Nearly all face temperatures that require them to dissipate excess heat at some times and conserve and generate heat at other times.

Heat-producing mechanisms of mammals are divided into two categories. Shivering thermogenesis is muscular activity that results in the generation of large amounts of heat, but little movement. Nonshivering thermogenesis involves heat production by general cellular metabolism, and the metabolism of special fat deposits called brown fat. These heat-generating processes are discussed in more detail in chapter 38.

Heat production is effective in thermoregulation because mammals are insulated by their pelage and/or fat deposits. Fat deposits are also sources of energy to sustain high metabolic rates.

Mammals without a pelage can conserve heat by allowing the temperature of surface tissues to drop. A walrus in cold, arctic waters has a surface temperature near 0° C; however, a few centimeters below the skin surface, body temperatures are about 35° C. Upon emerging from the icy water, the skin warms quickly by increasing peripheral blood flow. Most tissues cannot tolerate such rapid and extreme temperature fluctuations. Further investigations are likely to reveal some very unique biochemical characteristics of these skin tissues.

Even though most of the body of arctic mammals is unusually well insulated, appendages often have thin coverings of fur as an adaptation to changing thermoregulatory needs. Even in winter, an active mammal sometimes produces more heat than is required to maintain body temperature. Patches of poorly insulated skin allow excess heat to be dissipated. During periods of inactivity or extreme cold, however, heat loss from these exposed areas must be reduced, often by assuming heat-conserving postures. Mammals sleeping in cold environments conserve heat by tucking poorly insulated appendages and their faces under well-insulated body parts.

Countercurrent heat-exchange systems may help regulate heat loss from exposed areas (figure 31.14). Arteries passing peripherally through the core of an appendage are surrounded by veins that carry blood back toward the body. When blood returns to the body through these veins, heat is transferred from arterial blood to venous blood and returned to the body rather than lost to the environment. When excess heat is produced, blood is shunted away from the countercurrent veins toward peripheral vessels, and excess heat is radiated to the environment.

Mammals have few problems getting rid of excess heat in cool, moist environments. Heat can be radiated into the air from vessels near the surface of the skin or lost by evaporative cooling from either sweat glands or respiratory surfaces during panting.

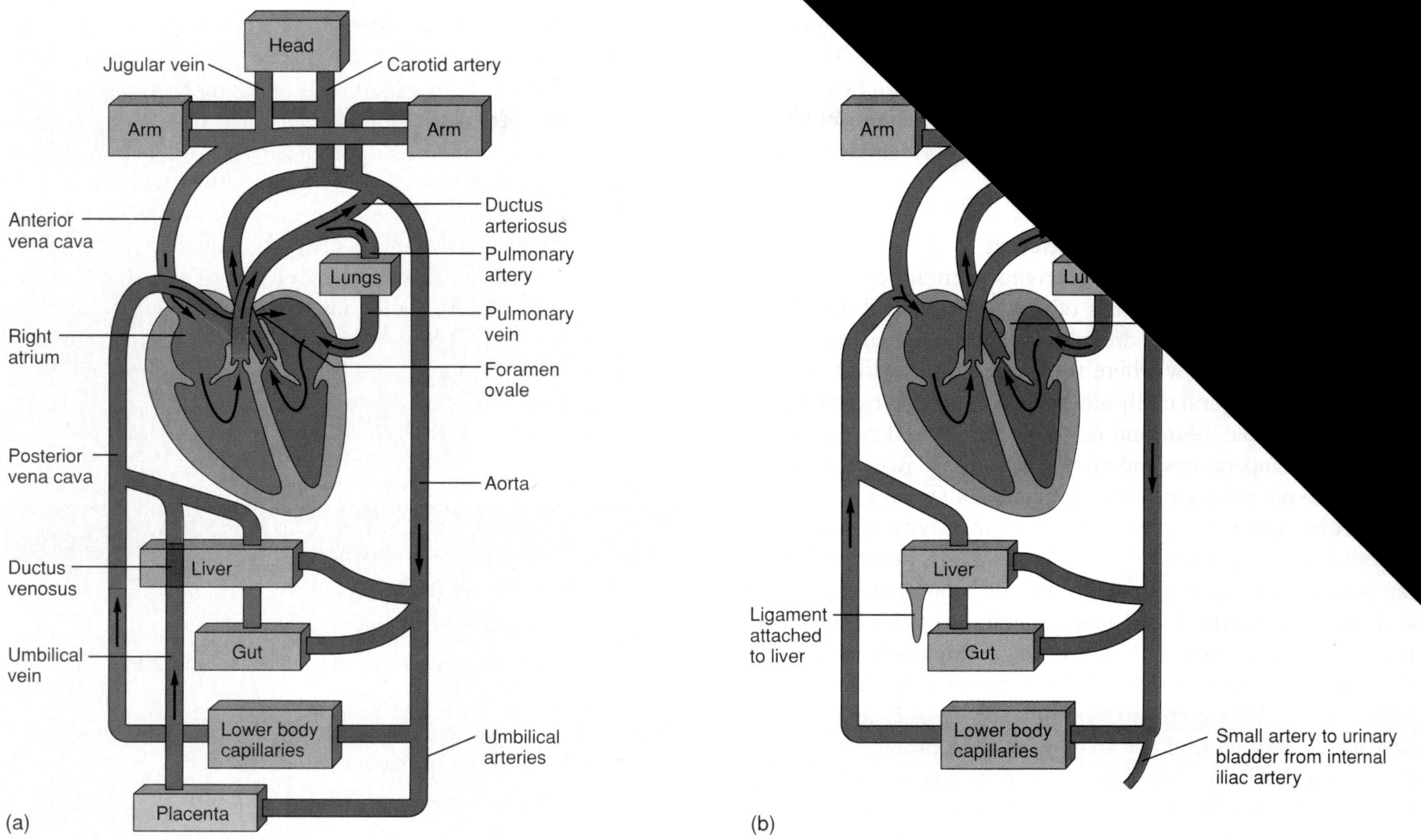

Head

Jugular vein — Carotid artery

Arm Arm

Anterior vena cava

Ductus arteriosus

Pulmonary artery

Lungs

Pulmonary vein

Right atrium

Foramen ovale

Posterior vena cava

Aorta

Ductus venosus — Liver

Umbilical vein

Gut

Lower body capillaries

Umbilical arteries

Placenta

(a)

Arm

Lu[ng]

Liver

Ligament attached to liver

Gut

Lower body capillaries

Small artery to urinary bladder from internal iliac artery

(b)

Figure 31.13

Mammalian Circulatory Systems. The circulatory patterns of (*a*) fetal and (*b*) adult mammals. Highly oxygenated blood is shown in red, and poorly oxygenated blood shown in blue.

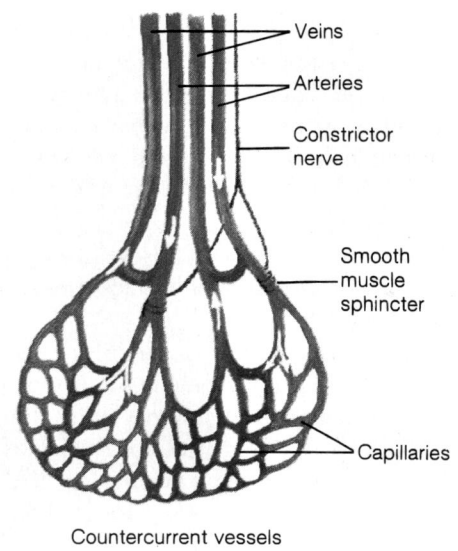

Veins

Arteries

Constrictor nerve

Smooth muscle sphincter

Capillaries

Countercurrent vessels

Figure 31.14

Countercurrent Heat Exchange. Countercurrent heat exchangers conserve body heat in animals adapted to cold environments. Systems similar to the one depicted here are found in the legs of reindeer (*Rangifer tarandus*) and in the flippers of dolphins. Venous blood returning from an extremity is warmed by heat transferred from blood moving peripherally in arteries. During winter, the lower part of a reindeer's leg may be at 10° C, while body temperature is about 40° C. Arrows indicate direction of blood flow.

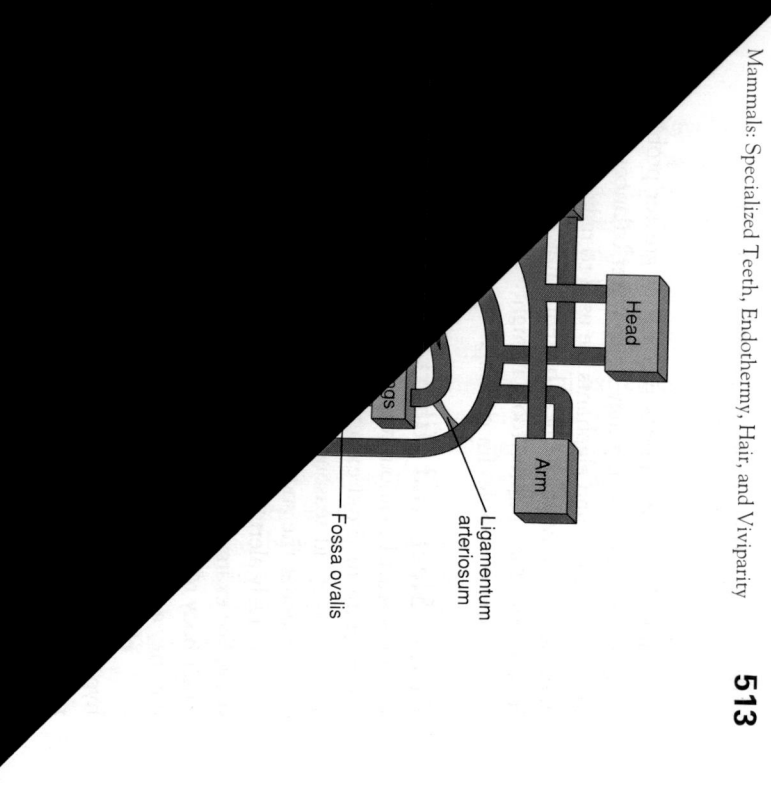

Head

Arm

Ligamentum
arteriosum

Fossa ovalis

ind to the middle ear. The sensory patch of the inner ear
at contains receptors for sound is long and coiled and is
led the cochlea. This structure provides more surface area for
ceptor cells and allows mammals greater sensitivity to pitch
d volume than is present in reptiles (box 31.2). Cranial casts
early mammals show well-developed auditory regions.

Vision is an important sense in many mammals, and the
ucture of the eye is similar to that described for other verte-
ates. Accommodation occurs by changing the shape of the
ns (*see figure 34.18*). Color vision is less well developed in
ammals than in reptiles and birds. The fact that the retinas of
ost mammals are dominated by rods supports the hypothesis
at early mammals were nocturnal. Primates, squirrels, and a
w other mammals have well-developed color vision.

Stop and Ask Yourself

9. In what way are the hearts of birds and mammals an
example of convergent evolution?

10. What are two ways that mammals can generate
metabolic heat?

11. How is excessive heat loss from the poorly insulated
legs of a reindeer prevented?

12. What is the difference between hibernation of a ground
squirrel and the winter sleep of a bear?

Excretion and Osmoregulation

Mammals, like all amniotes, have a metanephric kidney. Unlike reptiles and birds, which excrete mainly uric acid, mammals excrete urea. Urea is less toxic than ammonia and does
not require large quantities of water in its excretion. Unlike
uric acid, however, urea is highly water soluble and cannot be
excreted in a semisolid form; thus, some water is lost. Excretion
in mammals is always a major route for water loss.

In the nephron of the kidney, fluids and small solutes are
filtered from the blood through the walls of a group of capillary-
like vessels, called the glomerulus. The remainder of the
nephron consists of tubules that reabsorb water and essential
solutes and secrete particular ions into the filtrate.

The primary adaptation of the mammalian nephron is a
portion of the tubule system called the loop of the nephron (*see
figure 38.20*). The transport processes in this loop and the remainder of the tubule system allow mammals to produce urine
that is 2 to 22 times more concentrated than blood (e.g., beavers
and Australian hopping mice, respectively). ⑥ This accomplishes the same function that nasal and orbital salt glands
do in reptiles and birds.

Water loss varies greatly depending on activity, physiological state, and environmental temperature. Water is lost in
urine, feces, evaporation from sweat glands and respiratory surfaces, and during nursing. Mammals in very dry environments
have numerous behavioral and physiological mechanisms to

mammals usually accumulate large quantities of body fat. After
retreating to a burrow or a nest, the hypothalamus sets the body's
thermostat to about 2° C. The respiratory rate of a hibernating
ground squirrel falls from 100 to 200 breaths per minute to
about 4 breaths per minute. The heart rate falls from 200 to 300
beats per minute to about 20 beats per minute. During hibernation, a mammal may lose ⅓ to ½ of its body weight. Arousal
from hibernation occurs by metabolic heating, frequently using
brown fat deposits, and it takes several hours to raise body temperature to near 37° C.

Nervous and Sensory Functions

The basic structure of the vertebrate nervous system is retained
in mammals. The development of complex nervous and sensory
functions goes hand-in-hand with active life-styles and is most
evident in the enlargement of the cerebral hemispheres and the
cerebellum of mammals. The enlargement of the cerebral cortex (neocortex) is accompanied by most integrative functions
being shifted to this region.

In mammals, the sense of touch is well developed. Receptors are associated with the bases of hair follicles and are stimulated when a hair is displaced.

Olfaction was apparently an important sense in early
mammals, because fossil skull fragments show elongate snouts,
which would have contained olfactory epithelium. Cranial
casts of fossil skulls show enlarged olfactory regions. Olfaction
is still an important sense for many mammals. Olfactory stimuli
can be perceived over long distances during either the day or
night and are used to locate food, recognize members of the
same species, and avoid predators.

Auditory senses were similarly important to early mammals. More recent adaptations include an ear flap (the pinna)
and the auditory tube leading to the tympanum that directs

BOX 31.2   MAMMALIAN ECHOLOCATION

Imagine a pool's water made so murky that a human is only able to see a few centimeters below the surface. Also imagine a clear Plexiglas sheet with a dolphin-sized opening in the middle, dividing the pool in half. At one end of the pool is an eager dolphin; at the other end is a trainer. The trainer throws a dead fish into the water, and on signal, the dolphin unhesitatingly finds its way through the murky water to the opening in the Plexiglas and then finds the fish at the other end of the pool.

Although the dolphin in the above account was trained to find the fish, it relied on a sense that it shares with a few other mammals. Toothed whales, bats, and some shrews use the return echoes of high-frequency sound pulses to locate objects in their environment. This mechanism is called **echolocation.**

Echolocation has been studied in bats more completely than in any other group of mammals. The Italian scientist Lassaro Spallanzani discovered in the late 1700s that blinded bats could navigate successfully at night, whereas bats with plugged ears could not. Spallanzani believed that echoes of the sounds made by beating wings were used in echolocation. In 1938, however, ultrasonic bat cries (inaudible to humans) were electronically recorded, and their function in echolocation was described.

Insect-eating bats navigate through their caves and the night sky and locate food by echolocation. During normal cruising flight, ultrasonic (100 to 20 kHz) "clicks" are emitted approximately every 50 milliseconds. As insect prey is detected, the number of clicks per second increases, the duration between clicks decreases, and the wavelength of the sound decreases, increasing directional precision and making small flying insects more easily detected. On final approach, the sound becomes buzzlike, and the bat scoops up the insect with its wings or in the webbing of its hind legs (figure 1).

Modifications of the bat ear and brain allow bats to perceive faint echoes of their vocalizations and to precisely determine direction and distance. Enlarged ear flaps funnel sounds toward particularly thin eardrums and very sensitive ear ossicles. The auditory regions of the bat brain are very large, and special neural pathways enhance a bat's ability to determine the direction of echoes.

Bats must distinguish echoes of their own cries from the cries themselves and from other noises. Leaflike folds of the nostrils direct sound emitted from the nostrils forward, rather than in

FIGURE 1   Bat Echolocation. A greater horseshoe bat (*Rhinophus*) capturing a moth.

all directions from the head, much like the megaphone of a cheerleader. The ears, therefore, receive little stimulation from direct vocalizations. Fat and blood sinuses surrounding the middle and inner ears reduce transmission of sound from the mouth and pharynx. Some bats temporarily turn off their hearing during sound emission by making the ear ossicles insensitive to sound waves and then turn on their hearing an instant later when the reflected sound is returning to the bat.

reduce water loss. The kangaroo rat, named for its habit of hopping on large hind legs, is capable of extreme water conservation (figure 31.15). It is native to the southwestern deserts of the United States and survives without drinking water. Its feces are almost dry, and evaporative water loss is reduced by its nocturnal habits. Respiratory water loss is minimized by condensation as warm air in the respiratory passages encounters the cooler nasal passages. Excretory water loss is minimized by a diet low in protein, which reduces the production of urea. The nearly dry seeds that the kangaroo rat eats are rich sources of carbohydrates and fats. Metabolic oxidation of carbohydrates produces water as a by-product.

BEHAVIOR

Mammals have complex behaviors that enhance survival. Visual cues are often used in communication. The bristled fur, arched back, and open mouth of a cat communicates a clear message to curious dogs or other potential threats. A tail-wagging display of a dog has a similarly clear message. A wolf defeated in a fight with other wolves lies on its back and exposes its vulnerable throat. Similar displays may allow a male already recognized as being subordinate to another male to avoid conflict within a social group.

Pheromones are used to recognize members of the same species, members of the opposite sex, and the reproductive state

(a)

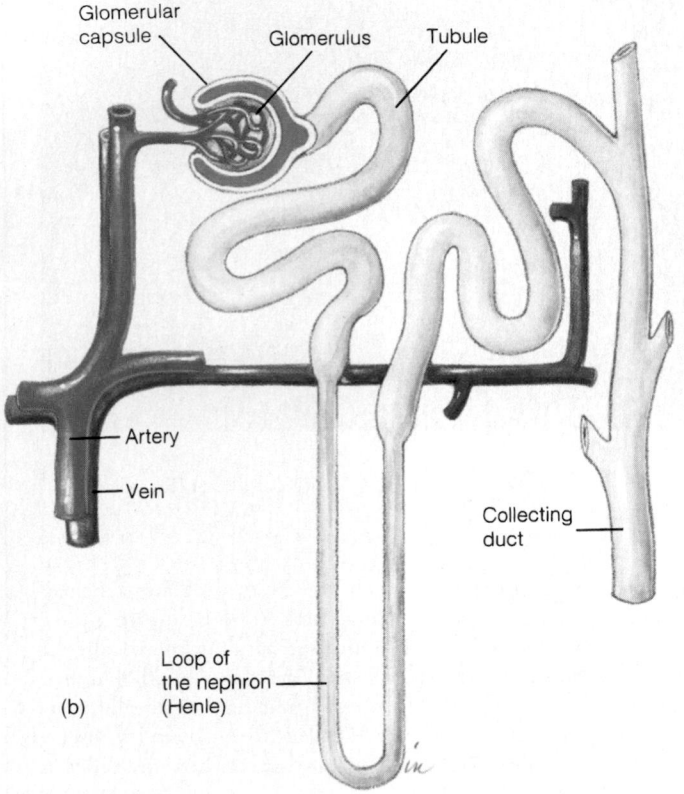

(b)

Figure 31.15

Order Rodentia. (*a*) The kangaroo rat (*Dipodomys ordii*). (*b*) The long loop of the nephron of this desert animal acts to conserve water, preventing dehydration.

of a member of the opposite sex. Pheromones may also induce sexual behavior, help establish and recognize territories, and ward off predators. The young of many mammalian species recognize their parents, and parents recognize their young, by smell. Bull elk smell the rumps of females during the breeding season to recognize those in their brief receptive period. They

also urinate on their own belly and underhair to advertise their reproductive status to females and other males. Male mammals urinate on objects in the environment to establish territories and to allow females to become accustomed to their odors. Rabbits and rodents spray urine on a member of the opposite sex to inform the second individual of the first's readiness to mate. Skunks use chemicals to ward off predators.

Auditory and tactile communication are also important in the lives of mammals. Herd animals are kept together and remain calm as long as the array of familiar sounds (e.g., bellowing, hooves walking over dry grasses and twigs, and rumblings from ruminating stomachs) are uninterrupted. Unfamiliar sounds may cause alarm and flight.

Vocalizations and tactile communication are important in primate social interactions. Tactile communication ranges from precopulatory "nosing" that occurs in many mammals to grooming. Grooming does much more than help maintain a healthy skin and pelage. It reinforces important social relationships within primate groups.

Territoriality

Many mammals mark and defend certain areas from intrusion by other members of the same species. ⑦ (When cats rub their face and neck on us or on furniture in our homes, we like to think the cat is being affectionate. Cats, however, are really staking claim to their territory, using odors from facial scent glands.) Some territorial behavior attracts females to, and excludes other males from, favorable sites for mating and rearing young.

Male California sea lions (*Zalophus californianus*) establish territories on shorelines where females come to give birth to young. For about 2 weeks, males engage in vocalizations, displays, and sometimes serious fighting to stake claim to favorable territories (figure 31.16). Older, dominant bulls are usually most successful in establishing territories, and young bulls generally swim and feed just offshore. When they arrive at the beaches, females select a site for giving birth. Selection of the birth site also selects the bull that will father next year's offspring. Mating occurs approximately 2 weeks after the birth of the previous year's offspring. Development is arrested for the 3 months during which the recently born young do most of their nursing. This mechanism is called embryonic diapause. Thus, even though actual development takes about 9 months, the female carries the embryo and fetus for a period of 1 year.

Reproduction and Development

In no other group of animals has viviparity developed to the extent it has in mammals. It requires a large expenditure of energy on the part of the female during development and on the part of one or both parents caring for young after they are born. Viviparity is advantageous because females are not necessarily tied to a single nest site, but can roam or migrate to find food or a proper climate. Viviparity is accompanied by the evolution of a portion of

Figure 31.16

Order Carnivora. California sea lions (*Zalophus californianus*) on a beach during the breeding season. The adult males in the foreground are vocalizing and posturing.

the reproductive tract where the young are nourished and develop. In viviparous mammals, the oviducts are modified into one or two uteri (s., uterus).

Reproductive Cycles

Most mammals have a definite time or times during the year in which ova (eggs) mature and are capable of being fertilized. Reproduction usually occurs when climatic conditions and resource characteristics favor successful development. Mammals living in environments with few seasonal changes and those that exert considerable control of immediate environmental conditions (e.g., humans) may reproduce at any time of the year. However, they are still tied to physiological cycles of the female that determine when ova can be fertilized.

Most female mammals undergo an **estrus** (Gr. *oistros*, a vehement desire) **cycle,** which includes a time during which the female is behaviorally and physiologically receptive to the male. During the estrus cycle, hormonal changes stimulate the maturation of ova in the ovary and induce ovulation (release of one or more mature ova from an ovarian follicle). A few mammals (e.g., rabbits, ferrets, and mink) are induced ovulators; ovulation is induced by coitus.

Hormones also mediate changes in the uterus and vagina. As the ova are maturing, the inner lining of the uterus proliferates and becomes more vascular in preparation for receiving developing embryos. Proliferation of vaginal mucosa is accompanied by external swelling in the vaginal area and increased glandular discharge. During this time, males show heightened interest in females, and females are receptive to males. If fertilization does not occur, the above changes in the uterus and vagina are reversed until the next cycle begins. No bleeding or sloughing of uterine lining usually occurs.

Many mammals are monestrus and go through only a single yearly estrus cycle that is sharply seasonal. Wild dogs, bears, and sea lions are monestrus; domestic dogs are diestrus. Other

mammals are polyestrus. Rats and mice have estrus cycles that are repeated every 4 to 6 days.

The menstrual cycle of female humans, apes, and monkeys is similar to the estrus cycle in that it results in a periodic proliferation of the inner lining of the uterus and is correlated with the maturation of an ovum. If fertilization does not occur before the end of the cycle, mensus—the sloughing of the uterine lining—occurs. Human menstrual and ovarian cycles are described in chapter 39.

Fertilization usually occurs in the upper ⅓ of the oviduct within hours of copulation. In a few mammals, fertilization may be delayed. In some bats, for example, coitus occurs in autumn, but fertilization is delayed until spring. Females store sperm in the uterus for periods in excess of 2 months. This example of **delayed fertilization** is apparently an adaptation to winter dormancy. Fertilization can occur immediately after females emerge from dormancy rather than having to wait until males attain their breeding state.

In many other mammals, fertilization occurs right after coitus, but development is arrested after the first week or two. This **embryonic diapause** was described previously for sea lions, and also occurs in some bats, bears, martens, and marsupials. The adaptive significance of embryonic diapause varies with species. In the sea lion, embryonic diapause allows the mother to give birth and mate within a short interval, but not have her resources drained by both nursing and pregnancy. It also allows young to be born at a time when resources favor their survival. In some bats, it allows fertilization to occur in the fall before hibernation, but birth is delayed until resources become abundant in the spring.

Modes of Development

Monotremes are oviparous. Ova are released from the ovaries with large quantities of yolk. After fertilization, shell glands in the oviduct deposit a shell around the ovum, forming an egg. Female echidnas incubate eggs in a ventral pouch. Platypus eggs are laid in their burrows.

All other mammals nourish young by a placenta through at least a portion of their development. Nutrients are supplied from the maternal bloodstream, not yolk.

In marsupials, most nourishment for the fetus comes from "uterine milk" secreted by uterine cells. Some nutrients diffuse from maternal blood into a highly vascular yolk sac that makes contact with the uterus. This connection in marsupials is a primitive placenta. The **gestation period** (the length of time young develop within the female reproductive tract) varies between 8 and 40 days in different species. The short gestation period is a result of the inability to sustain the production of hormones that maintain the uterine lining. After birth, tiny young crawl into the marsupium, and attach to a nipple, where they suckle for an additional 60 to 270 days (figure 31.17).

In eutherian mammals, the embryo implants deeply into the uterine wall. Embryonic and uterine tissues grow rapidly and become highly folded and vascular, forming the placenta. Although maternal and fetal blood do not mix, nutrients, gases, and wastes diffuse between the two bloodstreams. Gestation periods of eutherian mammals vary widely between 20 days (some

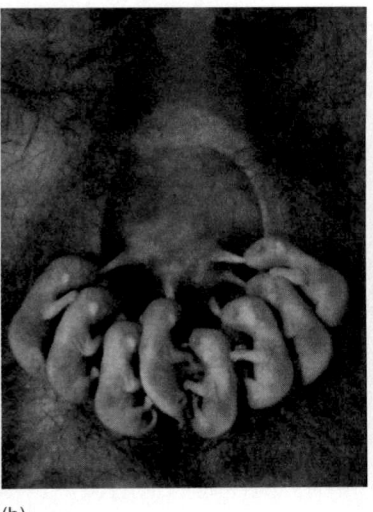

(a)   (b)

FIGURE 31.17

Order Marsupialia. (*a*) An opossum (*Didelphis marsupialis*) with young. (*b*) Opossum young nursing in a marsupial pouch.

rodents) and 19 months (the African elephant). Following birth, the placenta and other tissues that surrounded the fetus in the uterus are expelled as "afterbirth." The newborns of many species are helpless at birth (e.g., humans); others can walk and run shortly after birth (e.g., deer and horses).

Stop and Ask Yourself

13. What adaptation of the kidney allows mammals to excrete urine that is hypertonic to the blood?
14. What are the advantages of viviparity for mammals? In what way is viviparity costly?
15. What is embryonic diapause?
16. Why is the gestation period of a marsupial so short?

SUMMARY

1. Mammalian characteristics evolved in the synapsid lineage over a period of about 200 million years. Mammals evolved from a group of synapsids called therapsids.
2. Modern mammals include the monotremes, marsupial mammals, and placental mammals.
3. Hair is uniquely mammalian. It functions in sensory perception, temperature regulation, and communication.
4. Sebaceous, sudoriferous, scent, and mammary glands are present in mammals.
5. The teeth and digestive tracts of mammals are adapted for different feeding habits. Herbivores are characterized by flat, grinding teeth and fermentation structures for digesting cellulose. Predatory mammals have sharp teeth for killing and tearing prey.
6. The heart of mammals has four chambers, and circulatory patterns are adapted for viviparous development.
7. Mammals possess a diaphragm that alters intrathoracic pressure, which helps ventilate the lungs.
8. Metabolic heat production, insulating pelage, and behavior are used in mammalian thermoregulation.
9. Mammals react to unfavorable environments by migration, winter sleep, and hibernation.
10. The nervous system of mammals is similar to that of other vertebrates. Olfaction and hearing were important for early mammals. Vision, hearing, and smell are the dominant senses in many modern mammals.
11. The nitrogenous waste of mammals is urea, and the kidney is adapted for excreting a concentrated urine.
12. Mammals have complex behavior to enhance survival. Visual cues, pheromones, and auditory and tactile cues are important in mammalian communication.
13. Most mammals have specific times during the year when reproduction occurs. Estrus or menstrual cycles are present in female mammals. Monotremes are oviparous. All other mammals nourish young by a placenta.

SELECTED KEY TERMS

cecum (*p. 511*)

delayed fertilization (*p. 517*)

dental formula (*p. 508*)

diaphragm (*p. 512*)

embryonic diapause (*p. 517*)

estrus cycle (*p. 517*)

gestation period (*p. 517*)

heterodont (*p. 507*)

homodont (*p. 507*)

CRITICAL THINKING QUESTIONS

1. Why is tooth structure important in the study of mammals?
2. What does the evolution of secondary palates have in common with the evolution of completely separated, four-chambered hearts?
3. Why is the classification of mammals by feeding habits not particularly useful to phylogenetic studies?
4. Under what circumstances is endothermy disadvantageous for a mammal?
5. Discuss the possible advantages of embryonic diapause for marsupials that live in climatically unpredictable regions of Australia.

SUGGESTED READINGS

BOOKS

Aidley, D. J. (ed.). 1980. *Animal Migration.* Cambridge: Cambridge University Press.

Baker, R. 1984. *Bird Navigation: The Solution of a Mystery?* New York: Holmes & Meier Publishers, Inc.

———. (ed.). 1981. *The Mystery of Migration.* Minneapolis: The Viking Press.

Bakker, R. T. 1986. *The Dinosaur Heresies.* New York: William Morrow & Co., Inc.

Barnes, R., Calow, P., and Olive, P. 1993. *The Invertebrates: A New Synthesis.* 2nd ed. Boston: Blackwell Scientific.

Barrington, E. J. W. 1965. *The Biology of Hemichordata and Protochordata.* San Francisco: W. H. Freeman.

Binyon, J. 1972. *Physiology of Echinoderms.* New York: Pergamon Press, Inc.

Bliss, D. E. (ed.). 1982. *The Biology of Crustacea,* Vols. 1–5. San Diego: Academic Press, Inc.

Bogitsh, B., and Cheng, T. 1990. *Human Parasitology.* Philadelphia: W. B. Saunders Co.

Boitani, L., and Bartoli, S. 1983. *Simon and Schuster's Guide to Mammals.* New York: Simon and Schuster.

Borror, D. J., Tripplehorn, C. A., and Johnson, N. F. 1989. *An Introduction to the Study of Insects.* 6th ed. Philadelphia: Saunders College Publishing.

Boss, K. J. 1982. Mollusca. In S. P. Parker (ed.), *Synopsis and Classification of Living Organisms,* Vol. 1. New York: McGraw-Hill Book Co., Inc.

Brinkhurst, R. O., and Jamieson, B. B. 1972. *Aquatic Oligochaeta of the World.* Toronto: Toronto University Press.

Bristow, W. S. 1971. *The World of Spiders.* Minneapolis: William Collins Sons & Co., Ltd.

Brusca, R. C., and Brusca, G. J. 1990. *Invertebrates.* Sunderland, Mass.: Sinauer Associates, Inc.

Chapman, J. A., and Feldhamer, G. A. (eds.). 1982. *Wild Mammals of North America: Biology, Management, and Economics.* Baltimore: The Johns Hopkins University Press.

Corliss, J. D. 1979. *The Ciliated Protozoa: Characterization, Classification, and Guide to the Literature.* 2d ed. Elmford, New York: Pergamon Press, Inc.

Cousteau, J., and Diol'e, P. 1973. *Octopus and Squid, the Soft Intelligence.* Garden City, Mich.: Doubleday & Co.

Dethier, V. G. 1976. *The Hungry Fly.* Cambridge: Harvard University Press.

Duellman, W. E., and Trueb, L. 1986. *Biology of Amphibians.* New York: McGraw-Hill Book Co.

Duncan, T., and Stuessy, T. F. 1984. *Cladistics: Perspectives on the Reconstruction of Evolutionary History.* New York: Columbia University Press.

Dunn, D. F. 1982. Cnidaria. In S. P. Parker (ed.), *Synopsis and Classification of Living Organisms,* Vol. 1. New York: McGraw-Hill Book Co.

Eisenberg, J. F. 1981. *The Mammalian Radiations: An Analysis of Trends in Evolution, Adaptation, and Behavior.* Chicago: University of Chicago Press.

Eldredge, N., and Cracraft, J. 1980. *Phylogenetic Patterns and the Evolutionary Process, Method and Theory in Comparative Biology.* New York: Columbia University Press.

Faaborg, J. 1988. *Ornithology: An Ecological Approach.* Englewood Cliffs, N.J.: Prentice-Hall.

Farmer, J. N. 1980. *The Protozoa: Introduction to Protozoology.* St. Louis: C. V. Mosby Co.

Feduccia, A. 1980. *The Age of Birds.* Cambridge: Harvard University Press.

Fell, H. B. 1982. Echinodermata. In S. P. Parker (ed.), *Synopsis and Classification of Living Animals,* Vol. 2. New York: McGraw-Hill Book Co.

Fenchel, T. 1987. *Ecology of Protozoa.* New York: Springer-Verlag.

Foelix, R. F. 1982. *Biology of Spiders*. Cambridge: Harvard University Press.

Foreman, R. E., Gorbman, A., Dodd, J. M., and Olsson, R. (eds.). 1985. *Evolutionary Biology of Fishes*. NATO ASI Series, Vol. 103. New York: Plenum Press.

Frangsmyr, T. 1983. *Linnaeus: The Man and His Work*. Berkeley: University of California Press.

Gibson, R. 1972. *Nemerteans*. London: Hutchinson University Library.

————. 1982. *British Nemerteans: Keys and Notes for Identification of the Species*. New York: Cambridge University Press.

Gill, F. B. 1990. *Ornithology*. New York: W. H. Freeman.

Gillot, Cedric. 1980. *Entomology*. New York: Plenum Press.

Goin, C. J., and Goin, O. B. 1978. *Introduction to Herpetology*. 3d ed. San Francisco: W. H. Freeman.

Gould, S. J. 1989. *Wonderful Life: The Burgess Shale and the Nature of the History*. New York: W. W. Norton.

Grell, K. G. 1973. *Protozoology*. Berlin: Springer-Verlag.

Griffiths, M. 1978. *The Biology of Monotremes*. San Diego: Academic Press, Inc.

Halstead, L. B. 1968. *The Pattern of Vertebrate Evolution*. San Francisco: W. H. Freeman.

Harbison, G. R., and Madin, L. P. 1982. Ctenophora. In S. P. Parker (ed.), *Synopsis and Classification of Living Organisms*, Vol. 1. New York: McGraw-Hill Book Co.

Hardisty, M. W. 1979. *Biology of the Cyclostomes*. New York: Chapman and Hall, Ltd.

Hasler, A. D., and Scholz, A. T. 1983. *Olfactory Imprinting and Homing in Salmon*. New York: Springer-Verlag, Zoophysiology Series.

Holldobler, B., and Wilson, E. O. 1990. *The Ants*. Cambridge: Harvard University Press.

Horridge, G. A. (ed.) 1975. *The Compound Eye and Vision of Insects*. Atlanta: Clarendon Group, Inc.

Hyman, L. H. 1940. *The Invertebrates*. New York: McGraw-Hill Book Co., Inc.

————. 1951. *The Invertebrates*. Vol. II. *Platyhelminthes and Rhynchocela*. New York: McGraw-Hill.

Jacques, H. E. 1978. *How to Know the Insects*. 3d ed. Dubuque: Wm. C. Brown Publishers.

Jahn, T., Bovee, R., and Jahn, F. 1979. *How to Know the Protozoa*. Dubuque: Wm. C. Brown Publishers.

Kaston, B. J. 1972. *How to Know the Spiders*. 2d ed. Dubuque: Wm. C. Brown Publishers.

King, F. W., and Behler, J. 1979. *The Audubon Society Field Guide to North American Reptiles and Amphibians*. New York: Alfred A. Knopf, Inc.

King, P. E. 1973. *Pycnogonids*. New York: St. Martins Press, Inc.

Kozloff, E. 1990. *Invertebrates*. Philadelphia: W. B. Saunders Co.

Laybourn-Parry, J. 1984. *A Functional Biology of Free-Living Protozoa*. Berkeley: University of California Press.

Lee, J., Hunter, S., and Bovee, E. 1985. *An Illustrated Guide to the Protozoa*. Lawrence, Kan.: Allen Press, Society of Protozoologists.

Levandowsky, M., and Hunter, S. H. 1979. *Biochemistry and Physiology of Protozoa*, Vols. I–III. New York: Academic Press.

Levi, H. W. 1982. Crustacea. In S. P. Parker (ed.), *Synopsis and Classification of Living Organisms*, Vol. 2. New York: McGraw-Hill Book Co.

Lovtrup, S. 1977. *The Phylogeny of Vertebrata*. New York: John Wiley & Sons, Inc.

Margulis, L., and Schwartz, K. V. 1987. *Five Kingdoms: An Illustrated Guide to the Phyla of Life on Earth*. 2d ed. San Francisco: W. H. Freeman.

Matthews, T. W., and Matthews, J. R. 1978. *Insect Behavior*. New York: John Wiley & Sons, Inc.

McCafferty, W. P. 1981. *Aquatic Entomology: A Fisherman's and Ecologist's Illustrated Guide to Insects and Their Relatives*. Providence: Science Books International.

Meglitsch, P. A., and Schram, F. R. 1991. *Invertebrate Zoology*. 3d ed. New York: Oxford University Press.

Moyle, P. B., and Cech, J. J. 1982. *Fishes: An Introduction to Ichthyology*. Englewood Cliffs: Prentice-Hall, Inc.

Moynihan, M. H., and Rodaniche, A. F. 1977. Communication, crypsis, and mimicry among cephalopods. In T. A. Sebeok (ed.), *How Animals Communicate*. Indiana University Press.

Nelson, J. S. 1984. *Fishes of the World*. 2d ed. New York: John Wiley & Sons, Inc.

Nisbet, B. 1984. *Nutrition and Feeding Strategies in Protozoa*. London: Croom Helm Ltd.

Pearse, V., Pearse, J., Buchsbaum, M., and Buchsbaum, R. 1987. *Living Invertebrates*. New York: Blackwell Scientific Publications.

Pechenik, J. A. 1991. *Biology of the Invertebrates*. 2d ed. Dubuque: Wm. C. Brown Publishers.

Pennak, R. W. 1989. *Freshwater Invertebrates of the United States*. 3d ed. New York: John Wiley & Sons, Inc.

Peterson, R. T. 1980. *Field Guide to the Birds*. 2d ed. Boston: Houghton Mifflin Co.

Pettibone, M. H. 1982. Annelida. In S. P. Parker (ed.), *Synopsis and Classification of Living Organisms*. Vol. 2. New York: McGraw-Hill Book Co.

Poinar, G. O. 1983. *The Natural History of Nematodes*. Englewood Cliffs, N.J.: Prentice-Hall.

Pough, F. H., Heiser, J. B., and McFarland, W. N. 1989. *Vertebrate Life*. 3d ed. New York: Macmillan Publishing Co.

Rice, M. E., and Todorovic, M. (eds.). 1975. *Proceedings of the International Symposium on the Biology of the Sipuncula and Echiura*. Washington, D.C.: American Museum of Natural History.

Ridley, M. 1986. *Evolution and Classification: The Reformation of Cladism*. New York: Longman.

Riser, N. W., and Morse, M. P. (eds.). 1974. *Biology of the Turbellaria*. New York: McGraw-Hill.

Romer, A. S., and Parsons, T. S. 1986. *The Vertebrate Body*. 6th ed. Philadelphia: Saunders College Publishing.

Ruppell, G. 1975. *Bird Flight*. New York: Van Nostrand Reinhold Co.

Ruppert, E. E., and Barnes, R. D. 1994. *Invertebrate Zoology*. 6th ed. Philadelphia: Saunders College Publishing.

Russell-Hunter, W. D. 1979. *A Life of Invertebrates*. New York: Macmillan Publishing Co., Inc.

Savage, R. J. G., and Long, M. T. 1986. *Mammal Evolution*. New York: Facts On File Publications.

Savory, T. H. 1977. *Arachnida*. 2d ed. San Diego: Academic Press, Inc.

Schmidt, G. D., and Roberts, L. S. 1996. *Foundations of Parasitology*. Dubuque: Wm. C. Brown Publishers.

Schmidt, K. P., and Inger, R. F. 1975. *Living Reptiles of the World*. New York: Doubleday & Co., Inc.

Sleigh, M. 1989. *Protozoa and Other Protists*. New York: Routledge, Chapman, and Hall.

Smith, R. J. F. 1985. *The Control of Fish Migration*. New York: Springer-Verlag, Zoophysiology Series.

Solem, A. 1974. *The Shell Makers: Introducing Mollusks*. New York: John Wiley & Sons, Inc.

Stahl, B. J. 1974. *Vertebrate History: Problems in Evolution*. New York: McGraw-Hill Book Co.

Steele, R. S. 1985. *Sharks of the World*. New York: Facts on File Publications.

Stonehouse, B., and Gilmore, D. (eds.). 1977. *The Biology of Marsupials*. New York: Macmillan Publishing Co.

Terres, J. K. 1980. *The Audubon Society Encyclopedia of North American Birds*. New York: Alfred A. Knopf, Inc.

Thomas, R. D. K., and Olson, E. C. (eds.). 1980. *A Cold Look at the Warm-Blooded Dinosaurs*. AAAS Selected Symposium Series. Boulder: Westview Press, Inc.

Travola, W. N., Popper, A. N., and Fay, R. R. 1981. *Hearing and Sound Communication in Fishes*. New York: Springer-Verlag.

Tytler, P., and Calow, P. 1985. *Fish Energetics: New Perspectives*. Baltimore: Johns Hopkins University Press.

Vandenbergh, J. G. 1983. *Pheromones and Reproduction in Mammals*. San Diego: Academic Press.

Vaughan, T. A. 1978. *Mammalogy*. Philadelphia: W. B. Saunders Company.

Walker, W. F. 1987. *Functional Anatomy of the Vertebrates*. Philadelphia: Saunders College Publishing.

Welty, J. C. 1988. *The Life of Birds*. 4th ed. Philadelphia: W. B. Saunders Co.

Wigglesworth, V. B. 1982. *Principles of Insect Physiology*. 7th ed. New York: John Wiley & Sons, Inc.

Wiley, E. O. 1981. *Phylogenetics: The Theory and Practice of Phylogenetic Systematics*. New York: John Wiley and Sons.

Wilford, J. N. 1985. *The Riddle of the Dinosaur*. New York: Alfred A. Knopf.

Wilson, E. O. 1971. *The Insect Societies*. Cambridge: Harvard University Press.

Young, J. Z., and Hobbs, M. J. 1975. *The Life of Mammals: Their Anatomy and Physiology*. 2d ed. New York: Oxford University Press.

Zuckerman, B. M. (ed.). 1980. *Nematodes as Biological Models*. Vol. II: *Aging and Other Model Systems*. New York: Academic Press.

ARTICLES

Aldhous, P. 1993. Malaria: Focus on mosquito genes. *Science* 261(5121):546–548.

Alexander, R. M. How dinosaurs ran. *Scientific American* April, 1991.

Alldredge, A. L., and Madin, L. P. 1982. Pelagic tunicates: Unique herbivores in the marine plankton. *BioScience* 32:655–663.

Alverez, W., and Asaro, F. What caused mass extinction—an extra-terrestrial impact? *Scientific American* October, 1990.

Bakker, R. T. Dinosaur renaissance. *Scientific American* April, 1975.

Beard, J. 1992. Warding off bullets by a spider's thread. *New Scientist* 136(1847):18.

Beebee, T. J. C. 1992. Amphibian decline? *Nature* 355(6356):120.

Birkeland, C. 1989. The faustian traits of the crown-of-thorns starfish. *American Scientist* 72(2):154–163.

Blaustein, A. R. and Wake, D. B. The puzzle of declining amphibian populations. *Scientific American* April, 1995.

Bogan, A. E. 1993. Freshwater bivalve extinction (Mollusca: Unionoida): A search for causes. *American Zoologist* 33(6):599–610.

Boycott, B. B. Learning in the octopus. *Scientific American* March, 1965.

Brown, S. C. 1975. Biomechanics of water pumping by *Chaetopterus variopedatus* Renier: Skeletomusculature and mechanics. *Biological Review* 149:136–156.

Brownlee, S. 1987. Jellyfish aren't out to get us. *Discover* 8:42–52.

Buck, J., and Buck, E. Synchronous fireflies. *Scientific American* May, 1976.

Burnett, A. L. 1960. The mechanism employed by the starfish *Asterias forbesi* to gain access to the interior of the bivalve *Venus mercenaria*. *Ecology* 4:583–584.

Calder, W. A., III. The Kiwi. *Scientific American* July, 1978.

Camhi, J. M. The escape system of the cockroach. *Scientific American* December, 1980.

Carter, C. S., and Getz, L. L. Monogamy and the prairie vole. *Scientific American* June, 1993.

Cloney, R. A. 1982. Ascidian larvae and the events of metamorphosis. *American Zoologist* 22:817–826.

Cole, J. Unisexual lizards. *Scientific American* January, 1984.

Conniff, R. 1987. The little suckers have made a comeback. *Discover* 8:84–93.

Corliss, J. 1984. The kingdom Protista and its 45 phyla. *Biosystems* 17:87–126.

Cortillot, V. What caused mass extinction?—a volcanic eruption. *Scientific American* October, 1990.

Cox, F. E. G. 1988. Which way for malaria? *Nature* 331:486–487.

Cracraft, J. 1988. Early evolution of birds. *Nature* 335:630–632.

Dando, P. R., Southward, A. J., Southward, E. C., Dixon, D. R., Crawford, A., and Crawford, A. 1992 Shipwrecked tube worms. *Nature* 356(6371):667.

Daves, N. B., and Brooke, M. Coevolution of the cuckoo and its host. *Scientific American* January, 1991.

Day, S. 1992. A moving experience for sponges. *New Scientist* 136(1847):15–16.

Deaming, C., and Ferguson, F. 1989. In the heat of the nest. *New Scientist* 121:33–38.

D'Hondt, J. L. 1971. Gastroticha. *Annual Review Oceanography and Marine Biology* 9:141–150.

Duellman, W. E. 1985. Systematic Zoology: Slicing the Gordian knot with Ockham's razor. *American Zoologist* 25:751–762.

Dunelson, J., and Turner, M. How the trypanosome changes its coat. *Scientific American* February, 1985.

Evans, H. E., and O'Neill, K. M. Beewolves. *Scientific American* August, 1991.

Ewing, T. 1988. Thorny problem as Australia's coastline faces invasion. *Nature* 333:387.

Feder, H. M. Escape responses in marine invertebrates. *Scientific American* July, 1972.

Fingerman, M. (ed.). 1992. The compleat crab (symposium). *American Zoologist* 32(2):359–542.

Fischer, E. A., and Peterson, C. W. 1987. The evolution of sexual patterns in the seabasses. *BioScience* 37:482–489.

FitzGerald, G. J. The reproductive behavior of the stickleback. (fish) *Scientific American* April 1993.

Fleming, T. H. 1993. Plant-visiting bats. *American Scientist* 81(5):460–467.

Forey, P. L. 1988. Golden Jubilee for the coelacanth *Latimeria chalumnae*. *Nature* 336:727–732.

Franks, N. 1989. Army ants: A collective intelligence. *American Scientist* 77(2):138–145.

Fricke, Hans. 1988. Coelacanth: The fish that time forgot. *National Geographic* 173(6):824–838.

Funk, D. H. The mating of tree crickets. *Scientific American* August, 1989.

Gaffney, E. S., Hutchison, J. H., Jenkings, F. A., Jr., and Meeker, L. J. 1987. Modern turtle origins: The oldest known cryptodire. *Science* 237:289–291.

Gee, H. 1988. Taxonomy bloodied by cladistic wars. *Nature* 335:585.

Gerhard, S. The mammals of island Europe. *Scientific American* February, 1992.

Gibbons, J. W. 1987. Why do turtles live so long? *BioScience* 37(4):262–268.

Gilbert, J. J. 1984. To build a worm. *Science* 84(5):62–70.

Gore, R. Extinctions. *National Geographic* June, 1989.

Goreau, T. F., Goreau, N. I., and Goreau, T. J. Corals and coral reefs. *Scientific American* August, 1979.

Gorniak, G. C., and Gans, C. 1982. How does the toad flip its tongue? Test of two hypotheses. *Science* 216:1335–1337.

Gorr, T., and Kleinschmidt, T. 1993. Evolutionary relationships of the coelacanth. *American Scientist* 81(1):72–82.

Gould, J. L. 1980. The case for magnetic sensitivity in birds and bees (such as it is). *American Scientist* 68:256–267.

Gould, J. L., and Marler, P. Learning by instinct. *Scientific American* January, 1987.

Gould, S. J. 1976. The five kingdoms. *Natural History* 85(6):30.

Greenwood, J. J. D. 1992. In the pink. (snails) *Nature* 357(6375):192.

Griffiths, M. The Platypus. *Scientific American* May, 1988.

Grober, M. S. 1988. Brittle-star bioluminescence functions as an aposematic signal to deter crustacean predators. *Animal Behaviour* 36:493–501.

Gutzke, W. H. N., and Crews, D. 1988. Embryonic temperature determines adult sexuality in a reptile. *Nature* 332:832–834.

Handel, S. N., and Beattie, A. J. Seed dispersal by ants. *Scientific American* August, 1990.

Hanken, J. 1989. Development and evolution in amphibians. *American Scientist* 77(4):336–343.

Harvey, P. H., and Partridge, L. 1988. Of cuckoo clocks and cowbirds. *Nature* 335:630–632.

Hawking, F. The clock of the malaria parasite. *Scientific American* June, 1970.

Heinrich, B., and Esch, H. 1994. Thermoregulation in bees. *American Scientist* 82(2):164–170.

Herbert, S. Darwin as a geologist. *Scientific American* May, 1986.

Heslinga, G. A., and Fitt, W. K. 1987. The domestication of reef-dwelling clams. *BioScience* 37:332–339.

Horn, M. H., and Gibson, R. N. Intertidal fishes. *Scientific American* January, 1988.

Jaeger, R. G. 1988. A comparison of territorial and non-territorial behaviour in two species of salamanders. *Animal Behavior* 36:307–400.

Kabnick, K. S., and Peattie, D. A. 1991. *Giardia*: A missing link between prokaryotes and eukaryotes. *American Scientist* 79(1):34–43.

Kantor, F. S. Disarming Lyme disease. *Scientific American* September, 1994.

Kanwisher, J. W., and Ridgeway, S. H. The physiological ecology of whales and porpoises. *Scientific American* June, 1983.

Keeton, W. T. The mystery of pigeon homing. *Scientific American* December, 1974.

Kelly-Borges, M. M. 1995. Zoology: Sponges out of their depth. *Nature* 273(6512):284–285.

Kerstitch, A. 1992. Primates of the sea. (octupuses) *Discover* 13(2):34–37.

Kirchner, W. H., and Towne, W. F. The sensory basis of the honeybee's dance language. *Scientific American* June, 1994.

Klimley, A. P. 1994. The predatory behavior of the white shark. *American Scientist* 82(2):122–133.

Knoll, A. H. End of the Proterozoic eon. *Scientific American* October, 1991.

Konishi, M. Listening with two ears. *Scientific American* April, 1993.

Kristensen, R. M. 1983. Loricifera, a new phylum with Aschelminthes characters from the meiobenthos. *Zeitschrift Zoologie Systumatiks Evolution-Fforschung* 21:163–180.

Langston, W., Jr. Pterosaurs. *Scientific American* February, 1981.

Lemche, H. 1957. A new living deep-sea mollusk of the Cambro-Devonian class Monoplacophora. *Nature* 179:413.

Lenhoff, H. M., and Lenhoff, S. G. Trembly's polyps. *Scientific American* April, 1988.

Lent, C. M., and Dickinson, M. H. The neurobiology of feeding in leeches. *Scientific American* June, 1988.

Levine, N. D. 1980. A newly revised classification of the protozoa. *Journal of Protozoology* 27:37–58.

Linsle, R. M. 1978. Shell form and evolution of gastropods. *American Scientist* 66:432–441.

Lizotte, R. S., and Rovner, J. S. 1988. Nocturnal capture of fireflies by lycosid spiders: Visual versus vibratory stimuli. *Animal Behaviour* 36:1809–1815.

Lohman, K. J. How sea turtles navigate. *Scientific American* January, 1992.

Mackenzie, D. 1991. Where earthworms fear to tread. *New Scientist* 131(1781):31–34.

Mangum, C. 1970. Respiratory physiology in annelids. *American Scientist* 58(6):641–647.

Mann, J. 1992. Sponges to wipe away pain. *Nature* 358(6387):540.

Manzel, R., and Erber, J. Learning and memory in bees. *Scientific American* July, 1978.

Marshall, L. G. 1988. Land mammals and the great American interchange. *American Scientist* 76(4):380–388.

Marshall, L. G. The terror birds of South America. *Scientific American* February, 1994.

May, M. 1991. Aerial defense tactics of flying insects. *American Scientist* 79(4):316–328.

Mayr, E. 1981. Biological classification: Toward a synthesis of opposing methodologies. *Science* 241:510–516.

McClanahan, L. L., Ruibal, R., and Shoemaker, V. H. Frogs and toads in deserts. *Scientific American* March, 1994.

McMasters, J. H. 1989. The flight of the bumblebee and related myths of entomological engineering. *American Scientist* 72(2):164–169.

McMenamin, M. A. S. The emergence of animals. *Scientific American* April, 1987.

Messing, C. G. 1988. Sea lilies and feather stars. *Sea Frontiers* 34:236–241.

Millar, R. H. 1971. The biology of ascidians. *Advances Marine Biology* 9:1–100.

Miller, J. A. 1984. Spider silk, stretch, and strength. *Science News* 125:391.

Miller, L. H., Howard, R. J., Carter, R., Good, M. F., Nussenzwieg, V., and Nussenzwieg, R. S. 1986. Research toward malaria vaccines. *Science* 234:1349–1355.

Milne, L. J., and Milne, M. The social behavior of burying beetles. *Scientific American* August, 1978.

———. Insects of the water surface. *Scientific American* April, 1978.

Milner, A. 1989. Late extinctions of amphibians. *Nature* 338:117.

Mitchell, T. 1988. Coral-killing starfish meet their mesh. *New Scientist* 120:28.

Mock, D. W., Drummond, H., and Stinson, H. 1990. Avian siblicide. *American Scientist* 78(5):438–449.

Moffett, M. W. 1991. All eyes on jumping spiders. *National Geographic* 180(3):43–63.

Moore, J. Parasites that change the behaviour of their host. *Scientific American* January, 1984.

Morse, A. N. C. 1991. How do planktonic larvae know where to settle? *American Scientist* 79(2):154–167.

Newman, E. A., and Hartline, P. H. 1982. The infrared "vision" of snakes. *Scientific American* March 246:116–127.

Nordell, D. 1988. Milking leeches for drug research. *New Scientist* 117:43–44.

Ostrom, J. H. 1979. Bird flight: How did it happen? *American Scientist* 67:46–56.

Partridge, B. L. The structure and function of fish schools. *Scientific American* June, 1982.

Quicke, D. 1988. Spiders bite their way towards safer insecticides. *New Scientist* 120:38–41.

Raeburn, P. 1988. Ancient survivor. *National Wildlife* 26(5):36–38.

Rennie, J. Insects are forever. *Scientific American* November, 1993.

Reynolds, C. V. 1994. Warm blood for cold water. *Discover* 15(1):42–43.

Ricciuti, E. R. 1986. A genuine monster. *Audubon* 88:22–24.

Rinderer, T. E., Oldroyd, B. P., and Sheppard, W. S. Africanized bees in the U.S. *Scientific American* December, 1993.

Rinderer, T. E., Stelzer, J. A., Oldroyd, B. P., Buco, S. M., and Rubink, W. L. 1991. Hybridization between European and Africanized bees in neotropical Yucatan Peninsula. *Science* 253(5017):309–311.

Rismiller, P. D., and Seymour, R. S. The echidna. *Scientific American* February, 1991.

Roberts, L. 1988. Corals remain baffling. *Science* 239:256.

———. 1990. The worm project. *Science* 248:1310–1313.

Robinson, M. H. 1987. In a world of silken lines, touch must be exquisitely fine. *Smithsonian* 18:94–102.

Roe, P., and Norenburg, J. L. (eds.). 1985. Symposium on the comparative biology of nemertines. *American Zoologist* 25(1):1–151.

Rome, L. C., Swank, D., and Corda, D. 1993. How fish power swimming. *Science* 261(5119):340–343.

Roper, C. R. E., and Boss, K. J. The giant squid. *Scientific American* April, 1982.

Russell, D. A. 1982. The mass extinctions of the late Mesozoic. *Scientific American* January, 1982.

Ryan, M. J. 1990. Signals, species, and sexual selection. *American Scientist* 78(1):46–52.

Seeley, T. D. How honeybees find a home. *Scientific American* October, 1982.

————. 1989. The honeybee colony as a superorganism. *American Scientist* 77(6):546–553.

Shapiro, D. Y. 1987. Differentiation and evolution of sex change in fishes; a coral reef fish's social environment can control its sex. *BioScience* 490–497.

Shear, W. A. 1994. Untangling the evolution of the web. *American Scientist* 82(3):256–266.

Shimek, R. B. 1987. Sex among the sessile: With the onset of spring in cool northern Pacific waters, even sea cucumbers bestir themselves. *Natural History* 96:60–63.

Simmons, L. W. 1988. The calling song of the field cricket, *Gryllus bimaculatus* (De Geer): Constraints on transmission and its role in intermale competition and female choice. *Animal Behaviour* 36:380–394.

Sitwell, N. 1993. The grub and the Galapagos. (sea cucumbers) *New Scientist* 40(1903):32–35.

Stowe, M. K., Tumilinson, J. H., and Heath, R. R. 1987. Chemical mimicry: Bolas spiders emit components of moth prey species sex pheromones. *Science* 236:964–968.

Stuller, J. 1988. With the gales in their sails. *Audubon* 90:84–85.

Suga, N. Biosonar and neural computations in bats. *Scientific American* June, 1990.

Sutherland, W. J. 1988. The heritability of migration. *Nature* 334:471–472.

Tangley, L. 1987. Malaria: Fighting the African scourge. *BioScience* 37(2):94–98.

Tattersall, I. Madagascar's lemurs. *Scientific American* January, 1993.

Taylor, M. 1994. Amphibians that came to stay. *New Scientist* 141(1912):21–24.

Toner, M. 1992. Spin doctor. *Discover* 13(5):32–36.

Topoff, H. 1990. Slave-making ants. *American Scientist* 78(6):520–528.

Tumlinson, J. H., Lewis, W. J., and Vet, L. E. M. How parasitic wasps find their hosts. *Scientific American* March, 1993.

Tuttle, R. H. 1990. Apes of the world. *American Scientist* 78(2):115–125.

Verell, P. 1988. The chemistry of sexual persuasion. *New Scientist* 118:40–43.

Vickers-Rich, P., and Rich, T. H. Australia's polar dinosaurs. *Scientific American* July, 1993.

Vogel, S. 1988. How organisms use flow-induced pressures. *American Scientist* 76:92–94.

Vollrath, F. 1992. Spider webs and silks. *Scientific American* March, 1992.

Von Frisch, K. 1974. Decoding the language of the bee. *Science* 185:663–668.

Walsh, J. 1979. Rotifers, nature's water purifiers. *National Geographic* 155:286–292.

Ward, P., Greenwald, L., and Greenwald, O. E. The buoyancy of the chambered nautilus. *Scientific American* October, 1980.

Wellnhofer, P. *Archaeopteryx. Scientific American* May, 1990.

West, M. J., and King, A. P. 1990. Mozart's starling. *American Scientist* 78(2):106–114.

Wheatley, D. 1988. Whale size quandary. *Nature* 336:626.

Whittaker, R. H. 1969. New concept of kingdoms of organisms. *Science* 163:150–160.

Wicksten, M. D. Decorator crabs. *Scientific American* February, 1980.

Wilczynski, W., and Brenowitz, E. A. 1988. Acoustic cues mediate inter-male spacing in a neotropical frog. *Animal Behaviour* 36:1054–1063.

Wilkinson, C. R. 1987. Interocean differences in size and nutrition of coral reef sponge populations. *Science* 236:1654–1657.

Wood, R. 1990. Reef-building sponges. *American Scientist* 78(3):224–235.

Wootton, R. J. The mechanical design of insect wings. *Scientific American* November, 1990.

Yager, J. 1981. Remipedia, a new class of Crustacea from a marine cave in the Bahamas. *Journal of Crustacean Biology* 1:328–333.

Yonge, C. M. Giant clams. *Scientific American* April, 1975.

Zapol, W. M. Diving adaptations of the Weddell Seal. *Scientific American* June, 1987.

part SIX

FORM AND FUNCTION:
A COMPARATIVE PERSPECTIVE

Is the whole of an animal equal to the sum of its parts? A superficial answer would be "yes." However, the structure and function of an animal is never as simple as this answer implies. A body is composed of many parts (e.g., cells,  tissues, organs, and organ systems), yet rarely are any of these parts independent of one another. Simple additive relationships fail to describe adequately the interactions between the body's parts. Instead, an animal is the product of many complex interactions. In understanding the structure and function of any system, one only begins to understand the whole animal. Cells, tissues, organs, and organ systems all interact to maintain a steady homeostatic state compatible with life. Ultimately, one needs to look inward to see the genetic potential of the animal, outward to see how environmental constraints limit the fulfillment of that potential, and backward in time to see the evolutionary pressures that shaped the particular species.

Parts One through Five of this textbook examine animal life at molecular, cellular, genetic, developmental, behavioral, and taxonomic levels. Throughout these various parts, the evolutionary forces and pressures that influenced the development of a vast array of animal life forms were presented, concluding with five chapters on the vertebrates. Part Six (chapters 32 through 39) continues this coverage of animal life by presenting an overview of the various organ systems: integumentary, skeletal, muscular, nervous and sensory, endocrine, circulatory, lymphatic, respiratory, digestive, urinary, and reproductive.

Throughout, the major theme is that all organ systems are specialized and coordinated with each other and are constantly adjusting to changes inside and outside the animal. Although each system has its own specialized function, none operates without help from the others. As you will see, the structure of each system determines its particular function.

Frog, Smilisca phaeota.

chapter

PROTECTION, SUPPORT, AND MOVEMENT

Outline

Concepts

1. The integumentary system of animals consists of an outer protective body covering called the integument. The integument of most multicellular invertebrates consists of a single layer of cells. The vertebrate integument is multilayered and is called skin. Skin contains nerves and blood vessels, as well as derivatives such as glands, hair, and nails.
2. Skeletal systems function primarily in movement using muscle antagonism. Three types of skeletons are found in animals: fluid hydrostatic skeletons, rigid exoskeletons, and rigid endoskeletons. Many invertebrates have hydrostatic skeletons consisting of a core of liquid wrapped in a tension-resistant sheath containing muscles. A rigid exoskeleton completely surrounds an animal and functions as a site for muscle attachment and counterforces for muscle movements, as well as for protection and support. The vertebrate skeletal system is an endoskeleton. It consists mainly of supportive tissue called cartilage and bone.
3. Muscles provide the force for movement in animals as diverse as cnidarians and vertebrates. The latter use their endoskeleton in conjunction with muscles to accomplish movement. In vertebrates, striated skeletal muscles are involved in moving the body, smooth muscles in moving material through tubular organs and changing the size of tubular openings, and cardiac muscle in the beating of the heart.

Would You Like to Know:

1. how one can determine the age of a fish? (p. 529)
2. what is the function of toad "warts"? (p. 530)
3. why mammals have been able to colonize terrestrial environments? (p. 531)
4. how leather is made and where it comes from? (p. 531)
5. what "goose bumps" are? (p. 532)
6. what is "animal rubber" and how does it function? (p. 534)
7. where the expression "to clam up" comes from? (p. 539)
8. when a heart has time to relax? (p. 539)
9. why insects that jump have relatively long legs? (p. 541)

These and other useful questions will be answered in this chapter.

This chapter contains evolutionary concepts, which are set off in this font.

In animals, structure and function have evolved together. Several results of this evolution are protection, support, and movement. These functions are represented primarily by the integumentary, skeletal, and muscular systems.

PROTECTION: INTEGUMENTARY SYSTEMS

The **integument** (L. *integumentum*, cover) is the external covering of an animal. It functions primarily in protection against mechanical and chemical injury, and invasion by microorganisms. Many other diverse functions of the integument have evolved in different animal groups. These include regulation of body temperature; excretion of waste materials; conversion of sunlight into vitamins; the reception of environmental stimuli, such as pain, temperature, and pressure; and the movement of nutrients and gases.

THE INTEGUMENTARY SYSTEM OF INVERTEBRATES

Some single-celled protozoa have only a **plasma membrane** for an external covering. This membrane is structurally and chemically identical to the plasma membrane of multicellular organisms (*see figure 3.4*). In protozoa, the plasma membrane has a large surface area relative to body volume, so that gas exchange and removal of soluble wastes occur by simple diffusion. This high surface area also facilitates the uptake of dissolved nutrients from surrounding fluids. Other protozoa, such as *Paramecium*, have a thick protein coat called a **pellicle** (L. *pellicula*, thin skin) outside the plasma membrane. This pellicle offers further environmental protection, and provides a semirigid structure that transmits the force of cilia or flagella to the entire body of the protozoan as it moves.

Most multicellular invertebrates have an integument consisting of a single layer of columnar epithelial cells (figure 32.1). This outer layer, the **epidermis** (Gr. *epi*, upon + *derm*, skin), rests on a basement membrane. Beneath the basement membrane is a thin layer of connective tissue fibers and cells. When the epidermis is exposed at the surface of the animal, many of its cells may possess cilia. Glandular cells may also be found in the epidermis of some invertebrates. These cells secrete an overlying, noncellular material that encases part or most of the animal.

Some invertebrates possess **cuticles** (L. *cuticula*, *cutis*, skin) that are highly variable in structure (figure 32.2). For example, in some animals (rotifers) cuticles are thin and elastic, whereas in others (crustaceans, arachnids, insects) cuticles are thick and rigid, and support the body. Such cuticles consist of chitin and proteins in rigid plates linked by a flexible membrane. A disadvantage of possessing cuticles is that animals have difficulty growing within them. As a result, some of these invertebrates (e.g., arthropods) periodically shed the old, outgrown cuticle in a process called molting or ecdysis (*see figure 23.5*).

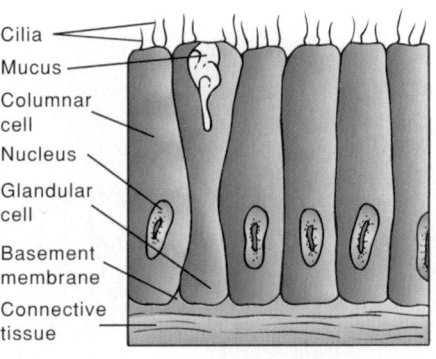

FIGURE 32.1

The Integument of Invertebrates. The integument of many invertebrates consists of a simple layer of columnar epithelial cells (epidermis) resting on a basement membrane. A thin layer of connective tissue lies under the basement membrane. Cilia and glandular cells may or may not be present.

In cnidarians, such as *Hydra*, the epidermis is only a few cell layers thick. Other cnidarians (e.g., the corals) contain mucous glands that secrete a calcium carbonate ($CaCO_3$) **shell.** The outer covering of parasitic flukes and tapeworms is a complex syncytium called a **tegument** (L. *tegumentum*, *tegere*, to cover). Its main functions are nutrient ingestion and protection against digestion by host enzymes. Nematodes and annelids have an epidermis that is one cell thick that secretes a multilayered cuticle. The integument of echinoderms consists of a thin, usually ciliated epidermis and an underlying connective tissue dermis. The dermis contains $CaCO_3$. Arthropods have the most complex of invertebrate integuments, in part because their integument serves as a specialized exoskeleton.

Stop and Ask Yourself

1. How would you define a plasma membrane? Pellicle? Cuticle? Shell? Tegument?
2. What is the function of each of the above structures?
3. In what group of organisms would you observe each of the above structures?

THE INTEGUMENTARY SYSTEM OF VERTEBRATES

Skin is the integument found in vertebrates. It is the largest organ of the vertebrate body and continues to grow as the animal grows. Skin has two main layers. Just as in invertebrates, the epidermis is the outermost layer of epithelial tissue, one to several cells in thickness. The **dermis** (Gr. *derma*, hide, skin) is a thicker layer of connective tissue beneath the epidermis. The skin is separated from deeper tissues by a **hypodermis** ("below the skin").

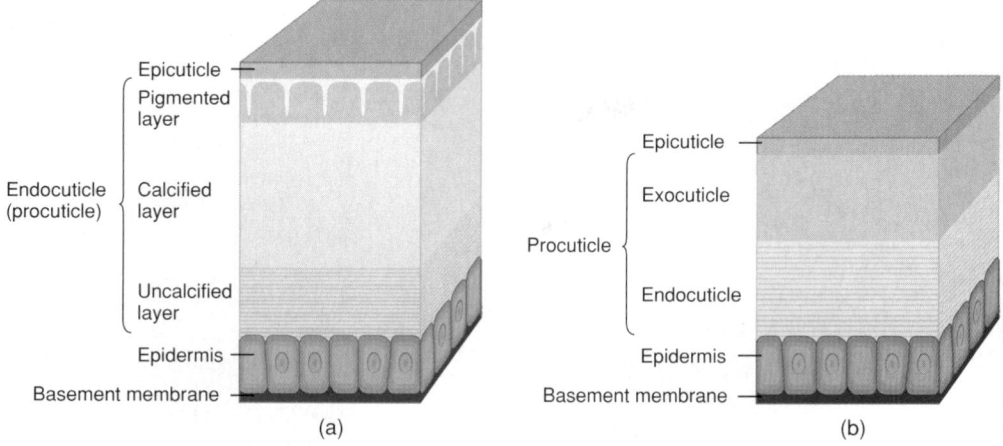

Figure 32.2

Cuticles. Drawings of the cuticle of (*a*) a crustacean and (*b*) an insect. The cuticles of both groups of animals are secreted by the underlying epidermis. *From: "A LIFE OF INVERTEBRATES" © 1979 W. D. Russell-Hunter.*

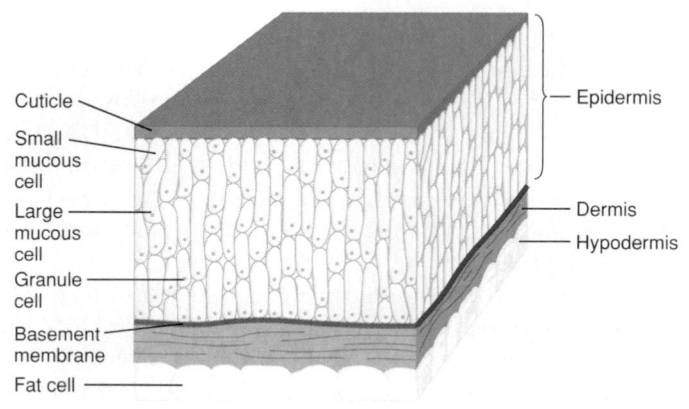

Figure 32.3

The Skin of Jawless Fishes. The skin of an adult lamprey has a multilayered epidermis with glandular cells and fat storage cells in the hypodermis.

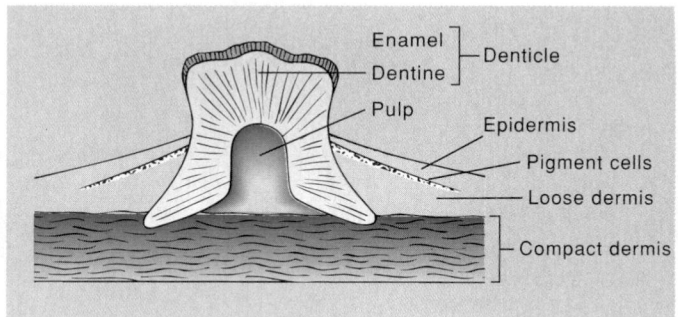

Figure 32.4

The Skin of Cartilaginous Fishes. Shark skin contains toothlike denticles that become exposed through loss of the epidermal covering. The skin is otherwise fishlike in structure.

The Skin of Jawless Fishes

Lampreys and hagfishes have relatively thick skin (figure 32.3). Of the several types of epidermal glandular cells that may be present, one secretes a protective cuticle. In hagfishes, multicellular slime glands produce large amounts of mucous slime that covers the body surface. This slime protects the animals from external parasites and has earned hagfishes the descriptive name "slime eels."

The Skin of Cartilaginous Fishes

The skin of cartilaginous fishes (e.g., sharks) is multilayered and contains mucous and sensory cells (figure 32.4). The dermis contains bone in the form of small placoid scales called **denticles** (L. *denticulus*, little teeth), blood vessels, and nerves. Denticles are similar to vertebrate teeth. Because cartilaginous fishes grow throughout life, the skin area must also increase,

which necessitates the production of new denticles to maintain enough of these protective structures at the skin surface. Like teeth, once denticles reach maturity they do not grow; thus, they are continually being worn down and lost. Since denticles project above the surface of the skin, they give cartilaginous fishes a "sandpaper texture."

The Skin of Bony Fishes

The skin of bony fishes (teleosts) contains **scales** (Fr. *escale*, shell, husk). Scales are normally covered by a thin layer of dermal tissue overlaid by the superficial epidermis (figure 32.5). Because scales are not shed, they grow at the margins and over the lower surface.   In many bony fishes, it is often possible to detect growth lines, which are useful in determining the age of a fish. In bony fishes, the skin is permeable and functions in gaseous exchange, particularly in the smaller fishes that have a large skin surface area relative to body volume. The dermis is richly supplied with capillary beds

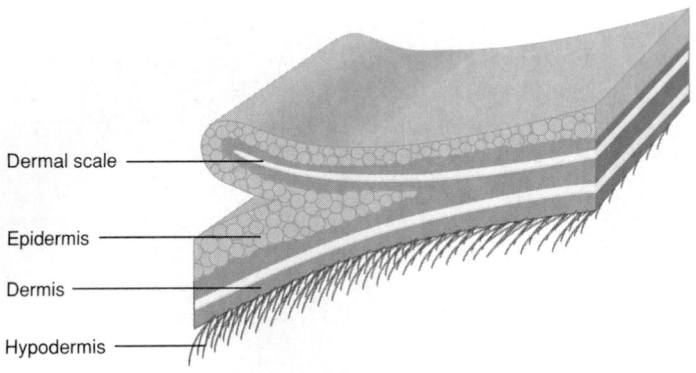

Figure 32.5

The Skin of Bony Fishes. This drawing of the skin of a typical bony fish shows two overlapping scales, which are layers of collagenous fibers covered by a thin, flexible layer of bone.

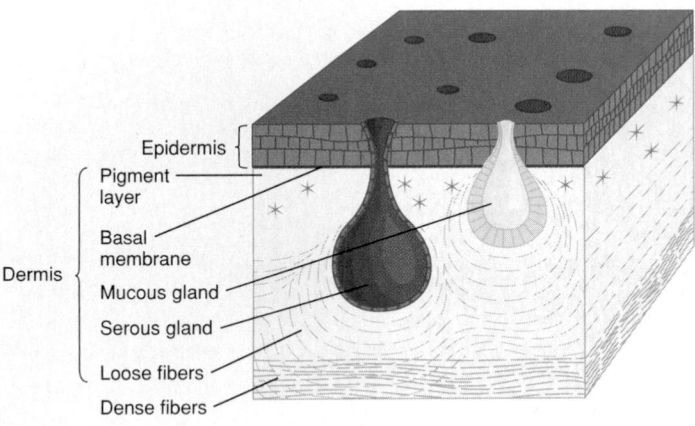

Figure 32.6

The Skin of Amphibians. This drawing of frog skin illustrates the stratified epidermis and several types of glands located in the dermis. Notice the pigment layer in the upper part of the dermis.

to facilitate its use in respiration. The epidermis also contains many mucous glands. Mucus production helps prevent bacterial and fungal infections, and reduces friction as the fish swims. Some species have granular glands that secrete an irritating, or to some species, poisonous alkaloid. Many teleosts that inhabit deep aquatic habitats have photophores that facilitate species recognition, lures, or warning signals.

The Skin of Amphibians

Amphibian skin consists of a stratified epidermis and a dermis containing mucous and serous glands plus pigmentation (figure 32.6). Three problems associated with terrestrial environments are desiccation, the damaging effects of UV light, and physical abrasion. During amphibian evolution, their skin became modified by increasing the production of keratin in the outer layer of cells. (Keratin is a tough and impermeable protein well suited

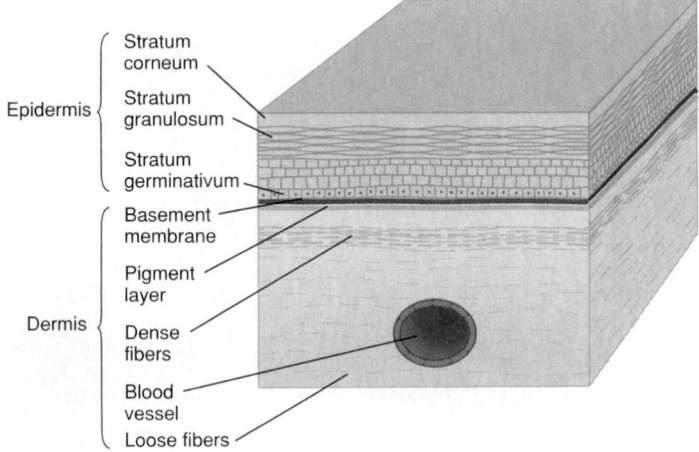

Figure 32.7

The Skin of Reptiles. This drawing of the skin of a lizard illustrates the heavily keratinized outer epidermis (scales) characteristic of reptiles.

to protect the skin in the physically abrasive, rigorous environment out of water.) The increased keratin in the skin also protects the cells, especially their nuclear material, from UV light. The mucus produced by the mucous glands helps prevent desiccation, facilitates gaseous exchange when the skin is used as a respiratory organ, and makes the body slimy, which facilitates escape from predators.

Within the dermis of some amphibians are poison glands that produce an unpleasant-tasting or toxic fluid that acts as a predator deterrent (*see box 28.1*). Sensory nerves penetrate the epidermis as free nerve endings.   ② Interestingly, the "warts" of toads seem to be specialized sensory structures since they contain numerous sensory cells.

The Skin of Reptiles

In reptiles, the outer layer of the epidermis (stratum corneum) is very thick (figure 32.7) and modified into keratinized scales, scutes, (thick scales) in snakes and turtles, beaks in turtles, rattles on snakes, and claws, plaques, and spiny crests on most other reptiles. This thick keratinized layer functions to resist abrasion, inhibits dehydration, and acts as a "suit of armor" for protection. During shedding or molting of the skin of many reptiles (e.g., snakes and lizards), the old outer layer separates from newly formed epidermis. This separation is aided by the diffusion of fluid between the layers.

The Skin of Birds

The skin of birds shows many typically reptilian features with no epidermal glands (the only epidermal gland of birds is the uropygial or preen gland). Over most of the bird's body, the epidermis is usually thin and only two or three cell layers deep (figure 32.8). Indeed, the term "thin skinned," sometimes applied

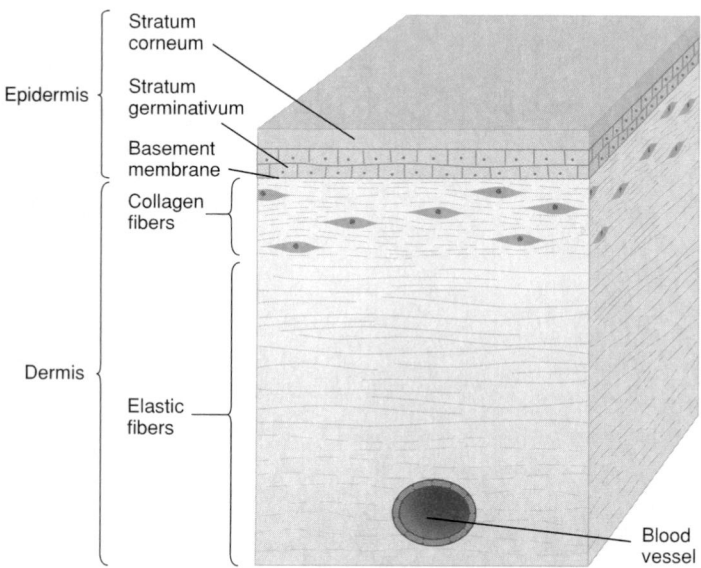

Epidermis
- Stratum corneum
- Stratum germinativum
- Basement membrane

Dermis
- Collagen fibers
- Elastic fibers

Blood vessel

FIGURE 32.8

The Skin of Birds. This drawing of the skin of a bird shows a relatively soft and thin epidermis with no epidermal glands.

figuratively to humans, is literal when applied to birds. The outer keratinized layer is often quite soft. The most prominent parts of the epidermis are the feathers. Feathers are derived from the scales of reptilian ancestors and the most complex of all the derivates of the vertebrate stratum corneum (*see figure 30.4*).

The dermis of birds is similar in structure to that of reptiles. Blood and lymphatic vessels, nerves, and epidermally derived sensory bodies are present. Air spaces that are part of the avian respiratory system extend into the dermis. These air spaces are involved in thermal regulation. Associated with the feathers and their normal functioning is an incredibly complicated array of dermal smooth muscle fibers. These muscle fibers control the position of the feathers. Feather position is important in thermal regulation, flying, and behavior. Aquatic birds may also have fat deposits in the hypodermal layer that function to store energy and help insulate the body.

The Skin of Mammals

The notable features of mammalian skin are: (1) hair; (2) a greater variety of epidermal glands than in any other vertebrate class; (3) a highly stratified, cornified epidermis; and (4) a dermis, which, for the first time, is many times thicker than the epidermis.

The epidermis of mammalian skin is stratified squamous epithelium consisting of several layers of a variety of cells. Rapid cell divisions in the deepest layer of the epidermis push cells toward the surface of the skin. As cells reach the surface, they die and become keratinized (contain the protein keratin) and make up the outer layer called the stratum corneum. Because keratin is virtually insoluble in water, the stratum corneum allows the

skin to act as a barrier to prevent dehydration and act as a first line of defense against many toxic substances and microorganisms.   ③   The prevention of dehydration is one of the evolutionary reasons mammals and other animals have been able to colonize terrestrial environments.

The thickest portion of the skin of mammals is composed of dermis. Within the dermis, blood vessels, lymphatic vessels, nerve endings, hair follicles, small muscles, and glands are present (figure 32.9).   ④   Of interest is the fact that leather is made from the dermal layer of mammalian skin by a special tanning process.

The hypodermis lies underneath the dermis. It is different from the hypodermis of other vertebrate classes in that it is composed of loose connective tissue, adipose tissue, and skeletal muscles. Adipose tissue serves to store energy in the form of fat and provide insulation in cold environments. Skeletal muscle allows the skin above it to move somewhat independently of underlying tissues. Blood vessels thread from the hypodermis to the dermis and are absent from the epidermis.

In humans and a few other animals (e.g., horses), the skin is an effective regulator of body temperature. This is accomplished by the opening and closing of sweat pores and the process of perspiration or sweating. The skin is an effective barrier for screening out excessive harmful ultraviolet rays from the sun, but it also lets in some necessary rays. These rays are used to convert a chemical in the skin into vitamin D. The skin is also an important sense organ, containing sensory receptors for heat, cold, touch, pressure, and pain. It helps protect an animal by means of its many nerve endings, which keep the animal responsive to factors in the environment that might cause harm to the animal.

The skin of humans and other mammals contains several types of glands. **Sudoriferous glands** (L. *sudor*, sweat) are also called sweat glands, and in humans are distributed over most of the body surface (figure 32.9). These glands secrete sweat by a process called **perspiration** (L. *per*, through + *spirare*, to breathe). Perspiration helps to regulate body temperature and maintain homeostasis, largely by the cooling effect of evaporation. In some mammals, certain sweat glands also produce pheromones. (A pheromone is a chemical secreted by an animal that communicates with other members of the same species to elicit certain behavioral responses.) **Sebaceous (oil) glands** (L. *sebum*, tallow or fat) are simple glands connected to hair follicles that are found in the dermis (figure 32.9). Their main functions are lubrication and protection, which they accomplish by secreting **sebum.** Sebum serves as a permeability barrier, an emollient (skin-softening agent), and a protective agent against microorganisms. Sebum can also act as a pheromone.

Mammalian skin has color. Skin color is due either to pigments or anatomical structures that absorb or reflect light. Pigments (e.g., melanin in human skin) may be found within the cells of the epidermal layer, in hair, or in specialized cells called chromatophores. Some skin color is due to the color of blood in superficial blood vessels reflected through the epidermis. Bright

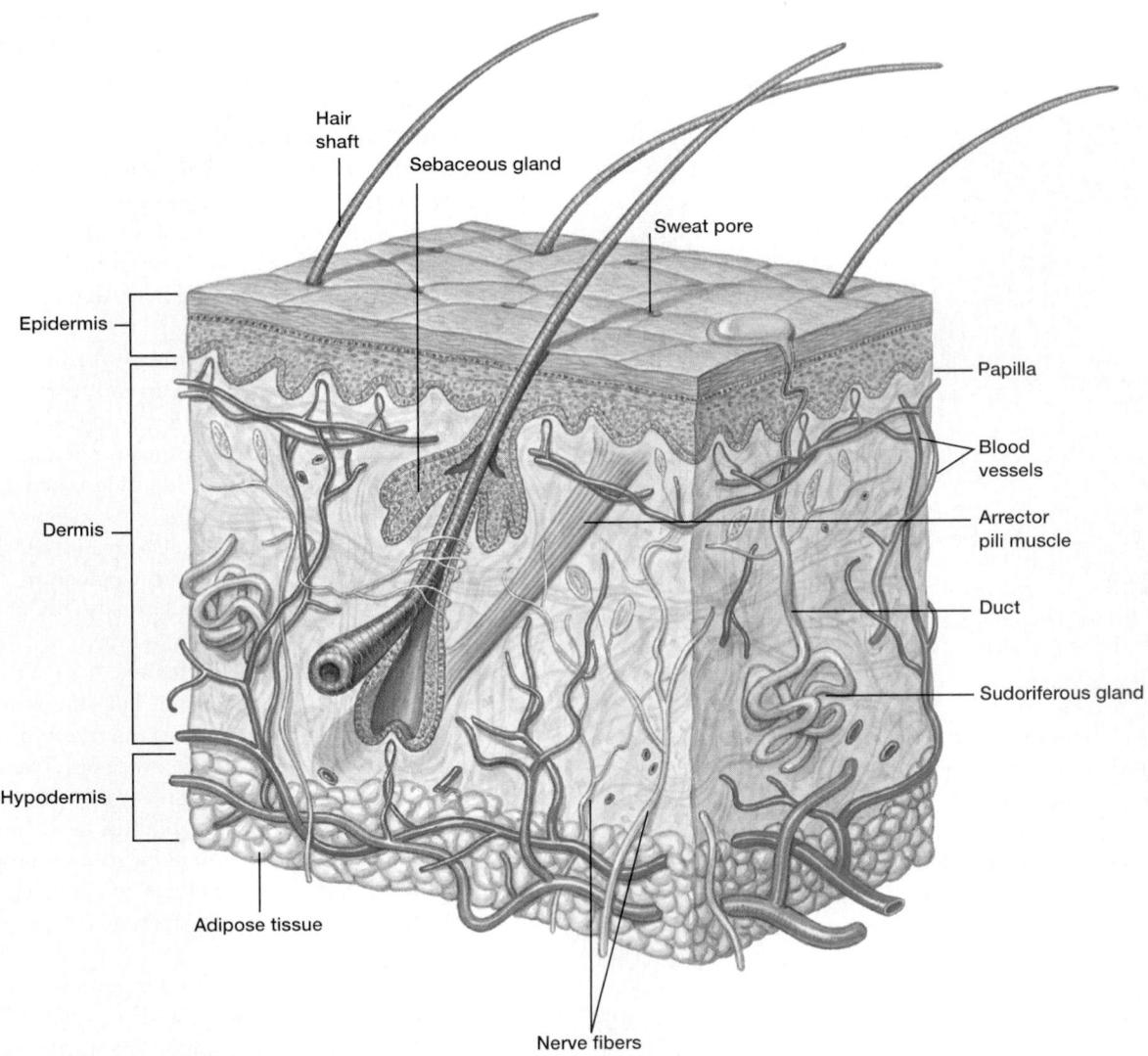

FIGURE 32.9

The Skin of Mammals. Notice the various cellular structures in the dermis. This drawing is of human skin.

skin colors in venomous, toxic, or bad-tasting animals may deter potential predators. Other skin colors may serve as camouflage for the animal. In addition, colors serve in social communication, to help members of the same species identify each other, their sex, reproductive status, or social rank.

Hair is composed of hardened cells that develop from the epidermis. The portion of hair that protrudes from the skin is the hair shaft, and the portion embedded beneath the skin is the root (figure 32.9). ⑤ An arrector pili muscle is attached to the connective tissue sheath of a hair follicle surrounding the bulb of the hair root. When this muscle contracts, it pulls the follicle and its hair to an erect position. In humans, this is referred to as a "goose bump." In other mammals, this action helps warm the animal by producing an insulating layer of warm air between the erect hair and skin. If hair is erect as a result of the animal being frightened instead of being cold, the erect hair also makes the animal look larger and less vulnerable to attack.

Nails, like hair, are modifications of the epidermis. Nails are composed of flat, horny plates on the dorsal surface of the distal segments of the digits (e.g., fingers and toes of primates). **Claws** and hooves (*see figure 31.7*) are found in other mammals. Other keratinized derivatives of mammalian skin are **horns** (not to be confused with bony antlers; *see box 31.1*) and the **baleen plates** of the toothless whales (*see box 37.2*).

Stop and Ask Yourself

4. What are some functions of skin?
5. What structures are found in the dermal layer of mammalian skin? What type of glands are found in this layer?
6. What determines the color of skin?

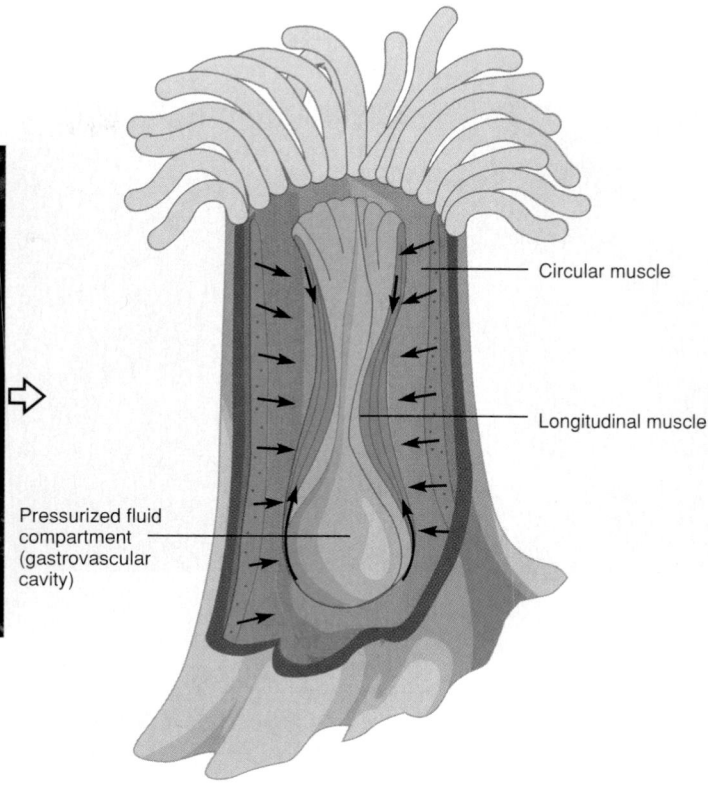

(a)

Figure 32.10

Hydrostatic Skeletons. (*a*) The hydrostatic skeleton of sea anemones (*Corynactis californic*) allows them to shorten or close when longitudinal muscles contract, or to lengthen or open when circular muscles contract. (*b*) How a hydrostatic skeleton functions to change shape in an invertebrate with only longitudinal muscles. (*c*) Because the fluid volume is constant, a change (increase) in the width must be compensated for by a change (decrease) in length brought about by the increase in internal hydrostatic pressure during muscle contraction.

Movement and Support: Skeletal Systems

As organisms evolved from the ancestral protists to the multicellular animals, body size increased dramatically. This increase in body size was accompanied by the evolution of systems involved in movement and support.

With respect to movement, four types of cell contribute to locomotion: (1) amoeboid cells, (2) flagellated cells, (3) ciliated cells, and (4) muscle cells. With respect to support, organisms have three kinds of skeletons: (1) fluid hydrostatic skeletons, (2) rigid exoskeletons, and (3) rigid endoskeletons. These three types of skeletal systems function in movement of an animal using muscles that work in opposition (antagonism) to each other.

The Skeletal System of Invertebrates

Many invertebrates use their body fluids for internal support. For example, sea anemones (figure 32.10a) and earthworms have a form of internal support called the hydrostatic skeleton.

Hydrostatic Skeletons

The **hydrostatic** (Gr. *hydro*, water + *statikos*, to stand) **skeleton** is composed of a core of liquid (water or a body fluid such as blood) surrounded by a tension-resistant sheath containing longitudinal and/or circular muscles. A hydrostatic skeleton is similar to a balloon filled with water, because the force exerted against the incompressible fluid in one region can be transmitted to other regions. Contracting muscles can push against a

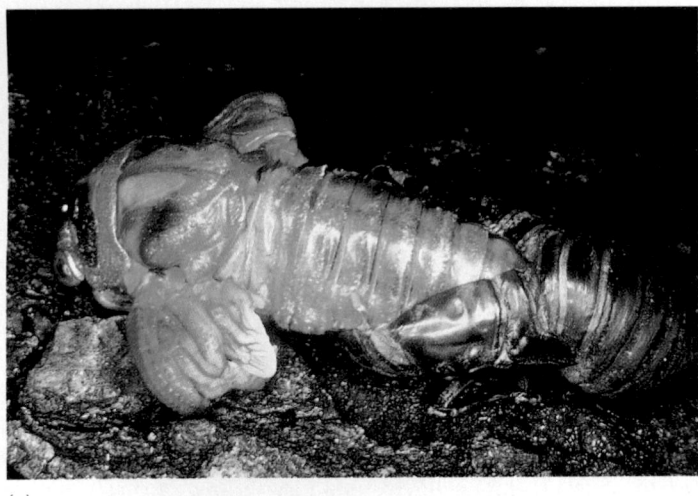

(a)

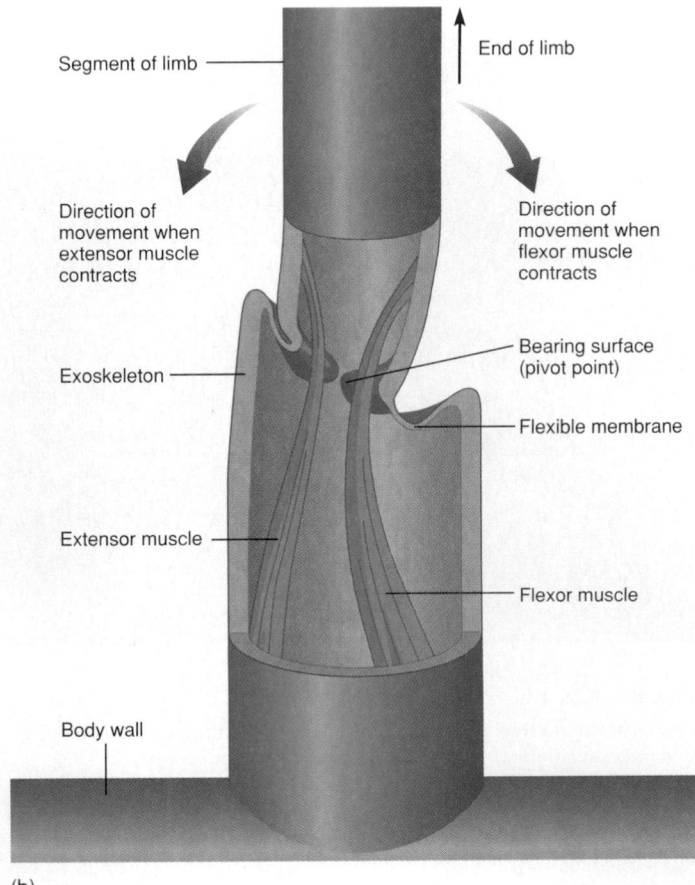

(b)

Figure **32.11**

Exoskeletons. (*a*) A cicada nymph (*Platypedia*) leaves its old exoskeleton as it molts. This exoskeleton provides external support for the body and attachment sites for muscles. (*b*) The exoskeleton and muscular arrangement in an arthropod consists of muscles attached to the interior of the exoskeleton. In this articulation of an arthropod limb, the cuticle is hardened everywhere except at the joint, where there is a flexible membrane. Notice that the extensor muscle is antagonistic to the flexor muscle. (*b*) *Source: After Russell-Hunter.*

hydrostatic skeleton, and the transmitted force generates body movements as illustrated by the movement of a sea anemone (figure 32.10*b,c*). Another example is the earthworm, *Lumbricus terrestris*. It uses its longitudinal and circular (antagonistic) muscles to contract alternately, creating a rhythm that moves the earthworm through the soil. In both of these examples, the hydrostatic skeleton keeps the body from collapsing when its muscles contract.

The invertebrate hydrostatic skeleton can take many forms and shapes, such as the gastrovascular cavity of acoelomates; a rhynchocoel in nemertines; a pseudocoelom in the aschelminths; or a coelom in the annelids. Overall, the hydrostatic skeleton of invertebrates is an excellent example of adaptation of major body functions to this simple but efficient principle of hydrodynamics—use of the internal pressure of body fluids.

Exoskeletons

Rigid **exoskeletons** (Gr. *exo*, outside + skeleton; figure 32.11*a*) also have locomotor functions. This is accomplished by providing sites for muscle attachment and counterforces for muscle movements. Exoskeletons also support and protect, but these are secondary functions.

In arthropods, the epidermis of the body wall secretes a thick, hard cuticle that waterproofs the body (*see figure 23.3*).

The cuticle also protects and supports the animal's soft internal organs. In crustaceans (e.g., crabs, lobsters, shrimp), the exoskeleton contains calcium carbonate crystals that make it hard and inflexible—except at the joints. Besides providing shieldlike protection from enemies and resistance to general wear and tear, the exoskeleton also prevents internal tissues from drying out. This evolutionary adaptation has been extremely important because it contributed to the successful colonization of land by arthropods. Animals with exoskeletons, however, are limited in their growth by the space within the exoskeleton, or they must shed the exoskeleton periodically, as arthropods do when they molt.

Arthropods have certain regions of their body where the cuticle is thin and flexible. Joints (articulations) are usually found in these areas (figure 32.11*b*). It is in these areas that pairs of antagonistic muscles function through a system of levers to accomplish coordinated movement.   ⑥   Interestingly, some arthropod joints (e.g., the wing joints of flying beetles and the joints of fleas that are involved in jumping) possess a highly elastic protein called "animal rubber," or **resilin.** Resilin stores energy on compression and then releases the energy to accomplish movement (*see figure 32.23*). From an evolutionary perspective, the development of a jointed, flexible exoskeleton that permitted flight is one of the reasons for the success of arthropods.

Endoskeletons

Like the term implies, **endoskeletons** (Gr. *endo,* within + skeleton) are enclosed by other body tissues. For example, the endoskeletons of sponges consist of mineral spicules and fibers of spongin that keep the body from collapsing (*see figure 18.4*). Since adult sponges remain attached to the substrate, they have no need for muscles attached to the endoskeleton. Similarly, the endoskeletons of echinoderms (starfishes, sea urchins) are made up of small, calcareous plates called ossicles. The most familiar endoskeletons, however, are found in vertebrates and discussed later in the chapter.

Mineralized Tissues and the Invertebrates

Hard, mineralized tissues are not unique to the vertebrates. In fact, over two-thirds of the living species of animals that contain mineralized tissues are invertebrates. Most invertebrates have inorganic calcium carbonate crystals embedded in a collagen matrix. (Vertebrates have calcium phosphate crystals.) Bone, dentin, cartilage, and enamel were all present in Ordovician ostracoderms (*see figure 27.3*).

Cartilage is the supportive tissue that makes up the major skeletal component of some gastropods, invertebrate chordates (amphioxus), jawless fishes such as hagfishes and lampreys, and sharks and rays. Since cartilage is lighter than bone, it affords the above predatory fishes the speed and agility that allows them to catch prey. It also provides buoyancy without the need for a swim bladder.

Stop and Ask Yourself

7. How does a hydrostatic skeleton function?
8. What animals possess a hydrostatic skeleton?
9. What are some of the differences between an endoskeleton and an exoskeleton? What are some examples of animals that possess exoskeletons? Endoskeletons?

THE SKELETAL SYSTEM OF VERTEBRATES

The skeletal system of vertebrates is an endoskeleton enclosed by other body tissues. This endoskeleton consists of two main types of supportive tissue: cartilage and bone.

Cartilage

Cartilage is a specialized type of connective tissue that provides a site for muscle attachment, aids in movement at joints, and provides support (*see figure 3.24* h–j). Like other connective tissues, it consists of cells (chondrocytes), fibers, and ground substance.

Bone or Osseous Tissue

Bone (osseous) tissue (figure 32.12a) is a specialized connective tissue that aids in the movement of an animal by providing a point of attachment for muscles and transmitting the force of muscular contraction from one part of the body to another during movement. In addition, bones of the skeleton support the internal organs of many animals, function as a storehouse and main supply of reserve calcium and phosphate, and serve as the site for the manufacture of red blood cells and some white blood cells.

Bone tissue is more rigid than other connective tissues because its homogeneous, organic ground substance also contains inorganic salts—mainly calcium phosphate and calcium carbonate. When an animal needs the calcium or phosphate that is stored within the bones, metabolic reactions (under endocrine control) release the required amounts.

As discussed in chapter 3, **bone cells** (osteocytes) are located in minute chambers called lacunae (s., lacuna), which are arranged in concentric rings around osteonic canals (formerly called Haversian systems) (figure 32.12b). These cells communicate with nearby cells by means of cellular processes passing through small channels called canaliculi (s., canaliculus).

The Skeleton of Fishes

Both cartilaginous and bony endoskeletons first appeared in the vertebrates. Since water has a buoyant effect on the fish body, the requirement for support by the skeleton is not as demanding in these vertebrates as it is in terrestrial vertebrates. Although most vertebrates have a well-defined vertebral column (the reason they are called "vertebrates"), the jawless vertebrates do not. For example, lampreys only have isolated cartilaginous blocks located along the notochord, and hagfishes do not even have these.

Most jawed fishes have an axial skeleton that includes a notochord, ribs, and cartilaginous or bony vertebrae (figure 32.13). The axial skeleton serves as a base for the attachment of the muscles used in locomotion.

The Skeleton of Tetrapods

Tetrapods must lift themselves in order to walk on land. The first amphibians needed support to replace the buoyancy of water. For the earliest terrestrial animals, support and locomotion were difficult and complicated processes. Adaptations for support and movement on land occurred over a period of approximately two hundred million years. For example, during this evolution, the tetrapod endoskeleton (figure 32.14) became modified for support on land. This added support resulted from the specializations of the intervertebral disks that articulate with adjoining vertebrae. The intervertebral disks help hold the vertebral column together while absorbing shock and providing joint mobility. The ribs ossified by replacing cartilage with bone and became more rigid. The various types of connective tissue that connect to the axial skeleton helped keep elevated portions from sagging. Appendages became elongated for support on a hard surface, and changes in the shoulder occurred that enabled the neck to move more freely.

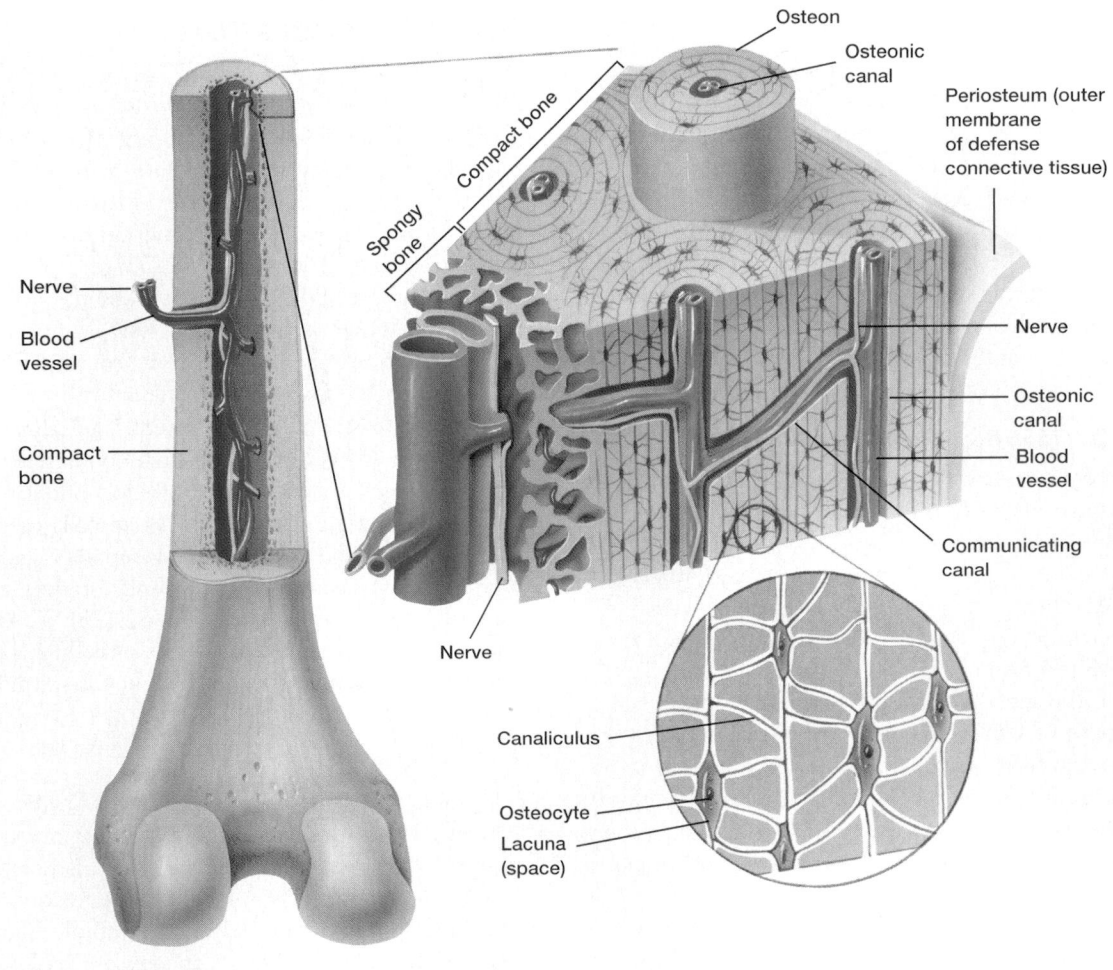

(a)

(b)

Figure 32.12

Bone. (*a*) Structural organization of a long bone (femur) of mammals. Compact bone is composed of osteons cemented together. Spongy bone is latticelike rather than dense. (*b*) The scanning electron micrograph is of a single osteon in compact bone. *(b) Photo appeared in TISSUES AND ORGANS: A TEXT-ATLAS OF SCANNING ELECTRON MICROSCOPY, BY RICHARD G. KESSEL AND RANDY H. KARDON.*

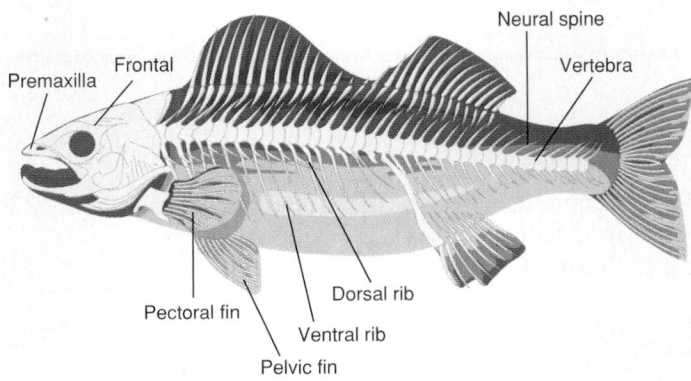

Figure 32.13

The Fish Endoskeleton. Lateral view of the entire skeleton of the perch.

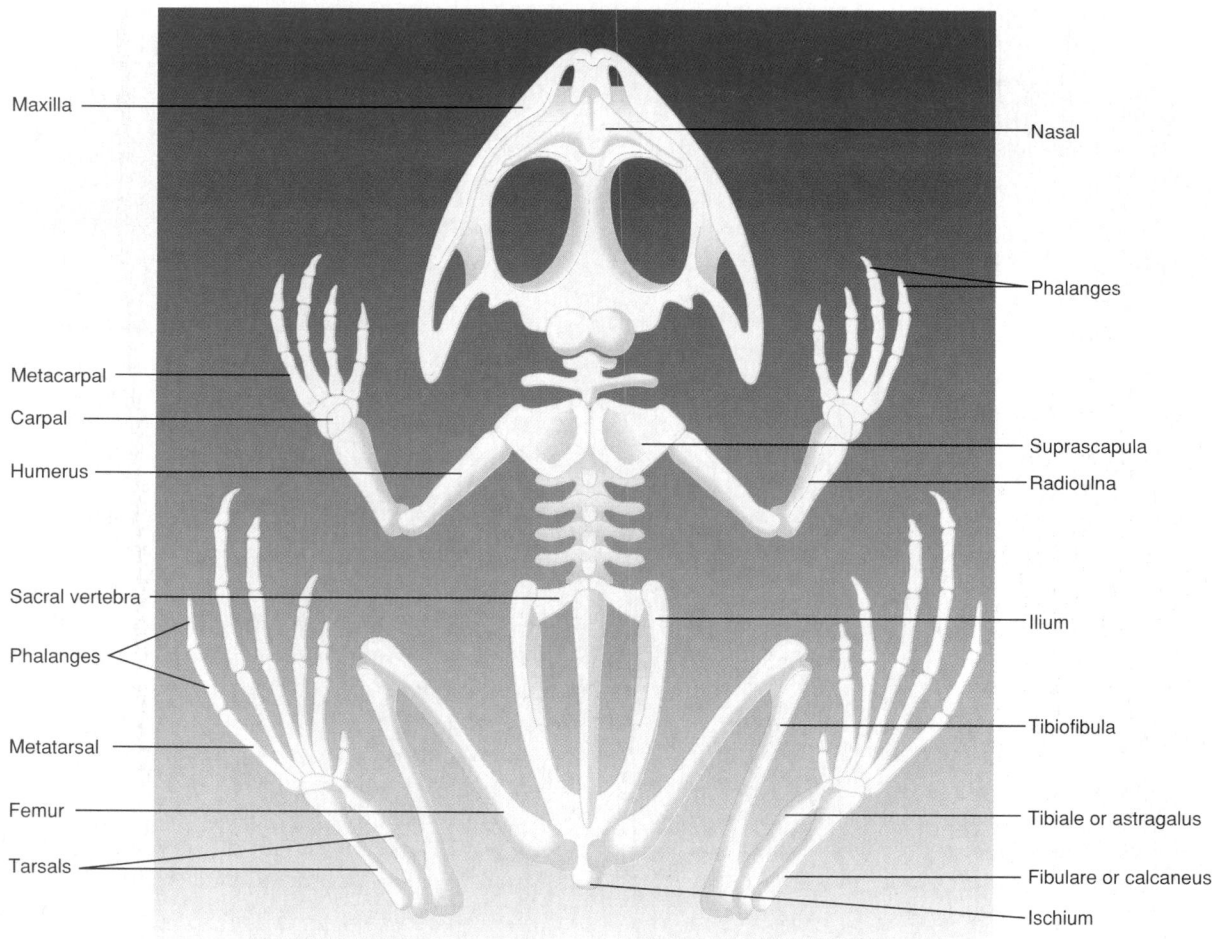

FIGURE 32.14

The Tetrapod Endoskeleton. Dorsal view of the frog skeleton.

The Human Endoskeleton

The human endoskeleton is divided into two major parts: the axial skeleton and the appendicular skeleton. The **axial skeleton** is so named because it forms the longitudinal axis of the body. It is made up of the skull, vertebral column, sternum, and ribs. The **appendicular skeleton** is composed of the appendages, the pectoral girdle, and the pelvic girdles. These girdles attach the upper and lower appendages to the axial skeleton.

Stop and Ask Yourself

10. What are some differences between cartilage and bone?
11. What are some differences between the endoskeleton of a fish and a frog?
12. What are the two major divisions of the human skeleton?

MOVEMENT: NONMUSCULAR MOVEMENT AND MUSCULAR SYSTEMS

Movement is a characteristic of certain cells, protists, and animals. For example, certain white blood cells, coelomic cells, and protists such as *Amoeba* utilize nonmuscular amoeboid movement. Amoeboid movement also occurs in embryonic tissue movements, in wound healing, and in many cell types growing in tissue culture. Other protists and some invertebrates utilize cilia or flagella for movement. Muscles and muscle systems are found in various invertebrate groups from the primitive cnidarians to the arthropods (e.g., insect flight muscles). In more complex animals, the muscles are attached to exo- and endoskeletal systems to form a motor system, which allows for complex movements.

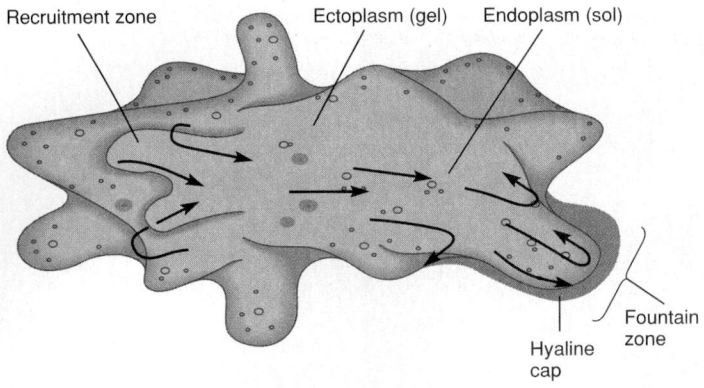

FIGURE 32.15

The Mechanism of Amoeboid Movement. Endoplasm (sol) flows into an advancing pseudopodium. At the tip (fountain zone) of the pseudopodium, endoplasm changes into ectoplasm (gel). At the opposite end (recruitment zone) of the amoeba, ectoplasm changes into endoplasm and begins flowing in the direction of movement.

NONMUSCULAR MOVEMENT

Nearly all cells have some capacity to move and change shape due to their cytoskeleton (*see figure* 3.19). It is from this basic framework of the cell that specialized contractile mechanisms emerged. For example, protozoan protists move by means of specific nonmuscular structures (pseudopodia, flagella, or cilia) that involve the contractile proteins, actin and myosin. Interactions between these proteins are also responsible for muscle contraction in animals, and the presence of actin and myosin in protozoa and animals is evidence of evolutionary ties between the two groups.

Amoeboid Movement

As the name suggests, **amoeboid movement** was first observed in *Amoeba*. The plasma membrane of an amoeba has adhesive properties since new **pseudopodia** (s., pseudopodium; Gr. *pseudes*, false + *podion*, little foot) attach to the substrate as they are formed. The plasma membrane also seems to slide over the underlying layer of cytoplasm when an amoeba moves. The plasma membrane may be "rolling" in a way that is (very roughly) analogous to a bulldozer track rolling over its wheels. A thin fluid layer between the plasma membrane and the ectoplasm may facilitate this rolling.

As an amoeba moves, the fluid endoplasm flows forward into the fountain zone of an advancing pseudopodium. As it reaches the tip of a pseudopodium, endoplasm is converted into ectoplasm. At the same time, ectoplasm near the opposite end in the recruitment zone is converted into endoplasm and begins flowing forward (figure 32.15).

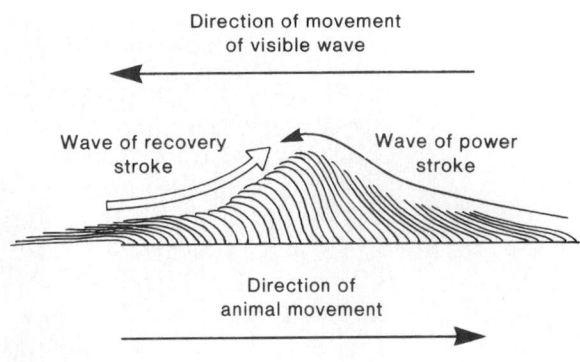

FIGURE 32.16

Ciliary Movement. A metachronal wave passing along a row of cilia. *Source: After Wells, after Sleigh.*

Ciliary and Flagellar Movement

With the exception of the arthropods, locomotory cilia and flagella occur in every animal phylum. Structurally, **cilia** (s., cilium; L. "eyelashes") and **flagella** (s., flagellum; L. "small whips") are very similar, but the former are shorter and more numerous, whereas the latter are long and generally occur singly or in pairs.

Ciliary movements are coordinated. For example, in some ciliated protozoa, pairs of cilia occur in rows. Rows of cilia beat slightly out of phase with one another so that ciliary waves periodically pass over the surface of the protozoan (figure 32.16). In fact, many ciliates can rapidly reverse the direction of ciliary beating, which changes the direction of the ciliary waves and the direction of movement.

The epidermis of free-living flatworms (e.g., turbellarians) and nemertines is abundantly ciliated. The smallest specimens (about 1 mm long) lie at the upper end of the size range for efficient locomotion using cilia. Larger flatworms (e.g., triclads and polyclads) have retained **ciliary creeping** as the principal means of locomotion, and the largest animals to move by ciliary creeping are the nemertines. The muscular activities of the flatworms and nemertines are varied and involve pedal locomotion, peristalsis, or looping movements with anterior and posterior adhesion. Since ciliary and muscular means of movement (locomotion) are found to coexist in some free-living flatworms and nemertines, the transition from ciliary to muscular locomotion is likely to have taken place among the flatwormlike ancestors.

> ### Stop and Ask Yourself
>
> 13. Considering protists and animals, where would you find amoeboid movement occurring?
> 14. What is the major difference between cilia and flagella?
> 15. How would you describe the process of amoeboid movement? Ciliary creeping?

The Muscular System of Invertebrates

Muscular tissue is the driving force, the power behind movement in most invertebrates and vertebrates. The basic physiological property of muscle tissue is contractility, the ability to contract or shorten. In addition, muscle tissue has three other important properties: excitability (or irritability), the capacity to receive and respond to a stimulus; extensibility, the ability to stretch; and elasticity, the ability to return to its original shape after being stretched or contracted.

Animals may have one or more of the following types of muscle tissue: smooth, cardiac, and skeletal. The contractile cells of these tissues are called **muscle fibers.**

Smooth muscle is also called involuntary muscle because its contractions are not controlled by higher brain centers. Smooth-muscle fibers have a single nucleus, are spindle shaped, and are arranged in a parallel pattern to form sheets (*see figure 3.24p*). Smooth muscle has the ability to maintain good tone (a normal degree of vigor and tension) even without nervous stimulation. Smooth muscle contracts slowly, but it can sustain prolonged contractions and does not fatigue (tire) easily.

Smooth muscle is the predominant muscle type in many invertebrates. For example, it forms part of the adductor ("catch") muscles that close the valves of clams and other bivalve molluscs. ⑦ These smooth muscles give bivalves the ability to "clam up" against predators for days with little or no energy expenditure.

Striated muscle fibers (cells) with single nuclei are common in invertebrates, but occur in adult vertebrates only in the heart, where it is called cardiac muscle. **Cardiac muscle** fibers are involuntary, have a single nucleus, are striated (have dark and light bands), and are branched (*see figure 3.24q*). This branching allows the fibers to interlock for greater strength during contraction. ⑧ Hearts do not fatigue because cardiac fibers relax completely between contractions.

Skeletal muscle, also a striated muscle, is called voluntary muscle because its contractions are consciously controlled by the nervous system. Skeletal muscle fibers are multinucleated and striated (*see figure 3.24o*). Skeletal muscles are attached to skeletons (both endo- and exoskeletons). When skeletal muscles contract, they shorten. Thus, muscles can only pull; they cannot push. Therefore, skeletal muscles work in antagonistic pairs. For example, one muscle of a pair bends (flexes) a joint and brings a limb close to the body. The other member of the pair straightens (extends) the joint and extends the limb away from the body (*see figure 32.11b*).

A few functional differences among invertebrate muscles are now mentioned to indicate some of the differences from the vertebrate skeletal muscles discussed next. In arthropods, a typical muscle fiber is innervated by at least two motor nerves. One motor nerve fiber causes a fast contraction and the other a slow contraction. Another variation occurs in certain insect (bees, wasps, flies, beetles) flight muscles. These muscles are called asynchronous muscles, since the upward wing movement (rather than a nerve impulse) activates the muscles that produce the downstroke. In the midge, for example, this can happen 1,000 times a second.

An understanding of the structure and function of invertebrate locomotion (movement) is crucial to an understanding

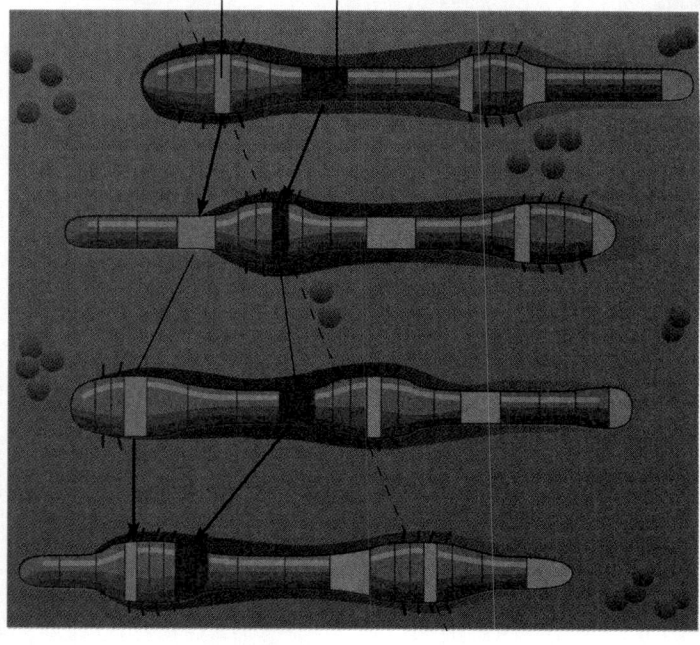

Longitudinal muscles contracted (setae protruded)   Circular muscles contracted (setae withdrawn)

Movement relative to the ground

Figure 32.17

A Diagram of the Successive Stages in the Movement of an Earthworm. When the longitudinal muscles are contracted and the circular muscles are relaxed, the segments of the earthworm bulge and are stationary with respect to the ground. In the front of each region of longitudinal muscle contraction, circular muscles contract, causing the segments to elongate and push forward. Contraction of longitudinal muscles in segments behind a bulging region cause those segments to be pulled forward. For reasons of simplification, the movements of the setae are not shown.

of the evolutionary origins of the various invertebrate groups. Discussion on several types of invertebrate locomotion that involve muscular systems follows.

The Locomotion of Soft-bodied Invertebrates

Many soft-bodied invertebrates are able to move over a firm substratum. For example, flatworms, some cnidarians, and the gastropod molluscs move by means of waves of activity in the muscular system that is applied to the substrate. This type of movement is called **pedal locomotion.** Pedal locomotion can be easily seen by examining the undersurface of a planarian or a snail while it crawls along a glass plate. In the land snail *Helix,* several waves crossing the length of the foot will be seen simultaneously, each moving in the same direction as the locomotion of the snail, but at a greater rate.

Many large flatworms and most nemertine worms exhibit a muscular component to their locomotion. In this type of movement, alternating waves of contraction of circular and longitudinal muscles generate retrograde peristaltic waves, which enhance the locomotion also provided by the surface cilia. This system is most highly developed in the septate coelomate worms, especially earthworms (figure 32.17).

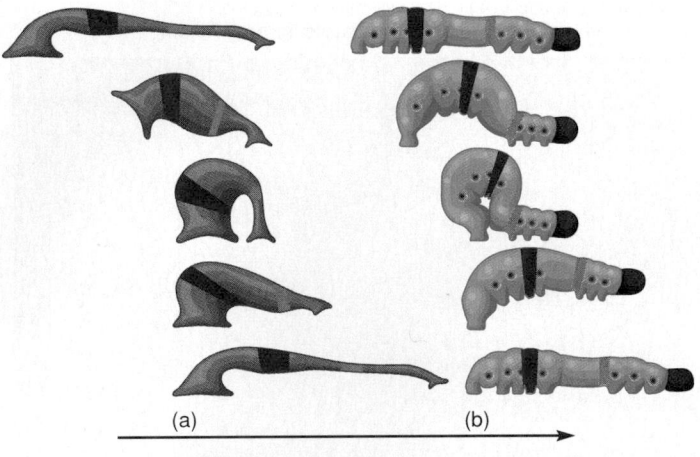

Movement relative to the ground

FIGURE 32.18

Looping Movements. (*a*) Leeches have anterior and posterior suckers, which they alternately attach to the substrate in looping movements in order to move forward. (*b*) Similar movements are exhibited by some insect larvae such as lepidopteran caterpillars. The caterpillar uses arching movements to move forward.

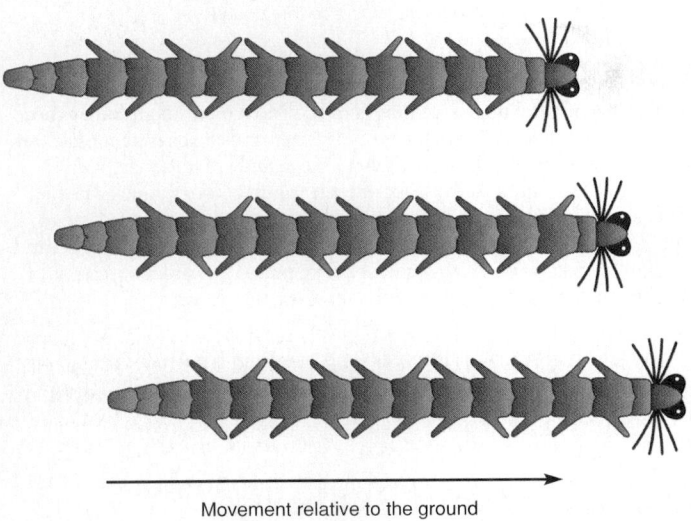

Movement relative to the ground

FIGURE 32.19

Diagrammatic Representation of Locomotion in a Polychaete. When a polychaete (e.g., *Nereis*) is crawling slowly, the tips of the multiple limbs (parapodia) move backwards relative to the body. Since the tips of the parapodia touch the ground, this causes the body to move forward. In addition, there is a metachronal wave of activity in the parapodia passing forwards from the tail to the head and with the left and right parapodia being exactly one-half wavelength out of phase. This ensures that each parapodium executes its power stroke without risk of interference with the parapodium immediately posterior. For simplification, the movements of the setae are not shown.

Leeches and some insect larvae exhibit **looping movements.** Leeches have anterior and posterior suckers that provide effective alternating temporary points of attachment (figure 32.18*a*). Similar movements are exhibited by lepidopteran caterpillars in which arching movements are equivalent to the contraction of longitudinal muscles (figure 32.18*b*).

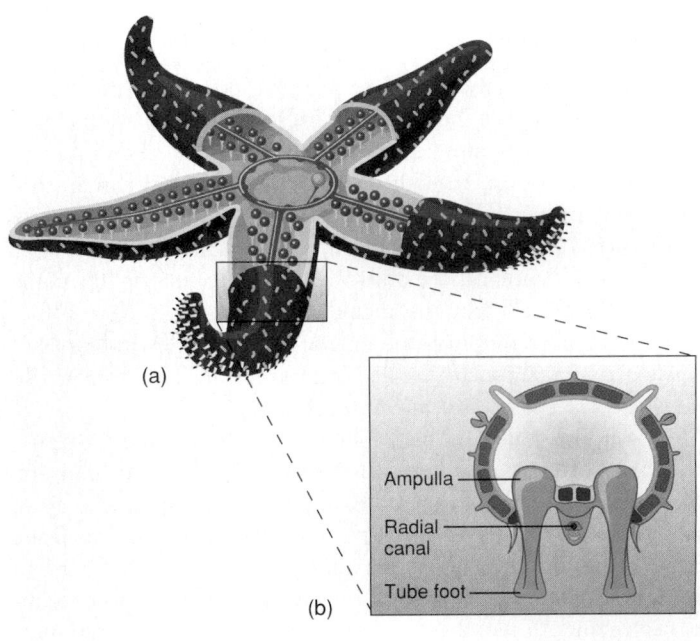

(a)

Ampulla

Radial canal

Tube foot

(b)

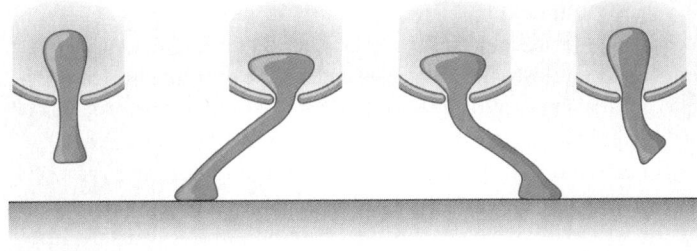

(c)

FIGURE 32.20

The Water-Vascular System of Echinoderms. (*a*) The general arrangement of the water-vascular system. (*b*) A cross section of an arm showing the radial canal, ampullae, and tube feet of the water-vascular system. (*c*) The stepping cycle of a single tube foot. For simplification, the retractor muscles in the tube foot are not shown.

Polychaete worms move by the alternate movement of multiple limbs (parapodia), the tips of which are made to move backwards relative to the body; however, since the tips are attached to the ground, this causes the body of the worm to move forward (figure 32.19).

The **water-vascular system** of echinoderms provides a unique means of locomotion. For example, in starfish, there are typically five arms and in each one there is a water-vascular canal. Along each canal are reservoir ampullae and tube feet (figure 32.20*a,b*). Contraction of the muscles comprising the ampullae drives water into the tube feet, whereas, contraction of the tube feet moves water into the ampullae. Thus, the tube feet are extended by hydraulic pressure and can perform simple steplike motions (figure 32.20*c*).

Terrestrial Locomotion in Invertebrates: Walking

Invertebrates (terrestrial arthropods) living in/on terrestrial environments are much denser than the air in which they

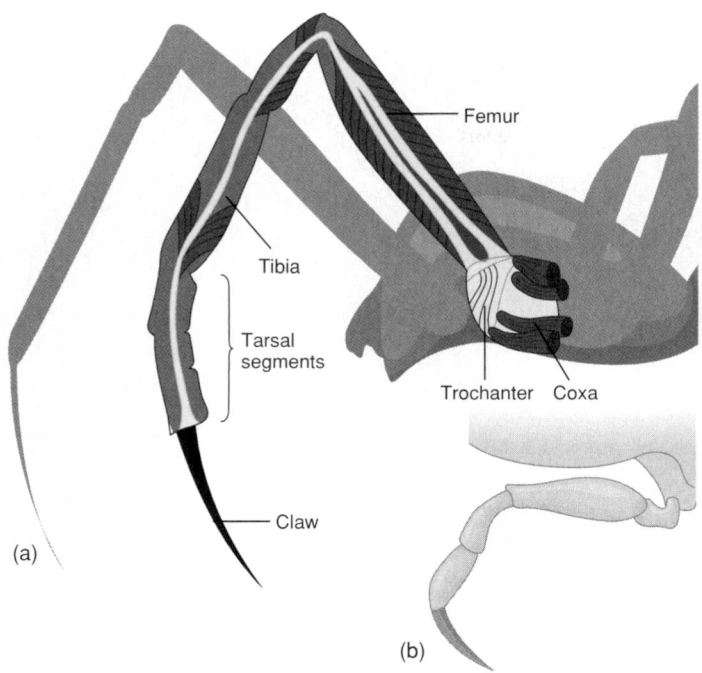

FIGURE 32.21
A Typical Arthropod Limb. (*a*) Notice that most of the muscles are in the basal section. (*b*) The characteristic projection of the arthropod limb.

FIGURE 32.22
Walking: The Limb Trajectories of Several Arthropods. (*a*) Crabs walk in a sideways fashion, protraction being achieved by extension of the lower limb joints. Other arthropods, such as (*b*) the lobster, (*c*) the spider, and (*d*) an insect have limb trajectories that do not overlap and move forward by rotating the basal joint of the limb relative to their body.

live. As a result they require structural support, and those that move quickly make use of rigid skeletal elements that interact with the ground. These elements include flexible joints, tendons, and muscles that are attached to a rigid cuticle and form limbs. The walking limbs of the most highly evolved arthropods (Crustacea, Chelicerata, and Uniramia) are remarkably uniform in structure. The limbs are composed of a series of jointed elements that become progressively less massive towards the tip (figure 32.21*a*). Each joint is articulated to allow movement in only one plane. These limb joints allow extension and flexion of the limb. Rotation of the limb plane at the basal joint with the body is also possible, which is responsible for forward movement. The body is typically carried slung between the laterally projected limbs (figure 32.21*b*) and walking movements do not involve raising or lowering the body. Depending on the arthropod, the trajectory of each limb is different and nonoverlapping (figure 32.22). Most arthropods walk forwards rotating the basal joint of the limb relative to the body, but crabs walk in a sideways fashion.

Terrestrial Locomotion in Invertebrates: Flight

The physical properties of a sclerotin-tanned arthropod cuticle are such that the evolution of true flight was possible for the pterygote insects. Flying insects evolved some 200 million years ago. There has, therefore, been a long time during which the

basic mechanism of flight has been modified. Consequently, present-day insects exhibit a wide range of structural adaptations and mechanisms for flight (*see figure 24.5*).

Terrestrial Locomotion in Invertebrates: Jumping

Some insects (fleas, grasshoppers, leafhoppers) have the ability to jump. Most of the time, this is an escape reaction. In order to jump, an insect must exert a force against the ground sufficient to impart a take-off velocity greater than its mass (figure 32.23). ⑨ Long legs increase the mechanical advantage of the leg extensor muscles. This is why insects that jump have relatively long legs. The limit to this line of evolution is probably set by the mechanical strength of the insect cuticle acting as the lever in this system.

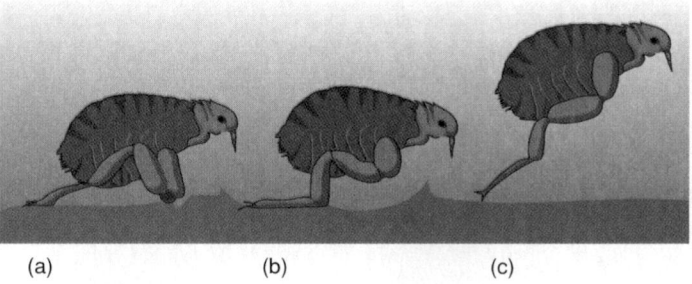

Figure **32.23**

The Jump of A Flea. (*a*) When a flea is resting, the femur of the leg (for simplicity only one is shown) is raised, the joints are locked, and energy is stored in the deformed elastic protein ("animal rubber" or resilin) of the cuticle. (*b*) As a flea begins to jump, the joints become unlocked by the relaxation of muscles. (*c*) The force exerted against the ground by the tibia gives the flea a specific velocity which will determine the height of the jump. The jump is the result of the explosive release of the energy stored in the cuticle.

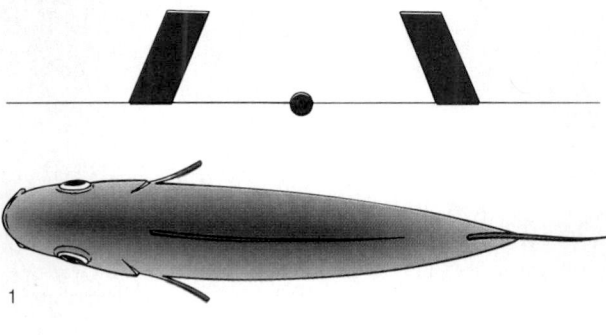

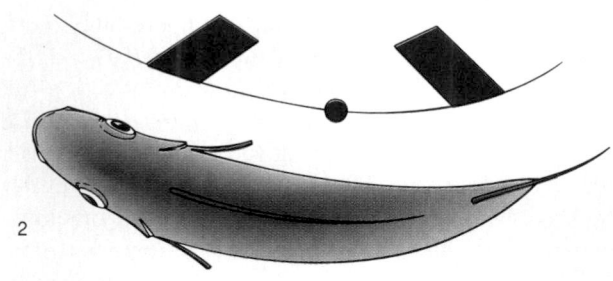

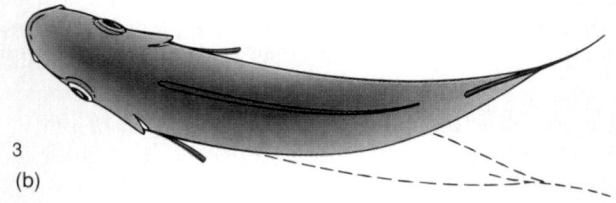

Figure **32.24**

Fish Musculature. (*a*) This drawing of the skeletal muscles of a bony fish (perch) shows mainly the large muscles of the trunk and tail. These muscles occur in blocks called myomeres separated by connective tissue sheaths. Notice that the myomeres are flexed so that they resemble the letter *W* tipped at a 90° angle. The different colors (red, orange, blue) represent different myomeres. (*b*) Diagram illustrating fish movements based on myomere contractions. Muscular forces cause the myomere segments to rotate rather than constrict (*1*). The rotation of cranial and caudal myomere segments causes the fish's body to bend about a point midway between the two segments (*2*). Alternate bends of the caudal end of the body propel the fish forward (*3*).

Stop and Ask Yourself

16. What are some physiological properties of muscle tissue?
17. What is meant by an asynchronous invertebrate muscle?
18. What invertebrates move by pedal locomotion? Looping movements? Water-vascular system? Walking? Jumping?

The Muscular System of Vertebrates

The endoskeleton of vertebrates provides sites for the attachment of skeletal muscles. Skeletal muscles are attached to the skeleton by **tendons,** which are tough, fibrous bands or cords.

Most of the musculature of fishes consists of segmental **myomeres** (Gr. *myo*, muscle + *meros*, part; figure 32.24*a*). This is an effective arrangement for causing the lateral undulations of the trunk and tail that are responsible for fish locomotion (figure 32.24*b*).

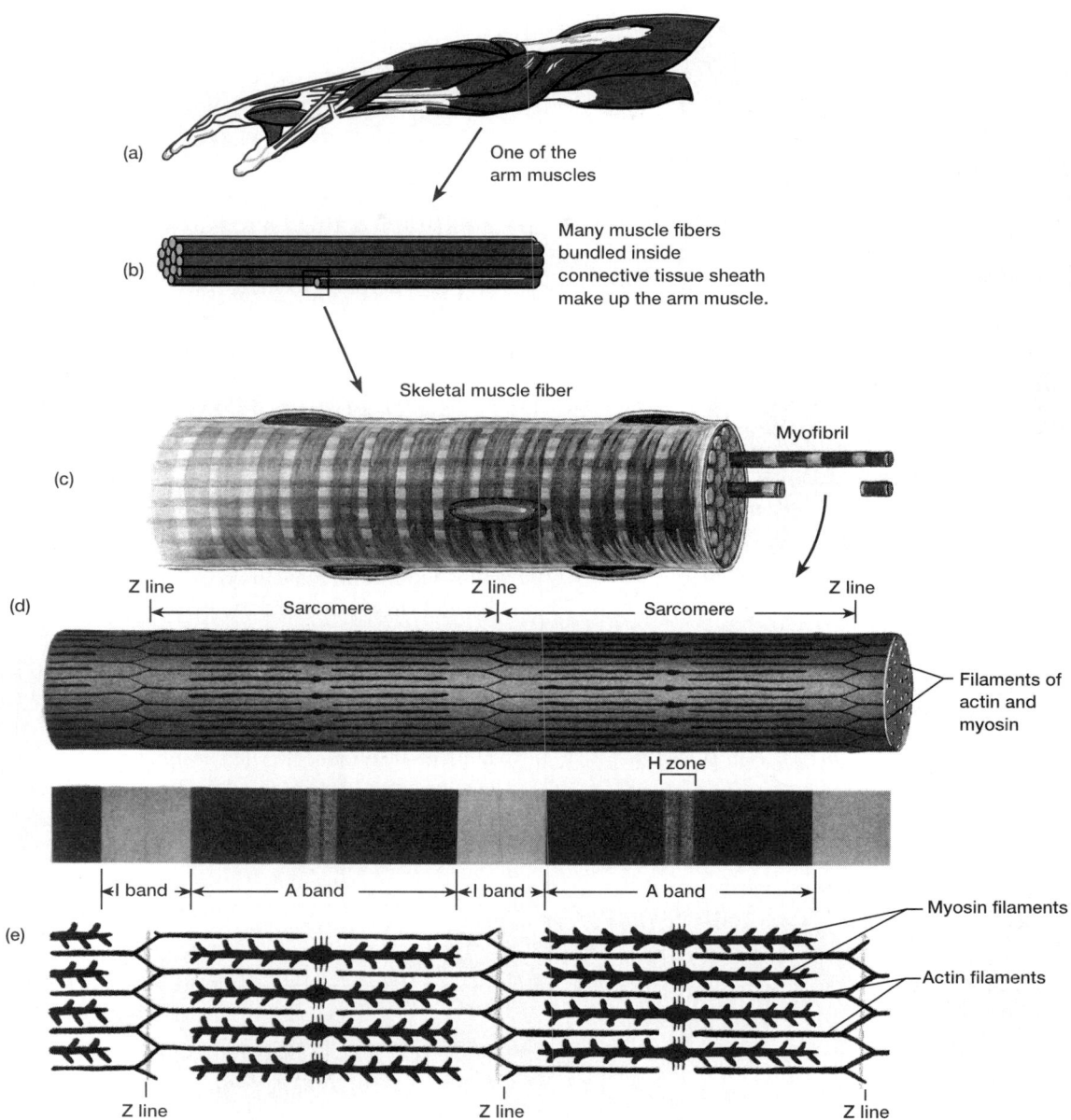

FIGURE 32.25

Structure of Skeletal Muscle Tissue. (*a*) A skeletal muscle in the forearm consists of many muscle fibers (*b*) bundled inside a connective tissue sheath. (*c*) A skeletal muscle fiber contains many myofibrils, each consisting of (*d*) functional units called sarcomeres. (*e*) The characteristic striations of a sarcomere are due to the arrangement of actin and myosin filaments.

The transition from water to land entailed changes in the body musculature. As previously noted, the appendages became increasingly important in locomotion, and movements of the trunk became less important. The segmental nature of the myomeres in the trunk muscles was lost. Back muscles became more numerous and powerful. These evolutionary adaptations are well illustrated by examining some of the major superficial muscles of the frog.

Skeletal Muscle Contraction

When observed with the light microscope, each skeletal muscle fiber has a pattern of alternate dark and light bands (*see figure 3.24o*). This striation of whole fibers arises from the alternating dark and light bands of the many smaller, threadlike **myofibrils** contained in each muscle fiber (figure 32.25*a–c*). Electron microscopy and biochemical analysis have shown that these bands are due to the placement of the muscle proteins **actin** and **myosin** within the myofibrils. Myosin occurs as thick filaments and actin as thin filaments. As figure 32.25*c–e* illustrates, the lightest region of a myofibril (the I band) contains only actin, whereas the darkest region (the A band) contains both actin and myosin.

The functional (contractile) unit of a myofibril is the **sarcomere,** each of which extends from one Z line to another Z line. Notice that the actin filaments are attached to the Z lines whereas myosin filaments are not (figure 32.25*e*). When a sarcomere contracts, the actin filaments slide past the myosin

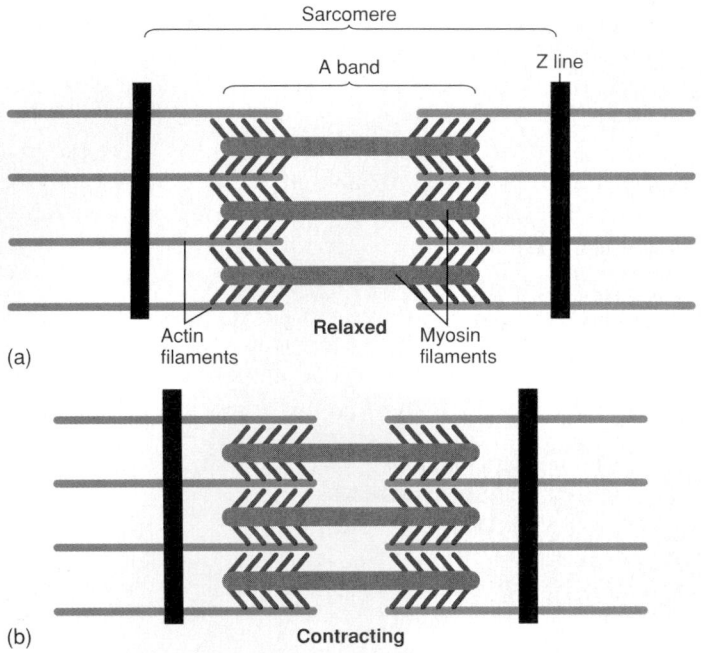

(a) **Relaxed**

Actin filaments   Myosin filaments

(b) **Contracting**

Figure 32.26

Sliding-Filament Model of Muscle Contraction. (*a*) A sarcomere in a relaxed position. (*b*) As the sarcomere contracts, the myosin filaments form attachments called cross-bridges to the actin filaments and pull them so that they slide past the myosin filaments. Compare the length of the sarcomere in (*a*) to that in (*b*).

filaments as they approach one another. This process shortens the sarcomere. The combined decreases in length of the individual sarcomeres account for contraction of the whole muscle fiber, and in turn, the whole muscle. This movement of actin in relation to myosin is called the sliding-filament model of muscle contraction.

The actual contraction is accomplished by a ratchet mechanism acting between the two filament types. Myosin contains globular projections that attach to actin at specific active binding sites, forming attachments called cross-bridges (figure 32.26). Once cross-bridges have formed, they exert a force on the thin actin filament and cause it to move.

Control of Muscle Contraction

When nerve impulses conducted by a motor nerve reach skeletal muscle fibers, the fibers are stimulated to contract via a motor unit. A **motor unit** consists of one motor nerve fiber and all the muscle fibers with which it communicates. A space separates the specialized end of the motor nerve fiber from the membrane (**sarcolemma**) of the muscle fiber. The motor end plate is the specialized portion of the sarcolemma of a muscle fiber surrounding the terminal end of the nerve. This arrangement of structures is called a **neuromuscular junction** or cleft (figure 32.27).

When nerve impulses reach the ends of the nerve fiber branches, a chemical called acetylcholine is released from storage synaptic vesicles in the nerve ending. Acetylcholine diffuses

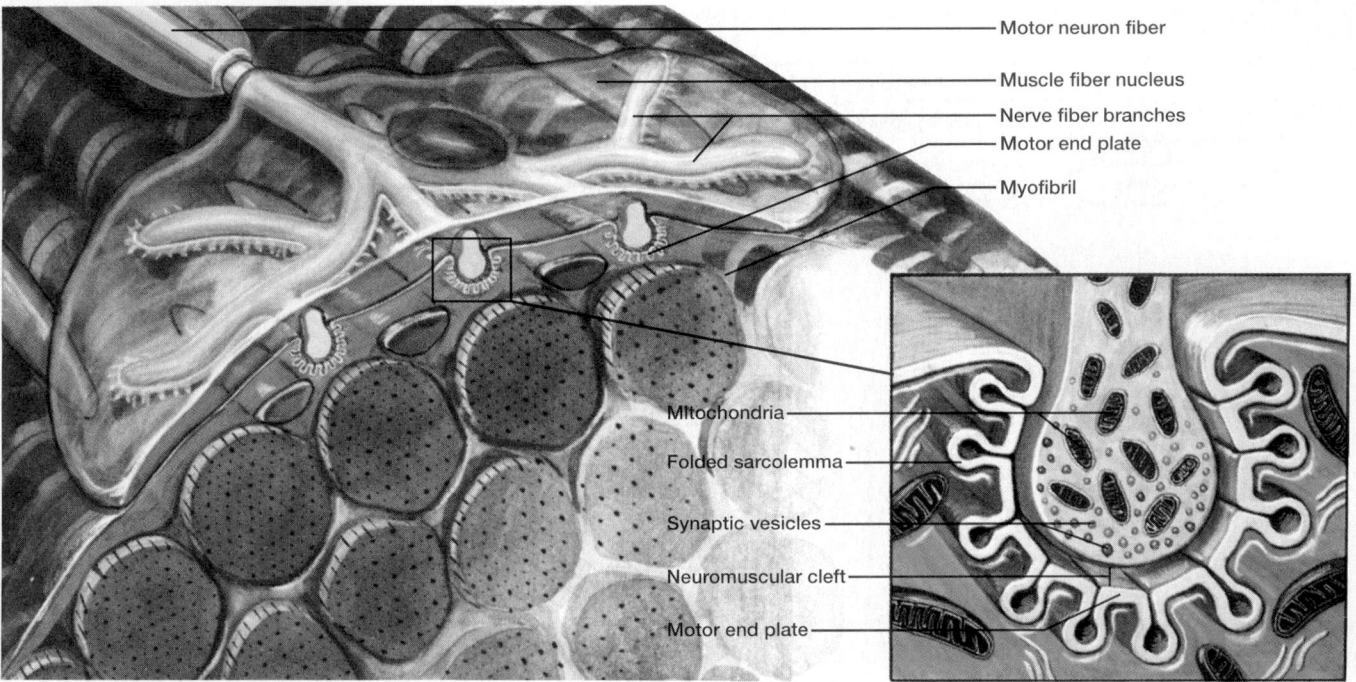

Motor neuron fiber
Muscle fiber nucleus
Nerve fiber branches
Motor end plate
Myofibril

Mitochondria
Folded sarcolemma
Synaptic vesicles
Neuromuscular cleft
Motor end plate

Figure 32.27

A Nerve-Muscle Motor Unit. A motor unit consists of one motor nerve and all the muscle fibers that it innervates. A neuromuscular junction, or cleft, is the site where the nerve fiber and muscle fiber meet.

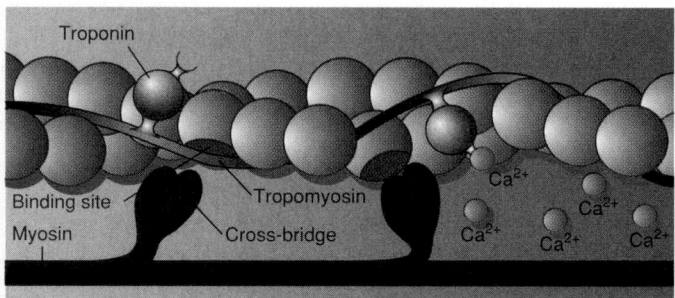

FIGURE 32.28

A Model of the Calcium-Induced Changes in Troponin, Allowing Cross-Bridges to Form between Actin and Myosin. The attachment of Ca^{2+} to troponin causes movement of the troponin-tropomyosin complex, which exposes a binding site on the actin. The myosin cross-bridge can then attach to actin and undergo a power stroke.

tubules is the endoplasmic reticulum (*see figure 3.15*) of muscle cells, called sarcoplasmic reticulum. The altered polarity of the transverse tubules causes calcium ions (Ca^{2+}) to be released from the sarcoplasmic reticulum and diffuse into the cytoplasm. The calcium then binds with a regulatory protein called troponin that is on another protein called tropomyosin. This binding exposes the myosin binding sites on the actin molecule that had been blocked by tropomyosin (figure 32.28). Once the binding sites are open, the myosin filament can form cross-bridges, and the filament can slide, via a power stroke, resulting in muscular contraction.

Relaxation follows contraction. During relaxation, an active transport system pumps calcium back into the sarcoplasmic reticulum for storage. By controlling the nerve impulses that reach the sarcoplasmic reticulum, the nervous system controls Ca^{2+} levels in skeletal muscle tissue, thereby exerting control over contraction.

across the neuromuscular cleft between the nerve ending and the muscle-fiber sarcolemma and binds with acetylcholine receptors on the sarcolemma. The sarcolemma is normally polarized; the outside is positive and the inside is negative. When acetylcholine binds to the receptors, ions are redistributed on both sides of the membrane and the polarity is altered. This altered polarity flows in a wavelike progression into the muscle fiber by conducting paths called transverse tubules. Associated with the transverse

Stop and Ask Yourself

19. What is a myofibril?
20. How does the sliding-filament model explain muscle contraction?
21. How do nerves cause skeletal muscles to contract?

SUMMARY

1. The integumentary system is the external covering of an animal. It functions primarily in protection against mechanical injury and invasion by microorganisms.

2. Some single-celled protozoa have only a plasma membrane for an external covering. Other protozoa have a thick protein coat, called a pellicle, outside the plasma membrane. Most invertebrates have an integument consisting of a single layer of columnar epithelial cells called an epidermis. Specializations may occur outside of this epithelial layer in the form of cuticles, shells, or teguments.

3. Skin is the integument found in vertebrates. It has two main layers: the epidermis and the dermis. Skin structure varies considerably among vertebrates. Some of these variable structures include scales, hairs, feathers, claws, nails, and baleen plates.

4. From a comparative perspective, the skin of jawless fishes (lampreys and hagfishes) is thick; the skin of cartilaginous fishes (sharks) is multilayered and contains bone in the form of denticles; the skin of bony fishes (teleosts) contains scales; the skin of amphibians is stratified and contains mucous and serous glands plus pigmentation; the skin of reptiles is very thick and modified into keratinized scales; the skin of birds is very thin and soft and contains feathers; and mammalian skin consists of several layers of a variety of cells.

5. Three types of skeletons are found in animals: hydrostatic skeletons, exoskeletons, and endoskeletons. These skeletons function in movement of an animal using muscles that work in opposition (antagonism) to each other.

6. The hydrostatic skeleton is composed of a core of liquid (water or a body fluid such as blood) surrounded by a tension-resistant sheath containing longitudinal and/or circular muscles. Hydrostatic skeletons are found in invertebrates and can take many forms and shapes such as the gastrovascular cavity of acoelomates, the rhynchocoel in nemertines, a pseudocoelom in aschelminths, a coelom in annelids, or a hemocoel in molluscs.

7. Rigid exoskeletons also have locomotor functions. This is accomplished by providing sites for muscle attachment and counterforces for muscle movements. Exoskeletons also support and protect, but these are secondary functions. In arthropods, the epidermis of the body wall secretes a thick, hard cuticle. In crustaceans (crabs, lobsters, shrimp), the exoskeleton contains calcium carbonate crystals that make it hard and flexible, except at the joints.

8. Rigid endoskeletons are enclosed by other body tissues. For example, the endoskeletons of sponges consist of mineral spicules, and the endoskeletons of echinoderms (starfishes, sea urchins) are made of calcareous plates called ossicles.

9. The most familiar endoskeletons, both cartilaginous and bony, first appeared in the vertebrates. Endoskeletons consist of two main types of supportive connective tissue: cartilage and bone. Cartilage provides a site for muscle attachment, aids in movement at joints, and provides support. Bone provides a point of attachment for muscles and for transmitting the force of muscular contraction from one part of the body to another.

10. Movement (locomotion) is characteristic of certain cells, protists, and animals. Amoeboid movement and movement by cilia and flagella are examples of locomotion that do not involve muscles.

11. The power behind muscular movement in both invertebrates and vertebrates is muscular tissue. The three types of muscular tissue are smooth, cardiac, and skeletal. Muscle tissue exhibits contractility, excitability, extensibility, and elasticity.

12. The functional (contractile) unit of a muscle fibril is the sarcomere. Nerves control skeletal muscle contraction.

SELECTED KEY TERMS

amoeboid movement (p. 538)

ciliary creeping (p. 538)

denticles (p. 529)

dermis (p. 528)

endoskeleton (p. 535)

epidermis (p. 528)

exoskeleton (p. 534)

hydrostatic skeleton (p. 533)

integument (p. 528)

neuromuscular junction (p. 544)

skin (p. 528)

CRITICAL THINKING QUESTIONS

1. How does the structure of skin relate to its functions of protection, temperature control, waste removal, radiation protection, vitamin production, and environmental responsiveness?

2. How does the epidermis of an invertebrate differ from that of a vertebrate?

3. Give an example of an animal with each type of skeleton (hydro-, exo-, endoskeleton) and explain how the contractions of its muscles produces locomotion.

4. Give one similarity and one difference between vertebrate skeletal muscle and the following: asynchronous insect muscle; the "catch" muscle of molluscs; the movement of cilia; amoeboid movement.

COMMUNICATION I:
NERVES

Concepts

1. The nervous system helps to communicate, integrate, and coordinate the functions of the various organs and organ systems in the body of an animal.
2. The flow of information through the nervous system occurs in three main steps: the collection of information from outside and inside the body (sensory activities), the processing of this information in the nervous system, and the initiation of appropriate responses.
3. Transmission between neurons is accomplished directly (electrically) or by means of chemicals called neurotransmitters.
4. The evolution of the nervous system in invertebrates has led to elaboration of organized nerve cords and centralization of responses in the anterior portion of the animal.
5. The nervous system of vertebrates consists of the central nervous system, made up of the brain and spinal cord, and the peripheral nervous system, which is composed of the nerves in the rest of the body.
6. Nervous systems evolved through the gradual layering of additional nervous tissue over reflex pathways of more ancient origin.

Would You Like to Know:

1.   how neurons and electrically active cells maintain an electrical charge? (p. 549)
2.   how flea sprays or powders work to kill fleas but not dogs or cats? (p. 551)
3.   how nerve pathways are analogous to a telephone cable? (p. 555)
4.   what part of the brain is involved with language, both written and spoken? (p. 557)

These and other useful questions will be answered in this chapter.

This chapter contains evolutionary concepts, which are set off in this font.

The two forms of communication in an animal that integrate body functions in order to maintain homeostasis are: (1) neurons, which transmit electrical signals that report information or initiate a quick response in a specific tissue; and (2) hormones, which are slower, chemical signals that initiate a widespread, prolonged response, often in a variety of tissues. This chapter focuses on the function of the neuron and the anatomical organization of the nervous system in animals. In the following chapter (chapter 34), the senses and the ways in which they collect information and transmit it along nerves to the central nervous system are presented. Chapter 35 will conclude the study of communication by presenting how hormones affect long-term changes in an animal's body.

NEURONS: THE BASIC UNITS OF THE NERVOUS SYSTEM

The functional unit of the nervous system is a highly specialized cell called the **neuron.** Neurons are specialized to produce signals that can be communicated over short to relatively long distances, from one part of an animal's body to another. Neurons have two important properties: excitability, the ability to respond to stimuli, and conductivity, the ability to conduct a signal.

There are three functional types of neurons. (1) **Sensory (receptor) neurons** either act as receptors of stimuli themselves or are activated by receptors (figure 33.1a). They are stimulated by changes in the internal or external environments and respond by sending signals to the major integrating centers where information is processed. (2) **Interneurons** (figure 33.1c) are the neurons that comprise the integrating centers and receive signals from the sensory neurons and transmit them to motor neurons. (3) **Motor (effector) neurons** (figure 33.1b) send the processed information via a signal to the body's effectors (e.g., muscles), causing them to contract, or to glands, causing them to secrete. The flow of information in the nervous system is summarized in figure 33.2.

NEURON STRUCTURE: THE KEY TO FUNCTION

Most neurons contain three principal parts: a cell body, dendrites, and an axon (*see figure 33.1*). The **cell body** has a large, central nucleus. The motor neuron shown in figure 33.1b has many short, threadlike branches called **dendrites** (Gr. *dendron*, tree), which are actually extensions of the cell body and conduct signals toward the cell body. The **axon** is a relatively long, cylindrical process that conducts signals (information) away from the cell body.

The neurons of hydras and sea anemones do not have a sheath covering the axon of the neuron. Other invertebrates and all vertebrates have sheathed neurons. When present, the laminated lipid sheath is called **myelin.** Some neurons have the myelin sheath wrapped in layers by a **neurolemmocyte** (formerly,

FIGURE 33.1

Types of Vertebrate Neurons. (*a*) Sensory neurons transmit information from the environment to the central nervous system. They tend to have long dendrites and short axons. (*b*) Motor neurons transmit information from the central nervous system to muscles or glands and tend to have short dendrites and long axons. (*c*) Interneurons connect other neurons, permitting integration of information to occur.

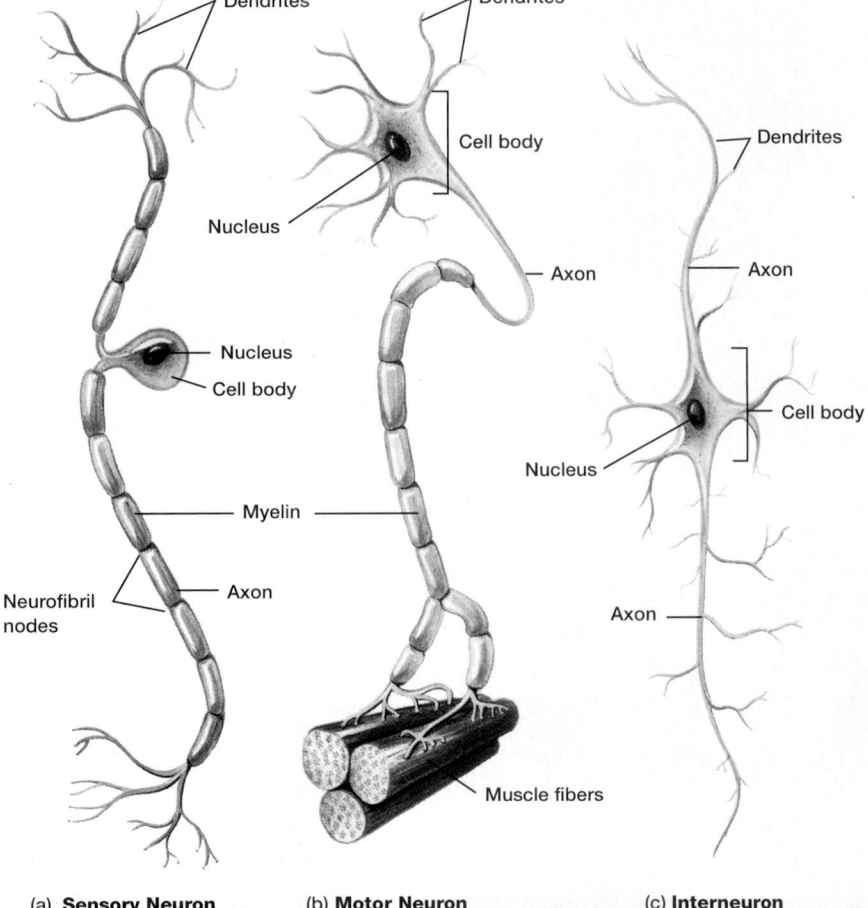

Dendrites

Dendrites

Cell body

Nucleus

Nucleus

Axon

Cell body

Myelin

Dendrites

Axon

Neurofibril nodes

Axon

Cell body

Nucleus

Axon

Muscle fibers

(a) **Sensory Neuron**   (b) **Motor Neuron**   (c) **Interneuron**

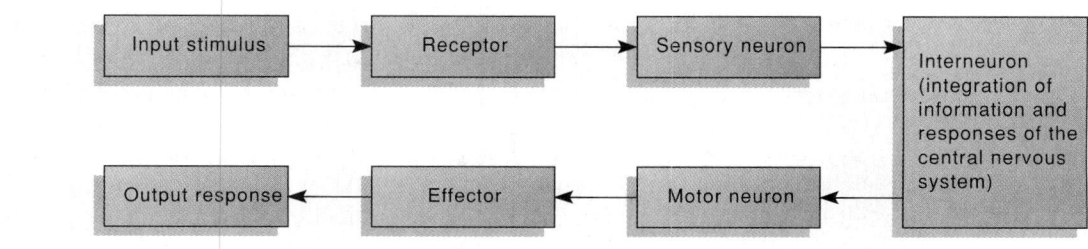

FIGURE 33.2

A Generalized Pathway for the Flow of Information within the Nervous System. An input stimulus initiates impulses within some sensory structure (the receptor); the impulses are then transferred via sensory neurons to interneurons. After response selection has occurred, nerve impulses are generated and transferred along motor neurons to an effector (e.g., a muscle or gland) where the appropriate output response is elicited.

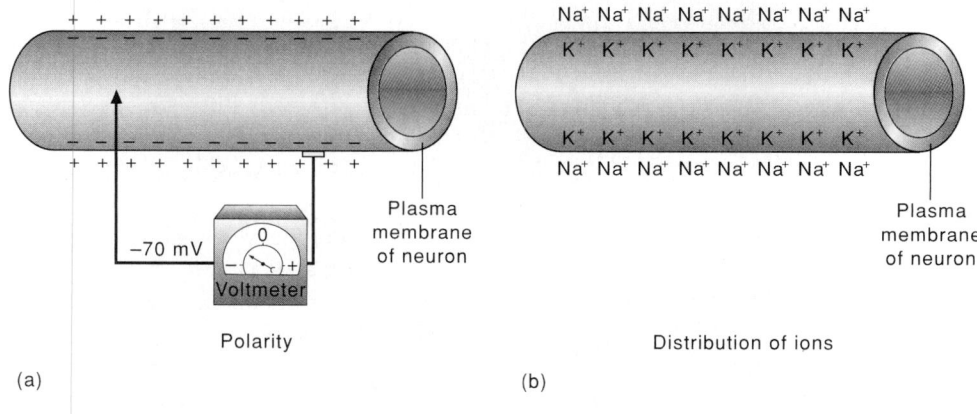

FIGURE 33.3

Resting Membrane Potential. (*a*) A voltmeter measures the difference in electrical potential between two electrodes. When one microelectrode is placed inside a neuron at rest, and one is placed outside, the electrical potential inside the cell is –70 mV relative to the outside. (*b*) In a neuron at rest, sodium is more concentrated outside and potassium is more concentrated inside the cell. When a neuron is in this resting condition, it is said to be polarized.

Schwann cell). In these neurons, the myelin sheath is segmented at regular intervals by gaps called **neurofibril nodes** (formerly, **nodes of Ranvier**). The neurolemmocyte also assists in the regeneration of injured myelinated neurons.

Recall that the nervous system receives data (input stimulus), integrates it, and effects a change (output response) in the physiology of the animal. In a given neuron, the dendrites are the receptors, the cell body the integrator, and the ends of the axon are the effectors.

NEURON COMMUNICATION

The language (signal) of a neuron is the nerve impulse or action potential. The key to this nerve impulse is the neuron's plasma membrane and its properties. Changes in membrane permeability and the subsequent movement of ions produce a nerve impulse that is conducted along the plasma membrane of the dendrites, cell body, and axon of each neuron.

RESTING MEMBRANE POTENTIAL

A "resting" neuron is one that is not conducting a nerve impulse. The plasma membrane of a resting neuron is polarized; the fluid on

the inner side of the membrane is negatively charged with respect to the positively charged fluid outside the membrane (figure 33.3). The difference in electrical charge between the inside and the outside of the membrane at any given point is due to the relative numbers of positive and negative ions in the fluids on either side of the membrane, and the permeability of the plasma membrane to these ions. The difference in charge is called the **resting membrane potential.** All cells have such a resting potential, but neurons and muscle cells are specialized to transmit and recycle it rapidly.

The resting potential is measured in millivolts (mV). A millivolt is 1/1,000 of a volt. Normally, the resting membrane potential is about –70 mV due to the unequal distribution of various electrically charged ions. Sodium (Na^+) ions are found in higher concentration in the fluid outside the plasma membrane, and potassium (K^+) and negative protein ions are found in higher concentrations inside.

The Na^+ and K^+ ions are constantly diffusing through the plasma membrane, moving from regions of high concentrations to regions of lower concentration. (There are also larger Cl^- ions and huge negative protein ions, which cannot move easily from the inside of the neuron to the outside.) ❶ However, the concentrations of Na^+ and K^+ ions on the two sides of the membrane remain constant due to the action of the **sodium-potassium ATPase pump,** which is powered by ATP

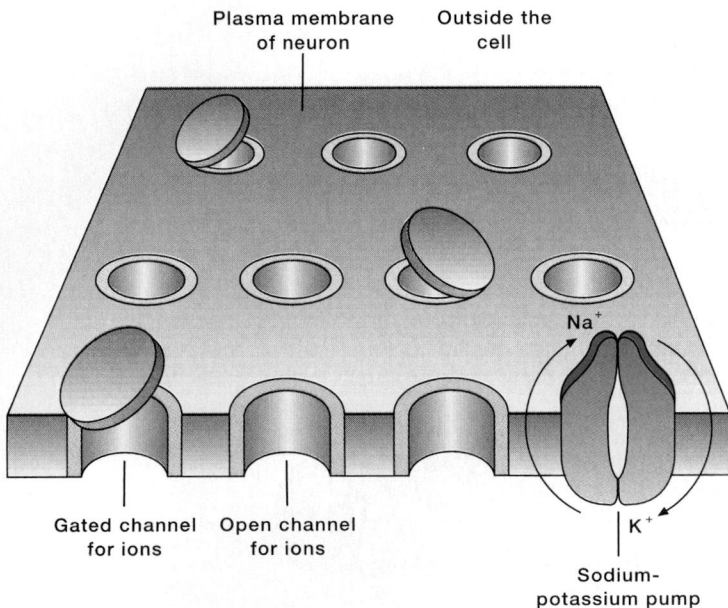

Plasma membrane   Outside the
of neuron   cell

Na⁺

Gated channel   Open channel
for ions   for ions

K⁺

Sodium-
potassium pump

FIGURE 33.4

Ion Channels and the Sodium-Potassium Pump. These mechanisms maintain a balance between the sodium ions and potassium ions on both sides of the membrane and create a membrane potential. Some channels are always open, but others are opened or closed by the position of gates, which are proteins that change shape to block or clear the channel. Whether a gate opens or closes a channel depends on the membrane potential, so that such gates are termed voltage regulated. Some of these membrane channels are specific for sodium ions, and others are specific for potassium ions.

(figure 33.4). The pump actively moves Na⁺ to the outside of the cell and K⁺ to the inside of the cell. Because it moves three Na⁺ molecules out for each two K⁺ that it moves in, the pump works to establish the resting potential across the membrane. Both ions leak back across the membrane—down their concentration gradients. K⁺ however, moves more easily back to the outside, adding to the positive charge there and contributing to the membrane potential of –70 mV.

MECHANISM OF NEURON ACTION: CHANGING THE RESTING MEMBRANE POTENTIAL INTO THE ACTION POTENTIAL (NERVE IMPULSE)

The change from the resting electrical potential across the plasma membrane is the key factor in the creation and subsequent conduction of a nerve impulse. A stimulus that is strong enough to initiate an impulse is called a threshold stimulus. When such a stimulus is applied to a point along the resting plasma membrane, the permeability to Na⁺ ions increases at that point. The inflow of positive charged Na⁺ ions causes the membrane potential to go from –70 mV toward 0. This loss in membrane polarity is called **depolarization** (figure 33.5). When depolarization reaches a certain level, special Na⁺ channels (voltage-gated) that are sensitive to changes in membrane potential quickly open, and more Na⁺

ions rush to the inside of the neuron. Shortly after the Na⁺ ions move into the cell, the Na⁺ gates close but now voltage-gated K⁺ channels open, and K⁺ ions rapidly diffuse outward. The movement of the K⁺ ions out of the cell builds up the positive charge outside the cell again, and the membrane becomes **repolarized.** This series of membrane changes triggers a similar cycle in an adjacent region of the membrane, and the wave of depolarization moves down the axon as an **action potential.** Overall, the transmission of an action potential along the neuron plasma membrane may be visualized as a wave of depolarization and repolarization.

After each action potential, there is an interval of time when it is impossible for another action potential to occur because the membrane has become hyperpolarized (more negative than –70 mV) due to the large number of K⁺ ions that rushed out. This brief period is called the **refractory period.** During this period, the resting potential is being restored at the part of the membrane where the impulse has just passed. Afterwards, the neuron is repolarized and is ready to transmit another impulse.

A minimum stimulus (threshold) is necessary to initiate an action potential, but an increase in the intensity of the impulse does not increase the strength of the action potential. The principle that states that an axon will "fire" at full power or not at all is known as the **all-or-none law.**

The speed of conduction of a nerve impulse can be increased by either increasing the axon diameter and/or by adding a myelin sheath. Axons with a large diameter transmit impulses faster than smaller ones. Large-diameter axons are common among many invertebrates (e.g., crayfishes, earthworms). The largest are those of the squid (*Loligo*), where they may be over 1 mm in diameter, and they have a conduction velocity greater than 36 m/second! (The giant squid axons provide a simple, rapid triggering mechanism for quick escape from predators. A single action potential elicits a maximal contraction of the mantle muscle that it innervates. Mantle contraction rapidly expels water, "jetting" the squid away from the predator.) Most vertebrate axons have a diameter of less than 10 μm; however, some fishes and amphibians have evolved large, unmyelinated axons 50 μm in diameter. These extend from the brain, down the spinal cord, and are used to activate many skeletal muscles that are used during rapid escape movements.

Regardless of an axon's diameter, the myelin sheath greatly increases conduction velocity. The reason for this velocity increase is that myelin is an excellent insulator and effectively stops the movement of ions across it. Action potentials are generated only at the neurofibril nodes. In fact, the action potential "jumps" from one node to the next node. For this reason, conduction along myelinated fibers is known as **saltatory conduction** (L. *saltare,* to jump). It takes less time for an impulse to jump from node to node along a myelinated fiber than if the impulse traveled smoothly along an unmyelinated fiber. Myelination makes rapid conduction in small neurons possible, and thus allows for the evolution of nervous systems that do not occupy a lot of space within the animal.

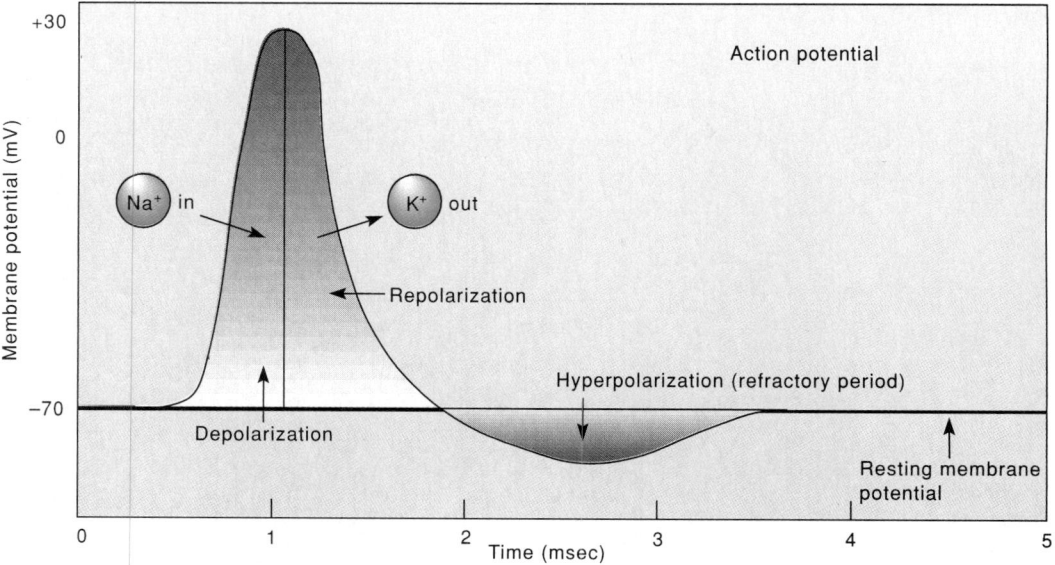

Figure 33.5

An Action Potential as Recorded on an Instrument Called an Oscilloscope. During the depolarization phase of the action potential, Na^+ ions rush to the inside of a neuron. The repolarization phase is characterized by a rapid increase of K^+ ions on the outside of the neuron. The action potential is sometimes called a "spike" because of its shape on an oscilloscope screen.

Transmission of the Action Potential between Cells

After an action potential travels along an axon, it reaches the end of a branching axon terminal called the **end bulb.** The **synapse** is the junction between the axon of one neuron and the dendrite of another neuron. The space (junction) between the end bulb and the dendrite of the next neuron is called a **synaptic cleft.** The neuron carrying the action potential toward a synapse is called the presynaptic ("before the synapse") neuron. It initiates a response in the receptive segment of a postsynaptic ("after the synapse") neuron leading away from the synapse. The presynaptic cell is always a neuron, but the postsynaptic cell can be a neuron, muscle cell, or gland cell.

There are two types of synapses: electrical and chemical. In an **electrical synapse,** nerve impulses are transmitted directly from neuron to neuron when positively charged ions move from one neuron to the next. These ions depolarize the postsynaptic membrane, as though the two neurons were electrically coupled. An electrical synapse can transmit impulses in both directions very rapidly. Electrical synapses are common in fishes and partially account for their ability to dart swiftly away from a threatening predator.

In a **chemical synapse,** two cells communicate by means of a chemical agent called a **neurotransmitter,** which is released by the presynaptic neuron. A neurotransmitter is capable of changing the resting potential in the plasma membrane of the receptive segment of the postsynaptic cell, creating an action potential in that cell, which continues the transmission of the impulse.

When a nerve impulse reaches an end bulb, it causes storage vesicles (containing the chemical neurotransmitter) to fuse with the plasma membrane. The neurotransmitter is released from the vesicles by exocytosis and empties into the synaptic cleft (figure 33.6). One common neurotransmitter (box 33.1) is the chemical **acetylcholine;** another is **norepinephrine.** (More than 50 other possible transmitters are known.)

When the released neurotransmitter (e.g., acetylcholine) binds with receptor protein sites in the postsynaptic membrane, it causes a depolarization similar to that of the presynaptic cell. As a result, the impulse continues its path to an eventual effector. Once acetylcholine has crossed the synaptic cleft, it is quickly inactivated by the enzyme acetylcholinesterase. Without this breakdown, acetylcholine would remain and would continually stimulate the postsynaptic cell, leading to a diseased state. Without knowing it, you have probably created a similar diseased state at the synapses of the fleas on your dog or cat.   The active ingredient in most flea sprays and powders is parathion. It prevents the breakdown of acetylcholine in the fleas, as well as pets and people. However, because fleas are so small, the low dose that immobilizes the fleas does not affect pets or humans.

Stop and Ask Yourself

1. What causes the resting membrane potential in a neuron?
2. How is a resting membrane potential maintained?
3. What are the different phases of an action potential?
4. What is saltatory conduction?
5. How is an action potential transmitted between neurons?

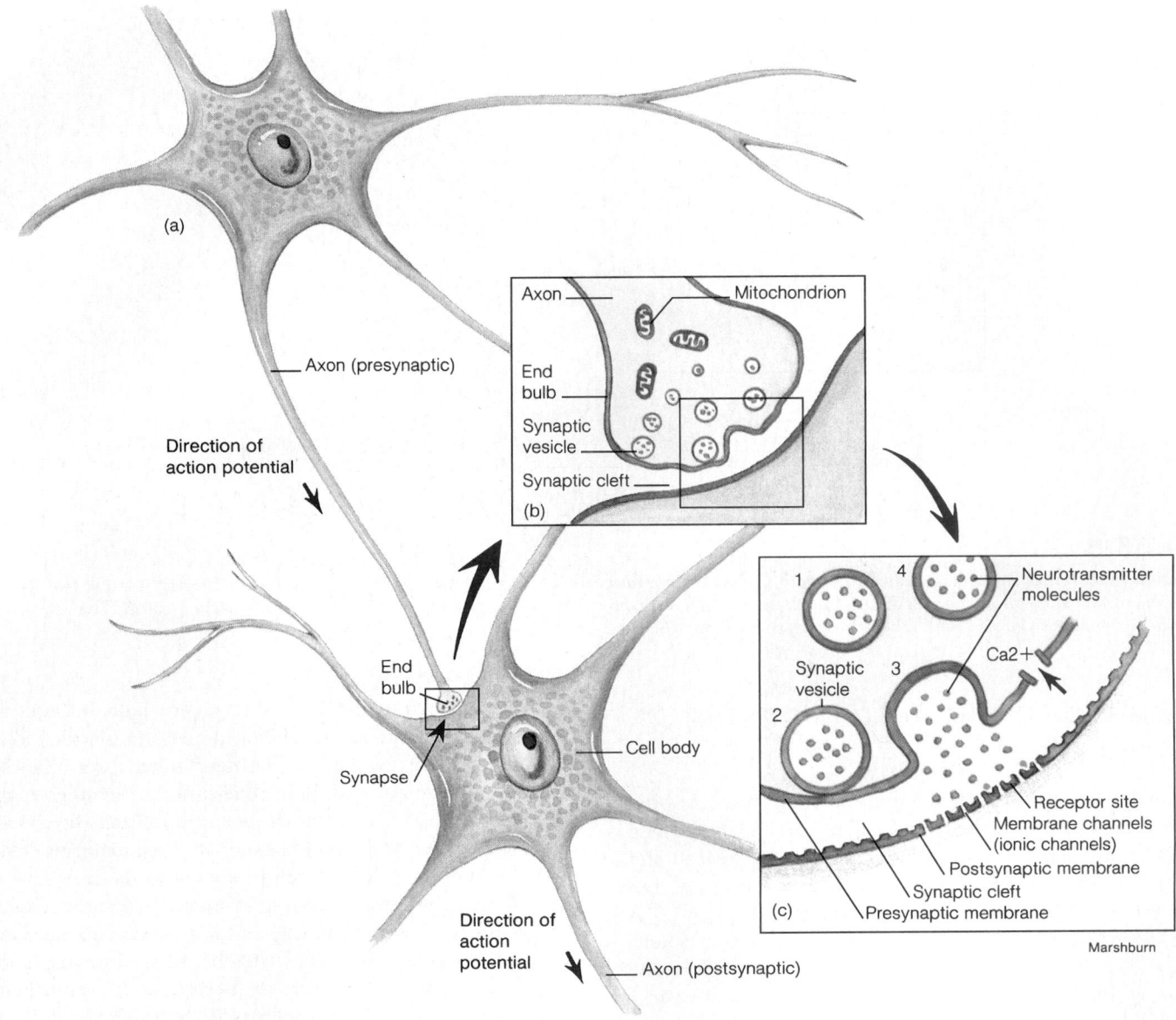

Figure 33.6

Chemical Transmission across a Synapse. (*a*) Pre- and postsynaptic neurons with synaptic end bulb. (*b*) An enlarged view of the end bulb containing synaptic vesicles. (*c*) An enlargement of a portion of the end bulb showing exocytosis. The sequence of events in neurotransmitter release involves (*1*) a synaptic vesicle containing neurotransmitter approaches the plasma membrane; (*2*) the vesicle fuses with the membrane; (*3*) exocytosis occurs; and (*4*) the vesicle reforms and begins to fill with more neurotransmitter.

INVERTEBRATE NERVOUS SYSTEMS

All cells respond to some stimuli and relay information both internally and externally. Thus, even when no real nervous system is present, such as in the protozoa and sponges, coordination and reaction to external and internal stimuli do occur. For example, the regular beating of protozoan cilia (*see figure 32.16*) or the response of flagellates to varying light intensities requires intracellular coordination. True nervous systems, however, are found only in animals that have achieved the tissue level of organization (e.g., the diploblastic and triploblastic animals). This clearly excludes the protozoa and sponges.

Among animals more complex than sponges, five general evolutionary trends in nervous system development are apparent. The first has been integrated throughout Part Five of this textbook: more complex animals possess more detailed nervous systems.

Of all animals, the cnidarians (hydras, jellyfishes, and sea anemones) have the simplest form of nervous organization. These animals have a **nerve net** (figure 33.7*a*), a latticework that permits the conduction of impulses from one area to another. In nerve nets, impulse conduction by neurons is bidirectional. Cnidarians lack brains and even local clusters of neurons. Instead, a nerve stimulus anywhere on the body initiates a nerve impulse that spreads across the nerve net to other regions

BOX 33.1 | NEUROTOXINS

Much of what we now know about synaptic transmission has been obtained by using chemicals produced by other animals. These chemicals are called **neurotoxins** because they block synaptic transmission. For example, tetrodotoxin is produced by symbiotic bacteria in a poison gland of the puffer fish, *Spheroides*. Tetrodotoxin blocks the sodium channels and prevents an action potential. Eating puffer fish without removing the neurotoxin often causes death by paralysis. In Japan, where this fish is a delicacy, specially trained chefs remove the organs of this fish that contain most of the neurotoxin before the fish is eaten. In spite of this precaution, about 100 diners die annually from improperly prepared puffer fish. A similar neurotoxin, saxitoxin, is produced by the dinoflagellates responsible for "red tides." Saxitoxin inhibits sodium transport in nerve cells, thus killing the fishes that eat the dinoflagellates. If filter-feeding molluscs consume the dinoflagel-

lates, and humans eat the "shellfish," they may suffer from paralytic "shellfish" poisoning (PSP). Another type of poisoning in humans is called "ciguatera." It results from eating marine fishes (red bass, moray eels, mackerel) that have consumed another dinoflagellate that produces the neurotoxin ciguatoxin. Ciguatoxin also blocks sodium transport. Batrachotoxin, from the poison-dart frog (*Phyllobates*) of South America, acts by keeping the sodium channels open, leading to a hyperpolarization and nerve dysfunction. Neurotoxins in the venom of the North African scorpion (*Leiurus*) and from the sea anemone (*Anemonia*) act by slowing the closing of the sodium channels at the end of an action potential. These neurotoxins normally help defend the above animals against predation, but are also useful tools for experimentation by neurophysiologists and have helped these scientists better understand the normal functioning of neurons.

of the body. In jellyfishes, this type of nervous system is involved in slow swimming movements and in keeping the body right-side up. At the cellular level, the neurons function in the way discussed earlier in this chapter.

Echinoderms (e.g., sea stars, sea urchins, sea cucumbers) still have nerve nets, but of increasing complexity. For example, sea stars have three distinct nerve nets. The one that lies just under the skin has a circumoral ring and five sets of nerve cords running out to the animal's arms. Another net serves the muscles between the skin plates called ossicles. The third net connects to the tube feet. This degree of nerve net complexity permits locomotion, a variety of useful reflexes, and some degree of "central" coordination. For example, when a sea star is flipped over, it can right itself.

Animals, such as flatworms and roundworms, that move in a forward direction have sense organs concentrated in the body region that first encounters new environmental stimuli. Thus, the second trend in nervous system evolution involves cephalization, which is a concentration of receptors and nervous tissue in the animal's anterior end. For example, a flatworm's nervous system contains **ganglia** (s., ganglion), which are distinct aggregations of nerve cells in the head region. Ganglia function as a primitive "brain" (figure 33.7b). Distinct lateral nerve cords (collections of neurons) on either side of the body carry sensory information from the periphery to the head ganglia and carry motor impulses from the head ganglia back to muscles, allowing the animal to react to environmental stimuli.

These lateral nerve cords reveal that flatworms also exhibit the third trend in nervous system evolution: bilateral symmetry. Bilateral symmetry (a body plan with roughly equivalent right and left halves) could have led to paired neurons, muscles, sensory structures, and brain centers. This pairing facilitates coordinated ambulatory movements, such as climbing, crawling, flying, or walking.

In other invertebrates, such as molluscs, segmented worms, and arthropods, the organization of the nervous system shows further advances. In these invertebrates, axons are joined into nerve cords, and, in addition to a small centralized brain, smaller peripheral ganglia help coordinate outlying regions of the animal's body. Ganglia can occur in each body segment or can be scattered throughout the body close to the organs they regulate (figure 33.7c,d,e). Regardless of the arrangement, these ganglia represent the fourth evolutionary trend: The more complex an animal, the more interneurons it will have. Because interneurons in ganglia do much of the integrating that takes place in nervous systems, the more interneurons, the more complex behavior patterns an animal can perform.

In echinoderms, such as starfishes, the nervous system is divided into several parts (figure 33.7f). The ectoneural system retains a primitive epidermal position and combines sensory and motor functions. A radial nerve extends down the lower surface of each arm. A deeper hyponeural system has a motor function, and the apical system may have some sensory functions.

The fifth trend in the evolution of invertebrate nervous systems is a consequence of the increasing number of interneurons. The brain contains the largest number of neurons, and the more complex the animal, and the more complicated its behavior, the more neurons (especially interneurons) it will have concentrated into an anterior brain and bilaterally organized ganglia. Vertebrate brains are an excellent example of this trend.

VERTEBRATE NERVOUS SYSTEMS

The basic organization of the nervous system is similar in all vertebrates. The evolution of vertebrate nervous systems is characterized by bilateral symmetry, the notochord, and the tubular nerve cord.

33.7

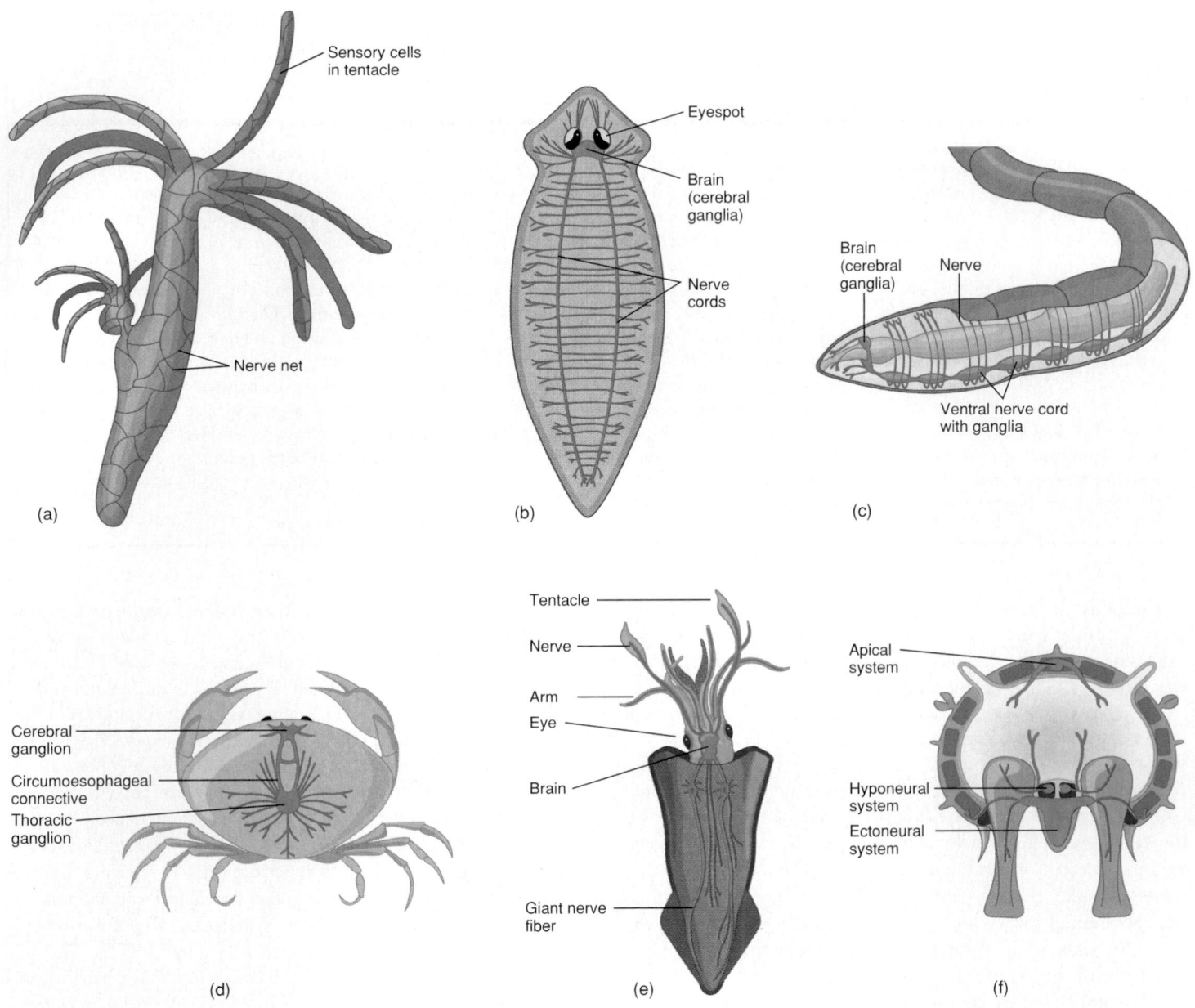

Figure 33.7

Some Invertebrate Nervous Systems. (*a*) The nerve net of *Hydra*, a cnidarian. (*b*) Brain and paired nerve cords of a planarian flatworm. (*c*) Brain, ventral nerve cord, ganglia, and the peripheral nerves of the earthworm, an annelid worm. (*d*) A mollusc, showing the principal ganglia and visceral connective nerves. Notice that the most primitive molluscs have nervous systems similar to those of the platyhelminths, whereas some cephalopods (such as the squid) have brains (*e*) and behavior as complex as those of fishes. (*f*) A cross section of a starfish arm. Nerves from the ectoneural system terminate on the surface of the hyponeural system but there is no contact between the two systems.

The **notochord** is a rod of mesodermally derived tissue encased in a firm sheath that lies ventral to the neural tube (*see figure 10.7*). It first appeared in marine chordates and is present in all vertebrate embryos, but is greatly reduced or absent in adults. In most vertebrate species, during embryological development, it is replaced by vertebrae serially arranged into a vertebral column. This vertebral column led to the development of strong muscles, allowing vertebrates to become fast-moving, predatory animals. Some

of the other bones developed into powerful jaws, which facilitated the predatory nature of these animals.

A related character in vertebrate evolution was the development of a single, tubular nerve cord above the notochord. During early evolution, the nerve cord underwent expansion, regional modification, and specialization into a spinal cord and brain. Over time, the anterior end became variably thickened with nervous tissue and functionally divided into the hindbrain, midbrain,

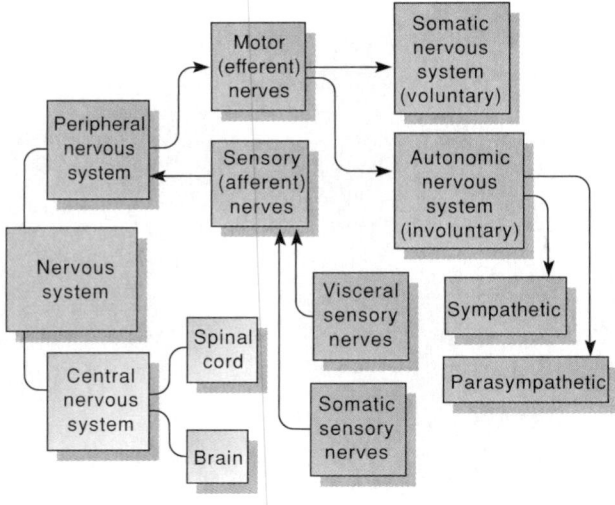

Figure 33.8

The Basic Organization of the Nervous System Is Similar in All Vertebrates. This flowchart shows the divisions and nerves of the vertebrate nervous system. Arrows indicate the directional flow of nerve impulses (information).

and forebrain. In the sensory world of the fast-moving and powerful vertebrates, the anterior sensory receptors became more complex and bilaterally symmetrical. For example, paired olfactory structures, such as eyes and ears, developed to better gather information from the outside environment.

The nervous system of vertebrates has two main divisions (figure 33.8). The **central nervous system** is composed of the brain and spinal cord, and is the site of information processing. The **peripheral nervous system** is composed of all the nerves of the body outside the brain and spinal cord. These nerves are commonly divided into two groups: **sensory (afferent) nerves,** which transmit information to the central nervous system; and **motor (efferent) nerves,** which carry commands away from the central nervous system. The motor nerves are divided into the **voluntary (somatic) nervous system,** which relays commands to skeletal muscles, and the **involuntary (visceral** or **autonomic) nervous system,** which stimulates other muscles (smooth and cardiac) and glands of the body. The nerves of the autonomic nervous system fall into two categories called **sympathetic** and **parasympathetic** systems.

3   Nervous system pathways are composed of individual neuronal axons bundled together like the strands of a telephone cable. In the central nervous system, these bundles of nerve fibers are called **tracts.** In the peripheral nervous system, they are called **nerves.** The cell bodies from which the axons extend are often clustered into groups. These groups are called nuclei if they are in the central nervous system and ganglia if they are part of the peripheral nervous system.

THE SPINAL CORD

The spinal cord serves two important functions in an animal; it is the connecting link between the brain and most of the body, and it is involved in spinal reflex actions. Thus, both voluntary

and involuntary movement of the limbs, as well as certain organ functions, depend on this link.

The spinal cord is the part of the central nervous system that extends from the brain to near or into the tail (figure 33.9). In cross section, there is a neural canal that contains cerebrospinal fluid. The gray matter consists of cell bodies and dendrites and is concerned mainly with reflex connections at various levels of the spinal cord. Extending from the spinal cord are the ventral and dorsal roots of the spinal nerves. These roots contain the main motor and sensory fibers (axons and/or dendrites), respectively, that contribute to the major spinal nerves. The white matter of the spinal cord gets its name from the myelin, which is a whitish color, that covers the axons.

The spinal cord of mammals is surrounded by three layers of protective membranes called **meninges** (pl. of *menix*, membrane). They are continuous with similar layers that cover the brain. The outer layer, the **dura mater,** is a tough, fibrous membrane. The middle layer, the **arachnoid,** is delicate and connects to the innermost layer, the **pia mater.** The pia mater contains small blood vessels that nourish the spinal cord.

SPINAL NERVES

Generally, the number of spinal nerves is directly related to the number of segments in the trunk and tail of a vertebrate. For example, a frog has evolved strong hind legs for swimming or jumping, a reduced trunk, and no tail in the adult. It has only 10 pairs of spinal nerves. By contrast, a snake, which moves by lateral undulations of its long trunk and tail, has several hundred pairs of spinal nerves.

THE BRAIN

Anatomically, the vertebrate brain develops at the anterior end of the spinal cord. During embryonic development, the brain undergoes regional expansion as a hollow tube of nervous tissue forms and develops into the hindbrain, midbrain, and forebrain (figure 33.10). The central canal of the spinal cord extends up into the brain and expands into chambers called ventricles. The ventricles are filled with cerebrospinal fluid.

Hindbrain

The **hindbrain** is continuous with the spinal cord and includes the medulla oblongata, cerebellum, and pons. The **medulla oblongata** is the enlargement where the spinal cord enters the brain. It contains reflex centers for breathing, swallowing, cardiovascular function, and gastric secretion. The medulla oblongata is well developed in all jawed vertebrates, reflecting its ability to control visceral functions and to serve as a screen for information that leaves or enters the brain.

The **cerebellum** is an outgrowth of the medulla oblongata. It functions in the coordination of motor activity associated with limb movement, maintaining posture, and spatial orientation. The cerebellum in cartilaginous fishes has distinct anterior and posterior lobes. In teleosts, the cerebellum ranges in size from large in active swimmers, to small in relatively inactive fishes.

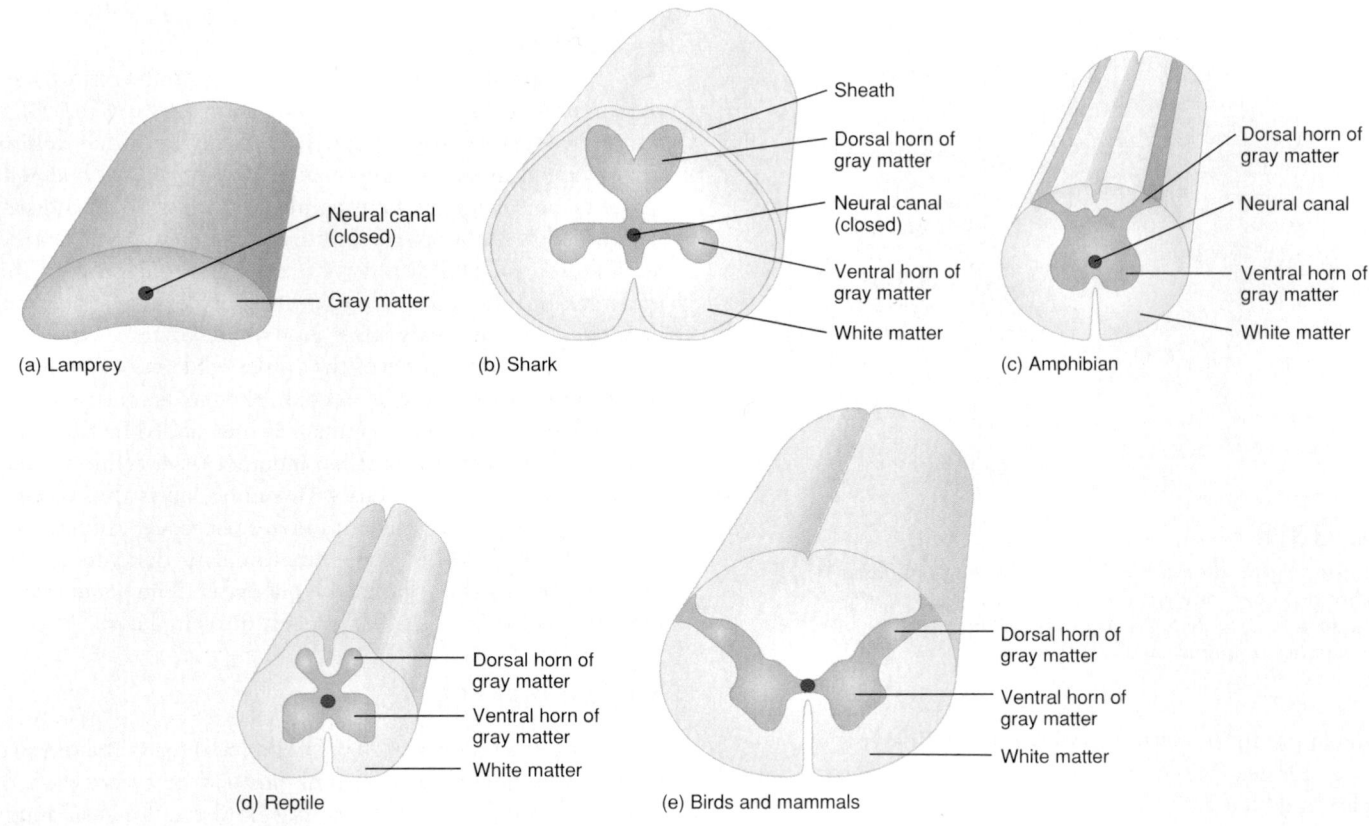

FIGURE 33.9

Spinal Cords of Vertebrates. (*a*) The spinal cord of a typical agnathan (lamprey) is flattened and possesses no myelinated axons. Its shape facilitates the diffusion of gases, nutrients, and other products. (*b,c*) In fishes and amphibians, the spinal cord is larger, well vascularized, and rounded. With more white matter, it bulges outward. The gray matter in the spinal cord of a (*d*) reptile and (*e*) birds and mammals has a characteristic butterfly shape.

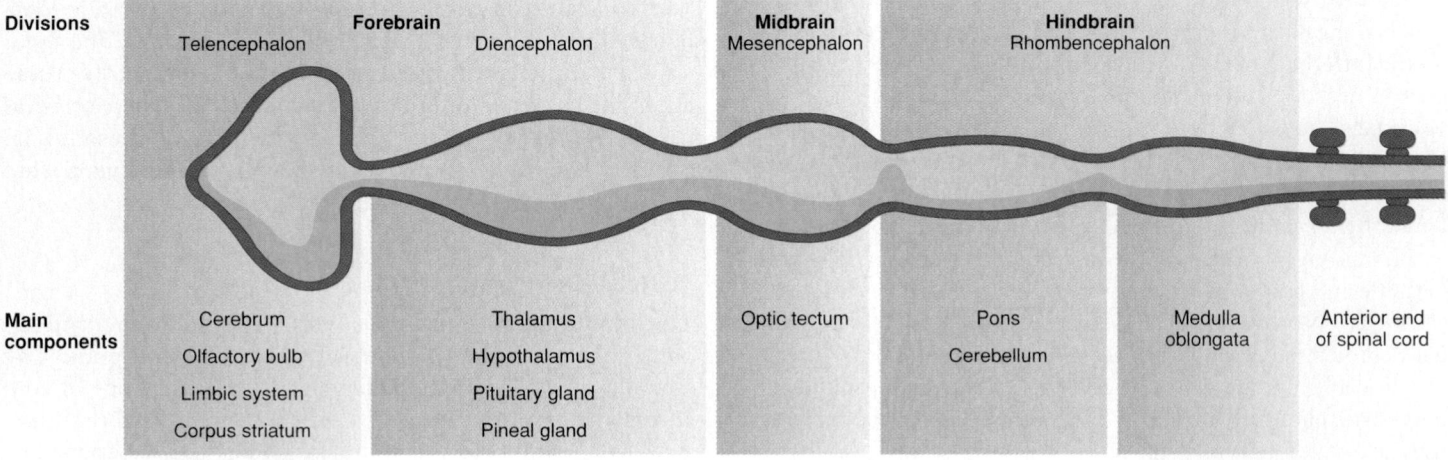

FIGURE 33.10

Development of the Vertebrate Brain. Summary of the three major subdivisions and some of the structures they contain. This drawing is highly simplified and flattened.

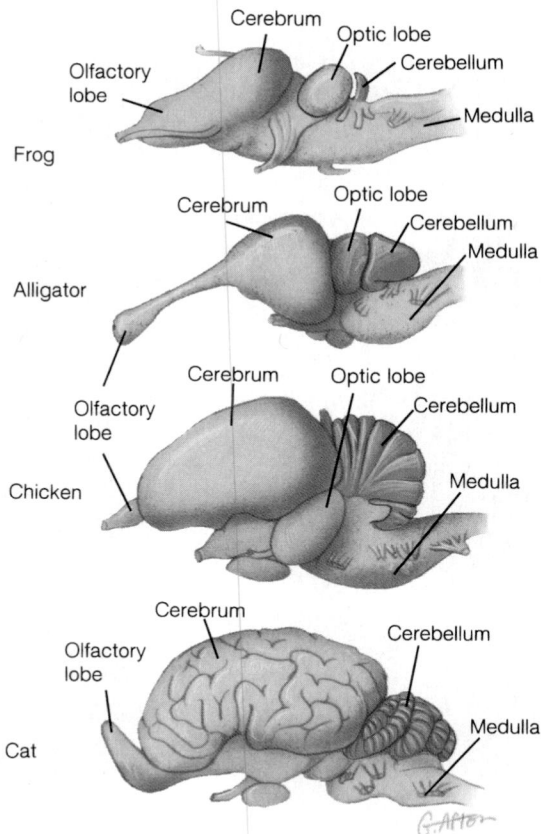

Figure 33.11

Vertebrate Brains. Comparison of several vertebrate brains, as viewed from the side. The drawings are not drawn to the same scale. Notice the increase in relative size of the cerebrum from amphibian (frog) to mammal (cat).

Amphibians often have a rudimentary cerebellum (figure 33.11), reflecting their relatively simple locomotor patterns. In tetrapods, the cerebellum is laterally expanded. It is from these expanded lateral lobes that locomotor control of muscles of the appendages occurs. The cerebellum is much larger in birds and mammals—a reflection of complex locomotor patterns and a common evolutionary history of limb development and phylogeny as terrestrial vertebrates.

The **pons** is a bridge of transverse nerve tracts from the cerebrum of the forebrain to both sides of the cerebellum. It also contains tracts that connect the forebrain and spinal cord in all vertebrates.

Midbrain

The **midbrain** was originally a center for coordinating reflex responses to visual input. As the brain evolved, it took on added functions relating to tactile (touch) and auditory (hearing) input, but it did not change in size. The roof of the midbrain is called the optic tectum. It is a thickened region of gray matter where visual and auditory signals are integrated.

Forebrain

The vertebrate forebrain has changed a great deal during vertebrate evolution. The **forebrain** has two main parts: the diencephalon and telencephalon (*see figure 33.10*). The diencephalon lies just in front of the midbrain and contains the pineal gland, pituitary gland, hypothalamus, and thalamus. The **thalamus** relays all sensory information to higher brain centers. The **hypothalamus** lies below the thalamus. This area controls many functions, such as regulation of body temperature, sexual drive, carbohydrate metabolism, hunger, and thirst. The pineal gland controls some body rhythms. The pituitary is a major endocrine gland and will be discussed in detail in chapter 35.

In fishes and amphibians, the diencephalon processes sensory (olfactory) information. In reptiles and birds, the most important part of the brain is the corpus striatum, which plays a role in their complex behavior patterns.

As the diencephalon slowly expanded during evolution and handled more and more sensory functions, the telencephalon (the front part of the forebrain) expanded rapidly in both size and complexity.

Outside the corpus striatum is the **cerebrum,** which is divided by a large groove into right and left cerebral hemispheres. The parts of the brain related to sensory and motor integration changed greatly as vertebrates became more agile and inquisitive animals (figure 33.12). Many functions shifted from the optic tectum to the expanding cerebral hemispheres. The increasing importance of the cerebrum affected many other brain regions, especially the thalamus and cerebellum. In mammals, there is a progressive increase in size and complexity of the outermost part of the cerebrum, called the cerebral cortex. This layer folds back on itself to a remarkable extent, suggesting that evolution of the mammalian cerebrum outpaced enlargement of the skullbones housing it.

Different parts of the cerebrum have specific functions. For example, the cerebral cortex contains primary sensory areas and primary motor areas. Other areas of the cortex are involved in perception of visual or auditory signals from the environment, and in humans, the ability to use language—both written and spoken.

Stop and Ask Yourself

6. How is the brain of a vertebrate related to the spinal cord?
7. What are the three parts of the vertebrate hindbrain?
8. What is the function of the midbrain?
9. What are the different parts of the forebrain and their respective functions?

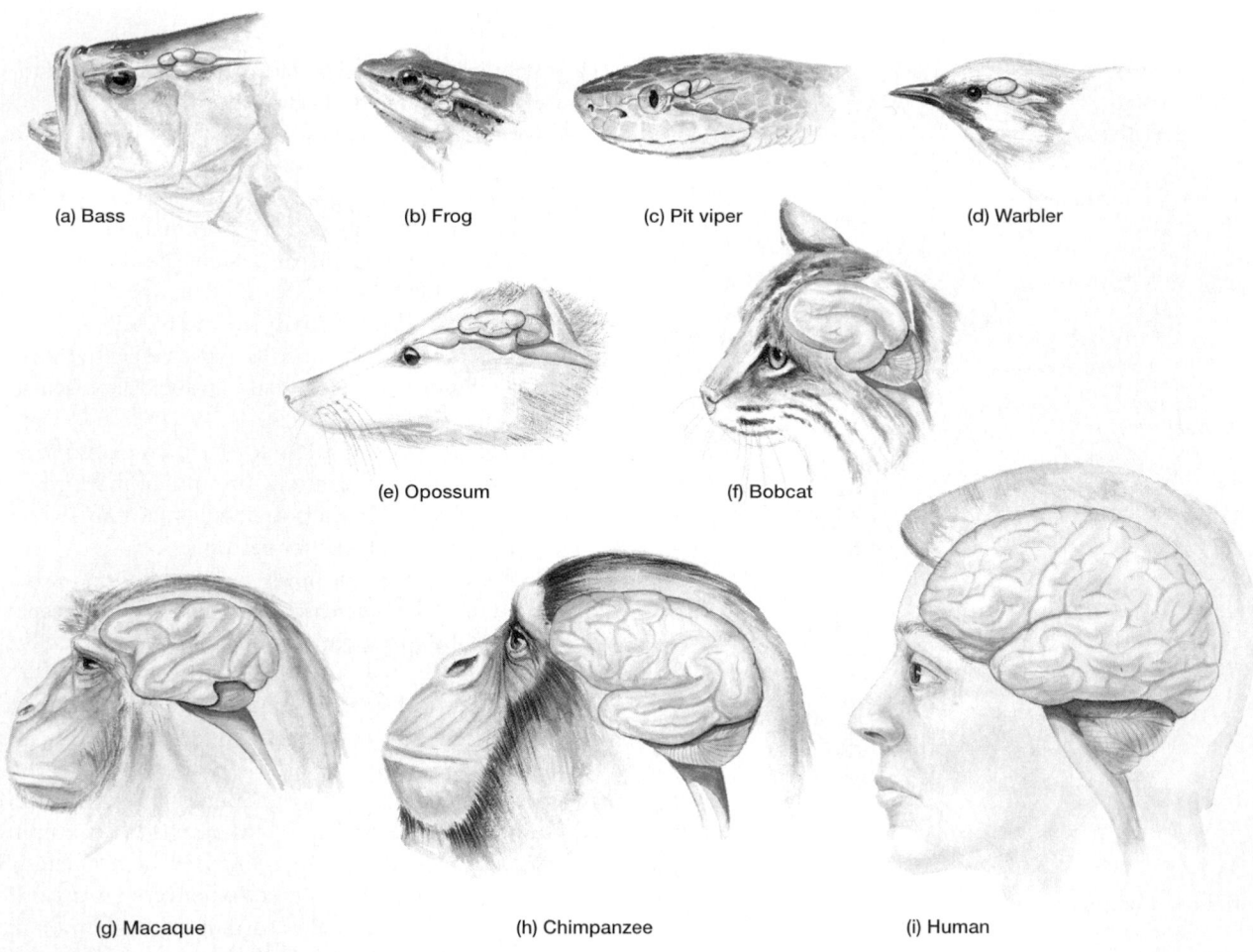

(a) Bass   (b) Frog   (c) Pit viper   (d) Warbler

(e) Opossum   (f) Bobcat

(g) Macaque   (h) Chimpanzee   (i) Human

FIGURE 33.12

The Cerebrum in Different Vertebrate Species. The cerebrum increases in both size and complexity of its neural connections in more advanced groups. (*a*) Fishes and (*b*) amphibians lack cerebral cortices, whereas (*c*) reptiles and (*d*) birds have a small amount of gray matter covering their cerebrums. Most primitive mammals, such as (*e*) the opossum, have smooth cortices. Carnivores, such as the (*f*) bobcat, have larger cerebrums, and the cortex has a few convolutions. In the (*g,h*) primates, the cerebrum is much increased relative to other brain structures, and the cortex is highly convoluted. (*i*) The human cerebrum dominates in brain evolution and is highly convoluted.

CRANIAL NERVES

In addition to the paired spinal nerves, the peripheral nervous system of vertebrates includes paired cranial nerves (table 33.1). There are 12 pairs of cranial nerves in reptiles, birds, and mammals. Fishes have only the first 10 pairs. Some of the nerves (e.g., optic nerve) contain only sensory axons, which carry signals to the brain. Others contain sensory and motor axons and are termed mixed nerves. For example, the vagus nerve has sensory axons leading to the brain as well as motor axons leading to the heart and smooth muscles of the visceral organs in the thorax and abdomen.

THE AUTONOMIC NERVOUS SYSTEM

The vertebrate autonomic nervous system is composed of two divisions that act antagonistically (in opposition to each other) to control the body's involuntary muscles (smooth and cardiac) and glands. The **parasympathetic nervous system** functions during times of calm relaxation. It contains nerves that arise from the brain and sacral region of the spinal cord and consists of a network of long efferent nerve fibers that synapse at ganglia in the immediate vicinity of organs, and short efferent neurons that extend from the ganglia to the organs. The **sympathetic nervous system** is responsible for the "fight-or-flight" response.

TABLE 33.1	FUNCTIONS OF THE CRANIAL NERVES OF REPTILES, BIRDS, AND MAMMALS	

NERVE	TYPE	INNERVATION AND FUNCTION
I Olfactory	Sensory	Smell
II Optic	Sensory	Vision
III Oculomotor	Primarily motor	Eyelids, eyes, adjust amount of light entering eyes, and focus lenses (motor)
IV Trochlear	Primarily motor	Condition of muscles (sensory)
		Eye muscles (motor)
V Trigeminal	Mixed	Condition of muscles (sensory)
Ophthalmic division		Eyes, tear glands, scalp, forehead, and upper eyelids (sensory)
Maxillary division		Upper teeth, upper gum, upper lip, lining of the palate, and skin of the face (sensory)
Mandibular division		Scalp, skin of the jaw, lower teeth, lower gum, and lower lip (sensory)
VI Abducens	Primarily motor	Jaws, floor of the mouth (motor)
		Eye muscles (motor)
VII Facial	Mixed	Condition of muscles (sensory)
		Taste receptors of the anterior tongue (sensory)
		Facial expression, tear glands, and salivary glands (motor)
VIII Vestibulocochlear	Sensory	
Vestibular branch		Equilibrium; vestibule
Cochlear branch		Hearing; cochlea
IX Glossopharyngeal	Mixed	Pharynx, tonsils, posterior tongue, and carotid arteries (sensory)
		Pharynx and salivary glands (motor)
X Vagus	Mixed	Speech and swallowing, heart, and visceral organs in the thorax and abdomen (motor)
		Pharynx, larynx, esophagus, and visceral organs of the thorax and abdomen (sensory)
XI Accessory	Motor	
Cranial branch		Soft palate, pharynx, and larynx
Spinal branch		Neck and back
XII Hypoglossal	Motor	Tongue muscles

It contains nerves that arise from the thoracic and lumbar regions of the spinal cord. It is a network of short, efferent central nervous system fibers that extend to ganglia located near the spine, and long efferent neurons extending from the ganglia directly to each organ. Organs often receive input from both the parasympathetic and sympathetic systems. For example, parasympathetic input is responsible for stimulation of salivary gland secretions, stimulation of intestinal movements, contraction of pupillary muscles in the eyes, and relaxation of sphincter muscles. Sympathetic input controls antagonistic actions: inhibition of salivary gland secretions and intestinal movements, relaxation of pupillary muscles, and contraction of sphincters.

Stop and Ask Yourself

10. How are cranial nerves named?
11. How would you describe the parasympathetic nervous system? The sympathetic system?

SUMMARY

1. The functional unit of the nervous system is the neuron. Neurons are specialized to produce signals that can be communicated from one part of an animal's body to another. Neurons have two important properties: excitability and conductivity.

2. A typical neuron has three anatomical parts: dendrites, a cell body, and an axon.

3. The language (signals) of neurons is the nerve impulse or action potential.

4. The plasma membrane of a resting neuron is polarized, meaning that the intracellular fluid on the inner side of the membrane is negatively charged with respect to the positively charged extracellular fluid outside the membrane. This state of affairs is maintained by the sodium-potassium pump and diffusion of ions through membrane channels.

5. When a threshold stimulus is applied to a resting neuron, the neuron depolarizes, causing an action potential. In myelinated neurons, the action potential jumps from one neurofibril node to the next in a process known as saltatory conduction.

6. Neuronal activity is transmitted between cells at the synapse. Although some animals have electrical synapses that transmit neuronal activity from one neuron to the next, most advanced animals use chemical neurotransmitter molecules.

7. Among animals more complex than sponges, five general evolutionary trends in the nervous system are apparent. That is, the more complex an animal

   a. the more detailed its nervous system.

   b. the more cephalization concentrates receptors and nervous tissue in an animal's anterior end.

   c. the more bilateral symmetry, which has led to paired nerves, muscles, sensory structures, and brain centers. This pairing facilitates ambulatory movements, such as climbing, crawling, flying, or walking.

   d. the more neurons it will have.

   e. the more complicated its behavior, the more neurons (especially interneurons) it will have concentrated into an anterior brain and bilaterally organized ganglia.

8. The vertebrate nervous system has two main divisions: the central nervous system is composed of the brain and spinal cord, and the peripheral nervous system is composed of all the nerves (bundles of axons and/or dendrites) outside the brain and spinal cord.

9. The spinal cord of a vertebrate serves two important functions: it is the connecting link between the brain of an animal and most of the body, and it is involved in spinal reflex actions. A reflex is a predictable, involuntary, response to a stimulus.

10. The number of spinal nerves is directly related to the number of segments in the trunk and tail of a vertebrate.

11. The vertebrate brain can be divided into the hindbrain, midbrain, and forebrain. The hindbrain is continuous with the spinal cord and includes the medulla oblongata, cerebellum, and pons.

12. The midbrain is a thickened region of gray matter where visual and auditory signals are integrated. The forebrain contains the pineal gland, hypothalamus, and thalamus. One part expanded during evolution to give rise to the cerebral cortex.

13. In addition to the paired spinal nerves, the peripheral nervous system includes 12 pairs of cranial nerves in reptiles, birds, and mammals. Fishes have only the first 10 pairs.

14. The autonomic nervous system consists of two antagonistic parts: the sympathetic and parasympathetic divisions.

SELECTED KEY TERMS

action potential (*p. 550*)   dendrites (*p. 548*)
axon (*p. 548*)   medulla oblongata (*p. 555*)
cell body (*p. 548*)   neuron (*p. 548*)
cerebellum (*p. 555*)   saltatory conduction (*p. 550*)
cerebrum (*p. 557*)   synapse (*p. 551*)

CRITICAL THINKING QUESTIONS

1. What are several ways in which drugs that are stimulants could increase activity of the human nervous system by acting at the synapse?

2. How can a neuron integrate information?

3. Surveying the functions of the evolutionarily oldest parts of the vertebrate brain gives us some idea of original functions of the brain. Explain this statement.

4. What possible advantages and disadvantages are there in the evolutionary trend toward cephalization of the nervous system?

5. How does an action potential cross a synapse?

chapter

34

COMMUNICATION II: SENSES

Concepts

1. Sensory receptors or organs permit an animal to detect changes in its body and objects and events in the world around it. Information collected by a sensory receptor is passed to the nervous system, which determines, evaluates, and initiates an appropriate response.
2. Sensory receptors initiate nerve impulses by opening channels in sensory neuron plasma membranes, depolarizing them, and causing a generator potential. Receptors differ from one another with respect to the nature of the environmental stimulus that triggers an eventual nerve impulse.
3. Many kinds of receptors have evolved among invertebrates and vertebrates, and each receptor is sensitive to a specific type of stimulus.
4. Each animal species has a unique perception of its body and environment due to the nature of its sensory receptors.

Would You Like to Know:

1. why it is so difficult to catch a fly with your hand? (p. 564)
2. how honeybees can recognize particular flowers? (p. 565)
3. what animal has the largest eye and how big it is? (p. 565)
4. how web-building spiders can sense struggling prey in their webs? (p. 566)
5. how certain fishes can detect electrical currents in the surrounding water? (p. 567)
6. why dogs can hear the sound from a high-pitched dog whistle while humans cannot? (p. 570)
7. what causes "motion sickness" or "seasickness" in humans? (p. 570)
8. how a sturgeon can taste food before the food reaches the sturgeon's mouth? (p. 574)

These and other useful questions will be answered in this chapter.

This chapter contains evolutionary concepts, which are set off in this font.

About 2,000 years ago, Aristotle identified five senses—sight, hearing, smell, taste, and touch—commonly referred to as the "five senses." Today zoologists know that other senses exist in animals. For example, invertebrates possess an impressive array of sensory receptors through which they receive information about their environment. Common examples include tactile receptors that sense touch; georeceptors that sense the pull of gravity; hygroreceptors that detect the water content of air; proprioceptors that respond to mechanically induced changes caused by stretching, compression, bending, and tension; phonoreceptors that are sensitive to sound; baroreceptors that respond to pressure changes; chemoreceptors that respond to air- and waterborne molecules; photoreceptors that sense light; and thermoreceptors that are influenced by temperature changes.

Most vertebrates have a sense of equilibrium (balance), a sense of body movement, fine touch, touch-pressure, heat, taste, vision, olfaction, audition, cold, pain, and various other tactile senses. In addition, receptors in the circulatory system register changes in blood pressure and blood levels of carbon dioxide and hydrogen ions, and receptors in the digestive system are involved in the perception of hunger and thirst.

Overall, an animal's impression of the environment is limited and defined by its senses. In fact, all awareness depends on the reception and decoding of stimuli from the external environment and from within an animal's body. This chapter examines how animals use sensory information to help maintain homeostasis.

Sensory Reception

Sensory receptors are structures made of cells that are capable of converting environmental information (stimuli) into nerve impulses. A **stimulus** (pl., stimuli) is any form of energy an animal is able to detect with its receptors. All receptors are **transducers** ("to change over"); that is, they convert one form of energy into another. Because all nerve impulses are the same, different types of receptors convert different kinds of stimuli, such as light or heat, into a local electrical potential called the **generator potential.** If the generator potential reaches the sensory neuron's threshold potential, it will cause channels to open in its plasma membrane and create an action potential. The impulse then travels along the cell's axon toward a synaptic junction and becomes information going to the central nervous system or brain.

As presented in chapter 33, all action potentials are alike. Furthermore, an action potential is an all-or-none phenomenon; it either occurs or it doesn't. How, then, does a common action potential give rise to different sensations, such as taste, color, or sound, or different degrees of sensation? In those animals that have brains, some nerve signals from specific receptors always end up in a specific part of the brain for interpretation; therefore, a stimulus that goes to the optic center will be

interpreted as a visual stimulus. Another factor that characterizes a particular stimulus is the intensity of the stimulus. When the strength of the stimulus increases, the number of action potentials per unit of time also increases. Thus, the passage of an all-or-none action potential can be used to transmit information about the intensity and type of stimulus by using the timing of the impulses and the "wiring" of neurons as additional sources of information for perception by the brain.

Sensory receptors have the following basic features:

1. They contain sensitive receptor cells or finely branched peripheral endings of sensory neurons that respond to a stimulus by creating a generator potential.
2. Their structure is designed to receive a specific stimulus.
3. Their receptor cells synapse with afferent nerve fibers that travel to the central nervous system along specific neural pathways.
4. In the central nervous system, the nerve impulse is translated into a recognizable sensation, such as sound.

Stop and Ask Yourself

1. What are the five basic senses Aristotle identified about 2,000 years ago? What are some additional senses found in different animals?
2. What does it mean to say that receptors function as transducers?
3. What is the difference between a generator potential and an action potential?
4. If all action potentials are alike, how is information regarding the type and intensity of a stimulus conveyed to the central nervous system of an animal?

Invertebrate Sensory Receptors

An animal's behavior is largely a function of its responses to environmental information. Invertebrates possess an impressive array of receptor structures through which they receive information about their environment. Some common examples are now discussed from a structural and functional perspective.

Baroreceptors

Baroreceptors (Gr. *baros*, weight + receptor) sense changes in pressure. However, no specific structures for baroreception have been identified in invertebrates. Nevertheless, responses to pressure changes have been identified in ocean-dwelling copepod crustaceans, ctenophores, jellyfish medusae, and squids. Some intertidal crustaceans coordinate migratory activity with daily tidal movements, possibly in response to pressure changes accompanying water depth changes.

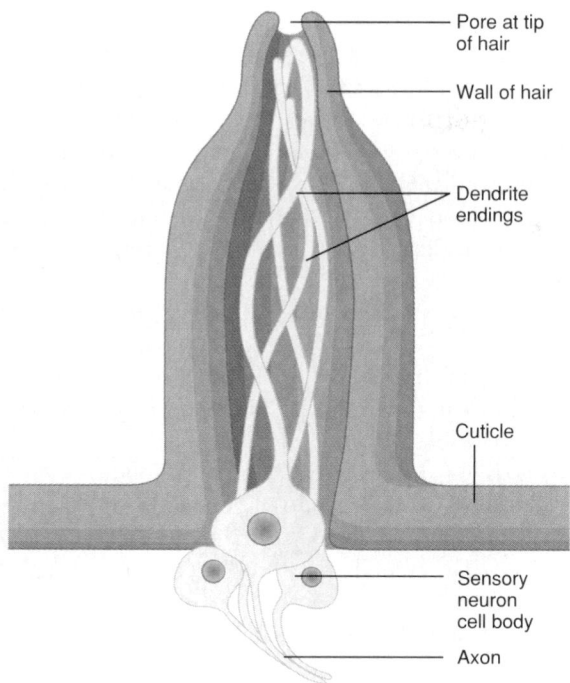

Figure 34.1

Invertebrate Chemoreceptor. Diagram of a cross section through an insect sensillum. The receptor is a projection of the cuticle with a pore at the tip. Each chemoreceptor generally contains four to five dendrites, which lead to sensory neuron cell bodies that lie underneath the cuticle. Each sensory cell has its own spectrum of chemical responses. Thus, a single sensillum with four or five dendrites and cell bodies may be capable of discriminating many different chemicals.

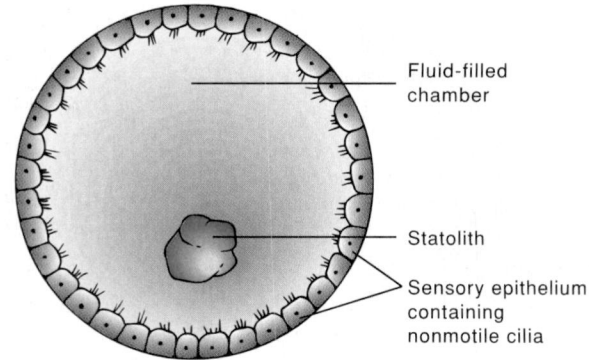

Figure 34.2

Invertebrate Georeceptor. A statocyst (cross section) consists of a fluid-filled chamber containing a solid granule called the statolith. The inner lining of the chamber contains tactile epithelium from which project cilia associated with underlying neurons.

CHEMORECEPTORS

Chemoreceptors (Gr. *chemeia,* pertaining to chemistry) respond to chemicals. Chemoreception is a direct sense in that molecules act specifically to stimulate a response. For example, protozoa have a chemical sense; they respond with avoidance behavior to acid, alkali, and salt stimuli. Predatory ciliates are attracted to their prey by specific chemicals. The chemoreceptors of many aquatic invertebrates are located in pits or depressions, through which water carrying the specific chemicals may be circulated. In arthropods, the chemoreceptors are usually found on the antennae, mouthparts, and legs in the form of hollow hairs (**sensilla;** s., sensillum) containing chemosensory neurons (figure 34.1).

The types of chemicals to which invertebrates respond are closely associated with their life-styles. Examples include chemoreceptors that provide information that the animal uses to perform tasks, such as analysis, humidity detection, pH assessment, prey tracking, food recognition, and mate location. With respect to mate location, the antennae of male *Cecropia* moths can detect one bombykol molecule in over a trillion molecules of air. Female silk moths secrete bombykol as a sex attractant, which enables a male to find a female in the dark.

GEORECEPTORS

Georeceptors (Gr. *ge,* earth + receptor) respond to the force of gravity. This gives an animal information about its orientation relative to "up" and "down." Most georeceptors are of the type known as **statocysts** (Gr. *statos,* standing + *kystis,* bladder; figure 34.2). Statocysts consist of a fluid-filled chamber lined with cilia-bearing sensory epithelium; within the chamber is a solid granule called a **statolith** (Gr. *lithos,* stone). Any movement of the animal causes changes in the position of the statolith and movement of the fluid, and thus alters the intensity and pattern of information arising from the sensory epithelium. For example, when an animal moves, both the movement of the statolith and the flow of fluid over the sensory epithelium provide information about the animal's linear and rotational acceleration relative to the environment.

Statocysts are found in various gastropods, chephalopods, crustaceans, nemertines, polychaetes, and scyphozoans. These animals utilize information from statocysts in different ways. For example, burrowing invertebrates cannot rely on photoreceptors for orientation; instead, they rely on georeceptors for orientation within the substratum. Planktonic animals orient in their three-dimensional aquatic environment using statocysts. This is especially important at night and in deep water where there is little light.

In addition to statocysts, a number of aquatic insects detect gravity by using information provided by air bubbles trapped in certain passageways (e.g., tracheal tubes). Analogous to the air bubble in a carpenter's level, these air bubbles move according to their orientation to gravity. The air bubbles stimulate sensory bristles that line the tubes.

HYGRORECEPTORS

Hygroreceptors (Gr. *hygros,* moist) are receptors that detect the water content of air. For example, some insects have hygroreceptors that can detect small changes in the ambient relative humidity. This sense enables them to seek environments

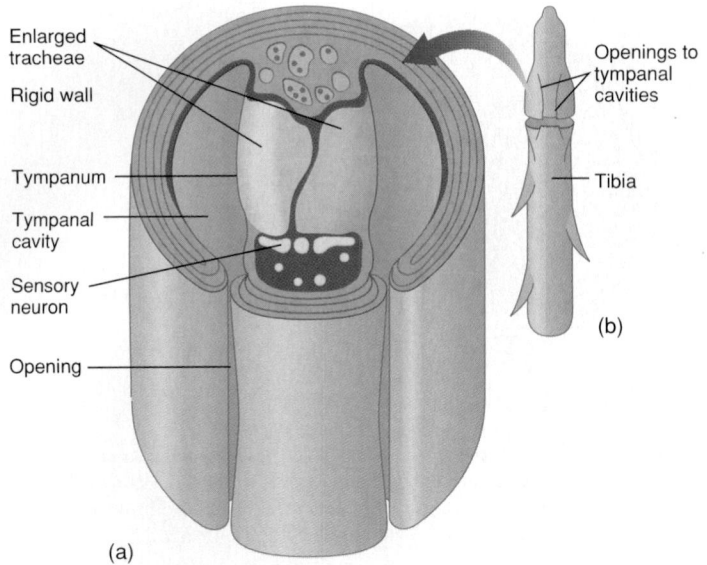

FIGURE 34.3

Invertebrate Phonoreceptor (Tympanic Organ). (*a*) The tympanic organ functions on the drumhead principle. The flattened outer wall (tympanum) of each trachea functions as a "drumhead." As they vibrate in response to sound waves, the pressure changes within the tracheae affect the sensory neuron, causing a generator potential. (*b*) The slit openings on the leg (tibia) of a cricket lead to the tympanal cavities.

that have a specific humidity or to modify their physiology or behavior with respect to the ambient humidity (e.g., to control the opening or closing of spiracles). A variety of hygrosensory structures have been identified on the antennae, palps, underside of the body, and near the spiracles of insects. However, how humidity is transduced by a hygroreceptor into an action potential is not known.

PHONORECEPTORS

True **phonoreceptors** (Gr. *phone*, voice + receptor) that respond to sound have been demonstrated only in insects, arachnids, and centipedes, although other invertebrates seem to respond to sound-induced vibrations of the substratum. For example, crickets, grasshoppers, and cicadas possess phonoreceptors called **tympanic organs** (figure 34.3). The anatomy of this organ consists of a tough, flexible tympanum that covers an internal sac that allows the tympanum to vibrate when struck by sound waves. Sensory neurons attached to the tympanum are stimulated and produce a generator potential.

Most arachnids possess phonoreceptors in their cuticle called slit sense organs that can sense sound-induced vibrations. Centipedes have organs of Tomosvary, which some zoologists believe may be sensitive to sound. However, the physiology of both slit sense organs and organs of Tomosvary are poorly understood.

PHOTORECEPTORS

Photoreceptors (Gr. *photos*, light + receptor) are sensitive to light. All photoreceptors possess light-sensitive pigments (e.g., carotenoids, rhodopsin). These pigments absorb photons of light energy and then produce a generator potential. Beyond this basic commonality, there is an incredible variation in the complexity and arrangement of photoreceptors within various animals.

Certain flagellated protozoa (*Euglena*) that contain chlorophyll possess a mass of bright red photoreceptor granules called the **stigma** (pl., stigmata) (figure. 34.4*a*). The granules are carotenoid pigments. The actual photoreceptor is the swelling at the base of the flagellum. The stigma probably serves as a shield, which is essential if the photoreceptor is to detect light coming from certain directions but not from others. Thus, the photoreceptor plus the stigma enable *Euglena* to orient itself so that its photoreceptor is exposed to light. This helps the protozoan maintain itself in the region of the water column where sufficient light is available for photosynthesis.

Some animals, such as the earthworm *Lumbricus*, have simple unicellular photoreceptor cells scattered over the epidermis or concentrated in particular areas of the body. Others possess multicellular photoreceptors that can be classified into three basic types: ocelli, compound eyes, and complex eyes.

An **ocellus** (L. dim of *oculus,* eye; pl., ocelli) is simply a small cup lined with light-sensitive receptors and backed by light-absorbing pigment (figure 34.4*b*). The light-sensitive cells are called retinular cells and contain a photosensitive pigment. Stimulation by light causes a chemical change in the pigment, leading to a generator potential, which causes an action potential that is carried by sensory neurons to be interpreted elsewhere in the animal's body. This type of visual system gives an animal information about light direction and intensity, but not image formation. Ocelli are common in many phyla (e.g., Annelida, Mollusca, and Arthropoda).

Compound eyes are composed of from just a few to many distinct units called **ommatidia** (Gr. *ommato,* eye + *ium,* little; s., ommatidium; figure 34.4*c*). Although compound eyes occur in some annelids and bivalve molluscs, they are best developed and understood in arthropods. A compound eye may contain thousands of ommatidia, each oriented in a slightly different direction from the others as a result of the eye's overall convex shape. The visual field of a compound eye is very wide, as anyone who has tried to catch a fly will know. Each ommatidium is supplied with its own nerve tract leading to a large optic nerve. ① The visual fields of adjacent ommatidia overlap to some degree; thus a shift of position of an object within the total visual field causes changes in the level of stimulation of several ommatidia. As a result of this physiology, as well as a sufficiently sophisticated central nervous system, compound eyes are very effective in detecting movements and are probably capable of forming an image. In addition, most compound eyes

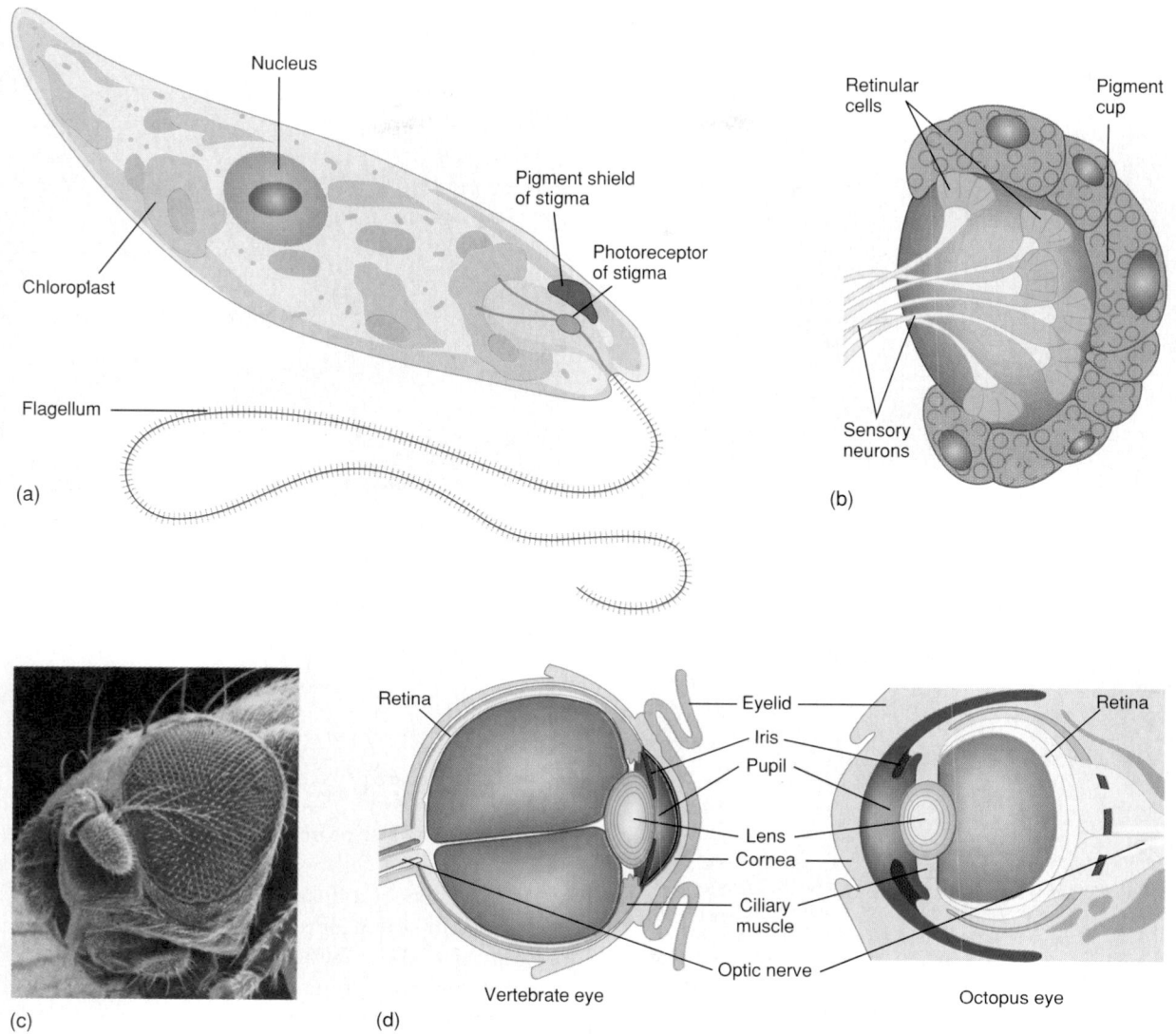

Figure **34.4**

Invertebrate Photoreceptors. (*a*) Stigma. The protozoan, *Euglena*, contains a mass of bright red granules called the stigma. The actual photoreceptor is the swelling at the base of the flagellum. (*b*) Ocellus. The inverted pigment cup ocellus of a flatworm. (*c*) Compound eye. The compound eye of a fly contains hundreds of ommatidia. Note the eye's convex shape; no two ommatidia are oriented in precisely the same direction (scanning electron micrograph). (*d*) Complex camera eyes. A comparison of a vertebrate eye and an octopus eye (vertical sections).

can adapt to changes in light intensities and some provide for color vision. ② Color vision is particularly important in active day-flying, nectar-drinking insects, such as honeybees. Honeybees learn to recognize particular flowers by color, scent, and shape.

The **complex camera eyes** of squids and octopuses are the best image-forming eyes among the invertebrates. ③ In fact, the giant squid's eye is the largest of any animal's, exceeding 38 cm in diameter. Cephalopod eyes are often compared with those of vertebrates (figure 34.4*d*) since they contain a thin transparent cornea, a lens that focuses light on the retina and is suspended by, and controlled by, ciliary muscles. However, the

complex eyes of squids are different from the vertebrate eye in that the receptor sites on the retinal layer face in the direction of light entering the eye. In the vertebrate eye, the retinal layer is inverted and the receptors are the deepest cells in the retina. Both eyes are focusing and image-forming, although the process differs in detail. In terrestrial vertebrates, light is focused by muscles that alter the shape (thickness) of the lens. In fishes and cephalopods, light is focused by muscles that move the lens toward or away from the retina (like moving a magnifying glass back and forth until proper focus is achieved) and by altering the shape of the eyeball.

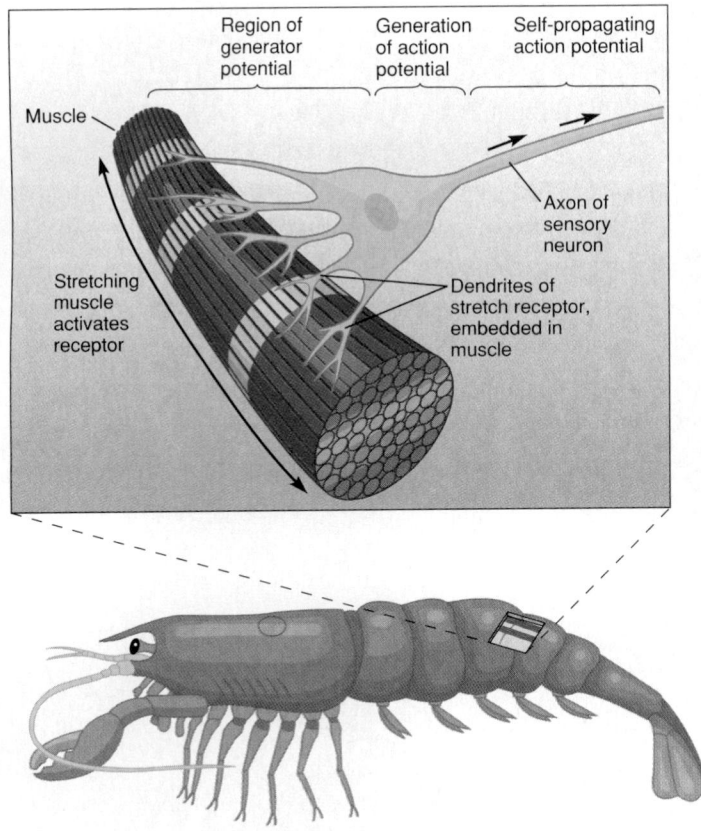

FIGURE 34.5

Invertebrate Proprioceptor. Crayfish stretch receptors are neurons attached to muscles. In this example, when the crayfish arches its abdomen while swimming, the stretch receptor detects the change in muscle length. When the muscle is stretched, so is the receptor. The stretch increases the sodium permeability of the receptor cell plasma membrane by mechanically opening sodium channels. The inflow of sodium ions produces depolarization and a generator potential that evokes an action potential. The action potential is then transmitted to the central nervous system, where interpretation takes place.

PROPRIOCEPTORS

Proprioceptors (L. *proprius*, one's self + receptor), commonly called "stretch receptors," are internal sense organs that respond to mechanically induced changes caused by stretching, compression, bending, or tension. These receptors give an animal information about the movement of its body parts and their positions relative to each other. Proprioceptors have been most thoroughly studied in arthropods, where they are associated with appendage joints and body extensor muscles (figure 34.5). In these animals, the sensory neurons involved in proprioception are associated with and attached to some part of the body that is stretched. These parts may be specialized muscle cells, elastic connective tissue fibers, or various membranes that span joints. As these structures change shape, sensory nerve endings of the attached nerves are distorted accordingly and initiate a generator potential.

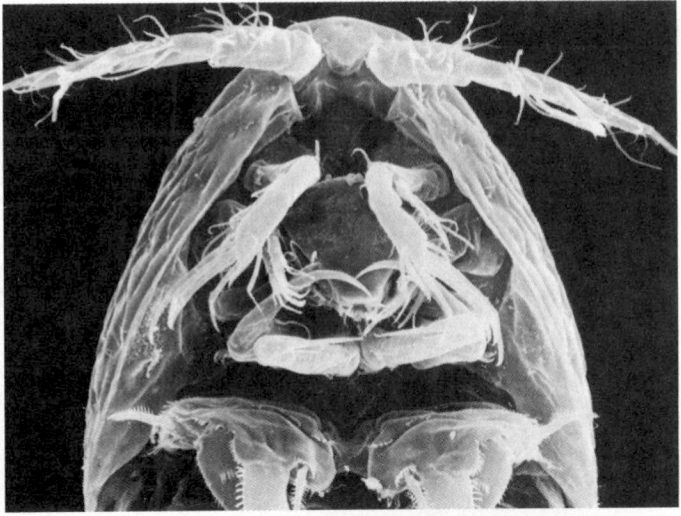

FIGURE 34.6

Invertebrate Tactile Receptor. Scanning electron micrograph of a copepod showing the head appendages covered with sensory bristles (×260).

TACTILE RECEPTORS

Tactile (touch) receptors are generally derived from modifications of epithelial cells associated with sensory neurons. Most tactile receptors of animals involve projections from the body surface. Examples include various bristles, spines, setae, and tubercles (figure 34.6). When an animal makes contact with an object in the environment, these receptors are mechanically deformed. These deformations activate the receptor, which in turn activates underlying sensory neurons, initiating a generator potential.

Most tactile receptors are also sensitive to mechanically induced vibrations propagated through water or a solid substrate. For example, tube-dwelling polychaetes bear receptors that allow them to retract quickly into their tubes in response to movements in their surroundings.   4   Web-building spiders have tactile receptors that can sense struggling prey in their webs through vibrations of the web threads.

THERMORECEPTORS

Thermoreceptors (Gr. *therme*, heat + receptors) respond to temperature changes. Evidence exists that some invertebrates are capable of directly sensing differences in environmental temperatures. For example, the protozoan *Paramecium* collects in areas where water temperature is moderate, and it avoids extremes in temperature. Somehow, leeches and ticks are drawn to warm-blooded hosts by some heat-sensing mechanism. Certain insects, some crustaceans, and the horseshoe crab (*Limulus*) can also sense thermal variations. In all of these cases, however, specific receptor structures have not been identified.

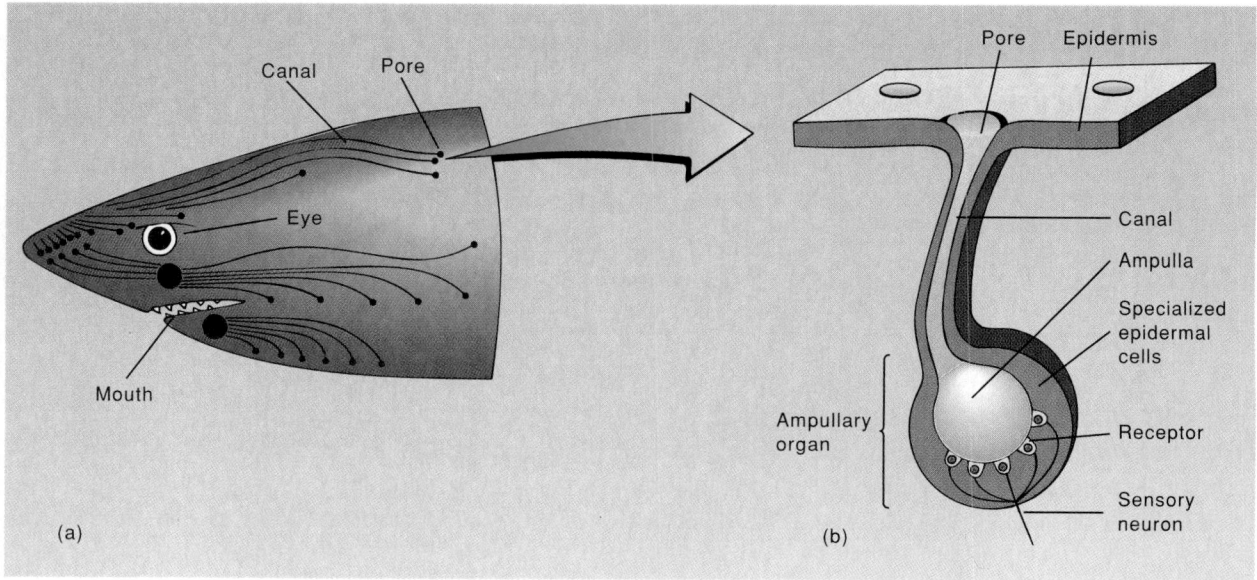

FIGURE 34.7

The Lateral-Line System and Electrical Sensing. (*a*) In jawless fishes, jawed fishes, and amphibians, electroreceptors are located in the epidermis along the sides of the head and body. (*b*)Pores of the lateral-line system lead into canals that connect to an ampullary organ that functions in electroreception and the production of a generator potential.

Stop and Ask Yourself

5. How does a statocyst function? In what animals do you find statocysts?

6. How does a tympanic organ function? What animals possess a tympanic organ?

7. What animals possess ocelli? Compound eyes? Complex camera eyes?

8. What is the difference between a proprioceptor and a tactile receptor?

VERTEBRATE SENSORY RECEPTORS

Vertebrate sensory receptors reflect adaptations to the nature of sensory stimuli in different external and internal environments. Each environment has chemical and physical characteristics that affect the kinds of energy and molecules that carry sensory information. For example, our external environment consists of the media that surrounds us: the earth that we stand on and the air that we breathe. Other animals, such as a trout, may be immersed in the cool, clear water of a mountain stream; a turtle may be located in the turbid water of a swamp, while a salmon may be swimming in the salty water of the sea.

Each of the above media contains only certain environmental stimuli. For example, air transmits light very well and conducts sound waves relatively efficiently. But air can carry only a limited assortment of small molecules detectable using the sense of smell and can pass little or no electrical energy. In water, however, sound travels both faster and farther than in air, and water dissolves and carries a wide range of chemicals. Water, especially seawater, is also an excellent conductor of electricity, but it absorbs (and hence fails to transmit) many wavelengths of light. As these examples indicate, vertebrate sensory receptors (organs), like invertebrate sensory receptors, have evolved in ways that relate to the environment in which they must function.

Many underlying similarities unite all vertebrate senses. For each sense, there is a fascinating story of environmental information, the evolutionary adaptation of receptor cells to detect that information, and the processing in the central nervous system of the information to make it usable by the animal. What follows is a discussion of particular vertebrate receptors (e.g., lateral-line systems, ears, eyes, skin sensors) that detect changes in the external environment, and of several receptors (e.g., pain, proprioception) that detect changes in the internal environment of some familiar vertebrate animals.

LATERAL-LINE SYSTEM AND ELECTRICAL SENSING

Specialized organs for equilibrium and gravity detection, audition, and magnetoreception have evolved from the lateral-line system of fishes. The **lateral-line system** for electrical sensing is located in the head and body areas of most fishes (figure 34.7*a*), some amphibians, and the platypus. It consists of sensory pores in the epidermis of the skin that connect to canals leading into **electroreceptors** called **ampullary organs** (figure 34.7*b*). These organs can sense electrical currents in the surrounding water.

⑤   Because most living organisms generate weak electrical

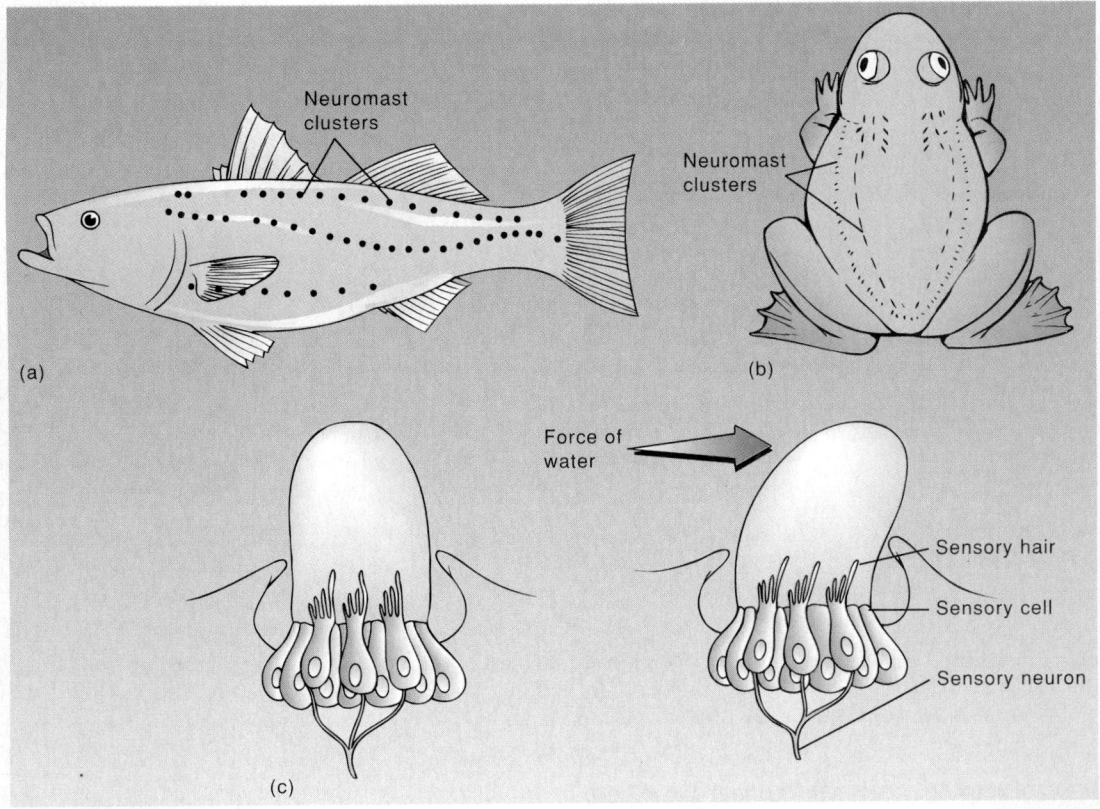

Figure 34.8

The Lateral-Line System and Mechanoreception. The lateral-line system of (*a*) a bony fish and (*b*) a frog, illustrating the various neuromast clusters. (*c*) The function of a neuromast. The water movement (arrow) forces the top of the cell to bend or distort, thereby distorting the small hairs on the inside, producing a generator potential.

fields, the ability to detect these fields may permit a fish to utilize electrolocation to find mates, capture prey, or avoid predators. This is an especially valuable sense in deep, turbulent, or murky water, where vision is of little use. In fact, some fishes actually generate electrical fields and then use their electroreceptors (electrocommunication) to detect how surrounding objects distort the field, allowing these fishes to navigate in murky or turbulent waters (*see figure 27.16*).

Lateral-Line System and Mechanoreception

A **mechanoreceptor** is a receptor that is excited by mechanical pressures or distortions (e.g., sound, touch, and muscular contractions). The lateral-line system of cyclostomes, some of the more advanced fishes, and aquatic amphibians includes several different kinds of hair-cell mechanoreceptors called **neuromasts.** Neuromasts are located in pits along the body, but not in the head region (figure 34.8*a,b*). All neuromasts are responsive to local water displacement or disturbance. When the water near the lateral line moves, it moves the water in the pits and distorts the hair cells, causing a generator potential in the associated sensory neurons (figure 34.8*c*). Thus, the animal can detect the direction and force of water currents and the movement of other

animals or prey in the water. For example, this sense enables a trout to orient with its head upstream.

Hearing and Equilibrium in Air

Hearing may initially have been important to vertebrates as a mechanism to alert the animal to either nearby or faraway activity that might be dangerous. It also became important in the search for food and mates, and in communication. Hearing (audition) and equilibrium (balance) are considered together because both sensations are received in the same vertebrate organ—the ear. The vertebrate ear has two functional units: (1) the auditory apparatus is concerned with hearing, and (2) the vestibular apparatus is concerned with equilibrium.

Sound results when energy is transmitted by pressure waves through some medium, such as air or water. Hearing in air poses serious problems for vertebrates since middle-ear transformers are sound pressure sensors, but in air, sound produces less than 0.1% of the pressure that the same intensity of sound produces in water. Adaptation to hearing in air resulted from the evolution of an acoustic transformer that incorporates a thin, stretched membrane, called either an eardrum, tympanic membrane, or tympanum, that is exposed to the air.

The tympanum first evolved in the amphibians. The ears of anurans (frogs) consist of a tympanum, a middle ear, and an

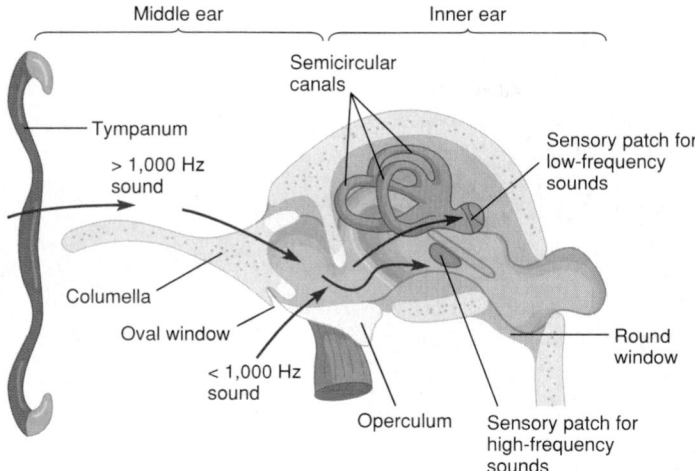

FIGURE 34.9

The Ear of an Anuran (Posterior View). Purple arrows show the pathway of low-frequency sounds, via the operculum. Red arrows show the pathway of high-frequency sounds, via the columella.

inner ear (figure 34.9). The tympanum is modified integument stretched over a cartilaginous ring; the tympanum vibrates in response to sounds, and transmits these movements to the middle ear, which is a chamber behind the tympanum. Touching the tympanum is an ossicle (a small bone or bony structure) called the columella or stapes. The opposite end of the columella (stapes) touches the membrane of the oval window, which stretches between the middle and inner ears. High-frequency (1,000 to 5,000 Hz) sounds strike the tympanum and are transmitted through the middle ear via the columella and cause pressure waves in the fluid of the inner ear. These pressure waves in the inner ear fluid stimulate receptor cells. A second small ossicle, the operculum, also touches the oval window. Substrate-borne vibrations transmitted through the front appendages and the pectoral girdle cause this ossicle to vibrate. The resulting pressure waves in the inner ear stimulate a second patch of sensory receptor cells that is sensitive to low-frequency (100 to 1,000 Hz) sounds. Muscles attached to the operculum and columella can lock either or both of these ossicles, allowing a frog to screen out either high- or low-frequency sounds. This mechanism is adaptive because low- and high-frequency sounds are used in different situations by frogs. For example, mating calls are high-frequency sounds that are of primary importance for only part of the year (breeding season). At other times, low-frequency sounds may warn of approaching predators.

Salamanders lack a tympanum and middle ear. They live in streams, ponds, and caves, and beneath leaf litter. They have no mating calls, and the only sounds they hear are probably transmitted through the substratum and skull to the inner ear.

The sense of equilibrium and balance in amphibians involves the semicircular canals. These canals help detect rotational movements and gravity. Since the function of the semicircular canals is similar in all vertebrates, they will be discussed with the human ear.

There are variations in the structure of reptilian ears. For example, the ears of snakes lack a middle-ear cavity and a

tympanum. A bone of the jaw articulates with the stapes and receives vibrations of the substratum. In other reptiles, a tympanum may be on the surface or in a small depression in the head. The inner ear of reptiles is similar to that of amphibians.

Hearing is well developed in most birds. The external ear opening is covered by loose, delicate feathers. Middle- and inner-ear structures are similar to mammals.

Auditory senses were also important to the early mammals. Adaptations include an ear flap (the auricle) and the auditory tube (external auditory canal), leading to the tympanum that directs sounds to the middle ear. In mammals, the sensory patch of the inner ear that contains receptors for sound is long and coiled and is called the cochlea. This structure provides more surface area for receptor cells and allows mammals greater sensitivity to pitch and volume than is present in other animals. Since the structure and function of all mammal ears is basically the same, we will use the familiar human ear as our example.

The human ear has three divisions: the outer, middle, and inner ear. The outer ear consists of the auricle and external auditory canal (figure 34.10). The middle ear begins at the tympanic membrane (eardrum) and ends inside the skull, where two small membranous openings, the oval and round windows, are located. Three small ossicles are located between the tympanic membrane and the oval window. They include the malleus (hammer), incus (anvil), and stapes (stirrup), so named because their shapes resemble these objects. The malleus adheres to the tympanic membrane and connects to the incus. The incus connects to the stapes, which adheres to the oval window. The auditory (eustachian) tube extends from the middle ear to the nasopharynx and permits equalization of air pressure between the middle ear and the throat.

The inner ear has three components. The first two, the vestibule and the semicircular canals, are concerned with equilibrium, and the third, the cochlea, is involved with hearing. The semicircular canals are arranged so that there is one in each dimension of space. The process of hearing can be summarized as follows:

1. Sound waves enter the outer ear and create pressure waves that reach the tympanic membrane.
2. Air molecules under pressure cause the tympanic membrane to vibrate. The vibrations move the malleus, on the other side of the membrane.
3. The handle of the malleus strikes the incus, causing it to vibrate.
4. The vibrating incus moves the stapes back and forth against the oval window.
5. The movements of the oval window set up pressure changes that vibrate the fluid in the inner ear. These vibrations are transmitted to the basilar membrane, causing it to ripple.
6. Receptor hair cells of the organ of Corti that are in contact with the overlying tectorial membrane are bent, causing a generator potential, which leads to an action potential that travels along the vestibulocochlear nerve to the brain for interpretation.
7. Vibrations in the cochlear fluid dissipate as a result of movements of the round window.

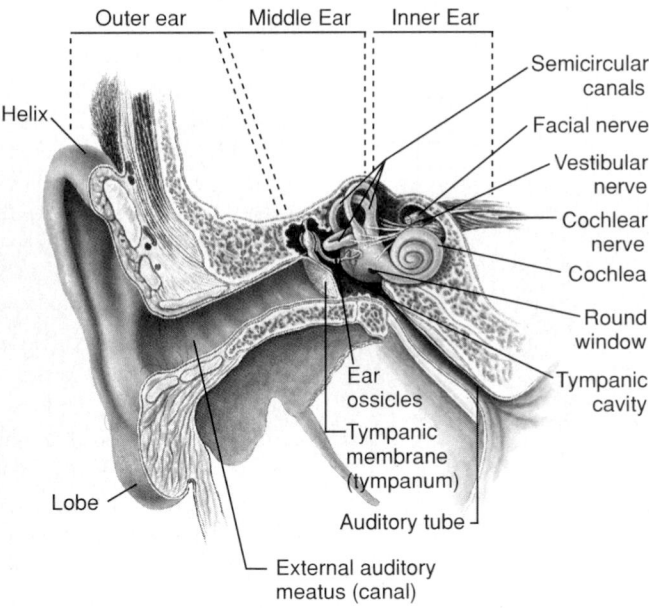

FIGURE 34.10

The Ear. Anatomy of the human ear. Note the outer, middle, and inner regions. The inner ear includes the semicircular canals, which are involved with equilibrium, and the cochlea, which is involved with hearing.

| BOX 34.1 | DEATH SOUNDS |

Zoologists have long wondered how huge whales, such as the sperm whale, catch fishes as small as 4 cm in length, and invertebrates as elusive and fast moving as squid. But size is not the only reason that the predatory habits of some of these animals known as odontocetes (toothed whales) are unusual. The fossil record shows that odontocete's teeth and beaks have become less, not more, functional over time. Then how do they catch their prey?

Recent evidence indicates that these sea mammals' secret weapon may be sound. Odontocetes are able to immobilize prey with loud vocalizations. Zoologists have been able to record the animals' loud hunting bursts, called bangs, and have found that they are of a different frequency from those used in echolocation, which is the normal form of auditory communication among whales and dolphins. Evidence indicates that when the "big bang" is emitted, at least one prey species—anchovies—is stunned, with hemorrhaging in their abdomens as a result of the power of the "bang." Studies are currently being done to measure the effects of low-frequency bangs on locomotion in a variety of other fish.

Humans are not able to hear low-pitched sounds, below 20 cycles per second, although some other vertebrates can (box 34.1). Young children can hear high-pitched sounds up to 20,000 cycles per second, but this ability decreases with age. ⑥ Other vertebrates can hear sounds at much higher frequencies. For example, dogs can easily detect sounds of 40,000 cycles per second. Thus, dogs can hear sounds from a high-pitched dog whistle that seems silent to a human.

The sense of equilibrium (balance) can be divided into two separate senses: Static equilibrium refers to sensing movement in one plane (either vertical or horizontal), and dynamic equilibrium refers to sensing angular and/or rotational movement.

When the body is still, the otoliths in the semicircular canals rest on hair cells (figure 34.11a). When the head or body moves horizontally, or vertically, the granules are displaced, causing the gelatinous material to sag (figure 34.11b). This displacement causes the hairs to bend slightly so that hair cells initiate a generator potential and then an action potential. ⑦ Continuous movement of the fluid in the semicircular canals may cause motion sickness or seasickness in humans.

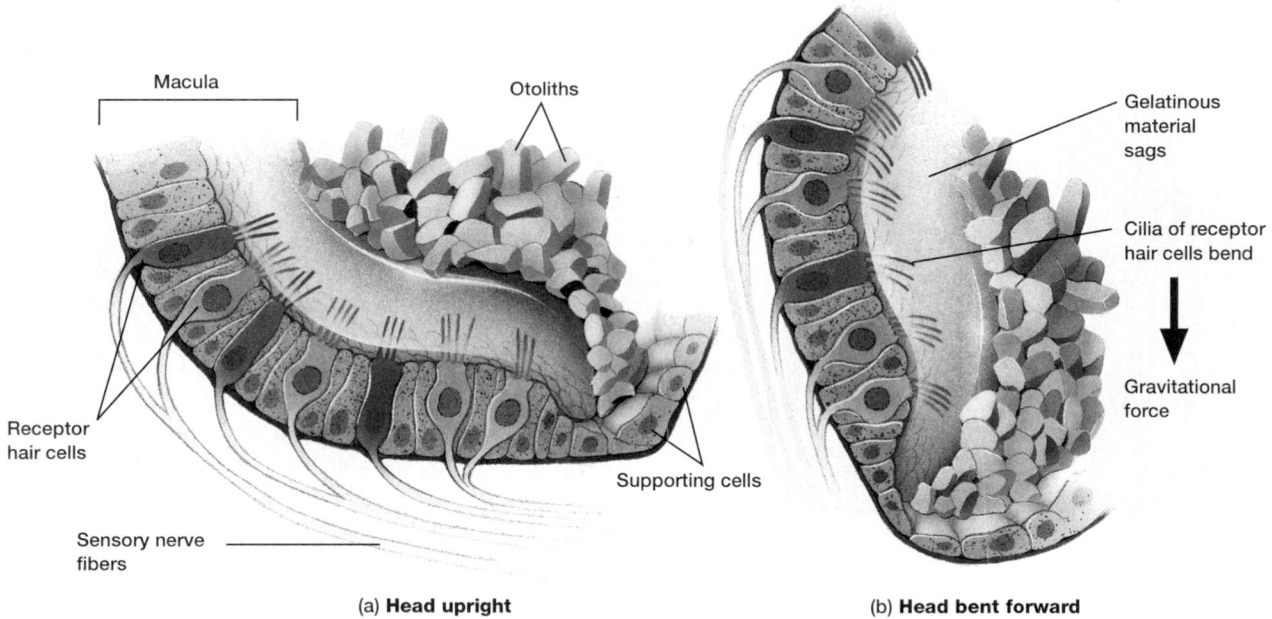

Macula

Otoliths

Gelatinous material sags

Cilia of receptor hair cells bend

Gravitational force

Receptor hair cells

Supporting cells

Sensory nerve fibers

(a) **Head upright**

(b) **Head bent forward**

Figure 34.11

Static Equilibrium (Balance). Receptor hair cells in the utricle and saccule are involved in responding to movement sideways or up or down. (*a*) When the head is upright, otoliths are balanced directly over the cilia of receptor hair cells. (*b*) When the head is bent forward, the otoliths shift, and the cilia of hair cells are bent. This bending of hairs causes a generator potential to be initiated.

HEARING AND EQUILIBRIUM IN WATER

In bony fishes, receptors for equilibrium, balance, and hearing are located in the inner ear (figure 34.12), and their functions are similar to those of other vertebrates. For example, semicircular canals detect rotational movements, and other sensory patches help with equilibrium and balance by detecting the direction of gravitational pull. Since fishes lack the outer and/or middle ear found in other vertebrates, vibrations are passed from the water through the bones of the skull to the inner ear. A few fishes have chains of bony ossicles (modifications of vertebrae) that pass between the swim bladder and the back of the skull. Vibrations that strike the fishes are thus amplified by the swim bladder and sent through the ossicles to the skull.

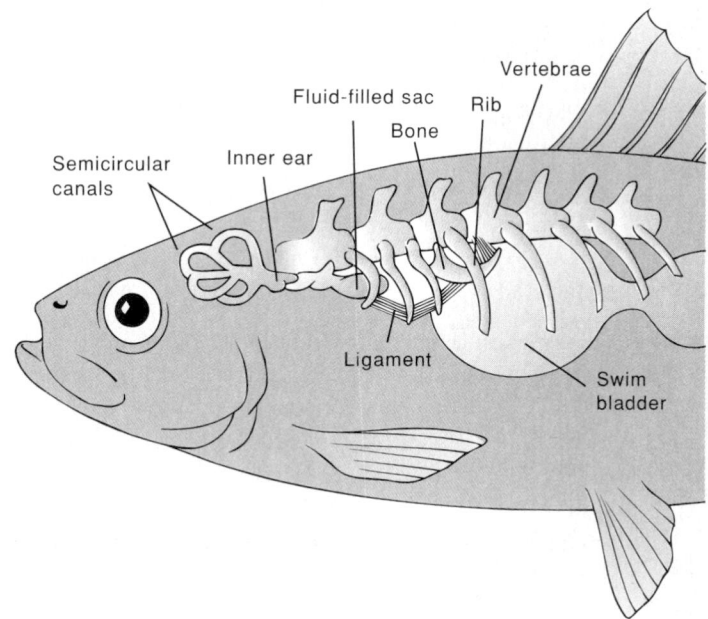

Vertebrae

Fluid-filled sac

Rib

Bone

Semicircular canals

Inner ear

Ligament

Swim bladder

Stop and Ask Yourself

9. How do fishes utilize electroreceptors?
10. How do neuromasts function?
11. Why is the tympanic membrane important to life on land?
12. What structures are involved in the sense of equilibrium?
13. Why don't fishes need either an outer or middle ear?

Figure 34.12

The Inner Ear of a Bony Fish. Sound waves that enter the pharynx are transmitted to gas in the swim bladder, causing it to expand and contract at frequencies and amplitudes corresponding to the incoming sound waves. Contacting the swim bladder is a bone that is suspended by ligaments and vibrates at the same frequency. The vibrations are passed forward along a chain of bones (ossicles) and then to a fluid-filled sac connected directly to the inner ear.

— Pit organ

Figure 34.13

Thermoreception. A rattlesnake (*Crotalus vergrandis*) has a pit organ between each eye and nostril that detects heat and allows the snake to locate warm prey in the dark.

Skin Sensors of Damaging Stimuli

Pain receptors are bare sensory nerve endings that are present throughout the body of mammals, except for the brain and intestines. These nerve endings are also called **nociceptors** (L. *nocere*, to injure + receptor). Severe heat, cold, irritating chemicals, and strong mechanical stimuli (e.g., penetration) may elicit a response from nociceptors that is interpreted in the brain as pain or itching. Details, however, of the structure and physiology of pain receptors are all but unknown.

Skin Sensors of Heat and Cold

Sensors of temperature (thermoreceptors) are also bare sensory nerve endings. Thermoreceptors may be present in either the epidermis or dermis. Mammals have a distinctly different distribution of areas sensitive to either cold or warm. These areas are called cold or warm spots. A spot refers to a small area of the skin that, when stimulated, yields a temperature sensation of warmth or cold. Cold receptors in the skin respond to temperatures below skin temperature, and heat receptors respond to temperatures above skin temperature. Materials coming into contact with the skin need not be warm or cold to produce temperature sensations. For example, when metal is placed on the skin, it absorbs heat and one feels a sense of coldness. If wood is placed on the skin, it absorbs less heat and, therefore, feels warmer than the metal.

The ability to detect changes in temperature has become well developed in a number of animals. For example, rattlesnakes and other pit vipers have heat-sensitive **pit organs** on each side of the face between the eye and nostril (figure 34.13). These depressions are lined with sensory epithelium containing receptor cells that respond to temperatures (in-

frared thermal regulation) different from the snakes' surroundings. Snakes use these pit organs to locate warm-blooded prey.

Skin Sensors of Mechanical Stimuli

Many animals rely on tactile (pertaining to touch) stimuli to obtain information about their environment. Mechanical sensory receptors in vertebrate skin detect stimuli that the brain interprets as light touch, touch-pressure, and vibration.

Light touch is perceived when the skin is touched, but not deformed. Receptors of light touch include **bare sensory nerve endings** and **tactile (Meissner's) corpuscles** (figure 34.14). Bare sensory nerve endings are the most widely distributed receptors in the vertebrate body, and are involved with pain and thermal stimuli, as well as light touch. The **bulbs of Krause** are mechanoreceptors, found in the dermis in certain parts of the body, that respond to some physical stimuli, such as position changes. Other receptors for touch-pressure are **Pacinian corpuscles** and the **organs of Ruffini.**

Many mammals have specially adapted sensory hairs called **vibrissae** (s., vibrissa) on their wrists, snout, and eyebrows (e.g., cat whiskers). Around the base of each vibrissa is a blood sinus. Nerves that border the sinus carry impulses from several kinds of mechanoreceptors to the brain for interpretation.

Sonar

Bats, shrews, several cave-dwelling birds (oilbird, cave swiftlet), whales, and dolphins can determine distance and depth by a form of echolocation called **sonar (biosonar).** These animals emit high-frequency sounds, then determine the time that it takes for these sounds to return to the animal after bouncing off objects in the environment. For example, some bats emit clicks that last from 2 to 3 milliseconds and are repeated several hundred times per second. The returning echo created when a moth or other insect flies past the bat can provide sufficient information for the bat to locate and catch its prey. Overall, the three-dimensional imaging achieved with such an auditory sonar system is quite sophisticated.

Smell

The sense of smell, or **olfaction** (L. *olere*, to smell + *facere*, to make) is due to olfactory neurons (receptor cells) located in the roof of the vertebrate nasal cavity (figure 34.15). These cells, which are specialized endings of the fibers that make up the olfactory nerve, lie among supporting epithelial cells. They are densely packed; for example, a dog has up to 40 million olfactory receptor cells per square centimeter. Each olfactory cell ends in a tuft of cilia containing receptor sites for various chemicals.

Several theories have been proposed to explain how odors are perceived. The most likely one is that odor molecules

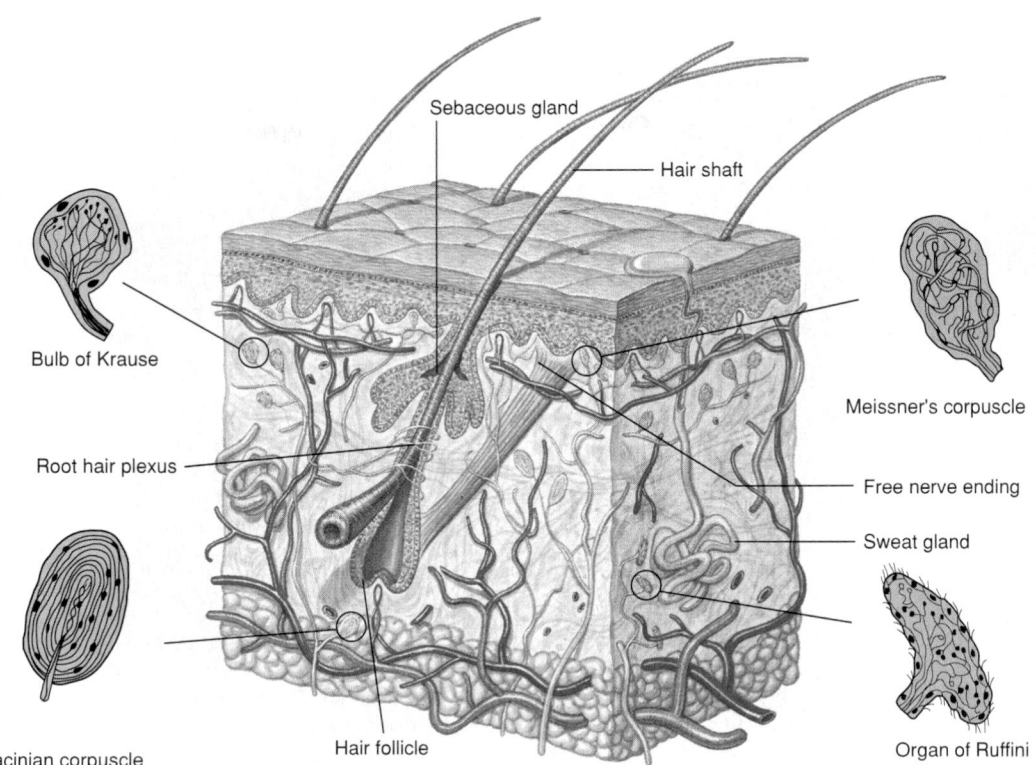

FIGURE 34.14

Different Sensory Receptors to Mechanical Stimuli. Sensory receptors located in the skin for light touch (Meissner's corpuscles), free nerve endings, touch-pressure (organs of Ruffini and Pacinian corpuscles), position (bulbs of Krause), and pain (free nerve endings).

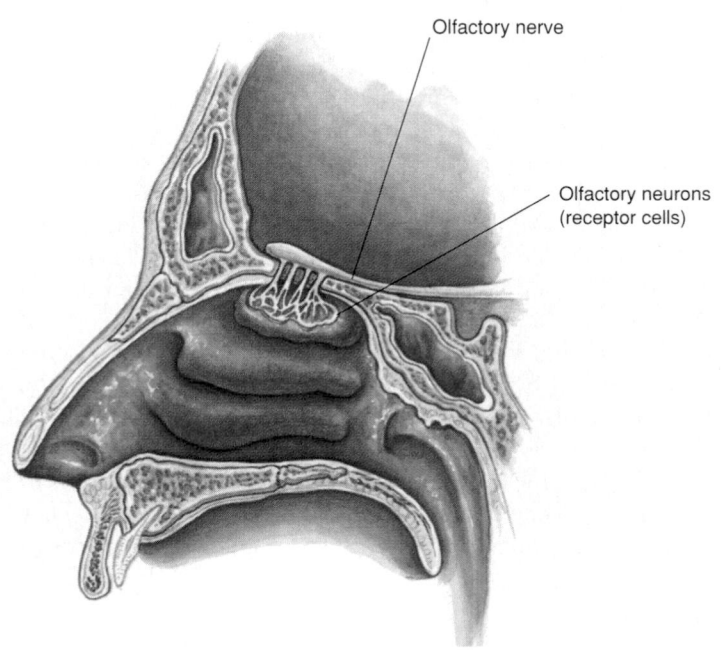

FIGURE 34.15

Smell. Position of olfactory receptors in a human nasal passageway. The receptor cells, which have hairlike processes (analogous to dendrites) projecting into the nasal cavity, are supported by columnar epithelial cells. When these receptor cells are stimulated by chemicals in the air, nerve impulses are conducted to the brain by the olfactory nerve.

have some kind of physical interaction with protein receptors located on the receptor-plasma membrane. Such an interaction somehow alters the membrane permeability and leads to a generator potential.

In most fishes, openings (external nares) in the snout lead to the olfactory receptors. Recent research has revealed that some fishes rely heavily on their sense of smell. For example, salmon and lampreys return to spawn in the same streams in which they hatched years earlier. Their migrations to these streams often involve distances of hundreds of miles and are guided by the fishes' perception of characteristic odors of their spawning stream.

Olfaction is an important sense for many amphibians. It is used in mate recognition, as well as detecting noxious chemicals and in locating food.

Olfactory senses are better developed in reptiles than in amphibians. In addition to having more olfactory epithelium, most reptiles (except crocodilians) possess blind-ending pouches that open into the mouth. These pouches, called **Jacobson's (vomeronasal) organs,** are best developed in snakes and lizards (figure 34.16). The protrusible, forked tongues of snakes and lizards are accessory olfactory organs that are used to sample airborne chemicals. A snake's tongue is flicked out and then moved to the Jacobson's organs, where odor molecules are perceived. In turtles and the tuatara, Jacobson's organs are used to taste objects held in the mouth.

34.13

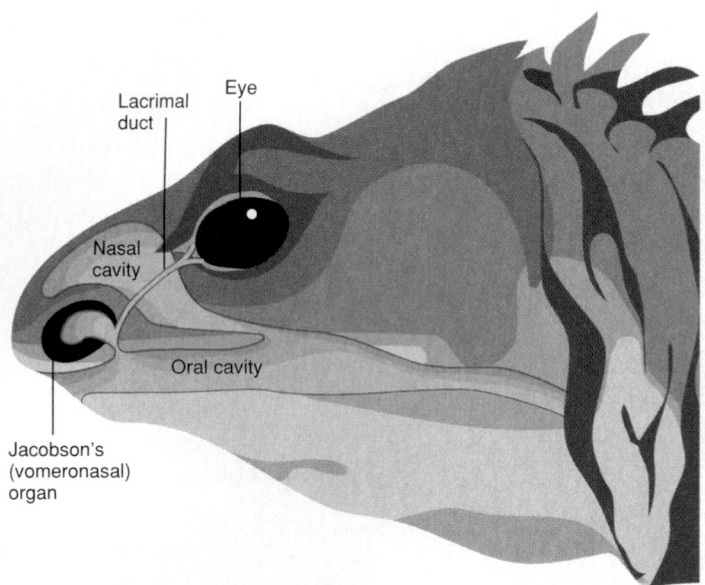

Figure 34.16

Smell. A drawing showing the anatomic relationships of Jacobson's (vomeronasal) organ in a generalized lizard. Only the left organ is shown located alongside the nasal cavity. Jacobson's organ is a spherical structure with the ventral side invaginated into a sphere the shape of a mushroom. A narrow duct connects the interior of Jacobson's organ to the oral cavity. In many lizards, fluid draining from the eye via the lacrimal duct may bring odoriferous molecules into contact with the sensory epithelium of Jacobson's organ.

Olfaction apparently plays a minor role in the lives of most birds. External nares open near the base of the beak, but the olfactory epithelium is poorly developed. An exception includes the vultures, which locate their dead and dying prey largely by smell.

Olfaction is an important sense for many mammals. Olfactory stimuli can be perceived over long distances during either the day or night and are used to locate food, recognize members of the same species, and avoid predators.

Taste

The receptors for taste, or **gustation** (L. *gustus*, taste), are chemoreceptors. They may be located on the body surface of an animal or in the mouth and throat. For example, the surface of the mammalian tongue is covered with many small protuberances called papillae (s., papilla). Papillae give the tongue its "bumpy" appearance (figure 34.17*a*). Located in the crevices between the papillae are thousands of specialized receptors called **taste buds** (figure 34.17*b*). Taste buds are barrel-shaped clusters of chemoreceptor cells called gustatory cells and supporting cells arranged like alternating segments of an orange. Extending from each receptor cell are gustatory hairs that project through a tiny opening called the taste pore. Sensory neurons are associated with the basal ends of the gustatory cells.

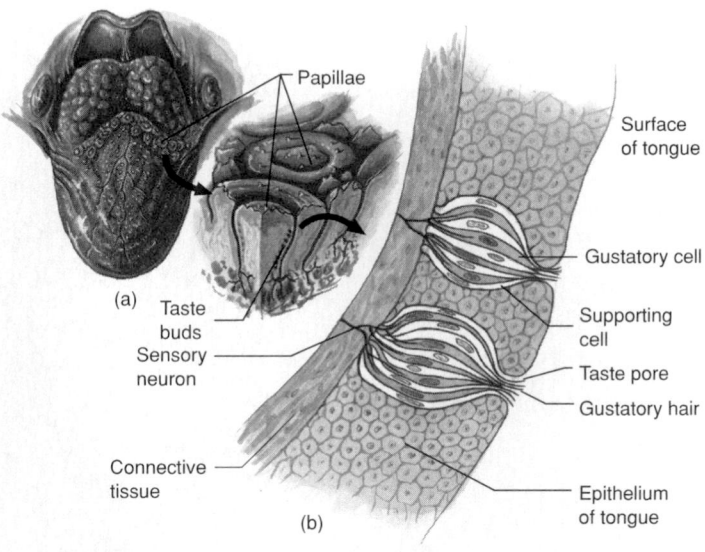

Figure 34.17

Taste. (*a*) Surface view of the human tongue showing the many papillae and the numerous taste buds found between papillae. (*b*) The gustatory cell and its associated gustatory hair is encapsulated by supporting cells.

The four generally recognized taste sensations are sweet (sugars), sour (acids), bitter (alkaloids), and salty (electrolytes). The exact mechanism(s) that stimulate a chemoreceptor taste cell are not known. One theory is that different types of gustatory stimuli cause proteins on the surface of the receptor-cell plasma membrane to change the permeability of the membrane, in effect, "opening and closing gates" to chemical stimuli and causing a generator potential.

In vertebrates other than mammals, taste buds may be found on other parts of the body. For example, taste buds are rarely found on the tongue of reptiles and birds. Instead, most are found in the pharynx. In fishes and amphibians, taste buds may also be found in the skin.   ⑧   For example, a sturgeon's taste buds are abundant on its projection called the rostrum. As the sturgeon glides over the bottom, it can obtain foretaste of potential food before the mouth reaches it. In other fishes, taste buds are widely distributed in the roof, side walls, and floor of the pharynx, where they monitor the incoming flow of water. In fish that feed on the bottom (catfish, carp, suckers), taste buds are distributed over the entire surface of the head and body to the tip of the tail. They are also very abundant on the barbels ("whiskers") of catfish.

Vision

Vision (photoreception) is the primary sense used by vertebrates that live in a light-filled environment, and consequently their photoreceptive structures are well-developed. Most vertebrates have eyes capable of forming visual images. As figure 34.18 indicates, the eyeball has a lens, a sclera (the tough outer coat), a

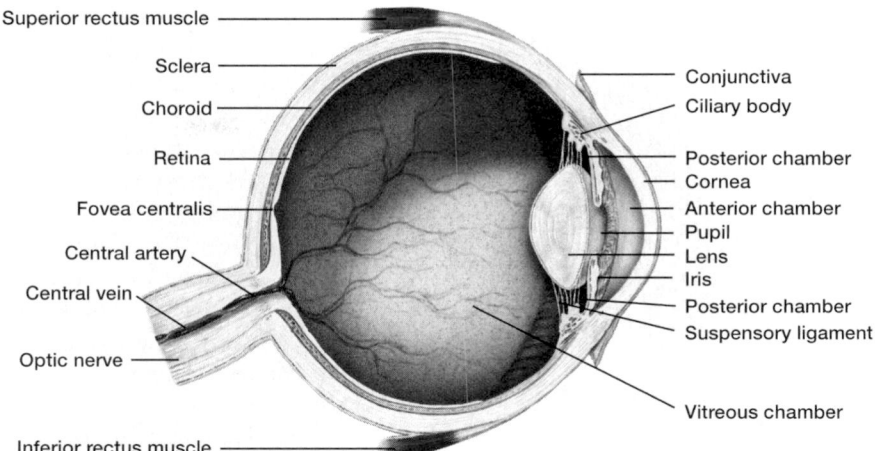

Figure 34.18

The Internal Anatomy of the Human Eyeball. Light passes through the transparent cornea and is focused by the lens on the rear surface of the eye, the retina, at a particular location called the fovea centralis. The retina is rich in rods and cones.

choroid layer (a thin middle layer), and an inner retina containing many light-sensitive receptor cells (photoreceptors). The transparent cornea is continuous with the sclera and covers the front of the eyeball. Choroid tissue also extends to the front of the eyeball to form the iris, ciliary body, and suspensory ligaments. The colored iris is heavily endowed with light-screening pigments, and it has radial and circular smooth muscles for regulating the amount of light entering the pupil. A clear fluid (aqueous humor) fills the anterior and posterior chambers, which lie between the lens and the cornea. The lens is located behind the iris, and a jellylike vitreous body fills the vitreous chamber behind the lens. The moist, mucous membrane that covers the eyeball is the conjunctiva.

Vertebrates can adjust the direction in which light from either close-up or distant objects converges on the photoreceptors. This process of focusing light rays precisely on the retina is called **accommodation.** Vertebrates rely on the coordinated stretching and relaxation of the eye muscles and fibers (the ciliary body and suspensory ligaments) that are attached to the lens for accommodation.

The eyes of the fishes are similar in most aspects of structure and function to those found in other vertebrates. However, fish eyes are lidless, and the lens is rounded and located close to the cornea. Focusing is accomplished by moving the lens forward or backward.

Vision is one of the most important senses in amphibians because they are primarily sight feeders. A number of adaptations allow the eyes of amphibians to function in terrestrial environments. For example, the eyes of some amphibians (e.g., anurans, salamanders) are located on the front of the head and provide the binocular vision and well-developed depth perception necessary for capturing prey. Other amphibians with smaller and more lateral eyes (e.g., some salamanders) lack binocular vi-

sion. However, the more laterally placed eyes permit these animals to see well off to their sides. The transparent **nictitating membrane** (an "inner eyelid") is movable and functions to clean and protect the eye.

Vision is the dominant sense in most reptiles, and their eyes are similar to those of amphibians. Upper and lower eyelids, a nictitating membrane, and a blood sinus protect and cleanse the surface of the eye. In snakes and some lizards, the upper and lower eyelids become fused in the embryo to form a protective window of clear skin called the spectacle. Some reptiles possess a **median (parietal) eye** (figure 34.19) that develops from outgrowths of the roof of the optic tectum (midbrain). In the tuatara, it is an eye complete with a lens, nerve, and retina. In other reptiles, the parietal eye is less developed. Parietal eyes are covered by skin and probably cannot form images. They can, however, differentiate light and dark periods and are used in orientation to the sun.

Vision is an important sense for most birds. The structure of the bird eye is similar to that of other vertebrates (*see figure 34.18*). Birds have a unique, double-focusing mechanism. Pad-like structures control the curvature of the lens, and ciliary muscles change the curvature of the cornea. Double, nearly instantaneous focusing allows an osprey, or other bird of prey, to remain focused on a fish throughout a brief, but breathtakingly fast, descent. Like reptiles, birds have a nictitating membrane that is drawn over the surface of the eyeball to cleanse and protect it.

In all vertebrates, the retina is well developed. Its basement layer is composed of pigmented epithelium that covers the choroid layer. Nervous tissue that contains photoreceptors lies on this basement layer. The photoreceptors are called **rod** and **cone cells** because of their shape. Rods are sensitive to dim light, whereas cones respond to high-intensity light and are involved in color perception.

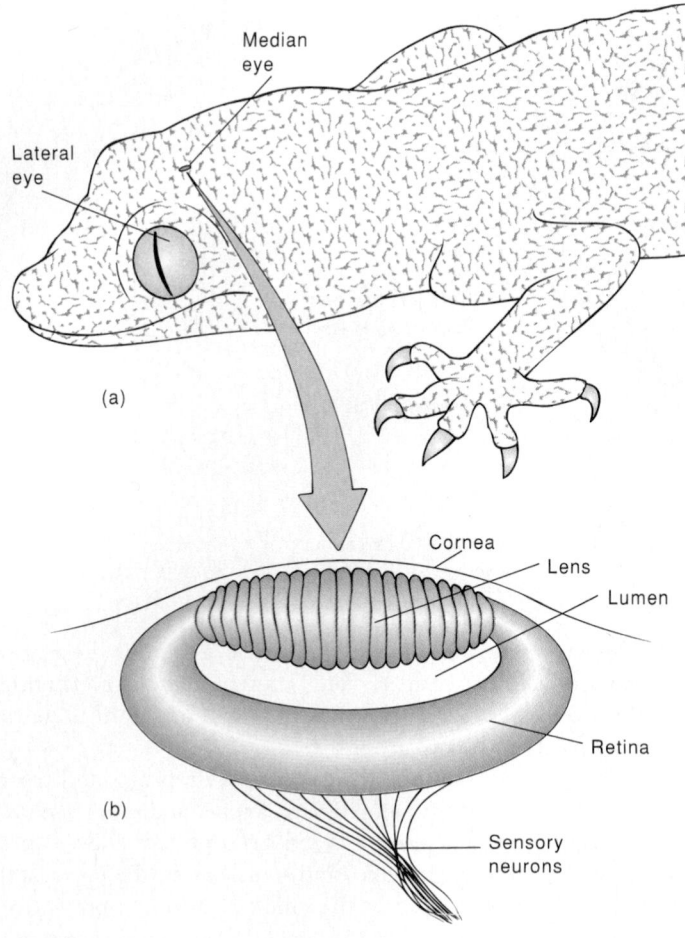

FIGURE 34.19

The Median Eye of Reptiles. (*a*) The median eye in a reptile and its relationship to the lateral eyes (dorsal view). (*b*) Sagittal section of the median eye.

When a pigment (**rhodopsin**) in a rod cell absorbs light energy, the energy release from this reaction triggers the generator potential in an axon and then an action potential that leaves the eyeball via the optic nerve. When the photoreceptor cells are not being stimulated (i.e., in the dark), energy from ATP along with vitamin A converts rhodopsin back to its light-sensitive form.

The nineteenth-century poet Leigh Hunt said, "Colors are the smiles of Nature." How does an animal distinguish one smile from another? The answer lies to a great extent in the three types of cone-shaped, color-sensitive cells in the retina of the eye. These three types of cone cells are found among primates, birds, reptiles, and fishes. Each type responds differently to light reflected from a colored object, depending on whether the cells have within them red-, green-, or blue-absorbing pigments. The pigments are light-absorbing proteins that are particularly sensitive to either the long-wavelength (red), intermediate-wavelength (green), or short-wavelength (blue) region of the visible spectrum. The relative amounts of light absorbed by each type of cone are translated into generator potentials by the retinal nerves and then transmitted as a nerve impulse to the brain, where the overall pattern evokes the sensation of a specific hue.

Stop and Ask Yourself

14. What is the function of a pit organ?
15. What animals possess a median eye?
16. What is rhodopsin, and how does it function?

SUMMARY

1. A stimulus is any form of energy an animal is able to detect by means of its receptors. Receptors are nerve endings of sensory neurons or specialized cells that respond to stimuli, such as chemical energy, mechanical energy, light energy, or radiant energy.

2. Receptors are transducers of energy from one form to another. When a receptor is stimulated, a generator potential is initiated, causing an action potential to travel along a nerve pathway to another part of the nervous system where it is perceived.

3. Invertebrates possess an impressive array of receptor structures through which they receive information about their environment. Examples include chemoreceptors that respond to chemicals in the environment; georeceptors, called statocysts, that respond to the force of gravity; hygroreceptors that detect the water content of air; phonoreceptors, such as tympanic organs that respond to sound; photoreceptors such as stigmata, ocelli, compound eyes, and complex camera eyes that respond to light; proprioceptors

that respond to mechanically induced changes caused by stretching; tactile receptors such as bristles, sensilla, spines, setae, and tubercles that sense touch; and thermoreceptors that respond to temperature changes.

4. Invertebrate and vertebrate sensory receptors (organs) have evolved in ways that relate to the environment in which they must function.

5. The lateral-line system for electrical sensing is located in the head area of most fishes, some amphibians, and the platypus. This system can sense electrical currents in the surrounding water. The lateral-line system of fishes and amphibians also contains neuromasts, which are responsive to local water displacement or disturbances.

6. The vertebrate ear has two functional units: the auditory apparatus is concerned with hearing, and the vestibular apparatus is concerned with posture and equilibrium.

7. Pain receptors (nociceptors) are bare sensory nerve endings that produce a painful or itching sensation.

8. Sensors of temperature (thermoreceptors) are bare sensory nerve endings that are the simplest vertebrate receptors. Some snakes have heat-sensitive pit organs on each side of the face.

9. Many vertebrates rely on tactile (pertaining to touch) stimuli to respond to their environment. Receptors include bare sensory nerve endings, tactile (Meissner's) corpuscles, bulbs of Krause, Pacinian corpuscles, organs of Ruffini, and vibrissae.

10. Bats, shrews, whales, and dolphins can determine distance and depth by sonar.

11. The receptors for taste (gustation) are chemoreceptors located on the body surface of an animal or in the mouth and throat.

12. Vision (photoreception) is the primary sense used by vertebrates that live in a light-filled environment; consequently, their photoreceptive structures are very well developed. Most vertebrates have eyes capable of forming visual images.

SELECTED KEY TERMS

accommodation (*p. 575*)

generator potential (*p. 562*)

median (parietal) eye (*p. 575*)

ocellus (*p. 564*)

pit organs (*p. 572*)

rhodopsin (*p. 576*)

sonar (*p. 572*)

statocysts (*p. 563*)

stigma (*p. 564*)

taste buds (*p. 574*)

CRITICAL THINKING QUESTIONS

1. The comparison of the vertebrate eye to a camera is not very accurate. Why is this so?

2. Most animals lack cones in their retinas. How then does such an animal view the visual world?

3. Why is the sense of gravity considered a sense of equilibrium?

4. How does vitamin A deficiency result in night blindness?

5. How would you expect your inner ear to behave in zero gravity?

35

COMMUNICATION III:
THE ENDOCRINE SYSTEM
AND CHEMICAL MESSENGERS

Outline

Concepts

1. Chemical messengers are involved in communication and maintaining homeostasis in an animal's body, and in the body's response to various stimuli. One type of chemical messenger is a hormone. Only those cells that have specific receptors for a hormone can respond to that hormone.
2. Hormones work along with nerves to communicate and integrate activities within the body of an animal.
3. Almost every invertebrate examined has been found to produce hormones. However, the physiology of invertebrate hormones is often quite different from that of vertebrates.
4. The major endocrine glands of vertebrates include the pituitary, thyroid, parathyroids, adrenals, pineal, thymus, pancreas, and gonads. Various other tissues, however, have also been shown to secrete hormones. Examples include the kidneys, heart, digestive system, and placenta.

Would You Like to Know:

1. what causes a crayfish to shed its skin (molt)? (p. 584)
2. what causes brooding behavior in some fishes? (p. 586)
3. why the thyroid gland is located in the neck on the ventral side of the pharynx in all vertebrates? (p. 586)
4. what hormones cause a tadpole to metamorphose into a frog? (p. 587)
5. how pigeons and doves produce "milk" to feed their young? (p. 589)
6. why some animals (including humans) possess the "fight-or-flight" response? (p. 594)

These and other useful questions will be answered in this chapter.

This chapter contains evolutionary concepts, which are set off in this font.

Chapters 33 and 34 discuss ways that the nervous and sensory systems work together to rapidly communicate information and maintain homeostasis in an animal's body. In addition, many animals have a second, slower form of communication—the endocrine system with its chemical messengers.

Some scientists suggest that chemical messengers may initially have evolved in single-celled organisms to coordinate feeding or reproduction. As multicellularity evolved, more complex organs also evolved to govern the many individual coordination tasks, but control centers relied on the same kinds of messengers that were present in the simpler organisms. Some of the messengers worked fairly slowly but had long-lasting effects on distant cells; these became the modern hormones. Others worked more quickly, but influenced only adjacent cells for short periods; these became the neurotransmitters and local chemical messengers. Clearly, chemical messengers must have a very ancient origin and must have been conserved for hundreds of millions of years.

Evolutionarily, new messengers are uncommon. Instead, "old" messengers are adapted to new purposes. For example, some protein hormones are very ancient and are found in species ranging from bacteria to humans.

One key to the survival of any group of animals is proper timing of activity so that growth, maturation, and reproduction coincide with the times of year when climate and food supply favor survival. It seems likely that the chemical messengers regulating growth and reproduction were among the first to appear. These messengers were probably secretions of neurons. Later, specific hormones developed to play important regulatory roles in molting, growth, metamorphosis, and reproduction in various invertebrates (as has been presented in specific chapters in Part Five

of this textbook). Chemical messengers and their associated secretory structures became even more complex with the appearance of vertebrates.

CHEMICAL MESSENGERS

Development of most animals commences with fertilization and the subsequent division of the zygote. Further development is then dependent upon continued cell proliferation, growth, and differentiation. The integration of these events, as well as the communication and coordination of physiological processes, such as metabolism, respiration, excretion, movement, and reproduction, are dependent on chemical messengers—molecules synthesized and secreted by specialized cells. Chemical messengers can be categorized as follows:

1. **Local chemical messengers.** Many cells secrete chemicals that alter physiological conditions in the immediate vicinity (figure 35.1a). Most of these chemicals act on adjacent cells and do not accumulate in the blood. Vertebrate examples include some of the chemicals called lumones produced in the gut that help regulate digestion. In a wound, a substance called histamine is secreted by mast cells and participates in the inflammatory response.

2. **Neurotransmitters.** As presented in chapter 33, neurons secrete chemicals called neurotransmitters (e.g., nitric oxide and acetylcholine) that act on immediately adjacent target cells (figure 35.1b). These chemical messengers reach high concentrations in the synaptic cleft, act quickly, and are actively degraded and recycled.

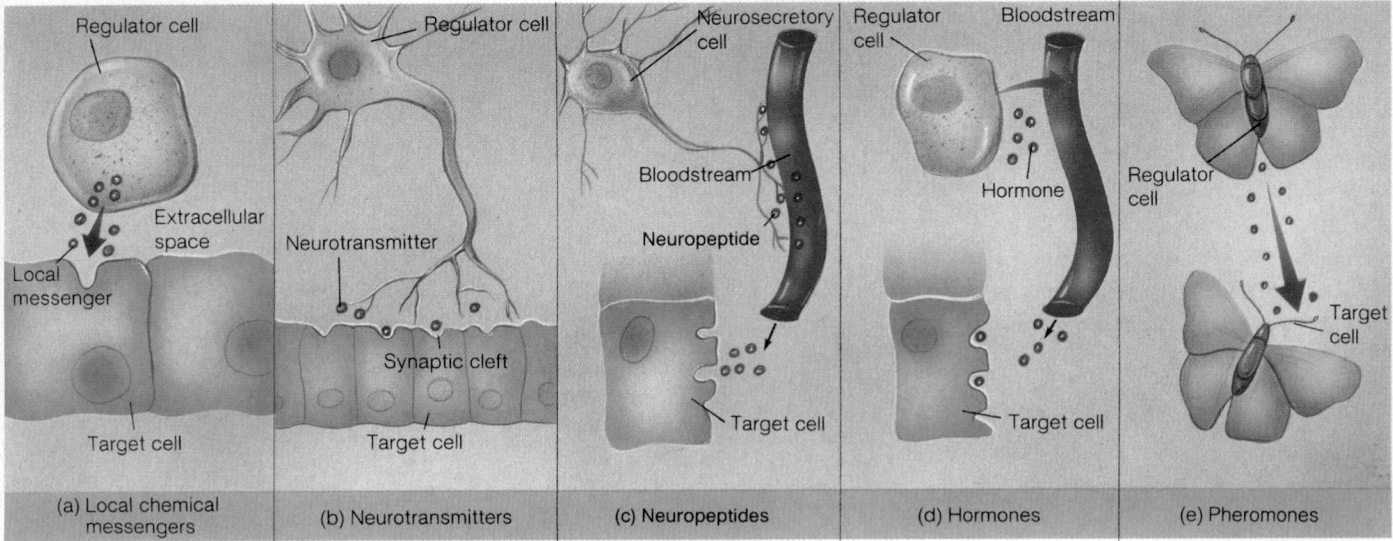

FIGURE 35.1

Chemical Messengers: Targets and Transport. (a) Short-distance local messengers act on an adjacent cell. (b) Individual nerve cells secrete neurotransmitters that cross the synaptic cleft to act on target cells. (c) Individual nerve cells can also secrete neuropeptides (neurohormones) that travel some distance in the bloodstream to reach a target cell. (d) Hormones are secreted by regulatory cells, usually in an endocrine gland, and enter the bloodstream, where they travel to target cells. (e) Pheromones are secreted by regulatory cells in exocrine glands. They leave the body and stimulate target cells in another animal.

3. **Neuropeptides.** Some specialized neurons (called neurosecretory cells) secrete **neuropeptides (neurohormones).** Neuropeptides enter the bloodstream or other body fluids and are transported to nonadjacent target cells where they exert their effects (figure 35.1c). In mammals, for example, certain nerve cells in the hypothalamus release a neuropeptide that causes the pituitary gland to release the hormone oxytocin, which induces powerful uterine contractions during the delivery of offspring.
4. **Hormones.** Endocrine glands or cells secrete hormones that are transported by the bloodstream to nonadjacent target cells (figure 35.1d). Many examples will be given in the rest of this chapter.
5. **Pheromones.** Pheromones are chemical messengers released to the exterior of one animal that affect the behavior of another individual of the same species (figure 35.1e; *see also table 24.2*).

Overall, scientists now recognize that the nervous and endocrine systems work together as an all-encompassing communicative and integrative network called the **neuroendocrine system.** In this system, chemical messengers achieve short- and long-term regulation of body function in an animal to maintain homeostasis by means of feedback systems.

HORMONES AND THEIR FEEDBACK SYSTEMS

A **hormone** (Gr. *hormaein*, to set in motion or to spur on) is a specialized chemical messenger produced and secreted by an endocrine gland or tissue. The study of endocrine glands and their hormones is called **endocrinology.** Hormones circulate through body fluids and affect the metabolic activity of a target cell or tissue in a specific way. By definition, a **target cell** is one having receptors to which chemical messengers either selectively bind to or on which they have an effect. Only rarely does a hormone operate independently. More typically, one hormone influences, depends upon, and balances another hormone in a controlled feedback network.

BIOCHEMISTRY OF HORMONES

Most hormones are proteins (polypeptides), derivatives of amino acids (amines), or steroids: a few are fatty acid derivatives. For example, most invertebrate neurosecretory cells produce polypeptides called neuropeptides. Hormones secreted by the vertebrate pancreas are proteins; those secreted by the thyroid gland are amines. Steroids are secreted by the ovaries, testes, and adrenal glands.

Hormones are effective in extremely small amounts. Only a few molecules of a hormone may be enough to produce a dramatic response in a target cell. In the target cell, hormones help control biochemical reactions in three different ways: (1) a hor-

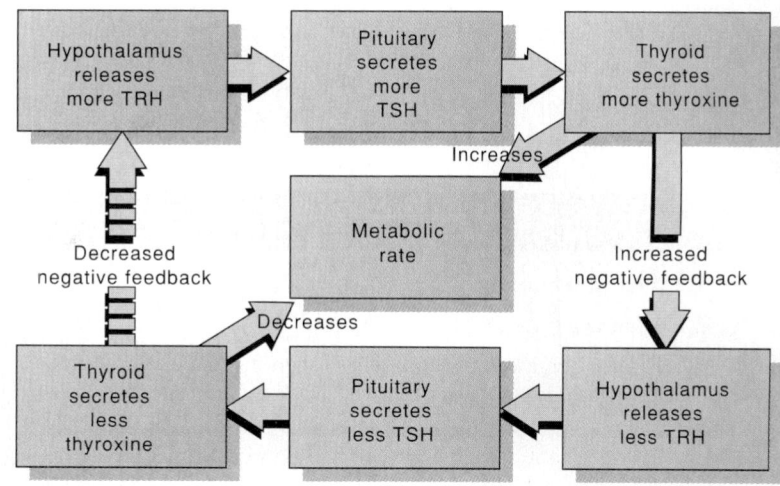

FIGURE 35.2
Hormonal Feedback. A negative feedback system that helps control metabolic rate in a vertebrate such as a dog.

mone can increase the rate at which other substances enter or leave the cell; (2) it can stimulate a target cell to synthesize enzymes, proteins, or other substances; or (3) it can prompt a target cell to activate or suppress existing cellular enzymes. As is the case for enzymes, hormones are not changed by the reaction they regulate.

FEEDBACK CONTROL SYSTEM OF HORMONE SECRETION

Although hormones are always present in some amount in endocrine cells or glands, they are not secreted continuously. Instead, the glands tend to secrete the amount of hormone that the animal needs to maintain homeostasis. Regulation occurs through a feedback control system, where changes in the animal or in the external environment are fed back to a central control unit (such as the central nervous system), where the adjustment is made. A feedback system that produces a response that counteracts the initiating stimulus is called a negative feedback system. In contrast, a positive feedback system is one in which the initial stimulus is reinforced. Positive feedback systems are relatively rare in animals, because they usually lead to instability or pathological states.

Negative feedback systems monitor the amount of hormone secreted, altering the amount of cellular activity as needed to maintain homeostasis. For example, suppose that the rate of chemical activity (metabolic rate) in the body cells of a dog slows down (figure 35.2). The hypothalamus responds to this slow rate by releasing more thyrotropin-releasing hormone (TRH), which causes the pituitary gland to secrete more thyrotropin, or thyroid-stimulating hormone (TSH). This hormone, in turn, causes the thyroid gland to secrete a hormone called thyroxine. Thyroxine increases the metabolic rate, restoring homeostasis. Conversely, if

35.3

the metabolic rate speeds up, the hypothalamus releases less TRH, the pituitary secretes less TSH, the thyroid secretes less thyroxine, and the metabolic rate decreases once again restoring homeostasis.

MECHANISMS OF HORMONE CONTROL

The function of a hormone is to modify the biochemical activity of a target cell or tissue. Two basic mechanisms are involved. The first, the fixed-membrane-receptor mechanism, applies to hormones that are proteins or amines. Because they are water-soluble and cannot diffuse across the plasma membrane, these hormones initiate their response by means of specialized receptors on the plasma membrane of the target cell. The mobile-receptor mechanism applies to steroid hormones. These hormones are lipid-soluble and diffuse easily into the cytoplasm, where they initiate their response by binding to cytoplasmic receptors.

FIXED-MEMBRANE-RECEPTOR MECHANISM

According to the fixed-membrane-receptor mechanism, a water-soluble hormone is secreted by an endocrine cell and circulates through the bloodstream (figure 35.3a). At the cells of the target organ, the hormone acts as a "first or extracellular messenger," binding to a specific receptor site for that hormone on the plasma membrane (figure 35.3b). The hormone-receptor complex activates the enzyme adenylate cyclase in the membrane (figure 35.3c). The activated enzyme converts ATP into a nucleotide called cyclic AMP, which will become the "second (or intracellular) messenger." Cyclic AMP diffuses throughout the cytoplasm and activates an enzyme called protein kinase, which causes the cell to respond with its distinctive physiological activity (figure 35.3d). After inducing the target cell to perform its specific function, cyclic AMP is inactivated by the enzyme phosphodiesterase. In the meantime, the receptor on the plasma membrane has lost the first messenger and now becomes available for a new reaction.

MOBILE-RECEPTOR MECHANISM

Because steroid hormones pass easily through the plasma membrane, their receptors are inside the target cells. The mobile-receptor mechanism involves the stimulation of protein synthesis. After being released from a carrier protein in the bloodstream, the

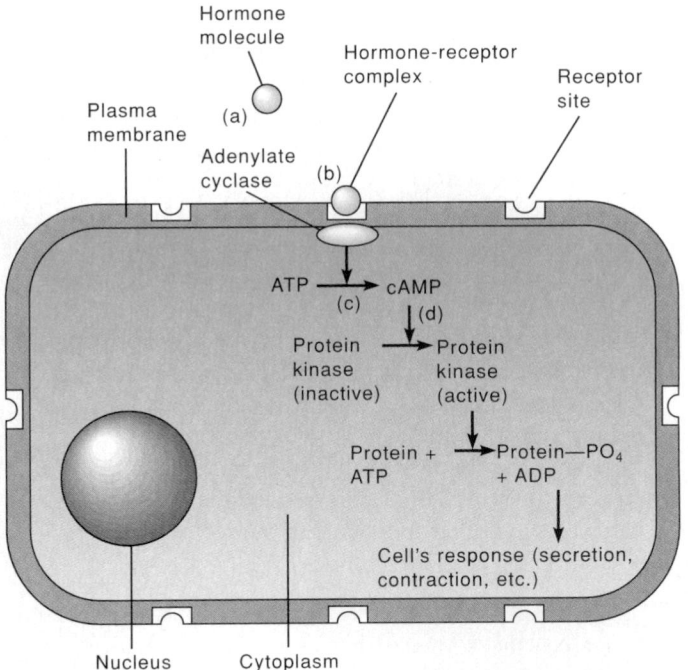

FIGURE 35.3

The Steps of the Fixed-Membrane-Receptor Mechanism of Hormonal Control. (a) A protein hormone molecule (such as epinephrine) diffuses from the blood to a target cell. (b) The binding of the hormone to a specific plasma membrane receptor activates adenylate cyclase (a membrane-bound enzyme system). (c) This enzyme system catalyzes cyclic AMP formation (the second messenger) inside the cell. (d) Cyclic AMP (cAMP) diffuses throughout the cytoplasm and activates an enzyme called protein kinase, which then phosphorylates specific proteins in the cell, thereby triggering the biochemical reaction, leading ultimately to the cell's response.

steroid hormone enters the target cell by diffusion and binds to a specific steroid receptor in the cytoplasm (figure 35.4a,b). This newly formed hormone-receptor complex acquires an affinity for DNA that causes it to enter the nucleus of the cell, where it binds to DNA and regulates the transcription of specific genes to form messenger RNA (figure 35.4c,d). The newly transcribed mRNA leaves the nucleus and moves to the rough endoplasmic reticulum, where it initiates protein synthesis (figure 35.4e,f). Some of the newly synthesized proteins may be enzymes whose effects on cellular metabolism constitute the cellular response (figure 35.4g) attributable to the specific steroid hormone.

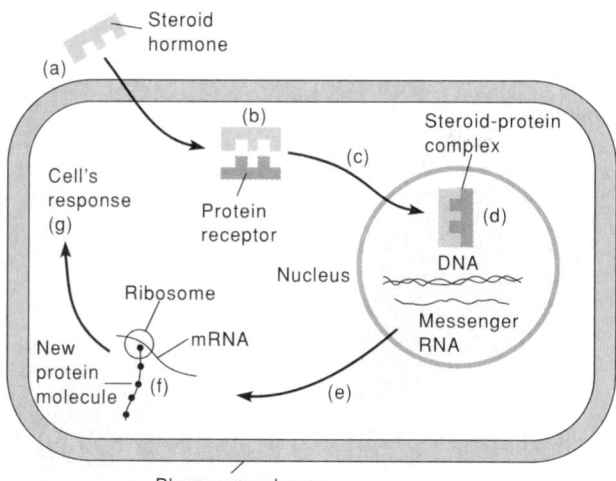

Figure 35.4

The Steps of the Mobile-Receptor Mechanism. (*a*) A steroid hormone molecule (e.g., testosterone) diffuses from the blood to a target cell and then through the plasma membrane of the target cell. (*b*) Once in the cytoplasm, the hormone binds to a receptor that carries it into the nucleus (*c*). (*d*) This steroid-protein complex triggers transcription of specific gene regions of DNA. (*e*) The messenger RNA transcript is then translated into a gene product via protein synthesis (*f*) in the cytoplasm. (*g*) The new protein then mediates the cell's response.

SOME HORMONES OF INVERTEBRATES

One key to the survival of any group of animals is the assurance that growth, maturation, and reproduction coincide with the most favorable seasons of the year so that climate and food supply are optimal. Thus, it seems likely that the chemicals regulating growth, maturation, and reproduction were among the first hormones to appear during the course of animal evolution.

The first hormones were probably neurosecretions. As presented below, most of the chemicals functioning as hormones in invertebrate animals are neurosecretions called neuropeptides. Only in a few of the more complex invertebrates (e.g., molluscs, arthropods, echinoderms) have hormones other than neurosecretions been identified. What follows is a brief overview of some invertebrate neuropeptides and hormones.

PORIFERA

The porifera (sponges) do not have classical endocrine glands. Since sponges do not have neurons, they also do not have neurosecretory cells.

CNIDARIANS

The nerve cells of *Hydra* contain a neuropeptide that stimulates budding, regeneration, and growth. For example, when the neuropeptide is present in the medium in which fragments of *Hydra* are incubated, head regeneration is accelerated. This so-called "head activator" also stimulates mitosis in *Hydra*.

PLATYHELMINTHES

Neurosecretory cells have been known in various flatworms for over three decades. These cells are located in the cerebral ganglion and along major nerve cords. The neuropeptides produced by the cells function in regeneration, asexual reproduction, and gonad maturation. For example, neurosecretory cells in the scolex of some tapeworms control shedding of the proglottids or the initiation of strobilization.

NEMERTEANS

Nemerteans have more cephalization than platyhelminthes and a larger brain composed of a dorsal and ventral pair of ganglia connected by a nerve ring. The neuropeptide produced by these ganglia appears to control gonadal development and regulation of water balance.

NEMATODES

Although no classical endocrine glands have been identified in nematodes, they do have neurosecretory cells associated with the central nervous system. The neuropeptide produced by this nervous tissue apparently controls ecdysis of the old cuticle. The neuropeptide is released after a new cuticle is produced and stimulates the excretory gland to secrete an enzyme (leucine aminopeptidase) into the space between the old and new cuticle. The accumulation of fluid in this space causes the old cuticle to split and be shed.

MOLLUSCS

The nervous system of molluscs is richly endowed with neurosecretory cells situated in the ring of ganglia that constitutes the central nervous system. The neuropeptides produced by these cells play a role in the regulation of heart rate, kidney function, and energy metabolism.

In certain gastropods, such as the common land snail *Helix*, a specific hormone stimulates spermatogenesis; another hormone termed egg laying hormone stimulates egg development; and hormones from the ovary and testis stimulate accessory sex organs. In all snails, the growth of the shell is under neuroendocrine control by way of a growth hormone.

In cephalopods, such as the octopus, and squid, the optic gland in the eye stalk produces one or more hormones that stimulates egg development, proliferation of spermatogonia, and the development of secondary sex characteristics.

ANNELIDS

Since annelids have a well-developed and cephalized nervous system, a well-developed circulatory system, and a large coelom, it is not surprising that they have a correspondingly well-developed endocrine control of physiological functions. The various endocrine systems of annelids are generally involved with morphogenesis, development, growth, regeneration, and gonadal maturation. For example, in polychaetes, juvenile hormone inhibits the gonads and stimulates growth and regeneration. Another hormone, gonadotropin, stimulates development of eggs. In leeches, a neuropeptide stimulates development of the gametes and triggers color changes. Osmoregulatory hormones have been reported in oligochaetes, and a hyperglycemic hormone that maintains a high concentration of blood glucose has been reported for the oligochaete, *Lumbricus*.

ARTHROPODS

The endocrine systems of advanced invertebrates (crustaceans and insects) are excellent examples of how hormones regulate growth, maturation, and reproduction. Since so much is known about hormones and their functioning in these animals, a more detailed discussion is now presented.

The endocrine system of a crustacean, such as a crayfish, controls functions such as ecdysis (molting), sex determination, and color changes. We will use only ecdysis as our example of how hormones function in this animal.

X-organs are neurosecretory tissues located in the crayfish eye stalks (figure 35.5a). Associated with each X-organ is a sinus gland that accumulates and releases the secretions of the X-organ. Other glands, called Y-organs, are located at the base of the maxillae.   ① Both the X-organ and Y-organ control ecdysis as follows. In the absence of an appropriate stimulus, the X-organ produces molt-inhibiting hormone (MIH), and the sinus gland releases it (figure 35.5b). The target of this hormone is the Y-organ. When molt-inhibiting hormone is present in high concentrations, the Y-organ is inactive. Under appropriate internal and external stimuli, molt-inhibiting hormone release is prevented and the Y-organ releases the hormone ecdysone, which leads to molting (figure 35.5c).

The sequence of events in insects is similar to that of crustaceans, but does not involve a molt-inhibiting hormone. In the presence of an appropriate stimulus to the central nervous system, certain neurosecretory cells (pars intercerebralis) in the optic lobes of the brain are activated (figure 35.6a). These cells secrete the hormone ecdysiotropin, which is carried by axonal transport to the corpora cardiaca (a mass of neurons associated with the brain). In the corpora cardiaca, thoracotropic hormone is produced and carried to the prothoracic glands, stimulating them to produce and release ecdysone, which induces molting (figure 35.6b)—in particular, the resorption of some of the old cuticle and the development of a new cuticle.

Other neurosecretory cells in the brain and nerve cords produce the hormone bursicon. Bursicon influences certain aspects of epidermal development such as tanning (i.e., hardening and darkening of the chitinous outer cuticle layer). Tanning is completed several hours after each molt.

Another hormone, juvenile hormone (JH), is also involved in the morphological differentiation that occurs during the molting of insects. Located just behind the insect brain are the paired corpora allata (figure 35.6a). These structures produce juvenile hormone. When the concentration of juvenile

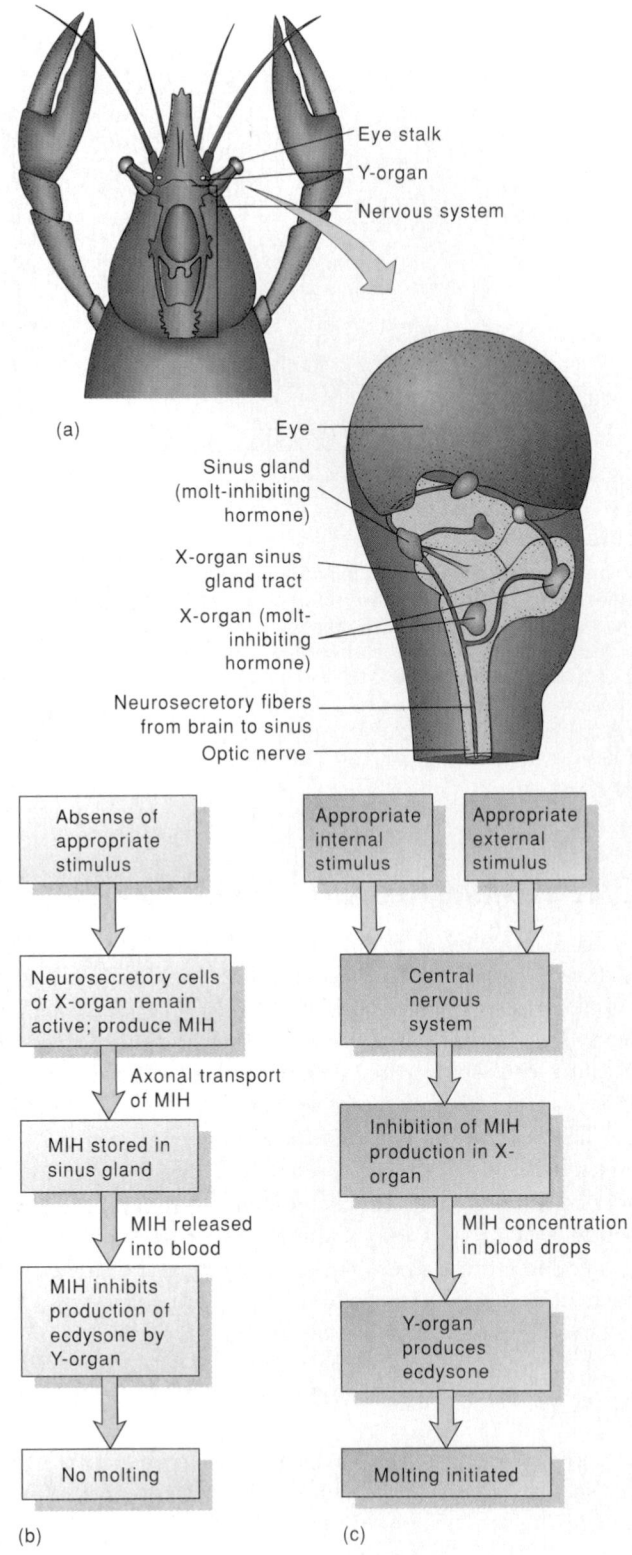

FIGURE 35.5

The Control of Ecdysis (Molting) in Crustaceans by Hormones.
(*a*) The neurosecretory apparatus in a crustacean eye stalk. (*b*) Flow diagram of the events inhibiting molting and (*c*) causing molting.

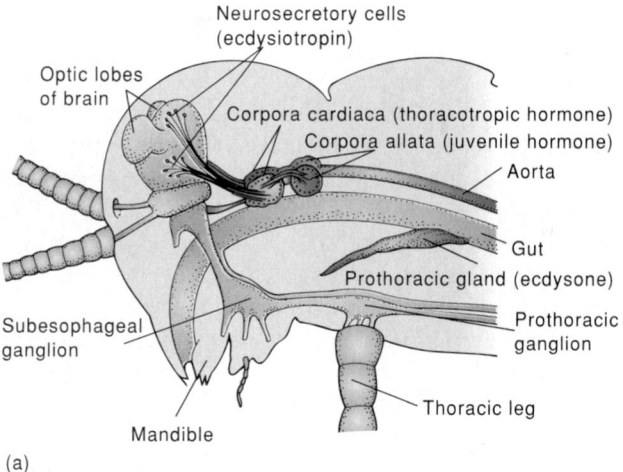

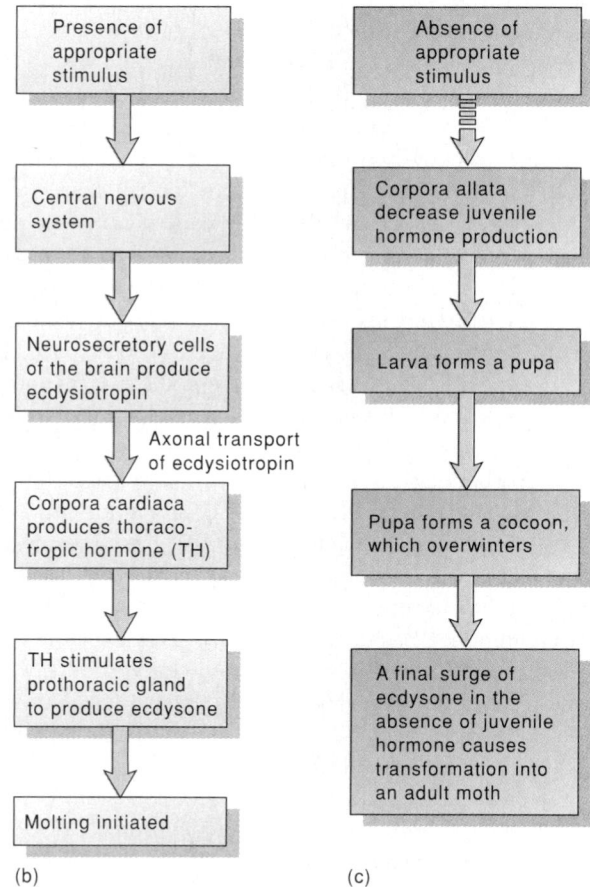

FIGURE 35.6

The Control of Ecdysis (Molting) and Development (Metamorphosis) in an Insect. (*a*) The anterior end of an insect showing the location of the brain hormone, juvenile hormone, and ecdysone secretory centers. (*b*) Flow diagram of the events initiating molting in an insect. (*c*) Flow diagram of the events of insect metamorphosis as regulated by a decrease in the production of juvenile hormone.

hormone in the blood of an insect is high, differentiation is inhibited. In the absence of an appropriate environmental stimulus, the corpora allata decrease the production of juvenile hormone, which causes the insect larva to differentiate into a pupa (figure 35.6*c*). The pupa then forms a cocoon to overwinter. In the spring, a final serge of ecdysone, in the absence of juvenile hormone, causes the pupa to transform into an adult moth.

ECHINODERMS

Since echinoderms are deuterostome animals, they are more closely allied to chordates than are the protostome invertebrates. However, the endocrine systems of echinoderms provide few insights into the evolution of chordate endocrine systems because the echinoderm hormones and endocrine glands are very different from those of chordates. With this in mind, zoologists do know that the radial nerves of starfishes contain a neuropeptide called gonad-stimulating substance. When this neuropeptide is injected into a mature starfish, it induces immediate shedding of the gametes, spawning behavior, and meiosis in the oocytes. The neuropeptide also causes the release of a hormone called maturation-inducing substance, which has various effects on the reproductive system.

Stop and Ask Yourself

7. Why were the first hormones probably neurosecretions?
8. How do hormones function in the common land snail, *Helix*?
9. How do the X- and Y-organs of crustaceans control ecdysis?
10. What is the function of juvenile hormone in insects? Of the hormone bursicon?

AN OVERVIEW OF THE VERTEBRATE ENDOCRINE SYSTEM

Since vertebrates have been studied more than invertebrates, vertebrates have the best understood system of hormonal control. As the earliest vertebrates evolved, hormone-producing cells and tissues developed and came to be controlled in several ways. Some, such as the adrenal glands, are directed by sets of nerve cells in the brain; others are controlled by the hypothalamus of the brain and the pituitary gland (hypophysis); and still others function independently of either nerves or the pituitary gland.

Vertebrates possess two types of glands (figure 35.7). One type, **exocrine** (Gr. *exo*, outside + *krinein*, to separate) **glands**, secrete chemicals into ducts that, in turn, empty into body cavities or onto body surfaces (e.g., mammary, salivary, and sweat glands). The second type, **endocrine** (Gr. *endo*, within + *krinein*, to separate) **glands** have no ducts, and instead secrete

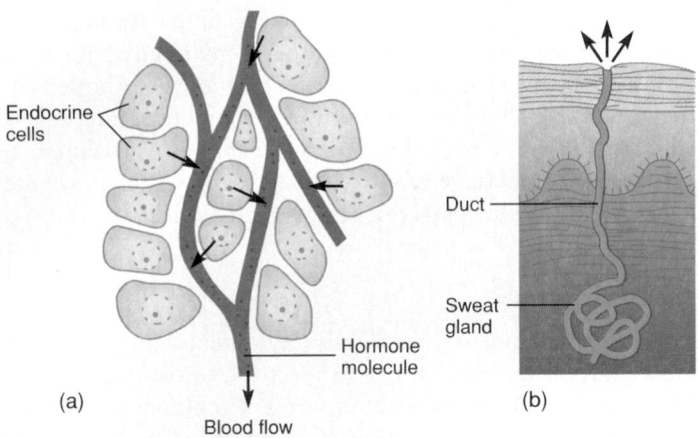

FIGURE 35.7

Vertebrate Glands with and without Ducts. (*a*) An endocrine gland, such as the thyroid, secretes hormones into the extracellular fluid. From there, the hormones pass into blood vessels and travel to distinct sites in the body. (*b*) An exocrine gland, such as a sudoriferous (sweat) gland, secretes material (sweat) into a duct that leads to a body surface.

chemical messengers, called hormones, directly into the tissue space next to each endocrine cell. The hormones then diffuse into the bloodstream and are carried throughout the body to their target cells.

ENDOCRINE SYSTEMS OF VERTEBRATES OTHER THAN BIRDS OR MAMMALS

Since a phylogenetic approach is being used in this textbook to describe form and function in animals, we will now briefly discuss endocrine regulation in vertebrates other than birds or mammals. Birds and mammals will be the subject of the last part of this chapter.

Vertebrates other than birds or mammals have somewhat similar endocrine systems, but differences do exist. Recent research has revealed the following three aspects of endocrinology that relate to species differences among these vertebrates:

1. Hormones (or neuropeptides) with the same function in different species may not be chemically identical.
2. Certain hormones are species-specific with respect to their function; conversely, some hormones produced in one species may be completely functional in another species.
3. A hormone from one species may elicit a different response in the same target cell or tissue of a different species.

The following examples will serve to illustrate the above three principles and also present a comparative survey of endocrine function in selected vertebrates.

When one compares more ancient groups of vertebrates with more recent ones, one general tendency surfaces—older groups seem to have simpler endocrine systems. For example, many of the hormones present in mammals are absent in fishes. In

fishes, the brain and spinal cord are the most important producers of hormones, with other glands being rudimentary (figure 35.8). In jawed fishes, three major regions have been identified that secrete neuropeptides. The two in the brain are the **pineal gland** of the epithalamus and the **preoptic nuclei** of the hypothalamus. The pineal gland produces neuropeptides that affect pigmentation and apparently inhibit reproductive development, both of which are stimulated by light. One specific hormone produced by the pineal gland, melatonin, has broad effects on body metabolism by synchronizing activity patterns with light intensity and day length. The preoptic nuclei produce various other neuropeptides that control various functions in fishes (e.g., growth, sleep, locomotion). The third major region of fishes that has neuropeptide function is the urophysis. The **urophysis** (Gr. *oura*, tail + *physis*, growth) is a discrete structure in the spinal cord of the tail. The urophysis produces neuropeptides that help control water and ion balance, blood pressure, and smooth muscle contractions. Other than these functions, little else is known of its functions or the significance of its absence in more complex vertebrates.

In many fishes, amphibians, and reptiles, hormones (e.g., **melatonin**) from the **pituitary gland** (hypophysis) control variations in skin color. When this hormone produced by one species is injected into another species, it can induce dramatic color changes (figure 35.9). From this type of experiment, one can conclude that there is a close chemical similarity in some hormones (point no. 2 at the beginning of this section) despite the distant evolutionary relationships between the animals producing them. Another example is the hormone prolactin (also produced by the pituitary gland). Prolactin stimulates reproductive migrations in many animals (e.g., the movement of salamanders to water). ② Prolactin causes brooding behavior in some fishes. It also helps control water and salt balances, and is essential for certain saltwater fishes to enter fresh water during spawning runs.

③ From an evolutionary perspective, there is evidence that the thyroid gland in the earliest vertebrates evolved from a pouch-like structure (the endostyle; *see box 26.2*) that carried food particles in the front end of the digestive tract. This explains why the thyroid gland is located in the neck on the ventral side of the pharynx in all vertebrates. How did this feeding mechanism turn into an endocrine gland? One possible hypothesis is that as the developing pouch gradually lost all connection with the pharynx, it became independent of the digestive system both functionally and structurally. As a result, a functionally novel structure arose from an ancestral structure with an unrelated function. The shape of the thyroid varies among vertebrates. It may be a single structure (e.g., many fishes, reptiles, and some mammals), or it may have several to many lobes. The major hormones produced by this gland are thyroxine (T_4) and triiodothyronine (T_3), which control the rate of metabolism, growth, and tissue differentiation in vertebrates.

As noted in point no. 3 at the beginning of this section, related but different processes may be regulated by the same hormone(s) in different vertebrates. The hormones thyroxine and triiodothyronine are excellent examples of this point. For example, in most animals, thyroxine and triiodothyronine regulate overall metabolism. In amphibians, they play an additional role

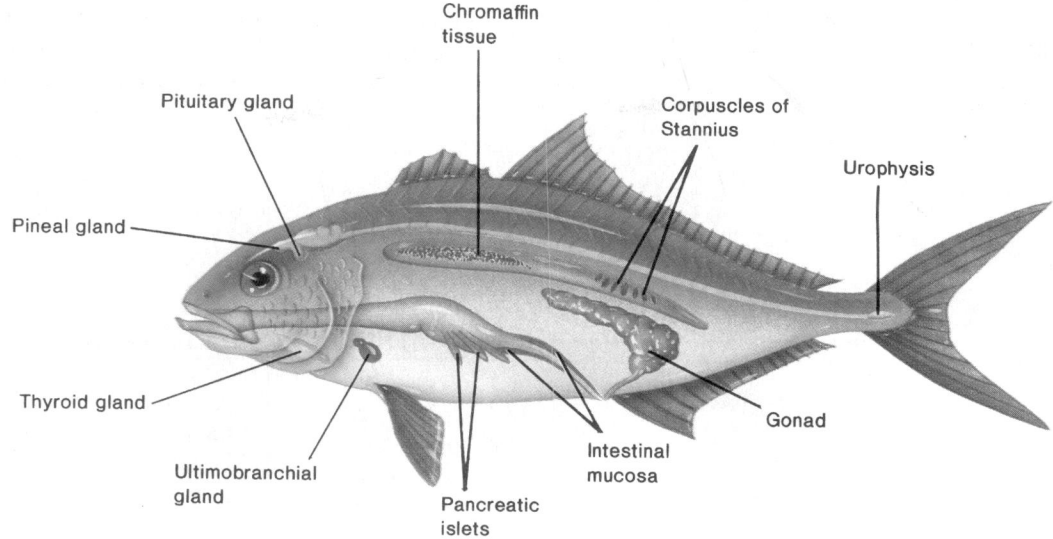

FIGURE 35.8

Diagram Showing Approximate Locations of Endocrine Tissues (Glands) in a Bony Fish.

FIGURE 35.9

Hormonal Control of Frog Skin Color. The light-colored frog on the left has been immersed in water containing the hormone melatonin. The dark-colored frog on the right has received an injection of melanocyte-stimulating hormone.

in metamorphosis (figure 35.10). Metamorphosis in the frog is controlled by specifically timed changes in the concentrations of three hormones: prolactin, thyroxine, and triiodothyronine. Low thyroxine and triiodothyronine concentrations and high prolactin concentrations in young tadpoles stimulate larval growth and prevent metamorphosis. As the hypothalamus and pituitary glands develop in the growing tadpole, thyroid-stimulating hormone-releasing hormone and prolactin-inhibiting hormone are released from the hypothalamus. Their release causes the pituitary gland to release thyroid-stimulating hormone and to cease production of

prolactin.   4   As a result, the concentration of thyroxine and triiodothyronine rise, triggering the onset of metamorphosis. Tail resorption and other metamorphic changes follow.

In jawed fishes and primitive tetrapods, several small glands form ventral to the esophagus and are called **ultimobranchial glands** (*see figure 35.8*). These glands produce the hormone calcitonin that helps regulate the concentration of blood calcium.

Specialized endocrine cells (**chromaffin tissue**) or glands (**adrenal glands**) located near the kidneys prepare the animals being discussed for stressful emergency situations (figure 35.11). These tissues and glands produce two hormones (epinephrine or adrenaline, and norepinephrine or noradrenaline) that cause vasoconstriction, increased blood pressure, changes in the heart rate, and increased blood glucose levels. These hormones are involved in the "fight-or-flight" reactions.

Stop and Ask Yourself

11. What are some differences between endocrine and exocrine glands?
12. What is the function of the urophysis?
13. What role do thyroxine and triiodothyronine play in amphibian metamorphosis?
14. What is the function of calcitonin? Melatonin?

ENDOCRINE SYSTEMS OF BIRDS AND MAMMALS

With some minor exceptions, birds and mammals have a similar complement of endocrine glands (figure 35.12). The major hormones produced by these vertebrates are summarized in table 35.1.

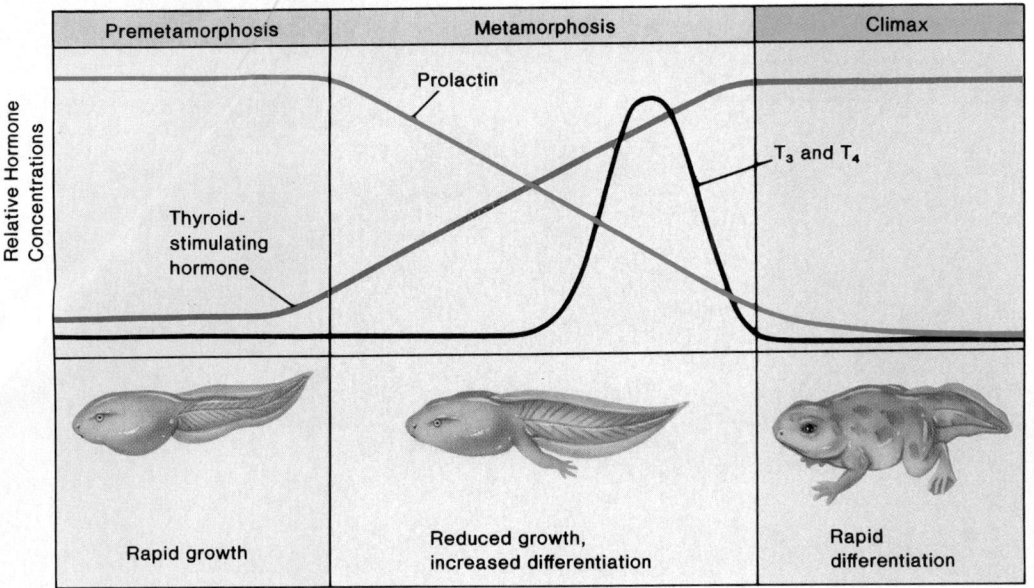

FIGURE 35.10

Frog Tadpole Metamorphosis. The metamorphosis of an aquatic frog tadpole into a semiterrestrial or terrestrial adult is regulated by the thyroid hormones triiodothyronine (T_3) and thyroxine (T_4). The activity of the thyroid gland is regulated by thyroid-stimulating hormone, secreted by the anterior pituitary gland. During the premetamorphosis (tadpole) stage, the pituitary and thyroid glands are relatively inactive. This keeps the concentration of thyroid-stimulating hormones, T_3 and T_4, at low concentrations. The high prolactin concentration in tadpoles stimulates larval growth and prevents metamorphosis. During metamorphosis, the concentrations of the thyroid hormones markedly increase and prolactin decreases. These hormonal fluctuations induce rapid differentiation, climaxing in the adult frog.

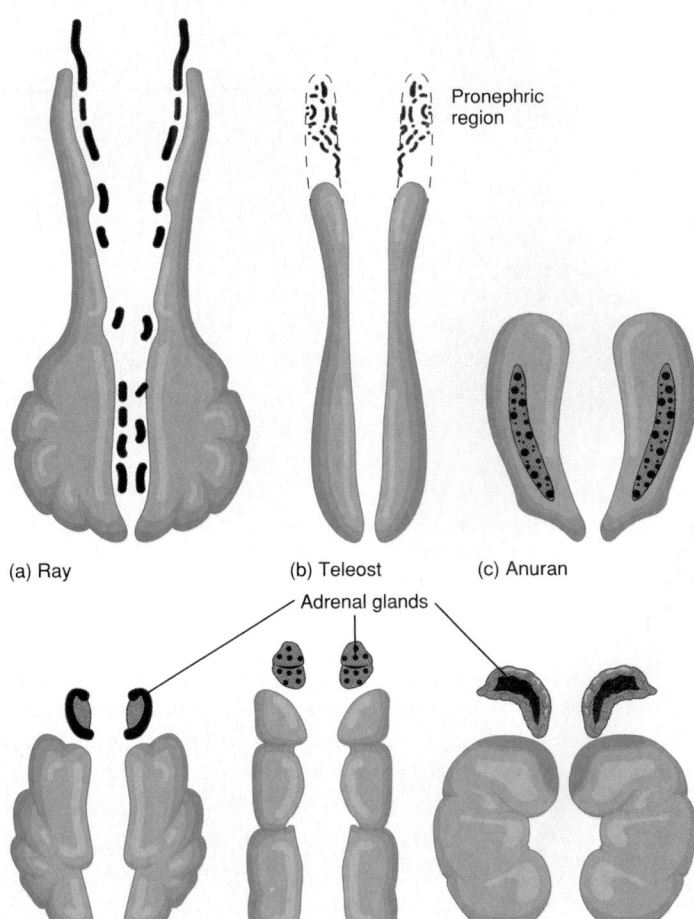

FIGURE 35.11

Chromaffin Tissue and Adrenal Glands in Selected Vertebrates. The chromaffin tissue (steroidogenic) produces steroid hormones and is shown in gray. The aminogenic tissue that produces norepinephrine and epinephrine is shown in black. The kidneys are shown in outline form. Note the reversed location of the two components in lizards and mammals. (*a*) In jawless and cartilaginous fishes (elasmobranchs), aminogenic tissue develops as clusters near the kidneys. (*b*) In teleosts, the chromaffin tissue is generally at the anterior end of the kidney (pronephric region). (*c*) In anurans, the chromaffin tissue is interspersed in a diffuse gland on the ventral surface of each kidney. (*d*) In lizards, the chromaffin tissue forms a capsule around the steroidogenic-producing tissue. (*e*) In birds, the chromaffin tissue is interspersed within an adrenal capsule. (*f*) In most mammals, the chromaffin tissue forms an adrenal medulla and the steroidogenic tissue forms the cortex.

35.10

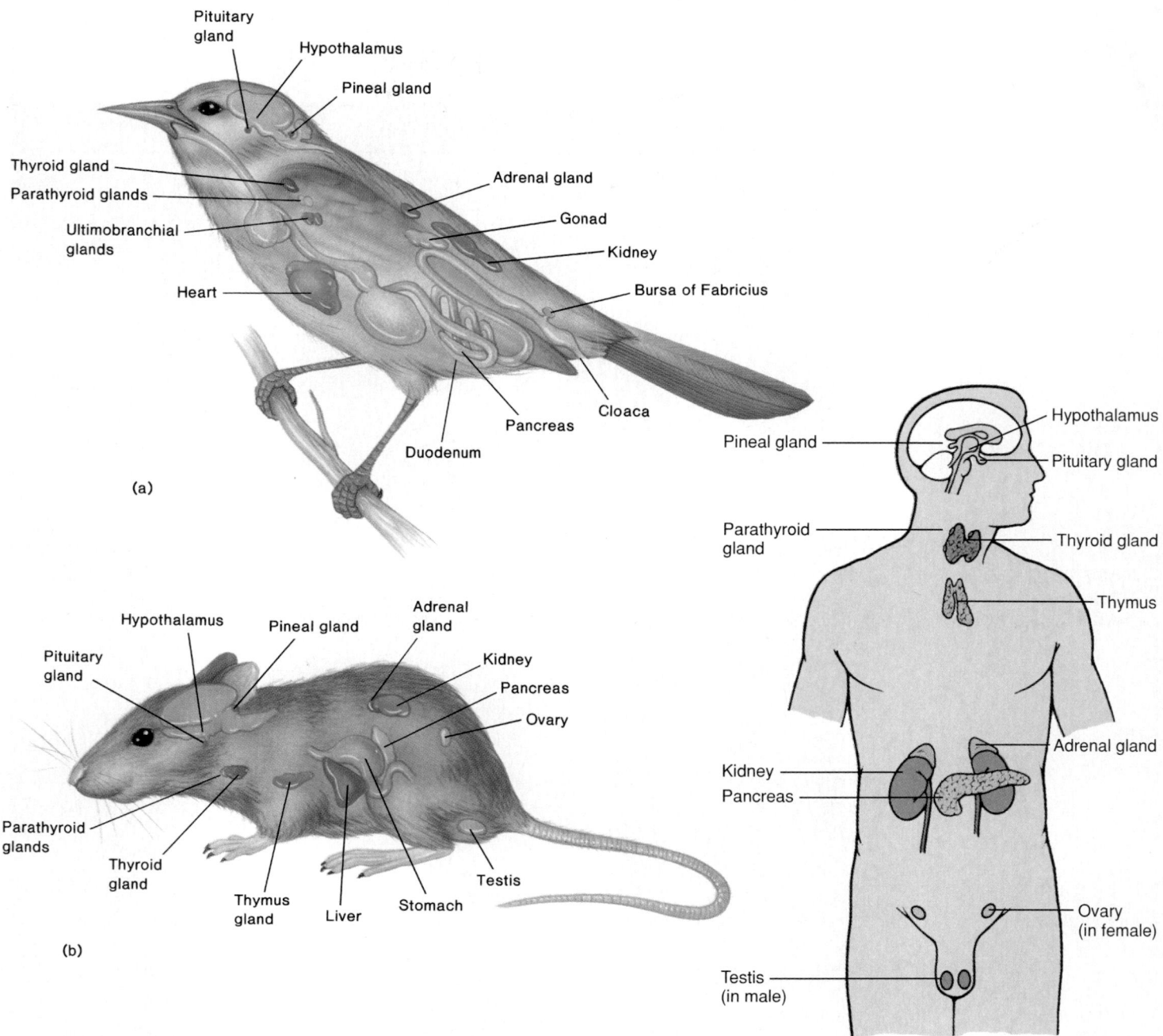

FIGURE 35.12

Endocrine Glands of Birds and Mammals. Drawings illustrating the location of the major endocrine glands of a bird (*a*), a rat (*b*), and a human (*c*).

BIRDS

The endocrine glands in birds include the ovary, testes, adrenals, pituitary, thyroid, pancreas, parathyroids, pineal, hypothalamus, thymus, ultimobranchial, and bursa of Fabricius (figure 35.12*a*). Since the hormones produced by most of these glands and their effects on target tissues are nearly the same as in mammals, they will be discussed in the next section on mammals. What follows is a discussion of some unique hormones and their functions in birds.

In some birds (e.g., pigeons and doves), the pituitary gland secretes the hormone prolactin.   Prolactin stimulates production of "pigeon's milk" by desquamation (sloughing off cells) in the pigeon's crop. Prolactin also stimulates and regulates broodiness and certain other kinds of parental behavior, and along with estrogen, stimulates full development of the **brood (incubation) patch** (figure 35.13). The brood patch helps keep the eggs at a temperature between 33 and 37° C.

The bird's thyroid gland produces the hormone thyroxine. In addition to the major vertebrate functions listed in table 35.1,

TABLE 35.1 MAJOR VERTEBRATE ENDOCRINE TISSUES AND HORMONES

SOURCE	HORMONES	TARGET CELLS AND PRINCIPAL ACTIONS
Anterior lobe of pituitary	Somatotropin (STH, or growth hormone [GH])	Growth of bone and muscle; promotes protein synthesis; affects lipid and carbohydrate metabolism; increases cell division
	Adrenocorticotropic hormone (ACTH)	Stimulates secretion of adrenocortical steroids; involved in stress response
	Thyrotropin (TSH) or thyroid-stimulating hormone	Stimulates thyroid gland to synthesize and release thyroid hormones concerned with growth, development, metabolic rate
	Endorphins	Decrease pain
	Gonadotropins:	In ovary: formation of corpora lutea; secretion of progesterone; probably acts in conjunction with FSH
	Luteinizing or interstitial cell-stimulating hormone (LH or ICSH)	In testis: stimulates the interstitial cells, thus promoting the secretion of testosterone
	Follicle-stimulating hormone (FSH)	In ovary: growth of follicles; functions with LH to cause estrogen secretion and ovulation
		In testis: acts on seminiferous tubules to promote spermatogenesis
	Prolactin (PRL)	Initiation of milk production by mammary glands; acts on crop sacs of some birds; stimulates maternal behavior in birds
Intermediate or posterior lobe of pituitary	Melanocyte-stimulating hormone (MSH)	Expansion of amphibian melanophores; contraction of iridophores and xanthophores; melanin synthesis; darkening of the skin; responds to external stimuli
Posterior lobe of pituitary	Antidiuretic hormone (ADH or vasopressin)	Elevates blood pressure by acting on arterioles; promotes reabsorption of water by kidney tubules
	Oxytocin	Affects postpartum mammary gland, causing ejection of milk; promotes contraction of uterus; possible action in parturition and in sperm transport in female reproductive tract
Hypothalamus	Thyrotropin-releasing hormone (TRH)	Stimulates release of TSH by anterior pituitary
	Adrenocorticotropin-releasing hormone (CRH)	Stimulates release of ACTH by anterior pituitary
	Gonadotropin-releasing hormone (GnRH)	Stimulates gonadotropin release by anterior pituitary
	Prolactin-inhibiting factor (PIF)	Inhibits prolactin release by anterior pituitary
	Somatostatin	Inhibits release of STH by anterior pituitary
Thyroid gland	Thyroxine, triiodothyronine	Growth; amphibian metamorphosis; molting; metabolic rate in birds and mammals; growth, development
	Calcitonin	Lowers calcium level in blood by inhibiting calcium reabsorption from bone
Parathyroid glands	Parathormone	Regulates calcium concentration
Pancreas, islet cells	Insulin (from beta cells)	Promotes glycogen synthesis and glucose utilization and uptake from blood
	Glucagon (from alpha cells)	Raises blood glucose concentration
Adrenal cortex	Glucocorticoids (e.g., cortisol)	Promote synthesis of carbohydrate; protein breakdown; antiinflammatory and antiallergic actions; mediates response to stress
	Mineralocorticoids (e.g., aldosterone)	Sodium retention and potassium loss through kidneys; water balance
Adrenal medulla	Epinephrine (adrenaline)	Mobilization of glucose; increased blood flow through skeletal muscle; increased oxygen consumption; increased heart rate
	Norepinephrine	Adrenergic neurotransmitter; elevation of blood pressure; constricts arterioles and venules
Testes	Androgens (e.g., testosterone)	Male sexual characteristics; spermatogenesis
Ovaries	Estrogens (e.g., estradiol)	Female sexual characteristics; oogenesis
Corpus luteum	Progesterone	Maintains pregnancy; stimulates development of mammary glands

35.12

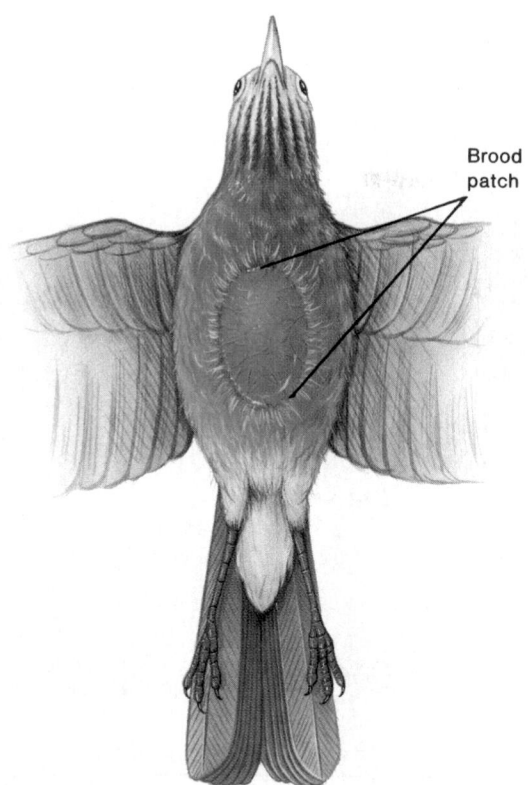

Brood patch

Figure 35.13

A Bird's Brood Patch. In this example, a robin's single brood patch appears (due to the effect of the hormone prolactin) a few days before eggs are laid. Prolactin causes the down feathers to drop from the abdomen of the incubating robin, and the bare patch becomes swollen and richly supplied with blood vessels. After the eggs are laid, the robin settles on its nest and brings this warm patch in contact with its eggs, thereby transferring heat to the developing embryos within the eggs.

thyroxine regulates normal development of feathers and the molt cycle, and plays a role in the onset of migratory behavior.

In male birds, the testes produce the hormone testosterone. Testosterone controls the secondary sexual characteristics of the male, such as bright plumage color, comb (when present), and spurs—all of which strongly influence sexual behavior.

The ultimobranchial glands are small paired structures lying in the neck just below the parathyroid glands. They secrete the hormone **calcitonin,** which is involved in the regulation of the concentration of blood calcium.

The **bursa of Fabricius** is a sac that lies just dorsal to the cloaca and empties into it. Although well developed during the bird's embryological development, it begins to get smaller soon after hatching. Its tissues produce secretions that are responsible for the maturation of white blood cells (B lymphocytes), which play an important role in immunological reactions.

Stop and Ask Yourself

15. What are several functions of the hormone prolactin in birds?

16. What is the function of the ultimobranchial glands in birds? The bursa of Fabricius?

Mammals

Zoologists know more about mammalian endocrine organs, their hormones, and target tissues than those of any animal group. This is especially true for the human body. What follows is a brief overview of mammalian endocrinology.

Pituitary Gland (Hypophysis)

The pituitary gland (also known as the hypophysis) is located directly below the hypothalamus (*see figure 35.12*c). The pituitary has two distinct lobes: the anterior lobe (adenohypophysis) and the posterior lobe (neurohypophysis) (figure 35.14). There are several differences between the two lobes: (1) the adenohypophysis is larger than the neurohypophysis; (2) secretory cells called pituicytes are found in the adenohypophysis, but not in the neurohypophysis; and (3) the neurohypophysis has a greater supply of nerve endings. Pituicytes produce and secrete hormones directly from the adenohypophysis, whereas the neurohypophysis obtains its hormones from the neurosecretory cells in the hypothalamus, stores them and secretes them when they are needed. These modified hypothalamic nerve cells project their axons down a stalk of nerve cells and blood vessels called the infundibulum, into the pituitary gland, creating a direct link between the nervous and the endocrine systems.

The pituitary of many vertebrates (but not in humans, birds, and cetaceans) also has a functional **intermediate lobe (pars intermedia)** of mostly glandular tissue. Its secretions (e.g., melanophore-stimulating hormone) induce changes in the coloration of the body's surface of many animals by responding to external stimuli.

Hormones of the Neurohypophysis

The neurohypophysis does not manufacture any hormones. Instead, the neurosecretory cells of the hypothalamus synthesize and secrete two hormones, antidiuretic hormone and oxytocin, which move down nerve axons into the neurohypophysis, where they are stored in the axon terminals until released.

A diuretic is a substance that stimulates the excretion of urine, whereas an antidiuretic decreases urine secretion. When a mammal begins to lose water and becomes dehydrated, antidiuretic hormone (ADH, or vasopressin) is released and increases water absorption in the kidneys so that less urine is secreted. Because less urine is secreted, water is retained; this negative feedback system thus restores water homeostasis.

Oxytocin plays a role in mammalian reproduction by its effect on smooth muscle. During labor, it stimulates contraction of the uterus or uteri to aid in expulsion of the offspring during birth, and promotes ejection of milk from the mammary glands to provide nourishment for the newborn during feeding.

Both ADH and oxytocin are thought to have evolved from a similar ancestral chemical messenger that helped control water loss and, indirectly, solute concentrations. For example, the neurohypophysis is notably larger in animals that live in arid parts of the world where water conservation is crucial. Also, the structure of the two hormones is similar except for a difference in two of the amino acids.

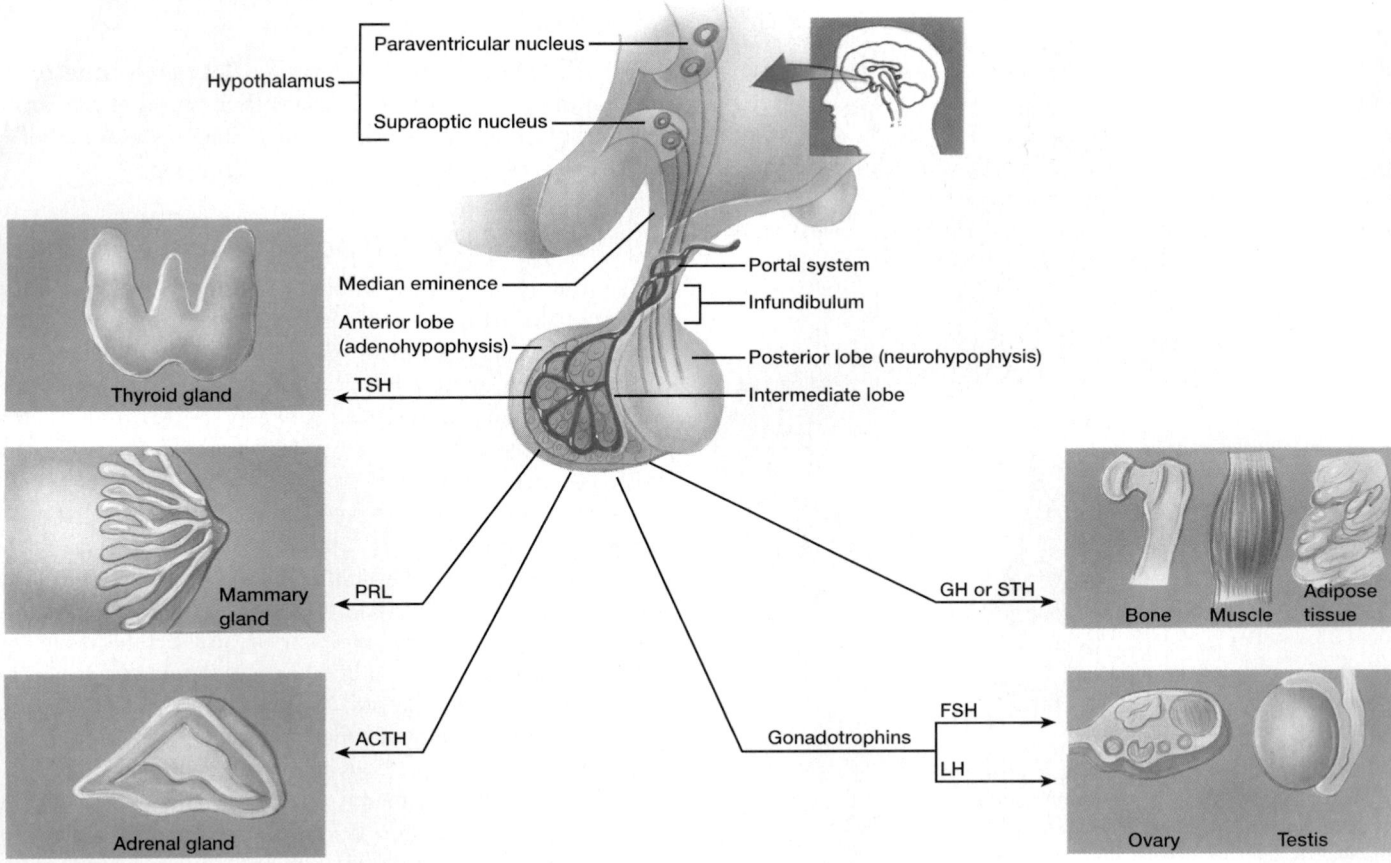

FIGURE 35.14

Functional Links between the Pituitary Gland and the Hypothalamus. Target areas for each hormone are shown in the relevant box. The blood vessels that make up the hypothalamic-hypophyseal portal system provide the functional link between the hypothalamus and the adenohypophysis, and the axons of the hypothalamic neurosecretory cells provide the link between the hypothalamus and neurohypophysis.

Hormones of the Adenohypophysis

The true endocrine portion of the pituitary is the adenohypophysis, which synthesizes six different hormones (figure 35.14). All of these hormones are polypeptides, and all but two are true tropic hormones, hormones whose primary target is another endocrine gland. The two nontropic hormones are growth hormone and prolactin.

Growth hormone (GH), or somatotropin (STH), does not influence a specific target tissue; rather, it affects all parts of the body that are concerned with growth. It directly induces the cell division necessary for growth and protein synthesis in most types of cells by stimulating uptake of amino acids, RNA synthesis, and ribosome activity.

Prolactin (PRL) has the widest range of actions of the adenohypophyseal hormones. It plays an essential role in many aspects of reproduction. For example, it stimulates reproductive migrations in many mammals such as elk and caribou. Prolactin also enhances mammary gland development and milk production in female mammals. (Recall that oxytocin stimulates milk ejection from the mammary glands, but not its production.)

Thyrotropin, or thyroid-stimulating hormone (TSH), stimulates the synthesis and secretion of thyroxine, the main thyroid hormone.

Adrenocorticotropic hormone (ACTH) stimulates the adrenal gland to produce and secrete steroid hormones called glucocorticoids. Secretion of ACTH is regulated by the secretion of corticotropin-releasing factor from the hypothalamus, which in turn is regulated by a feedback system that involves such factors as stress, insulin, ADH, and other hormones.

Two gonadotropins (hormones that stimulate the gonads) are produced by the adenohypophysis: luteinizing hormone and follicle-stimulating hormone. Luteinizing hormone (LH) received its name from the corpus luteum, a temporary endocrine tissue in the ovaries that secretes the female sex hormones estrogen and progesterone. In the female, an increase of LH in the blood simulates ovulation, the release of a mature egg(s) from an ovary. In the male, the target cells of LH are cells in the testes that secrete the male hormone testosterone. In the female, follicle-stimulating hormone (FSH) stimulates the follicle cells in the ovaries to develop into mature eggs and also stimulates them to produce estrogen. In the male, FSH stimulates the cells of the testes to produce sperm.

The **pineal gland,** so named because it is shaped like a pine cone, is found only in the brain of mammals. Its distinctive cells have evolved from the photoreceptors of lower vertebrates; they synthesize melatonin, and are most active in the dark. Light inhibits the enzymes needed for melatonin synthesis. Because of its cyclical production, melatonin has the potential of affecting many physiological processes and adjusting them to diurnal and seasonal cycles. The use of melatonin by mammals is an evolutionary adaptation to help ensure that periodic activities of mammals occur at a time of the year when environmental conditions are optimal for those activities. In humans, decreased melatonin secretion may help trigger the onset of puberty, the age at which reproductive structures start to mature.

Stop and Ask Yourself

17. What hormones are secreted by the adenohypophysis?
18. What hormones are secreted by the neurosecretory cells of the hypothalamus?
19. What are the effects of gonadotropins in both the male and female?
20. What is the function of melatonin?

Thyroid Gland

The **thyroid gland** is located in the neck, anterior to the trachea (*see figure 35.12*). Two of its secretions are thyroxine and triiodothyronine, both of which influence overall growth, development, and metabolic rates. Another thyroid hormone, calcitonin, plays a role in controlling extracellular levels of calcium ions (Ca^{2+}) by promoting deposition of these ions into bone tissue when their concentrations rise. Once calcium returns to its homeostatic concentration, the thyroid cells decrease their secretion of calcitonin.

Parathyroid Glands

The **parathyroid glands** are tiny, pea-sized glands embedded in the thyroid lobes, usually two glands in each lobe (*see figure 35.12*). The parathyroids secrete parathormone (PTH), which regulates the concentrations of calcium (Ca^{2+}) and phosphate (HPO_2^{-4}) ions in the blood.

When the concentration of calcium in the blood bathing the parathyroid glands is low, PTH secretion increases and has the following effects. It stimulates the activity of bone cells to break down bone tissue and release calcium ions into the blood. It also enhances the absorption of calcium from the small intestine into the blood. Finally, PTH promotes the reabsorption of calcium by the kidney tubules, so that the amount of calcium excreted in the urine is decreased. The negative feedback system for parathormone is shown in figure 35.15.

Adrenal Glands

In mammals, two **adrenal glands** rest on top of the kidneys. Each gland is made up of two separate glandular tissues. The inner portion is called the medulla, and the outer portion, which surrounds the medulla, is the cortex (figure 35.16).

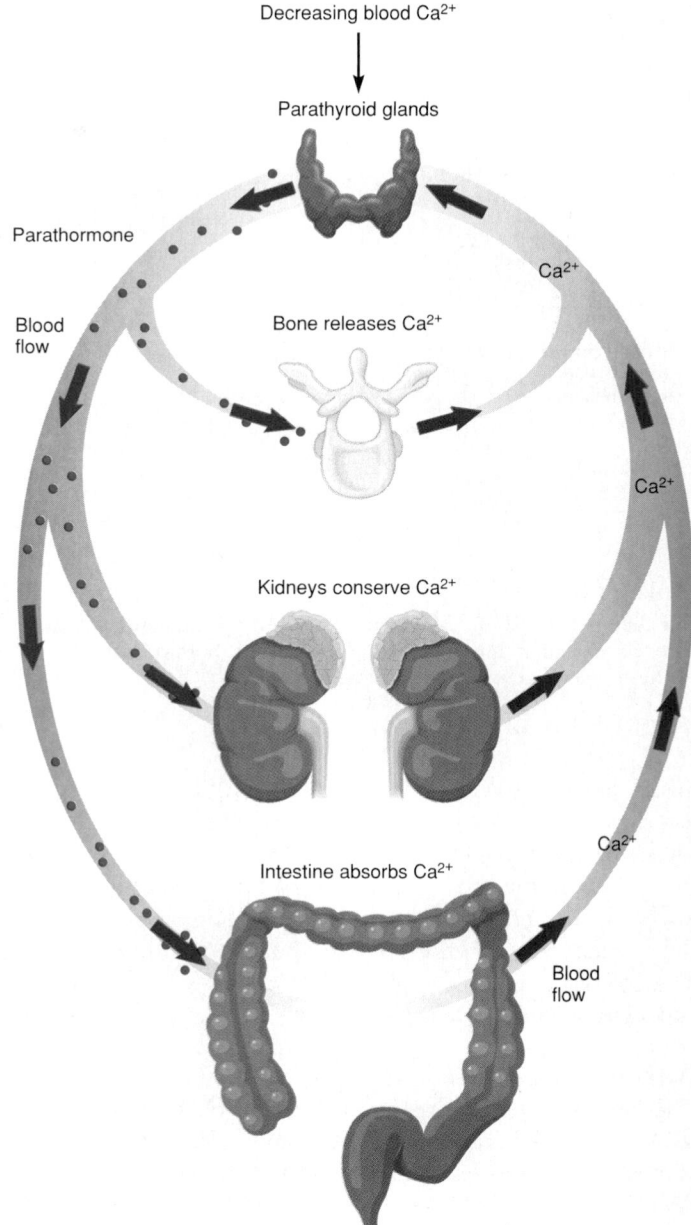

FIGURE 35.15

Hormonal Feedback. The negative feedback mechanism of the parathyroid glands (parathormone). Parathormone stimulates the release of calcium from bone and the conservation of calcium by the kidneys. It indirectly stimulates the absorption of calcium by the intestine. The result increases blood calcium, which then inhibits the secretion of parathormone.

Adrenal Cortex

The adrenal cortex secretes three classes of steroid hormones: glucocorticoids (hydrocortisone, cortisol), a single mineralocorticoid (aldosterone), and sex hormones (androgens, estrogens). The glucocorticoids, such as **cortisol,** help regulate overall metabolism and the concentration of blood sugar. They also function in defense responses to infection or tissue injury. Aldosterone helps maintain concentrations of solutes (such as sodium) in the extracellular fluid when either food intake or

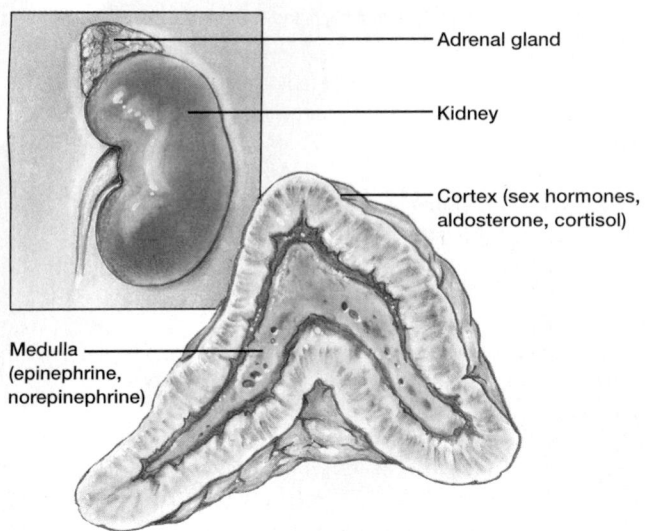

Figure 35.16

The Adrenal Gland of a Mammal. An adrenal gland consists of an outer cortex and an inner medulla. The different hormones produced by the cortex and medulla are indicated.

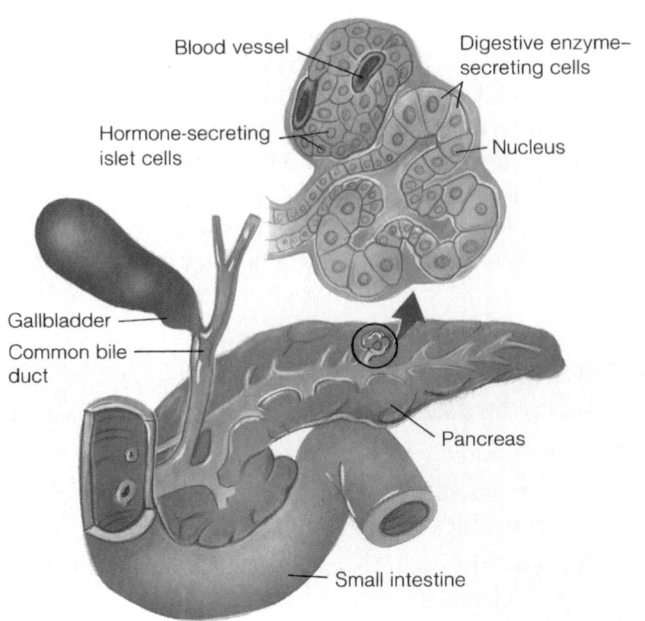

Figure 35.17

The Pancreas. The hormone-secreting cells of the pancreas are arranged in clusters or islets that are closely associated with blood vessels. Other pancreatic cells secrete digestive enzymes into ducts.

metabolic activity change the amount of solutes entering the bloodstream. Aldosterone also promotes sodium reabsorption in the kidneys and thus water reabsorption; hence it plays a major role in maintaining the homeostasis of extracellular fluid. Normally, the sex hormones secreted by the adrenal cortex have only a slight effect on the gonads of both the male and female. They consist mainly of weak male hormones called androgens and lesser amounts of female hormones called estrogens.

Adrenal Medulla

The adrenal medulla is under neural control. It contains neurosecretory cells that secrete epinephrine (adrenaline) and norepinephrine (noradrenaline), both of which help control blood circulation and carbohydrate metabolism. Brain centers and the hypothalamus govern their secretion via sympathetic nerves.

⑥ During times of excitement, emergencies, or stress, the adrenal medulla contributes to the overall mobilization of the body through the sympathetic nervous system. In response to epinephrine and norepinephrine, the heart rate increases, blood flow increases to many vital organs, the airways in the lungs dilate, and more oxygen is delivered to all cells of the body. This group of events is sometimes called the "fight-or-flight" response and permits the body to react strongly and quickly to emergencies.

Pancreas

The **pancreas** (figure 35.17) is an elongated fleshy organ located posterior to the stomach. It is a mixed gland because it functions both as an exocrine (with ducts) gland to secrete digestive enzymes, and as an endocrine (ductless) gland. The endocrine portion of the pancreas makes up only about 1% of the gland. It is this portion that synthesizes, stores, and secretes hormones from clusters of cells called pancreatic islets.

The pancreas contains between 200,000 and 2,000,000 **pancreatic islets** scattered throughout the gland. Each islet contains four special groups of cells, called alpha (α), beta (β), delta (δ), and F cells. The alpha cells produce the hormone glucagon, and beta cells produce insulin. The delta cells secrete somatostatin, the hypothalamic growth-hormone inhibiting factor that also inhibits the secretion of both glucagon and insulin. F cells secrete a pancreatic polypeptide of unknown function that is released into the bloodstream after eating a meal.

When the glucose concentrations in the blood are high, such as after eating a meal, beta cells secrete insulin. Insulin promotes the uptake of glucose by the body's cells, including liver cells, where excess glucose can be converted to glycogen (a storage polysaccharide; *see figure 2.11*). Insulin and glucagon are crucial to the regulation of blood glucose concentrations. When the concentration of glucose in the blood is low, the alpha cells secrete glucagon. Glucagon stimulates the breakdown of glycogen into glucose units, which can be released into the bloodstream to raise the concentration of blood glucose to restore the homeostatic level. Figure 35.18 illustrates the negative feedback system that regulates the secretion of glucagon and insulin and maintenance of appropriate blood glucose concentrations (box 35.1).

Gonads

The **gonads** (ovaries and testes) secrete hormones that help regulate reproductive functions. In the male, testosterone is secreted by the testes and acts with luteinizing and follicle-stimulating hormones produced by the adenohypophysis to stimulate spermatogenesis. It is also necessary for the growth and maintenance of the male sex organs, it promotes the development and

BOX 35.1 | DIABETES

Several disorders classified under the term **diabetes** (Gr. *diabetes*, syphon) are associated with insulin deficiency or with the inability of cells to take up glucose. In type I diabetes (juvenile diabetes), the afflicted person (or other mammal such as a dog or cat) has little or no insulin because the beta cells have been destroyed. This form of diabetes is relatively uncommon and usually occurs early in life. It can occur as a result of a genetic susceptibility, viral infection, or an autoimmune response mounted against the beta cells. Without enough insulin, glucose accumulates in the blood but does not enter the cells. Because the cells cannot use the accumulated glucose, the body actually begins to starve. Brain, retinal, and gonadal tissues are particularly endangered because glucose is the only nutrient that can be utilized by these tissues. The use of fats (to replace glucose) for energy production in other tissues

causes the accumulation of acetoacetic acid and keto acids in the blood. This buildup leads to acidosis, which can cause coma and death. Survival for type I diabetes is absolutely dependent on regular injections of insulin. (Insulin is a small protein molecule and cannot be taken by mouth because it would be rapidly inactivated by protein-digesting enzymes in the digestive tract.) Without injections, the person (or other mammal) would suffer severe metabolic and urinary disruptions.

In type II (maturity-onset) diabetes, insulin concentrations are nearly normal or even above normal; however, the target cells cannot respond to the hormone. Either the cells have an insufficient number of insulin receptors, or the receptors themselves are abnormal. Diet, exercise, and oral glycemic agents, which facilitate the uptake of glucose, are used to treat this type of diabetes.

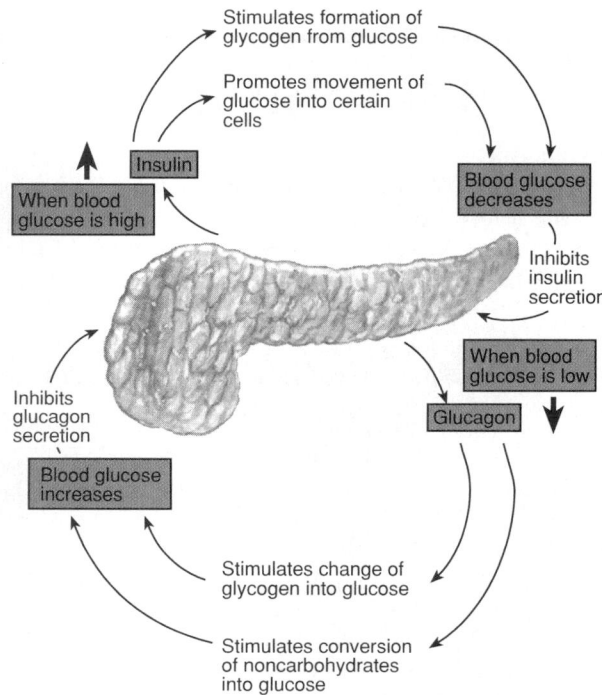

FIGURE 35.18

Two Pancreatic Hormones (Insulin and Glucagon) Regulate the Concentration of Blood Glucose. The negative feedback mechanism for regulating the secretion of glucagon and insulin functions together to help maintain a relatively stable blood glucose concentration.

maintenance of sexual behavior, and in humans stimulates the growth of facial and pubic hair, as well as enlargement of the larynx, which causes the voice to deepen.

Three major classes of ovarian hormones help to regulate female reproductive functions. Estrogens (estrin, estrone, and estradiol) help regulate the menstrual and estrus cycles and the development of the mammary glands and other female secondary sex characteristics. The progestins (primarily progesterone) also regulate the menstrual and estrus cycles, the development of the mammary glands, and aid in the formation of the placenta during pregnancy. Relaxin, which is produced in small quantities, softens the opening of the uterus (cervix) at the time of delivery.

Thymus

The **thymus gland** is located near the heart (*see figure 35.12*). It is large and conspicuous in young birds and mammals, but diminishes in size throughout adulthood. The major hormonal product of the thymus is a family of peptide hormones, including thymopoietin (TP) and alpha$_1$ and beta$_4$ thymosin, that appear to be essential for the normal development of the immune system.

Other Sources of Hormones

In addition to the major endocrine glands, other glands and organs carry on hormonal activity. Some of these are summarized in table 35.2.

Stop and Ask Yourself

21. What effect does parathormone have on the concentration of calcium in the blood?

22. What types of hormones are secreted by the adrenal cortex? By the three cell types in the pancreatic islets?

23. How do norepinephrine and epinephrine help an animal respond to stress?

24. How does glucagon function in opposition to insulin?

TABLE 35.2		OTHER SOURCES OF VERTEBRATE HORMONES	

GLAND/ORGAN	HORMONE	FUNCTION	TARGET AREA
Placenta	Estrogens, progesterone, human chorionic gonadotropin (hCG)	Maintains pregnancy	Ovaries, mammary glands, uterus
Digestive tract	Secretin	Stimulates release of pancreatic juice to neutralize stomach acid	Cells of pancreas
	Gastrin	Produces digestive enzymes and HCl in stomach	Stomach mucosa
	Cholecystokinin (CCK)	Stimulates release of pancreatic enzymes and bile from gallbladder	Pancreas, gallbladder
Heart	Atriopeptin	Lowers blood pressure, maintains fluid balance	Blood vessels, kidneys
Kidneys	Erythropoietin	Stimulates red blood cell production	Bone marrow

SUMMARY

1. For metabolic activity to proceed smoothly in an animal, the chemical environment of each cell must be maintained within fairly narrow limits (homeostasis). This is accomplished using negative feedback systems that involve integrating, communicating, and coordinating molecules called messengers.

2. Chemical messengers are molecules secreted by specialized cells. These chemical messengers can be categorized as follows: local chemical messengers (lumones), neurotransmitters such as acetylcholine, neuropeptides, hormones, and pheromones (e.g., sex attractants).

3. A hormone is a specialized chemical messenger produced and secreted by an endocrine cell or tissue. Hormones are usually steroids, amines, proteins, or fatty acid derivatives. Secretion of hormones is often regulated by negative feedback systems.

4. The function of a hormone is to modify the biochemical activity of a target cell or tissue, so called because it has receptors to which hormone molecules can bind. Hormonal activity may be accomplished by either the fixed-membrane-receptor mechanism (water soluble hormones) or the mobile-receptor mechanism (steroid hormones).

5. Most of the chemicals functioning as hormones in invertebrate animals are neurosecretions called neuropeptides. Only in a few of the more advanced invertebrates (e.g., molluscs, arthropods, echinoderms) have nonneurosecretory hormones been identified.

6. In all vertebrates, a neuroendocrine control center helps communicate and integrate activities for the entire body. This center consists of the hypothalamus and pituitary gland.

7. The vertebrate endocrine system consists of several major glands: the pituitary gland, thyroid gland, parathyroid glands, adrenal glands, pancreas, and gonads. In addition to these major glands, other glands and organs carry on hormonal activity. Examples include the placenta, thymus, digestive tract, heart, and kidneys.

SELECTED KEY TERMS

endocrinology (p. 581)
hormones (p. 581)
local chemical messengers (p. 580)
neuroendocrine system (p. 581)
neuropeptides (p. 581)
neurotransmitters (p. 580)
pheromones (p. 581)
target cell (p. 581)

CRITICAL THINKING QUESTIONS

1. How is information encoded by hormones? How do cells "know what to do" in response to hormonal information?

2. Summarize your knowledge of how endocrine systems work by describing the "life" of a hormone molecule from the time it is secreted until it is degraded or used up.

3. All cells secrete or excrete molecules, and all cells respond to certain biochemical factors in their external environments. Could the origin of endocrine control systems lie in such ordinary cellular events? How might the earliest multicellular organisms have evolved some sort of endocrine coordination?

4. Mental states strongly affect the function of many endocrine glands. This link between the mind and the body occurs through the hypothalamus. Can you describe how thoughts are transformed into physiological responses in the hypothalamus?

5. Compared to enzymes and genes, hormones are remarkably small molecules. Wouldn't larger molecules be able to carry more information? Explain.

CIRCULATION, IMMUNITY, AND GAS EXCHANGE

Outline

Concepts

1. Animal transport and circulatory systems move substances from one part of the body to another, and between the animal's external environment and extracellular fluid.
2. Some invertebrates have specific transport systems such as gastrovascular cavities. The circulatory system of more complex animals consists of a central pumping heart, blood vessels, blood, and an ancillary lymphatic system.
3. Invertebrates do not have immune systems with special cells that recognize and destroy specific foreign agents. Vertebrates defend themselves against microorganisms, foreign matter, and cancer cells by both nonspecific and specific mechanisms.
4. Some invertebrates depend solely on the diffusion of gases, nutrients, and wastes between body surfaces and individual cells. Others have either open or closed circulatory systems for the transport of gases, wastes, and nutrients.
5. Animals use five main types of respiratory surfaces to accomplish respiration: simple diffusion across plasma membranes, tracheae, cutaneous (integument or body surface) exchange, gills, and lungs.
6. Gas movement occurs between the environment and cells of an animal's body by diffusion down concentration gradients (from areas of higher to areas of lower concentration). In large and active animals, gas exchange is increased by respiratory pigments and ventilation—the active movement of air into and out of a respiratory system.

Would You Like to Know:

1. why a mammalian red blood cell is shaped like a doughnut without a complete hole? (*p. 601*)
2. if blood in our veins is bluish, why it appears red when we cut a vein and begin to bleed? (*p. 601*)
3. what a blood pressure reading of 120/80 mm Hg means? (*p. 606*)
4. why organ and tissue transplants are often rejected except between identical twins? (*p. 609*)
5. how land snails breathe? (*p. 612*)
6. how salamanders that do not have lungs breathe? (*p. 613*)

These and other useful questions will be answered in this chapter.

This chapter contains evolutionary concepts, which are set off in this font.

RNAL TRANSPORT
AND CIRCULATORY SYSTEMS

All animals must maintain a homeostatic balance in their bodies. This need requires that nutrients, metabolic wastes, and respiratory gases be circulated through the animal's body. Any system of moving fluids that reduces the functional diffusion distance that nutrients, wastes, and gases must traverse may be referred to as an internal transport or circulatory system. The nature of the system is directly related to the size, complexity, and life-style of the animal in question. The first part of this chapter discusses some of these transport and circulatory systems.

TRANSPORT SYSTEMS IN INVERTEBRATES

Because protozoa are small, with high surface-area-to-volume ratios (*see figure 3.3*), all they need for gas, nutrient, and waste exchange is simple diffusion. In protozoa, the cytoplasm itself serves as the medium through which materials diffuse to various parts of the organism, or between the organism and the environment (*see figure 36.16a*).

Some invertebrates have evolved specific transport systems. For example, sponges circulate water from the external environment through their bodies, instead of circulating an internal fluid (figure 36.1a). Cnidarians, such as *Hydra*, have a fluid-filled internal **gastrovascular cavity** (figure 36.1b). This cavity supplies nutrients for all body cells lining the cavity, obtains oxygen from the water in the cavity, and releases carbon dioxide and other wastes into it. Simple body movement causes the fluid to move.

The gastrovascular cavity of flatworms, such as the planarian *Dugesia*, is more complex than that of *Hydra*. In the planarian, branches penetrate to all parts of the body (figure 36.1c). Because this branched gastrovascular cavity runs close to all body cells, diffusion distances for nutrients, gases, and wastes are not great. Body movement helps distribute materials to various parts of the body. However, one disadvantage of this system is that it limits these animals to relatively small sizes or to shapes that maintain low diffusion distances.

Pseudocoelomate invertebrates, such as rotifers, gastrotrichs, and nematodes, use the coelomic fluid of their body cavity for transport (figure 36.1d). Most of these animals are small, and adequate transport is accomplished by the movements of the body against the coelomic fluids, which are in direct contact with the internal tissues and organs. A few other invertebrates (e.g., ectoprocts, sipunculans, echinoderms) also depend largely on the body cavity as a coelomic transport chamber.

Beginning with the molluscs, transport functions occur as separate circulatory systems. A **circulatory** or **cardiovascular system** (Gr. *kardia*, heart + L. *vascular*, vessel) is a specialized system that moves the fluid medium called either hemolymph or blood in a specific direction determined by the presence of unidirectional blood vessels. Movement is accomplished by a muscular pumping heart.

There are two basic types of circulatory systems: open and closed. In an **open circulatory system,** the heart pumps hemolymph out into the body cavity or at least through parts of the cavity, where the hemolymph bathes the cells, tissues, and organs. In a **closed circulatory system,** blood is circulated in the confines of tubular vessels. The coelomic fluid of some invertebrates also has a circulatory role either in concert with, or instead of, the hemolymph or blood.

The annelids, such as the earthworm, have a closed circulatory system in which blood travels through vessels delivering nutrients to cells and removing wastes (figure 36.1e).

Most molluscs and arthropods have open circulatory systems, where hemolymph directly bathes the cells and tissues rather than being carried only in vessels (figure 36.1f). For example, an insect's heart pumps hemolymph through vessels that open into a body cavity (hemocoel).

CHARACTERISTICS OF INVERTEBRATE COELOMIC FLUID, HEMOLYMPH, AND BLOOD CELLS

As previously noted, some animals (e.g., echinoderms, annelids, sipunculans) use coelomic fluid as a supplementary or sole circulatory system. Coelomic fluid may be either identical in composition to interstitial fluids, or differ particularly with respect to specific proteins and cells. Coelomic fluid functions in the transport of gases, nutrients, and waste products. It also may function in certain invertebrates (annelids) as a hydrostatic skeleton (*see figure 32.10*).

Hemolymph (Gr. *haima*, blood + *lympha*, water) is the circulating fluid of animals with an open circulatory system. Hemolymph is found in most arthropods, ascidians, and many molluscs. In these animals, hemolymph is pumped by a heart at low pressures through vessels to tissue spaces (hemocoel) and sinuses. Generally, the hemolymph volume is high and the circulation slow. In the process of movement, essential gases, nutrients, and wastes are transported.

Many times hemolymph has noncirculatory functions. For example, in insects, hemolymph pressure assists in molting of the old cuticle and in inflation of the wings. In certain jumping spiders, hydrostatic pressure of the hemolymph provides a hydraulic mechanism for limb extension.

The coelomic fluid, hemolymph, or blood of most animals contains circulating cells called blood cells or **hemocytes.** Some cells contain a respiratory pigment such as hemoglobin and are called erythrocytes or red blood cells. These cells are usually present in high numbers to facilitate oxygen transport. Other cells do not contain respiratory pigments and have other functions such as blood clotting.

The number and types of blood cells vary dramatically in different invertebrates. For example, annelid blood contains hemocytes that are phagocytic. The coelomic fluid contains a variety of coelomcytes (amebocytes, eleocytes, lampocytes, linocytes) that function in phagocytosis, glycogen storage, encapsulation, defense responses, and excretion. The hemolymph of molluscs has two general types of hemocytes (amoebocytes and granulocytes) that have most of the aforementioned functions as well as nacrezation (pearl formation) in some bivalves. Insect hemolymph contains large numbers of various hemocyte types (figure 36.2) that function in phagocytosis, encapsulation, and clotting.

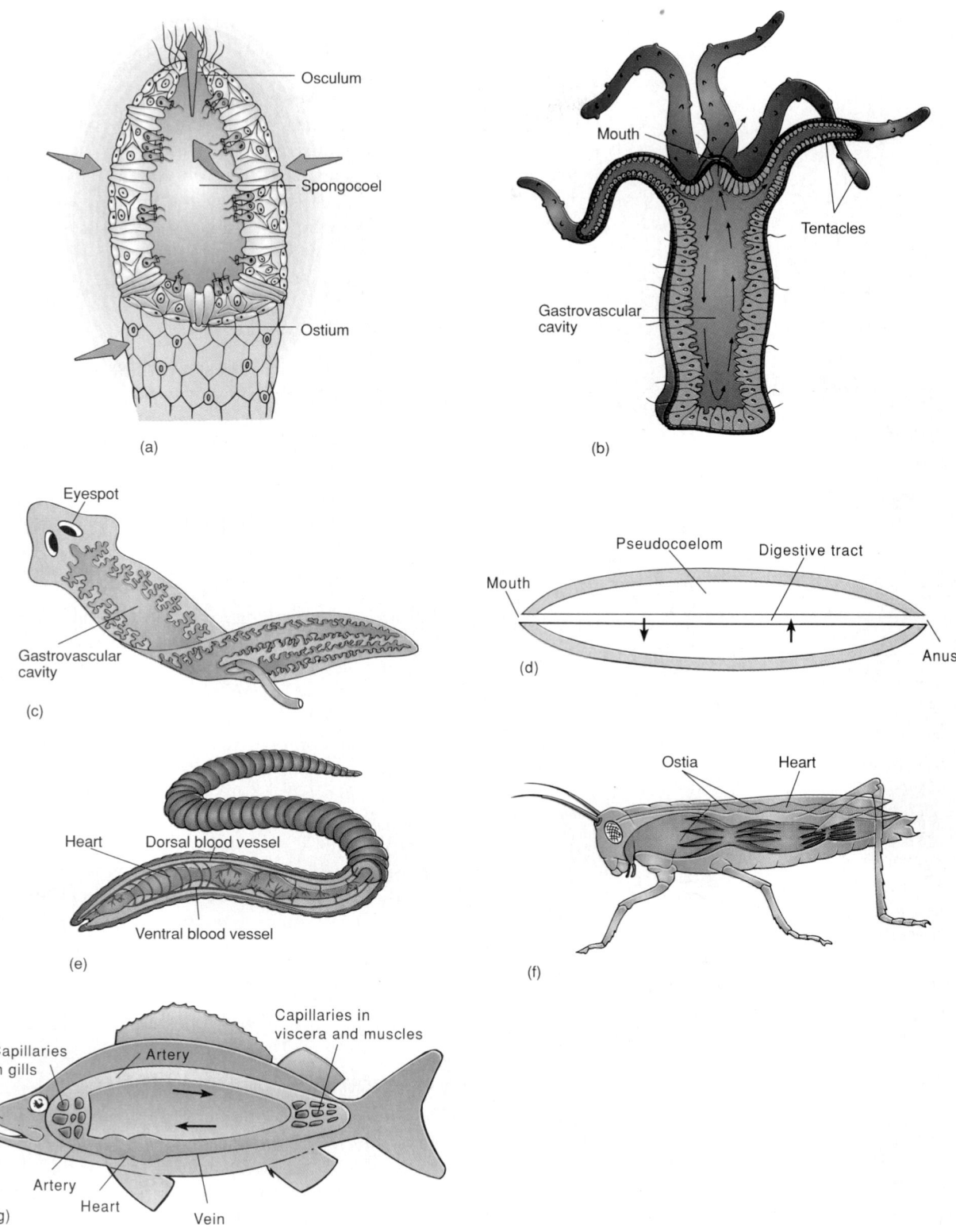

(a)

(b)

(c)

(d)

(e)

(f)

(g)

Figure 36.1

Some Transport and Circulatory Systems. (*a*) Sponges use water from the environment as a circulatory fluid by passing it through their bodies (arrows). (*b*) Cnidarians, such as this *Hydra,* also use water from the environment and circulate it (arrows) through the gastrovascular cavity. Cells lining the cavity can exchange gases and nutrients from the water and release waste into it. (*c*) The planarian's gastrovascular cavity is branched, allowing for more effective distribution of materials. (*d*) Pseudocoelomates use their body cavity fluid for internal transport from and to the digestive tract as indicated by the arrows. (*e*) The circulatory system of an earthworm contains blood that is kept separate from the coelomic fluid. This is an example of a closed circulatory system. (*f*) The dorsal heart of an arthropod, such as this grasshopper, pumps blood through an open circulatory system. In this example, blood and body cavity (hemocoelic) fluid are one and the same. (*g*) Octopuses, other cephalopod molluscs, annelids, and vertebrates, such as this fish, have closed circulatory systems. In a closed system, the walls of the heart and blood vessels are continuously connected, and blood never leaves the vessels. Arrows indicate the direction of blood flow.

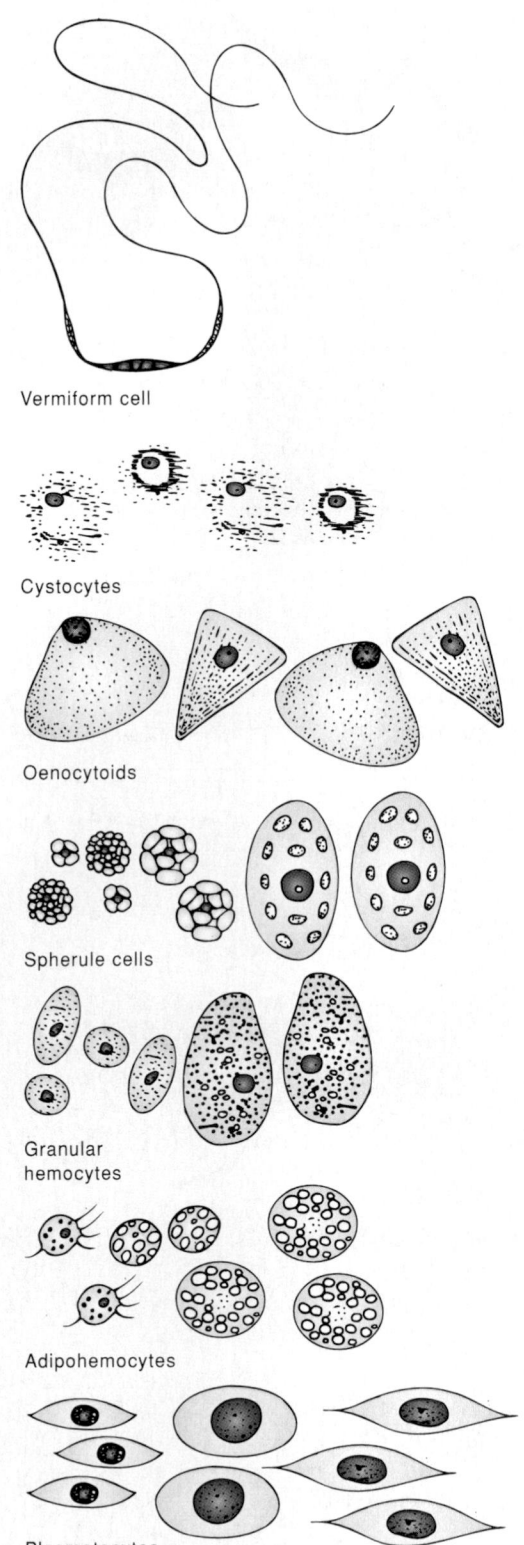

Vermiform cell

Cystocytes

Oenocytoids

Spherule cells

Granular hemocytes

Adipohemocytes

Plasmatocytes

Figure 36.2

Some Examples of Invertebrate Hemocytes. These hemocytes are representative of those found in an insect. The different cells function in phagocytosis, agglutination, storage of nutrients, wound repair, forming connective tissue cells, and in lipid transport.

Transport Systems in Vertebrates

All vertebrates have a closed circulatory system in which the walls of the heart and blood vessels are continuously contracted, and blood never leaves the blood vessels (figure 36.1g). Blood generally is conducted from the heart, through arteries, arterioles, capillaries, venules, veins, and back to the heart. It is only at the capillary level that exchange occurs between the blood and extracellular fluid.

Characteristics of Vertebrate Blood and Blood Cells

Overall, vertebrate blood transports oxygen, carbon dioxide, and nutrients; defends against harmful microorganisms, cells, and viruses; prevents blood loss through coagulation (clotting); and helps regulate body temperature and pH. Because it is a liquid, vertebrate blood is classified as a specialized type of connective tissue. As do other connective tissues, blood contains a fluid matrix called plasma and cellular elements called formed elements.

Plasma

Plasma, (Gr., anything formed or molded) is the straw-colored liquid part of blood. In mammals, plasma is about 90% water and provides the solvent for dissolving and transporting nutrients. A group of proteins (albumins, fibrinogen, and globulins) comprise another 7% of the plasma. It is the concentration of these plasma proteins that influences the distribution of water between the blood and extracellular fluid. Because albumin represents about 60% of the total plasma proteins, it plays important roles with respect to water movement. Fibrinogen is necessary for blood coagulation (clotting), and the globulins transport lipids and fat-soluble vitamins. **Serum** is plasma from which the proteins involved in blood clotting have been removed. The gamma globulin portion functions in the immune response because it consists mostly of antibodies. The remaining 3% of plasma is composed of electrolytes, amino acids, glucose and other nutrients, various enzymes, hormones, metabolic wastes, and traces of many inorganic and organic molecules.

Formed Elements

The **formed-element fraction** (cellular component) of vertebrate blood (figure 36.3) consists of erythrocytes (red blood cells; RBCs), leukocytes (white blood cells; WBCs), and platelets (thrombocytes). White blood cells are present in lower number than are red blood cells, generally being 1 to 2% of the blood by volume. White blood cells are divided into agranulocytes (without granules in the cytoplasm) and granulocytes. There are two types of agranulocytes: lymphocytes and monocytes. The granulocytes have granules in the cytoplasm. There are three types of granulocytes: eosinophils, basophils, and neutrophils. Fragmented cells are called platelets (thrombocytes). Each of these cell types is now discussed in more detail.

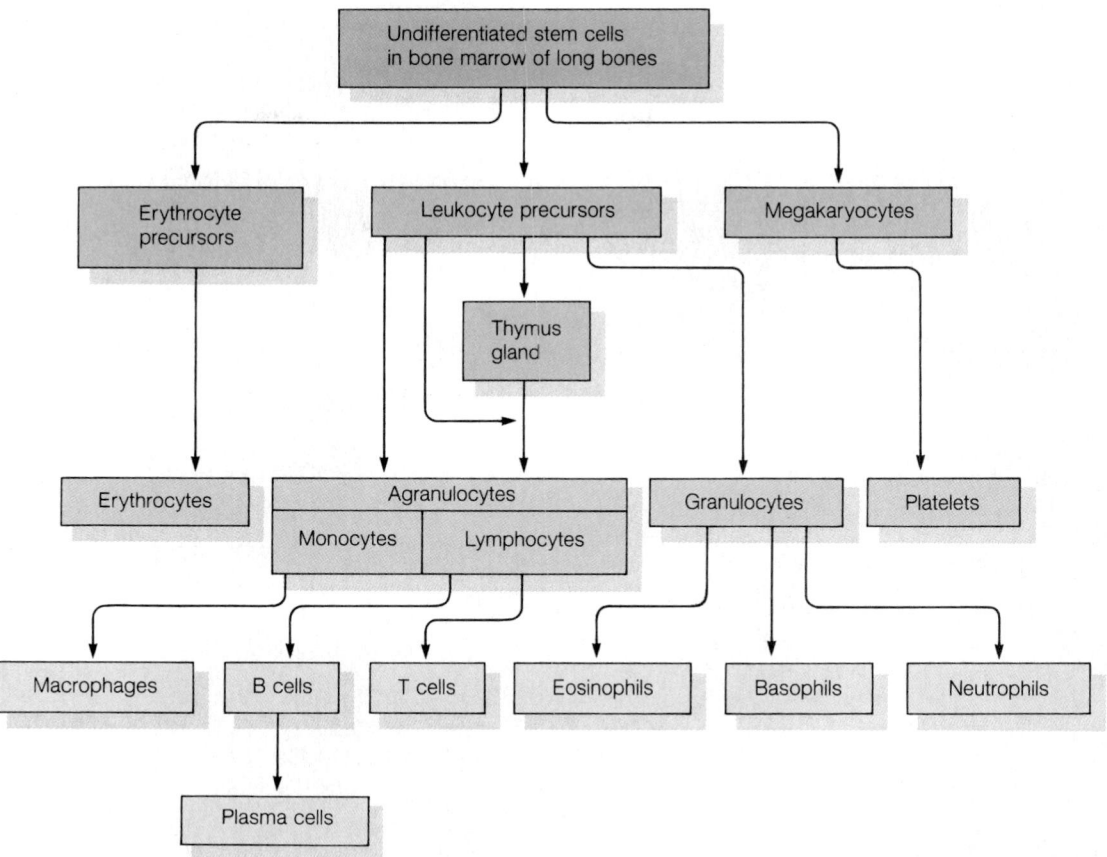

FIGURE 36.3

Cellular Components of Vertebrate Blood. The process of blood cell production is called hematopoiesis. Notice that all blood cells initially begin their life in the bone marrow of long bones within a vertebrate's body.

Red Blood Cells

Red blood cells (erythrocytes; Gr. *erythros*, red + cells) vary dramatically in size, shape, and number in the different vertebrates (figure 36.4; *see also figure 36.5a*). For example, the RBCs of most vertebrates are nucleated, but mammalian RBCs are enucleated (without a nucleus). Some fishes and amphibians also have enucleated RBCs. Among all vertebrates, the salamander *Amphiuma* has the largest RBC (figure 36.4*a*). Avian RBCs (figure 36.4*c*) are oval-shaped, nucleated, and larger than mammalian RBCs. Among birds, the ostrich has the largest RBC. Most mammalian RBCs are biconcave disks (*see figure 36.5a*); however, the camel (figure 36.4*e*) and llama have elliptical RBCs. ❶ The shape of a biconcave disk provides a larger surface for gas diffusion than a flat disk or sphere. Generally, the lower vertebrates tend to have fewer but larger RBCs than the higher invertebrates.

Almost the entire mass of a RBC consists of **hemoglobin** (Gr. *haima*, blood + L. *globulus*, little globe), an iron-containing protein. The major function of an erythrocyte is to pick up oxygen from the environment, bind it to hemoglobin to form **oxyhemoglobin,** and transport it to body tissues. Blood rich in oxyhemoglobin is bright red; as oxygen diffuses into the tissues, blood becomes darker and appears blue when observed through the blood vessel walls. ❷ However, when this deoxygenated blood is ex-posed to oxygen (such as when a vein is cut and a mammal begins to bleed), it instantaneously turns bright red. Hemoglobin also carries waste carbon dioxide (in the form of **carbaminohemoglobin**) from the tissues to the lungs (or gills) for removal from the body.

White Blood Cells

White blood cells (leukocytes) (Gr. *leukos*, white + cells) serve as scavengers that destroy microorganisms at infection sites, remove foreign chemicals, and remove debris that results from dead or injured cells. All WBCs are derived from immature cells (called stem cells) in bone marrow by a process called **hematopoiesis** (Gr. *hemato*, blood + *poiein*, to make; *see figure 36.3*).

Among the granulocytes, **eosinophils** are phagocytic, and ingest foreign proteins and immune complexes rather than bacteria (figure 36.5*b*). In mammals, eosinophils also release chemicals that counteract the effects of certain inflammatory chemicals released during allergic reactions. **Basophils** are the least numerous WBC (figure 36.5*c*). When they react with a foreign substance, their granules release histamine and heparin. Histamine causes blood vessels to dilate and leak fluid at a site of inflammation, and heparin prevents blood clotting. **Neutrophils** are the most numerous of the white blood cells (figure 36.5*d*). They are chemically attracted to sites of inflammation and are active phagocytes.

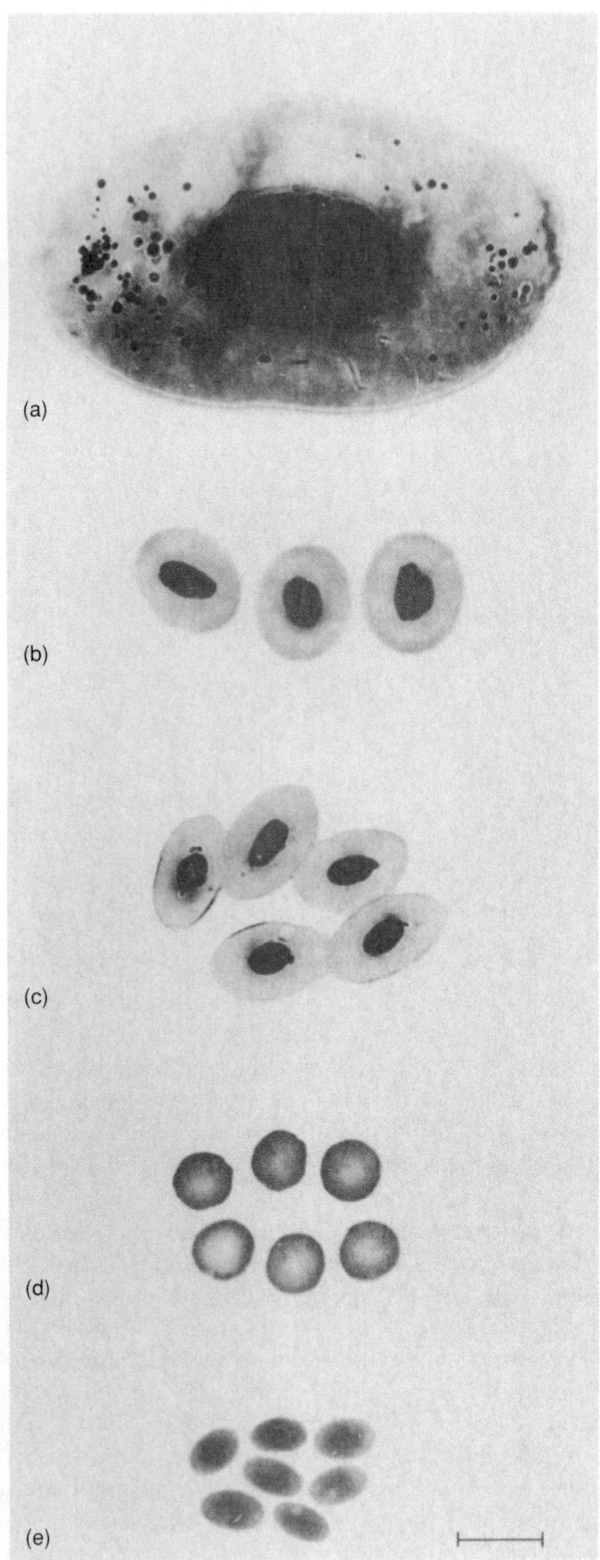

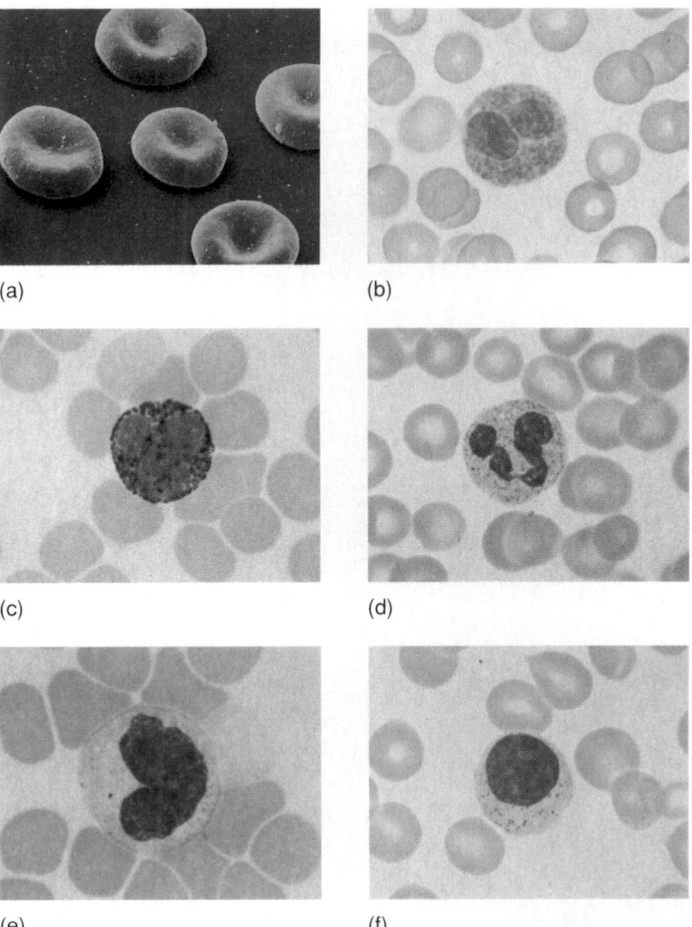

FIGURE 36.5

Blood Cells. (*a*) Scanning electron micrograph showing the biconcave shape of human erythrocytes (× 1,500). (*b*) An eosinophil is characterized by the presence of red-staining cytoplasmic granules. (*c*) A basophil is characterized by blue-staining granules. (*d*) A neutrophil is characterized by light-pink granules and a multilobed nucleus. Cells shown in *b–d* are also known as granulocytes. The agranulocytes consist of large monocytes (*e*) and lymphocytes (*f*). (*b–f* are light micrographs × 710.)

The two types of agranulocytes are the **monocytes** and **lymphocytes** (figure 36.5*e,f*). Two distinct types of lymphocytes are recognized: B cells and T cells, both of which are central to the immune response. **B cells** originate in the bone marrow, and colonize the lymphoid tissue, where they mature. In contrast, **T cells** are associated with and influenced by the thymus gland before they colonize lymphoid tissue and play their role in the immune response. When B cells are activated, they divide and differentiate to produce **plasma cells.**

Platelets (Thrombocytes)
Platelets (so named because of their platelike flatness), or **thrombocytes** (Gr. *thrombus*, clot + cells), are disk-shaped cell fragments that function to initiate blood clotting. When a blood vessel is injured, platelets immediately move to the site and begin to clump together, attaching themselves to the damaged area, and begin the process of blood coagulation.

FIGURE 36.4

Comparison of the Form of Red Blood Cells from a Variety of Vertebrates. Light micrographs of (*a*) a nucleated cell from a salamander; (*b*) nucleated cells from a snake; (*c*) nucleated cells from an ostrich; (*d*) enucleated cells (biconcave disk) from a red kangaroo; and (*e*) enucleated cells (ellipsoid) from a camel (bar = 10 μm).

36.6

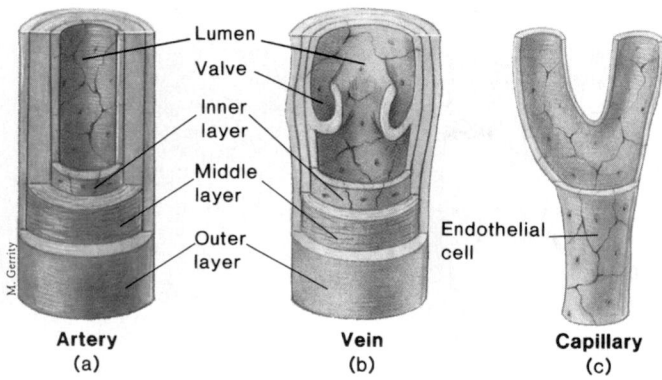

FIGURE 36.6

Structure of Blood Vessels. (*a*) The walls of arteries and (*b*) veins have three layers (tunicae); the outermost layer consists of connective tissue, the middle layer has elastic and smooth muscle tissue, and the inner layer consists of a single layer of smooth endothelial cells (endothelium). Notice that the wall of an artery is much thicker than the wall of a vein. The middle layer is greatly reduced in a vein. (*c*) A capillary consists of a single layer of endothelial cells.

VERTEBRATE BLOOD VESSELS

Arteries are elastic blood vessels that carry blood away from the heart to the organs and tissues of the body. The central canal of an artery (and of all blood vessels) is called a lumen. Surrounding the lumen of an artery is a thick wall composed of three layers, or tunicae (L. *tunica*, covering) (figure 36.6*a*).

Most **veins** are relatively inelastic, large vessels that carry blood from the body tissues to the heart. The wall of a vein contains the same three layers (tunicae) as arterial walls, but the middle layer is much thinner, and one or more valves is present (figure 36.6*b*). The valves permit blood flow in only one direction, which is important in returning the blood to the heart.

Arteries lead to terminal **arterioles** (those closest to a capillary). The arterioles branch to form **capillaries** (L. *capillus*, hair), which are connected to **venules** and then to veins. Capillaries are generally composed of a single layer of endothelial cells (figure 36.6*c*) and are the most numerous blood vessels in an animal's body. An abundance of capillaries makes an enormous surface area available for the exchange of gases, fluids, nutrients, and wastes between the blood and nearby cells.

Stop and Ask Yourself

1. Why don't protozoa need a circulatory system?
2. How does circulation occur in sponges and cnidarians? In pseudocoelomates?
3. What is the difference between an open and closed circulatory system? What type of cells are found in each of these systems?
4. What are the different blood vessels found in a vertebrate?

THE HEARTS AND CIRCULATORY SYSTEMS OF BONY FISHES, AMPHIBIANS, AND REPTILES

The heart and blood vessels changed greatly as vertebrates moved from water to land and as endothermy evolved. Examples of these trends are now presented.

The bony fish heart has four chambers: the sinus venosus, atrium, ventricle, and conus arteriosus through which blood flows in sequence (figure 36.7*a*). Blood leaves the heart via the ventral aorta, which goes to the gills. In the gills, blood becomes oxygenated, loses carbon dioxide, and enters the dorsal aorta. The dorsal aorta distributes blood to all of the body organs, and then blood is returned to the heart via the venous system. Because blood only passes through the heart once, this system is called a single circulation circuit. This circuit has the advantage of circulating oxygenated blood from the gills to the systemic capillaries in all organs almost simultaneously. However, the circulation of blood through the gill capillaries offers resistance to flow. Blood pressure and rates of flow to other organs are thus appreciably reduced. This arrangement probably could not support the very high metabolic rates present in some birds and mammals.

In amphibians and reptiles, the slow blood flow problem has been overcome by the evolution of a double circulatory circuit, in which blood passes through the heart twice during its circuit through the body. Amphibians and most reptiles have hearts that are not fully divided in two. In amphibians (figure 36.7*b*), there is a single ventricle that pumps blood both to the lungs and the rest of the body. However, because most amphibians absorb more oxygen through their skin than through their lungs or gills, blood returning from the skin also contributes oxygenated blood to the ventricle. The blood that is pumped out to the rest of the body is thus highly oxygenated.

In the heart of most reptiles (figure 36.7*c*), the ventricle is partially divided into a right and left side. Oxygenated blood from the lungs returns to the left side of the heart via the pulmonary vein, and little mixing with deoxygenated blood in the right side of the heart occurs. When the ventricles contract, blood is pumped out two aortae for distribution throughout the body, as well as to the lungs. The incomplete separation of the ventricles is an important adaptation for reptiles, such as turtles, because it allows blood to be diverted away from the pulmonary circulation during diving and when the turtle is withdrawn into its shell. This conserves energy and diverts blood to vital organs during the time when the lungs cannot be ventilated.

THE HEARTS AND CIRCULATORY SYSTEMS IN BIRDS AND MAMMALS

Even though the physiological separation of blood in left and right ventricles is almost complete in reptiles, the complete anatomical separation of ventricles occurs only in crocodilians, birds, and mammals (figure 36.7*d*). This facilitates the double circulation that is required to maintain high blood pressure. High blood pressure is important in the rapid delivery of oxygenated nutrient-rich blood to tissues with very high metabolic rates.

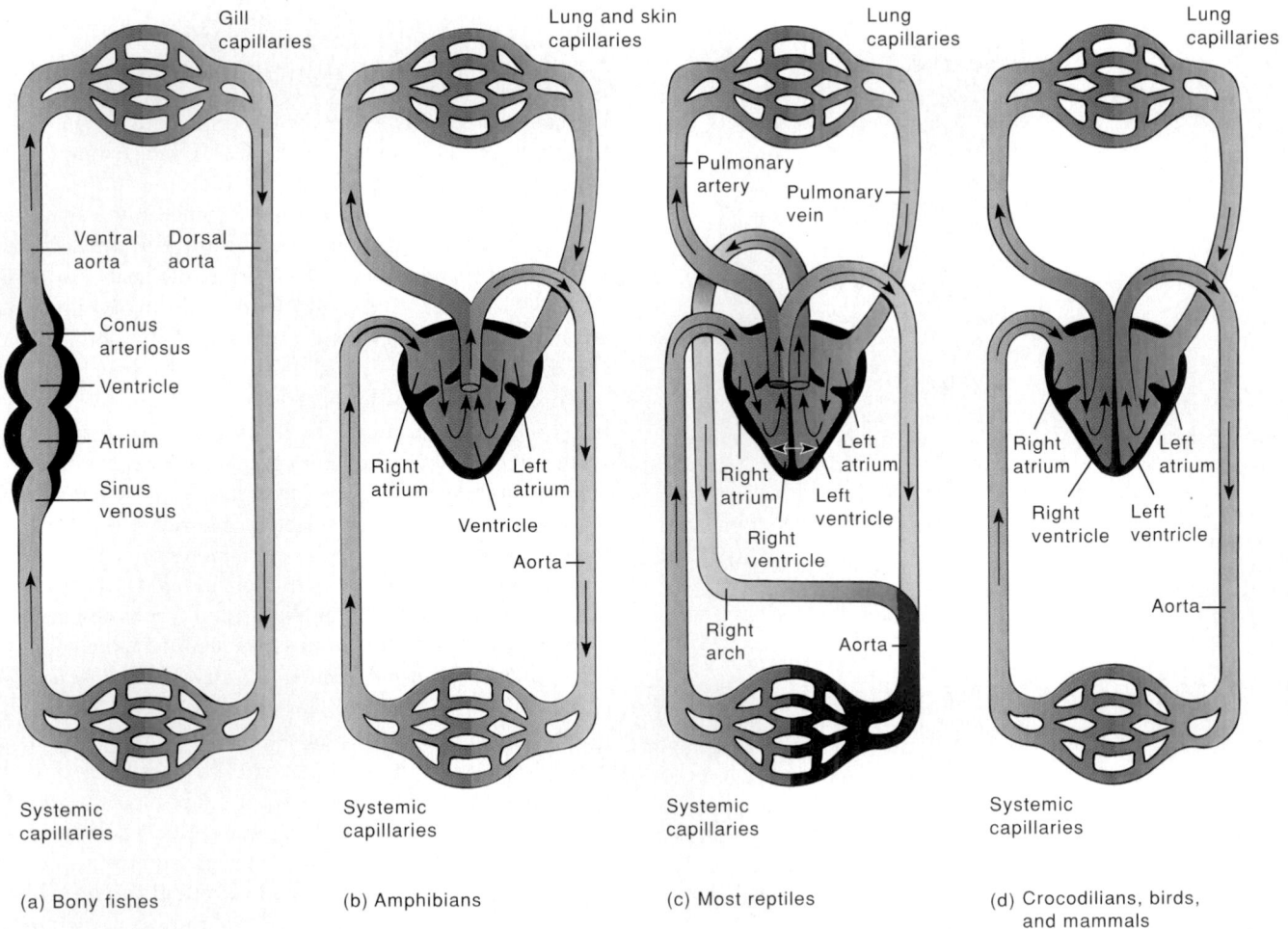

Figure 36.7

The Heart and Circulatory Systems of Various Vertebrates. Oxygenated blood is red; deoxygenated blood is blue; a mixture of oxygenated and deoxygenated blood is purple. (*a*) In bony fishes, the heart's four chambers (sinus venosus, atrium, ventricle, and conus arteriosus) pump in series. There is no separation of respiratory and systemic circulation. (*b*) The amphibian heart has two atria and one ventricle. Blood from the lungs enters the left atrium, and blood from the body enters the right atrium. The blood from both atria empties into one ventricle, which then pumps it into the respiratory and systemic circulations. (*c*) In most reptiles, there is a greater degree of anatomical division of the ventricle into two halves. (*d*) In crocodilians, birds, and mammals, the ventricle is completely divided, forming a four-chambered heart, with the flow of blood through the lungs completely separated from the flow to other tissues. The arrows indicate the direction of the blood flow. *Redrawn from N. K. Wessels and J. L. Hopson, Biology, 3d ed. Copyright © 1988 McGraw-Hill, Inc. Used by permission.*

Blood circulates throughout the avian and mammalian body in two main circuits: the pulmonary and systemic circuits (figure 36.8). The **pulmonary circuit** supplies the blood only to the lungs. It carries oxygen-poor (deoxygenated) blood from the heart to the lungs, where carbon dioxide is removed, and oxygen is added. It then returns the oxygen-rich (oxygenated) blood to the heart for distribution to the rest of the body. The **systemic circuit** supplies all the cells, tissues, and organs of the body with oxygen-rich blood and returns the oxygen-poor blood to the heart.

THE HUMAN HEART

The human heart is a hardworking pump that moves blood through the body. It pumps its entire blood volume (about 5 liters) every minute; about 8,000 liters of blood moves through 96,000 km (60,000 mi) of blood vessels every day. The heart of an average adult beats about 70 times per minute—more than

100,000 times per day. In a 70-year lifetime, the heart beats more than 2.6 billion times without tiring.

Most of the human heart is composed of cardiac muscle tissue called myocardium (Gr. *myo*, muscle). The outer protective covering of the heart, however, is fibrous connective tissue called the epicardium (Gr. *epi*, upon). Connective tissue and endothelium form the inside of the heart, the endocardium (Gr. *endo*, inside). (Endothelium is a single layer of epithelial cells lining the chambers of the heart, as well as the lumen of blood vessels; *see figure 36.6*.)

The left and right halves of the heart are two separate pumps, each containing two chambers (figure 36.9). In each half, blood first flows into a thin-walled atrium (L. *antichamber*, waiting room; pl. atria), then into a thick-walled ventricle. Valves are located between the upper (atria) and lower (ventricles) chambers. The tricuspid valve is located between the right atrium and right ventricle, and the bicuspid valve between the left atrium and left

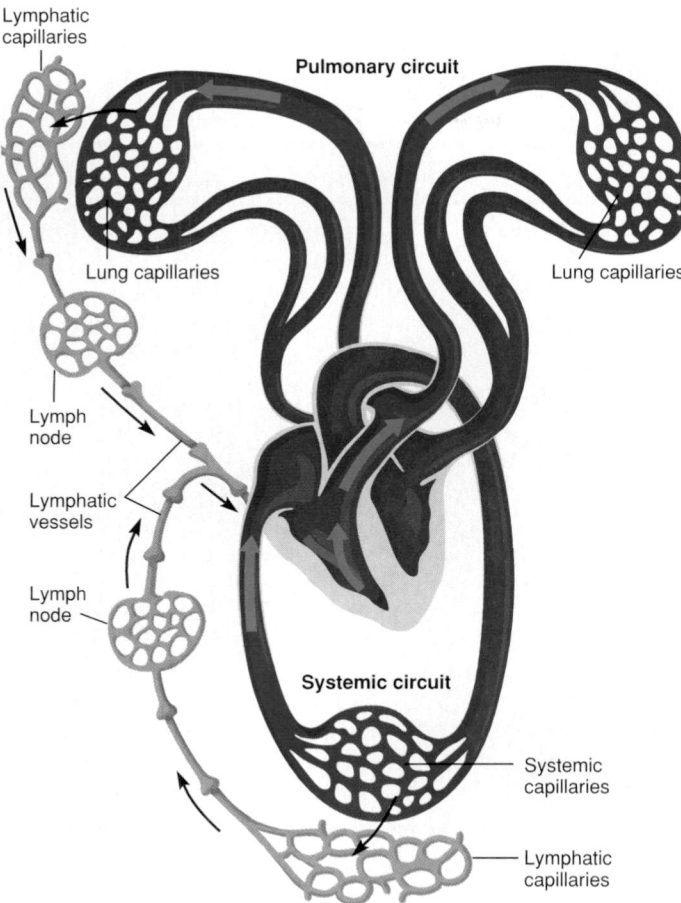

FIGURE 36.8

Circulatory Circuits. The cardiovascular system of a bird or mammal has two major capillary beds and transport circuits: the pulmonary circuit and systemic circuit. The lymphatic system consists of one-way vessels that are also involved in returning tissue fluid, called lymph, back to the heart. The black arrows indicate the direction of lymph flow, and the light arrows indicate the direction of blood flow.

ventricle. (Collectively, these are referred to as the AV valves—atrioventricular valves.) The pulmonary semilunar valve is located at the exit of the right ventricle, and the aortic semilunar valve at the exit of the left ventricle. (Collectively, these are referred to as the semilunar valves.) All of these valves open and close due to blood pressure changes that are produced when the heart contracts during each heart beat. Just as do the valves in veins, heart valves keep blood moving in one direction, preventing backflow.

The heartbeat is a sequence of muscle contractions and relaxations called the cardiac cycle. Each heartbeat is initiated by a "pacemaker," which is a small mass of tissue called the sinoatrial node (SA node) located at the entrance to the right atrium (figure 36.10). (Because the pacemaker is in the heart, nervous innervation is not necessary, which is why a heart transplant without nerves is possible.) The SA node initiates the cardiac cycle by producing an action potential that spreads over both atria, causing them to contract simultaneously. The action potential then passes to the atrioventricular node (AV node), which is located on the inferior portion of the interatrial septum. From here, the action potential continues through the

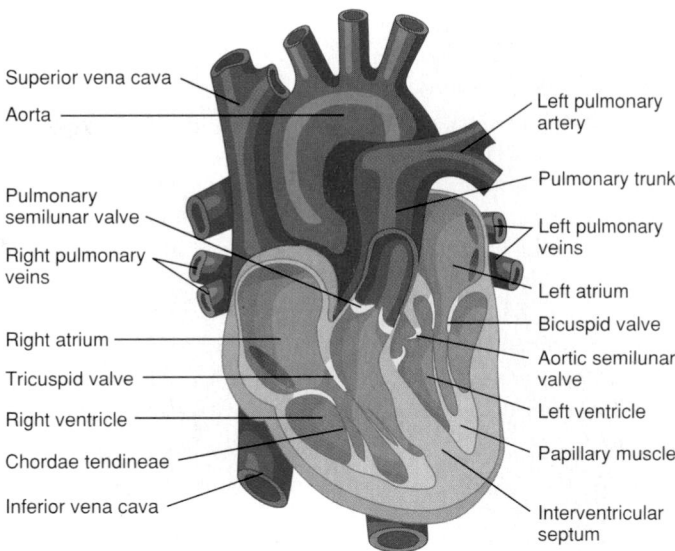

FIGURE 36.9

The Structures of the Human Heart. Deoxygenated blood from the tissues of the body returns to the right atrium and flows through the tricuspid valve into the right ventricle. The right ventricle pumps the blood through the pulmonary semilunar valve into the pulmonary circuit, from which it returns to the left atrium and flows through the bicuspid valve into the left ventricle. The left ventricle then pumps blood through the aortic semilunar valve into the aorta.

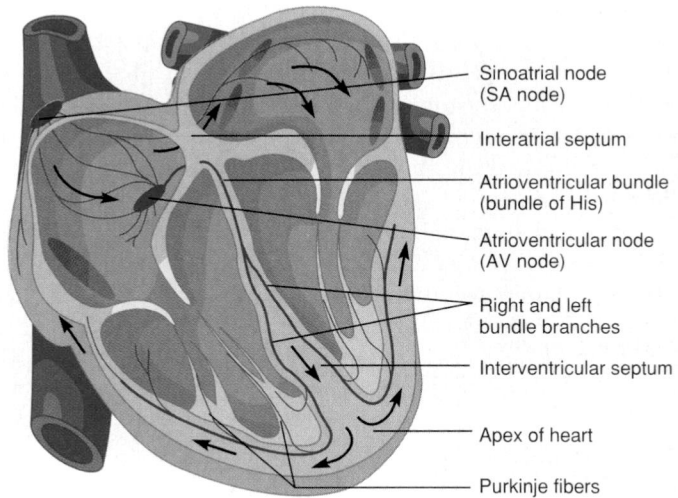

FIGURE 36.10

The Electrical Conduction System of the Human Heart. The depolarization wave is initiated by the SA node and passes successively through the atrial myocardium to the AV node, the AV bundle, the right and left bundle branches, and the Purkinje fibers in the ventricular myocardium. Arrows indicate the direction of the electrical current flow.

atrioventricular bundle (bundle of His), located at the tip of the interventricular septum. The atrioventricular bundle divides into right and left branches, which are continuous with the Purkinje fibers in the ventricular walls. Stimulation of these fibers causes the ventricles to contract simultaneously and eject blood into the pulmonary and systemic circulations.

The action potential moving over the surface of the heart causes current flow, which can be recorded at the surface of the body as an electrocardiogram (ECG or EKG).

During each cycle, the atria and ventricles go through a phase of contraction called **systole** and a phase of relaxation called **diastole.** Specifically, while the atria are relaxing and filling with blood, the ventricles are also relaxed. As more and more blood accumulates in the atria, the blood pressure rises, and the atria contract, forcing the AV valves open and causing blood to rush into the ventricles. When the ventricles contract, the AV valves close, and the semilunar valves open, allowing blood to be pumped into the pulmonary arteries and aorta. After the blood has been ejected from the ventricles, they relax and start the cycle anew.

BLOOD PRESSURE

The fluid pressure that is generated by the ventricles contracting forces blood through the pulmonary and systemic circuits; the fluid pressure is called **blood pressure.** More specifically, blood pressure is the force exerted by the blood against the inner walls of blood vessels. Although such a force occurs throughout the vascular system, the term blood pressure is most commonly used to refer to systemic arterial blood pressure.

Arterial blood pressure rises and falls in a pattern corresponding to the phases of the cardiac cycle. When the ventricles contract (ventricular systole), their walls force the blood in them into the pulmonary arteries and the aorta. As a result, the pressure in these arteries rises sharply. The maximum pressure achieved during ventricular contraction is called the **systolic pressure.** When the ventricles relax (ventricular diastole), the arterial pressure drops, and the lowest pressure that remains in the arteries before the next ventricular contraction is called the **diastolic pressure.**

③   In humans, normal systolic pressure for a young adult is about 120 mm Hg, which is the amount of pressure required to make a column of mercury [Hg] in a sphygmomanometer (sfig″mo-mah-nom′e-ter) rise a distance of 120 mm. Diastolic pressure is approximately 80 mm Hg. These readings are by convention expressed as 120/80.

THE LYMPHATIC SYSTEM

The vertebrate **lymphatic system** begins with very small closed vessels called lymphatic capillaries, which are in direct contact with the extracellular fluid surrounding tissues (*see figure 36.8*). The system has four major functions: (1) to collect and drain most of the fluid that seeps from the bloodstream and accumulates in the extracellular fluid; (2) to return small amounts of proteins that have left the cells; (3) to transport lipids that have been absorbed from the small intestine; and (4) to transport foreign particles and cellular debris to disposal centers called lymph nodes. The small lymphatic capillaries merge to form larger lymphatic vessels called lymphatics. Lymphatics are thin-walled vessels with valves that ensure the one-way flow of lymph. **Lymph** (L. *lympha,* clear water) is the extracellular fluid that accumulates in the lymph vessels. These vessels pass through the

TABLE 36.1	MAJOR STRUCTURAL AND FUNCTIONAL COMPONENTS OF THE LYMPHATIC SYSTEM IN VERTEBRATES	
STRUCTURE	**FUNCTION**
Lymphatic capillaries	Collect excess extracellular fluid in tissues
Lymphatics	Carry lymph from lymphatic capillaries to veins in the neck where it is returned to the bloodstream
Lymph nodes	House the WBCs that destroy foreign substances, play a role in antibody formation
Spleen	Filters foreign substances from blood, manufactures phagocytic lymphocytes, stores red blood cells, releases blood to the body when there is blood loss
Thymus gland (in mammals)	Forms antibodies in the newborn; is involved in the initial development of the immune system; site of T-cell differentiation
Bursa of Fabricius (in birds)	A lymphoid organ found at the lower end of the alimentary canal in birds; the site of B-cell maturation

lymph nodes on their way back to the heart. Large concentrations of lymph nodes occur in several areas of the body and play an important role in the body's defense against disease.

In addition to the above parts, the lymphatic system of birds and mammals consists of lymphoid organs, the spleen and either the bursa of Fabricius in birds or the thymus gland, tonsils, and adenoids in mammals. The major components of the lymphatic system are summarized in table 36.1. The lymphatic system is also the bridge to the next section, on immunity, because it is vital to an animal's defense against injury and attack.

Stop and Ask Yourself

5. What is a single circulatory circuit? A double circulatory circuit?

6. What is the cardiac cycle? What is blood pressure?

7. What are the four major functions of the lymphatic system?

IMMUNITY

Mechanisms (defenses) have evolved in animals which prevent unwanted cells, microorganisms, or agents from upsetting the animal's homeostasis. We will now briefly examine the general innate

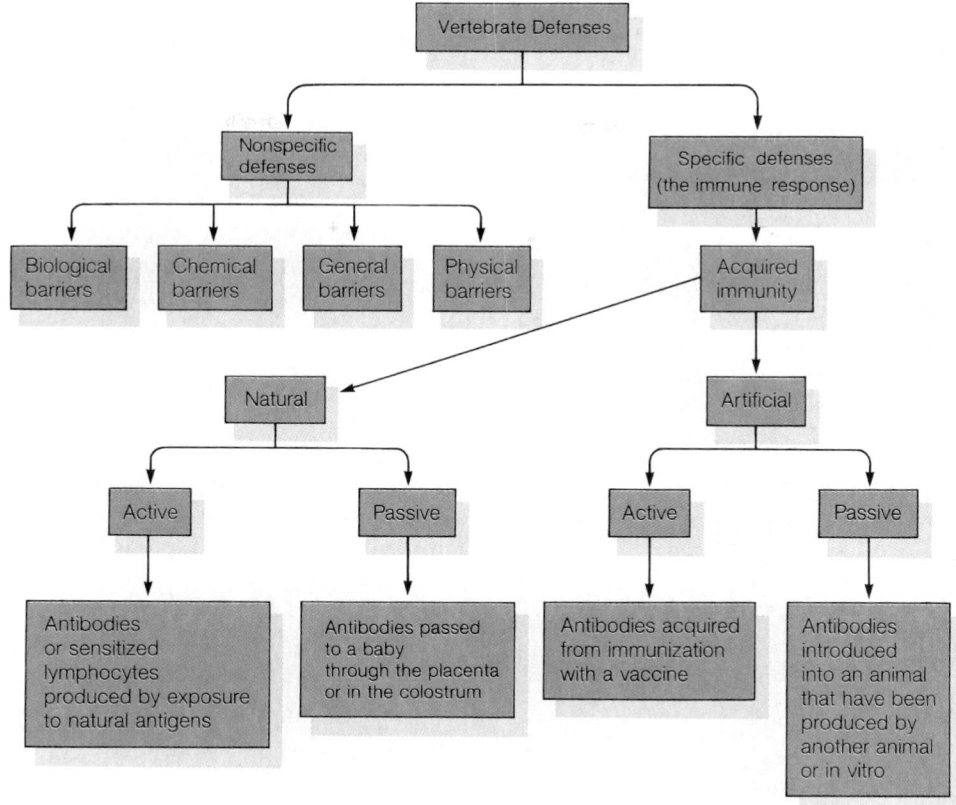

Figure 36.11

Various Aspects of the Immune Response: Different Vertebrate Defenses.   The details of the vertebrate immune system are astonishingly complex; many events have been omitted so that the overall organization of the immune response can be clearly seen.

defenses of various animals, and then the acquired immune response of vertebrates.

It is generally agreed that invertebrates do not have immune systems with special cells that recognize and destroy very specific foreign agents. However, many do have innate, internal defense mechanisms. For example, molluscs and insects have granulocytes that are highly phagocytic to foreign agents, and in arthropods (primarily insects) these cells are capable of encapsulating foreign agents. Arthropods also possess another type of internal defense mechanism called melanization. This process is characterized by the deposition of the dark pigment melanin around the foreign agent. Nacrezation, or pearl formation, is another innate defense mechanism found in molluscs.

Vertebrates are continuously exposed to microorganisms, foreign macromolecules, or cancer cells that can cause disease. Fortunately, they are equipped with an immune system that responds in defensive ways to this exposure. **Immunity** (L. *immunis*, free of burden) refers to the general ability of an animal to resist harmful attack. The immune response that results is a large and specific complex of defensive elements, widely distributed throughout the body, that help the animal defend against attack. These defenses can be divided into nonspecific and specific categories (figure 36.11). **Immunology** is the study of these defenses.

NONSPECIFIC DEFENSES

Nonspecific defenses refer to those general mechanisms that are inherited as part of the innate structure and function of each animal. These mechanisms act in concert as a first line of defense against intruders, before they can cause disease. Nonspecific defenses include biological barriers (inflammation and phagocytosis), chemical barriers (enzymatic action, interferons), general barriers (fever), and physical barriers (skin, mucous membranes).

SPECIFIC DEFENSES: THE IMMUNE RESPONSE

If nonspecific defenses are breached, the specific immune response is called upon for protection. This system consists of a number of immunological mechanisms in which certain white blood cells (lymphocytes) recognize the presence of particular foreign invaders or substances (antigens) and act to eliminate them. This elimination can occur by direct destruction of the antigens by the lymphocytes or by the formation of specialized proteins (antibodies) that either destroy the invader or target it for destruction by other cells (table 36.2).

As an overview, when B cells are stimulated by a foreign invader, they divide into plasma cells. Plasma cells respond to invaders by secreting specific proteins (antibodies) into the

TABLE 36.2	SPECIFIC DEFENSES OF THE VERTEBRATE IMMUNE SYSTEM

DEFENSE	FUNCTION
White Blood Cells	
B cells	Lymphocytes that differentiate into plasma cells after stimulation by antigen
Plasma cells	Cells that are formed from stimulated B cells and secrete antibody
T cells	Lymphocytes that are produced in bone marrow and mature in the thymus gland
Helper T cells	Stimulate the rapid divisions of lymphocytes and along with them, mount an attack against foreign invaders
Natural killer cells	Destroy body cells infected with viruses or fungal parasites as well as cancer cells
Suppressor T cells	Slow down or stop the immune response
Memory cells	A portion of the B and T cells produced during a first-time encounter with a specific invader that are held in reserve; they make possible a rapid response to subsequent encounters with the same type of invader
Macrophages	Highly phagocytic lymphocytes; alert helper T cells' response to the presence of foreign intruders
Secreted Chemicals	
Antibodies	Receptor molecules that bind specific foreign targets and tag them for destruction by phagocytes or the complement system
Lymphokines, interleukins	Secretions by which white blood cells communicate with each other
Perforin-1	A protein secreted by certain T cells that punches a hole in target cells and kills them

into close physical contact with foreign cells or infected cells in order to destroy them, they are said to provide **cell-mediated immunity.**

Acquired Immunity

Acquired immunity refers to the type of specific immunity that develops after exposure to an antigen or is produced after antibodies are transferred from one animal to another. It can be obtained by natural or artificial means, either actively or passively (figure 36.11).

Naturally Acquired
Naturally acquired active immunity occurs when an animal's immune system comes into contact with an appropriate antigenic stimulus during the course of daily activities. The immune system responds by producing antibodies and sensitized lymphocytes that inactivate the antigen. The immunity produced can be either lifelong (e.g., measles or chicken pox) or last for only a few years (e.g., tetanus).

Naturally acquired passive immunity involves the transfer of antibodies from one host to another. For example, in a pregnant mammal, some of the female's antibodies pass across the placenta to the fetus. Whatever immunity the female has will be transferred to the newborn. Certain other antibodies are able to pass from the female to her offspring in the first secretions (called colostrum) from the mammary glands. Unfortunately, naturally acquired passive immunity generally lasts only a short time (weeks or months at the most).

Artificially Acquired
Artificially acquired active immunity results from immunizing an animal with a vaccine. A **vaccine** consists of a preparation of either killed microorganisms; living, weakened (attenuated) microorganisms; or inactivated bacterial toxins (called toxoids) that is administered to an animal to induce immunity. Such deliberate causing of antibody production is called **immunization.**

Artificially acquired passive immunity results from introducing into an animal antibodies that have been produced either in another animal or by specific in vitro methods. Although this type of immunity is immediate, it is short-lived (about 3 weeks). An example would be botulinum antitoxin produced in a horse and given to a human suffering from botulism food poisoning.

Antigens

The mammalian immune system distinguishes between "self" and "nonself" by an elaborate recognition system. Prior to birth, the body makes an inventory of the proteins and various other large molecules that are present in the body ("self") and inactivates most of the genetic programming for making antibodies to "self" molecules. Subsequently, the self-molecules can be distinguished from foreign, nonself substances, and lymphocytes can produce specific immunological reactions against the foreign material, leading to its removal. Foreign ("nonself") substances (markers) to which lymphocytes respond are called

blood and lymph. These antibodies are specifically directed against proteins (antigens) on the invader that caused their formation. Because antibodies are soluble in blood and lymph, they provide **humoral** (L. *humor,* a liquid) **immunity.** The humoral response defends mostly against bacteria, bacterial toxins, and viruses that enter the animal's various body-fluid systems.

T cells do not secrete antibodies. Instead, they attack host cells that have been infected by microorganisms, tissue cells transplanted from one animal to another, or cancer cells. T cells (e.g., helper T cells) also influence the activity of other components of the immune system. Because T cells must come

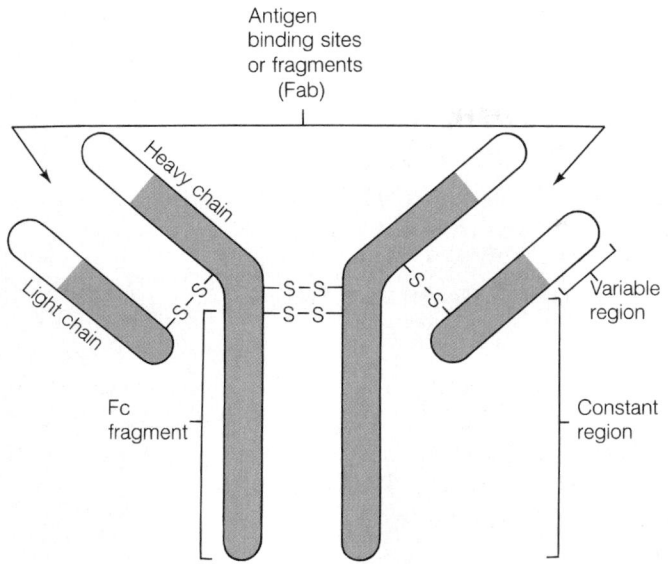

FIGURE 36.12

Antibody Structure. The antibody molecule consists of two identical heavy chains and two light chains held together by disulfide bonds. There are five types of the heavy chain, giving rise to the five types of immunoglobulins (IgG, IgA, IgM, IgD, IgE) with distinct functions. There are antibodies against virtually any potential antigen, because the variable regions can form millions of different attachment sites that bind to different antigens.

antigens (antibody generator). Most antigens are large proteins or other complex molecules with a molecular weight generally greater than 10,000.

Antibodies

Antibodies (immunoglobulins) are a group of recognition glycoproteins manufactured by plasma cells and present in the blood and tissue fluids of birds and mammals. All antibody molecules have a basic Y structure composed of four chains of polypeptides (figure 36.12) connected to each other by disulfide bonds. The arms of the Y contain binding sites or fragments (Fab) for specific invaders (i.e., antigens). The tail of the Y can activate the complement system or bind to receptors on phagocytic cells.

Antibody-Mediated (Humoral) Immune Response

B cells are of great importance in fighting invading organisms because they produce the antibodies that identify the antigens for destruction. The B cells carry some of their particular antibodies on their plasma membrane. When an antigen comes into contact with a B cell whose antibodies recognize the antigen, the B cell binds to the antigen. When stimulated by one kind of T cell, a helper T cell, the B cell divides many times, producing plasma cells that begin producing and secreting more of this particular antibody. These antibody molecules are carried through the circulation. If they encounter antigens, the

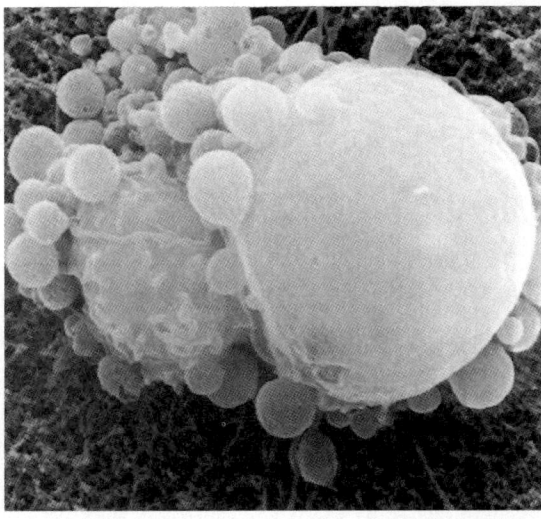

FIGURE 36.13

A Natural Killer (NK) Cell Destroying a Cancer Cell. Upon contact with a cancer cell, a natural killer cell releases toxic chemicals, such as perforin-1, which punch holes in the cancer cell's plasma membrane causing the cancer cell to die.

antibodies bind to the antigen molecules, which are now marked for destruction by other parts of the immune system (e.g., macrophages).

Cell-Mediated Immune Response

Unlike B cells that produce the antibodies that subsequently mark antigens for destruction, T cells are directly involved with the destruction of invading cells, as well as with the regulation of other parts of the immune system. T cell responses are called the cell-mediated immune response.

Natural killer (NK) cells, also called cytotoxic T cells, help in a bird or a mammal's defense by recognizing cell surface changes on cancer cells, virus-infected cells, fungi, bacteria, protozoa, or helminth parasites (figure 36.13).

④ The action of NK cells is also the reason why tissue and organ transplants are rejected in birds or mammals. In the rejection mechanism, NK cells enter the transplanted tissue through the blood vessels, recognize it as foreign, attach to the tissue, and destroy it. However, the body will tolerate tissue and organ transplants between identical twins who have identical sets of DNA and hence identical self-recognition marker regions.

T cells are also involved with regulating the activity of other parts of the immune system. For example, suppose several bacteria penetrate the first line of defense (the skin) through an abrasion or cut. Inflammation occurs, and the bacteria are phagocytized by macrophages (figure 36.14). The macrophage destroys most of the antigens (bacteria), but some of the antigens are moved to the surface of the plasma membrane of both macrophages and B cells, where they are displayed alongside the self-recognition marker. It is this specific combination of self-recognition marker and antigen that is recognized by helper T cells.

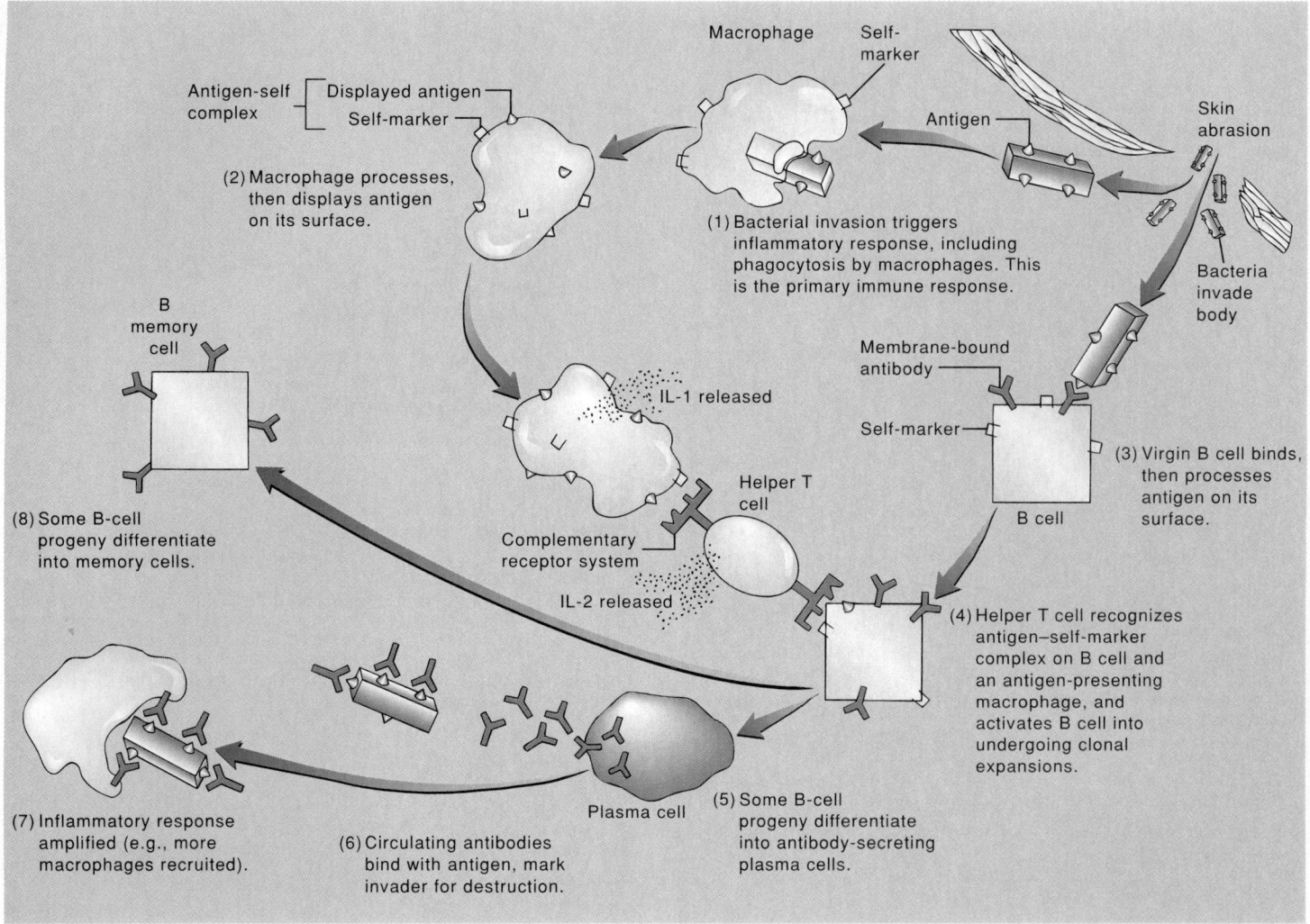

FIGURE 36.14

Cell-Mediated Immune Response. Helper T cells activate B cells to differentiate into plasma cells that produce antibodies. Notice that different cells are involved: macrophages, helper T cells, and B cells. It is the interaction of these three cells that finally causes B cells to differentiate into antibody-producing plasma cells. The self-markers consist of the major histocompatibility complex.

When the macrophage reacts with a helper T cell, it releases interleukin-1 (IL-1). Interleukin-1 stimulates other helper T cells to secrete interleukin-2 (IL-2), which stimulates their growth and cell division. Some of the interleukin-2 produced by helper T cells acts on sensitized B cells. Sensitized B cells are ones that have recognized and processed the antigen onto their plasma membrane alongside their self-recognition marker (figure 36.14). These stimulated B cells mature and divide into differentiated plasma cells.

Primary and Secondary Immune Responses: Immunological Memory

The **primary immune response** is the response an animal generates during its first encounter with an antigen. During this response, the antigen disappears from the blood because it is either bound to antibody and/or phagocytized by macrophages.

Most of the B cells that are producing the antibodies also die. However, if the same antigen enters the body a second time, a **secondary immune response** is mounted that is faster and more extensive than the primary response (figure 36.15). This rapid response occurs because the immune system has stored a "memory" of the antigen: some of the original B cells did not die but differentiated into **memory cells** (*see figure 36.14*) that will remain in the body for life. Memory cells from B-cell clones continually expose antibodies on their plasma-membrane surface. If the antigen invades the body again, these memory cells rapidly produce large numbers of antibody-secreting B cells.

Evolution of the Vertebrate Immune System

The evolution of the immune system in vertebrates parallels that of the lymphatic system. Jawless vertebrates (cyclostomes), cartilaginous fishes (chondrichthians), and bony fishes (osteichthians)

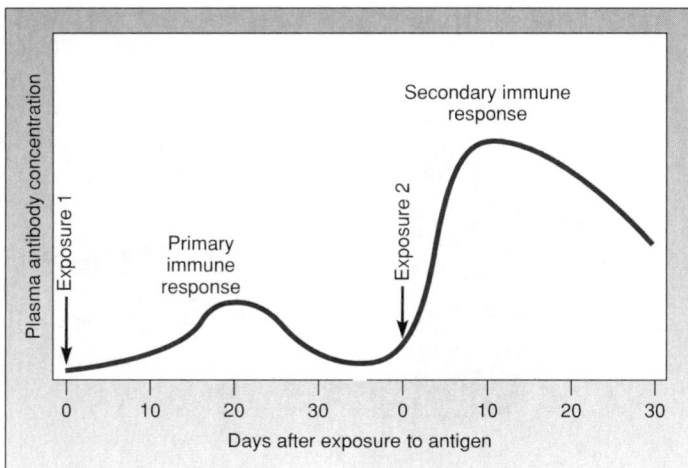

Figure 36.15

Primary and Secondary Immune Responses: Immunological Memory. The antibody concentration increases more rapidly during a secondary immune response than during a primary response. Note that the secondary response peaks in 10 days, whereas the primary response does not peak for about 20 days. The magnitude (plasma antibody concentration) of the secondary response is also many times that of the primary response.

have networks of small, blind vessels that accompany the veins and help the capillaries drain the tissues. These vessels developed from veins and empty into them at frequent intervals. They represent the earliest stage in the evolution of the lymphatic system; however, no lymph nodes or lymphocytes are present.

Teleosts and tetrapods have independently evolved lymphatic systems in which lymphatic capillaries help drain most of the tissues of the body. Lymph nodes and lymphocytes occur in a few aquatic birds and are abundant in mammals. Additional aggregations of lymphatic tissue, T cells, and immunoglobulins evolved in birds and mammals, such as the distinct bursa of Fabricius in birds and the thymus gland in mammals (see table 36.1). Both of these organs are particularly large and active in late fetal and young individuals but gradually regress as the animal matures. They play a functional role in the processing of lymphocytes and the development of immunological maturity.

Stop and Ask Yourself

8. What is the relationship between the lymphatic and immune systems?
9. What is a self-recognition marker? How does it function?
10. How does an antibody differ from an antigen?
11. What is the difference between an antibody-mediated immune response and a cell-mediated immune response?
12. How do NK cells function?
13. How does immunological memory occur?

Gas Exchange

To take advantage of the rich source of energy represented by the organic matter on our planet, animals must solve two practical problems. First, they must break down and digest the organic matter so that it can enter the cells that are to metabolize it (this digestive process is described in the next chapter). Second, they must provide the cells with both an adequate supply of oxygen required for aerobic respiration and a way of eliminating the carbon dioxide produced by this type of respiration. This process of gas exchange with the environment, also called external respiration, is the subject of the rest of this chapter.

Respiratory Surfaces

Protists and animals use five main types of respiratory systems (surfaces) to accomplish respiration: simple diffusion across plasma membranes, tracheae, cutaneous (integument or body surface) exchange, gills, and lungs. Each of these surfaces will now be discussed.

Invertebrate Respiratory Systems

In single-celled protists, such as protozoa, **diffusion** across the plasma membrane is all that is needed to move gases into and out of the organism (figure 36.16a). Some multicellular invertebrates (figure 36.16b,c) either have very flat bodies (e.g., flatworms) in which all body cells are relatively close to the body surface or are thin-walled and hollow (e.g., Hydra). Again, diffusion is sufficient to move gases into and out of the animal.

Other invertebrates, such as earthworms, that live in moist environments use **integumentary exchange.** Earthworms have capillary networks just under their integument, and they exchange gases with the air spaces among soil particles (see figure 22.14).

Most aquatic invertebrates carry out gas exchange with **gills.** The simplest gills are small, scattered projections of the skin, such as the gills of starfishes. Other aquatic invertebrates have their gas exchange structures in more restricted areas. For example, marine and annelid worms have prominent lateral projections called parapodia (see figure 22.7) that are richly supplied with blood vessels and function as gills.

Crustaceans and molluscs have gills that are compact and protected with hard covering devices (see figure 21.11). Such gills are finely divided into highly branched structures to maximize the area for gas exchange.

Some terrestrial invertebrates (e.g., insects, centipedes, and some mites, ticks, and spiders) have **tracheal systems** consisting of highly branched chitin-lined tubes called tracheae (figure 36.17a). Tracheae open to the outside of the body through spiracles, which are usually provided with some kind of closure device to prevent excessive water loss. Spiracles lead to tracheal trunks that branch, eventually giving rise to smaller branches called tracheoles, whose blind ends lie close to all cells of the body. Since no cells are more than 2 or 3 μm from a tracheole (figure 36.17b), gases move between the tracheole

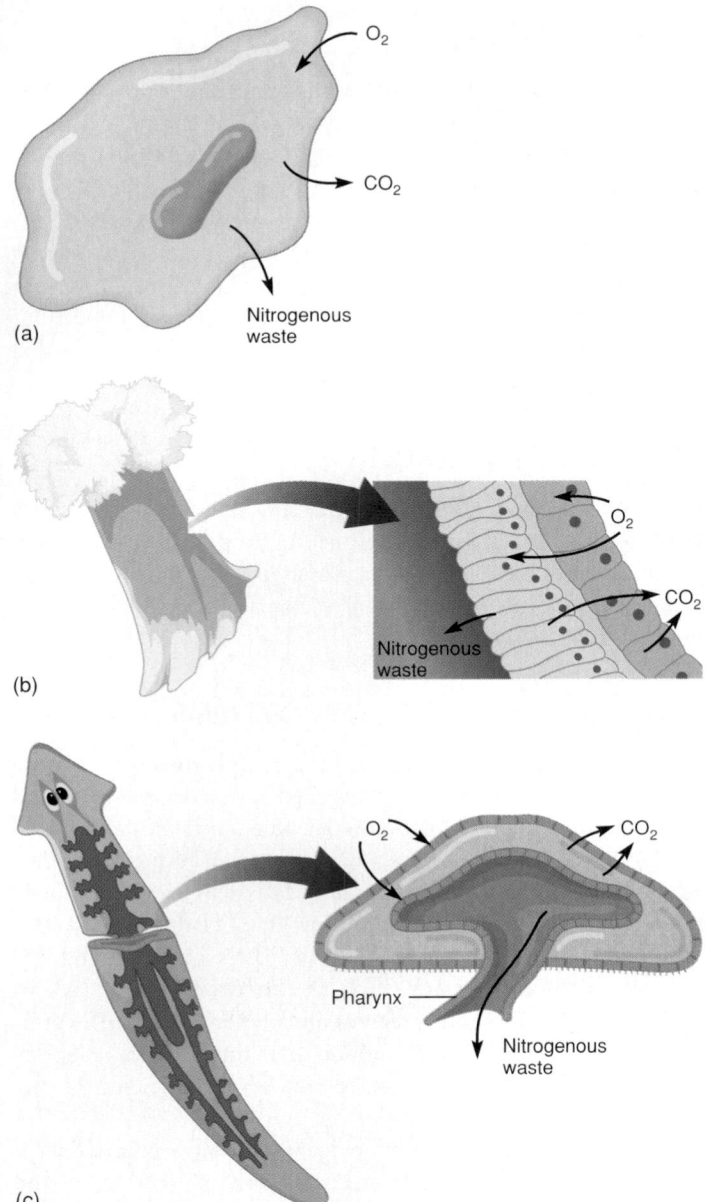

FIGURE 36.16

Invertebrate Respiration: Diffusion through Body Surfaces. The cells of small organisms such as protozoa (*a*), cnidarians (*b*), and flatworms (*c*) maintain close enough contact with the environment that they have no need for a respiratory system. Diffusion is all that is needed to move gases, as well as waste products, into and out of these organisms.

and the tissues of the body by diffusion. Most insects have ventilating mechanisms that move air into and out of the trachea. For example, alternate compression and expansion of the large tracheal trunks by contracting flight muscles of insects ventilate the tracheae.

Arachnids possess tracheae, book lungs, or both. **Book lungs** are paired invaginations of the ventral body wall that are folded into a series of leaflike lamellae (figure 36.18). Air enters the book lung through a slitlike opening called a spiracle and

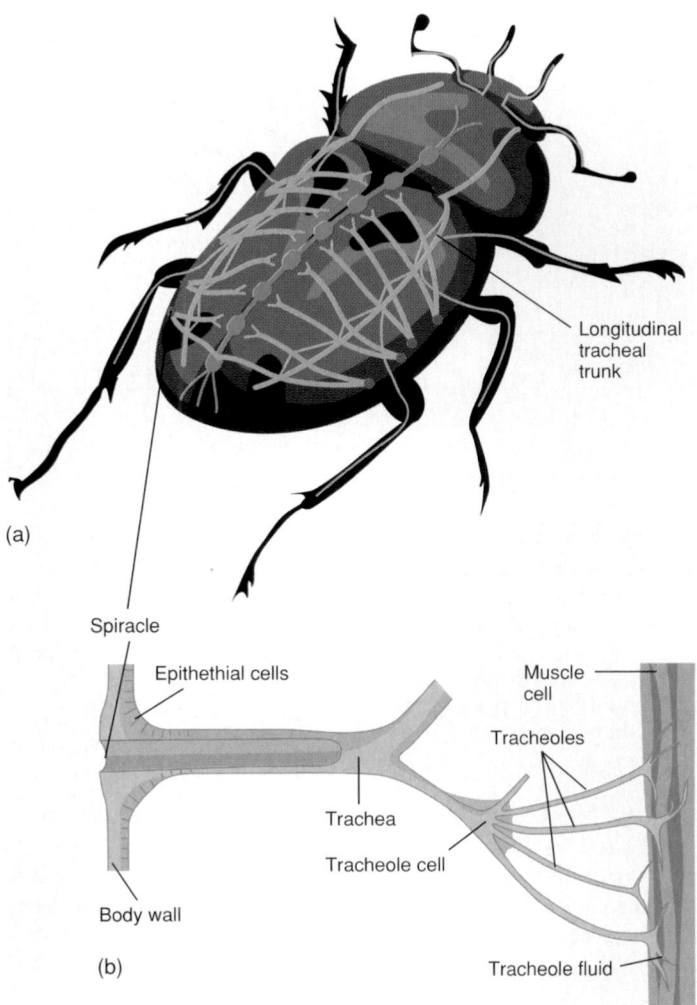

FIGURE 36.17

Invertebrate Respiration: A Tracheal System. (*a*) The tracheal system of an insect showing the major tracheal trunks. (*b*) Tracheoles end at cells, and the terminal portions of tracheoles are fluid filled. The fluid acts as a solvent for gases.

circulates between lamellae. Diffusion of respiratory gases occurs between the blood moving along the lamellae and the air in the air chamber. Some ventilation also results from the contraction of a muscle attached to the dorsal side of the air chamber. This contraction dilates the chamber and opens the spiracle, but most gas movement is still by diffusion.

The only other major group of terrestrial invertebrates whose members have distinct air-breathing structures is the molluscan subclass Pulmonata—the land snails and slugs. ⑤ The gas exchange structure in these animals is a **pulmonate lung** that opens to the outside via a pore called a **pneumostome** (Gr. *pneumo,* breath + *stoma,* mouth; figure 36.19). This lung is derived from a feature common to molluscs in general, the mantle cavity, which in other molluscs houses the gills and other organs. Some of the more primitive pulmonate snails are aquatic (fresh water). During submergence, the pneumostome is closed. When the snail comes to the surface to breathe air, the

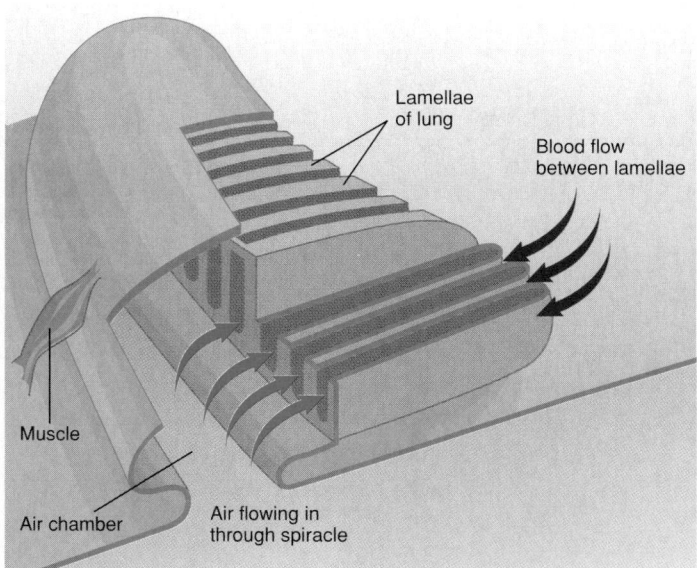

Figure 36.18

Invertebrate Respiration: A Book Lung. Structure of an arachnid (spider) book lung. Air enters through a spiracle into the air chamber by diffusion and ventilation due to muscle contraction. Air diffuses from the air chamber into the lamellar spaces; hemolymph circulates through the blood lamellar spaces that alternate with air lamellar spaces. The lamellae are held apart by small peglike surface projections. Thus, due to this structural arrangement, air and blood move on opposite sides of a lamella (arrows) in a countercurrent flow, allowing the exchange of respiratory gases by diffusion.

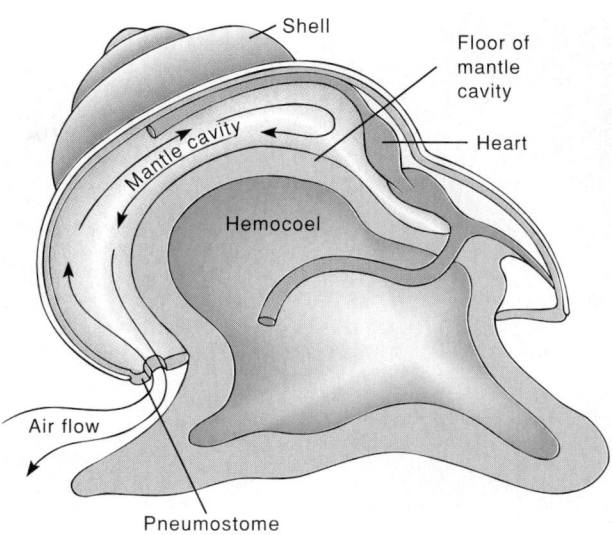

Figure 36.19

Invertebrate Respiration: The Pulmonate Lung. The mantle cavity in this drawing of the pulmonate snail, *Lymnaea*, is highly vascularized and functions as a lung. Downward movement of the floor of the cavity increases the cavity's volume, so that air is drawn into the mantle cavity for respiration. The air is then expelled by decreasing the volume of the mantle cavity. Flow of air into and out of the lung occurs through a single pore called the pneumostome.

pneumostome opens. Most of the higher pulmonates are terrestrial and rely on their lungs for gas exchange. The lung may be ventilated by arching and then flattening the body, but most gas exchange occurs by diffusion through the pneumostome, which is open most of the time.

Vertebrate Respiratory Systems

Aquatic vertebrates (fish, amphibians, and some reptiles) rely on one, or a combination of, the following surfaces for gas exchange: the cutaneous body surface, external filamentous gills, and internal lamellar gills. **Bimodal breathing** is the ability of an organism to exchange respiratory gases simultaneously with both air and water. A bimodal organism (e.g., some salamanders, crabs, barnacles, bivalve molluscs, and fishes [blennies] uses gills for water breathing and lungs for air breathing. However, it should be remembered that there is always some cutaneous gas exchange, and that some bimodal breathers are trimodal [skin, gills, and lungs]). Bimodal breathing was an important respiratory adaptation present in animals that made possible the evolutionary transition between aquatic and terrestrial habitats. The transition from water to air-breathing was accompanied by fundamental changes in the structure and function of the respiratory organs. Gills are replaced in air-breathing terrestrial vertebrates (other reptiles, birds, and mammals) by lungs. These vertebrate surfaces and transitions are now discussed.

Cutaneous Exchange

Cutaneous (respiration) or **integumentary exchange** is also used to supplement gas exchange by some vertebrates that have lungs or gills, such as some aquatic turtles, salamanders with lungs, snakes, fishes, and mammals. However, cutaneous exchange is most highly developed in frogs, toads, lungless salamanders, and newts.

Amphibian skin has the simplest structure of all the major vertebrate respiratory organs (*see figure 32.6*). In frogs, a uniform capillary network lies in a plane directly beneath the epidermis. This vascular arrangement facilitates gas exchange between the capillary bed and the environment by both diffusion and convection. To facilitate this exchange, amphibian skin is kept moist and is protected from injury by a slimy, mucous layer.   ⑥   Some amphibians obtain about 25% or more of their oxygen by this exchange, and the lungless salamanders carry out all of their gas exchange through the skin and buccal-pharyngeal region.

Gills

Gills are respiratory organs that have either a thin, moist, vascularized layer of epidermis to permit gas exchange across thin gill membranes, or a very thin layer of epidermis over highly vascularized dermis. Larval forms of a few fishes and amphibians have external gills projecting from their body (figure 36.20). Adult fishes have internal gills.

Gas exchange across internal gill surfaces is extremely efficient (figure 36.21). It occurs as blood and water move in opposite

Figure 36.20

Vertebrate Respiration: External Gills. This axolotl (*Ambystoma tigrinum*) has elaborate external gills that have a large surface for exchanging gases with the water.

directions on either side of the lamellar epithelium. For example, the water that passes over a gill first encounters vessels that are transporting blood with a low oxygen concentration into the body. Because the concentration (partial pressure) of the oxygen is lower in the blood than in the water, oxygen diffuses into the blood. Water then passes over the vessels carrying blood relatively high in oxygen from deep within the body. More oxygen diffuses inward, because this blood still has less oxygen than the surrounding water. Carbon dioxide also diffuses into the water because its concentration (pressure) is higher in the blood than in the water. This countercurrent exchange mechanism provides very efficient gas exchange by maintaining a concentration gradient between the blood and water over the length of the capillary bed.

LUNGS

A **lung** is an internal sac-shaped respiratory organ. The typical lung of a terrestrial vertebrate comprises one or more internal blind pouches into which air is either drawn or forced. The respiratory epithelium of lungs is thin, well vascularized, and divided into a large number of small units, which greatly increase the surface area for gaseous exchange between the lung air and the blood. This blind-pouch construction, however, limits the efficiency with which oxygen and carbon dioxide are exchanged with the atmosphere because only a portion of the lung air is ever replaced with any one breath. Birds are an exception in that they have very efficient lungs with a one-way pass-through system (*see figure 30.11*). For example, a mammal removes approximately 25% of the oxygen from air with each breath, whereas a bird removes approximately 90%.

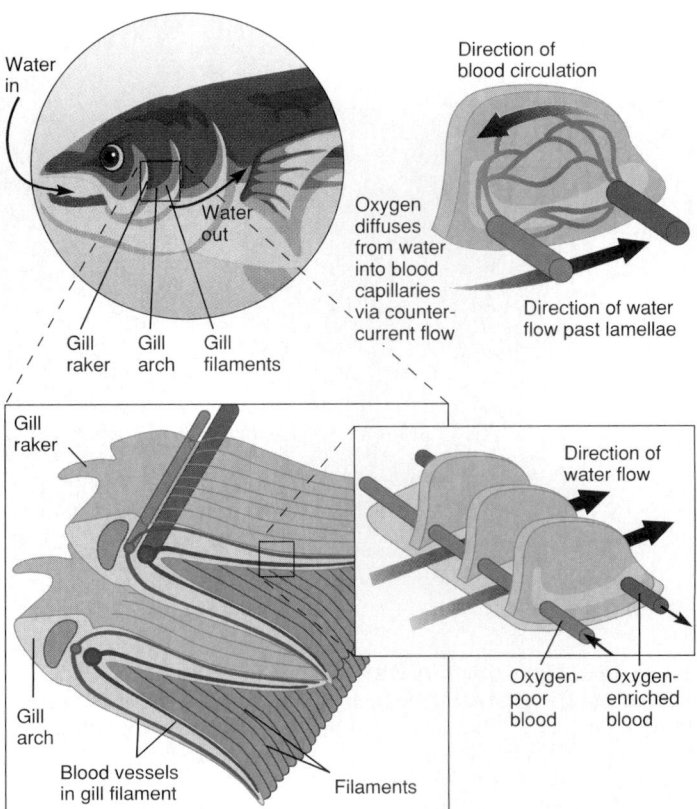

Figure 36.21

Vertebrate Respiration: Internal Gills. When the protective operculum is removed, the feathery internal gills of this bony fish are visible. Each side of the head has four gill arches, and each arch consists of many filaments. A filament houses capillaries within lamellae. Note that the direction of water flow opposes that of blood flow. This countercurrent flow allows the maximal amount of oxygen to be extracted from the water.

The evolution of the vertebrate lung is related to the evolution of the swim bladder. The swim bladder is an air sac located dorsal to the digestive tract in the body of many modern fishes. Evidence indicates that both lungs and swim bladder evolved from a lunglike structure present in primitive fishes that were ancestors of both present-day fishes and tetrapods (amphibians, reptiles, birds, and mammals). These ancestral fishes probably had a ventral sac attached to their pharynx (*see figure 27.16*). This sac may have served as a supplementary gas-exchange organ when the fishes could not obtain enough oxygen through their gills (e.g., in stagnant or oxygen-depleted water). By swimming to the surface and gulping air into this sac, gas exchange could take place through its wall.

Further evolution of this blind sac proceeded in two different directions (*see figure 27.15*). One adaptation is seen in the majority of modern bony fishes, where the swim bladder lies dorsal to the digestive tract. The other adaptation is in the form of the lungs, which are ventral to the digestive tract. Ventral lungs are found in a few present-day fishes and in the tetrapods. The evolution of the

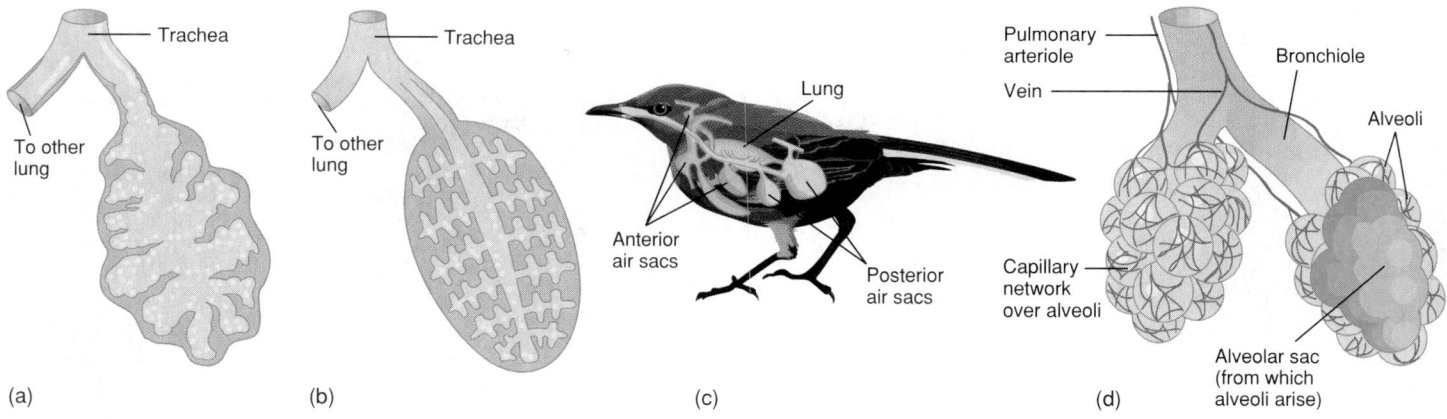

FIGURE 36.22

Vertebrate Respiration: Lungs. The evolution of the vertebrate lung showing the increased surface area from (*a*) amphibians and (*b*) reptiles to (*c*) birds and (*d*) mammals. This evolution has paralleled the evolution of large body size and higher metabolic rates.

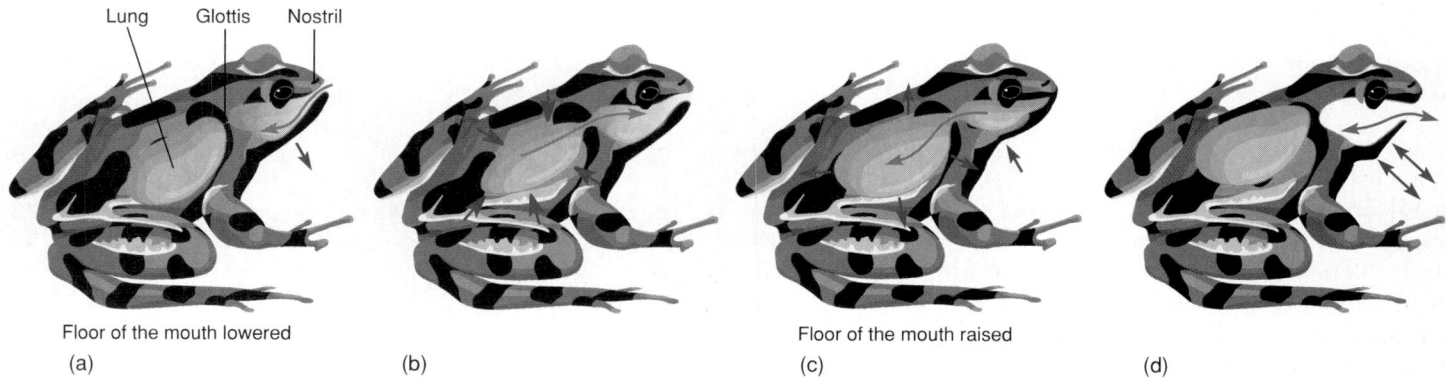

FIGURE 36.23

Ventilation in Amphibians. The positive pressure pumping mechanism in a frog (*Rana*). The breathing cycle has several stages. (*a*) Air is taken into the mouth and pharynx by lowering the floor of the mouth. Notice that the glottis is closed. (*b*) The glottis is then opened, and air is permitted to escape from the lungs, passing over the air that was just taken in. (*c*) With the nostrils and mouth firmly shut, the floor of the mouth is raised. This positive pressure forces air into the lungs. (*d*) With the glottis closed, fresh oxygenated air can again be brought into the mouth and pharynx. Some gas exchange occurs in the mouth cavity (buccopharyngeal respiration), and frogs may repeat this "mouth breathing" movement several times before ventilating the lungs again.

structurally complex lung (figure 36.22) has paralleled the evolution of the large body sizes and high metabolic rates found in endothermic vertebrates (birds and mammals), which necessitated an increase in lung surface area for gas exchange, compared to the smaller body size and lower metabolic rates found in the ectothermic vertebrates.

LUNG VENTILATION

External respiration is based on several physiological principles that apply to all air-breathing animals that have lungs:

1. Air moves by bulk flow into and out of the lungs in the process called ventilation.
2. Oxygen and carbon dioxide diffuse across the respiratory surface of the lung tissue from pulmonary capillaries.

3. At systemic capillaries, oxygen and carbon dioxide diffuse between the blood and interstitial fluid in response to concentration gradients.
4. Oxygen and carbon dioxide diffuse between the interstitial fluid and body cells.

Utilizing these physiological principles, two different mechanisms for lung ventilation are found among vertebrate animals. Amphibians and some reptiles use a positive pressure pumping mechanism. They push air into their lungs. Most reptiles and all birds and mammals, however, use a negative pressure system; that is, they inhale (breathe in) by suction.

The positive pressure pumping mechanism of an amphibian is illustrated in figure 36.23. The muscles of the mouth and pharynx create a positive pressure to force air into the lungs.

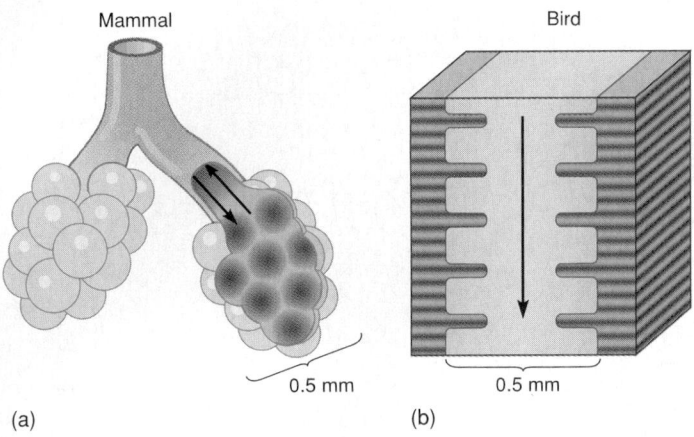

Figure 36.24

Gas Exchange Surfaces in Mammals and Birds. (*a*) The gas exchange surfaces in a mammal's lung are in saclike alveoli. Ventilation is by an ebb and flow mechanism (arrows), and the replacement of air inside the alveoli can never be complete. (*b*) The finest passages in a bird lung are tubes that are open on both ends. Ventilation is by one-way flow (arrow), and there is continual complete replacement of air in the tubes.

Lung ventilation occurs in most reptiles (e.g., snakes, lizards, crocodilians) by expanding the body cavity with a posterior movement of the ribs. This expansion decreases pressure in the lungs and air is drawn into the lungs. Air is expelled by the elastic recoil of the lungs and the movement of the ribs and body wall, which compress the lungs. The ribs of turtles are a part of the shell (*see figure 29.5*); thus, movements of the body wall to which they are attached are impossible. Turtles exhale by contracting muscles that force the viscera upward, compressing the lungs. They inhale by contracting muscles that increase the volume of the visceral cavity, creating negative pressure to draw air into the lungs.

Because of high metabolic rates associated with flight, birds have a greater rate of oxygen consumption than any other vertebrate. Birds also use a negative pressure system to move air into and out of their lungs in an ebb and flow breathing pattern similar to mammals. However, birds also have a special lung ventilation mechanism that permits one-way flow over the surfaces where gas exchange occurs. This mechanism makes birds' lungs more efficient than mammals' lungs (figure 36.24). This is why bird lungs are smaller than the lungs of mammals of comparable body size. The lungs of birds have tunnellike passages called parabronchi, which lead to air capillaries in which gas exchange occurs, and the one-way air flow through them is made possible by the arrangement and functioning of a system of air sacs. These air sacs ramify throughout the body cavity, are collapsible, and they open and close as a result of muscle contractions around them. Inhaled air bypasses the lungs and enters the abdominal (posterior) air sacs. It then passes through the lungs into the thoracic (anterior) air sacs. Finally, air is exhaled from the thoracic air sacs. This whole process requires two complete breathing cycles (figure 36.25).

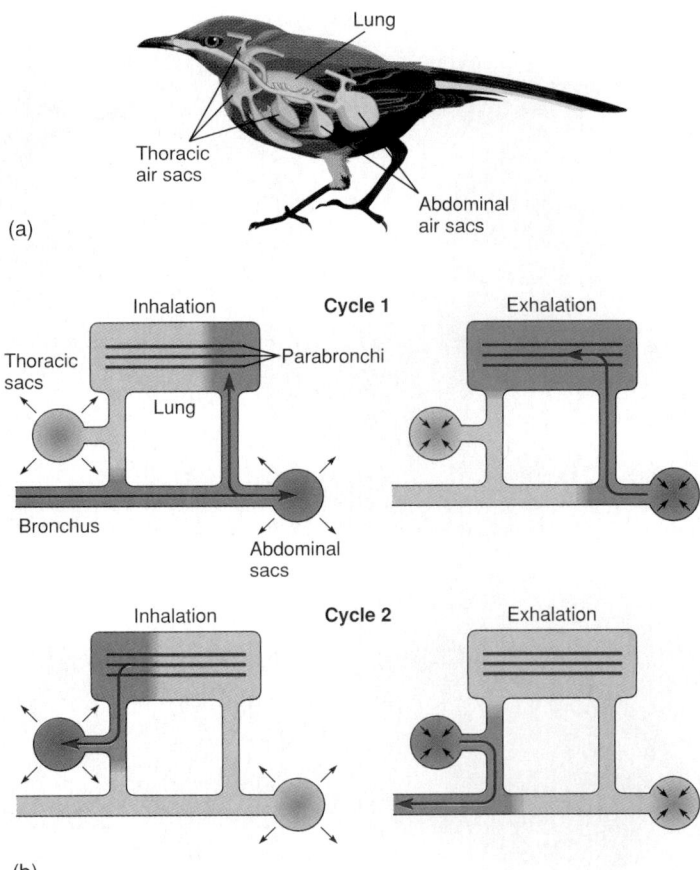

Figure 36.25

Gas Exchange Mechanism in Birds. (*a*) Birds have a number of large air sacs; some of them (abdominal) are posterior to the small pair of lungs, and others (thoracic) are anterior to the lungs. The main bronchus (air passageway) that runs through each lung has connections to air sacs, as well as to the lung. The schematic diagrams below the bird show these structures. Abdominal and thoracic air sacs are sketched as single functional units to clarify their relationship to the lung and bronchus. (*b*) The flow of air through the bird respiratory system. The darker blue portion in each diagram represents the volume of a single inhalation and distinguishes it from the remainder of the air in the system. Two full breathing cycles are needed to move the volume of gas taken in during a single inhalation through the entire system and out of the body. This system is associated with one-way flow through the gas exchange surfaces in the lungs. Arrows indicate expansion and contraction of air sacs.

HUMAN RESPIRATORY SYSTEM

The structure and function of external respiration in humans is typical of mammals. As a result, the human will be used to describe those principles that apply to all air-breathing mammals.

Air-Conducting Portion

The various organs of the human respiratory system are shown in figure 36.26. Air normally enters and leaves this system

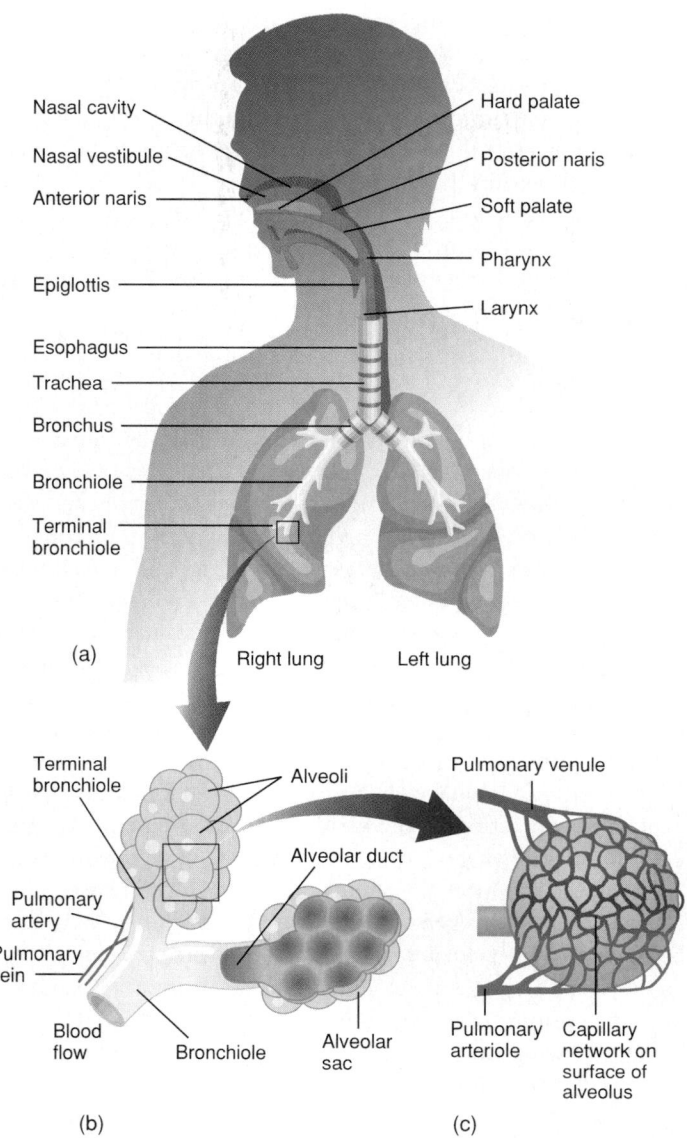

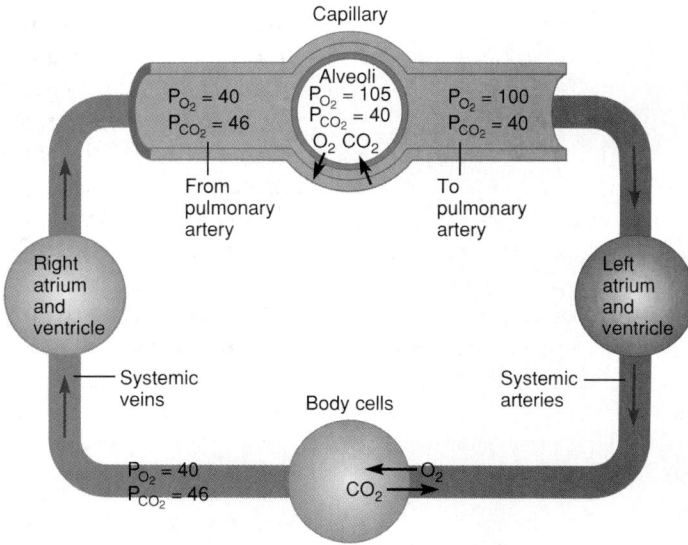

FIGURE 36.27

Gas Exchange between the Lungs and Tissues. Gases diffuse according to partial pressure (P) differences, as indicated by the numbers and arrows.

FIGURE 36.26

Organs of the Human Respiratory System. (*a*) The basic anatomy of the respiratory system. (*b,c*) The respiratory tubes end in minute alveoli, each of which is surrounded by an extensive capillary network.

through either nasal or oral cavities. From these cavities, air moves into the pharynx, which is a common area for both the respiratory and digestive tracts. The pharynx connects with the larynx (voice box) and with the esophagus that leads to the stomach. The epiglottis is a flap of cartilage that allows air to enter the trachea when breathing. It covers the trachea when swallowing to prevent food or water from entering.

During inhalation, air from the larynx moves into the trachea (windpipe), which branches into a right and left bronchus (pl., bronchi). After each bronchus enters the lungs, it branches into smaller tubes called bronchioles, then even smaller tubes called terminal bronchioles, and finally, respiratory bronchioles that connect to the gas exchange portion of the respiratory system.

Gas-Exchange Portion

The respiratory bronchioles have small tubes called alveolar ducts leading from them that connect to grapelike outpouchings from their walls called **alveoli** (s., alveolus; L. *alveus*, hollow) (figure 36.26*b*). The alveoli are clustered together to form an alveolar sac. Surrounding the alveoli are many capillaries (figure 36.26*c*). Alveoli are the functional units of the lungs (gas exchange portion) because it is here that oxygen moves into the blood and carbon dioxide moves from the blood into the alveoli. Passive diffusion, driven by a partial pressure gradient, is enough to move oxygen across the respiratory surface and into the blood, and to move carbon dioxide from the blood into the alveoli (figure 36.27). Collectively, the alveoli provide a large surface area for gas exchange. To illustrate this important point, if the alveolar epithelium of a human were removed from the lungs and put into a single layer of cells side by side, the cells would cover the area of a tennis court.

Ventilation

Breathing (also called pulmonary ventilation) has two phases: inhalation, the intake of air, and exhalation, the outflow of air. These air movements result from the rhythmic increases and decreases in the volume of the thoracic cavity. It is these changes in thoracic volume that lead to reversals in the pressure gradients between the lungs and the atmosphere; gases in the respiratory system follow these gradients. The mechanism of inhalation operates in the following way (figure 36.28):

1. Several sets of muscles contract, the main ones being the diaphragm and intercostal muscles. The intercostal muscles

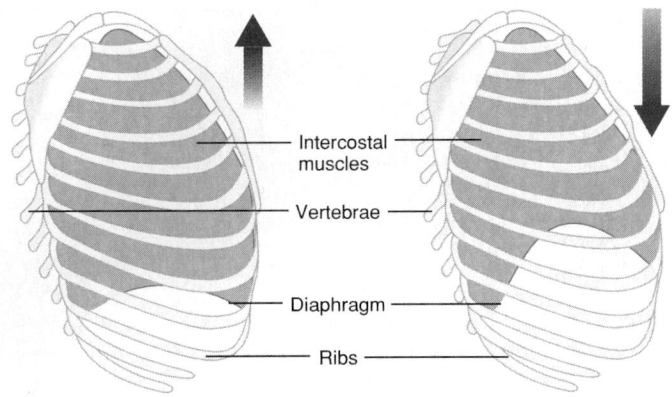

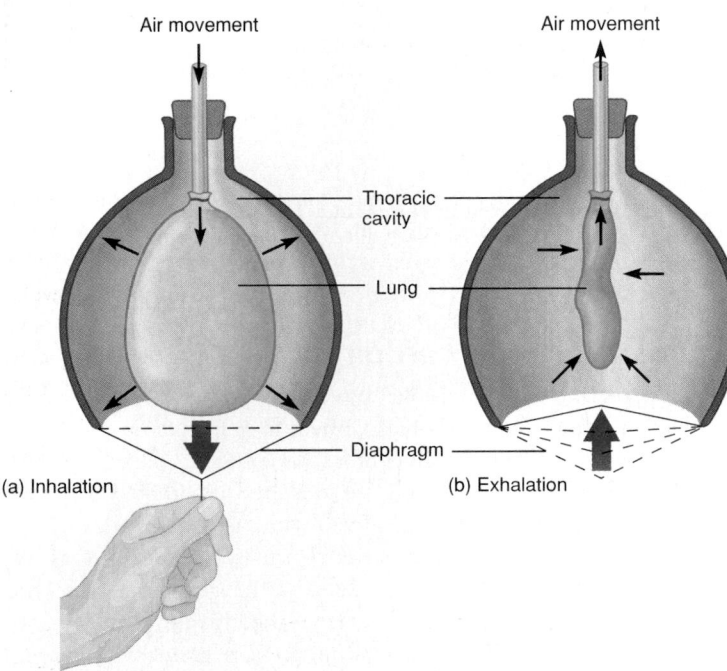

FIGURE 36.28

Ventilation of Human Lungs as an Example of Breathing in Mammals. (*a*) During inhalation, muscle contractions lift the ribs up and out (upper diagram arrows) and lower the diaphragm. These movements increase the size of the thoracic cavity and decrease the pressure around the lungs. This negative pressure causes more air to enter the lungs. (*b*) Exhalation follows the relaxation of the rib cage and diaphragm muscles, as the increased pressure forces the air out of the lungs. The arrows indicate the direction pressure changes take in the thoracic (lower diagrams) cavity during inhalation and exhalation.

stretch from rib to rib, and when they contract, they pull the ribs closer together, causing the enlargement of the thoracic cavity.

2. The thoracic cavity is enlarged further when the diaphragm contracts and flattens.
3. The increased size of the thoracic cavity causes the pressure in the cavity to drop below the atmospheric pressure, allowing air to rush into the lungs, and they inflate.

During ordinary exhalation, the expulsion of air from the lungs occurs in the following way:

1. The intercostal muscles and the diaphragm relax, allowing the thoracic cavity to return to its original, smaller size, and increasing the pressure in the thoracic cavity.
2. Abdominal muscles contract, pushing the abdominal organs against the diaphragm, further increasing the pressure within the thoracic cavity.
3. The above action causes the elastic lungs to contract and compress the air in the alveoli. With this compression, the alveolar pressure becomes greater than atmospheric pressure causing air to be expelled (exhaled) from the lungs.

GAS TRANSPORT

As noted in the above discussion, oxygen must be transported from the sites of environmental gas exchange to the various cells of an animal's body. Various systems (e.g., tracheae, cutaneous exchange, gills, lungs) help accomplish this transport.

As animals acquired increased body size and higher metabolic rates, simple diffusion became increasingly inadequate as a means of delivering oxygen to the tissues. Consequently, in most animals that have high metabolic rates and tissues more than a few millimeters from respiratory surfaces, there is a specialized circulatory system (*see figure 36.1*) for circulating body fluids to aid in the internal distribution of oxygen (box 36.1). In general, more active animals have an increased demand for oxygen. However, simply creating a convection of a water-based body fluid does not in itself guarantee internal transport of sufficient quantities of oxygen to meet this increased demand. The reason is the low solubility of oxygen in water-based body fluids. Thus, fluid-borne respiratory pigments specialized for reversibly binding large quantities of oxygen evolved in most phyla. Respiratory pigments help the various transport systems satisfy this increased oxygen demand. In addition to oxygen transport, respiratory pigments may also function in short-term oxygen storage.

Respiratory pigments are organic compounds that have either metallic copper or iron that bind oxygen. These pigments may be in solution within the blood or body fluids, or they may be in specific blood cells. In general, the pigments respond to a high oxygen concentration by combining with oxygen and to low oxygen concentrations by releasing oxygen. The four most common respiratory pigments are hemoglobin, hemocyanin, hemerythrin, and chlorocruorin.

Hemoglobin is a reddish pigment that contains iron as the oxygen-binding metal. It is the most common respiratory pigment in animals, being found in a variety of invertebrates (e.g., protozoa, platyhelminths, nemerteans, nematodes, annelids, crustaceans, some insects and molluscs), and with the exception of a few fishes, in all vertebrates. This wide distribution suggests that hemoglobin evolved very early in the history of animal life. Hemoglobin may be carried within red blood cells (erythrocytes; *see figure 36.5a*) or simply dissolved in the blood or coelomic fluid.

Hemocyanin is the most commonly occurring respiratory pigment in molluscs and certain crustaceans. Hemocyanin contains metallic copper, has a bluish color when

36.1   HOW DEEP-DIVING MARINE MAMMALS ADAPT TO OXYGEN-POOR ENVIRONMENTS

Deep-diving marine animals, such as the sperm whale, have evolved several mechanisms for remaining submerged for up to 1 hour. Most have a large number of red blood cells per milliliter of blood, large quantities of the oxygen-binding pigment **myoglobin** in their muscles, and hemoglobin that releases oxygen much more easily than other mammalian hemoglobin.

The **diving reflex** is an evolutionary adaptation that occurs in those mammals that dive (e.g., whales) downward in the sea. In this reflex, blood is shunted away from most regions of the body during a dive, and diverted mainly to the heart, brain, and skeletal muscles. Also, the skeletal muscles can incur an oxygen debt; they can

continue to contract even after all oxygen is depleted building up lactic acid. The ATP energy for contraction comes from glycolysis, which forms lactic acid that accumulates in the tissues. When the whale surfaces, it quickly exhales its moist, oxygen-poor air, which condenses to form the "spout." A large amount of carbon dioxide is blown off in the "spout," and oxygen quickly combines with hemoglobin passing through the lungs.

The second part of the diving reflex is the slowing of the heart rate (called bradycardia). This slowing is an adaptation to ensure less rapid depletion of oxygen until the whale can return to the air for more oxygen.

---

oxygenated, and always occurs dissolved in hemolymph. Unlike most hemoglobin, hemocyanin tends to release oxygen easily and provide a ready source of oxygen to the tissues as long as there are relatively high concentrations of oxygen in the environment.

Hemerythrin contains iron and is pink when oxygenated. It is found in nucleated cells rather than free in body fluids or hemolymph. Hemerythrin is found in sipunculan, priapulids, in a few brachiopods, and some polychaetes.

Chlorocruorin also contains iron but is green when associated with low concentrations of oxygen and bright red when associated with high concentrations of oxygen. Chlorocruorin occurs in several families of polychaete worms.

As just discussed, respiratory pigments raise the oxygen-carrying capacity of body fluids far above what would be achieved by simple transport in a dissolved state. Similarly, carbon dioxide concentrations in animal body fluids (and in seawater as well) are much higher than would be expected strictly on the basis of its solubility. The reason for this increased transport lies in the fact that in addition to being transported bound to hemoglobin and in the dissolved state, some carbon dioxide is transported in the form of carbonic acid (H_2CO_3) and the bicarbonate ion (HCO_3^-) in a series of reversible reactions:

$$CO_2 + H_2O \rightleftharpoons H_2CO_3 \rightleftharpoons H^+ + HCO_3^-$$

Thus, by "tying up" carbon dioxide in other forms, the concentration of CO_2 in solution is lowered, thus raising the overall carrying capacity of a body fluid such as blood.

From an evolutionary perspective, there seems to be no obvious phylogenetic reason for the occurrence of these pigments among various taxa. Their sporadic distribution suggests that some of them may have evolved more than once, through parallel evolution. Interestingly, respiratory pigments are rare in the successful insects. The general absence of respiratory pigments among most insects reflects the fact that most of them do not use blood as a medium for gas transport, but employ extensive tracheal systems to carry gases directly to the tissues (*see figure 36.16*). In those insects that do not have well developed trachea, oxygen is simply carried in solution in the hemolymph.

Stop and Ask Yourself

14. What are the five types of respiratory surfaces animals use to accomplish external respiration?

15. How does cutaneous exchange accomplish respiration? Gills? Lungs?

16. What different parts comprise the air-conducting portion of the mammalian respiratory system?

17. Why are alveoli called the functional units of the respiratory system in mammals?

18. What are four respiratory pigments, and where would you find each one?

SUMMARY

1. Any system of moving fluids that reduces the functional diffusion distance that nutrients, wastes, and gases must transverse may be referred to as an internal transport system or circulatory system.

2. There are two basic types of circulatory systems: open and closed. Open systems generally circulate hemolymph and closed systems circulate blood.

3. Blood is a type of connective tissue made up of blood cells (red blood cells and white blood cells), plasma, and platelets.

4. The heart pumps blood through a series of vessels in the following order: arteries, arterioles, capillaries, venules, veins, and back to the heart.

5. The action of the heart consists of cyclic contraction (systole) and relaxation (diastole). It is the systolic contraction that generates blood pressure that forces blood through the closed system of vessels.

6. The lymphatic system consists of one-way vessels that help return fluid and protein to the circulatory system.

7. The vertebrate body uses nonspecific and specific immune responses to protect itself against the continuous onslaught of microorganisms, foreign invaders, and cancer cells.

8. The nonspecific response includes biological barriers (inflammation and phagocytosis), chemical barriers (enzymatic action, interferons, the complement system), general barriers (fever), and physical barriers (skin, mucous membranes).

9. The specific immune response is due to the coordinated activity of specialized cells (macrophages and T cells) and antibodies produced by B cells.

10. Acquired immunity can be either active or passive.

11. An immunization is the deliberate provocation of memory lymphocytes by a vaccine.

12. In those animals that respire aerobically, a constant supply of oxygen is needed. The process of acquiring oxygen and eliminating carbon dioxide is called external respiration.

13. The exchange of oxygen and carbon dioxide occurs across respiratory surfaces. Such surfaces include gills, cutaneous surfaces, and lungs.

14. The air-conducting portion of the respiratory system of air-breathing vertebrates moves air into (inhalation) and out of (exhalation) this system. This process of air movement is called ventilation.

15. Exchange of oxygen and carbon dioxide occurs by diffusion from areas of higher to areas of lower concentrations.

16. Once in the blood, oxygen diffuses into red blood cells and is bound to hemoglobin for transportation to the tissues. Carbon dioxide is transported in the form of the bicarbonate ions, carbonic acid, and bound to hemoglobin.

17. Respiratory pigments are organic compounds that have either metallic copper or iron that bind oxygen. Examples include hemoglobin, hemocyanin, hemerythrin, and chlorocruorin.

SELECTED KEY TERMS

alveoli (p. 617)

antibodies (p. 609)

antigens (p. 609)

bimodal breathing (p. 613)

immunity (p. 607)

lung (p. 614)

lymph (p. 606)

plasma (p. 600)

serum (p. 600)

vaccine (p. 608)

CRITICAL THINKING QUESTIONS

1. Many invertebrates utilize the body cavity as a circulatory system. However, in humans the body cavity plays no role whatsoever in circulation. Why?

2. Describe the homeostatic functions of the vertebrate circulatory system. What functions are maintained at relative stability?

3. One of the most important goals of immunological research is developing techniques for transplanting skin between individuals. Why is this so important, and why is it such a difficult problem?

4. The area of an animal's respiratory surface is usually directly related to the body weight of the animal. What does this tell you about the mechanism of gas exchange?

5. How can seals and whales stay under water for long periods of time?

NUTRITION AND DIGESTION

Concepts

1. Animals are heterotrophic organisms that use food to supply both raw materials and energy. Nutrition includes all of those processes by which an animal takes in, digests, absorbs, stores, and uses food in order to meet its metabolic needs.
2. Digestion is the chemical and/or mechanical breakdown of food into particles that can be absorbed by the individual cells of an organism. Digestion can occur either inside a cell (intracellular), outside a cell (extracellular), or in both places.
3. Most animals must work for their nutrients. The number of specializations that have evolved for food procurement (feeding) and extracellular digestion are almost as numerous as the number of animal species. Some examples include continuous versus discontinuous feeding, suspension feeding, deposit feeding, herbivory, predation, surface nutrient absorption, and fluid feeding.
4. Intracellular digestion occurs in some invertebrates (e.g., in sponges); others (e.g., some cnidarians and molluscs) utilize both intracellular and extracellular digestion; and most higher invertebrates (e.g., insects) have evolved variations in extracellular digestion that allow them to exploit different food sources.
5. In primitive, multicellular animals, such as cnidarians, the gut is a blind (closed) sac called a gastrovascular cavity. It has only one opening that serves as both entrance and exit; thus, it is an incomplete digestive tract. The development of an anus and complete digestive tract in the aschelminths was an evolutionary breakthrough. The many variations of the basic plan of a complete digestive tract are correlated with different food-gathering mechanisms and diets.
6. Vertebrate digestive systems have evolved into assembly lines where food is first broken down mechanically and then chemically by digestive enzymes. The simple sugars, fats, triglycerides, amino acids, vitamins, and minerals that result are then taken into the circulatory systems for distribution throughout the animal's body and used in maintenance, growth, and energy production.

Would You Like to Know:

① why a light beer that is advertised as containing only 95 Calories per 12 oz actually contains 95,000 calories? (*p. 622*)

② why a high-fiber diet is good for you? (*p. 622*)

③ what mammals feed exclusively on blood? (*p. 628*)

④ why birds do not have teeth? (*p. 632*)

⑤ why some snakes have salivary glands that produce venoms? (*p. 632*)

⑥ why some birds eat pebbles or stones? (*p. 634*)

⑦ why some mice and rabbits eat some of their own feces? (*p. 636*)

⑧ why vomiting causes a burning sensation in our esophagus and mouth? (*p. 640*)

⑨ what causes "hunger pangs"? (*p. 640*)

These and other useful questions will be answered in this chapter.

This chapter contains evolutionary concepts, which are set off in this font.

Nutrition includes all of those processes by which an animal takes in, digests, absorbs, stores, and uses food (nutrients) in order to meet its metabolic needs. **Digestion** (L. *digestio*, from + *dis*, apart + *gerere*, to carry) is the chemical and/or mechanical breakdown of food into particles that can be absorbed by the individual cells of an animal. This chapter discusses animal nutrition, the different strategies animals use for consuming and using food, and various animal digestive systems.

EVOLUTION OF NUTRITION

Nutrients in the food an animal consumes provide the necessary chemicals for growth, maintenance, and energy production. Overall, the nutritional requirements of an animal are inversely related to its ability to synthesize molecules essential for life: the fewer such biosynthetic abilities an animal has, the more kinds of nutrients it must obtain from its environment. Green plants and photosynthetic protists have the fewest such nutritional requirements because they can synthesize all their own complex molecules from simpler inorganic substances; they are called **autotrophs** (Gr. *auto*, self + *trophe*, nourishing). Animals, fungi, and bacteria that are called **heterotrophs** (Gr. *heteros*, another or different + *trophe*, nourishing), cannot synthesize many of their own organic molecules and must obtain them by consuming other organisms or their products. Animals, such as rabbits, that subsist entirely on plant material are called **herbivores** (L. *herba*, plant + *vorare*, to eat). **Carnivores** (L. *caro*, flesh), such as hawks, are animals that eat only meat. **Omnivores** (L. *omnius*, all), such as humans, bears, raccoons, and pigs eat both plant and animal matter, and **insectivores,** such as bats, eat primarily arthropods.

    Much of animal evolution has been marked by losses in biosynthetic abilities. Once an animal routinely obtains essential, complex organic molecules in its diet, it can afford to lose the ability to synthesize those molecules. Moreover, the loss of this ability confers a selective advantage on the animal because the animal stops expending energy and resources to synthesize these molecules that are already in its diet. Thus, as the diet of animals became more varied, they tended to lose their abilities to synthesize such widely available molecules as some of the amino acids.

THE METABOLIC FATES OF NUTRIENTS IN HETEROTROPHS

The nutrients ingested by a heterotroph can be divided into macronutrients and micronutrients. **Macronutrients** are needed in large quantities and include the carbohydrates, lipids, and proteins. The **micronutrients** are needed in small quantities and include organic vitamins and inorganic minerals. Together, these nutrients make up the animal's dietary requirements. Besides these nutrients, animals require water.

CALORIES AND ENERGY

The energy value of food is measured in terms of calories or Calories. A **calorie** (L. *calor*, heat) is the amount of energy required to raise the temperature of 1 g of water 1° C. A calorie, with a small *c*, is also called a gram calorie. A **kilocalorie,** also known as a **Calorie** or kilogram calorie (kcal), is equal to 1,000 calories. In popular usage, we talk about calories but actually mean Calories, because the larger unit is more useful for measuring the energy value of food.   ① (If an advertisement says that a so-called light beer contains 95 calories per 12 oz, it really means 95,000 calories, 95 Calories, or 95 kcal.)

> **Stop and Ask Yourself**
>
> 1. How do autotrophs and heterotrophs differ?
> 2. What are some macronutrients? Micronutrients?
> 3. Why has much of animal evolution been marked by losses in biosynthetic abilities?
> 4. What is the difference between a calorie and a Calorie?

MACRONUTRIENTS

With a few notable exceptions, heterotrophs require organic molecules, such as carbohydrates, lipids, and proteins, in their diets. When these molecules are broken down by enzymes into their components, they can be used for energy production or as sources for the "building blocks" of life.

Carbohydrates: Carbon and Energy from Sugars and Starches

The major dietary source of energy for heterotrophs is complex carbohydrates (figure 37.1*a*). Most carbohydrates originally come from plant sources. This dietary need can be met by various polysaccharides, disaccharides, or any of a variety of simple sugars (monosaccharides). Carbohydrates also serve as a major carbon source for incorporation into important organic compounds. Many plants also supply cellulose, an indigestible polysaccharide, for humans and other animals (with the exception of herbivores). Cellulose is sometimes called dietary fiber.   ② It assists in the passage of food through the alimentary canal of mammals. Cellulose may also reduce the risk of cancer of the colon because mutagenic compounds that can occur during the storage of feces are fewer if fecal elimination is more frequent.

Lipids: Highly Compact Energy-Storage Nutrients

Neutral lipids (fats) or triacylglycerols are contained in fats and oils, meat and dairy products, nuts, and avocados (figure 37.1*b*). Lipids are the most concentrated source of food energy. They

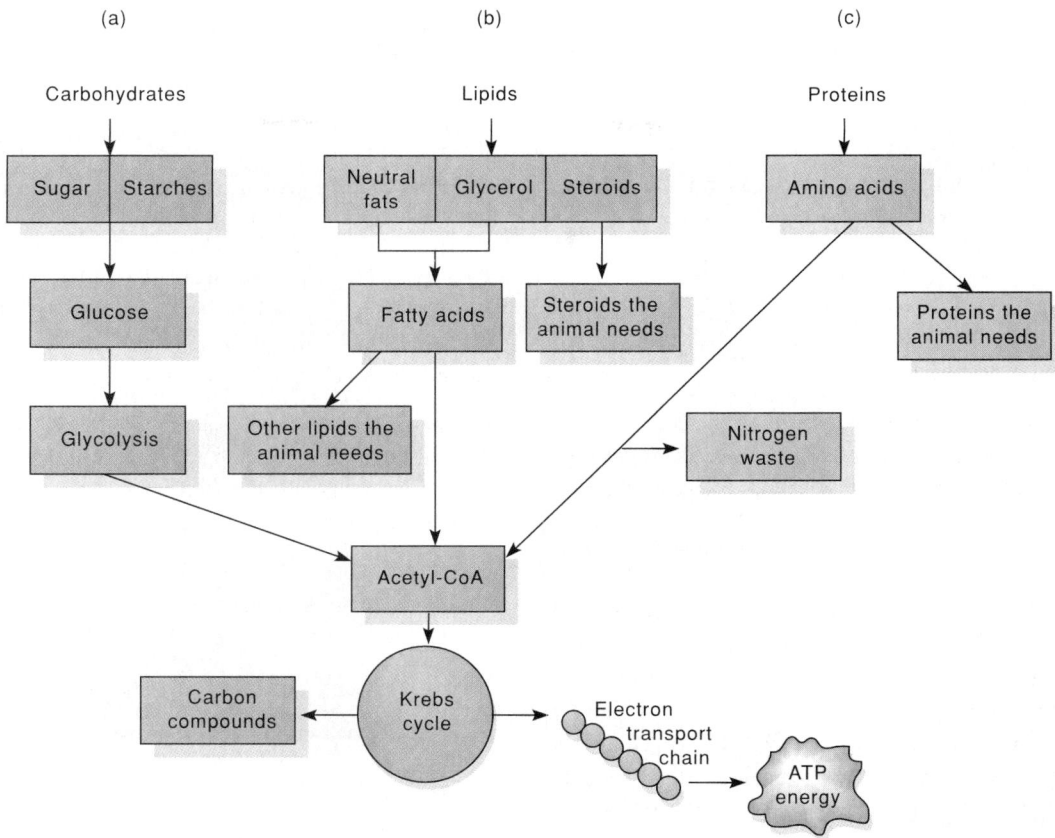

(a) Carbohydrates

(b) Lipids

(c) Proteins

Figure **37.1**

Macronutrients in the Diet. (*a*) Carbohydrate foods are broken down to their constituent sugars and starches and ultimately into glucose. Individual cells use this sugar in glycolysis and aerobic respiration to create new carbon compounds or ATP energy. (*b*) Lipids (fats and oils) in the diet are broken down to neutral fats, glycerol, and steroids. These molecules can be modified and incorporated into the lipids or steroids the animal needs for storing fat or generating hormones, or they can be converted to acetyl-CoA and enter the Krebs cycle and electron transport chain for ATP production. (*c*) Proteins are broken down to amino acids, which are incorporated into new proteins or modified to enter the Krebs cycle and electron transport chain to produce ATP energy.

produce about 9 Calories (kcal) of usable energy per gram, more than twice the energy available from an equal mass of carbohydrate or protein (table 37.1).

Many heterotrophs have an absolute dietary requirement for lipids, sometimes for specific types. For example, unsaturated fatty acids (e.g., linoleic acid, linolenic acid, and arachidonic acid) are required by a variety of animals. Their most obvious function is to act as precursor molecules for the synthesis of sterols, the most common of which is cholesterol. The sterols are required for the synthesis of steroid hormones and incorporated into cell membranes. Other lipids insulate the body of some vertebrates and help maintain a constant temperature.

Proteins: Basic to the Structure and Function of Cells

The animal sources of protein include, for example, other animals and milk. The plant sources include, for example, beans, peas, and nuts. Proteins (figure 37.1*c*) are needed for their amino acids, which heterotrophs use to build their own body proteins.

TABLE 37.1	THE AVERAGE CALORIC VALUES OF MACRONUTRIENTS	

MACRONUTRIENT	CALORIES PER GRAM
Carbohydrates	4.1
Lipids	9.3
Proteins	4.4

Micronutrients

Micronutrients are usually small ions, organic vitamins, inorganic minerals, and molecules that are used over and over for enzymatic reactions or as parts of certain proteins (e.g., copper in hemocyanin and iron in hemoglobin). Even though they are needed in small amounts, animals cannot synthesize them rapidly (if at all); thus, they must be obtained from the diet.

TABLE 37.2	PHYSIOLOGICAL ROLES OF THE ESSENTIAL MINERALS (MACROMINERALS) REQUIRED IN LARGE AMOUNTS BY ANIMALS
MINERAL	**MAJOR PHYSIOLOGICAL ROLES**
Calcium (Ca)	Component of bone and teeth; essential for normal blood clotting; needed for normal muscle, neuron, and cell function
Chlorine (Cl)	Principal negative ion in extracellular fluid; important in acid-base and fluid balance; needed to produce stomach HCl
Magnesium (Mg)	Component of many coenzymes; needed for normal neuron and muscle function, as well as carbohydrate and protein metabolism
Potassium (K)	Major constituent of bones, blood plasma; needed for energy metabolism
Phosphorus (P)	Major positive ion in cells; influences muscle contraction and neuron excitability; part of DNA, RNA, ATP, energy metabolism
Sodium (Na)	Principal positive ion in extracellular fluid; important in fluid balance; essential for conduction of action potentials, active transport
Sulfur (S)	Protein structure; detoxification reactions and other metabolic activity

TABLE 37.3	SOME PHYSIOLOGICAL ROLES OF TRACE MINERALS (MICROMINERALS) IN ANIMALS
MINERAL	**PHYSIOLOGICAL ROLES**
Cobalt (Co)	Component of vitamin B_{12}; essential for red blood cell production
Copper (Cu)	Component of many enzymes; essential for melanin and hemoglobin synthesis; part of cytochromes
Fluorine (F)	Component of bone and teeth; prevents tooth decay
Iodine (I)	Component of thyroid hormones
Iron (Fe)	Component of hemoglobin, myoglobin, enzymes, and cytochromes
Manganese (Mn)	Activates many enzymes; an enzyme essential for urea formation and parts of the Krebs cycle
Molybdenum (Mo)	Constituent of some enzymes
Selenium (Se)	Needed in fat metabolism
Zinc (Zn)	Component of at least 70 enzymes; needed for wound healing and fertilization

Minerals

Some minerals are needed in relatively large amounts and are called essential minerals, or macrominerals. For example, sodium and potassium are vital to the functioning of every nerve and muscle in an animal's body. Large quantities of these minerals, especially sodium, are lost in the urine every day. In those animal's that sweat to help regulate body temperature, sodium loss also becomes important. A daily supply of calcium is needed for muscular activity and, with phosphorous, for bone formation. The function of the major essential minerals is given in table 37.2.

Other minerals are known as trace minerals, trace elements, or microminerals. These are needed in only very small amounts for various enzymatic functions. The function of some trace minerals is given in table 37.3.

Vitamins

Normal metabolic activity depends on very small amounts of more than a dozen organic substances called vitamins. A **vitamin** (L. *vita*, life) is the general term for a number of chemically unrelated, organic substances that occur in many foods in small amounts and are necessary for the normal metabolic functioning. Vitamins may be water soluble or fat soluble. Most water-soluble vitamins, such as the B vitamins and vitamin C, are coenzymes needed in metabolism (table 37.4). The fat-soluble vitamins have various functions (table 37.5).

The dietary need for vitamin C and the fat-soluble vitamins (A, D, E, and K) tends to be limited to the vertebrates. Even in closely related groups, vitamin requirements vary. For example, among vertebrates, humans and guinea pigs require vitamin C, but rabbits do not. Some birds require vitamin A; others do not.

Stop and Ask Yourself

5. What are some functions of carbohydrates in vertebrates? Lipids? Proteins?
6. What is the difference between essential minerals and trace minerals?
7. What is a vitamin?
8. What are some water-soluble vitamins? Fat-soluble vitamins?

DIGESTION

Recall from chapters 17 and 18 that in some of the simplest forms of life (the protists and sponges), some cells take in whole food particles directly from the environment by diffusion, active transport, and/or endocytosis and break them down with enzymes to obtain nutrients. This strategy is called **intracellular** ("within the cell") **digestion** (figure 37.2a). Intracellular digestion circumvents the need for the mechanical breakdown of food or for a gut or other cavity in which to chemically digest

TABLE 37.4	WATER-SOLUBLE VITAMINS		
VITAMIN	**CHARACTERISTICS**	**FUNCTIONS**	**SOURCES**
Thiamine (vitamin B_1)	Destroyed by heat and oxygen, especially in alkaline environment	Part of coenzyme needed for oxidation of carbohydrates, and coenzyme needed in synthesis of ribose	Lean meats, liver, eggs, whole-grain cereals, leafy green vegetables, legumes
Riboflavin (vitamin B_2)	Stable to heat, acids, and oxidation; destroyed by alkalis and light	Part of enzymes and coenzymes needed for oxidation of glucose and fatty acids and for cellular growth	Meats, dairy products, leafy green vegetables, whole-grain cereals
Niacin (nicotinic acid)	Stable to heat, acids, and alkalis; converted to niacinamide by cells; synthesized from tryptophan	Part of coenzymes needed for oxidation of glucose and synthesis of proteins, fats, and nucleic acids	Liver, lean meats, poultry, peanuts, legumes
Vitamin B_6	Group of three compounds; stable to heat and acids; destroyed by oxidation, alkalis, and ultraviolet light	Coenzyme needed for synthesis of proteins and various amino acids, for conversion of tryptophan to niacin, for production of antibodies, and for synthesis of nucleic acids	Liver, meats, fish, poultry, bananas, avocados, beans, peanuts, whole-grain cereals, egg yolk
Pantothenic acid	Destroyed by heat, acids, and alkalis	Part of coenzyme needed for oxidation of carbohydrates and fats	Meats, fish, whole-grain cereals, legumes, milk, fruits, vegetables
Cyanocobalamin (vitamin B_{12})	Complex, cobalt-containing compound; stable to heat; inactivated by light, strong acids, and strong alkalis; absorption regulated by intrinsic factor from gastric glands; stored in liver	Part of coenzyme needed for synthesis of nucleic acids and for metabolism of carbohydrates; plays role in synthesis of myelin	Liver, meats, poultry, fish, milk, cheese, eggs
Folacin (folic acid)	Occurs in several forms; destroyed by oxidation in acid environment or by heat in alkaline environment; stored in liver where it is converted into folinic acid	Coenzyme needed for metabolism of certain amino acids and for synthesis of DNA; promotes production of normal red blood cells	Liver, leafy green vegetables, whole-grain cereals, legumes
Biotin	Stable to heat, acids, and light; destroyed by oxidation and alkalis	Coenzyme needed for metabolism of amino acids and fatty acids and for synthesis of nucleic acids	Liver, egg yolk, nuts, legumes, mushrooms
Ascorbic acid (vitamin C)	Closely related to monosaccharides; stable in acids, but destroyed by oxidation, heat, light, and alkalis	Needed for production of collagen, conversion of folacin to folinic acid, and metabolism of certain amino acids; promotes absorption of iron and synthesis of hormones from cholesterol	Citrus fruits, citrus juices, tomatoes, cabbage, potatoes, leafy green vegetables, fresh fruits

From John W. Hole, Jr., Human Anatomy and Physiology, 6th ed. Copyright © 1993 Wm. C. Brown Communications, Inc. Reprinted by permission of Times Mirror Higher Education Group, Inc., Dubuque, Iowa. All Rights Reserved.

food. At the same time, however, intracellular digestion puts an upper limit on an animal's size and complexity—only very small pieces of food can be used. This mechanism of intracellular digestion provides all or some of the nutrients in protozoa, sponges, cnidarians, platyhelminthes, rotifers, bivalve molluscs, and primitive chordates.

Larger animals have evolved structures and mechanisms necessary for **extracellular digestion:** the enzymatic breakdown of larger pieces of food into constituent molecules, usually in a special organ or cavity (figure 37.2b). Nutrients from the food then pass into body cells lining the organ or cavity and can take part in energy metabolism or biosynthesis.

37.5

TABLE 37.5	FAT-SOLUBLE VITAMINS		
VITAMIN	CHARACTERISTICS	FUNCTIONS	SOURCES
Vitamin A	Occurs in several forms; synthesized from carotenes; stored in liver, stable in heat, acids, and alkalis; unstable in light	Necessary for synthesis of visual pigments, mucoproteins, and mucopolysaccharides; for normal development of bones and teeth; and for maintenance of epithelial cells	Liver, fish, whole milk, butter, eggs, leafy green vegetables, and yellow and orange vegetables and fruits
Vitamin D	A group of sterols; resistant to heat, oxidation, acids, and alkalis; stored in liver, skin, brain, spleen, and bones	Promotes absorption of calcium and phosphorous; promotes development of teeth and bones	Produced in skin exposed to ultraviolet light; in milk, egg yolk, fish-liver oils, fortified foods
Vitamin E	A group of compounds; resistant to heat and visible light; unstable in presence of oxygen and ultraviolet light; stored in muscles and adipose tissue	An antioxidant; prevents oxidation of vitamin A and polyunsaturated fatty acids; may help maintain stability of cell membranes	Oils from cereal seeds, salad oils, margarine, shortenings, fruits, nuts, and vegetables
Vitamin K	Occurs in several forms; resistant to heat, but destroyed by acids, alkalis, and light; stored in liver	Needed for synthesis of prothrombin; needed for blood clotting	Leafy green vegetables, egg yolk, pork liver, soy oil, tomatoes, cauliflower

From John W. Hole, Jr., Human Anatomy and Physiology, 6th ed. Copyright © 1993 Wm. C. Brown Communications, Inc. Reprinted by permission of Times Mirror Higher Education Group, Inc., Dubuque, Iowa. All Rights Reserved.

ANIMAL STRATEGIES FOR GETTING AND USING FOOD

As noted above, only a few protists and animals can absorb nutrients directly from their external environment via intracellular digestion. Most animals must work for their nutrients. The number of specializations that have evolved for food procurement (feeding) and extracellular digestion are almost as numerous as the number of animal species. What follows is a brief discussion of the major feeding strategies animals utilize.

CONTINUOUS VERSUS DISCONTINUOUS FEEDERS

One variable related to the structure of digestive systems is whether an animal is a continuous or discontinuous feeder. Many **continuous feeders** are slow moving or completely sessile animals (they remain permanently in one place). For example, aquatic **suspension feeders** (box 37.1), such as tube worms and barnacles, remain in one place and continuously "strain" small food particles from the water.

Discontinuous feeders tend to be active, sometimes highly mobile, animals. Typically, discontinuous feeders have more digestive specializations than continuous feeders because discontinuous feeders take in large meals that must be either ground up or stored, or both. Many carnivores, for example, pursue and capture relatively large prey. When successful, they must eat large meals so that they need not spend their time in the continuous pursuit of prey. Thus, carnivores have digestive systems that permit storage and gradual digestion of large, relatively infrequent meals.

Herbivores spend more time eating than carnivores do, but they are also discontinuous feeders. They need to move from area to area when food is exhausted and, at least in natural environments, must limit their grazing time to avoid excessive exposure to predators. Thus, their digestive systems permit relatively rapid food gathering and gradual digestion.

SUSPENSION FEEDERS

Suspension feeding is the removal of suspended food particles from the surrounding water by some sort of capture, trapping, or filtration structure. This feeding strategy involves three steps: (1) transport of water past the feeding structure, (2) removal of nutrients from the water, and (3) transport of the nutrients to the mouth of the digestive system. Suspension feeding is utilized by sponges, ascidians, branchiopods, ectoprocts, entoprocts, phoronids, most bivalves, and many crustaceans, polychaetes, gastropods, and some nonvertebrate chordates (*see box 37.1*).

DEPOSIT FEEDERS

Deposit feeding involves primarily omnivorous animals. These animals obtain their nutrients from the sediments of soft-bottom habitats (muds and sands) or terrestrial soils. Direct deposit feeders simply swallow large quantities of sediment (mud, soil, sand, organic matter). The usable nutrients are digested and the remains pass out the anus. Direct deposit feeding occurs in many polychaete annelids, some snails, some sea urchins, and in most earthworms. Other direct deposit feeders utilize tentaclelike structures to consume sediment. Examples include sea cucumbers, most sipunculans, certain clams, and several types of polychaetes.

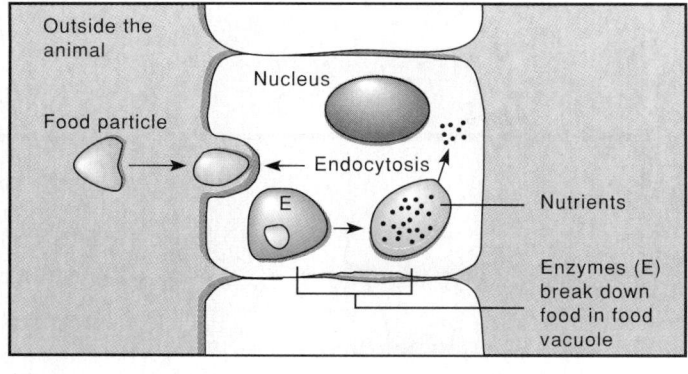

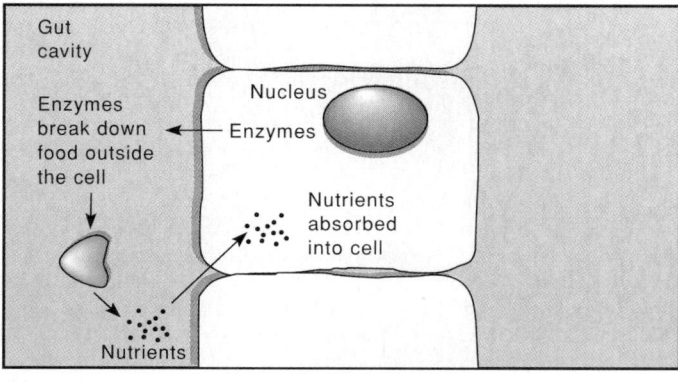

FIGURE 37.2

Intracellular and Extracellular Digestion. (*a*) A simple invertebrate, such as a sponge, has no gut and thus carries out intracellular digestion. Tiny food particles are taken into the body wall cells by endocytosis. Digestive enzymes in the vacuole then break the small particles into constituent molecules. (*b*) A dog, for example, has a gut and so can take in and digest (extracellularly) relatively large food particles. Cells lining the gut cavity secrete enzymes into the cavity. There, the enzymes break down food materials into constituent nutrients, and the nearby cells absorb these nutrients.

HERBIVORY

Herbivory (L. *herba*, herb + *vorare*, to eat) is the consumption of macroscopic plants. This feeding strategy is very common in animals and requires the ability to "bite and chew" large pieces of plant matter (macroherbivory). Although the evolution of biting and chewing mechanisms took place within the architectural framework of a number of invertebrate lineages, it is often characterized by the development of hard surfaces (e.g., teeth) that are manipulated by powerful muscles. Examples of invertebrate animals that evolved macroherbivory include molluscs, polychaete worms, arthropods, and sea urchins.

Many molluscs have a radula. A radula is a muscularized, beltlike rasp armed with chitinous teeth (*see figure 21.6*). Molluscs use the radula to scrape algae off rocks or tear the leaves off terrestrial plants. Polychaetes have sets of large chitinous teeth on an eversible proboscis or pharynx that is used to scrape off algae. This toothed pharynx is also suitable for carnivory when plant material is scarce. Macroherbivory is found in almost every group of arthropods. For example, insects and crustaceans have large, powerful mandibles capable of biting off plant material and subsequently grinding and chewing it before passing the plant material on to the mouth.

PREDATION

Predation (L. *praedator*, a plunderer, pillager) is one of the most sophisticated feeding strategies since it requires the capture of live prey. Only a few generalizations about the many kinds of predation are presented here; discussions of various taxa are presented in their appropriate chapters.

Predators may be classified by how they capture their prey: motile stalkers, lurking predators, sessile opportunists, or grazers. Motile stalkers actively pursue their prey. Examples include ciliate protozoa, nemerteans, polychaete worms, gastropods, octopuses and squids, crabs, sea stars, and many vertebrates. Lurking predators are those that sit and wait for their prey to come within capture distance, whereupon they quickly seize their prey. Examples include certain species of preying mantises, shrimp, crabs, spiders, polychaetes, and many vertebrates. Sessile opportunists usually are not very mobile. Examples include certain protozoa, barnacles, and cnidarians. Grazing carnivores move about the substrate picking up small organisms. Their diet usually consists largely of sessile and slow-moving animals, such as sponges, ectoprocts, tunicates, snails, worms, and small crustaceans.

SURFACE NUTRIENT ABSORPTION

Some highly specialized animals have dispensed entirely with all mechanisms for prey capture, ingestion of food particles, and digestive processes. They instead rely on the direct absorption of nutrients across their body surfaces from the external medium. This medium may be nutrient-rich seawater, fluid in other animals' digestive tracts, or body fluids of other animals. For example, some free-living protozoa, such as *Chilomonas*, are able to absorb all of their nutrients across their body surface. The endoparasitic protozoa, cestode worms, endoparasitic gastropods, and crustaceans (all of which lack mouths and digestive systems) also absorb all of their nutrients across their body surface.

A few nonparasitic multicellular animals also lack a mouth and digestive system and absorb nutrients across their body surface. Examples include the gutless bivalves and pogonophoran worms. Interestingly, many pogonophoran worms absorb some nutrients from seawater across their body surface and also supplement their nutrition with organic carbon fixed within the pogonophoran's tissues by symbiotic bacteria.

FLUID FEEDERS

The biological fluids of animals and plants are a rich source of nutrients. Feeding on this fluid is called **fluid feeding.** Fluid feeding is especially characteristic of some parasites, such as the intestinal nematodes that bite and rasp off host tissue or suck blood. External

BOX   37.1   SUSPENSION FEEDING IN INVERTEBRATES AND NONVERTEBRATE CHORDATES

Most suspension feeders are marine rather than freshwater animals because seawater contains an abundance of microscopic food particles. Suspension-feeding invertebrates and some nonvertebrate chordates generally consume bacteria, phytoplankton, zooplankton, and some detritus. In order to capture food particles from the environment, suspension feeders must either move part or all of their body through the water, or water must be moved past the feeding structures. Only a relatively few suspension feeders (some ciliate protozoa, certain bivalve molluscs, many tunicates, some large crustaceans) use true filter feeding. The reason is that it is energetically costly to drive water through a fine-meshed filter. An analogy would be moving molasses through a fine-mesh filter. Thus, most invertebrates utilize one of the following less energetically costly methods of capturing food particles from the water.

Among some aquatic arthropods, such as the sessile barnacles, certain thoracic appendages are modified with rows of featherlike cirri adapted for generating water currents across parts of the body and removing food from it (figure 1a).

A second method is called "scan and trap." The general strategy here is to move water over all or part of the body, detect suspended food particles, isolate the particles in a small parcel of water, and process only that water by some method of particle extraction. This method is employed by many copepods, ectoprocts, and a variety of invertebrate larval forms.

A third suspension-feeding device is the mucous bag or mucous trap. In this method, patches or sheets of mucus are used to trap suspended food particles. A classic example is seen in the annelid worm *Chaetopterus* (figure 1b). This invertebrate lives in a U-shaped tube in a sediment and pumps water through the tube and through a mucous net. As the net fills with trapped food particles,

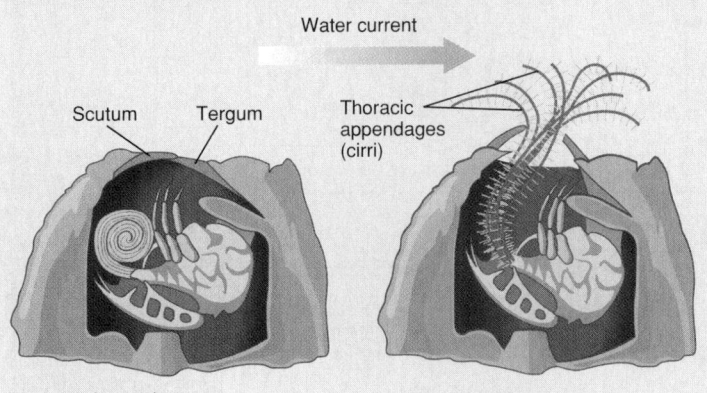

(a) Acorn barnacle

FIGURE 1   Suspension Feeding in Invertebrates. (a) In the free-living barnacle *Balanus* spp. (an acorn barnacle), the scutum and tergum can move apart, allowing the animal to extend cirri in the water currents (arrows) and gather food particles. (b) In the polychaete *Chaetopterus* (tube worm), water currents are generated by the fanlike parapodia. One pair of anterior parapodia is modified for holding a mucous bag, which filters out food particles as water moves through the tube. The bag is held posteriorly by a food cup, which continuously gathers the food-laden mucus into a ball. Periodically, the ball is released from the rest of the net and passed forward along a ciliated tract to the mouth for ingestion. (c) In a typical ascidian (a nonvertebrate chordate; sea squirt), an elongated gland called the endostyle extends along the ventral surface of the pharynx. Mucus secreted by the endostyle is drawn across the pharynx in a thin sheet, so that water passing through the stigmata must pass through the mucous sheet as well. Pharyngeal cilia continually move the particle-laden sheet of mucus to the esophagus for ingestion. (d) A crinoid echinoderm (sea lily). Crinoids collect food by extending the arms (pinnules) and tube feet into the surrounding water current. As food particles in the water contact the podia, the particles are entangled in mucus and then flicked into the mouth by the cirri. *Sources: (c) Modified after Bullough and other sources, (d) Modified from Hyman after Clark.*

parasites (ectoparasites), such as leeches, ticks, mites, lampreys, and certain crustaceans use a wide variety of mouthparts to feed on body fluids. For example, the sea lamprey (*see figure 37.6a*) has a funnel structure surrounding its mouth. The funnel is lined with over 200 rasping teeth and a rasplike tongue. The lamprey uses the funnel like a suction cup to grip its fish host, and then with its tongue, rasps a hole in the fish's body wall. The lamprey then sucks blood and body fluids from the wound, usually killing the fish.

The most highly developed sucking structures for fluid feeding are found in the insects. For example, butterflies, moths, and aphids have tubelike mouthparts that enable them to suck up plant fluids. Blood-sucking mosquitos have complex mouthparts with piercing stylets.

Most pollen- and nectar-feeding birds have long bills and tongues. In fact, the bill is often specialized (in shape, length,

and curvature) for particular types of flowers. The tongues of some birds have a brushlike tip or are hollow, or both, to collect the nectar from flowers. Other nectar-feeding birds have short bills; they make a hole in the base of a flower and use their tongue to obtain nectar through the hole.

3 The only mammals that feed exclusively on blood are the vampire bats, such as *Desmodus*, of tropical South and Central America. These bats attack birds, cattle, and horses, using knife-sharp front teeth to pierce the surface blood vessels and lap at the oozing wound. Nectar-feeding bats have a long tongue to extract the nectar from flowering plants, and by comparison to the blood-feeding bats, have reduced dentition. In like manner, the nectar-feeding honey possum has a long, brush-tipped tongue and reduced dentition.

37.8

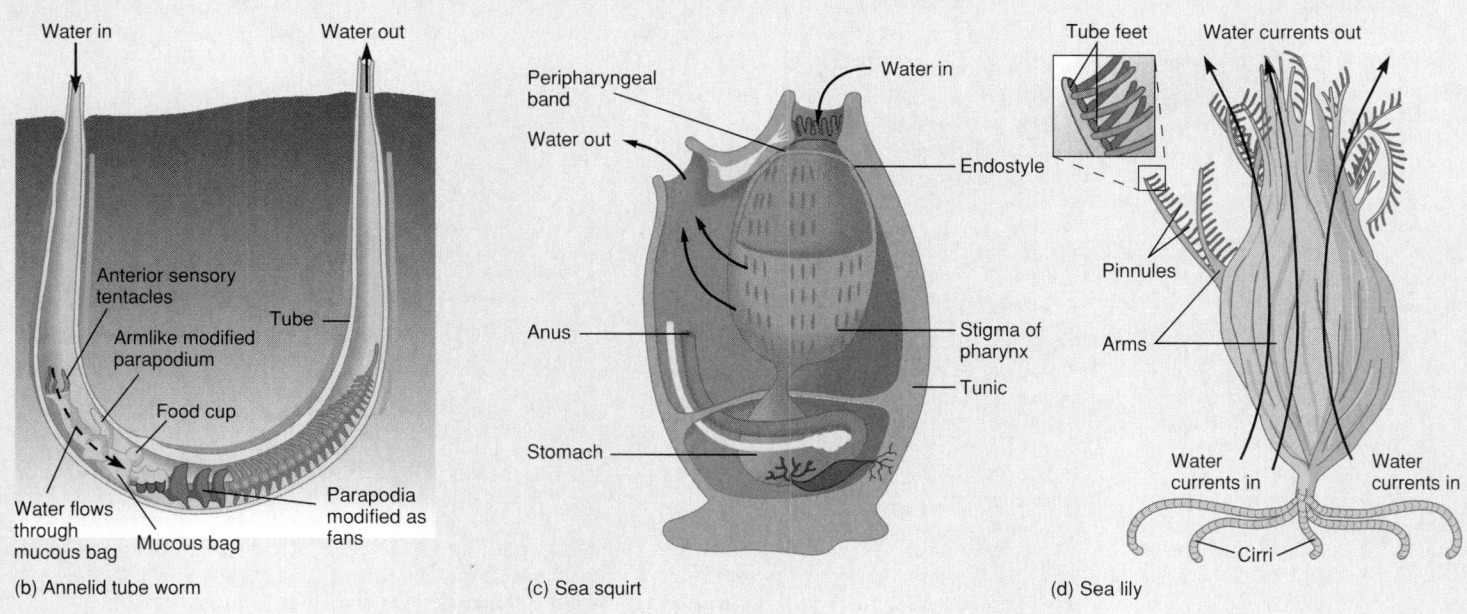

(b) Annelid tube worm

(c) Sea squirt

(d) Sea lily

it is periodically manipulated and rolled into a ball. The ball is eventually passed to the mouth and swallowed.

A fourth type of suspension feeding is the ciliary mucous mechanism. In this mechanism, rows of cilia carry a mucous sheet across some structure while water is passed through or across it. A good example of this method of suspension feeding is seen in sea squirts (ascidians). These nonvertebrate chordates move a continuous sheet of mucus across their sievelike pharynx, while pumping water through it (figure 1c). Fresh mucus is secreted at

one side of the pharynx, while the food-laden mucus is ingested at the other side using the esophagus.

A fifth type of suspension feeding is tentacle or tube feet suspension feeding. In this strategy, a tentaclelike structure captures larger food particles, with or without the aid of mucus (figure 1d). Examples of this food-gathering mechanism are most commonly encountered in the echinoderms (e.g., many brittle stars and crinoids such as the sea lily) and cnidarians (e.g., some sea anemones and corals).

Stop and Ask Yourself

9. What is the difference between continuous and discontinuous feeding?
10. How does suspension feeding occur? Deposit feeding?
11. What are some different types of predation?
12. What protists and animals utilize surface nutrient absorption? Fluid feeding?

DIVERSITY IN DIGESTIVE STRUCTURES: INVERTEBRATES

In primitive, multicellular animals, such as cnidarians, the gut is a blind (closed) sac called a **gastrovascular cavity.** It has only one

opening that serves as both entrance and exit (figure 37.3a); thus, it is an incomplete digestive tract. Some specialized cells in the cavity secrete digestive enzymes that begin the process of extracellular digestion. Other phagocytic cells that line the cavity engulf food material and continue intracellular digestion inside food vacuoles. Similar digestive patterns are seen in some flatworms (figure 37.3b).

The development of the anus and complete digestive tract in the aschelminths (figure 37.3c) was an evolutionary breakthrough. A complete digestive tract permits the one-way flow of ingested food without mixing it with previously ingested food or waste. Complete digestive tracts also have the advantage of progressive digestive processing in specialized regions along the system. Food can be digested efficiently in a series of distinctly different steps. The many variations of the basic plan of a complete digestive tract (figure 37.3d) are correlated with different food-gathering mechanisms and diets. Most of these have been presented in the discussion of the many different protists and invertebrates

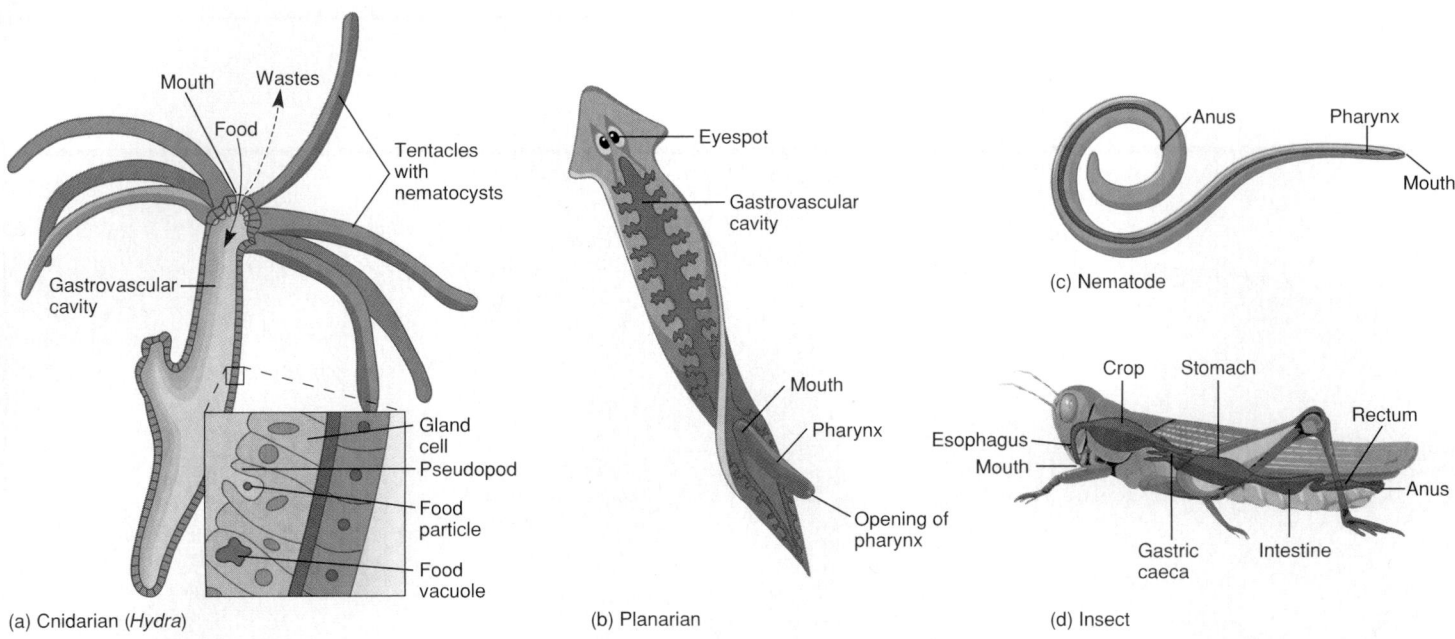

FIGURE 37.3

Various Types of Digestive Structures in Invertebrates. (*a*) The gastrovascular cavity of a cnidarian (*Hydra*) is an incomplete digestive tract because it has only one opening, a mouth, that must serve as the entry and exit point for food and waste. Extracellular digestion occurs in the gastrovascular cavity, and intracellular digestion occurs inside food vacuoles formed when phagocytic cells engulf food particles. (*b*) Even though the gastrovascular cavity in a platyhelminth (planarian) branches extensively, it is also an incomplete digestive tract with only one opening. When a planarian feeds, it sticks its muscular pharynx out of its mouth and sucks in food. (*c*) An aschelminth (*Ascaris*) has a complete digestive tract with a mouth, pharynx, and anus. (*d*) The complete digestive tract of an insect (grasshopper) has an expanded region called a crop that functions as a food storage organ.

covered in chapters 18 to 24 and will not be repeated in this chapter. Instead, to further illustrate digestive systems in protozoa and invertebrates, three examples will be presented: (1) the incomplete digestive system of a ciliated protozoan will be used as an example of an intracellular digestive system; (2) the bivalve mollusc will be used as an example of an invertebrate that has both intracellular and extracellular digestion; and (3) an insect will be used as an example of an invertebrate that has extracellular digestion and a complete digestive tract.

PROTOZOA

As presented in chapter 17, protozoa may be autotrophic, saprozoic, or heterotrophic (ingest food particles). Ciliated protozoa are good examples of protists that utilize heterotrophic nutrition. Food from the environment is directed by ciliary action into the buccal cavity and cytostome (figure 37.4). The cytostome opens into the cytopharynx, which enlarges as food enters, and pinches off a food-containing vacuole. The detached food vacuole then moves through the cytoplasm. During this movement, excess water is removed from the vacuole, the contents are acidified and then made alkaline, and digestive enzymes are added by a lysosome. The food particles are then digested within the vacuole and the nutrients absorbed into the cytoplasm. The residual vacuole then excretes its waste products via the cytopyge.

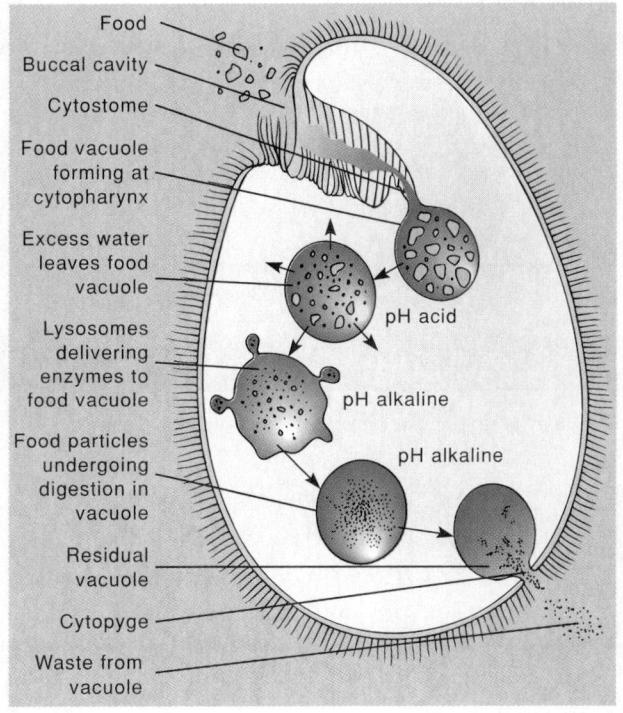

FIGURE 37.4

Intracellular Digestion in a Ciliated Protozoan. Food is directed by cilia toward the cytostome ("mouth") and enters the cytopharynx, where a food vacuole forms and detaches from the cytopharynx. The detached vacuole undergoes acidic and alkaline digestion, and the waste vacuole moves to the cytopyge ("anus") for excretion.

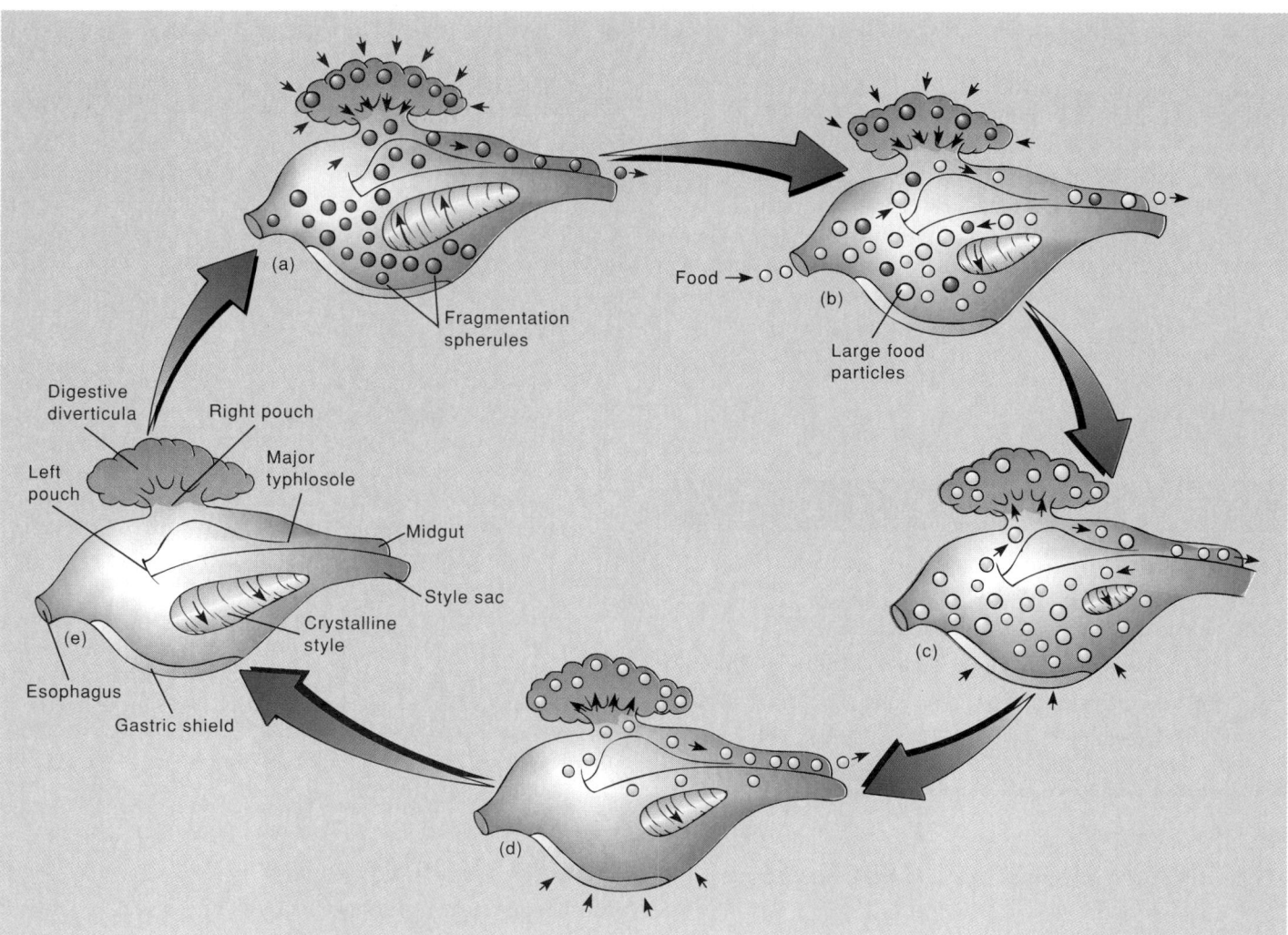

Figure 37.5

Extracellular and Intracellular Digestion in a Bivalve Mollusc. (*a*) The process of extracellular digestion begins before food ingestion by the dissolving of the crystalline style and the formation of fragmentation spherules in the stomach. (*b*) As food enters the stomach, it is mechanically and enzymatically broken down by the rotating style and the enzymes released by the gastric shield. (*c*) The small food particles are then moved into the digestive diverticulae for intracellular digestion. (*d*) Cessation of feeding is followed by a progressive passage of food particles from the stomach to the digestive diverticulae. (*e*) During this resting phase, the stomach empties and the style re-forms, while intracellular digestion in the diverticulae is completed, and fragmentation spherules begin to form again. The movement of fragmentation spherules starts the next feeding cycle.

BIVALVE MOLLUSCS

Many bivalve molluscs suspension feed and ingest small food particles. The digestive tract has a short esophagus opening into a stomach, midgut, hindgut, and rectum. The stomach contains a crystalline style, gastric shield, and diverticulated region. These diverticulae are blind-ending sacs that function by increasing the surface area for absorption and intracellular digestion. The midgut, hindgut, and rectum function in extracellular digestion and absorption (figure 37.5).

Digestion is a coordination of three cycles: (1) feeding, (2) extracellular digestion, and (3) intracellular digestion. The resting phase is preparative for extracellular digestion. The mechanical and enzymatic breakdown of food during feeding provides the small particles for intracellular digestion. Intracellular digestion releases the nutrients into the blood and produces the fragmentation spherules that are both excretory and lower the pH for optimal extracellular digestion. These three cycles are linked to tidal immersion and emersion of the mollusc.

INSECTS

The grasshopper is a representative insect (*see figure 37.3d*) that has a complete digestive tract and extracellular digestion. When feeding, food is first broken up (masticated) by the mandibles and maxillae, taken into the mouth, and passed to the crop via the esophagus. During mastication, saliva from the salivary glands is added to the food to lubricate it for passage through the digestive tract. Saliva also contains the enzyme amylase, which begins the enzymatic digestion of carbohydrates. This digestion continues during food storage in the crop. Other enzymes (carbohydrases, lipases, proteases) are secreted by the midgut and enter the crop. Food passes slowly from the crop to the stomach, where it is mechanically reduced and the nutrient particles sorted. Large particles are returned to the crop for further processing; the small particles enter the gastric cecae, where extracellular digestion is completed. Most absorption of nutrients then occurs in the intestine. Undigested food is moved along the intestine and passes into the rectum, where water and ion absorption occur. The solid fecal pellets that are formed are then passed out of the animal via the anus. During this entire feeding process, there is considerable control of enzyme production at various points in the digestive tract by (1) the nervous system, (2) the endocrine system, and (3) the presence of food.

Stop and Ask Yourself

13. What is the difference between an incomplete and complete digestive tract?
14. How do heterotrophic protozoa feed?
15. What is the function of diverticulae in bivalve molluscs?
16. Where does digestion begin in an insect?
17. What is the difference between intracellular and extracellular digestion?

DIVERSITY IN DIGESTIVE STRUCTURES: VERTEBRATES

The complete vertebrate digestive tract (gut tube) is highly specialized in both structure and function for the digestion of a wide variety of foods. The basic structures of the gut tube include the buccal cavity, pharynx, esophagus, stomach, small intestine, large intestine, rectum, and anus/cloaca. In addition, there are three important glandular systems associated with the digestive tract: (1) the salivary glands; (2) the liver, gallbladder, and bile duct; and (3) the pancreas and pancreatic duct.

Because most vertebrates spend the majority of their time acquiring food, feeding can be referred to as the universal pastime. The oral cavity (mouth), teeth, intestines, and other major digestive structures usually reflect the way an animal gathers food (box 37.2), the type of food it eats, and the way it digests that food. These major digestive structures are now discussed in order to illustrate the diversity of form and function among different vertebrates.

TONGUES

A tongue or tonguelike structure develops in the floor of the oral cavity in many vertebrates. For example, a lamprey has a protrusible tongue that bears horny teeth and is used to rasp its prey's flesh (figure 37.6a). In fishes, a primary tongue may be present that bears teeth that help hold prey; however, this type

of tongue is not muscular (figure 37.6b). Tetrapods have evolved mobile tongues that are used for gathering food. Frogs and salamanders and some lizards can rapidly project part of their tongue from the mouth to capture an insect (figure 37.6c). A woodpecker has a long and spiny tongue (figure 37.6d) that is used to gather insects and grubs. Ant- and termite-eating mammals also gather food with long, sticky tongues. Spiny papillae on the tongues of cats and other carnivores help these animals rasp flesh from a bone.

TEETH

With the exception of birds, turtles, and baleen whales, most vertebrates have teeth. ④ (Birds lack teeth, probably to reduce body weight for flight.) Teeth are specialized, depending on whether an animal is feeding on plants or animals, and how it obtains its food. The teeth of snakes slope backward to aid in the retention of prey while swallowing (figure 37.7a), and the canine teeth of wolves are specialized for ripping food (figure 37.7b). The teeth of herbivores, such as deer, have predominantly grinding teeth, the front teeth of a beaver are used for chiseling trees and branches, and the elephant has two of its upper, front teeth specialized as weapons and for moving objects (figure 37.7c–e). Because humans, pigs, bears, raccoons, and a few other mammals are omnivores, they contain teeth that can perform a number of tasks—tearing, ripping, chiseling, and grinding (figure 37.7f).

SALIVARY GLANDS

Most fishes lack salivary glands in the head region. Lampreys are an exception because they have a pair of glands that secrete an anticoagulant that is needed to keep their prey's blood flowing as they feed. Terrestrial vertebrates have well-developed salivary glands. ⑤ Modified salivary glands of some snakes produce venoms that are injected through their fangs to immobilize their prey. Because the secretion of oral digestive enzymes is not an important function in amphibians or reptiles, salivary glands are absent.

ESOPHAGI

The esophagus (pl., esophagi) is short in fishes and amphibians but much longer in amniotes due to their longer necks. Grain- and seed-eating birds have a crop that develops from the caudal portion of the esophagus (figure 37.8a). Storing food in the crop ensures an almost continuous supply of food to the stomach and intestine for digestion. This structure allows these birds to reduce the frequency of feeding and still maintain a high metabolic rate.

STOMACHS

The stomach is an ancestral vertebrate structure that evolved as these animals began to feed on larger organisms that were caught at less frequent intervals and required storage. Some zoologists believe that

BOX 37.2 | FILTER FEEDING IN VERTEBRATES

The baleen, or whalebone whales, include the humpback and gray whales (figure 1*a*). These are the largest living animals on earth, and because they lack teeth, they have evolved a different approach to feeding. A full-grown gray whale exceeds 30 m in length and weighs as much as 120,000 kg. What food could support the life of such a large animal? The answer is krill. **Krill** (Norw., *kril*, fry or young fish) are small, shrimplike crustaceans.

Baleen whales are named for the fringes of baleen, or whale bone (not true bone) that hang down in "mustachelike" sheets inside their mouths (figure 1*b*). Baleen is nothing more than hardened, shredded sheets of the gum epithelial layers. When these animals feed, they swim through dense schools of krill, straining huge amounts of water through the baleen meshwork. A large whale's expandable mouth holds 60 m³, or 60 tons, of water, which it filters in a few seconds. The filtering process allows the smaller plant life (phytoplankton) to escape with the seawater while the krill is retained to be swallowed at leisure. Tons of krill can be eaten by a whale in a short time.

Flamingos are also filter feeders. They have fringed filters hanging from the upper bill and a deep-sided, curved lower bill (figure 1*c,d*). This bill represents a similar evolutionary adaptation to the same problem—removing small particles from a dilute medium.

Flamingos are commonly misportrayed as denizens of lush tropical islands. In fact, many dwell in one of the world's harshest habitats—shallow, hypersaline lakes. Few animals can tolerate the unusual environments of these saline lakes. Those that can, thrive in the absence of competitors and build up their populations to enormous numbers. Hypersaline lakes provide these predators with ideal conditions for filter feeding on small molluscs, crustaceans, and insect larvae.

Flamingos pass water through their bills either by swinging their heads back and forth, permitting water to flow passively through, or by an active pump maintained by a large and powerful tongue. The tongue fills a large channel in the lower beak. It moves rapidly back and forth, up to five times per second, drawing water through the filters on the backwards pull and expelling it on the forward drive.

(a)

(b)

(c)

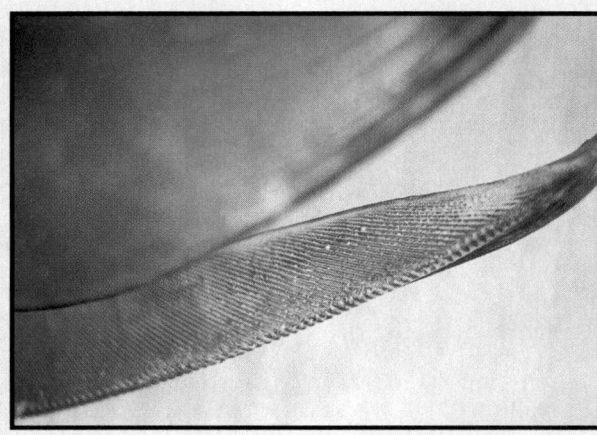
(d)

FIGURE 1   **Vetebrate Filter Feeders.** (*a*) Gray whale (*Eschrichtius robustus*) feeding in a kelp bed. (*b*) Baleen. (*c*) Flamingos (*Phoenicopterus minor*) feeding. (*d*) Filters on the bill of a flamingo.

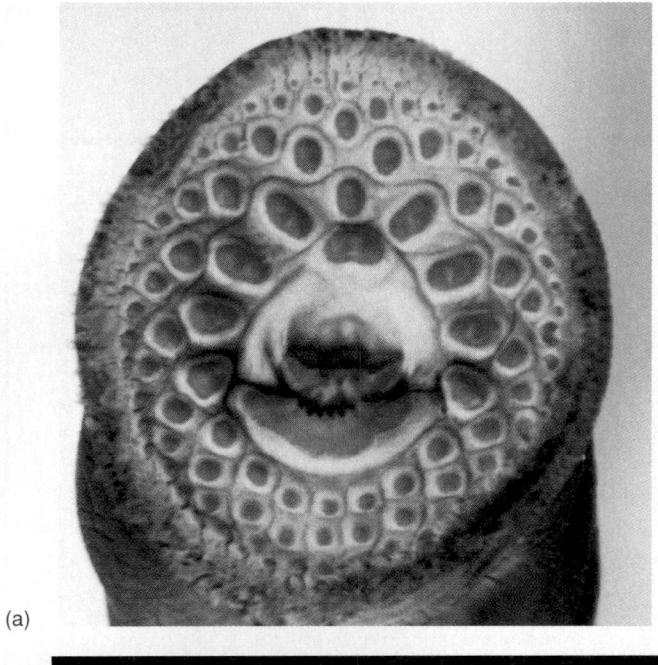

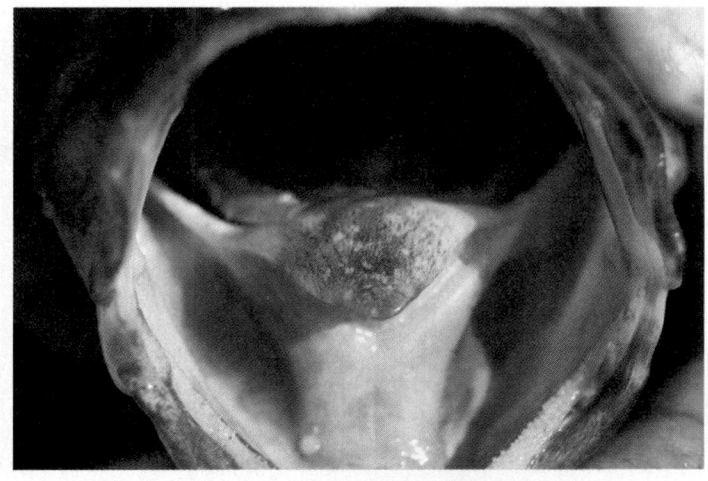

FIGURE 37.6

Tongues. (*a*) The rasping tongue and mouth of a lamprey. (*b*) A fish tongue. (*c*) The tongue of a chameleon catching an insect. (*d*) The tongue of a woodpecker is used to help extract insects from the bark of a tree.

the gastric glands and their HCl production evolved in the context of killing bacteria and helping preserve food. The synthesis of the enzyme pepsinogen may have evolved later because the stomach is not essential for digestion. In fact, in those vertebrates that feed on very small particulate matter, the stomach may be lost, as probably occurred in some lungfishes, chimaeras, and teleosts (figure 37.8*b,c*).

GIZZARDS

Some fishes, some reptiles such as crocodilians, and all birds have a gizzard (figure 37.8*a*) that is used to grind up food. The bird's gizzard develops from the posterior part of the stomach called the ventriculus.   6   Pebbles (grit) that have been swallowed are often retained in the gizzard of grain-eating birds and facilitate the grinding process.

RUMENS

Some of the most unusual modifications of the stomach are seen in ruminant mammals—animals that "chew their cud." Examples include cows, sheep, and deer. This method of digestion has evolved in animals that need to eat large amounts of food relatively quickly, but can chew the food at a more comfortable or safer location. More important though, the ruminant stomach provides an opportunity for large numbers of microorganisms to digest the cellulose walls of grass and other vegetation. Cellulose contains a large amount of energy; however, animals generally lack the ability to produce the enzyme cellulase, which is needed to digest cellulose and obtain its energy. Because gut microorganisms can produce this enzyme, they have made the herbivorous life-style more effective.

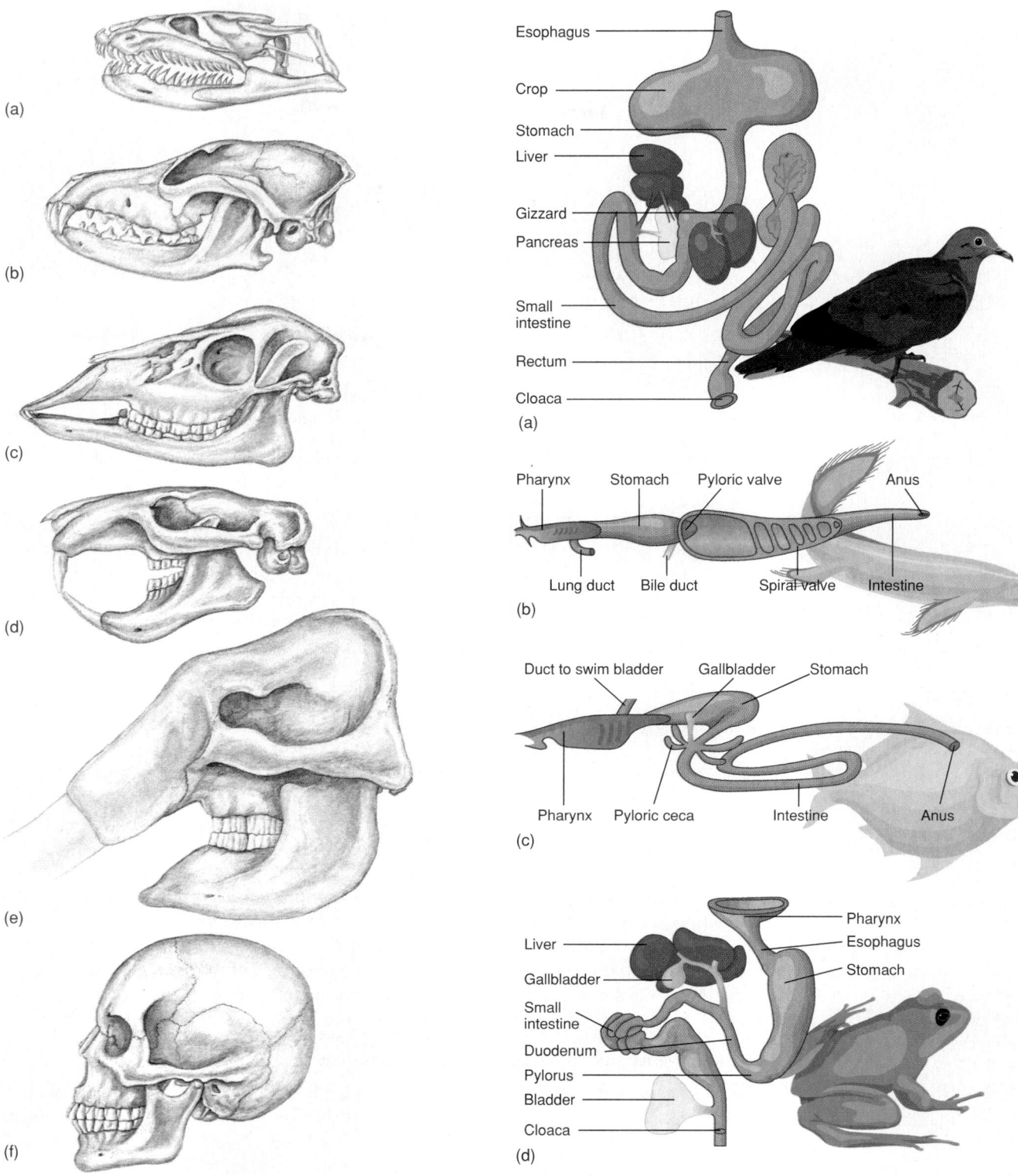

Figure 37.7
The Arrangement of Teeth in a Variety of Vertebrates. (*a*) Snake. (*b*) Wolf. (*c*) Deer. (*d*) Beaver. (*e*) Elephant. (*f*) Human.

Figure 37.8
The Arrangement of Stomachs and Intestines in a Variety of Vertebrates. (*a*) Pigeon. (*b*) Lungfish. (*c*) Teleost fish. (*d*) Frog.

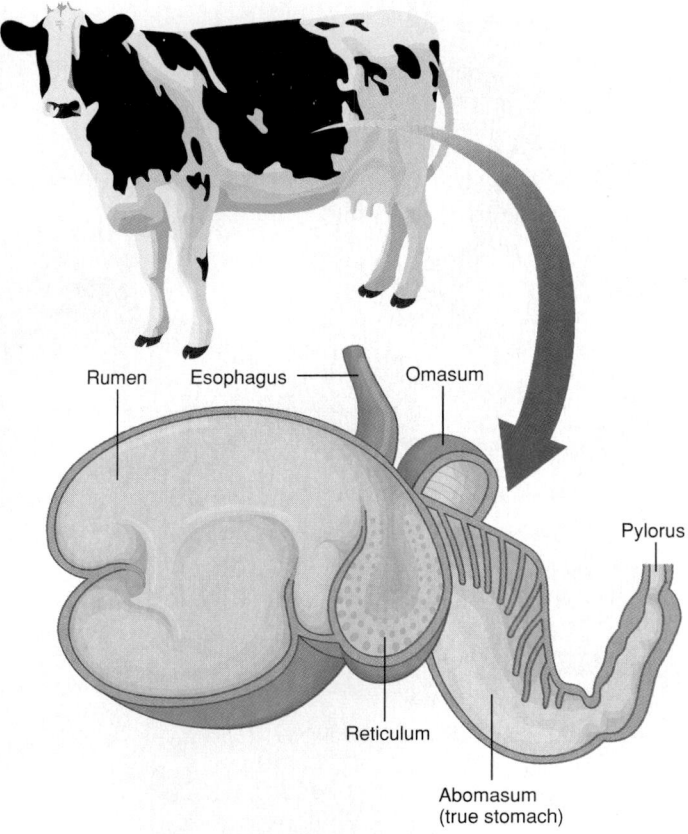

Figure **37.9**

A Ruminant Mammal. The four-chambered stomach of a cow, where cellulose is digested by symbiotic microorganisms.

In ruminants, the upper portion of the stomach expands to form a large pouch, the rumen, and a smaller reticulum. The lower portion of the stomach consists of a small antechamber, the omasum, with a "true" stomach, or abomasum, behind it (figure 37.9). Food first enters the rumen, where it encounters the microorganisms. Aided by copious secretions of fluid, body heat, and churning of the rumen, the food is partially digested and reduced to a pulpy mass. Later, the pulpy mass moves into the reticulum, from which mouthfuls are regurgitated as "cud" (L. *ruminare,* to chew the cud). At this time, food is thoroughly chewed for the first time. When reswallowed, the food enters the rumen where it becomes more liquid in consistency. When it is very liquid, the digested food material flows out of the reticulum and into the omasum and then the glandular region, the abomasum. Here the digestive enzymes are first encountered, and digestion continues.

Cecae

The food of ruminants is attacked by microorganisms before gastric digestion, but in the typical nonruminant herbivore, microbial action on cellulose occurs after digestion. Rabbits, horses, and rats accomplish cellulose digestion by maintaining a population of microorganisms in their unusually large cecum,

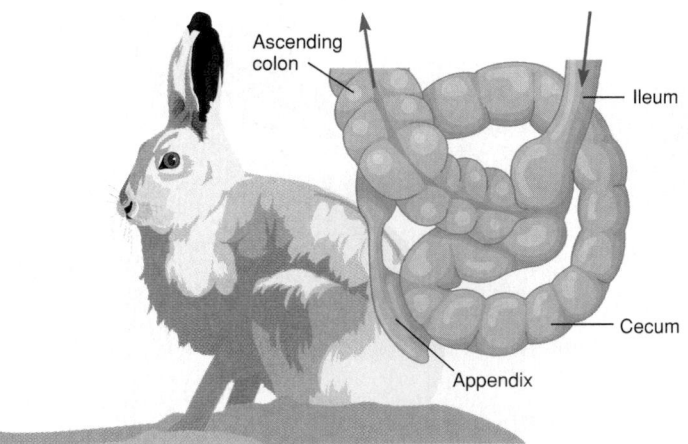

Figure **37.10**

The Extensive Cecum of a Nonruminant Herbivore, Such as a Rabbit. The cecum contains microorganisms that produce digestive enzymes (e.g., cellulase that help break down cellulose).

the blind pouch that extends from the colon (figure 37.10). ⑦ Adding further to this efficiency, a few nonruminant herbivores, such as mice and rabbits, eat some of their own feces to process the remaining materials in them, such as vitamins.

Livers and Gallbladders

In those vertebrates that have a gallbladder, it is closely associated with the liver. The liver manufactures bile which is then stored in the gallbladder. **Bile** is a fluid containing bile salts and bile pigments. Bile salts play an important role in the digestion of fats, although they are not digestive enzymes. They emulsify dietary fat, breaking it down into small globules (emulsification) on the surface of which the fat-digesting enzyme lipase can function. Bile pigments result from phagocytosis of red blood cells in the spleen, liver, and red bone marrow. Phagocytosis cleaves the hemoglobin molecule, iron is released, and the remainder of the molecule is converted into pigments that enter the circulation. These pigments are subsequently extracted from the circulation in the liver and excreted in the bile as bilirubin ("red bile") and biliverdin ("green bile").

Because of the importance of bile in fat digestion, the gallbladder is relatively large in carnivores and vertebrates in which fat is an important part of the diet. It is much reduced or absent in bloodsuckers, such as the lamprey, and in animals that feed primarily on plant food (e.g., some teleosts, many birds, rats, and other mammals such as whales).

Pancreata

Every vertebrate has a pancreas (pl., pancreata); however, in lampreys and lungfishes it is embedded in the wall of the intestine and is not a visible organ. Both endocrine and exocrine tissues are present, but the cell composition varies. Pancreatic fluid containing many enzymes is emptied into the small intestine via the pancreatic duct.

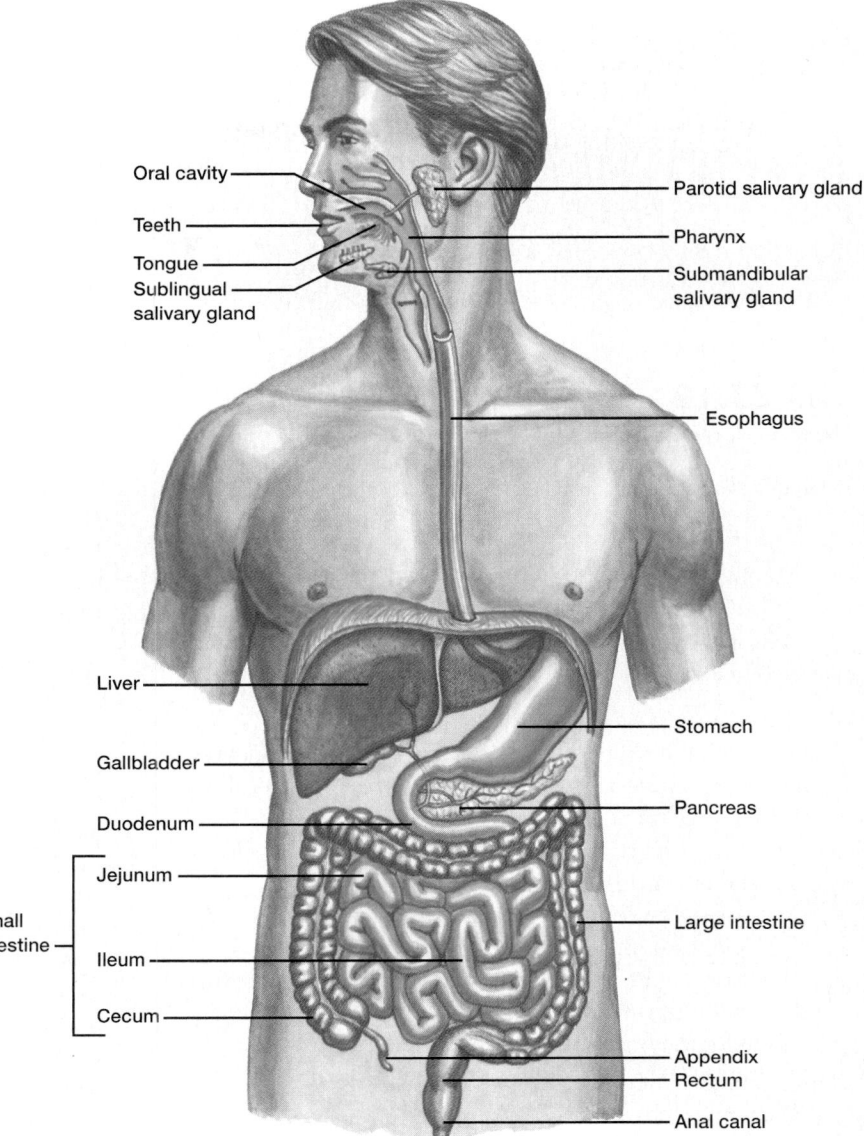

Oral cavity
Teeth
Tongue
Sublingual salivary gland
Parotid salivary gland
Pharynx
Submandibular salivary gland
Esophagus
Liver
Gallbladder
Duodenum
Jejunum
Small intestine
Ileum
Cecum
Stomach
Pancreas
Large intestine
Appendix
Rectum
Anal canal

FIGURE 37.11

Major Organs and Parts of the Human Digestive System. Food passes from the mouth through the pharynx and esophagus to the stomach. From the stomach, it passes to the small intestine, where nutrients are broken down and absorbed into the circulatory and lymphatic systems. Nutrients then move to the large intestine, where water is reabsorbed, and feces are formed. Feces exit the body via the anal canal.

INTESTINES

The configuration and divisions of the small and large intestines vary greatly among vertebrates. Intestines are closely related to the animal's type of food, body size, and levels of activity. For example, cyclostomes, chondrichthian fishes, and primitive bony fishes have short, nearly straight intestines that extend from the stomach to the anus (see figure 37.8b). In more advanced bony fishes, the intestine increases in length and begins to coil (see figure 37.8c). The intestines are moderately long in most amphibians and reptiles (see figure 37.8d). In birds (see figure 37.8a) and mammals, the intestines are longer and have more surface area than those of other tetrapods. Birds typically have two ceca, and mammals a single cecum at the beginning of the large intestine. The large intestine is much longer in mammals than in birds, and it empties into the cloaca in most vertebrates.

Stop and Ask Yourself

18. How do vertebrate teeth reflect the eating habits of various animals?
19. How does the stomach of a ruminant function?

THE MAMMALIAN DIGESTIVE SYSTEM

Humans, pigs, bears, raccoons, and a few other mammals are omnivores. The digestive system of an omnivore possesses the mechanical and chemical ability to process many kinds of foods. The following sections will examine the control of gastrointestinal motility, the major parts of the alimentary canal, and the accessory organs of digestion (figure 37.11).

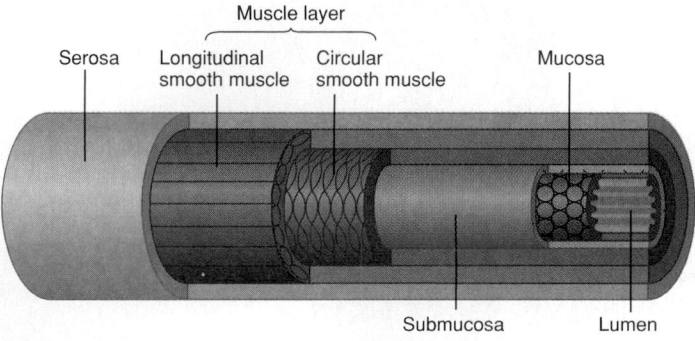

Muscle layer

Serosa | Longitudinal smooth muscle | Circular smooth muscle | Mucosa

Submucosa | Lumen

FIGURE 37.12

The Mammalian Gastrointestinal Tract. A generalized illustration of the common structural layers of the gastrointestinal tract. The central lumen extends from the mouth to the anus.

The process of digesting and absorbing nutrients in a mammal includes:

1. Ingestion—eating
2. Peristalsis and segmentation—the involuntary, sequential muscular contractions that move ingested nutrients along the digestive tract
3. Secretion—the release of hormones, enzymes, and specific ions and chemicals that take part in digestion
4. Digestion—the conversion of large nutrient particles or molecules into small particles or molecules
5. Absorption—the passage of usable nutrient molecules from the small intestine into the bloodstream and lymphatic system for the final passage to body cells
6. Defecation—the elimination from the body of undigested and unabsorbed material as waste

GASTROINTESTINAL MOTILITY AND ITS CONTROL

As with any organ, the function of the gastrointestinal tract is determined by the type of tissues it contains. Most of the mammalian gastrointestinal tract has the same anatomical structure along its entire length (figure 37.12). From the outside inward, there is a thin layer of connective tissue called the serosa. (The serosa forms a moist epithelial sheet called the peritoneum. This peritoneum lines the entire abdominal cavity and covers all internal organs. The space it encompasses is the coelom.) Next is the longitudinal smooth muscle layer and circular smooth muscle layer. Underneath this muscle layer is the submucosa. The submucosa contains connective tissue that contains blood and lymphatic vessels. The mucosa faces the central opening called a lumen.

It is the coordinated contractions of the muscle layers of the gastrointestinal tract that mix the food material with various secretions, and move the food from the oral cavity to the rectum. The two types of movement involved are peristalsis and segmentation.

During **peristalsis** (Gr. *peri*, around + *stalsis*, contraction), food advances through the gastrointestinal tract when the rings of circular smooth muscle contract behind it and relax in front of it (figure 37.13*a*). Peristalsis is analogous to squeezing icing from a pastry tube. The small and large intestines also have rings of smooth muscles that repeatedly contract and relax, creating an oscillating back-and-forth movement in the same place, called **segmentation** (figure 37.13*b*). This movement mixes the food with digestive secretions and increases the efficiency of absorption.

Sphincters also influence the flow of material through the gastrointestinal tract and prevent backflow. Sphincters are rings of smooth or skeletal muscle located at the beginning or ends of specific regions of the gut tract. For example, there is a sphincter called the cardiac sphincter located between the esophagus and stomach, and a pyloric sphincter located between the stomach and small intestine.

The control of gastrointestinal activity is based on the volume and composition of food in the lumen of the gut. For example, ingested food distends the gut and stimulates mechanical receptors located in the gut wall. In addition, as carbohydrates, lipids, and proteins are digested, various chemical receptors in the gut wall are also stimulated. Signals from these mechanical and chemical stimuli travel through nerve plexuses in the gut wall to control the muscular contraction that leads to peristalsis and segmentation, as well as the secretion of various substances (e.g, mucus, enzymes) into the gut lumen. In addition to this local control, long-distance nerve pathways connect the receptors and effectors with the central nervous system. Either or both of these pathways function to maintain homeostasis in the gut. The endocrine cells of the gastrointestinal tract also produce hormones that help regulate secretion, digestion, and absorption.

ORAL CAVITY

The **oral cavity** (mouth) is protected by a pair of lips. The lips are highly vascularized, skeletal muscle tissue with an abundance of sensory nerve endings. Lips help retain food as it is being chewed and play a role in phonation (the modification of sound).

The oral cavity contains the teeth (figure 37.14) and tongue. The mechanical processing of a wide range of foods by mammals is possible because the teeth are covered with enamel, the hardest material in the body, and because of the large force exerted by the jaws and teeth. The oral cavity is continuously bathed by **saliva,** a watery fluid secreted by three pairs of salivary glands. Saliva moistens food and binds it together with mucins (glycoproteins), and forms the ingested food into a moist mass called a bolus. Saliva also contains bicarbonate ions (HCO_3^-) that buffer chemicals in the mouth, thiocyanate ions (SCN^-) and the enzyme lysozyme that kill microorganisms, and it contributes an enzyme (amylase) necessary for the initiation of carbohydrate digestion.

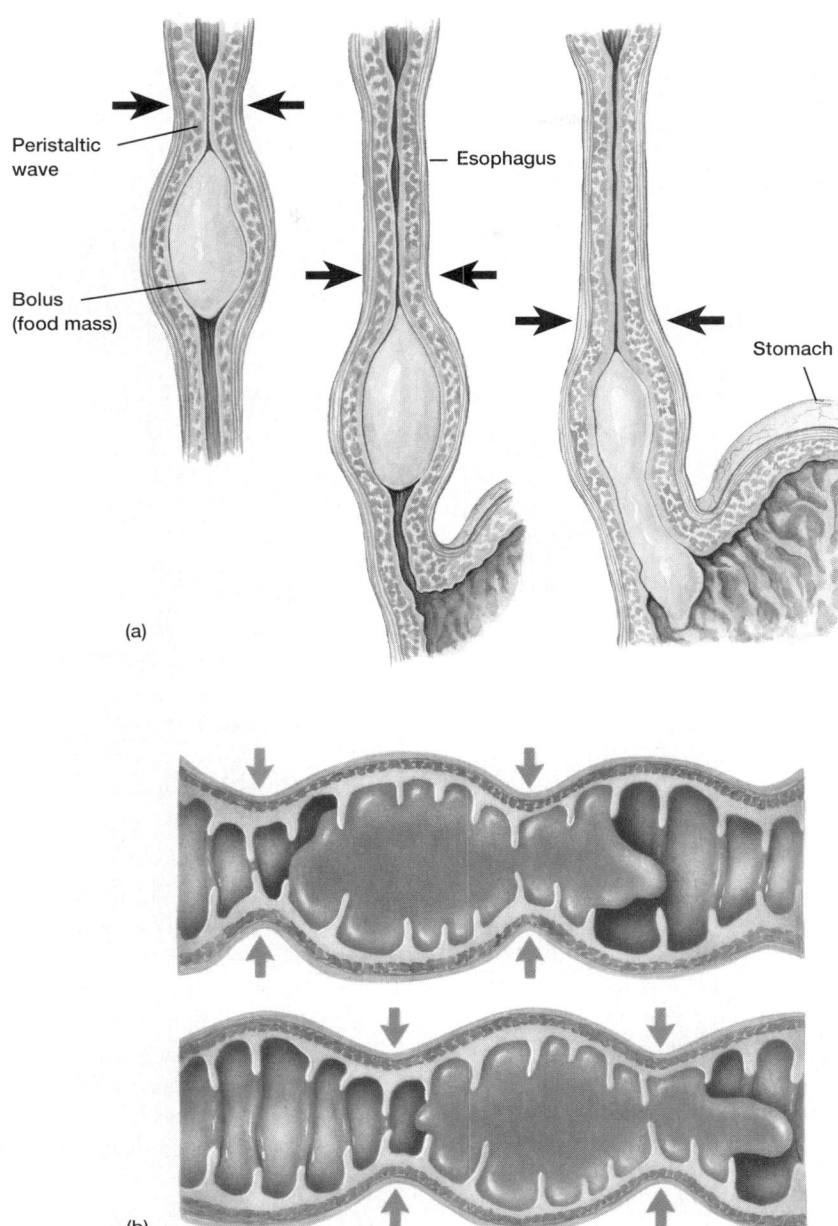

Peristaltic wave

Bolus (food mass)

Esophagus

Stomach

(a)

(b)

Figure 37.13

Peristalsis and Segmentation. (*a*) Peristaltic waves move food through the esophagus to the stomach. (*b*) In segmentation, simultaneous muscular contractions of many sections of the intestine (arrows) help mix nutrients with digestive secretions.

PHARYNX AND ESOPHAGUS

Chapter 36 presented the fact that both air and swallowed foods and liquids pass from the mouth into the **pharynx**—the common passageway for both the digestive and respiratory tracts. The epiglottis temporarily seals off the opening (glottis) to the trachea so that swallowed food will not enter the trachea. Initiation of the swallowing reflex can be voluntary, but most of the time it is involuntary. When swallowing begins, sequential, involuntary contractions of smooth muscles in the

Stop and Ask Yourself

20. What are the component parts of the mammalian gastrointestinal tract? What are the accessory organs of digestion?
21. How do peristalsis and segmentation differ?
22. How is gastrointestinal motility controlled?
23. What is the function of saliva?

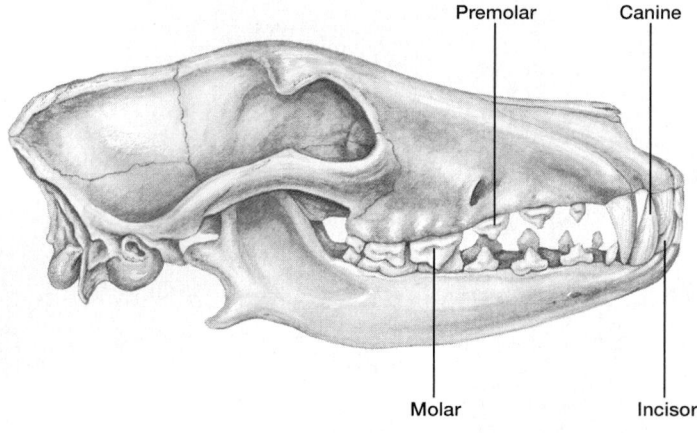

(a)

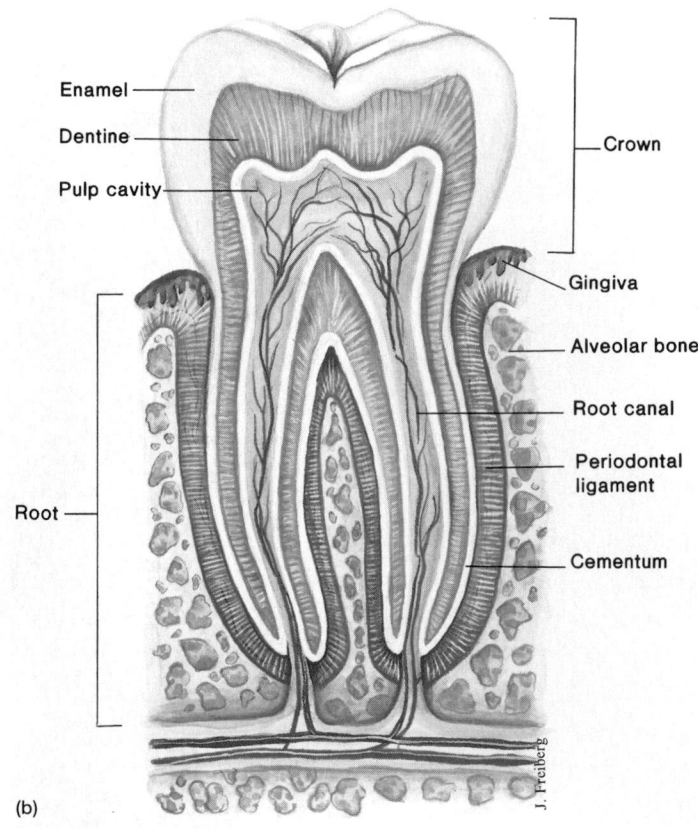

(b)

Figure 37.14

Teeth. (*a*) The teeth of an omnivorous mammal, such as this wolf, are specialized for slicing, puncturing, tearing, and grinding, all of which are used to consume both animal flesh and plant material. (*b*) The anatomy of a typical mammalian tooth.

walls of the **esophagus** propel the bolus or liquid to the stomach. Neither the pharynx nor the esophagus contribute to digestion.

Stomach

The mammalian **stomach** (figure 37.15*a*) is a muscular distensible sac having three main functions. It (1) stores and mixes the food bolus received from the esophagus, (2) secretes substances (enzymes, mucus, and HCl) that start the digestion of proteins, and (3) helps control the rate at which food moves into the small intestine via the pyloric sphincter.

The stomach is made up of an inner mucous membrane containing thousands of gastric glands (figure 37.15*b*). Three types of cells are found in these glands. **Parietal cells** secrete a solution containing HCl, and **chief cells** secrete pepsinogen, the precursor of the enzyme pepsin. Both of the cells are located in the pits of the gastric glands. The surface of the mucous membrane at the openings of the glands contains numerous **mucous cells** that secrete mucus that coats the surface of the stomach and protects it from the HCl and digestive enzymes. ⑧ The surfaces of the upper gastrointestinal tract, esophagus and mouth, have a much thinner mucous-cell layer than the stomach, which is why vomiting can cause a burning sensation in the esophagus or mouth. Endocrine cells in one part of the stomach mucosa release the hormone gastrin, which travels to target cells in the gastric glands, further stimulating them.

When the bolus of food enters the stomach, it causes the walls of the stomach to distend. This distention, as well as the act of eating, causes the gastric pits to secrete HCl (as H⁺ and Cl⁻) and pepsinogen. The H⁺ ions cause pepsinogen to be converted into the active enzyme pepsin. As pepsin, mucus, and HCl mix with and begin to break down proteins, smooth mucosal

muscles contract and vigorously churn and mix the food bolus. About 3 to 4 hours after a meal, the stomach contents have been sufficiently mixed and are a semiliquid mass called **chyme** (Gr. *chymos*, juice). The pyloric sphincter regulates the release of the chyme into the small intestine.

When the stomach is empty, peristaltic waves cease; however, after about 10 hours of fasting, new waves may occur in the upper region of the stomach. ⑨ It is these waves that can cause "hunger pangs" as sensory nerve fibers carry impulses to the brain.

Small Intestine: Main Site of Digestion

Most of the food a mammal ingests is digested and absorbed in the **small intestine.** The human small intestine is about 4 cm in diameter and 7 to 8 m in length (*see figure 37.11*). It is intermediate in length between the small intestines of typical carnivores and herbivores of similar size, and reflects the human's omnivorous eating habits. The length of the small intestine is directly related to the total surface area available for absorbing nutrients, as determined by the many circular folds and minute projections of the inner gut surface (figure 37.16*a*). On the circular folds, thousands of fingerlike projections called **villi** (s., **villus;** L. "tuft of hair") project from each square centimeter of mucosa (figure 37.16*b*). Both the circular folds and villi are covered by simple columnar epithelial cells, each bearing numerous microvilli (figure 37.16*d*). These minute projections are so dense that the inner wall of the human small intestine has a total surface area of approximately 300 m² — the size of a tennis court.

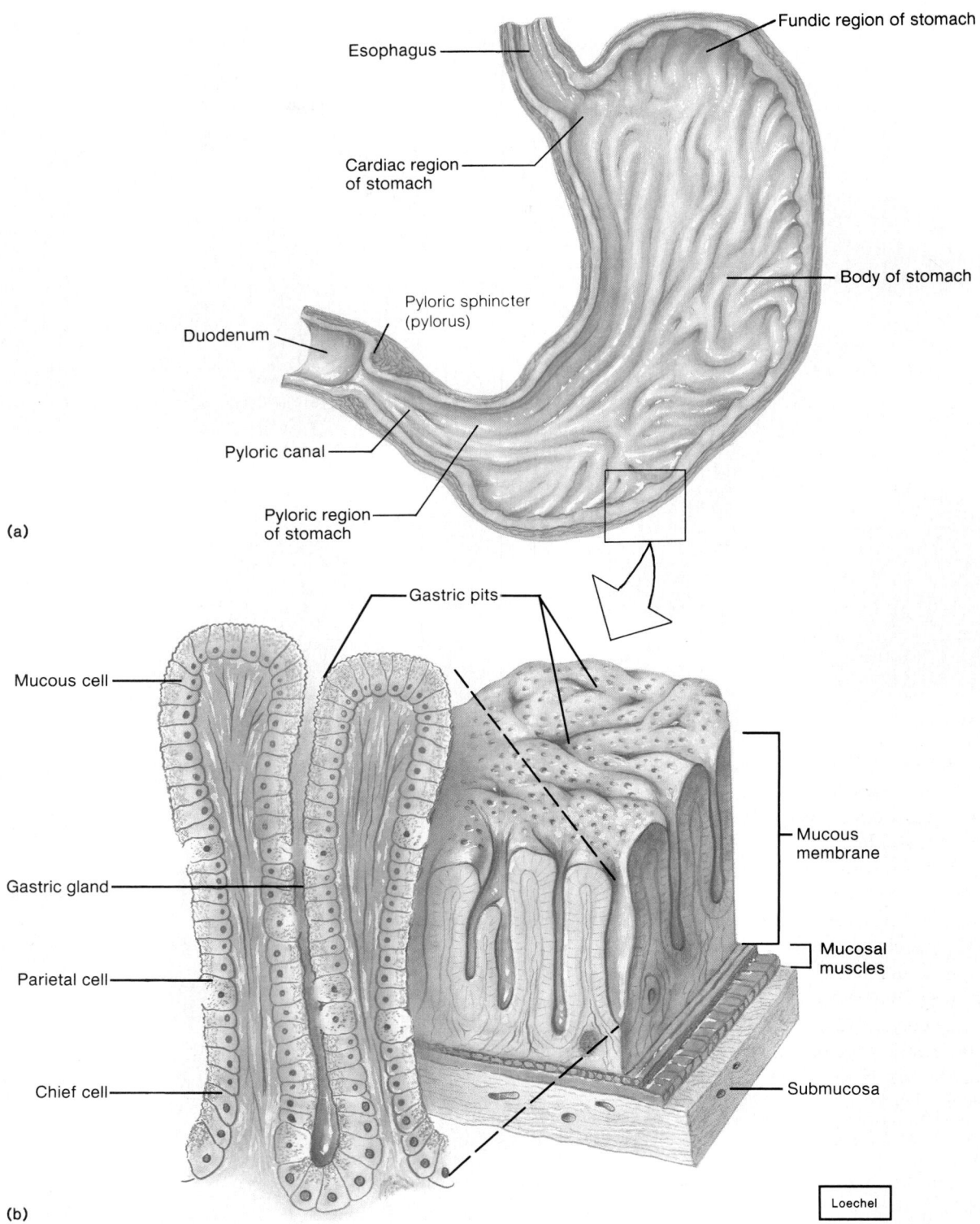

Esophagus

Fundic region of stomach

Cardiac region
of stomach

Body of stomach

Duodenum

Pyloric sphincter
(pylorus)

Pyloric canal

Pyloric region
of stomach

(a)

Gastric pits

Mucous cell

Gastric gland

Parietal cell

Chief cell

Mucous
membrane

Mucosal
muscles

Submucosa

Loechel

(b)

Figure 37.15

The Stomach. (*a*) Food enters the stomach from the esophagus. (*b*) The mucosa of the stomach is covered with gastric glands. The gastric glands include mucous cells, parietal cells, and chief cells—each type producing a different secretion.

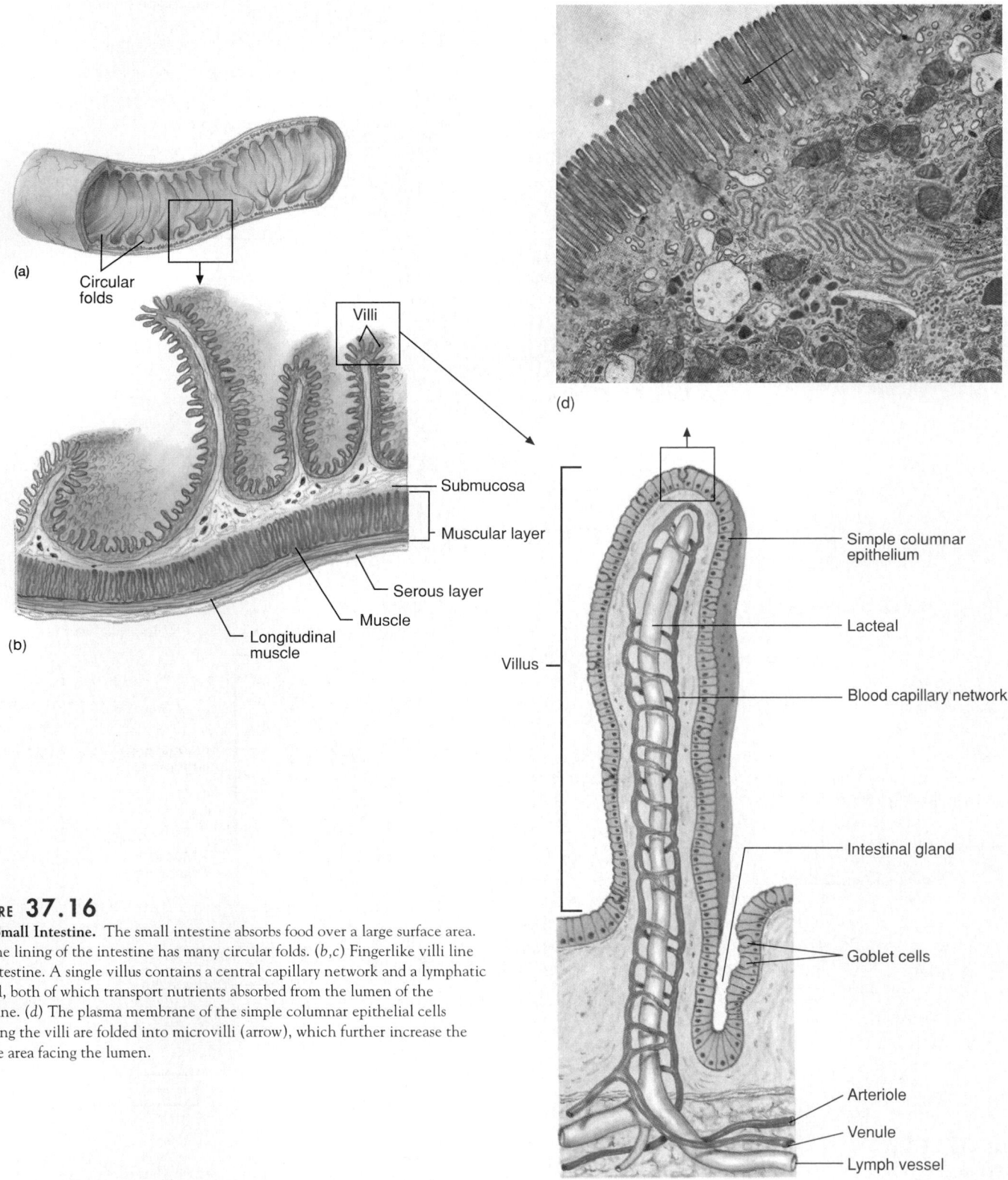

(a) Circular folds

Villi

Submucosa

Muscular layer

Serous layer

Muscle

Longitudinal muscle

(b)

Villus

(d)

Simple columnar epithelium

Lacteal

Blood capillary network

Intestinal gland

Goblet cells

Arteriole

Venule

Lymph vessel

(c)

Figure 37.16

The Small Intestine. The small intestine absorbs food over a large surface area. (*a*) The lining of the intestine has many circular folds. (*b,c*) Fingerlike villi line the intestine. A single villus contains a central capillary network and a lymphatic lacteal, both of which transport nutrients absorbed from the lumen of the intestine. (*d*) The plasma membrane of the simple columnar epithelial cells covering the villi are folded into microvilli (arrow), which further increase the surface area facing the lumen.

37.22

The first part of the small intestine is called the duodenum, and functions primarily in digestion. The next part is the jejunum and the last part is the ileum: both function in the absorption of nutrients.

The duodenum contains many digestive enzymes that are secreted by intestinal glands in the duodenal mucosa; other enzymes are secreted by the pancreas. It is here that digestion of carbohydrates and proteins is completed, and where the digestion of most lipids occurs. In the jejunum and ileum, absorption of the end products of digestion (amino acids, simple sugars, fatty acids, glycerol, nucleotides, water) takes place. Much of this absorption involves active transport and the sodium-dependent ATPase pump. Sugars and amino acids are absorbed into the capillaries of the villi, whereas free fatty acids enter the epithelial cells of the villi and are recombined with glycerol to form triglycerides. The triglycerides are coated with proteins to form small droplets called **chylomicrons,** which enter the lacteals of the villi (figure 37.16c). From the lacteals, the chylomicrons move into the lymphatics and eventually into the bloodstream to be transported throughout the body.

Besides absorbing organic molecules, the small intestine absorbs water and dissolved mineral ions. About 9 liters of water are absorbed per day in the small intestine, and the rest is absorbed in the large intestine.

LARGE INTESTINE

Unlike the small intestine, the **large intestine** has no circular folds, villi, or microvilli; thus, the surface area is much smaller. The small intestine joins the large intestine near a blind-ended sac, the **cecum** (L. *caecum*, blind gut) (*see figure 37.11*). The human cecum and its extension, the **appendix,** are nonfunctional storage sites and possibly represent evolutionary remains of a larger, functional cecum, such as is found in herbivores (*see figure 37.10*). The appendix contains an abundance of lymphoid tissue, and may function as part of the immune system.

The major functions of the large intestine include the reabsorption of water and minerals, and the formation of feces. As food residue is moved along by peristaltic waves, minerals diffuse or are actively transported from the residue across the epithelial surface of the large intestine into the bloodstream. Water follows osmotically and is returned to the lymphatic system and bloodstream. When sufficient water reabsorption does not occur, diarrhea (Gr. *rhein*, to flow) results. If too much water is reabsorbed, fecal matter becomes too thick, and constipation results.

Many bacteria and fungi exist symbiotically in the large intestine. They feed on the food residue and further break down its organic molecules to waste products. In turn, they secrete amino acids and vitamin K, which are absorbed by the host's gut. What remains, feces, is a mixture of a large number of bacteria, fungi, undigested plant fiber, sloughed-off intestinal cells, and other waste products.

Stop and Ask Yourself

24. What are three functions of the stomach?
25. How does the small intestine provide a large surface area for absorption of nutrients?
26. What are the major functions of the large intestine?
27. What is absorbed in the small intestine? The large intestine?

ROLE OF THE PANCREAS IN DIGESTION

The **pancreas** (Gr. *pan*, all + *kreas*, flesh) is an organ that lies just ventral to the stomach and has both endocrine and exocrine functions. Exocrine cells in the pancreas secrete digestive enzymes into the pancreatic duct, which merges with the hepatic duct from the liver to form a common bile duct that enters the duodenum. The pancreatic enzymes complete the digestion of carbohydrates and proteins and initiate the digestion of lipids. Trypsin, carboxypeptidase, and chymotrypsin digest proteins into small peptides and individual amino acids. Pancreatic lipases split triglycerides into smaller, absorbable glycerol and free fatty acids. Pancreatic amylase converts polysaccharides into disaccharides and monosaccharides. Table 37.6 summarizes the major glands, secretions, and enzymes of the mammalian digestive system.

The pancreas also secretes bicarbonate (HCO_3^-) ions that help neutralize the acidic food residue coming from the stomach. Bicarbonate raises the pH from 2 to 7 for optimal digestion to occur. If there were no such neutralization, the pancreatic enzymes could not function.

ROLE OF THE LIVER AND GALLBLADDER IN DIGESTION

The **liver** is the largest organ in the mammalian body and is located just under the diaphragm (*see figure 37.11*). In the liver are millions of specialized cells called hepatocytes. Hepatocytes take up nutrients absorbed from the intestines and release them into the bloodstream. Hepatocytes also manufacture the blood proteins prothrombin and albumin.

In addition to the above, some major metabolic functions of the liver include:

1. Removal of amino acids from organic compounds.
2. Formation of urea from proteins and conversion of excess amino acids into urea to decrease body levels of ammonia.
3. Manufacturing most of the plasma proteins (albumins), forming fetal erythrocytes, destroying worn-out erythrocytes, and helping to synthesize the blood-clotting agents prothrombin and fibrinogen from amino acids.
4. Synthesis of nonessential amino acids.

| TABLE 37.6 | MAJOR DIGESTIVE GLANDS, SECRETIONS, AND ENZYMES IN MAMMALS |

PLACE OF DIGESTION	SOURCE	SECRETION	ENZYME	DIGESTIVE FUNCTION
Mouth	Salivary glands	Saliva	Salivary amylase	Begins the digestion of carbohydrates; inactivated by stomach HCl
	Mucous glands	Mucus	—	Lubricates food bolus
Esophagus	Mucous glands	Mucus	—	Lubricates food bolus
Stomach	Gastric glands	Gastric juice	Lipase	Digests lipids into fatty acids and glycerol
			Pepsin	Digests proteins into polypeptides
	Gastric mucosa	HCl	—	Converts pepsinogen into active pepsin; kills microorganisms
	Mucous glands	Mucus	—	Lubricates
Small intestine	Liver	Bile	—	Emulsifies lipids; activates lipase
	Pancreas	Pancreatic juice	Amylase	Digests starch into maltose
			Chymotrypsin	Digests proteins into peptides and amino acids
			Lipase	Digests lipids into fatty acids and glycerol (requires bile salts)
			Nuclease	Digests nucleic acids into mononucleotides
			Trypsin	Digests proteins into peptides and amino acids
	Intestinal glands	Intestinal juice	Enterokinase	Digests inactive trypsinogen into active trypsin
			Lactase	Digests lactose into glucose and galactose
			Maltase	Digests maltose into glucose
			Peptidase	Digests polypeptides into amino acids
			Sucrase	Digests sucrose into glucose and fructose
	Mucous glands	Mucus	—	Lubricates
Large intestine	Mucous glands	Mucus	—	Lubricates

5. Conversion of galactose and fructose to glucose.
6. Oxidation of fatty acids.
7. Formation of lipoproteins, cholesterol, and phospholipids (essential cell membrane components).
8. Conversion of carbohydrates and proteins into fat.
9. Modification of waste products, toxic drugs, and poisons (detoxification).
10. Synthesis of vitamin A from carotene, and along with the kidneys, participates in the activation of vitamin D.
11. Maintenance of a stable body temperature by raising the temperature of the blood passing through it. Its many metabolic activities make the liver the major heat producer in a mammal's body.
12. The manufacture of bile salts, which are used in the small intestine for the emulsification and absorption of simple fats, cholesterol, phospholipids, and lipoproteins.
13. The liver is also a main storage center. It stores glucose in the form of glycogen, and with the help of insulin and enzymes, it converts glycogen back into glucose as it is needed by the body. The liver also stores fat-soluble vitamins (A, D, E, and K), and minerals, such as iron, from the diet. The liver can also store fats and amino acids and convert them into usable glucose as required.

The **gallbladder** (L. *galbinus*, greenish yellow) is a small organ located near the liver (*see figure 37.11*). The gallbladder stores the greenish fluid called bile that is continuously produced by the liver cells. Bile is very alkaline and contains pigments, cholesterol, lecithin, mucin, bilirubin, and bile salts that act as detergents to emulsify fats (form them into droplets suspended in water) and aid in fat digestion and absorption. (Recall that fats are insoluble in water.) Bile salts also combine with the end products of fat digestion to form micelles. **Micelles** are lipid aggregates (fatty acids and glycerol) with a surface coat of bile salts. Because they are so small, they are able to cross the microvilli of the intestinal epithelium.

SUMMARY

1. Nutrition describes all of those processes by which an animal takes in, digests, absorbs, stores, and uses food (nutrients) in order to meet the metabolic needs of the animal. Digestion is the mechanical and chemical breakdown of food into smaller particles that can be absorbed by the individual cells of an animal.

2. Much of animal evolution has been marked by losses in biosynthetic abilities. This tendency has led to the evolution of the following nutritional types: insectivores, herbivores, carnivores, and omnivores.

3. The nutrients ingested by a heterotroph can be divided into macronutrients and micronutrients. Macronutrients are needed in large quantities and include the carbohydrates, lipids, and proteins. Micronutrients are needed in small quantities and include the vitamins and minerals.

4. Only a few protists and animals can absorb nutrients directly from their external environment. Most animals must work for their nutrients. Various specializations have evolved for food procurement (feeding) in animals. Some examples include continuous versus discontinuous feeding, suspension feeding, deposit feeding, herbivory, predation, surface nutrient absorption, and fluid feeding.

5. The evolution and structure of the digestive system in various invertebrates and vertebrates reflects their eating habits, their rate of metabolism, and their body size.

6. The digestive system of vertebrates is one-way, leading from the mouth (oral cavity), to the pharynx, esophagus, stomach, small intestine, large intestine, rectum, and anus.

7. It is the coordinated contractions of the muscle layer of the gastrointestinal tract that mixes food material with various secretions and moves it from the oral cavity to the rectum. The two types of movement involved are segmentation and peristalsis.

8. Most digestion occurs in the duodenal portion of the small intestine. The products of digestion are absorbed in the walls of the jejunum and ileum. In the process of digestion, fats are made soluble by bile secreted from the liver. The liver has many diverse functions. It controls the fate of newly synthesized food molecules, stores excess glucose as glycogen, synthesizes many blood proteins, and converts nitrogenous and other wastes into a form that can be excreted by the kidneys.

9. The large intestine has little digestive or nutrient absorptive activity; it functions principally to absorb water, to compact the material that is left over from digestion, and to serve as a storehouse for microorganisms.

SELECTED KEY TERMS

autotrophs (*p. 622*)
carnivores (*p. 622*)
digestion (*p. 622*)
herbivores (*p. 622*)
heterotrophs (*p. 622*)
macronutrients (*p. 622*)

micronutrients (*p. 622*)
nutrition (*p. 622*)
omnivores (*p. 622*)
suspension feeding (*p. 626*)
vitamin (*p. 624*)

CRITICAL THINKING QUESTIONS

1. What advantages are there to digestion? Would it not be simpler for a vertebrate to simply absorb carbohydrates, lipids, and proteins from its food and use these molecules without breaking them down?

2. What might have been some evolutionary pressures acting on animals that led to the internalization of digestive systems?

3. Many digestive enzymes are produced in the pancreas and released into the duodenum. Why then, has the mammalian stomach evolved the ability to produce pepsinogen?

4. Human vegetarians, unlike true herbivores, have no highly specialized fermentation chambers. Why is this so?

5. Trace the fate of a hamburger from the mouth to the anus, identifying sites and mechanisms of digestion and absorption.

38

TEMPERATURE AND BODY FLUID REGULATION

Concepts

1. Thermoregulation is a complex and important physiological process that maintains, to varying degrees, an animal's body temperature, despite variations in environmental temperature. Based on this regulation, animals can be categorized as endotherms or ectotherms, and homeotherms or heterotherms.
2. For osmoregulation, some invertebrates have contractile vacuoles, flame-cell systems, antennal (green) glands, maxillary glands, coxal glands, nephridia, or malpighian tubules.
3. A vertebrate's urinary system functions in osmoregulation and excretion, both of which are necessary for internal homeostasis. Osmoregulation governs water and salt balance, and excretion eliminates metabolic wastes. In fishes, reptiles, birds, and mammals, the kidneys are the primary osmoregulatory structures.

Would You Like to Know:

1. how sweating cools the body? (*p. 649*)
2. why hummingbirds have to spend so much time feeding compared to larger birds? (*p. 650*)
3. why bluefin tuna and great white sharks can swim faster than other fishes of a comparable size? (*p. 652*)
4. why frogs have to live in warm, moist environments? (*p. 652*)
5. why goose down was traditionally used as an insulator in outdoor vests and jackets? (*p. 652*)
6. what blubber is? (*p. 653*)
7. why freshwater fishes usually do not drink much water? (*p. 660*)
8. why saltwater fishes drink large quantities of water? (*p. 660*)
9. why a dog's nose is normally cold and wet? (*p. 663*)
10. how kangaroo rats can live in a desert environment drinking little or no water? (*p. 665*)

These and other useful questions will be answered in this chapter.

This chapter contains evolutionary concepts, which are set off in this font.

The earth's environments vary dramatically in temperature and amount of water present. In the polar regions, high mountain ranges, and deep in the oceans, the temperature remains near or below 0° C (32° F) throughout the year. Temperatures exceeding 40° C (103° F) are common in equatorial deserts. Between these two extremes, in the earth's temperate regions, wide fluctuations in temperature are common. The temperate regions have varying amounts of water, as well as varied habitats—fresh water, salt water, wetlands, mountains, and grasslands.

Animals have successfully colonized these varied places on earth by possessing homeostatic mechanisms for maintaining a relatively constant internal environment, despite fluctuations in the external environment. This chapter covers three separate but related homeostatic systems that enable animals to survive the variations in temperature, water availability, and salinity (salt concentration) on the earth. The thermoregulatory system maintains an animal's body temperature and/or its responses to shifts in environmental temperature; the osmoregulatory system maintains the level and concentration of water and salts in the body; and the urinary system eliminates metabolic wastes from the body and functions in osmoregulation.

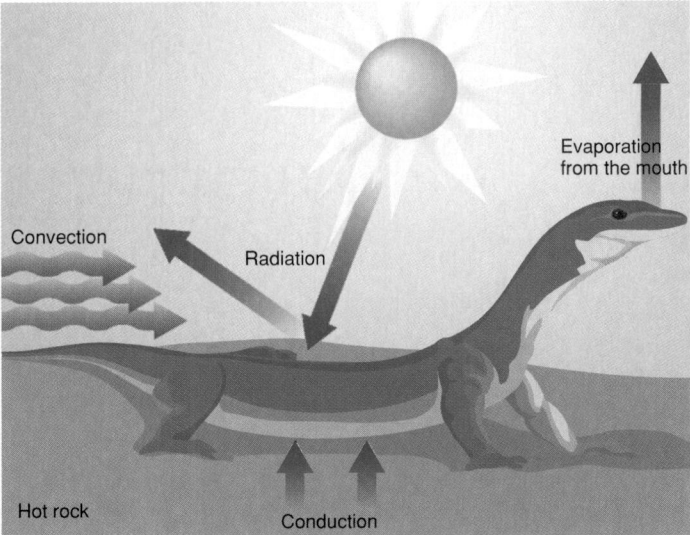

Figure 38.1

Heat Gain and Loss for a Terrestrial Reptile in a Typical Terrestrial Environment. Heat is either gained or lost by objects in direct contact with the animal (conduction), by air currents (convection), by exhaled air (evaporation), or by electromagnetic waves (radiation).

Homeostasis and Temperature Regulation

As presented in chapters 4 and 5, the temperature of a living cell affects the rate of its metabolic processes. An animal can grow faster and respond to the environment more rapidly if its cells are kept warm. In fact, the ability of some higher animals to maintain a constant (homeostatic), relatively high body temperature, is believed to be a major reason for their evolutionary success. This ability to control the temperature of the body is called **thermoregulation** ("heat control") and involves the nervous, endocrine, respiratory, and circulatory systems in higher animals.

The Impact of Temperature on Animal Life

Every animal's physiological functions are inexorably linked to temperature, because metabolism is very sensitive to changes in internal temperature. Thus, temperature has been a strong source of selective pressure on all animals. The rate of cellular respiration increases with temperature up to a certain point. When the temperature rises beyond the temperature optima at which enzymes most efficiently catalyze their chemical reactions, the rates decline as the enzymes begin to denature. The chemical interactions holding the enzymes together in their three-dimensional shape are also disrupted. Thus, the results of enzyme evolution have frequently been enzymes with temperature optima that reflect an animal's habitat. For example, a digestive enzyme in a trout might function optimally at 10° C, whereas another enzyme in the human body that catalyzes the same reaction functions best at 37° C (see figure 4.6). High temperatures

cause the proteins in nucleic acids to denature and low temperatures may cause membranes to change from a fluid to a solid state, which can interfere with many cellular processes, such as active-transport pumps.

Animals can guard against these damaging effects of temperature fluctuations by balancing heat gains and heat losses with their environment.

Heat Gains and Losses

Animals produce heat as a by-product of metabolism, and either gain heat from, or lose it to, the environment. The total body temperature is a product of these factors and can be expressed as:

Body temperature = heat produced metabolically
+ heat gained from the environment
− heat lost to the environment

Animals use four physical processes to exchange heat with the environment: conduction, convection, evaporation, and radiation (figure 38.1). **Conduction** is the direct transfer of thermal motion (heat) between molecules of the environment and those on the body surface of an animal. This transfer is always from an area of higher to one of lower temperature, because heat moves down thermal gradients. For example, when you sit on the cold ground you will lose heat, and when you sit on warm sand, you will gain heat.

Convection is the movement of air (or a liquid) over the surface of a body and contributes to heat loss (if the air is cooler than the body) or heat gain (if the air is warmer than the body). On a cool day, your body loses heat by convection because your skin temperature is higher than the surrounding air temperature.

Evaporation is loss of heat from a surface as water molecules escape in the form of a gas. It is useful only to terrestrial animals. For example, recall that humans and some other mammals have sweat glands that actively move watery solutions through pores to the skin surface. When the skin temperature is high, water at the surface absorbs enough thermal energy to break the hydrogen bonds holding the individual water molecules together, and they depart from the surface, carrying heat with them. ❶ As long as the environmental humidity is low enough to permit complete evaporation, sweating can rid the mammalian body of excess heat; however, the water must evaporate. Sweat dripping from a mammal has no cooling effect at all.

Radiation is the emission of electromagnetic waves produced by objects, such as another animal's body or the sun. Radiation can transfer heat between objects that are not in direct contact with each other, as happens when an animal suns itself (figure 38.2).

SOME SOLUTIONS TO TEMPERATURE FLUCTUATIONS

Animals cope with temperature fluctuations in one of three basic ways: (1) they can occupy a place in the environment where the temperature remains constant and compatible with their physiological processes; (2) their physiological processes may have adapted to the range of temperatures in which the animals are capable of living; or (3) they can generate and trap heat internally to maintain a constant body temperature, despite fluctuations in the temperature of the external environment.

Animals can be categorized as ectotherms or endotherms, based on whether their source of body heat is from internal processes or derived from the environment. **Ectotherms** (Gr. *ectos,* outside) derive most of their body heat from the environment rather than from their own metabolism (figure 38.3). They have low rates of metabolism and are poorly insulated. In general, reptiles, amphibians, fishes, and invertebrates are ectotherms, although a few reptiles, insects, and fishes can generate

FIGURE 38.2
Radiation Warms an Animal. After a cold night in its den on the Kalahari Desert, a meerkat (*Suricata suricatta*) stands at attention, allowing the large surface area of its body to absorb radiation from the sun.

Maximize heat gain   Minimize heat gain

FIGURE 38.3
Heat Gain in an Insect. Postures adopted by a dragonfly to either maximize or minimize heat gain.

some internal heat. Ectotherms tend to move about the environment and find places where they will minimize heat or cold stress to their bodies.

Birds and mammals are called **endotherms** (Gr. *endos*, within) because they obtain their body heat from cellular processes. Having a constant source of internal heat allows them to maintain a nearly constant core temperature despite the fluctuating environmental temperature. ("Core" refers to the body's internal temperature as opposed to the temperature near its surface.)

Most endotherms have bodies insulated by fur or feathers and a large amount of fat. This insulation enables heat to be retained more efficiently and a high core temperature to be maintained. Endothermy allows animals to stabilize their core temperature so that biochemical processes and nervous system functions can proceed at steady high levels of activity. Endothermy has allowed some animals to colonize habitats denied to ectotherms.

Another way of categorizing animals is based on whether they maintain a constant or variable body temperature. Although most endotherms are **homeotherms** (maintain a relatively constant body temperature), and most ectotherms are **heterotherms** (have a variable body temperature), there are many exceptions. Some endotherms vary their body temperatures seasonally (e.g., hibernation); others vary it on a daily basis.

For example, some birds (e.g., hummingbirds) and mammals (e.g., shrews) can only maintain a high body temperature for a short period because they usually weigh less than 10 g and have a body mass so small that not enough heat can be generated to compensate for the heat that is lost across their relatively large surface area. ② Hummingbirds must devote much of the day to locating and sipping nectar (a very high-calorie food source) as a constant energy source for metabolism. When not feeding, hummingbirds would rapidly run out of energy unless their metabolic rates decreased considerably. When resting at night, hummingbirds enter a sleeplike state, called **daily torpor,** and their body temperature approaches that of the cooler surroundings.

There are also some ectotherms that can maintain fairly constant body temperatures. Among these are a number of reptiles that can maintain fairly constant body temperatures by changing position and location during the day to equalize heat gain and loss.

In general, ectotherms are more common in the tropics because they do not have to expend as much energy in maintaining body temperature, and more energy can be devoted to food gathering and reproduction. Indeed, in the tropics, amphibians are far more abundant than mammals. Conversely, in moderate to cool environments, endotherms have a selective advantage and are more abundant. Their high metabolic rates and insulation allow them to occupy even the polar regions (e.g., polar bears). In fact, the efficient circulatory systems of birds and mammals can be thought of as adaptations to endothermy and a high metabolic rate.

TEMPERATURE REGULATION IN INVERTEBRATES

As previously noted, environmental temperature is critical in limiting the distribution of all animals and in controlling metabolic reactions. Many invertebrates have relatively low metabolic rates and have no thermoregulatory mechanisms; thus, they passively conform to the temperature of their external environment. These invertebrates are termed **thermoconformers.**

Evidence exists that some higher invertebrates are capable of directly sensing differences in environmental temperatures; however, specific receptors are either absent or unidentified. What zoologists do know is that many arthropods, such as insects, crustaceans, and the horseshoe crab (*Limulus*), can sense thermal variation. For example, ticks of warm-blooded vertebrates are able to sense the "warmth of a nearby meal" and drop on the vertebrate host.

Many arthropods have unique mechanisms for surviving temperature extremes. For example, temperate-zone insects avoid freezing by reducing the water content in their tissues as winter approaches. Other insects can produce glycerol or other glycoproteins that act as an antifreeze. Some moths and bumblebees warm up prior to flight by shivering contractions of their thoracic flight muscles. Most large, flying insects have evolved a mechanism to prevent overheating during flight; blood circulating through the flight muscles carries heat from the thorax to the abdomen, which gets rid of the heat—much as coolant circulating through an automobile engine passes through the radiator. Certain cicadas (*Diceroprocta apache*) that live in the Sonoran Desert have independently evolved the complete repertoire of evaporative cooling mechanisms used by vertebrates. When threatened with overheating, these cicadas extract water from their blood and transport it through large ducts to the surface of their body, where it passes through sweat pores and evaporates. In other words, these insects can sweat.

Body posture and orientation of the wings to the sun can markedly affect the body temperature of basking insects. For example, perching dragonflies and butterflies can regulate their radiation heat gain by postural adjustments (figure. 38.3).

To prevent overheating, many ground-dwelling arthropods (*Tenebrio* beetles, locusts, scorpions) raise their bodies as high off the ground as possible to minimize heat gain from the

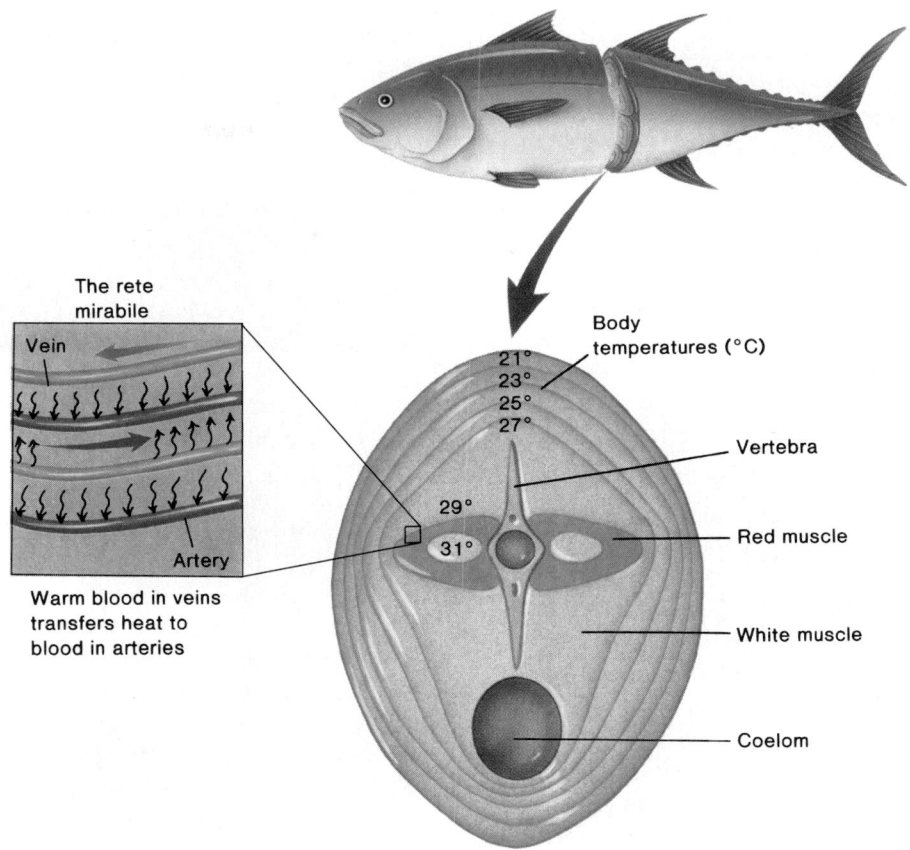

FIGURE 38.4

Thermoregulation in Large, Active Fishes. In the bluefin tuna, the rete mirabile of arteries and veins acts as a countercurrent exchange system that helps reduce the loss of body heat. The cross section through the body shows that the temperature is highest around the red swimming muscles.

ground. Some caterpillars and locusts orient with reference to both the sun and wind, to vary both radiation heat gain and convective heat loss. Some desert-dwelling beetles can exude waxes from thousands of tiny pores on their cuticle. These "wax blooms" provide a critical barrier to water, preventing dehydration, and the excreted wax provides an extra barrier against the desert sun.

Color has a significant effect on thermoregulation since 50% of the radiant energy from the sun is in the visible spectrum. A black surface reflects less radiant energy than a white surface. Thus, based on color, many black beetles seem to be more active earlier in the day because they absorb more radiation and heat faster. Conversely, white beetles are more active in the hotter parts of the day because they absorb less heat.

The above examples of invertebrate temperature regulation give clues to how thermoregulation may have evolved in vertebrates. The endothermic temperature regulation of active insects apparently evolved because locomotion produced sufficient metabolic heat that thermoregulatory strategies could evolve. An increased locomotor metabolism could well have preceded the evolution of thermoregulation in vertebrates.

TEMPERATURE REGULATION IN FISHES

The body temperature of most fishes is determined by their surrounding water temperature. Fishes that live in extremely cold water have "antifreeze" materials in their blood. Polyalcohols (e.g., sorbitol, glycerol) or water-soluble peptides and glycopeptides lower the freezing point of blood plasma and other body fluids. These fishes also have proteins or protein-sugar compounds that stunt the growth of ice crystals that begin to form. These adaptations enable these fishes to stay flexible and swim freely in a supercooled state (i.e., at a temperature below the normal freezing temperature of a solution).

Some very active fishes maintain a core temperature significantly above the temperature of the water. Bluefin tuna and the great white shark have their major blood vessels just under the skin. Branches deliver blood to the deeper, powerful, red swimming muscles, where smaller vessels are arranged in a countercurrent heat exchanger called the **rete mirabile** ("miraculous net") (figure 38.4). The heat generated by these red muscles is not lost because it is transferred in the rete mirabile from venous blood passing outward to cold arterial blood passing inward from the body surface. This arrangement of blood vessels enhances vigorous activity by keeping the swimming muscles several degrees warmer than the tissue near the surface of the fish. This system has been adaptive for these fishes. ③ The power of their muscular contractions can be four times greater than those of similar muscles in fishes with cooler bodies. Thus, they can swim faster and range more widely through various depths in search of prey than can other predatory fishes more limited to given water depths and temperatures.

TEMPERATURE REGULATION IN AMPHIBIANS AND REPTILES

Animals, such as amphibians and reptiles, that have air rather than water as a surrounding medium are subjected to marked daily and seasonal temperature changes. Most of these animals are ectotherms, they derive heat from their environment, and their body temperatures vary with external temperatures.

Most amphibians have difficulty in controlling body heat because they produce little of it metabolically and rapidly lose most of it from their body surfaces. However, as previously noted, behavioral adaptations enable them to maintain their body temperature within a homeostatic range most of the time. Amphibians have an additional thermoregulatory problem because they must exchange oxygen and carbon dioxide across their skin surface, and this moisture layer acts as a natural evaporative cooling system. ④ This problem of heat loss through evaporation limits the habitats and activities of amphibians to warm, moist areas. Some amphibians, such as bullfrogs, can vary the amount of mucus they secrete from their body surface—a physiological response that helps regulate evaporative cooling.

Reptiles have dry rather than moist skin, which reduces loss of body heat through the skin through evaporative cooling. They also have an expandable rib cage, which allows for more powerful and efficient ventilation. Reptiles are almost completely ectothermic. They have a low metabolic rate and warm themselves by behavioral adaptations. In addition, some of the more sophisticated regulatory mechanisms found in mammals are first found in reptiles. For example, in diving reptiles (e.g., sea turtles, sea snakes) body heat is conserved by routing blood through circulatory shunts into the center of the body. These animals can also increase heat production in response to the hormones thyroxine and epinephrine. In addition, tortoises and land turtles can cool themselves through salivating and frothing at the mouth, urinating on the back legs, moistening of the eyes, and panting.

TEMPERATURE REGULATION IN BIRDS AND MAMMALS

Birds and mammals are the most active and behaviorally complex vertebrates. They can live in habitats all over the earth because they are homeothermic endotherms; they can maintain body temperatures between 35 and 42° C with metabolic heat.

Various cooling mechanisms prevent excessive warming in birds. Because they have no sweat glands, birds pant to lose

(a)

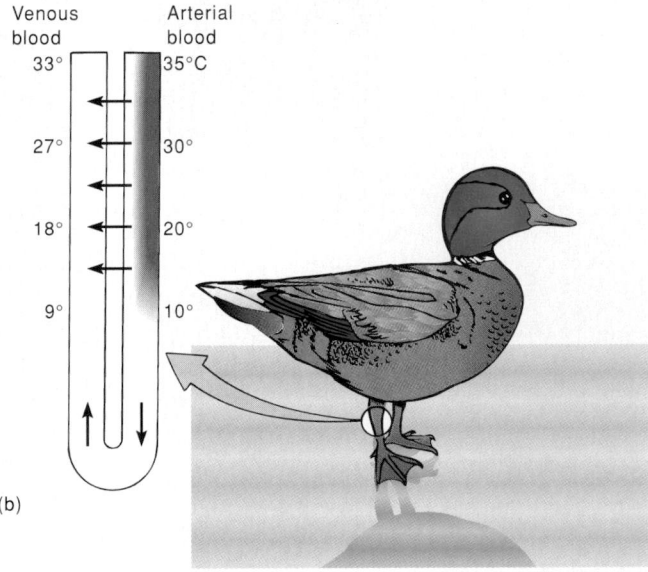

(b)

FIGURE 38.5

Insulation and Countercurrent Heat Exchange. (*a*) The thick layer of down feathers keeps these Chinstrap penguins (*Pygocelis antarctia*) warm. Their covering of short, stiff feathers interlocks to trap air, forming the ornithological equivalent of a diver's suit. (*b*) The countercurrent heat exchanger in a bird foot. Some aquatic birds, such as this duck, possess countercurrent systems of arteries and veins (rete mirabile) in their legs that reduce heat loss. The arteries carry warm blood down the legs to warm the cooler blood in the veins, so that the heat is carried back to the body rather than lost through the feet that are in contact with a cold surface.

heat through evaporative cooling. Some species have a highly vascularized pouch (gular pouch) in their throat that they can flutter (a process called **gular flutter**) to increase evaporation from the respiratory system.

⑤ Some birds possess mechanisms for preventing heat loss. Feathers are excellent insulators for the body, especially downy-type feathers that trap a layer of air next to the body to reduce heat loss from the skin (figure 38.5a). (This mechanism explains why goose down is such an excellent insulator and is used in outdoor vests and coats where protection from extreme cold is needed.) Aquatic species face the problem of heat loss from their legs and feet. To help solve this problem, they have

Figure 38.6

Temperature Regulation. This antelope jackrabbit (*Lepus alleni*) must get rid of excess body heat. Its huge, thin, highly vascularized ears have a large surface area for heat exchange.

peripheral countercurrent heat exchange vessels called a rete mirabile (figure 38.5b) in their legs to reduce heat loss. (Mammals that live in cold regions, such as the arctic fox and barren-ground caribou, also have these exchange vessels in their extremities [e.g., legs, tails, ears, nose].) Animals in hot climates, such as jackrabbits, have mechanisms (e.g., large ears) to rid the body of excess heat (figure 38.6).

6 Marine animals, such as seals and whales, maintain a body temperature around 36 to 38° C by having thick pelts and a thick layer of insulating fat called **blubber** just under the skin. In the tail and flippers, where there is no blubber, a countercurrent system of arteries and veins helps keep heat loss to a minimum.

Birds and mammals also use behavioral mechanisms to cope with external temperature changes. As do ectotherms, they can sun themselves or seek shade as the temperature fluctuates. Many animals huddle together to keep warm; others share burrows for protection from temperature extremes. Migration to warm climates and hibernation enable many different birds and mammals to survive through the harsh winter months. Others, such as the desert camel, have a multitude of evolutionary adaptations for surviving in some of the hottest and driest climates on earth (box 38.1).

HEAT PRODUCTION IN BIRDS AND MAMMALS

In endotherms, heat generation can warm the body as it dissipates throughout tissues and organs. Birds and mammals can generate heat (**thermogenesis**) by muscle contraction, ATPase pump enzymes, oxidation of fatty acids in brown fat, and metabolic processes.

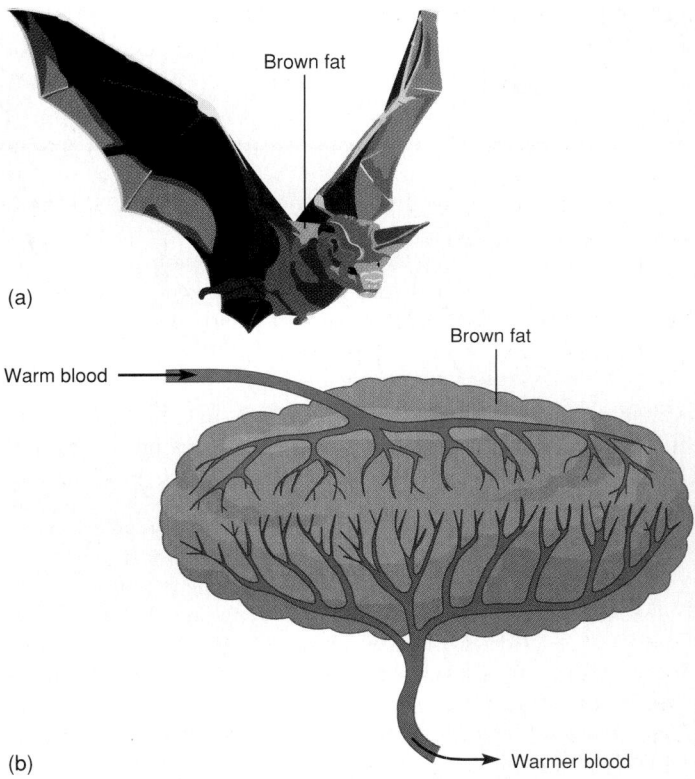

Figure 38.7

Brown Fat. (*a*) Many mammals, such as this bat, have adipose tissue called brown fat located between the shoulder blades. (*b*) The area of brown fat is much warmer than the rest of the body. As blood flows through the brown fat, it is warmed.

Every time a muscle cell contracts, heat is generated by the actin and myosin filaments sliding over each other and the hydrolysis of ATP molecules. Both voluntary muscular work (e.g., running, flying, jumping) and involuntary muscular work (e.g., shivering) generate heat. The generation of heat by shivering is called **shivering thermogenesis.**

Birds and mammals have a unique capacity to generate heat by using specific enzymes of ancient evolutionary origin—the ATPase pump enzymes found in the plasma membranes of most cells. When the body cools, the hormone thyroxine is released from the thyroid gland. Thyroxine increases the permeability of many cells to Na⁺ ions, which leak into the cells. These ions are then quickly pumped out by the ATPase pump. In the process, ATP is hydrolyzed, releasing heat energy. The hormonal triggering of heat production is called **nonshivering thermogenesis.**

Brown fat is a specialized type of fat found in newborn mammals, in mammals that live in cold climates, and in mammals that hibernate (figure 38.7). The brown color of this fat comes from the large number of mitochondria with their iron-containing cytochromes. Deposits of brown fat are found beneath the ribs and in the shoulders. A large amount of heat is

BOX 38.1
HOW THE ONE-HUMPED DROMEDARY (CAMEL) OF THE ARABIAN AND AFRICAN DESERTS THRIVES IN SOME OF THE HOTTEST AND DRIEST CLIMATES ON EARTH

During the past 3 million years, various physiological and behavioral mechanisms have evolved in the dromedary or one-humped camel (*Camelus dromedarius;* figure 1) that enable it to survive on the Arabian and African deserts where temperatures in the summer can exceed 140° F (60° C). What particularly distinguishes the desert camel is its ability to relinquish strict homeothermy and allow its body temperature to fluctuate with that of the environment. As a result, the difference between a camel's body temperature and that of the environment is never large; thus, the flow of heat from the air to the body is reduced.

Another of the camel's physiological adaptations to heat is its "adjustable" metabolic rate. As the desert temperature increases, the camel's metabolic rate slows down. Due to slow dehydration, there is also a drop in the amount of thyroxine produced by the thyroid gland (*see figure 38.8*). With less thyroxine, the camel's respiratory rate also slows, thereby reducing water loss via breathing.

Camel blood is unusual in two ways: its plasma contains more water than that of other animals, and its oval-shaped (*see figure 36.4e*) red blood cells stay intact even when the plasma surrounding the cells has a high osmolarity (they do not crenate; *see figure 3.11b*). Under similar conditions, the red blood cells of other mammals would crenate, and the blood would cease flowing and transporting body heat outward to the skin, leading to a heatstroke. But even after a camel has lost more than half of its body water, its blood continues to circulate and dissipate heat.

The camel also conserves water by excreting extremely dry feces and recycling water from the kidneys to the stomach and back to the blood. (By contrast, other ruminants [cows and goats] cannot recycle water and lose so much fluid when heat stressed that the alimentary tract and kidneys cease functioning entirely.) A camel, after recycling water for weeks, can drink forty gallons of water and rehydrate its blood in less than an hour.

To counteract heat and dehydration, the camel also modifies its behavior. When possible, it lies down, thereby reducing the heat

FIGURE 1   *Camelus dromedarius.*

energy produced by muscle activity and metabolism. Camels also take advantage of the shade cast by other camels and squat close to each other, creating an even larger cooled area. At the same time, each camel faces the sun so that the hump absorbs most of the direct sunlight and the smallest possible body area is exposed. The hump is a concentration of body fat that acts as a kind of sun screen, shielding the camel's vital organs. The camel also urinates on its long legs, and as the urine evaporates, the blood vessels on the legs are cooled.

produced when the brown fat cells oxidize fatty acids because little ATP is made. Blood flowing past brown fat is heated and contributes to warming the body.

The basal metabolic rate of birds and mammals is high and also produces heat as an inadvertent but useful by-product (*see figure 4.10*).

In amphibians, reptiles, birds, and mammals, thermoregulation is controlled by specialized cells in the hypothalamus of the brain. There are two hypothalamic thermoregulatory areas: the heating center and the cooling center. The heating center controls vasoconstriction of superficial blood vessels, erection of hair and fur, and shivering or nonshivering thermogenesis. The cooling center controls vasodilation of blood vessels, sweating, or panting. Overall, body temperature is controlled by

feedback mechanisms (with the hypothalamus acting as a thermostat) that trigger either the heating or cooling of the body (figure 38.8). Specialized neuronal receptors that sense temperature changes are located in the skin and other parts of the body. The warm neuron receptors excite the cooling center and inhibit the heating center; the cold receptors have the opposite effects.

During the winter, various endotherms (e.g., skunks, woodchucks, chipmunks, ground squirrels) go into **hibernation** (L. *hiberna,* winter). When hibernating, the metabolic rate slows as do the heart and breathing rates. Mammals prepare for hibernation by building up fat reserves and growing long winter pelts. All hibernating animals have brown fat. Both increased fat deposition and fur growth are stimulated by

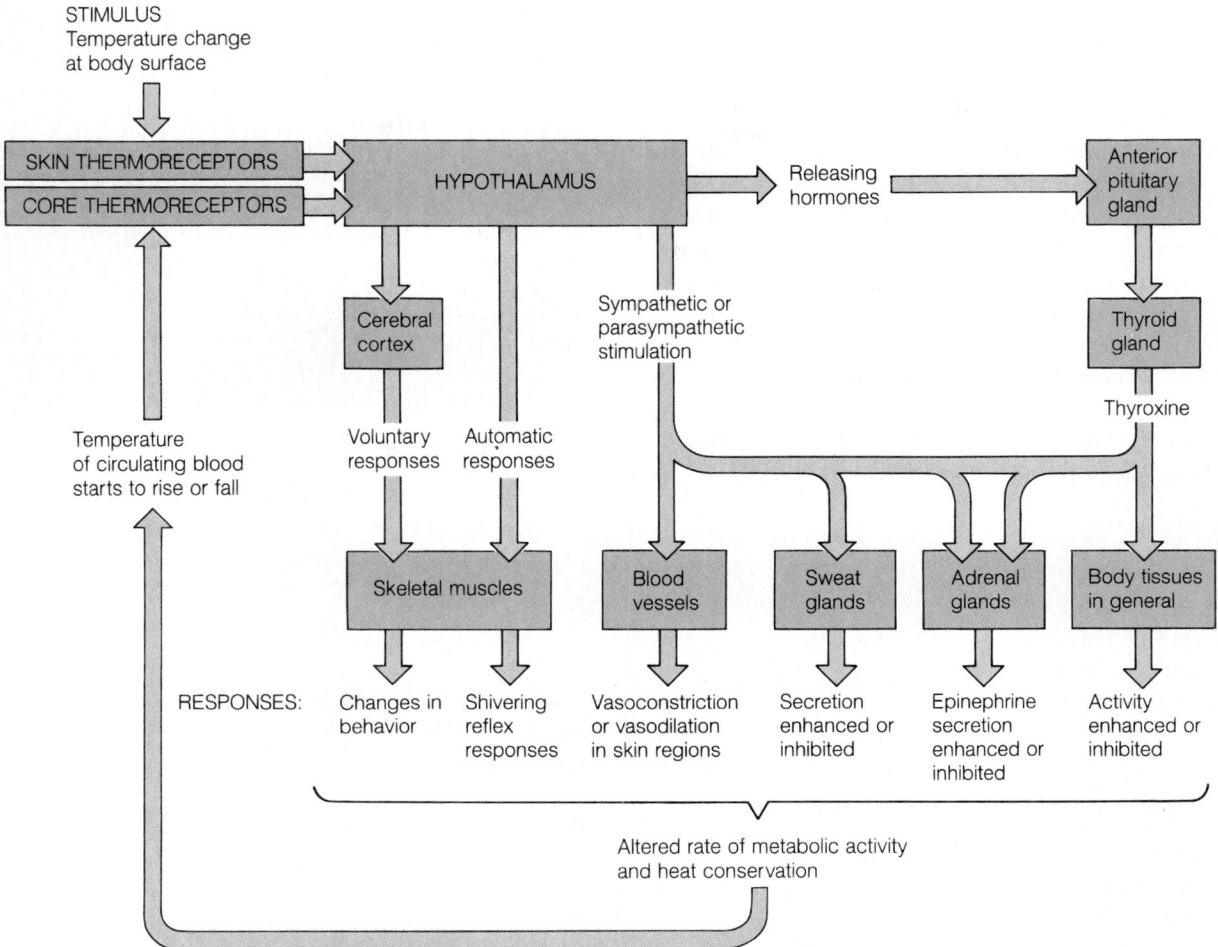

Figure 38.8

Thermoregulation. An overview of the feedback pathways that control the core body temperature of a mammal. The arrows are the major control pathways.

decreasing day length. Another physiological state characterized by slow metabolism and inactivity is **aestivation** (L. *aestivus*, summer), which allows certain mammals to survive long periods of elevated temperature and diminished water supplies.

Some animals, such as badgers, bears, opossums, raccoons, and skunks, enter a state of prolonged sleep in the winter. Since their body temperature remains near normal and does not decrease, this is not true hibernation.

Stop and Ask Yourself

5. What is the function of a rete mirabile?
6. How do amphibians maintain their body temperature?
7. How do birds and mammals generate heat?
8. What is the difference between hibernation and aestivation?

THE CONTROL OF WATER AND SOLUTES (OSMOREGULATION AND EXCRETION)

Excretion (L. *excretio*, to eliminate) can be defined broadly as the elimination of metabolic waste products from an animal's body. These products include carbon dioxide and water (which are produced primarily by cellular respiration), excess nitrogen (which is produced as ammonia from deamination of amino acids), and solutes (various ions). The excretion of respiratory carbon dioxide was covered in chapter 36.

The excretion of nitrogenous wastes is usually associated with the regulation of water and solute (ionic) balance by a physiological process called **osmoregulation.** Osmoregulation is necessary for animals in all habitats. If the osmotic concentration of the body fluids of an animal is equal to that of the medium (environment) in which it lives, this animal is called an **osmoconformer.** When the osmotic concentration of the environment changes, so does that of the animal's body fluids. Obviously, this type of osmoregulation is not very efficient and has limited the distribution of those animals using it. In contrast, if an animal maintains its body fluids at a different osmotic concentration from that of its surrounding environment, it is called an **osmoregulator.**

Animals living in seawater have body fluids with an osmotic concentration that is about ⅓ less (hypoosmotic) than the surrounding seawater, and water tends to leave their bodies continually. To compensate for this problem, mechanisms evolved in these animals to conserve water and prevent dehydration. Freshwater animals have body fluids that are hyperosmotic with respect to their environment, and water tends to continually enter their bodies. To compensate for this problem, mechanisms evolved in these animals that excrete water and prevent fluid accumulation. Land animals have a higher concentration of water in their fluids than in the surrounding air. They tend to lose water to the air through evaporation, and may use considerable amounts of water to dispose of wastes.

The form and function of organs or systems associated with excretion and osmoregulation are related both to environmental conditions (salt water, fresh water, terrestrial) and to body size (especially the surface-to-volume ratio). Some of the ways animals accomplish excretion and osmoregulation, and the structures involved, are discussed next.

INVERTEBRATE EXCRETORY SYSTEMS

Aquatic invertebrates occur in a wide range of media, from fresh water to markedly hypersaline water (e.g., salt lakes). Generally, marine invertebrates have about the same osmotic concentration as seawater (i.e., they are osmoconformers). This avoids any need to osmoregulate. Most water and ions are gained across the integument, via gills, by drinking, and in food. Ions and wastes are mostly lost by diffusion via the integument, gills, or urine.

Freshwater invertebrates are strong osmoregulators because it is impossible to be isosmotic with dilute media. Any water gain is usually eliminated as urine.

A number of invertebrate taxa have more or less successfully invaded terrestrial habitats. The most successful terrestrial invertebrates are the arthropods, particularly the insects, spiders, scorpions, ticks, mites, centipedes, and millipedes. Overall, the water and ion balance of terrestrial invertebrates is quite different from that of aquatic animals because of the limited availability of water and water loss by evaporation from their integument. Some of the invertebrate excretory mechanisms and systems are now discussed.

CONTRACTILE VACUOLES

Some protists and marine invertebrates (e.g., protozoa, cnidarians, echinoderms, sponges) do not have specialized excretory structures because wastes simply diffuse into the surrounding isoosmotic water. In some freshwater species, cells on the body surface actively pump ions into the animal. Many freshwater species (protozoa, sponges), however, have contractile vacuoles that pump out excess water. **Contractile**

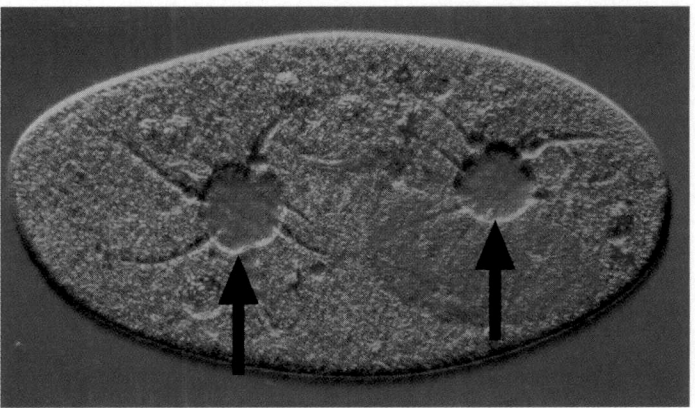

FIGURE 38.9

Contractile Vacuoles. A photomicrograph showing the location of two contractile vacuoles (arrows) in a stained *Paramecium*. Notice the small tubules surrounding each vacuole. These tubes collect water and deliver it to the contractile vacuole, which expels the fluid through a pore (×100).

vacuoles are energy-requiring devices that expel excess water from individual cells exposed to hypoosmotic environments (figure 38.9).

PROTONEPHRIDIA

Although a few groups of metazoan invertebrates possess no known excretory structures, most have **nephridia** (Gr. *nephros*, kidney; s., nephridium) that serve for excretion, osmoregulation, or both. Probably the earliest type of nephridium to appear in the evolution of animals was the **protonephridium** (Gr. *protos*, first + nephridium).

Among the simplest of the protonephridia are flame-cell systems, such as those found in rotifers, some annelids, larval molluscs, and some flatworms (figure 38.10). The protonephridial excretory system is composed of a network of excretory canals that open to the outside of the body through excretory pores. Bulblike **flame cells** are located along the excretory canals. Fluid filters into the flame cells from the surrounding interstitial fluid and is propelled by the beating cilia through the excretory canals and out of the body through the excretory pores. Flame-cell systems function primarily in eliminating excess water. Nitrogenous waste simply diffuses across the body surface into the surrounding water.

METANEPHRIDIA

A more advanced type of excretory structure among invertebrates is the **metanephridium** (Gr. *meta*, beyond + nephridium; pl., metanephridia). There is a critical structural difference between protonephridia and metanephridia. Both open to the outside, but metanephridia (1) also open internally to the body fluids and (2) are multicellular.

Most annelids (such as the common earthworm) and a variety of other invertebrates have a metanephridial excretory

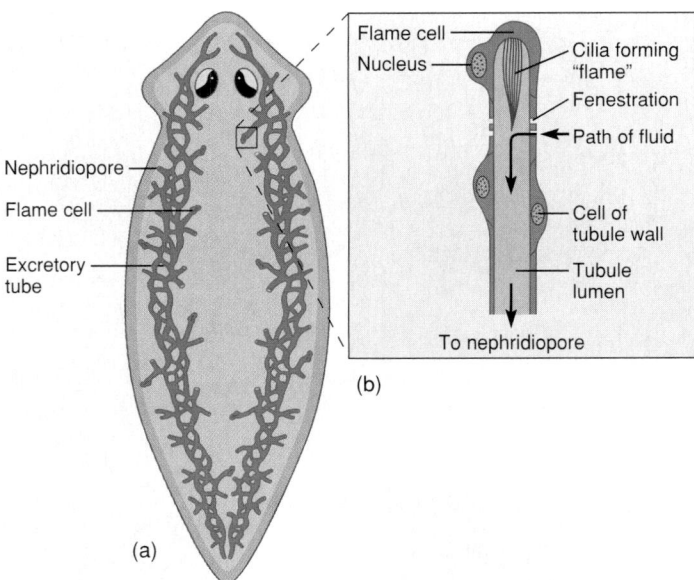

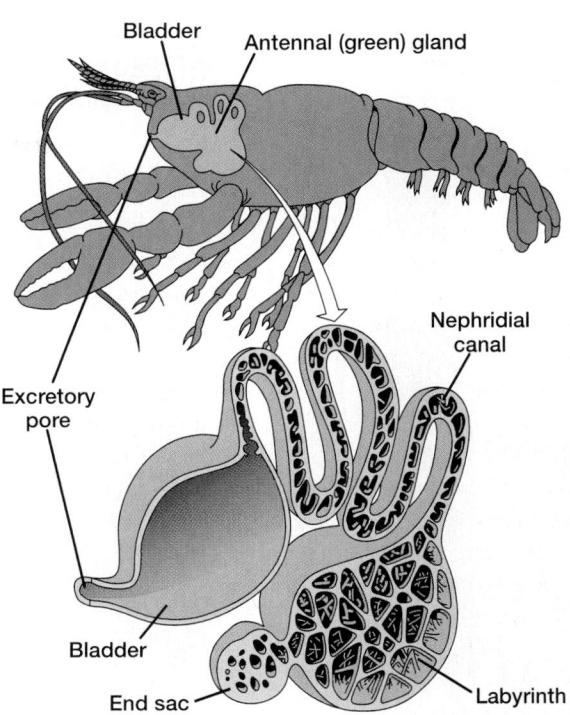

FIGURE 38.10

Protonephridial (Excretory) System in a Turbellarian. (*a*) The system lies in the mesenchyme and consists of a network of fine tubules that run the length of the animal on each side and open to the surface by minute excretory pores called nephridiopores. (*b*) Numerous fine side branches from the tubules originate in the mesenchyme in enlargements called flame cells.

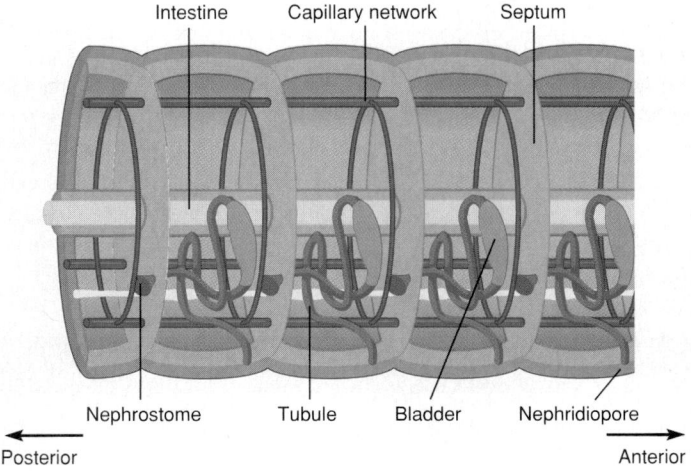

FIGURE 38.11

The Earthworm Metanephridium. The metanephridium opens by a ciliated nephrostome into the cavity of one segment, and the next segment contains the nephridopore. The main tubular portion of the metanephridium is coiled and is surrounded by a capillary network. Waste can be stored in a bladder before being expelled to the outside. Most segments contain two metanephridia.

FIGURE 38.12

Antennal (Green) Gland of the Crayfish. The end sac, which lies in front of and to both sides of the esophagus, is divided into an end sac, where fluid collects by filtration, and a labyrinth. The labyrinth walls are greatly folded and glandular and appear to be an important site for reabsorption. The labyrinth leads via a nephridial canal into a bladder. From the bladder, a short duct leads to an excretory pore.

system. Recall that the earthworm's body is divided into segments, and that each segment has a pair of metanephridia. Each metanephridium (figure 38.11) begins with a ciliated funnel, the nephrostome, that opens from the body cavity of a segment into a coiled tubule. As the fluid is moved through the tubule by beating cilia, ions are reabsorbed and carried away by a network of capillaries surrounding the tubule. Each tubule leads to an enlarged bladder that empties to the outside of the body through an opening called the nephridiopore.

The excretory system of molluscs includes protonephridia in larval stages and metanephridia in adults.

ANTENNAL (GREEN) AND MAXILLARY GLANDS

In those crustaceans that have gills, nitrogenous wastes are removed by simple diffusion across the gills. Most crustaceans release ammonia, although some urea and uric acid are also produced as waste products. Thus, the excretory organs of freshwater species may be more involved with reabsorption of ions and elimination of water than with discharge of nitrogenous wastes. The excretory organs in some crustaceans (crayfish, crabs) are **antennal glands** or **green glands** because of their location near the antenna and their green color (figure 38.12). Fluid filters into the antennal gland from the hemocoel. Hemolymph pressure from the heart is the main driving force for filtration. Marine crustaceans have a short nephridial canal and produce urine that is isoosmotic to their hemolymph. The nephridial canal is longer in freshwater crustaceans, which allows more surface area for the transport of ions.

In other crustaceans (some malacostracans [crabs, shrimp, pillbugs]), the excretory organs are located near the maxillary segments and are termed **maxillary glands.** In maxillary glands,

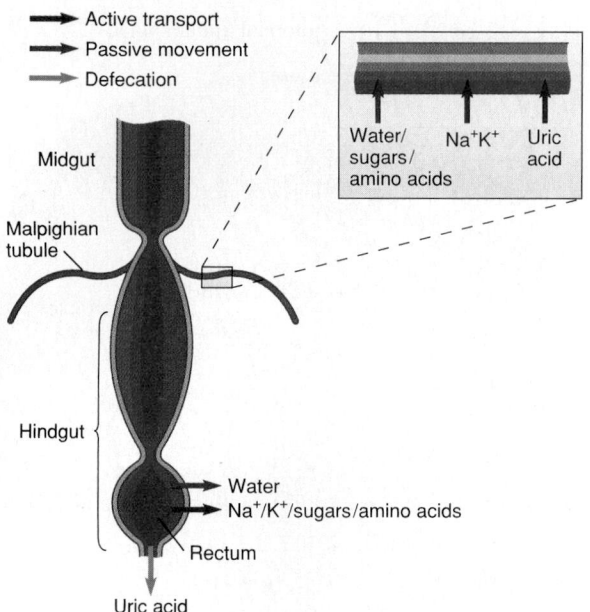

FIGURE 38.13

Malpighian Tubules. Malpighian tubules remove nitrogenous wastes from the hemocoel. Various ions are actively transported across the outer membrane of the tubule. Water follows these ions into the tubule and carries amino acids, sugars, and some nitrogenous wastes along passively. Some water, ions, and organic compounds are reabsorbed in the basal portion of the malpighian tubules and the hindgut: the rest are reabsorbed in the rectum. Uric acid moves into the hindgut and is excreted.

fluid collects within the tubules from the surrounding blood of the hemocoel, and this primary urine is modified substantially by selective reabsorption and secretion as it moves through the excretory system and rectum.

MALPIGHIAN TUBULES

Insects have an excretory system made up of **malpighian tubules** attached to the gut (figure 38.13). The malpighian tubules and the gut together serve as the excretory system. Excretion involves the active transport of potassium ions from the blood surrounding the tubules into the tubules and osmotic movement of water follows. Nitrogenous waste (uric acid) also enters the tubules. As the fluid moves through the malpighian tubules, some of the water and certain ions are recovered. All of the uric acid passes into the gut and out of the body.

COXAL GLANDS

Coxal glands are common among arachnids (spiders, scorpions, ticks, mites). These are spherical sacs resembling annelid nephridia (figure 38.14). Wastes are collected from the surrounding blood of the hemocoel and discharged through pores on from one to several pairs of appendages. Recent evidence suggests that the coxal glands may also function in the release of pheromones.

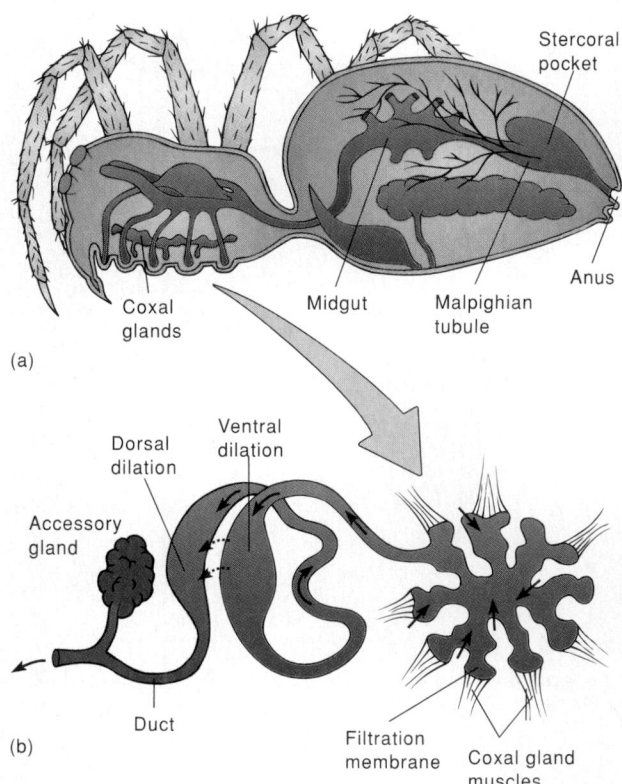

FIGURE 38.14

Coxal Glands in Arachnids. (*a*) A drawing of the gut and excretory systems of a spider. (*b*) Coxal gland muscles attach to the thin saccular filtration membrane. These muscles promote filtration and fluid flow (arrows) by contracting and relaxing along the tubular duct. Water and solutes are reabsorbed along the tubular duct.

Other arachnid species have malpighian tubules instead of, or in addition to, the coxal glands. In some of these species, however, the malpighian tubules seem to function in silk production rather than in excretion.

Stop and Ask Yourself

9. What is the difference between excretion and osmoregulation?

10. What is the function of the contractile vacuole, and where would you find one?

11. How do protonephridia and metanephridia function?

12. How do antennal (green) glands, maxillary glands, and coxal glands function?

VERTEBRATE EXCRETORY SYSTEMS

The problems faced by invertebrates in controlling their water and ion balance are also faced by vertebrates. Generally, water losses are balanced precisely by water gains (table 38.1).

TABLE 38.1	WATER GAIN AND LOSS IN A HUMAN AND KANGAROO RAT				
VERTEBRATE	**WATER GAIN (ML)**			**WATER LOSS (ML)**	
Human (daily)	Ingested in solid food	1,200	Feces	100
	Ingested as liquids	1,000	Urine	1,500
	Metabolically produced	350	Skin and lungs	950
	Total	2,550		2,550
Kangaroo rat (over 4 weeks)	Ingested in solid food	6	Feces	3
	Ingested in liquids	0	Urine	13
	Metabolically produced	54	Skin and lungs	44
	Total	60		60

Vertebrates gain water by absorption from liquids and solid foods in the small and large intestines, and metabolic reactions that yield water as an end product. Water is lost by evaporation from respiratory surfaces, evaporation from the integument, sweating or panting, elimination in feces, and excretion by the urinary system.

Solute losses also must be balanced by solute gains. Solutes are taken in by absorption of minerals from the small and large intestines, through the integument or gills, from secretions of various glands or gills, and metabolism (e.g., the waste products of degradative reactions). Solutes are lost in sweat, feces, urine, gill secretions, and as metabolic wastes. The major metabolic wastes that must be eliminated are ammonia, urea, or uric acid.

Vertebrates live in salt water, fresh water, and on land; each of these environments presents different water and solute problems that have been solved in different ways. The next section of this chapter will present the various ways vertebrates employ to keep from losing or gaining too much water and, in turn, maintain a homeostatic solute concentration in their body fluids. The disposal (excretion) of certain metabolic waste products is also coupled with osmotic balance and will be discussed with the urinary system (box 38.2).

HOW OSMOREGULATION IS ACHIEVED IN VERTEBRATES

A variety of mechanisms have evolved in vertebrates to cope with their osmoregulatory problems, and most of them are adaptations of the urinary system. As presented in chapter 36, vertebrates have a closed circulatory system containing blood that is under pressure. This pressure forces blood through a membrane filter in a kidney where the following four key functions take place:

1. Filtration, in which blood is passed through a filter that retains blood cells, proteins, and other large solutes but lets small molecules, ions, and urea pass through

2. Reabsorption, in which selective ions and molecules are taken back into the bloodstream from the filtrate
3. Secretion, whereby select ions and end products of metabolism (e.g., K^+, H^+, NH_3) that are in the blood are added to the filtrate for removal from the body
4. Excretion, in which urine is voided from the body

VERTEBRATE KIDNEY VARIATIONS

Vertebrates have two kidneys that are located in the back of the abdominal cavity, on either side of the aorta. Each kidney has a coat of connective tissue called the renal capsule (L. *renes*, kidney). The inner portion of the kidney is called the medulla; the region between the capsule and the medulla is the cortex.

The structure and function of vertebrate kidneys differ depending on the vertebrate groups and the developmental stage. Overall, there are three kinds of vertebrate kidneys: the pronephros, mesonephros, and metanephros. The **pronephros** (figure 38.15a) appears only briefly in many vertebrate embryos, and not at all in mammal embryos. In some vertebrates, the pronephros is the first osmoregulatory and excretory organ of the embryo (tadpoles and other amphibian larvae); in others (hagfishes) it remains as the functioning kidney. During embryonic development of amniotes, or during metamorphosis in amphibians, the pronephros is replaced by the mesonephros (figure 38.15b). The **mesonephros** is the functioning embryonic kidney of many vertebrates and also adult fishes and amphibians. The mesonephros gives way during embryonic development to the **metanephros** in adult reptiles, birds, and mammals (figure 38.15c).

The physiological differences between these kidney types are primarily related to the number of blood-filtering units they contain. The pronephric kidney forms in the anterior portion of the body cavity and contains fewer blood-filtering units than either the mesonephric or metanephric kidneys. The larger number of filtering units in the latter have allowed vertebrates to face the rigorous osmoregulatory and excretory demands of freshwater and terrestrial environments.

38.2   WASTE PRODUCTS OF NITROGEN METABOLISM

Proteins and nucleic acids are the two main sources of nitrogenous wastes. Proteins are the source of over 95% of the total amount of excreted nitrogen; nucleic acids make up the remaining 5%. The major problem is to get rid of the ammonia (NH_3) that forms when amino groups ($-NH_2$) are split from amino acids derived from the metabolized protein or from excess dietary protein. Because ammonia is very toxic to most vertebrates, it is kept in low concentrations (0.0001 to 0.003 mg/100 ml) in the blood; higher concentrations can be lethal. For example, a mouse will die if the ammonia concentration in its blood reaches 5 mg/100 ml.

Most vertebrates convert ammonia to a less toxic form immediately after it is formed; thus, allowing it to be retained until it can be excreted. Exceptions are teleost fishes, which excrete almost all of their nitrogen as ammonia through the gills and in the urine. The excretion of most of the nitrogen as ammonia is called **ammonotelic excretion.**

As noted in the text, most mammals need to drink water or eat food containing it to maintain a water balance. Mammals produce only a moderate amount of urine, not the quantities necessary to dilute the toxic ammonia. Most of the ammonia formed from amino acid metabolism is therefore converted to urea, which is less toxic than ammonia. The excretion of urea as the primary nitrogenous waste is called **ureotelic excretion.**

In a third category are animals that, because they inhabit dry habitats or for other reasons of water conservation, excrete a minimal amount of urine that contains little or no water. These animals (e.g., reptiles, some frogs, and birds) convert ammonia to uric acid or another highly insoluble substance. Because the substances are insoluble in water, only small amounts are retained in solution thus greatly limiting their toxicity. (For any substance to be toxic and achieve a biological effect, it must be in solution.) The excretion of nitrogen in the form of uric acid is called **uricotelic excretion.** Most uricotelic animals excrete their nitrogenous waste as a solid or semi-solid urine, or uric acid crystals.

Ammonia, urea, and uric acid are the most common nitrogenous waste products, but not the only ones. Some sharks secrete trimethylamine oxide (TMO). Creatine and creatinine are also excreted in small quantities by a variety of animals. Some animals even wastefully excrete some of their excess amino acids.

Because urea, uric acid, and TMO are less toxic than ammonia, why don't more animals excrete most of their nitrogen in these forms? The answer is in the form of biological economics. The synthesis of these compounds from urea requires an expenditure of ATP energy. An animal using energy for an unnecessary function might be selected against during evolution. Therefore, an animal usually excretes its nitrogen in the form requiring the least expenditure of energy, given the environment in which it lives.

A few animals excrete nitrogen that comes from the metabolism of purines (e.g., adenine and guanine). Purines can be broken down to ammonia only if the animal has the enzymes. Most animals excrete purine nitrogen as uric acid or as one or more intermediate products.

What follows is a presentation of how a few vertebrates maintain their water and solute concentrations in different habitats—in the seas, in fresh water, and on land (table 38.2).

Sharks

Sharks and their relatives (skates and rays) have mesonephric kidneys (*see figure 38.15*b) and have solved their osmotic problem in ways different from the bony fishes. Instead of actively pumping ions out of their bodies through the kidneys, they have a **rectal gland** that secretes a highly concentrated salt (NaCl) solution. To reduce water loss, they use two organic molecules, urea and trimethylamine oxide (TMO), in their body fluids to raise the osmotic pressure to a level equal to or higher than that of the seawater.

Urea denatures proteins and inhibits enzymes, whereas TMO stabilizes proteins and activates enzymes. Together in the proper ratio, they counteract each other, raise the osmotic pressure, and do not interfere with enzymes or proteins. This reciprocity is termed the **counteracting osmolyte strategy.**

A number of other fishes and invertebrates have evolved the same mechanism and employ pairs of counteracting osmolytes to raise the osmotic pressure of their body fluids.

Teleost Fishes

Most teleost fishes have mesonephric kidneys (*see figure 38.15*b). Because the body fluids of freshwater fishes are hyperosmotic relative to fresh water (*see table 38.2*), water tends to enter the fishes, causing excessive hydration or bloating (figure 38.16a). At the same time, body ions tend to move outward into the water.   (7)   To solve this problem, freshwater fishes usually do not drink much water; their bodies are coated with mucus, which helps stem the inward movement of water; they absorb salts and ions by active transport across their gills; and they excrete a large volume of water as dilute urine.

Although most groups of animals probably evolved in the sea, many marine bony fishes probably had freshwater ancestors, as presented in chapter 27.   (8)   Marine fishes faced a different problem of water balance—their body fluids are hypoosmotic

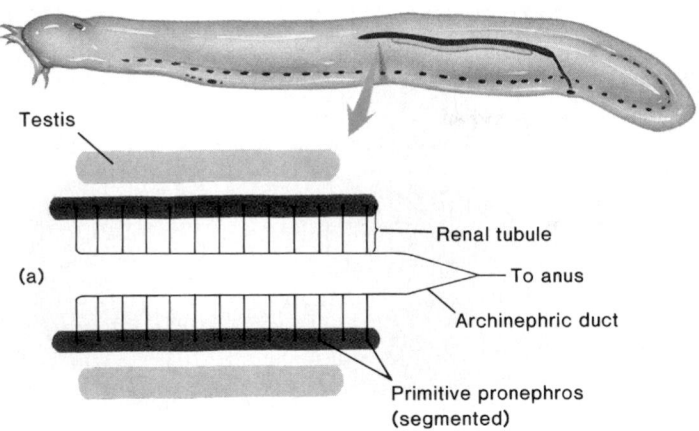

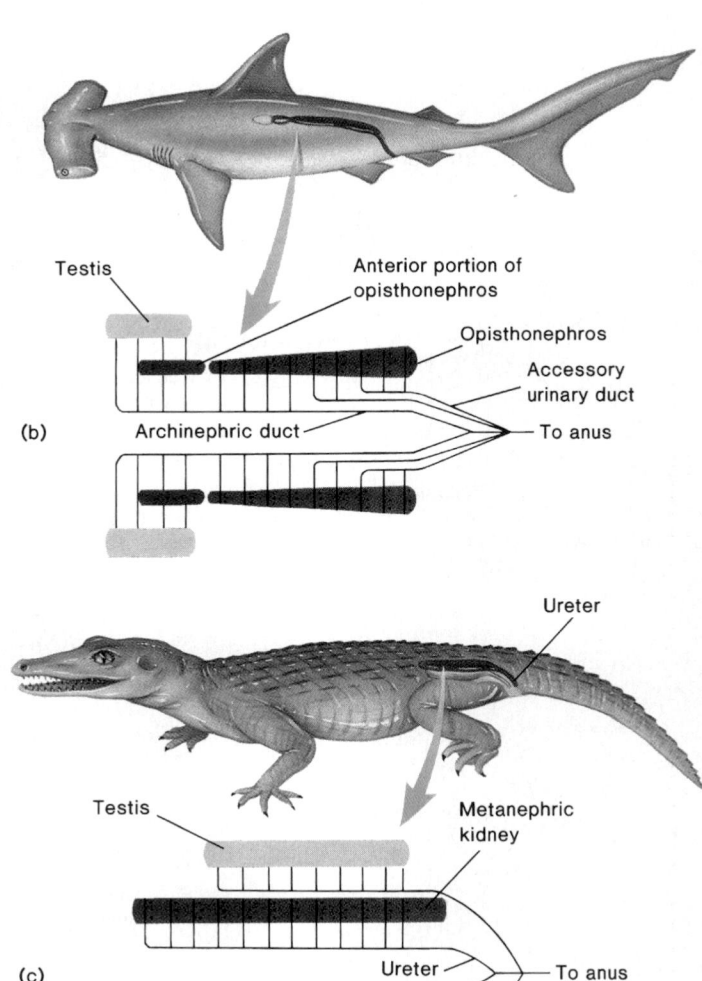

Figure 38.15

Types of Kidneys in Vertebrates and Their Association with the Male Reproductive System. The shaded portions of the drawings represent the mesoderm that forms both the kidneys and gonads. Notice that it extends much of the length of the body during development. (*a*) The primitive pronephric kidney is found in adult hagfishes and embryonic fishes and amphibians. It is located anterior in the body and contains segmental renal tubules that lead from the body of the pronephros to the archinephric duct. Notice that the testes are separated from the kidneys. (*b*) The mesonephros is the functional kidney in the amniote embryo, adult fishes, and amphibians. It is structurally similar to the nonsegmented opisthonephric (advanced mesonephric) kidney of most nonamniote vertebrates such as sharks. The anterior portion of the opisthonephros functions in blood cell formation and secretion of sex hormones. Notice that the testes occupy the position of the anterior opisthonephros, and the archinephric duct carries both sperm and urine. (*c*) The metanephric kidney of adult amniotes (reptiles, birds, and mammals) is the most advanced kidney. Notice the separate ureters (new ducts) for carrying urine; the archinephric duct becomes the ductus deferens for carrying sperm; and the kidney is more compact and located more caudally in the body.

TABLE 38.2	How Various Vertebrates Maintain Water and Salt Balance			
Organism	Environmental Concentration Relative to Body Fluids	Urine Concentration Relative to Blood	Major Nitrogenous Waste	Key Adaptation
Freshwater fishes	Hypoosmotic	Hypoosmotic	Ammonia	Absorb ions through gills
Saltwater fishes	Hyperosmotic	Isoosmotic	Ammonia	Secrete ions through gills
Sharks	Isoosmotic	Isoosmotic	Ammonia	Secrete ions through rectal gland
Amphibians	Hypoosmotic	Very hypoosmotic	Ammonia and urea	Absorb ions through skin
Marine reptiles	Hyperosmotic	Isoosmotic	Ammonia and urea	Secrete ions through salt gland
Marine mammals	Hyperosmotic	Very hyperosmotic	Urea	Drink some water
Desert mammals	No comparison	Very hyperosmotic	Urea	Produce metabolic water
Marine birds	No comparison	Weakly hyperosmotic	Uric acid	Drink seawater and uses salt glands
Terrestrial birds	No comparison	Weakly hyperosmotic	Uric acid	Drink fresh water

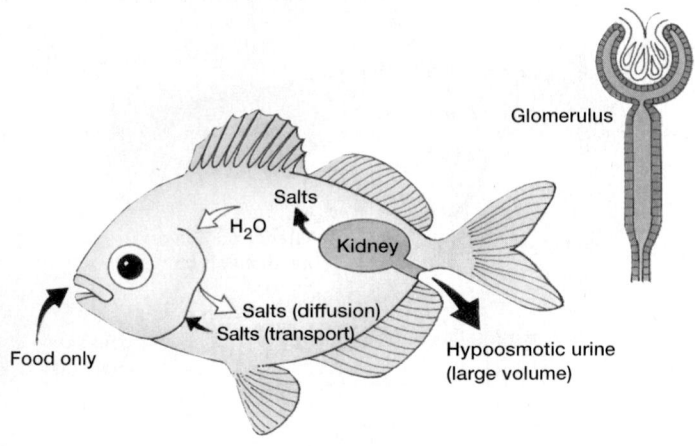

(a) Freshwater teleosts
(hypertonic blood)

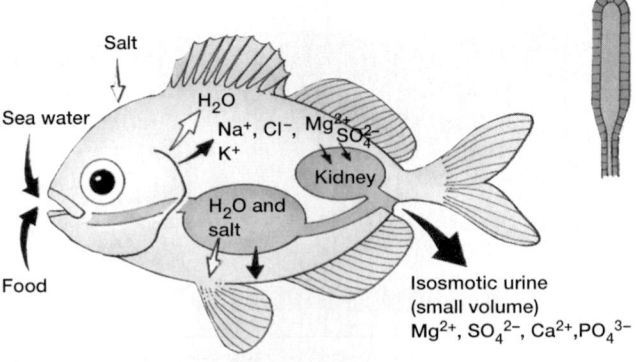

(b) Marine teleosts
(hypotonic blood)

Figure 38.16

Osmoregulation. Osmoregulation by (*a*) freshwater and (*b*) marine fishes. Large arrows indicate passive uptake or loss of water or ions. Small arrows indicate active transport processes occurring at gill membranes and kidney tubules. Insets of kidney nephrons depict adaptations within the kidney. Water, ions, and small organic molecules are filtered from the blood at the glomerulus of the nephron. Essential components of the filtrate can be reabsorbed within the tubule system of the nephron. Marine fishes conserve water by reducing the size of the glomerulus of the nephron, and thus reducing the quantity of water and ions filtered from the blood. Salts can be secreted from the blood into the kidney tubules. Marine fishes can produce urine that is isoosmotic with the blood. Freshwater fishes have enlarged glomeruli and short tubule systems. They filter large quantities of water from the blood, and tubules reabsorb some ions from the filtrate. Freshwater fishes produce a hypoosmotic urine.

with respect to the seawater, and water tends to leave their bodies resulting in dehydration (figure 38.16*b*). To compensate, marine fishes (*see table 38.2*) need to drink large quantities of water, and they secrete Na^+, Cl^-, and K^+ ions through secretory cells in their gills. There are channels in plasma membranes of the kidneys that actively transport the multivalent ions that are

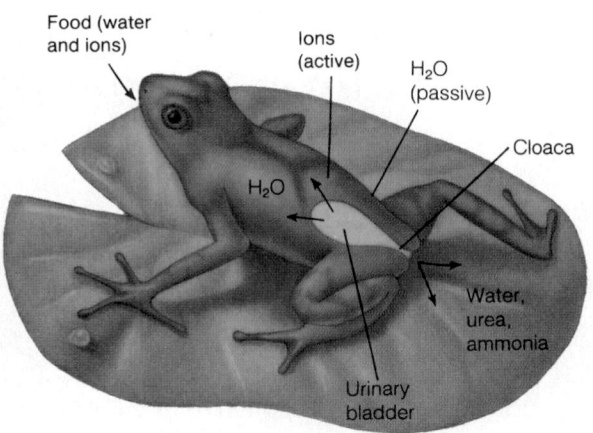

Figure 38.17

Water and Ion Uptake in an Amphibian. Water can enter this frog via food, through its highly permeable skin, or from the urinary bladder. The skin also actively transports ions such as Na^+ and Cl^- from the environment. The kidney forms a dilute urine by reabsorbing Na^+ and Cl^-. Urine then flows into the urinary bladder, where most of the remaining ions are reabsorbed. *Redrawn from N. K. Wessels and J. L. Hopson, Biology, 3d ed. Copyright © 1988 McGraw-Hill, Inc. Used by permission.*

abundant in seawater (e.g., Ca^{2+}, Mg^{2+}, SO_4^{2-}, and PO_4^{3-}) out of the extracellular fluid and into the nephron tubes. The ions are then excreted in a concentrated urine.

Some fishes encounter both fresh and salt water during their life. Newborn Atlantic salmon swim downstream from the freshwater stream of their birth and enter the sea. Instead of continuing to pump ions in, as they have done in fresh water, the salmon must now rid their bodies of salt. Years later, these same salmon migrate from the sea to their freshwater home to spawn. As they do, the pumping mechanisms reverse themselves.

Amphibians

The amphibian kidney is identical to that of freshwater fishes (*see figure 38.16a*), which is not surprising because amphibians spend a large portion of their time in fresh water, and when on land, they tend to seek out moist places. Amphibians take up water and ions in their food and drink, through the skin that is in contact with moist substrates, and through the urinary bladder (figure 38.17). This uptake counteracts what is lost through evaporation and prevents osmotic imbalance (*see table 38.2*).

The urinary bladder of a frog, toad, or salamander is an important water and ion reservoir. For example, when the environment becomes dry, the bladder becomes larger for storing more urine. If an amphibian becomes dehydrated, a brain hormone causes water to leave the bladder and enter the body fluid.

Reptiles, Birds, and Mammals

Reptiles, birds, and mammals all possess metanephric kidneys (*see figure 38.15c*). Their kidneys are by far the most complex animal kidneys, well suited for the high rates of metabolism present in these animals.

BOX 38.3 | EXTRARENAL SECRETION BY AVIAN AND REPTILIAN SALT GLANDS

Salt glands have been described in many species of birds and reptiles, including nearly all marine birds, ostriches, marine iguanas, sea snakes, sea turtles, crocodilians, and many terrestrial reptiles. In general, these animals are subjected to osmotic stress of a marine or desert environment.

The salt glands of some reptiles and birds occupy shallow depressions in the skull above the eye (figure 1a,b). These glands consist of many lobes, each of which drains via branching secretory tubules, and a central canal into a collecting duct that empties into the nostril. Active secretion takes place across the epithelial cells of the secretory tubules. These cells have a large surface area and many mitochondria. As in other transport epithelia, adjacent cells are tied together by tight junctions, which prevent the massive leakage of water or solutes past the cells, from one side of the epithelium to another.

The avian salt gland is organized as a countercurrent system that aids in concentrating the secreted salt solution. The capillaries are arranged so that the flow of blood is in the direction opposite to the flow of secretory fluid. This flow maintains a minimum concentration gradient between blood and the tubular lumen along the entire length of the tubule.

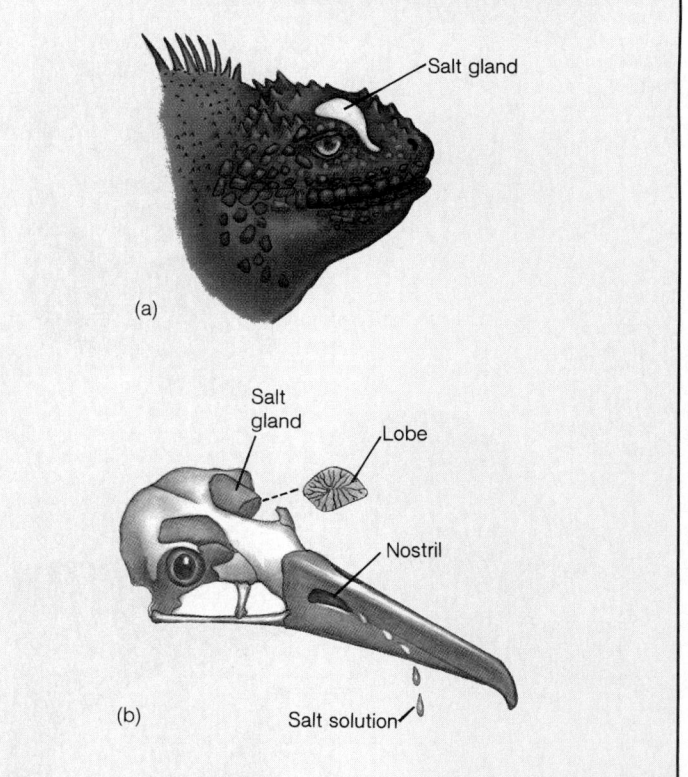

FIGURE 1 **Salt Glands.** (*a*) The reptilian salt gland is often located above the eyes. (*b*) The many-lobed salt glands of birds empty into the nostril.

In most reptiles, birds, and mammals, far more water can be removed from the kidneys than in amphibians, and the kidneys are the primary regulatory organs for controlling the osmotic balance of the body fluids. Some desert and marine reptiles and birds often build up high salt (NaCl) concentrations in their bodies because they consume salty foods or seawater, and they lose water through evaporation and in their urine and feces. To rid themselves of this excess salt, these animals also have salt glands near the eye or in the tongue to remove excess salt from the blood and secrete it as tearlike droplets (box 38.3).

A major site of water loss in mammals is the lungs. To reduce this evaporative loss, many mammals have nasal cavities that act as countercurrent exchange systems to combat such loss (figure 38.18). ⑨ When the animal inhales, air passes through the nasal cavities and is warmed by the surrounding tissues. In the process, the temperature of this tissue drops. When the air gets deep into the lungs, it is further warmed and humidified. During exhalation, as the warm moist air passes up the respiratory tree, it gives up its heat to the nasal cavity. As the air cools, much of the water condenses on the nasal surfaces and does not leave the body. This mechanism explains why a dog's nose is usually cold and moist.

Stop and Ask Yourself

13. How do freshwater fishes osmoregulate? Saltwater fishes?
14. What is the function of the rectal gland of sharks?
15. How do amphibians conserve water?
16. What is a salt gland?
17. How do nasal cavities help conserve water?

HOW THE METANEPHRIC KIDNEY FUNCTIONS

The filtration device of the metanephric kidney (figure 38.19*a*) consists of over one million individual filtration, secretion, and absorption structures called **nephrons** (Gr. *nephros*, kidney + *on*, neuter). At the beginning of the nephron is the filtration apparatus called the glomerular capsule (formerly Bowman's capsule), which looks rather like a tennis ball that has been punched in on one side (figure 38.19*b*). The capsules are located in the cortical (outermost) region of the kidney. In each capsule, an afferent ("going to") arteriole enters and branches into a fine network of capillaries called the **glomerulus.** The

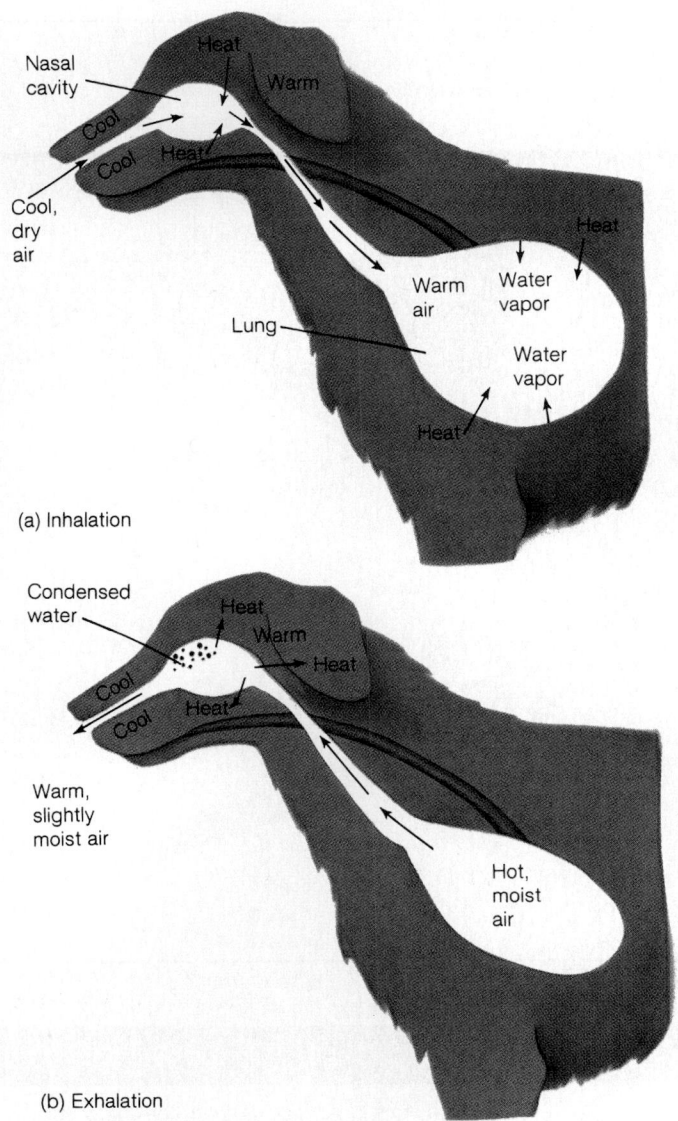

Figure 38.18

Water Retention by Countercurrent Heating and Cooling in a Mammal. (*a*) When this animal inhales, the cool, dry air passing through its nose is heated and humidified. At the same time, its nasal tissues are cooled. (*b*) When the animal exhales, it gives up heat to the previously cooled nasal tissue. The air carries less water vapor, and condensation occurs in the animal's nose. *Redrawn from N. K. Wessels and J. L. Hopson, Biology, 3d ed. Copyright © 1988 McGraw-Hill, Inc. Used by permission.*

walls of these glomerular capillaries contain small perforations that act as filters. Blood pressure forces fluid through these filters. The fluid is now known as glomerular filtrate and contains small molecules, such as glucose, ions (Ca^{2+}, PO_4^{3-}), and the primary nitrogenous waste product of metabolism, urea or uric acid. Because the perforations are so small, large proteins and blood cells are retained in the blood and leave the glomerulus via the efferent ("outgoing") arteriole. The efferent arteriole then divides into a set of capillaries called the peritubular capillaries (figure 38.20) that wind profusely around

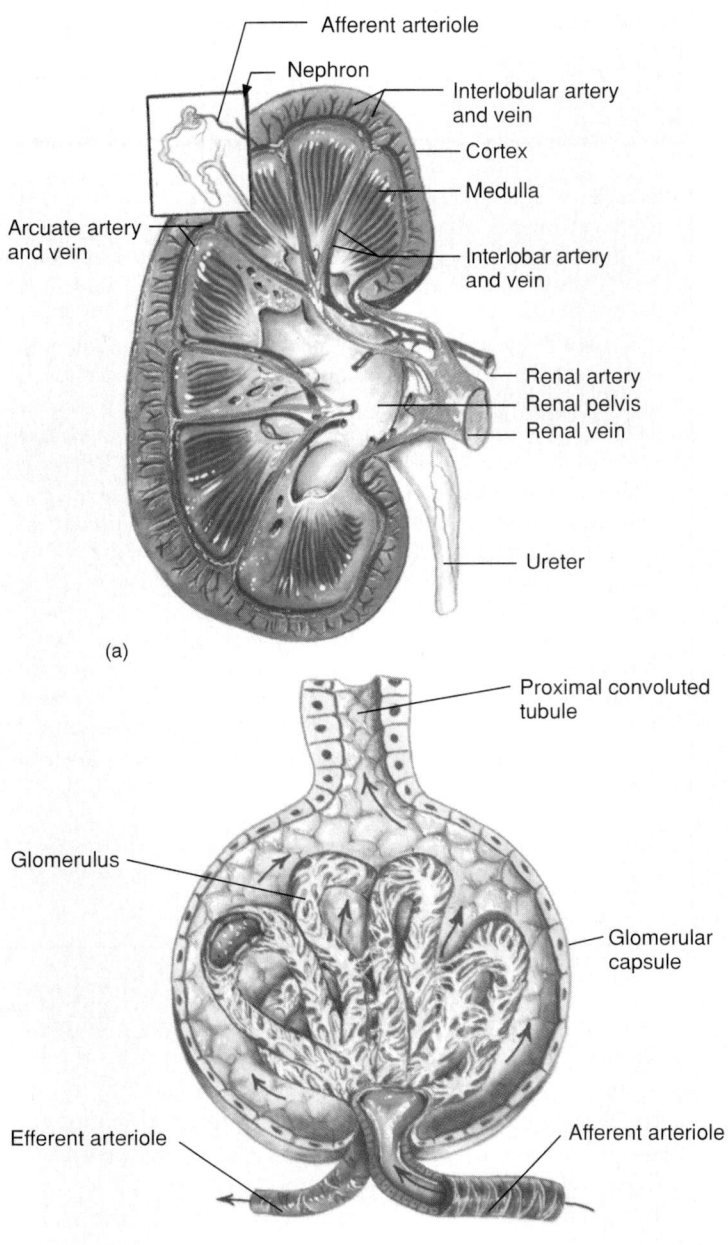

Figure 38.19

The Filtration Device of the Metanephric Kidney. (*a*) Interior of a kidney showing the positioning of the nephron and the blood supply to and from the kidney. (*b*) The glomerular capsule with arrows illustrating that high blood pressure forces water and ions through small perforations in the walls of the glomerular capillaries to form the glomerular filtrate.

the tubular portions of the nephron. Eventually they merge to form veins that carry blood out of the kidney.

Beyond the glomerular capsule are the proximal convoluted tubule, the loop of the nephron (formerly the loop of Henle), and the distal convoluted tubule. At various places along these structures, selective reabsorption of the glomerular

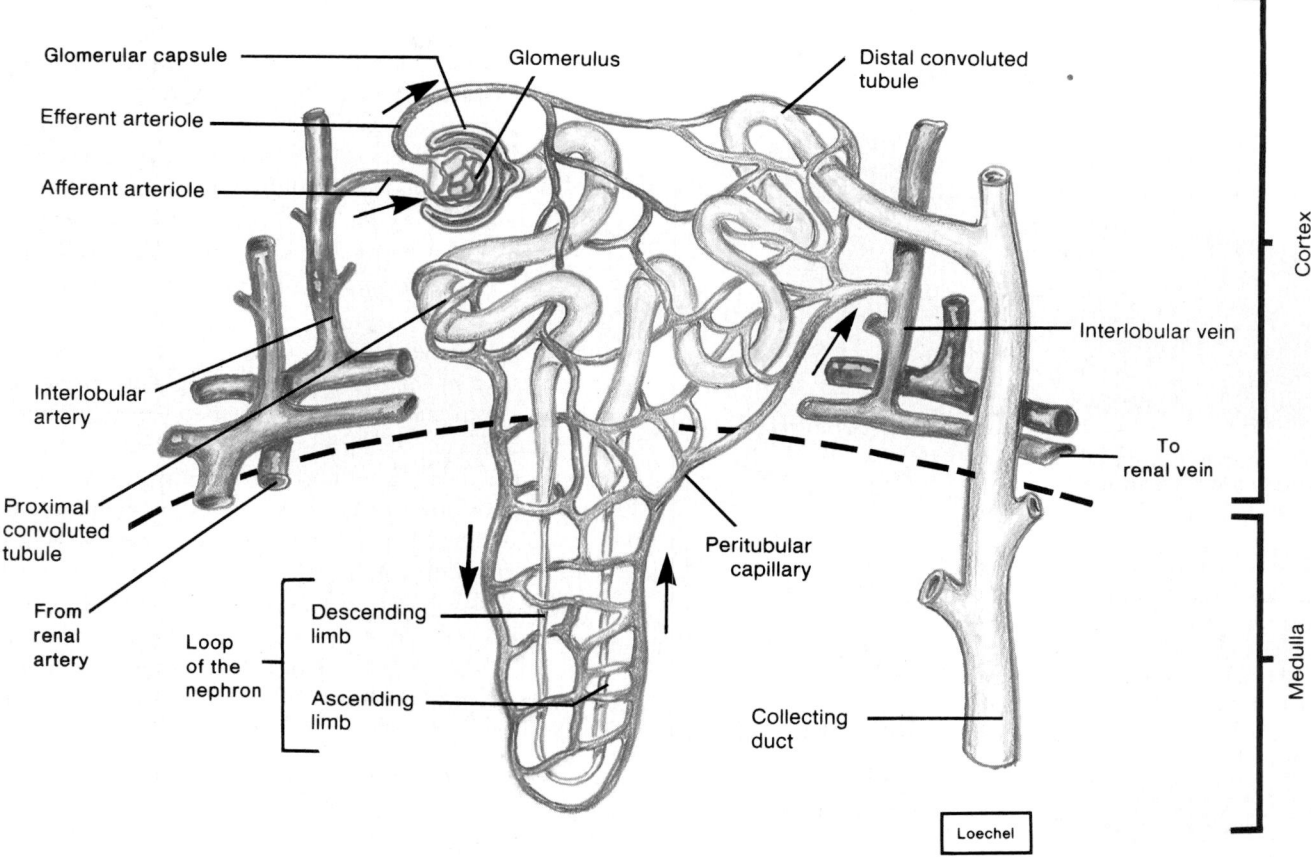

Figure 38.20

A Metanephric Nephron. Glucose and some ions are reabsorbed in the proximal convoluted tubule; other ions and water are reabsorbed in the distal convoluted tubule. Final water reabsorption takes place in the collecting duct. Arrows indicate the direction of movement of materials in the nephron.

filtrate occurs, returning certain ions (e.g., Na^+, K^+, Cl^-) to the bloodstream. Both active (ATP-requiring) and passive procedures are involved in the recovery of these substances. Potentially harmful compounds, such as hydrogen (H^+) and ammonium (NH_4^+) ions, drugs, and various other foreign materials are secreted into the nephron lumen. In the last portion of the nephron, called the collecting duct, final water reabsorption takes place so that the urine contains an ion concentration well above that of the blood. Thus the filtration, secretion, and reabsorption activities of the nephron do not simply remove wastes. They also maintain water and ion balance, and therein lies the importance of the homeostatic function of the kidney.

Mammalian, and to a lesser extent avian and reptilian, kidneys can remove far more water from the glomerular filtrate than can the kidneys of amphibians. For example, human urine is 4 times as concentrated as blood plasma, a camel's urine is 8 times as concentrated, a gerbil's is 14 times as concentrated as the plasma, and some desert rats and mice have urine more than 20 times as concentrated as their plasma. This concentrated waste enables them to live in dry or desert environments, where there is little water available for them to

drink. Most of their water is metabolically produced from the oxidation of carbohydrates, fats, and proteins in the seeds that they eat (see table 38.1). Mammals and, to a lesser extent birds, achieve this remarkable degree of water conservation by a unique, yet simple, evolutionary adaptation—the bending of the nephron tube in the form of a loop. By bending, the nephron can greatly increase the salt concentration in the tissue through which the loop passes and use this gradient to draw large amounts of water out of the tube.

Countercurrent Exchange

The loop of the nephron increases the efficiency of reabsorption by a countercurrent flow similar to that in the gills of fishes or in the legs of birds, but with water and ions being reabsorbed instead of oxygen or heat. **10** Generally, the longer the loop of the nephron, the more water and ions that can be reabsorbed. It follows that desert rodents (e.g., kangaroo rat) that form highly concentrated urine, have very long nephron loops (figure 38.21). Similarly, amphibians that are closely associated with aquatic habitats have nephrons that lack a loop.

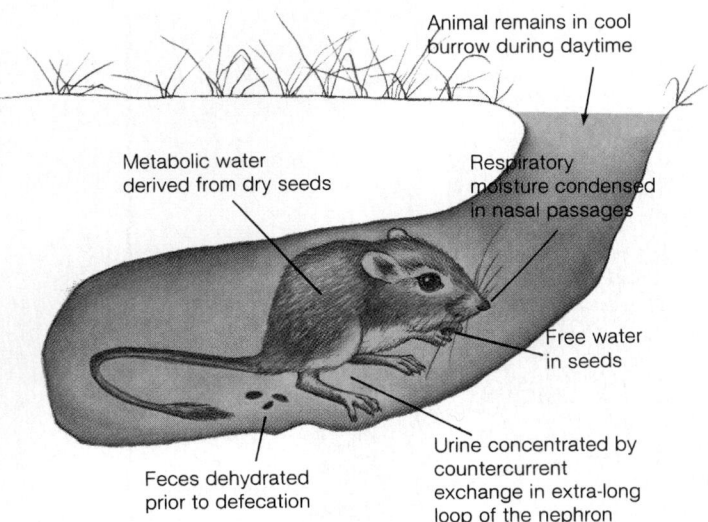

FIGURE 38.21

The Kangaroo Rat (*Dipodomys ordii*) Is a Master of Water Conservation. It has such efficient kidneys that it can concentrate urine 20 times that of its blood plasma. As a result, these kidneys as well as other adaptations prevent the unnecessary loss of water to the environment.

The countercurrent flow mechanism used for concentrating urine is illustrated in figure 38.22. The process of reabsorption in the proximal convoluted tubule removes some salt (NaCl) and water from the glomerular filtrate and reduces its volume by approximately 25%. However, the concentrations of salt and urea are still isosmotic with the extracellular fluid.

As the filtrate moves to the descending limb of the loop of the nephron, it becomes further reduced in volume and more concentrated. Water moves out of the tubule by osmosis due to the high salt concentration (the "brine-bath") in the extracellular fluid.

Notice in figure 38.22 that the highest urea-brine bath concentration is around the lower portion of the loop of the nephron. As the filtrate passes into the ascending limb, sodium (Na⁺) ions are actively transported out of the filtrate into the extracellular fluid with chloride (Cl⁻) ions following passively. Water cannot flow out of the ascending limb because the cells of the ascending limb are impermeable to water. Thus, the salt concentration of the extracellular fluid becomes very high. The salt flows passively into the descending loop, only to move out again in the ascending loop, creating a recycling of salt through the loop and the extracellular fluid. Because the flows in the descending and ascending limbs are in opposite directions, a

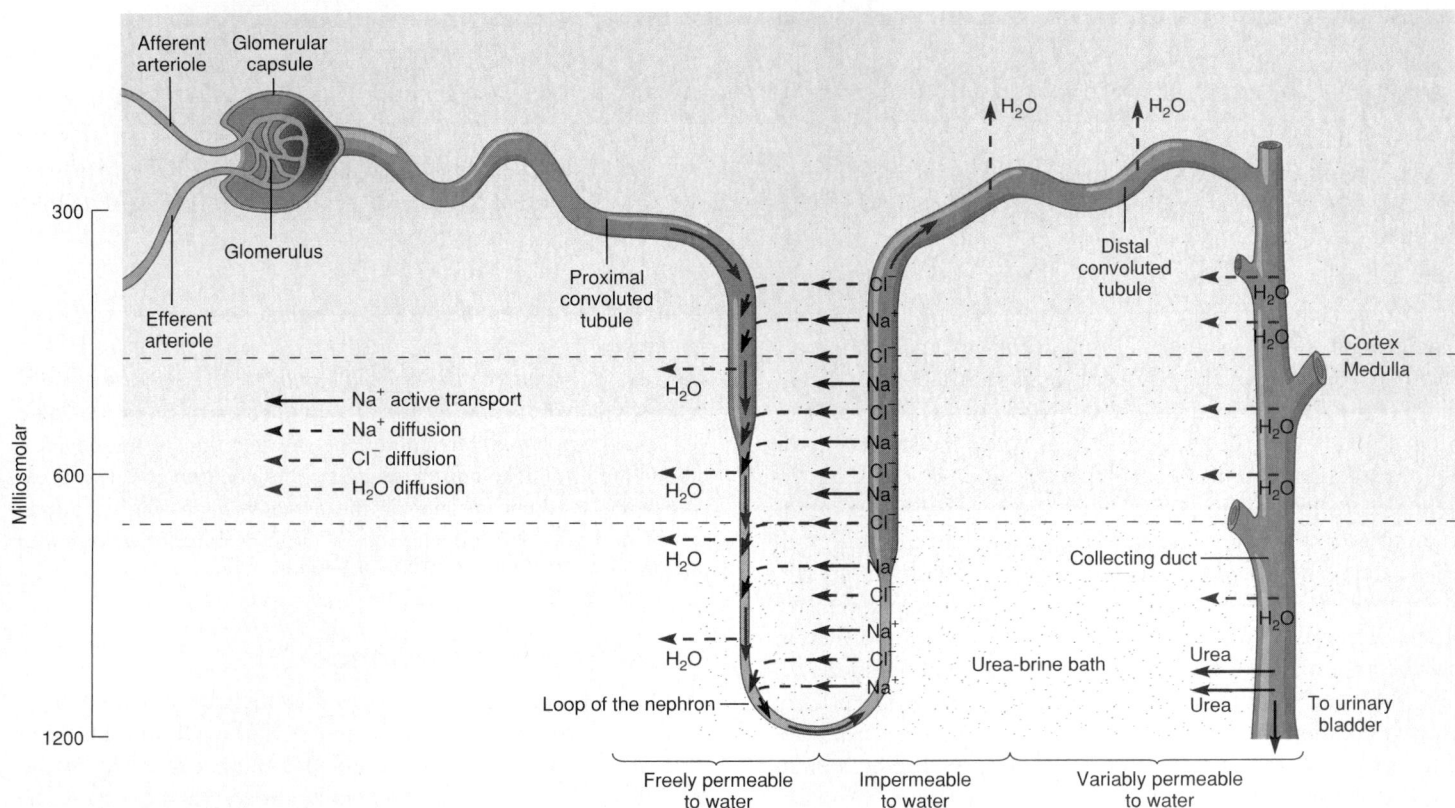

FIGURE 38.22

Countercurrent Exchange. The movement of materials in the nephron and collecting duct. Active transport is shown with solid arrows; passive transport with dashed arrows. The shading at intervals along the tubules illustrates the relative concentration of the filtrate in milliosmoles.

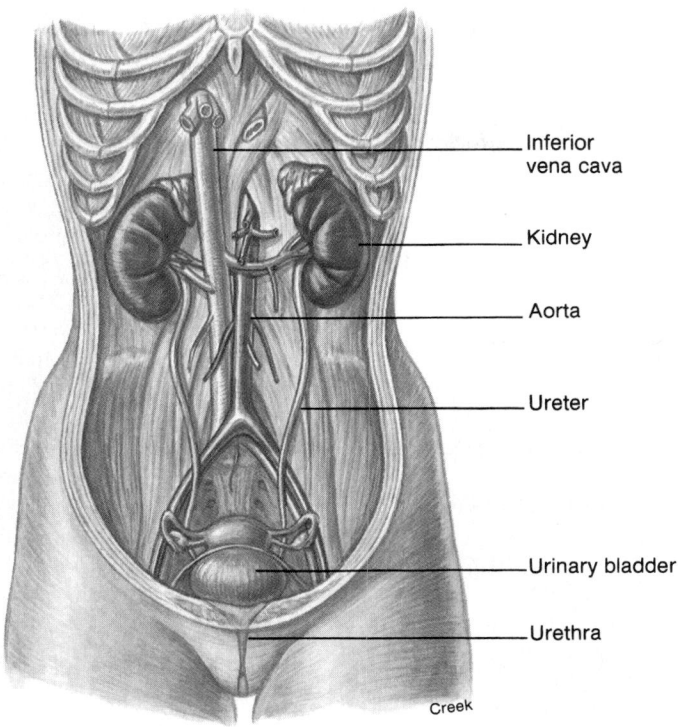

Figure 38.23

Component Parts of the Human Urinary System.   The position of the kidneys, ureters, urinary bladder, and urethra are shown.

countercurrent gradient in salt is set up. The osmotic pressure of the extracellular brine bath is made even higher because of the abundance of urea that moves out of the collecting ducts.

Finally, the distal convoluted tubule empties into the collecting duct, which is permeable to urea, and the concentrated urea in the filtrate diffuses out into the surrounding extracellular fluid. The high urea concentration in the extracellular fluid, coupled with the high concentration of salt, forms the urea-brine bath that causes water to move out of the filtrate by osmosis as it moves down the descending limb. The water is finally collected by the many peritubular capillaries surrounding each nephron and returned to the systemic circulation.

The renal pelvis of the mammalian kidney is continuous with a tube called the **ureter** that carries urine to a storage organ called the **urinary bladder** (figure 38.23). Urine from two ureters (one from each kidney) accumulates in this organ. It leaves the body through a single tube, the **urethra,** which opens at the body surface at the end of the penis (in human males) or just in front of the vaginal entrance (in human females). As the urinary bladder fills with urine, tension increases in its smooth muscle walls. In response to this tension, a reflex response relaxes sphincter muscles at the entrance to the urethra. This involuntary reflex response is called urination. The two kidneys, two ureters, urinary bladder, and urethra constitute the urinary system of mammals.

Stop and Ask Yourself

18. How does a vertebrate lose water from its body? How does it gain water?
19. How do vertebrates achieve osmoregulation?
20. What are four functions of the kidneys?
21. What is the anatomy of the nephron?
22. How does the countercurrent flow mechanism in the kidney function?

SUMMARY

1. Thermoregulation is a complex and important physiological process for maintaining heat homeostasis despite environmental changes.

2. Ectotherms generally obtain heat from the environment, whereas endotherms generate their own body heat from metabolic processes.

3. Homeotherms generally have a relatively constant core body temperature, and heterotherms have a variable body temperature.

4. The high, constant body temperature of birds and mammals also depends on insulation, panting, sweating, specific behaviors, vasoconstriction or vasodilation of the peripheral blood vessels, and in some species, a rete mirabile system.

5. Thermogenesis involves mainly shivering, enzymatic activity, brown fat, and high cellular metabolism.

6. The hypothalamus is the temperature regulating center that functions as a thermostat with a fixed set point. This set point can either rise or fall during hibernation or torpor.

7. Some invertebrates have contractile vacuoles, flame-cell systems, antennal (green) glands, maxillary glands, coxal glands, nephridia, or malpighian tubules for osmoregulation.

8. The osmoregulatory system of vertebrates governs the concentration of water and ions; the excretory system eliminates metabolic wastes, water, and ions from the body.

9. Freshwater animals tend to lose ions and take in water. To avoid hydration, freshwater fishes rarely drink much water, have impermeable body surfaces covered with mucus, excrete a dilute urine, and take up ions through their gills.

10. Marine animals tend to take in ions from the seawater and to lose water. To avoid dehydration, they frequently drink water, have relatively permeable body surfaces, excrete a small volume of concentrated urine, and secrete ions from their gills.

11. Amphibians can absorb water across the skin and urinary bladder wall. Desert and marine reptiles and birds have salt glands to remove and secrete excess salt (NaCl).

12. In reptiles, birds, and mammals, the kidneys are important osmoregulatory structures. The functional unit of the kidney is the nephron, composed of the glomerular capsule, proximal tubule, loop of the nephron, and distal tubule, and collecting duct. Mammalian and some avian nephrons also have a loop of the nephron. The loop and the collecting duct are in the kidney's medulla; the other nephron parts lie in the kidney's cortex. Urine passes from the pelvis of the kidney to the bladder.

13. To make urine, kidneys produce a filtrate of the blood and reabsorb most of the water, glucose, and needed ions, while allowing wastes to pass from the body. Four physiological mechanisms are involved: filtration of the blood through the glomerulus, reabsorption of the useful substances, secretion of toxic substances, and concentration of the filtrate. In those animals with a loop of the nephron, salt (NaCl) and urea are concentrated in the extracellular fluid around the loop, allowing water to move by osmosis out of the loop and into the peritubular capillaries.

SELECTED KEY TERMS

brown fat (*p. 653*)

ectotherms (*p. 649*)

endotherms (*p. 650*)

heterotherms (*p. 650*)

hibernation (*p. 654*)

homeotherms (*p. 650*)

nephrons (*p. 663*)

osmoconformers (*p. 655*)

osmoregulation (*p. 655*)

thermoregulation (*p. 648*)

CRITICAL THINKING QUESTIONS

1. Reptiles are said to be behavioral homeotherms. Explain what this means.

2. Why do very small birds and mammals go into a state of torpor at night?

3. How does the countercurrent mechanism help regulate heat loss?

4. In endotherms, what controls the balance between the amount of heat lost and the amount gained?

5. If marooned on a desert isle, do not drink seawater; it is better to be thirsty. Why is this true?

REPRODUCTION AND DEVELOPMENT

Concepts

1. All animals have the capacity for reproduction. The simplest form of reproduction is asexual. Asexual reproduction permits production of new individuals from one parent, but it does not produce new genetic combinations among offspring, as does sexual reproduction.
2. Almost all animals reproduce sexually, at least sometimes. Sexual reproduction involves mechanisms that bring sperm and egg together for fertilization, and ensure that the fertilized egg has a suitable place to develop until the new animal is ready to function on its own.
3. Sexual reproduction evolved in aquatic environments, and its modification for organisms living on dry land entailed evolutionary innovations to prevent the gametes and embryos from drying out.
4. Mammalian fertilization and embryonic development are both internal.
5. Hormones coordinate the reproductive functions in both males and females. In female mammals, hormones also maintain pregnancy, and after childbirth, stimulate the production and letdown of milk from the mammary glands.

Would You Like to Know:

1. how the earliest organisms reproduced? (*p. 670*)
2. how lobsters can reproduce without sperm? (*p. 670*)
3. what is one of the greatest disadvantages to asexual reproduction? (*p. 672*)
4. why the human testes are the only abdominal organs that lie outside of the abdominal cavity? (*p. 675*)
5. what causes a common inguinal hernia in humans? (*p. 675*)
6. why some males are circumcised? (*p. 676*)
7. what determines the size of a female's breasts? (*p. 680*)
8. why urine is used to determine if a female is pregnant? (*p. 681*)
9. when a female is considered pregnant? (*p. 682*)

These and other useful questions will be answered in this chapter.

This chapter contains evolutionary concepts, which are set off in this font.

Reproduction is a basic attribute of all forms of life. Chapters 6 through 10 describe the general features of animal development and the control processes that allow a genotype to be translated into its phenotype. Although in modern zoology, development is "the center stage" in reproduction, the whole process includes the behavior, anatomy, and physiology of adults—whether in protists, invertebrates, or vertebrates. This chapter begins with a comparative focus on the different reproductive strategies observed in protists, the invertebrates, and the five major groups of vertebrates. The chapter concludes with a discussion of human reproduction, not only because of the subject's basic interest to everyone, but because scientists know more about the biochemistry, hormones, anatomy, and physiology involved in human reproduction than they do for any other species.

Asexual Reproduction in Invertebrates

In the biological sense, reproduction means producing offspring that may (or may not) be exact copies of the parents. Reproduction is part of a life cycle, a recurring frame of events in which animals grow, develop, and reproduce according to a program of instruction encoded in the DNA they inherit from their parents. One of the two major types of reproduction that occur in the biological world is asexual reproduction.

(1) The first organisms to evolve probably reproduced by pinching in two, much as do the simplest organisms that exist today. This is a form of **asexual reproduction,** which is reproduction without the union of gametes or sex cells. In the first 2 billion years or more of evolution, forms of asexual reproduction were probably the only means by which the primitive organisms could increase their numbers. While asexual reproduction is effective in increasing the numbers of a species, those species reproducing asexually tend to evolve very slowly because all offspring of any one individual will be alike, providing less genetic diversity for evolutionary selection.

Asexual reproduction is common among the protozoa, as well as in lower invertebrates, such as sponges, jellyfishes, flatworms, and many segmented worms. Asexual reproduction is rare among the higher invertebrates. The ability to reproduce asexually is often correlated with a marked capacity for regeneration.

In the lower invertebrates, the most common forms of asexual reproduction are fission, budding (both internal and external), and fragmentation. Parthenogenesis, which is comparatively uncommon, also occurs in a few invertebrates.

Fission

Protists and some multicellular animals (cnidarians, annelids) may reproduce by fission. **Fission** (L. *fissio,* the act of splitting) is the division of one cell, body, or body part into two (figure 39.1a). In this process, the cell pinches in two by an inward furrowing of the plasma membrane. Binary fission is where the division is equal; each offspring contains approximately equal amounts of protoplasm and associated structures. Binary fission is common in protozoa; for some, it is their only means of reproduction.

In fission, the plane of division may be asymmetrical, transverse, or longitudinal, depending on the species. For example, the multicellular, free-living flatworms, such as the common planarian, reproduce by longitudinal fission (figure 39.1b). Some flatworms and annelids reproduce by forming numerous constrictions along the length of the body; a chain of daughter individuals results (figure 39.1c). This type of asexual reproduction is called multiple fission.

Budding

Another method of asexual reproduction found in lower invertebrates is **budding.** For example, in the cnidarian *Hydra* and many species of sponges, certain cells divide rapidly and develop on the body surface to form an external bud (figure 39.1d). The bud cells proliferate to form a cylindrical structure, which develops into a new animal, usually breaking away from the parent. If the buds remain attached to the parent, they form a colony. A **colony** is a group of closely associated individuals of one species. In internal budding, as in the freshwater sponges, gemmules, which are collections of many cells surrounded by a body wall, are produced. When the body of the parent dies and degenerates, each gemmule gives rise to a new individual.

Fragmentation

Fragmentation is a type of asexual reproduction whereby a body part is lost and then regenerates into a new organism. Fragmentation occurs in some cnidarians, platyhelminthes, rhynchocoels, and echinoderms. For example, in sea anemones, as the organism moves, small pieces break off from the adult and develop into new individuals (figure 39.1e).

Parthenogenesis

Certain flatworms, rotifers, roundworms, insects, and lobsters can reproduce without sperm and normal fertilization. (2) These animals carry out what is called **parthenogenesis** (Gr. *parthenos,* virgin + *genesis,* production). (However, most parthenogenetic animals also can reproduce sexually at some point in their life history.) Parthenogenesis is a spontaneous activation of a mature egg, followed by normal egg divisions and subsequent embryonic development. In fact, mature eggs of species that do not undergo parthenogenesis can sometimes be activated to develop without fertilization by pricking them with a needle, by exposing them to high concentrations of calcium or by altering their temperature.

Because parthenogenetic eggs are not fertilized, they do not receive male chromosomes. One would thus expect the offspring to have only a haploid set of chromosomes. In some animals, however, meiotic division is suppressed, so the diploid

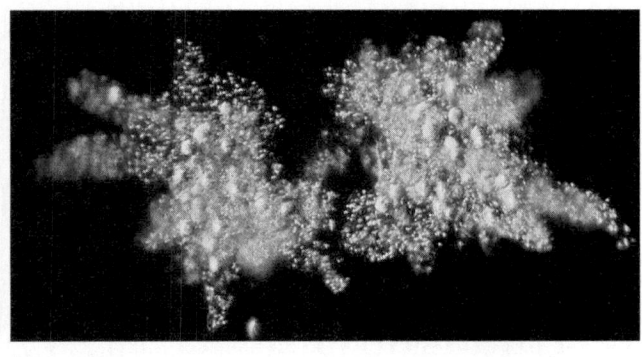

(a)

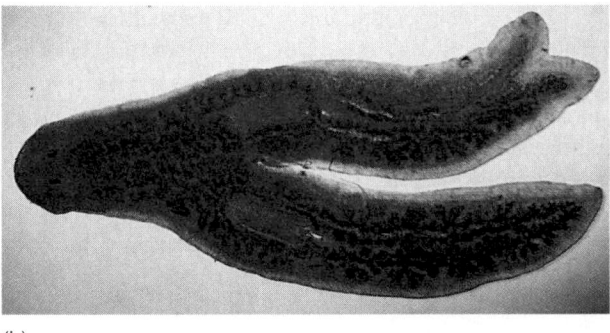

(b)

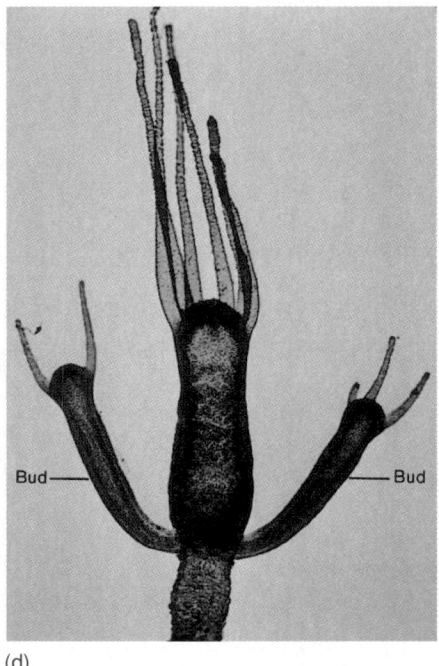

(d)

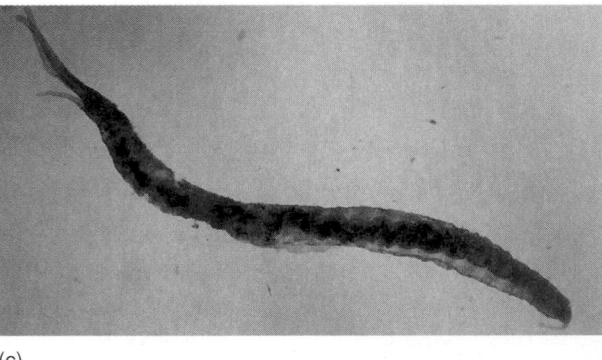

(c)

(e)

FIGURE 39.1

Asexual Reproduction. (*a*) An amoeba (a protist) undergoes fission to form two individual organisms. (*b*) Planarian worms undergoing longitudinal fission. (*c*) The annelid, *Autolysis*, undergoing various constrictions. (*d*) A hydra with developing buds. (*e*) Small sea anemones produced by fragmentation.

number is conserved. In other animals, meiosis occurs, but an unusual mitosis returns the haploid embryonic cells to the diploid condition.

Overall, animals that reproduce parthenogenetically have substantially less genetic variability than do animals with chromosome sets from two parents. This condition may be an advantage for animals that are well adapted to a relatively stable environment. However, in meeting the challenges of a changing environment, parthenogenetic animals may have less flexibility, which may explain why this form of reproduction is relatively uncommon.

Parthenogenesis also plays an important role in the social organization in colonies of certain bees, wasps, and ants. In these insects, large numbers of males (drones) are produced parthenogenetically, whereas sterile female workers and reproductive females (queens) are produced sexually.

ADVANTAGES AND DISADVANTAGES OF ASEXUAL REPRODUCTION

The predominance of asexual reproduction in protists and some invertebrates can be partially explained by the environment in which they live. The marine environment is usually very stable. Stable environments may favor this form of reproduction because a combination of genes that matches the relatively unchanging environment would be an advantage over a greater number of gene combinations, many of which would not match the environment. In other habitats, asexual reproduction is seasonal. The season during which asexual reproduction occurs coincides with the period when the environment is predictably hospitable. Under such conditions, it is advantageous for the animal to produce asexually a large number of progeny with identical characteristics. A large number of animals, well adapted to a given environment, can be produced even if only one parent is present.

39.3

Without the tremendous genetic variability bestowed by meiosis and sexual processes, however, a population of genetically identical animals stands a greatly increased chance of being devastated by a single disease or environmental insult, such as a long drought. A given line of asexually reproducing animals can cope with a changing environment only through the relatively rare spontaneous mutations (alterations in genetic material) that prove to be beneficial.   3   Paradoxically, however, most mutations are detrimental or lethal, and herein lies one of the greatest disadvantages of asexual reproduction: all such mutations will be passed on to every offspring along with the normal, unmutated genes. Consequently, the typical asexual animal may have only one "good" copy of each hereditary unit (gene); the one on the homologous chromosome may be a mutated form that is nonfunctional or potentially lethal.

Sexual Reproduction in Invertebrates

In **sexual reproduction,** the offspring have unique combinations of genes inherited from the two parents. Offspring of a sexual union are somewhat different from their parents and siblings—they have genetic diversity. Each new individual represents a combination of traits derived from two parents, because the union of two gametes in syngamy, or fertilization, unites one gamete from each parent.

Sexual reproductive strategies and structures in the invertebrates are overwhelming. What follows is simply an overview of some principles of reproductive structure and function. More specific details can be found in the coverage of each invertebrate phylum in chapters 18 through 26.

External Fertilization

Many invertebrates (e.g., sponges and corals) simply release their gametes into the water in which they live **(broadcast spawning),** allowing external fertilization to occur. In these invertebrates, the gonads are usually simple, often transient structures associated with just getting the gametes out of the body. This release is achieved through various arrangements of coelomic ducts, metanephridia, sperm ducts, or oviducts.

Internal Fertilization

Other invertebrates (from flatworms to insects) utilize internal fertilization to transfer sperm from male to female and have structures that facilitate such transfer (figure 39.2).

In the male, sperm are produced in the testes and transported via a sperm duct to a storage area called the seminal vesicle. Prior to mating, some invertebrates (e.g., arrowworms, leeches, some insects) incorporate many sperm into packets termed spermatophores. Spermatophores provide a protective casing for sperm and facilitate the transfer of large numbers of sperm with minimal loss. Some spermatophores are even motile and act as independent sperm carriers. Sperm or the spermatophores are then passed into an ejaculatory duct to a copulatory organ (e.g.,

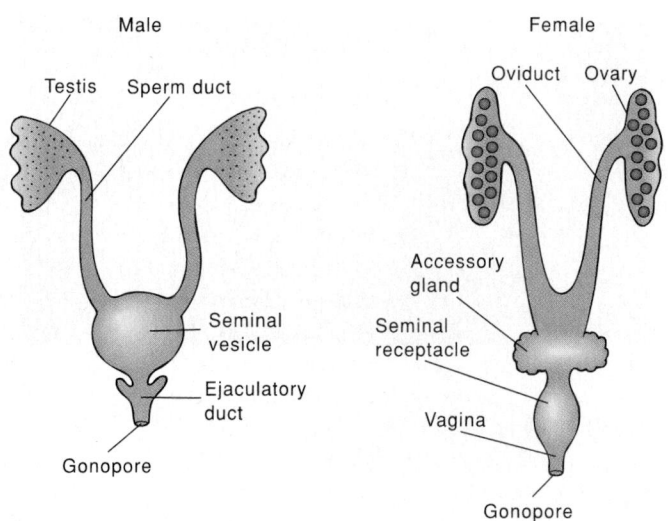

Figure 39.2
Stylized Male and Female Reproductive Systems in Invertebrates. Sexual reproduction is possible via these systems.

penis, cirrus, gonopore). The copulatory organ is used as an intromittent structure to introduce sperm into the female's system. Various accessory glands (e.g., seminal vesicle) may be present in males that produce seminal fluid or spermatophores.

In the female, ova (eggs) are produced in the ovaries and transported to the oviduct. Sperm move up the oviduct where they encounter the ova and fertilization takes place. Accessory glands (e.g., those that produce egg capsules or shells) may also be present in females.

As noted above, sexual reproduction usually involves the fusion of gametes from a male and female parent. However, some sexually reproducing animals occasionally depart from this basic reproductive mode and exhibit variant forms of sexual reproduction.

Hermaphroditism (Gr. *hermaphroditos*, an organism with the attributes of both sexes) occurs when an animal has both functional male and female reproductive systems. This dual sexuality is sometimes called the **monoecious** (Gr. *monos*, single + *oikos*, house) condition. Although some hermaphrodites fertilize themselves, most also mate with another member of the same species (e.g., earthworms and sea slugs). When this occurs, each animal serves as both male and female—donating and receiving sperm. Hermaphroditism is especially beneficial to sessile (attached) animals (e.g., barnacles) that may only occasionally encounter the opposite sex.

Another variation of hermaphroditism, **sequential hermaphroditism,** occurs when an animal is one sex during one phase of its life cycle and the opposite sex during another phase. Hermaphrodites are either **protogynous** (Gr. *protous*, first + *gyne*, women) or **protandrous** (Gr. *protos*, first + *andros*, man). In protandry, an animal is a male during its early life history and becomes a female later in the life history. The reverse is true for protogynous animals. A change in the sex ratio of a population is one factor that can induce sequential hermaphroditism, which is common in oysters.

ADVANTAGES AND DISADVANTAGES OF SEXUAL REPRODUCTION

New combinations of traits can arise more rapidly in sexually reproducing animals because of genetic recombinations. The resulting genetic diversity or variability increases the chances of the species surviving sudden environmental changes. Furthermore, variation is the foundation for evolution. In contrast to the way asexual reproduction can retain mutations, copies of deleterious and lethal mutations tend to be eliminated from sexually reproducing populations.

Sexual reproduction also has some disadvantages. For example, an animal that cannot reproduce asexually can never bequeath its own exact set of genetic material to its progeny. Sexual reproduction bestows on the progeny a reassortment of maternal and paternal chromosomes. Thus, the same mixing processes that created the adaptive gene combinations in the adult, work to dismantle it partially in the offspring. In addition, many of the gametes that are released will not be fertilized, leading to a significant waste of metabolic effort.

Stop and Ask Yourself

1. What is the difference between asexual and sexual reproduction?
2. What are some advantages to asexual reproduction in invertebrates? Some disadvantages?
3. How do each of the following types of asexual reproduction occur in invertebrates: Binary fission? Fragmentation? Budding?
4. What is the difference between hermaphroditism and parthenogenesis?
5. What are some advantages and disadvantages of sexual reproduction?

SEXUAL REPRODUCTION IN VERTEBRATES

Since the evolution of the first animals, the basic use of male and female gametes has been preserved. Vertebrate evolution has also given rise to the close link between reproductive biology and sexual behavior. The strong drive to mate or reproduce dominates the lives of many vertebrates, as illustrated by the salmon's fateful spawning run or the rutting of bull elk. Females of most mammal species come into heat or **estrus** (Gr. *oistros*, a most vehement desire; the period of sexual receptivity) about the same time each year. Estrus is usually timed by genetic, hormonal, and nervous system controls so that the young will be born when environmental conditions make their survival most likely.

SOME BASIC VERTEBRATE REPRODUCTIVE STRATEGIES

Fishes are well known for their high potential fecundity, with most species releasing thousands to millions of eggs and sperm

annually. Fish species have reproductive methods, structures, and an attendant physiology that have allowed them to adapt to a great variety of aquatic conditions.

The diversity of reproductive strategies in amphibians is much greater than those observed in other groups of vertebrates. In each of the three living orders of Amphibia (caecilians, salamanders, anurans) there are trends toward terrestriality. The variety of these adaptations is especially noteworthy in anurans. These reproductive adaptations have been viewed as pioneering evolutionary experiments in the conquest of terrestrial environments by vertebrates. Noteworthy is the evolution of direct development of terrestrial eggs, ovoviviparity, and viviparity that have been important in successful invasion of mountainous environments by amphibians.

The reproductive adaptations of reptiles, birds, and early mammals foreshadow changes evident in the reproductive systems of later mammals, including humans. The reptilian system includes shelled, desiccation-resistant eggs. These eggs had the three basic embryonic membranes that still characterize the mammalian embryo, as well as a flat embryo that developed and underwent gastrulation atop a huge yolk mass. The same process of gastrulation is still seen in mammalian embryos, even though the massive yolk mass has been lost.

It was in the early mammals that the mechanisms for maintaining the developing embryo within the female for long periods of time evolved. During this time, called **gestation** (L. *gestatio*, from + *gestare*, to bear), the embryo was nourished with nutrients and oxygen, yet it was protected from attack by the female's immune system. After birth, the first mammals nourished their young with milk from the mammary glands, just as primates do today.

Female apes and monkeys are asynchronous breeders: mating and births can take place over much of the year. Females mate only when in estrus, increasing the probability of fertilization. Human females show a less distinctive estrus phase and can reproduce throughout the year. They can also engage in sexual activity without reproductive purpose; no longer is sexual behavior precariously tied to ovulation. The source of this important reproductive adaptation may be physiological or a result of concomitant evolution of the brain—a process that gave humans some conscious control over their emotions and behaviors that are controlled solely by hormones, instincts, and the environment in other animals. This separation of sex from a purely reproductive function has evolved into the long-lasting pair bonds between human males and females (e.g., marriage) that further support the offspring. This type of behavior has also resulted in the transmission of culture—a key to the evolution and success of the human species.

With this background, the reproductive anatomy and physiology of selected vertebrate classes will now be presented.

EXAMPLES OF REPRODUCTION AMONG VARIOUS VERTEBRATE CLASSES

Almost all vertebrates reproduce sexually; only a few lizards and fishes normally reproduce parthenogenetically. Sexual reproduction evolved among aquatic animals and then spread to the land as animals became terrestrial.

Fishes

All fishes reproduce in aquatic environments. In bony fishes, fertilization is usually external, and eggs are produced that contain only enough yolk to sustain the developing fish for a short time. After this yolk is consumed, the growing fish must seek food. Although many thousands of eggs are produced and fertilized, very few survive and grow to maturity. Some succumb to fungal and bacterial infections, others to siltation, and still others to predation. Thus, to assure reproductive success, the development of the fertilized egg is very rapid, and the young that result achieve maturity within a short period of time.

Amphibians

The invasion of land by vertebrates meant facing for the first time the danger of drying out or desiccating—especially the small and vulnerable gametes. Obviously, the gametes could not simply be released near one another on the land, because the gametes would quickly desiccate.

The amphibians were the first vertebrates to invade the land. They have not, however, become adapted to a completely terrestrial environment; their life cycle is still inextricably linked to water. Among most amphibians, fertilization is still external, just as it is among the fishes. Among the frogs and toads, the male grasps the female and discharges fluid containing sperm onto the eggs as she releases them into the water (figure 39.3a).

The developmental period is much longer in amphibians than in fishes, although the eggs do not contain appreciably more yolk. An evolutionary adaptation present in amphibians is the presence of two periods of development: larval and adult stages. The development of the aquatic larval stage is rapid, and the animal spends a lot of time eating and growing. When a sufficient size has been reached, the larval form undergoes a developmental transition called metamorphosis into the adult (often terrestrial) form.

Reptiles

The reptiles were the first group of vertebrates to completely abandon the aquatic habitat because of adaptations that permitted sexual reproduction on land. A crucial adaptation first found in reptiles is internal fertilization (figure 39.3b). With internal fertilization, the gametes are protected from drying out, freeing the animals from returning to the water to breed.

Many reptiles are **oviparous** (L. *ovum*, egg + *parere*, to bring forth), and the eggs are deposited outside the body of the female. Others are **ovoviviparous** (L. *ovum*, egg + *vivere*, to live, + *parere*, to bring forth). They form eggs that hatch in the body of the female, and the young are born alive.

The shelled egg and extraembryonic membranes, also first seen in reptiles, constitute two other important evolutionary adaptations to life on land. By enclosing the developing organism in a shell and having an egg that contains a large amount of yolk encased in a membranous covering, the eggs can be laid in dry places without danger of desiccation. As the embryo develops, the extraembryonic chorion and amnion help protect it, the latter by creating a fluid-filled sac for the embryo. The allantois

39.6

(a)

(b)

(c)

(d)

Figure 39.3

Vertebrate Reproductive Strategies. (*a*) A male wood frog (*Rana sylvatica*) clasping the female in amplexus, a form of external fertilization. As the female releases eggs into the water, the male releases sperm over them. (*b*) Reptiles, such as these turtles, were the first terrestrial vertebrates to develop internal fertilization. (*c*) Birds are oviparous animals. Their shelled eggs have large yolk reserves, and the young develop and hatch outside the mother's body. Birds may show advanced parental care. (*d*) A placental mammal. This female dog is nursing her puppies.

permits gas exchange and stores excretory products. Complete development can occur within the eggshell. When the animal hatches, it has developed to the point that it is able to survive on its own or with some parental care.

Birds

Birds have retained the important adaptations for life on land that evolved in the early reptiles. With the exception of most waterfowl, birds lack a penis. Internal fertilization is achieved by males simply depositing semen against the cloaca. Sperm then migrate up the cloaca and fertilize the eggs before their hard shells are formed. This method of mating occurs more quickly than the internal fertilization practiced by reptiles. All birds are oviparous, and the eggshells are much thicker than those of reptiles. Thicker shells permit birds to sit on their eggs and warm them. This brooding, or incubation, hastens the development of the embryo. When many birds hatch from their eggs, they are incapable of surviving on their own. Extensive parental care and feeding of young are more common among birds than in fishes, amphibians, or reptiles (figure 39.3c).

Mammals

The most primitive mammals, the monotremes (e.g., the duck-billed platypus and spiny anteater), lay eggs, as did the reptiles from which they evolved. All other mammals are viviparous.

Mammalian viviparity was another major evolutionary adaptation, and it has taken two forms. The marsupials developed the ability to nourish their young in a pouch after a short gestation inside the female. The other, much larger group, the placentals, retains the young inside the female, where they are nourished by the mother by means of a placenta. Even after birth, mammals continue to nourish their young. Mammary glands are a unique mammalian adaptation that permit the female to nourish the young with milk that she produces (figure 39.3d). Some mammals nurture their young until adulthood, when they are able to mate and fend for themselves. As noted at the beginning of this section, mammalian reproductive behavior also contributes to the transmission and evolution of culture that is the key to the evolution of our species.

Stop and Ask Yourself

6. What reproductive strategy developed in bony fishes to increase the chances of survival? In amphibians? In reptiles?
7. What is the difference between a bird egg and an amphibian egg?
8. What reproductive adaptation evolved in humans that is not present in other mammals?
9. What is the advantage and disadvantage of estrus?

THE HUMAN MALE REPRODUCTIVE SYSTEM

The reproductive role of the male is to produce sperm and deliver them to the vagina of the female. This function requires the following four structures:

1. Two testes produce sperm and the male sex hormone, testosterone.
2. Accessory glands and tubes furnish a fluid for carrying the sperm to the penis. This fluid, together with the sperm, is called semen.
3. Accessory ducts store and carry secretions from the testes and accessory glands to the penis.
4. The penis deposits semen into the vagina during sexual intercourse.

PRODUCTION AND TRANSPORT OF SPERM

The paired **testes** (s., testis; L. *testis*, witness; the paired testes were believed to bear witness to a man's virility) are the male reproductive organs (gonads) that produce sperm (figure 39.4). Shortly after birth, the testes descend from the abdominal cavity into the **scrotum** (L. *scrautum*, a leather pouch for arrows), which hangs between the thighs. Because the testes hang outside the body, the temperature inside the scrotum is about 34° C compared to a 38° C core temperature. ④ The lower temperature is necessary for active sperm production and survival. Muscles elevate or lower the testes depending on the outside air temperature.

Each testis contains over 800 tightly coiled **seminiferous tubules** (figure 39.5a,b), which produce thousands of sperm each second in healthy young men (*see figure 6.11*). The walls of the seminiferous tubules are lined with two types of cells: spermatogenic cells, which give rise to sperm, and sustentacular cells, which provide nourishment for the sperm as they are being formed and secrete a fluid (as well as the hormone inhibin) into the tubules to provide a liquid medium for the sperm. Between the seminiferous tubules are clusters of endocrine cells, called interstitial endocrinocytes, which secrete the male sex hormone testosterone.

The sperm produced in a testis are carried to the penis by a system of tubes. The seminiferous tubules merge into a network of tiny tubules called the rete tesis (L. *rete*, net), which merge into a coiled tube called the epididymis. The epididymis has three main functions: (1) it stores sperm until they are mature and ready to be ejaculated, (2) it contains smooth muscle that helps propel the sperm toward the penis by peristaltic contractions, and (3) it serves as a duct system for the passage of sperm from the testis to the ductus deferens. The ductus deferens (formerly called the vas deferens or sperm duct) is the dilated continuation of the epididymis. Continuing upward after leaving the scrotum, the ductus deferens passes through the lower part of the abdominal wall via the inguinal canal. ⑤ If the abdominal wall weakens at the point where the ductus deferens passes through, an inguinal hernia may result. (In an inguinal hernia, the intestine may protrude downward into the scrotum.) The ductus deferens then passes around the urinary bladder (*see figure 39.4*) and becomes enlarged to form the ampulla. The ampulla stores some sperm until they are ejaculated. Distal to the ampulla, the ductus deferens becomes the ejaculatory duct. The urethra is the final section of the reproductive duct system.

After the ductus deferens passes around the urinary bladder, several accessory glands add their secretions to the sperm as they are propelled through the ducts. These accessory glands are the seminal vesicles, prostate gland, and bulbourethral glands (*see figure 39.4*). The **seminal vesicles** secrete water, fructose, prostaglandins, and vitamin C. This secretion provides an energy source for the motile sperm and helps to neutralize the natural protective acidity of the vagina. (The pH of the vagina is about 3 to 4, but sperm motility and fertility are enhanced when it increases to about 6.) The **prostate gland** secretes water, enzymes, cholesterol, buffering salts, and phospholipids. The **bulbourethral glands** secrete a clear alkaline fluid that acts as a lubricant in the urethra to facilitate the ejaculation of semen and to lubricate the penis prior to sexual intercourse. The fluid that results from the combination of sperm and glandular secretions is **semen** (L. *seminis*, seed). The average human ejaculation produces about 3 to 4 ml of semen and contains 300 to 400 million sperm.

The penis has two functions. It carries urine through the urethra to the outside during urination, and it transports semen through the urethra during ejaculation. In addition to the urethra, the penis contains three cylindrical strands of erectile tissue: two corpora cavernosa and the corpora spongiosum (*see figure 39.4*). The corpora spongiosum extends beyond the corpora cavernosa and becomes the expanded tip of the penis called the glans penis.

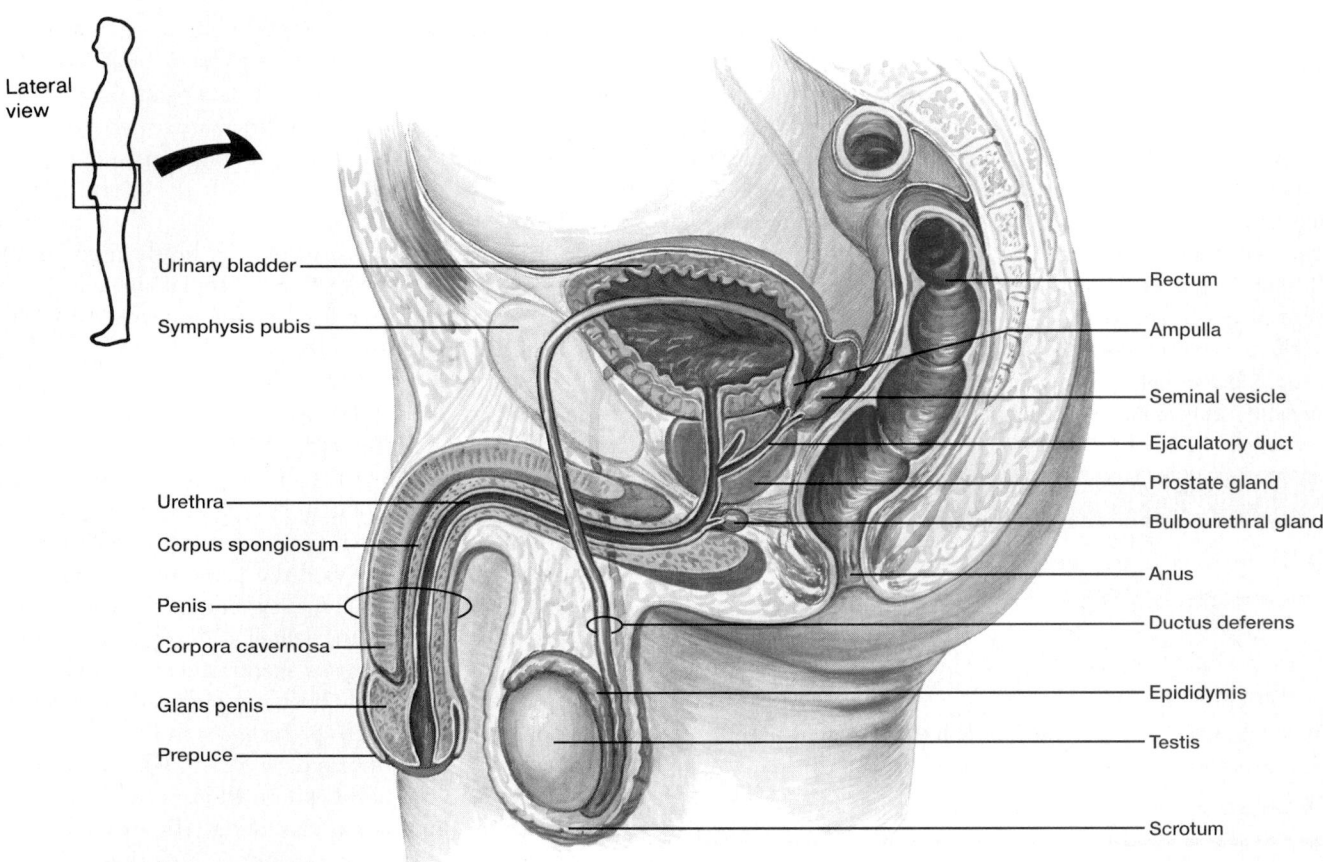

Figure **39.4**

Sagittal View of the Human Male Reproductive System. There are two each of the following structures: testis, epididymis, ductus deferens, seminal vesicle, ejaculatory duct, and bulbourethral gland.

The loosely fitting skin of the penis is folded forward over the glans to form the prepuce or foreskin. **Circumcision** is the removal of the prepuce for religious or health reasons. Today, many circumcisions are performed in the belief that the operation may decrease the occurrence of cancer of the penis.

A mature human sperm consists of a head, midpiece, and tail (figure 39.5c). The head contains the haploid nucleus, which is mostly DNA. The acrosome, a cap over most of the head, contains an enzyme called acrosin, that assists the sperm in penetrating the outer layer surrounding a secondary oocyte. The sperm tail contains an array of microtubules that bend to produce whiplike movements. The spiral mitochondria in the midpiece supply the ATP necessary for these movements.

Hormonal Control of Male Reproductive Function

Before a male can mature and function sexually, special regulatory hormones must come into play (table 39.1). Male sex hormones are collectively called **androgens** (Gr. *andros,* man + *gennan,* to produce). The hormones that travel from the brain and pituitary gland to the testes (and ovaries in the female) are called **gonadotropins.** As previously noted, the interstitial endocrinocytes

produce the male sex hormone **testosterone.** Figure 39.6 shows the feedback mechanisms that regulate the production and secretion of testosterone, as well as its actions. When the level of testosterone in the blood decreases, the hypothalamus is stimulated to secrete GnRH (gonadotropin-releasing hormone). GnRH stimulates the secretion of FSH (follicle-stimulating hormone) and LH (luteinizing hormone), also called ICSH (interstitial cell-stimulating hormone), into the bloodstream. (FSH and LH were first named for their functions in females, but their molecular structure is exactly the same in males.) FSH causes the spermatogenic cells in the seminiferous tubules to initiate spermatogenesis, and LH stimulates the interstitial endocrinocytes to secrete testosterone. The cycle is completed when testosterone inhibits the secretion of LH, and another hormone, inhibin, is secreted. Inhibin inhibits the secretion of FSH from the anterior pituitary. This cycle maintains a constant rate (homeostasis) of spermatogenesis.

Stop and Ask Yourself

10. What are the major constituents of semen?
11. How do LH and FSH function in males?

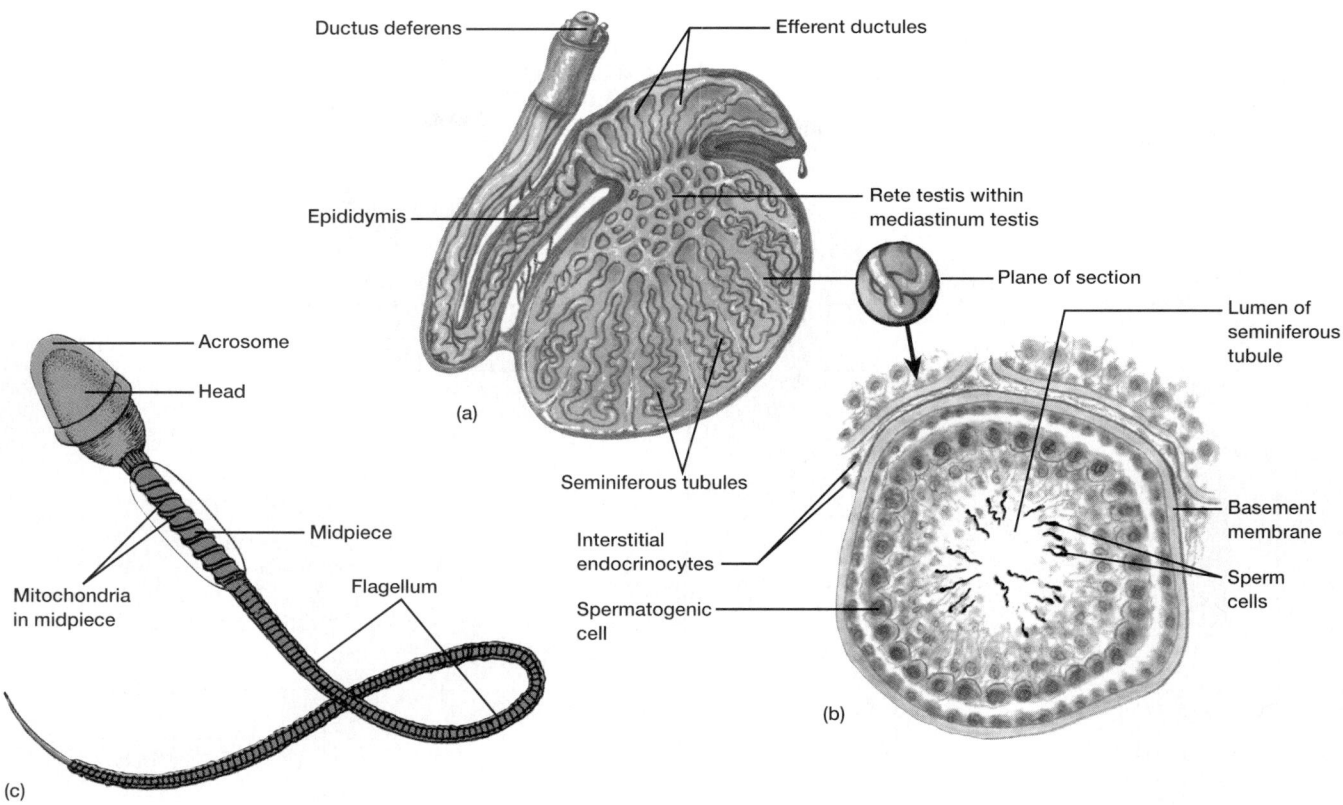

FIGURE 39.5

The Human Male Testis. (*a*) Sagittal section through a testis. (*b*) Cross section of a seminiferous tubule showing the location of spermatogenesis. (*c*) A mature sperm.

TABLE 39.1	MAJOR HUMAN MALE REPRODUCTIVE HORMONES IN AN ADULT	
HORMONE	**FUNCTIONS**	**SOURCE**
FSH (follicle-stimulating hormone)	Aids sperm maturation; increases testosterone production	Pituitary gland
GnRH (gonadotropin-releasing hormone)	Controls pituitary secretion	Hypothalamus
Inhibin	Inhibits FSH secretion	Sustentacular cells in testes
LH (luteinizing hormone) or ICSH (interstitial cell-stimulating hormone)	Stimulates testosterone secretion	Pituitary gland
Testosterone	Increases sperm production; stimulates development of male primary and secondary sex characteristics; inhibits LH secretion	Interstitial endocrinocytes in testes

THE HUMAN FEMALE REPRODUCTIVE SYSTEM

The reproductive role of females is more complex than that of males. Not only do females produce gametes (eggs or ova), but after fertilization, they also nourish, carry, and protect the developing embryo. After the offspring is born, the mother may nurse it for a time. Another difference between the sexes is the monthly rhythmicity of the female reproductive system.

The female reproductive system consists of a number of structures with specialized functions (figure 39.7):

1. Two ovaries produce eggs and the female sex hormones called estrogens, and progesterone.
2. Two uterine tubes, one from each ovary, carry eggs from the ovary to the uterus. Fertilization usually occurs in the upper ⅓ of a uterine tube.

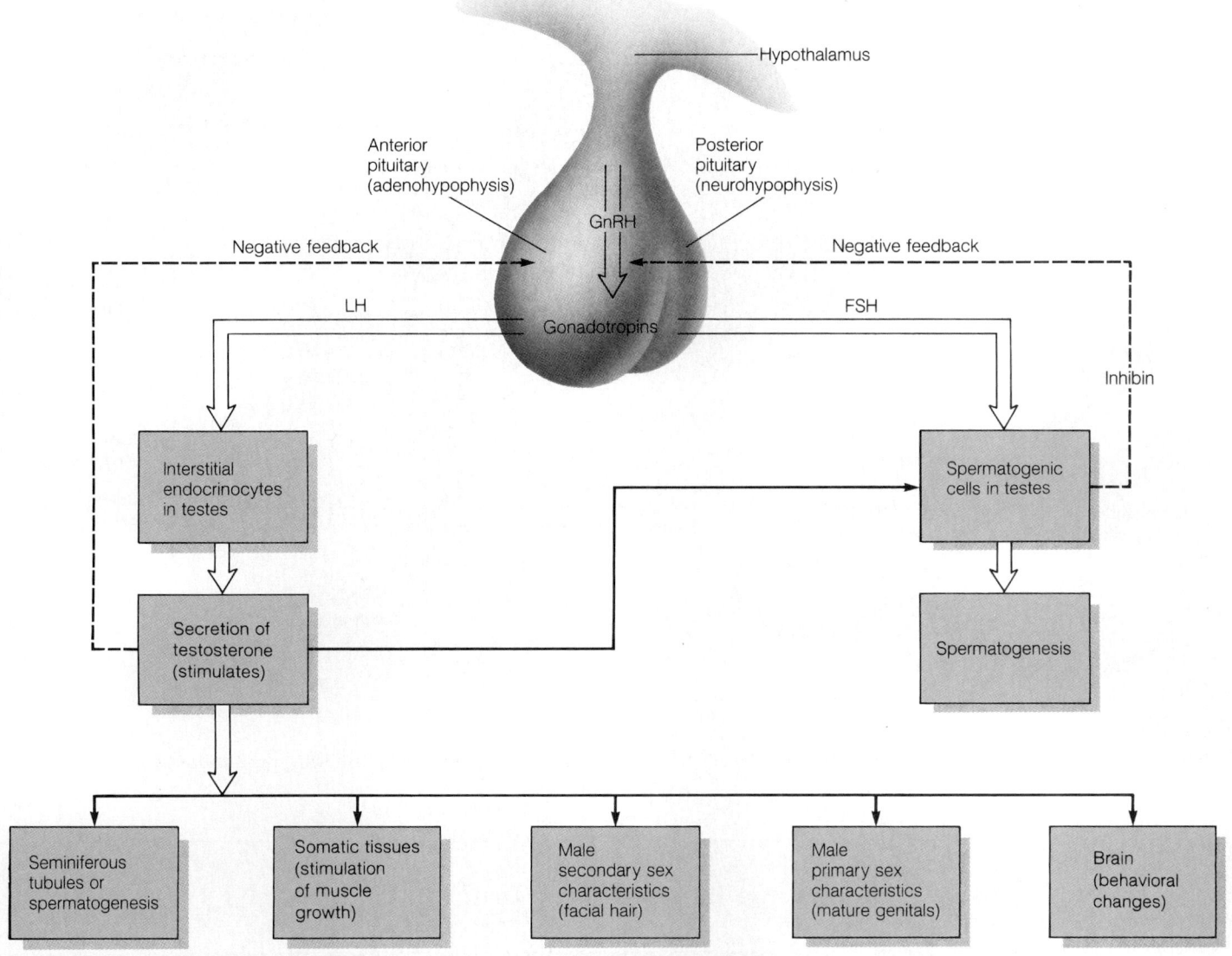

Figure 39.6

Hormonal Control of Reproductive Function in Adult Human Males. The feedback mechanisms by which the hypothalamus controls the maturation of sperm and the development of male secondary sexual characteristics are shown.

3. If fertilization occurs, the uterus receives the blastocyst and houses the developing embryo.

4. The vagina receives semen from the penis during sexual intercourse. It is the exit point for menstrual flow and is the canal through which the baby passes from the uterus during childbirth.

5. The external genital organs have protective functions and play a role in sexual arousal.

6. The mammary glands, contained in the paired breasts, produce milk for the newborn baby.

PRODUCTION AND TRANSPORT OF THE EGG

The female gonads are the paired **ovaries** (L. *ovum*, egg), which produce eggs and female hormones. The ovaries are located in the pelvic part of the abdomen, one on each side of the uterus.

A cross section of an ovary reveals rounded vesicles called follicles, which are the actual centers of egg production (oogenesis) (figure 39.8). Each follicle contains an immature egg called a primary oocyte, and follicles are always present in several stages of development. After release of a secondary oocyte (commonly called an egg) in the process called **ovulation,** the lining of the follicle grows inward, forming the corpus luteum ("yellow body"), which serves as a temporary endocrine tissue and continues to secrete the female sex hormones estrogen and progesterone.

The paired tubes that receive the secondary oocyte from the ovary and convey it to the uterus are called either the **uterine tubes** or **fallopian tubes** (*see figure 39.7*). The part of the uterine tube that encircles the ovary is fringed with feathery fimbriae. Each month, as a secondary oocyte is released, it is swept by the motion of the fimbriae across a tiny space between the uterine tube and the ovary into the tube.

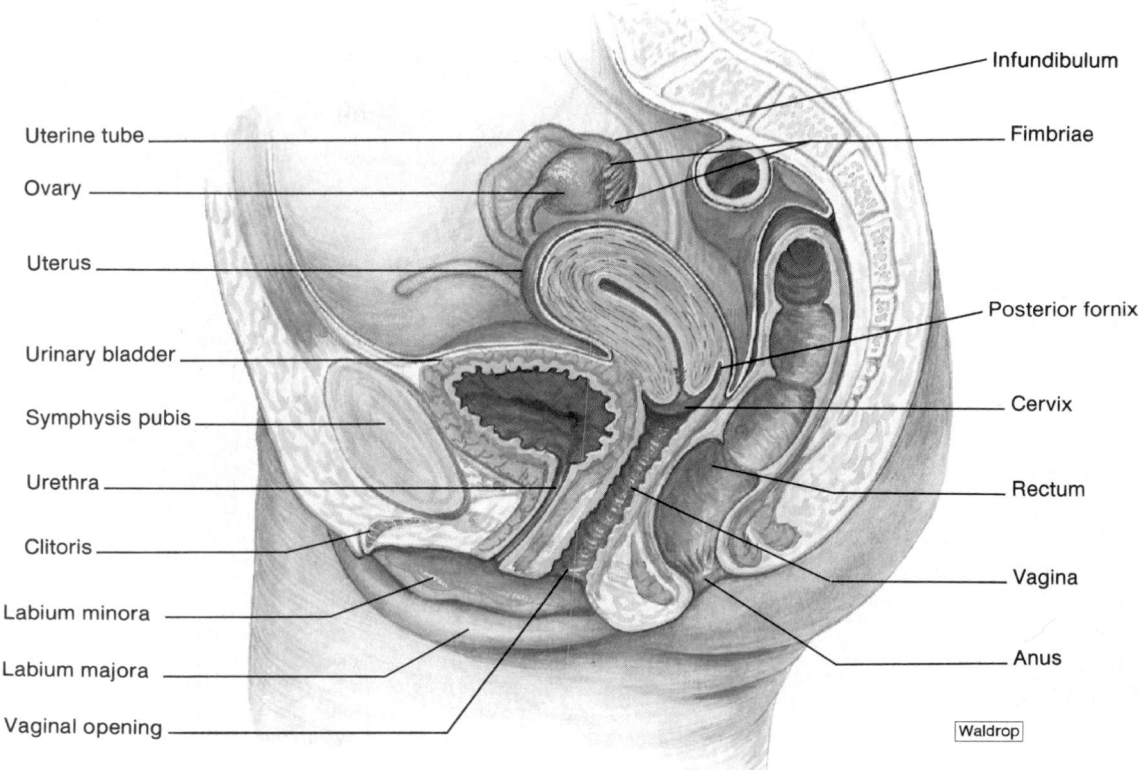

FIGURE 39.7

Sagittal View of the Human Female Reproductive System.   There are two uterine tubes that lead into the uterus and two ovaries.

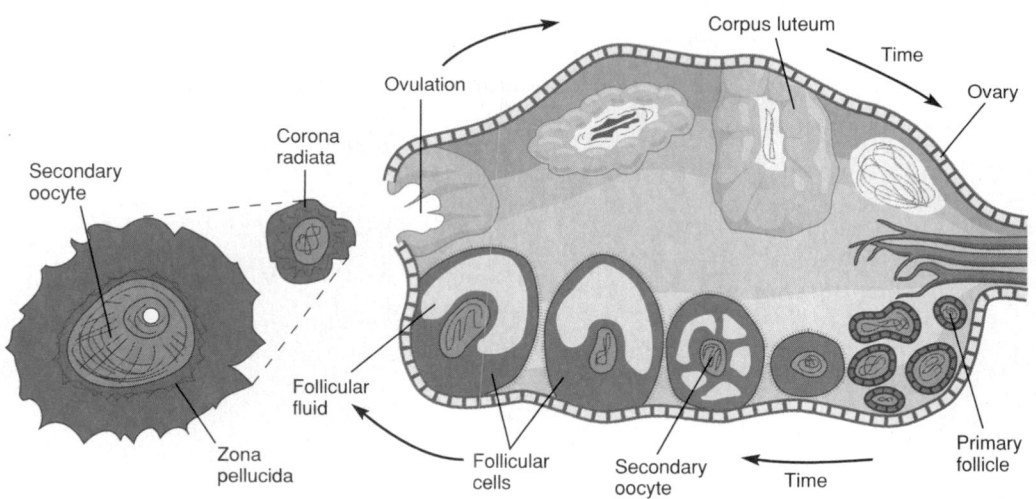

FIGURE 39.8

Cross Section through a Human Ovary.   The events in the ovarian cycle proceed from the growth and maturation of the primordial follicle, through ovulation (rupture of a mature follicle with the concurrent release of a secondary oocyte), through the formation and maintenance (during pregnancy) or degeneration (no pregnancy) of an endocrine structure called the corpus luteum. The positions of the oocyte and corpus luteum are varied for illustrative purposes only. The maturation of an oocyte occurs at the same site, from the beginning of the cycle to ovulation.

FIGURE **39.9**

Cilia Lining the Uterine Tubes. The electron micrograph shows the tiny, beating cilia on the surfaces of the uterine tube cells. They propel the secondary oocyte downward and perhaps the sperm upward.

Unlike sperm, the secondary oocyte is unable to move on its own. Instead, it is carried along the uterine tube toward the uterus by the peristaltic contractions of the tube and the waving motions of the cilia in the mucous membrane of the tube (figure 39.9). Fertilization usually occurs in the uppermost third of the uterine tube. A fertilized oocyte (zygote) continues its journey toward the uterus, where it will implant. The journey takes 4 to 7 days. If fertilization does not occur, the secondary oocyte degenerates in the uterine tube.

The uterine tubes terminate in the **uterus,** a hollow, muscular organ located in front of the rectum and behind the urinary bladder (figure 39.10). The uterus terminates in a narrow portion called the cervix, which joins the uterus to the vagina. The uterus is made up of three layers of tissues. The outer layer (perimetrium) extends beyond the uterus to form the two broad ligaments that stretch from the uterus to the lateral walls of the pelvis. The middle muscular layer (myometrium [Gr. *myo*, muscle + *metra*, womb]) makes up most of the uterine wall. The endometrium is the specialized mucous membrane that contains an abundance of blood vessels and simple glands.

The cervix leads to the **vagina,** a muscle-lined tube about 8 to 10 cm long. The wall of the vagina is composed mainly of smooth muscle and elastic tissue.

The external genital organs, or genitalia, include the mons pubis, labia majora, labia minora, vestibular glands, clitoris, and vaginal opening (*see figure 39.7*). As a group, these organs are

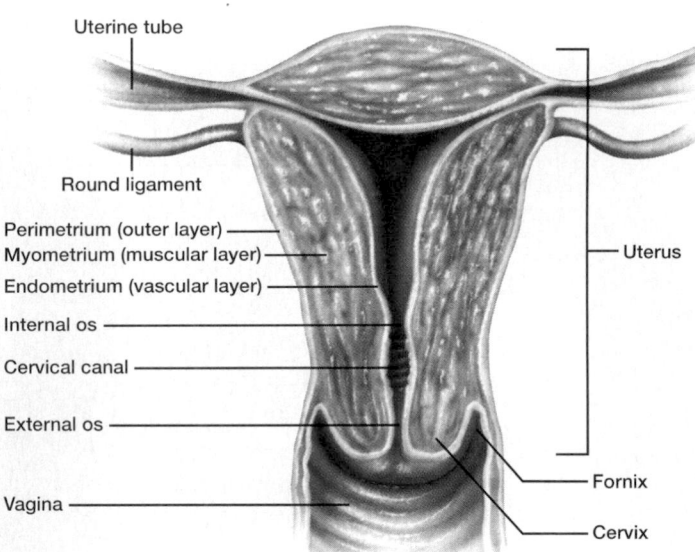

FIGURE **39.10**

The Human Female Uterus. This cross section of a uterus shows the three major tissue layers. The outer layer is the perimetrium. The middle myometrium makes up the bulk of the uterine wall. It is composed of smooth muscle fibers. The innermost layer is composed of a specialized mucous membrane called the endometrium, which is deep and velvety in texture. When the endometrium breaks down, this makes up part of the menstrual flow.

called the **vulva.** In most young women, the vaginal opening is partially covered by a thin membrane, the hymen, which may be ruptured during normal strenuous activities or may be stretched or broken during sexual activity.

The **mammary glands** (L. *mammae*, breasts) are modified sweat glands that produce and secrete milk. They contain varying amounts of adipose tissue.   ⑦   The amount of adipose tissue determines the size of the breasts, but the amount of mammary tissue does not vary widely from one woman to another.

HORMONAL CONTROL OF FEMALE REPRODUCTIVE FUNCTION

The male is continuously fertile from puberty to old age, and throughout that period, sex hormones are continuously secreted. The female, however, is fertile only during a few days each month, and the pattern of hormone secretion is intricately related to the cyclical release of a secondary oocyte from the ovary.

The development of a secondary oocyte in a follicle is controlled by the cyclical production of hormones (figure 39.11; table 39.2). Gonadotropin-releasing hormone (GnRH) from the hypothalamus acts on the anterior pituitary gland, which releases follicle-stimulating hormone (FSH) and luteinizing hormone (LH) to bring about the oocyte's maturation and release from the ovary. These hormones regulate the **menstrual cycle,** which is the cyclic preparation of the uterus to receive a fertilized egg, and the **ovarian cycle,** during which the oocyte matures, and ovulation occurs. This monthly preparation of the

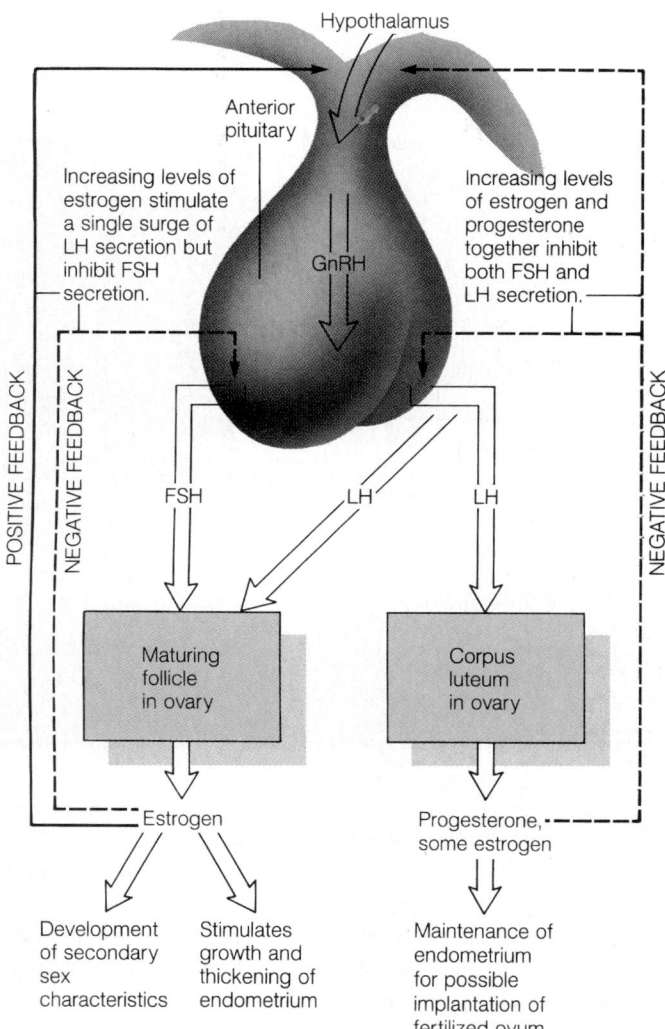

Figure **39.11**

Hormonal Control of Reproductive Functions in an Adult Human Female. Feedback loops involving the hypothalamus, anterior pituitary, and ovaries are included. GnRH stimulates the release of both FSH and LH. Two negative feedback systems and a positive feedback system (one of the few in the human body) control the ovarian cycle.

uterine lining for the fertilized egg normally begins at puberty. When a female reaches about 45 to 55 years of age, the ovaries lose their sensitivity to FSH and LH, they stop making normal amounts of progesterone and estrogen, and the monthly menstrual cycle ceases in what is called the **menopause** (Gr. *men*, month + *pausis*, cessation).

One way to understand the hormonal pattern in the normal monthly cycle is to follow the development of the oocyte and the physical events in the menstrual cycle (figure 39.12; table 39.3). On the average, it takes about 28 days to complete one menstrual cycle, although the range may be from 22 to 45 days. During this time, the following events take place:

1. The controlling center for ovulation and menstruation is the hypothalamus. It releases, on a regular cycle, GnRH,

which stimulates the anterior pituitary to secrete FSH and LH (*see figure 39.11*).
2. FSH promotes the development of the oocyte in one of the immature ovarian follicles.
3. Estrogen is produced by the follicles, causing a buildup and enrichment of the endometrium, as well as the inhibition of FSH production.
4. The elevated estrogen level about midway in the cycle triggers the anterior pituitary to secrete LH, which causes the mature follicle to enlarge rapidly and release the secondary oocyte (ovulation). LH also causes the collapsed follicle to become another endocrine tissue, the corpus luteum.
5. The corpus luteum secretes estrogen and progesterone, which act to complete the development of the endometrium and maintain it for 10 to 14 days.
6. If the oocyte is not fertilized, the corpus luteum disintegrates into a corpus albicans, and estrogen and progesterone secretion cease.
7. Without estrogen and progesterone, the endometrium breaks down, and **menstruation** occurs. The menstrual flow is composed mainly of sloughed-off endometrial cells, mucus, and blood.
8. As the progesterone and estrogen levels decrease further, the pituitary renews active secretion of FSH, which stimulates the development of another follicle, and the monthly cycle begins again.

HORMONAL REGULATION IN THE PREGNANT FEMALE

Pregnancy sets a new series of physiological events into motion. The ovaries are directly affected, because as the embryo develops, the cells of the embryo and placenta release the hormone human chorionic gonadotropin (hCG), which keeps the corpus luteum from disintegrating. The progesterone that it secretes is necessary to maintain the uterine lining. After a time, the placenta takes over the production of progesterone, and the corpus luteum degenerates. 8 By the end of 2 weeks following implantation, the concentration of hCG is so high in the female's blood, and therefore in her urine as well, that an hCG immunological test is used to test for pregnancy. As the embryo develops, other hormones are secreted. For example, prolactin and oxytocin induce the mammary glands to secrete and eject milk after childbirth. Oxytocin and prostaglandins also stimulate the uterine contractions that expel the baby from the uterus during childbirth.

Stop and Ask Yourself

12. What is the anatomy of a human uterus?
13. What are the external genital organs in a human female?
14. What events take place in the menstrual cycle?

TABLE 39.2	MAJOR HUMAN FEMALE REPRODUCTIVE HORMONES	
HORMONE	FUNCTIONS	SOURCE
Estrogen	Stimulates thickening of uterine wall; stimulates maturation of oocyte; stimulates development of female sex characteristics; inhibits FSH secretion; increases LH secretion	Ovarian follicle, corpus luteum
FSH (follicle-stimulating hormone)	Causes immature oocyte and follicle to develop; increases estrogen secretion; stimulates new gamete formation and development of uterine wall after menstruation	Pituitary gland
GnRH (gonadotropin-releasing hormone)	Controls pituitary secretion	Hypothalamus
hCG (human chorionic gonadotropin)	Prevents corpus luteum from disintegrating; stimulates estrogen and progesterone secretion by corpus luteum	Embryonic membranes and placenta
LH (luteinizing hormone)	Stimulates further development of oocyte and follicle; stimulates ovulation; increases progesterone secretion; aids development of corpus luteum	Pituitary gland
Oxytocin	Stimulates uterine contractions during labor; milk release during nursing	Pituitary gland
Prolactin	Promotes milk secretion by mammary glands after childbirth	Pituitary gland
Progesterone	Stimulates thickening of uterine wall	Corpus luteum

TABLE 39.3	SUMMARY OF THE MENSTRUAL CYCLE EVENTS	
PHASE	EVENTS	DURATION IN DAYS*
Follicular	Follicle matures in the ovary; menstruation (endometrium breaks down); endometrium rebuilds	1–5
Ovulation	Secondary oocyte released from ovary	6–14
Luteal	Corpus luteum forms; endometrium thickens and becomes glandular	15–28

*Using a 28-day menstrual cycle as an example.

PRENATAL DEVELOPMENT AND BIRTH

This section covers the main event in reproduction—the 9-month pregnancy period, during which time the female's body carries, nourishes, and protects the embryo as it grows to a full-term baby.

EVENTS OF PRENATAL DEVELOPMENT: FROM ZYGOTE TO NEWBORN

The development of a human being may be divided into prenatal ("before birth") and postnatal ("after birth") periods. During the prenatal period, the developing individual begins life as a zygote, then becomes a ball of cells called a morula, and eventually becomes a blastocyst that implants in the endometrium. From two weeks after fertilization until the end of the eighth week of its existence, the individual is called an embryo. From nine weeks until birth it is a fetus, and is called a newborn, or baby, when it is completely outside its mother's body.

Pregnancy is arbitrarily divided into trimesters, periods of three months each. The first trimester begins at fertilization and is the time when most of the organs are formed. The next two trimesters are mainly periods of growth for the fetus.

The First Trimester

After fertilization, usually in the first ⅓ of the uterine tube, the zygote goes through several cleavages as it is transported down the tube (figure 39.13). It eventually becomes a solid ball of cells called a **morula** and by the fourth day, it develops into a 50- to 120-cell blastula stage called a **blastocyst.**

The next stage of development occurs when the blastocyst adheres to the uterine wall and implants. During implantation, the outer cells of the blastocyst, called the trophoblast, invade the endometrium.   9   Implantation is usually completed 11 to 12 days after fertilization; from then on the female is considered to be pregnant.

One of the most unique features of mammalian development is that most of the cells of the early embryo make no contribution to the embryo's body, giving rise instead to supportive and protective membranes. Only the inner cell mass gives rise to the embryonic body. Eventually, these cells become arranged in a flat sheet that undergoes a gastrulation similar to that of reptiles and birds (see figure 10.12).

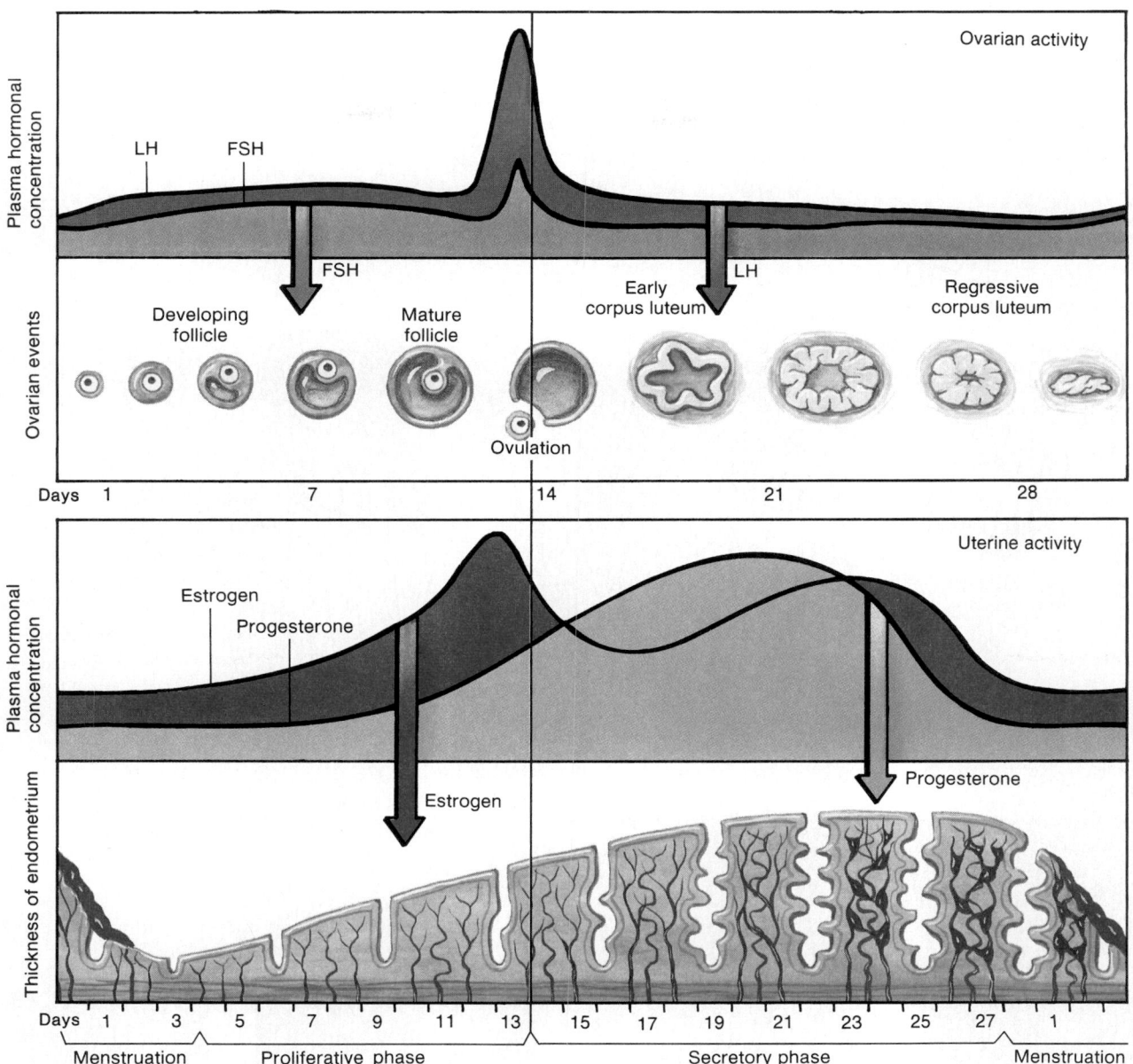

FIGURE 39.12

The Major Events in the Female Ovarian and Menstrual Cycles. The two charts correlate the gonadotropins, ovarian hormones, follicle development, ovulation, and changes in uterine anatomy during the cycles.

Once gastrulation is completed, the rest of the first trimester is devoted to organogenesis and growth (figure 39.14). Regulatory events and inductive-tissue interactions occur that shape most of the organ systems. By the middle of the first trimester, all the major body systems have begun their development.

The Second Trimester

In the second trimester (fourth month), growth is spectacular. By now, the pregnant mother is quite aware of fetal movements. The heartbeat can be heard with a stethoscope.

During the sixth month, the upper and lower eyelids separate, and the eyelashes form. During the seventh month, the eyes open. It is during this period that the bones begin to ossify.

The Third Trimester

The third trimester extends from the seventh month until birth. It is during this time that the fetus has developed sufficiently (with respect to the circulatory and respiratory systems) to potentially survive if born prematurely. During the last month, the weight of the fetus doubles.

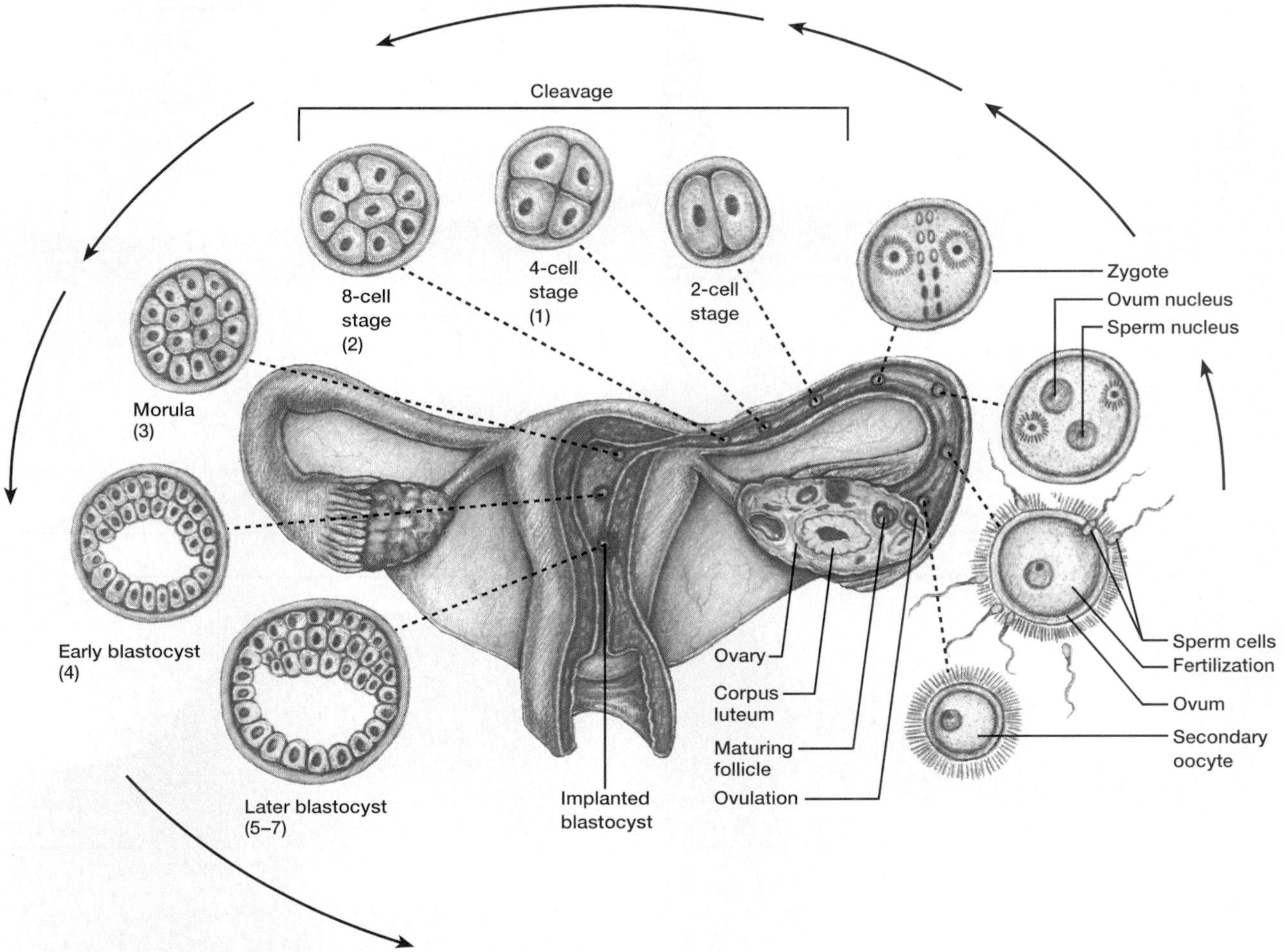

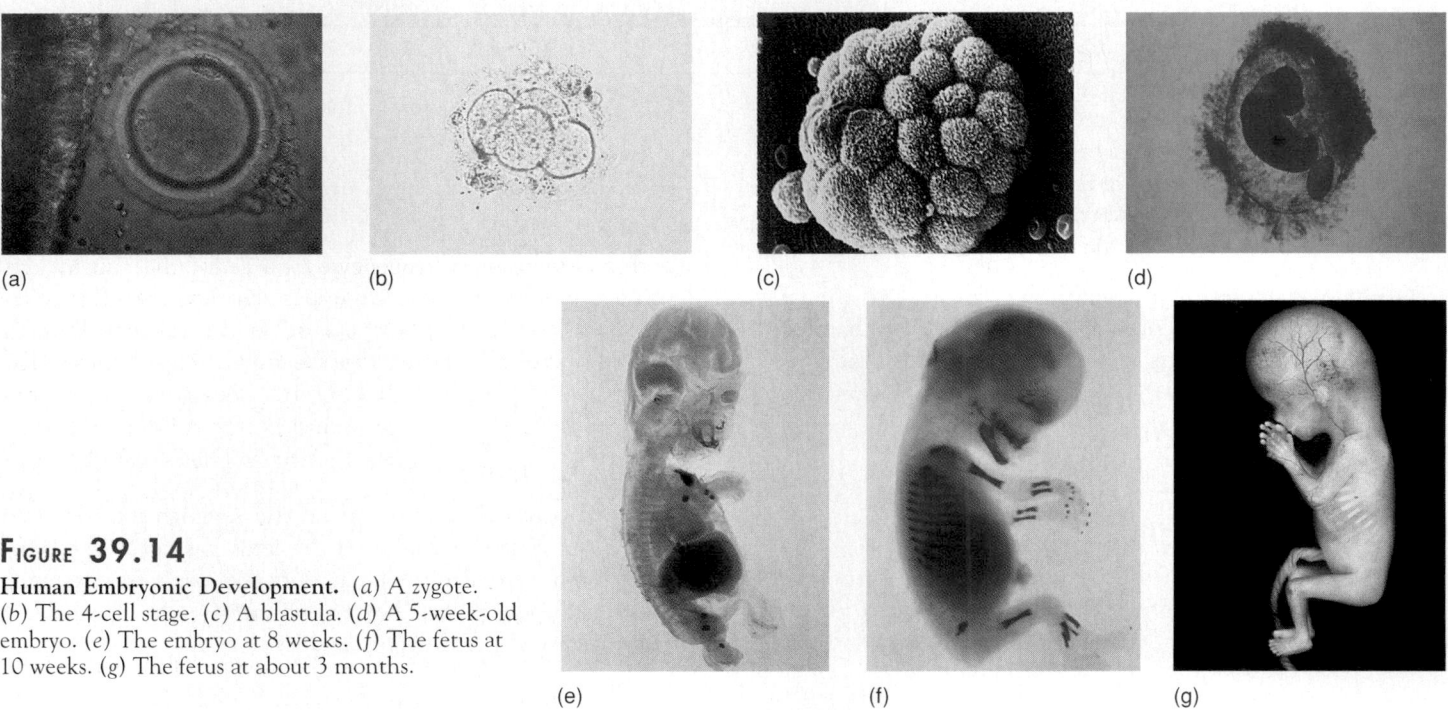

FIGURE 39.13

The Early Stages in Human Development. The numbers indicate the days after fertilization. The secondary oocyte is fertilized in the upper $\frac{1}{3}$ of the uterine tube, undergoes cleavage while traveling down the tube, and finally implants in the endometrium of the uterus.

(a) (b) (c) (d)

FIGURE 39.14

Human Embryonic Development. (*a*) A zygote. (*b*) The 4-cell stage. (*c*) A blastula. (*d*) A 5-week-old embryo. (*e*) The embryo at 8 weeks. (*f*) The fetus at 10 weeks. (*g*) The fetus at about 3 months.

(e) (f) (g)

FIGURE **39.15**

The Fetus and Placenta as They Appear during the Seventh Week of Development. The circulations of mother and fetus come into close contact at the site of the chorionic villi, but they do not actually mix. Branches of the mother's arteries in the wall of her uterus open into pools near the chorionic villi. Oxygen and nutrients from the mother's blood diffuse into the fetal capillaries of the placenta. The fetal capillaries lead into the umbilical vein, which is enclosed within the umbilical cord. From here, the fresh blood circulates through the fetus's body. Blood that the fetus has depleted of nutrients and oxygen returns to the placenta in the umbilical arteries, which branch into capillaries, from which waste products diffuse to the maternal side.

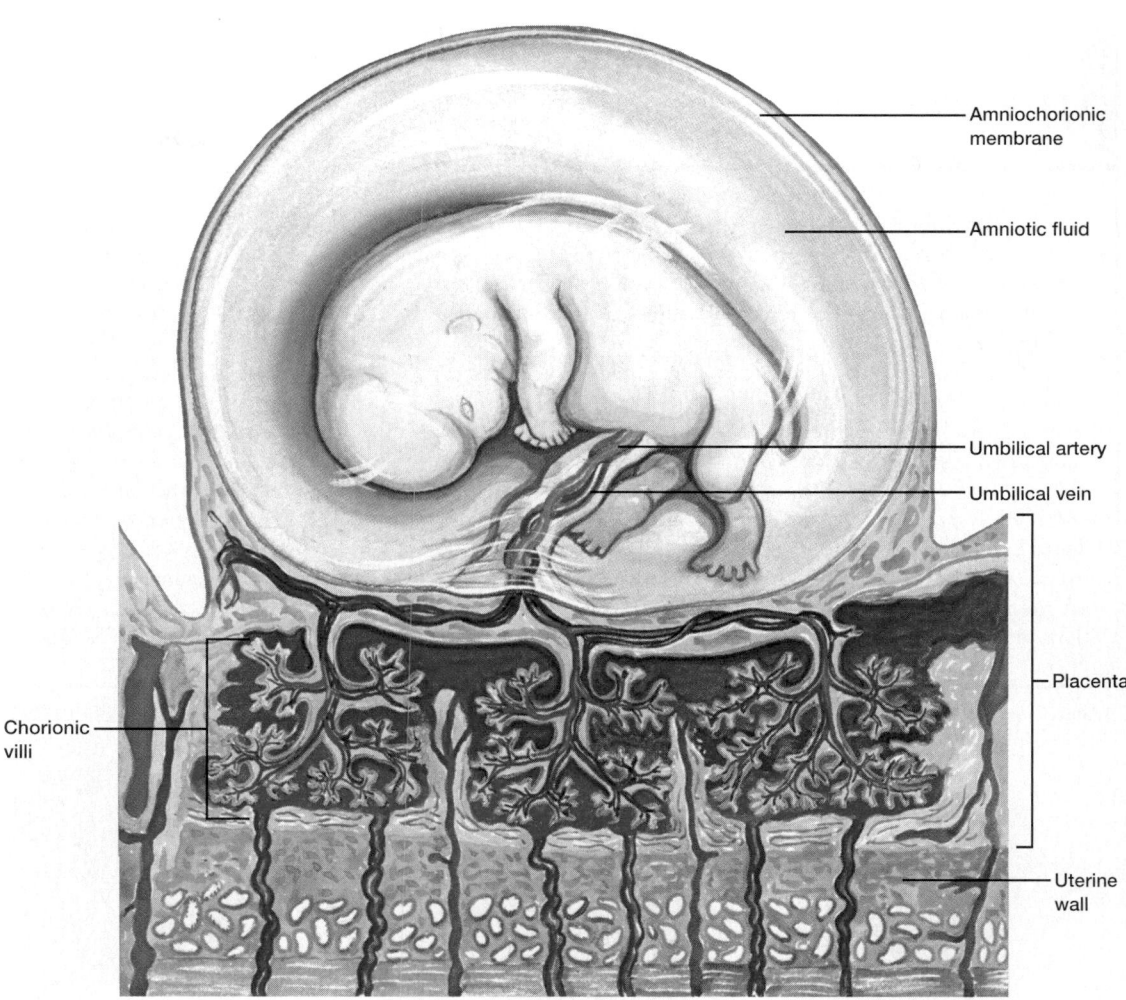

Amniochorionic membrane

Amniotic fluid

Umbilical artery

Umbilical vein

Placenta

Uterine wall

Chorionic villi

THE PLACENTA: EXCHANGE SITE AND HORMONE PRODUCER

The lengthy pregnancy characteristic of mammals is possible in part because of the embryonic membranes that originated in the reptiles: the amnion, yolk sac, chorion, and allantois (*see figure 10.13*). The latter two gave rise to the embryonic parts of the placenta. The **placenta** is the organ that sustains the embryo and fetus throughout the pregnancy and through which an exchange of gases, nutrients, and wastes takes place between the maternal and fetal systems (figure 39.15). The tiny, fingerlike projections that were sent out from the blastocyst during implantation develop into numerous chorionic villi, which contain embryonic blood vessels. These blood vessels do not merge with the mother's; the two bloodstreams remain separate throughout the pregnancy. The placenta remains connected to the abdomen of the fetus by the **umbilical cord,** in which the fetus's umbilical arteries and veins spiral about each other.

BIRTH: AN END AND A BEGINNING

About 266 days after fertilization, or 280 days from the beginning of the last menstrual period, the human infant is born. The birth process is called **parturition** (L. *parturire*, to be in labor). During parturition, the mother's uterine muscles begin to contract, and the cervix begins to dilate, or open. The hormone relaxin, produced by the ovaries and placenta, acts to cause the mother's pelvic bones to slightly separate so that the baby can pass through the birth canal.

Changing hormone levels initiate parturition (box 39.1). When it is time for the baby to be born, its pituitary gland secretes adrenocorticotropic hormone (ACTH), which stimulates the adrenal glands to secrete steroids. These steroids stimulate the placenta to produce prostaglandins that, along with the hormone oxytocin from the mother's pituitary, cause the uterus to begin powerful muscular contractions. The contractions build in length and increase in frequency over a period that usually lasts anywhere from 2 to 18 hours. During that time, the cervix becomes fully dilated, and the amniotic sac ruptures. Usually within an hour of these events, the baby is expelled from the uterus (figure 39.16*a*–*c*). After the baby emerges, uterine contractions continue, and the **afterbirth** is expelled (figure 39.16*d*). The umbilical cord is severed, and the newborn embarks on its nurtured existence in the outside world. (In mammals other than humans, the female bites through the cord to sever it.)

MILK PRODUCTION AND LACTATION

Lactation (L. *lactare*, to suckle) includes both milk secretion (production) by the mammary glands and milk release from the breasts.

BOX 39.1 THE FUNCTION OF THE FETUS DURING CHILDBIRTH

Until recently it was thought that the fetus played no active role in its own birth process. There is now evidence that the fetus triggers the release of "stress" hormones during parturition that help it survive the arduous process of birth and adjust to life outside the mother's uterus.

In addition to the pressure the fetus feels while passing through the birth canal, it is also periodically deprived of oxygen when powerful uterine contractions compress the umbilical cord and placenta. During these periods of stress, the fetus produces very high levels of epinephrine and norepinephrine, both of which are classified as catecholamines. Catecholamines are generally produced to help a person react favorably to incidents of extreme stress. The secretion of catecholamines allows the fetus to counteract the period of low oxygen and other potentially harmful situations throughout most of parturition.

The above stress situations are beneficial, because the presence of unusually high levels of catecholamines permits the newborn to adjust to new conditions outside the mother's uterus immediately after birth. Postnatal adjustments include the necessity to breathe, the breakdown of fat and glycogen into usable fuel for cells, the acceleration of the heart rate and cardiac output, and the increase of blood flow to the brain, heart, and skeletal muscles.

The surge of catecholamines during parturition also causes the newborn's pupils to dilate, even when strong light is present. This alertness may help the infant form an early bond with its mother.

The production of fetal catecholamines is a direct result of the adrenal glands' response to stress. In adults, however, the secretion of catecholamines begins with the stimulation of the sympathetic nervous system. It is also of interest that the adrenal glands of the fetus are proportionately larger than those of the adult.

Adapted from Robert Carola, John P. Harley, and Charles R. Noback, *Human Anatomy and Physiology*, 2d ed. Copyright © 1992 McGraw-Hill, Inc. Used by permission.

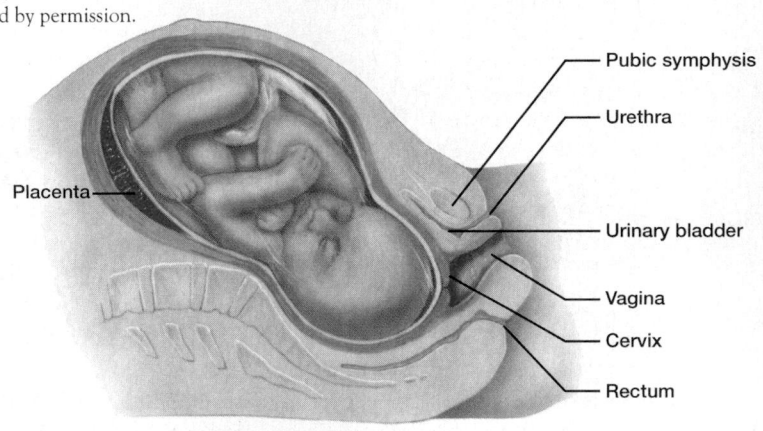

(a) 9-month-old fetus

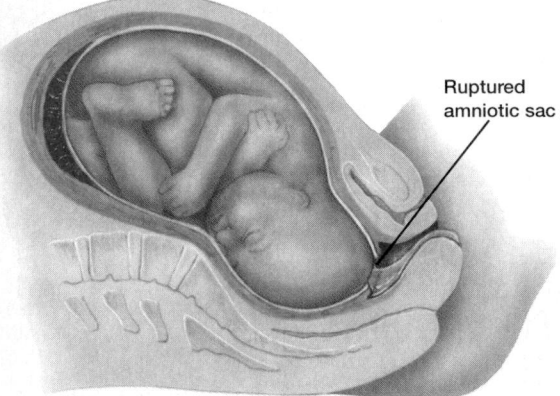

(b) First stage of birth

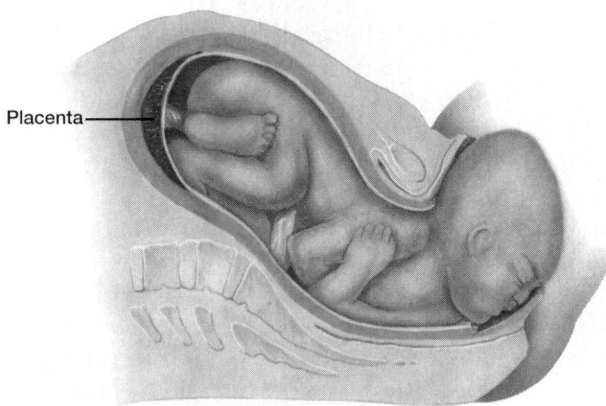

(c) Second stage of birth

(d) Third stage of birth

FIGURE 39.16

The Stages of Labor and Parturition. (*a*) The position of the fetus prior to labor. (*b*) The ruptured amniotic sac and early dilation of the cervix. (*c*) The expulsion stage of parturition. (*d*) Passage of the afterbirth.

(Mammary glands, a unique characteristic of mammals, evolved from sweat glands in the skin.) During pregnancy, the breasts enlarge in response to increasing levels of the hormone prolactin. Before birth, placental secretions of estrogen and progesterone inhibit the secretion of milk from the breasts. After the placenta has been expelled from the uterus, the concentrations of estrogen and progesterone drop, and the breasts begin to produce copious amounts of milk.

The actual release of milk from the mother's breasts does not occur until 1 to 3 days after the baby is born. During these first days, the suckling baby receives **colostrum,** a high-protein fluid that is present in the breast at birth. Colostrum contains an abundance of maternal antibodies and thus helps strengthen the baby's immune system. It also functions as a laxative, removing fetal wastes called **meconium,** which had been retained in the intestines. After about 3 days, the prolactin secreted

from the pituitary stimulates milk production. When the newborn suckles, the pituitary is stimulated into releasing oxytocin as well as prolactin. Oxytocin triggers the release of milk from the mammary glands.

Stop and Ask Yourself

15. What five stages comprise the prenatal period?
16. What are the main events of the first trimester of pregnancy? The second and third trimesters?
17. What is the function of the placenta?
18. What causes parturition to occur?
19. How does lactation occur?

Summary

1. Asexual reproductive processes do not involve the production and subsequent fusion of haploid cells but rely solely on vegetative growth through mitosis.
2. Sexual reproduction involves the formation of haploid cells through meiosis and the subsequent fusion of pairs of those cells to produce a diploid zygote.
3. The forms of asexual reproduction in invertebrates are binary fission, budding (both external and internal), and fragmentation.
4. Sexual reproductive strategies and structures in the invertebrates are numerous and varied.
5. Sexual reproduction first evolved in aquatic animals. The invasion of land meant facing the danger of the gametes and embryos desiccating. The five major groups of vertebrates have reproductive adaptations for the environment in which they reproduce.
6. The reproductive role of the human male is to produce sperm and deliver them to the vagina of the female. This function requires four different structures. The testes produce sperm and the male sex hormone, testosterone. Accessory glands furnish a fluid, called semen, for carrying the sperm to the penis. Accessory ducts store and carry secretions from the testes and accessory glands to the penis. The penis deposits semen into the vagina during sexual intercourse.

7. Before a male can mature and function sexually, special regulatory hormones (FSH, GnRH, inhibin, LH, and testosterone) must function.
8. The reproductive roles of the human female are more complex than those of the male. Not only do females produce eggs, but after fertilization, they also nourish, carry, and protect the developing embryo. They may also nourish the infant for a time after it is born. The female reproductive system consists of two ovaries, two uterine tubes, a uterus, vagina, and external genitalia. The mammary glands contained in the paired breasts produce milk for the newborn baby.
9. The human female is fertile only during a few days each month, and the pattern of hormone secretion is intricately related to the cyclical release of a secondary oocyte from the ovary. Various hormones regulate the menstrual and ovarian cycles.
10. Pregnancy sets a new series of physiological events into motion that are directed to housing, protecting, and nourishing the embryo.
11. The development of a human may be divided into prenatal and postnatal periods. Pregnancy is arbitrarily divided into trimesters.
12. The placenta is the organ that sustains the embryo and fetus throughout the pregnancy. The birth process is called parturition and occurs about 266 days after fertilization.
13. Lactation includes both milk secretion (production) by the mammary glands and milk release from the breasts.

SELECTED KEY TERMS

asexual reproduction (p. 670)

broadcast spawning (p. 672)

budding (p. 670)

estrus (p. 673)

fission (p. 670)

fragmentation (p. 670)

gestation (p. 673)

parthenogenesis (p. 670)

sequential hermaphroditism (p. 672)

sexual reproduction (p. 672)

CRITICAL THINKING QUESTIONS

1. Is the fertility of a woman affected by the length of a given menstrual cycle or whether the cycles are regular or irregular? Explain.

2. Looking at a variety of animals, what are the advantages to restricting reproduction to a limited time period? Why do so many animals have a sharply defined reproductive season during the year?

3. In most sexual species, males produce far more gametes than do females. Why does this occur when in most cases, only one male gamete can fertilize one female gamete?

4. Why are the accessory glands of the male so important in reproduction?

SUGGESTED READINGS

BOOKS

Allport, S. 1986. *Explorers of the Black Box: The Search for the Cellular Basis of Memory*. New York: W. W. Norton, Co.

Barlow, H. B., and Mollon, J. D. 1982. *The Senses*. Cambridge: Cambridge University Press.

Baulieu, E., and Kelley, P. 1990. *Hormones*. Paris: Hermann Press.

Bruely, D. 1985. *Oxygen Transport to Tissues*. New York: Plenum.

Christian, J. L., and Gregor, J. L. 1985. *Nutrition for Living*. Menlo Park, Calif.: Benjamin Cummings.

Crapo, L. 1985. *Hormones: The Messengers of Life*. New York: W. H. Freeman.

Hadley, M. 1988. *Endocrinology*. Englewood Cliffs: Prentice-Hall.

Hancox, N. M. 1972. *Biology of Bone*. Cambridge: Cambridge University Press.

Hochachka, P., and Somero, G. 1984. *Biochemical Adaptations*. Princeton, N.J.: Princeton University Press.

Jones, R. E. 1984. *Human Reproduction and Sexual Behavior*. Englewood Cliffs, N.J.: Prentice-Hall.

Kandel, E., and Schwartz, J. H. 1985. *Principles of Neural Science*. 2d ed. New York: Elsevier.

Margulis, L., and Sagan, D. 1986. *Origins of Sex: Three Billion Years of Genetic Recombination*. New Haven, Conn.: Yale University Press.

Masters, W. H., and Johnson, V. E. 1966. *Human Sexual Response*. Boston: Little, Brown.

Nilsson, L. 1977. *A Child Is Born*. New York: Delacorte Press.

———. 1986. *Behold Man: A Photographic Journey of Discovery Inside the Body*. Boston: Little, Brown.

Rankin, J. C., and Davenport, J. 1981. *Animal Osmoregulation*. New York: John Wiley & Sons.

Ruckenusch, Y., and Thivend, P. 1980. *Digestive Physiology and Metabolism in Ruminants*. Westport, Conn.: AVI Publishing Company.

Singer, P., and Wells, D. 1985. *Making Babies: The New Science and Ethics of Conception*. New York: Charles Scribner and Sons.

Smith, H. 1961. *From Fish to Philosopher*. New York: Doubleday.

Tregear, R. 1966. *Physical Functions of the Skin*. New York: Academic Press.

ARTICLES

Ada, G., and Nossal, G. The clonal-selection theory. *Scientific American* August, 1987.

Alexander, R. M. How dinosaurs ran. *Scientific American* April, 1991.

American Zoologist. 1983. Evolution of endocrine systems in lower vertebrates, a symposium honoring professor Aubrey Gorbman. pp. 595–739.

Atkinson, M., and Macharen, N. What causes diabetes? *Scientific American* July, 1990.

Avery, M., Wang, N., and Taeusch, W. The lung of the newborn infant. *Scientific American* April, 1973.

Baldwin, R. L. 1984. Digestion and metabolism of ruminants. *BioScience* 34(4):244–249.

Barlow, R. What the brain tells the eye. *Scientific American* April, 1990.

Beaconsfield, P., Birdwood, G., and Beaconsfield, R. The placenta. *Scientific American* August, 1980.

Berridge, M. The molecular basis of communication within the cell. *Scientific American* October, 1985.

Binkley, S. A timekeeping enzyme in the pineal gland. *Scientific American* April, 1979.

Bloom, F. E. Neuropeptides. *Scientific American* October, 1981.

Bonn, D. Hormones for healthy bones. *New Scientist* (February 19, 1987): 32–35.

Cantin, M., and Genest, J. The heart as an endocrine gland. *Scientific American* February, 1986.

Caplan, A. I. Cartilage. *Scientific American* October, 1981.

Carafoli, F. D., and Penniston, J. T. The calcium signal. *Scientific American* November, 1985.

Carey, F. G. Fishes with warm bodies. *Scientific American* February, 1983.

Carmichael, S. W., and Winkler, H. The adrenal chromaffin cell. *Scientific American* August, 1985.

Cave, L. J. 1983. Brain's unsung cells. *BioScience* 33:614–621.

Clements, J. A. Surface tension in the lungs. *Scientific American* December, 1962.

Cohen, L. A. Diet and cancer. *Scientific American* November, 1987.

Comroe, J. H. The lung. *Scientific American* February, 1966.

Coutant, C. Thermal niches of striped bass. *Scientific American* February, 1986.

Cowan, W. The development of the brain. *Scientific American* September, 1979.

Crews, D. The hormonal control of behavior in a lizard. *Scientific American* August, 1979.

Crick, F. H. C. Thinking about the brain. *Scientific American* September, 1979.

Davenport, H. W. Why the stomach does not digest itself. *Scientific American* January, 1972.

Degabriele, R. The physiology of the koala. *Scientific American* July, 1980.

Dunant, Y., and Isrel, M. The release of acetylcholine. *Scientific American* April, 1985.

Eastman, J., and DeVries, A. L. Antarctic fishes. *Scientific American* November, 1986.

Edelson, R., and Fink, J. The immunological function of the skin. *Scientific American* June, 1985.

Engelhard, V. How cells present antigens. *Scientific American* August, 1994.

Epel, D. The program of fertilization. *Scientific American* November, 1977.

Fedder, M., and Burggren, W. Skin breathing in vertebrates. *Scientific American* November, 1985.

Fen, W. The mechanism of breathing. *Scientific American* June, 1960.

Fernstrom, J. D., and Wurtman, R. J. Nutrition and the brain. *Scientific American* February, 1974.

Finke, R. Mental imagery of the visual system. *Scientific American* May, 1986.

Flam, F. Antifreezes in fish work quite similarly. *Science News* June 30, 1989.

French, A. R. 1988. The patterns of mammalian hibernation. *American Scientist* 76(6):568–575.

Frisch, R. E. Fatness and fertility. *Scientific American* March, 1988.

Geldard, F. A., and Sherrick, C. E. Space, time and touch. *Scientific American* July, 1986.

Gibbons, B. The intimate sense of smell. *National Geographic* September, 1986.

Golde, D. The stem cell. *Scientific American* December, 1991.

Golde, D., and Gasson, J. Hormones that stimulate the growth of blood cells. *Scientific American* July, 1988.

Gombrich, E. H. The visual image. *Scientific American* September, 1972.

Gottlieb, D. I. GABAergic neurons. *Scientific American* February, 1988.

Grobstein, C. External human fertilization. *Scientific American* June, 1979.

Guillemin, R., and Burgus, R. The hormones of the hypothalamus. *Scientific American* November, 1972.

Heatwole, H. 1978. Adaptations of marine snakes. *American Scientist* 66:594–604.

Heinrich, B. The raven's feast. *Natural History* February, 1989.

———. Thermoregulation in winter moths. *Scientific American* March, 1987.

Heinrich, B., and Bartholomew, G. A. Temperature regulation in flying moths. *Scientific American* June, 1972.

Hoberman, J. The history of synthetic testosterone. *Scientific American* February, 1995.

Hubel, D. H. Special issues on neurobiology. *Scientific American* September, 1979.

Hudspeth, A. J. The hair cells of the inner ear. *Scientific American* January, 1983.

Hume, I. Reading the entrails of evolution. *New Scientist* April, 1989.

Irving, J. Adaptations to cold. *Scientific American* January, 1966.

Kalil, R. Synapse formation in the developing brain. *Scientific American* December, 1989.

Kappas, A., and Alveares, A. P. How the liver metabolizes foreign substances. *Scientific American* June, 1975.

Keynes, R. Ion channels in the nerve-cell membrane. *Scientific American* March, 1987.

Kimelberg, H. K., and Norenberg, M. D. Astrocytes. *Scientific American* April, 1989.

Knudsen, E. I. The hearing of the barn owl. *Scientific American* December, 1981.

Kolata, G. 1987. Managing the inland sea. *Science* 224:703–710.

Koretz, J., and Handelman, G. How the human eye focuses. *Scientific American* July, 1988.

Kretchmer, N. Lactose and lactase. *Scientific American* October, 1972.

Lagercrantz, H., and Slotkin, A. The stress of being born. *Scientific American* April, 1986.

Lee, R. E. 1989. Insect cold-hardiness: To freeze or not to freeze. *BioScience* 39:308–313.

Lester, H. The response of acetylcholine. *Scientific American* February, 1977.

Liem, K. 1988. Form and function of lungs: The evolution of air breathing mechanisms. *American Zoologist* 28:739–759.

Linas, R. Calcium in synaptic transmission. *Scientific American* October, 1982.

Livingston, M. S. Art, illusion, and the visual system. *Scientific American* January, 1988.

Loeb, G. E. The functional replacement of the ear. *Scientific American* February, 1985.

Luria, A. R. The functional organization of the brain. *Scientific American* March, 1970.

Masland, R. H. The functional architecture of the retina. *Scientific American* December, 1986.

Mcewen, B. Interactions between hormones and nerve tissue. *Scientific American* July, 1976.

Merton, P. A. How we control the contraction of our muscles. *Scientific American* May, 1972.

Miller, J. 1990. A matter of taste. *BioScience* 40(2):78–82.

Mommsen, T., and Walsh, P. 1989. Evolution of urea synthesis in vertebrates. *Science* 243:72–75.

Montagna, W. The skin. *Scientific American* February, 1965.

Moog, F. The lining of the small intestine. *Scientific American* November, 1981.

Morell, P., and Norton, W. Myelin. *Scientific American* May, 1980.

Murray, J. H., and Weber, A. The cooperative action of muscles. *Scientific American* February, 1974.

Napier, J. The antiquity of human walking. *Scientific American* April, 1967.

Nassau, K. The causes of color. *Scientific American* October, 1980.

Nathan, J., and Greengard, P. Second messengers in the brain. *Scientific American* August, 1977.

Nathans, J. 1989. The genes for color vision. *Scientific American* February, 1989.

Notkins, A. The cause of diabetes. *Scientific American* November, 1979.

O'Malley, B., and Schrader, W. The receptors of steroid hormones. *Scientific American* February, 1976.

Orei, L., Yassalli, J. D., and Perrelet, A. The insulin factory. *Scientific American* September, 1988.

Oster, G. Muscle sounds. *Scientific American* March, 1984.

Parker, D. E. The vestibular apparatus. *Scientific American* November, 1980.

Perutz, M. F. The hemoglobin molecule. *Scientific American* November, 1964.

Pike, J. E. Prostaglandins. *Scientific American* November, 1971.

Poggio, T., and Koch, C. Synapses that communicate motion. *Scientific American* May, 1987.

Rassmussen, H. The cycling of calcium as an intracellular messenger. *Scientific American* October, 1989.

Rennie, J. The body against itself. *Scientific American* December, 1990.

Renouf, D. Sensory function in the harbor seal. *Scientific American* April, 1989.

Robinson, T., Factor, S., and Sonnenblick, E. The heart as a suction pump. *Scientific American* June, 1986.

Ross, R., and Borstein, P. Elastic fibers in the body. *Scientific American* June, 1971.

Ruppert, E., and Smith, P. 1988. The functional organization of filtration nephridia. *Biol. Rev.* 63:231–258.

Sanderson, S., and Wassersug, R. Suspension-feeding vertebrates. *Scientific American* March, 1990.

Schmidt-Nielsen, B. 1988. Excretory mechanisms as examples of the principle "The whole is greater than the sum of its parts." *Physiol. Zool.* 61:312–321.

Schmidt-Nielsen, K. Countercurrent systems in animals. *Scientific American* May, 1981.

———. How birds breathe. *Scientific American* December, 1971.

———. Salt glands. *Scientific American* January, 1959.

Schmidt-Nielsen, K., and Schmidt-Nielsen, B. The desert rat. *Scientific American* July, 1953.

Schnapf, J. L., and Baylor, D. A. How photoreceptor cells respond to light. *Scientific American* April, 1987.

Scrimshaw, N. S., and Young, V. R. The requirements of human nutrition. *Scientific American* September, 1976.

Segal, S. J. The physiology of human reproduction. *Scientific American* March, 1974.

Smith, H. The kidney. *Scientific American* January, 1953.

Smith, K., and Kier, W. 1989. Trunks, tongues, and tentacles: Moving with skeletons of muscles. *American Scientist* 77:28–35.

Spector, R., and Johanson, C. The mammalian choroid plexus. *Scientific American* November, 1989.

Storey, K., and Syorey, V. Frozen and alive. *Scientific American* December, 1990.

Stryer, L. The molecules of visual excitation. *Scientific American* July, 1987.

Suga, N. Biosonar and neural computation in bats. *Scientific American* June, 1990.

Synder, S. The molecular basis of communication between cells. *Scientific American* October, 1985.

Timmerman, M. Nerve and muscle: Bridging the gap. *New Scientist* (September 10, 1987):63–66.

Todd, J. T. The perception of human growth. *Scientific American* February, 1980.

Tonegawa, S. The molecules of the immune system. *Scientific American* October, 1985.

Triantafyllou, M. An efficient swimming machine. *Scientific American* March, 1995.

Ulmann, A., Teutsch, G., and Philibert, D. RU 486. *Scientific American* June, 1990.

Ulvnas-Moberg, K. The gastrointestinal tract in growth and reproduction. *Scientific American* July, 1990.

von Boehmer, H., and Kisielow, P. How the immune system learns about self. *Scientific American* October, 1991.

Vonrekesy, G. The ear. *Scientific American* August, 1957.

Wassarman, P. M. Fertilization in mammals. *Scientific American* December, 1988.

Webb, P. 1988. Simple physical principles and vertebrate aquatic locomotion. *American Zoologist* 28:709–725.

Wiggers, C. The heart. *Scientific American* May, 1967.

Winson, J. The meaning of dreams. *Scientific American* November, 1990.

Wood, W. White blood cells versus bacteria. *Scientific American* February, 1971.

Wurtman, R. Nutrients that modify brain function. *Scientific American* August, 1982.

Young, J., and Cohn, Z. How killer cells kill. *Scientific American* January, 1988.

Young, V. R., and Scrimshaw, N. S. The physiology of starvation. *Scientific American* October, 1971.

Zivin, J., and Choi, D. Stroke therapy. *Scientific American* July, 1991.

Zucker, M. The functioning of blood platelets. *Scientific American* June, 1980.

39.22

glossary

A

abdomen (ab′do-men) 1. The portion of a tetrapod's body between the thorax and pelvic girdle. 2. The region of an arthropod's body behind the thorax. It contains the visceral organs. 386

aboral (ab-or′al) The end of a radially symmetrical animal opposite the mouth. 238

acanthella (a-kan′thel-a) Developing acanthocephalan larva between an acanthor and a cystacanth, in which the definitive organ systems are developed; develops in the intermediate host. 316

Acanthocephala (a-kan′tho-sef-a-la) The phylum of aschelminths commonly called the spiny-headed worms. 308

acanthor (a-kan′thor) Acanthocephalan larva (first larval stage) that hatches from the egg. The larva has a rostellum with hooks that are used in penetrating the host's tissues. 316

acclimation (ak′li-ma′-shun) The change in tolerance of an animal for a condition in its environment. 194

accommodation (ah-kom″o-da′shun) The adjustment of the eye for various distances. 575

acetabulum (as″e-tab′u-lum) Sucker; the ventral sucker of a fluke; a sucker on the scolex of a tapeworm. 294

Acetospora (ah-seat-o-spor′ah) The protozoan phylum characterized by members having multicellular spores; all parasitic in invertebrates. Examples: acetosporans (*Paramyxa, Halosporidium*). 252

acetylcholine (as-e-tel-ko′len) A neurotransmitter liberated by certain neurons. It is excitatory at neuromuscular junctions and inhibitory at other synapses. 551

acid A substance that ionizes in water to release hydrogen ions (H⁺). 20

acid rain The combination of sulfur dioxide and nitrogen oxides with water in the atmosphere. This combination produces acidic precipitation called acid rain. The burning of fossil fuels is a major contributor to acid rain. 224

acoelomate (a-se′lah-māt) Without a body cavity. 239

acquired immunity The type of specific immunity that develops after exposure to a suitable antigen or is produced after antibodies are transferred from one individual to another. 608

acrosome (ak-ro-sōm′) The enzyme-filled cap on the head of a sperm. Used in egg penetration. 134

actin A protein in a muscle fiber that, together with myosin, is responsible for contraction and relaxation. 543

action potential The sequence of electrical changes occurring when a nerve cell membrane is exposed to a stimulus that exceeds its threshold. 550

activational effects of hormones (ak′ti-va′shun-el i-fekts ov hor′monz) Events that occur in the behavior of an animal where an external stimulus triggers a hormonally mediated response by the organism. 187

active transport A process that requires an expenditure of ATP energy to move molecules across a cell membrane; usually moved against the concentration gradient with the aid of specific transport proteins. 40

adaptation Structures or processes that increase an organism's potential to successfully reproduce in a specified environment. 160

adaptive radiation Evolutionary change that results in the formation of a number of new characteristics from an ancestral form. 173

Adenophorea (a-den″o-for′e-a) The class of nematodes formerly called Aphasmidia. Examples: *Trichinella, Trichuris*. 303

adenosine diphosphate (ah-dēn′o-sēn di-phos′phate) A nucleoside composed of the pentose sugar D-ribose, adenine, and two phosphates; ADP. 61

adenosine monophosphate (ah-dēn′o-sēn mon-o-phos′phate) AMP molecule; created when the terminal phosphate is lost from a molecule of adenosine diphosphate. 61

adenosine triphosphate (ah-dēn′o-sēn tri-phos′phate) ATP molecule; stores energy and releases energy for use in cellular processes. 61

adhesive gland Attachment glands in Turbellaria that produce a chemical that attaches part of the turbellarian to a substrate. 289

adipose tissue (ad′i-pos tish′u) Fat-storing tissue. 48

adrenal gland (ah-dre′nal gland) The endocrine gland located on the top of the kidney. 587, 593

aerobic (a″er-ob′ik) Having molecular oxygen present; an oxygen-dependent form of respiration. 66

aerobic respiration *See* **cellular respiration.**

aestivation (es′te-va-shun) The condition of dormancy or torpidity during the hot summer months. 196, 655

afterbirth The placental and fetal membranes expelled from the uterus after childbirth. 685

age structure The proportion of a population that is in prereproductive, reproductive, and postreproductive classes. 223

Agnatha (ag-nath′ah) A superclass of vertebrates whose members lack jaws and paired appendages and possess a cartilaginous skeleton and a persistent notochord. Lampreys and hagfishes. 417

airfoil A surface, such as a wing, that provides lift by using currents of air it moves through. 489

allantois (ah-lan′tois) One of the extraembryonic membranes formed in the embryo of an amniote; forms as a ventral outgrowth of the gut, enlarges during development, and functions in waste (uric acid) storage and gas exchange. 146

alleles (al-els′) Alternate forms of a gene that occur at the same locus of a chromosome. 97

allopatric speciation (al′o-pat′rik spe′se-a′shun) Speciation that occurs in populations separated by geographical barriers.   173

all-or-none law The phenomenon in which a muscle fiber contracts completely when it is exposed to a stimulus of threshold strength. Also, the principle that states a neuron will "fire" at full power or not at all.   550

altricial (al-trish′al) An animal that is helpless at hatching or birth.   496

altruism (al′troo-iz′em) The principle or practice of unselfish concern for, or devotion to, the welfare of others.   191

alula (al′u-lah) A group of feathers on the wing of a bird that is supported by the bones of the medial digit. The alula reduces turbulent airflow over the upper surface of the wing.   489

alveolus (al-ve′o-lus) An air sac of a lung; a saclike structure.   617

ambulacral groove (am′byul-ac″ral groov) The groove along the length of the oral surface of a sea star arm. Ambulacral grooves contain tube feet.   404

ametabolous metamorphosis (a′me-tab′a-lus met′ah-mor′fe-sis) Development in which the number of molts is variable; immature stages resemble adults, and molting continues into adulthood.   392

amictic (e-mik′tic) Pertaining to female rotifers that produce only diploid eggs that cannot be fertilized. The eggs develop directly into amictic females.   308

amino acid (ah-me′no as′id) A relatively small organic compound that contains an amino group (—NH_2) and a carboxyl group (—COOH); the structural unit of a protein molecule.   25

ammonotelic excretion (ah-mo″no-tel′ik) Having ammonia as the chief excretory product of nitrogen metabolism; occurs in freshwater fishes.   660

amnion (am′ne-on) One of the extraembryonic membranes of the embryos of reptiles, birds, and mammals. The amnion encloses the embryo in a fluid-filled sac.   146

amniote lineage (am′ne-ōt lin′e-ij) The evolutionary lineage of vertebrates leading to modern reptiles, birds, and mammals.   452

amniotic egg (am′ne-ot-ik) The egg of reptiles, birds, and mammals. It possesses a series of extraembryonic membranes that help prevent desiccation, store wastes, and promote gas exchange. These adaptations allowed vertebrates to invade terrestrial habitats.   465, 468

amoeboid movement (ah-me′boid) A form of movement similar to that found in amoebae. Fluid endoplasm (plasmasol) flows forward inside the cell and changes state to viscous ectoplasm (plasmagel) on reaching the tip of a pseudopodium. At the opposite end of the cell, ectoplasm is converted into endoplasm.   538

Amphibia (am-fib′e-ah) The class of vertebrates whose members are characterized by skin with mucoid secretions, which serves as a respiratory organ. Developmental stages are aquatic and are usually followed by metamorphosis to an amphibious adult. Frogs, toads, and salamanders.   433

amphid (am″fed) One of a pair of chemosensory organs found on the anterior end of certain nematodes.   310

amplexus (am-plek′sus) The positioning of a male amphibian dorsal to female amphibian, his forelimbs around her waist. During amplexus, the male releases sperm as the female releases eggs.   463

ampullary organ (am′pu-la″re) A receptor that can detect electrical currents. These electroreceptors are found in most fishes, some amphibians, and the platypus.   567

anabolism (an-nab′o-lizm) Any constructive metabolic process by which organisms convert substances into other components of the organism's chemical architecture. System of biosynthetic reactions in a cell by which large molecules are made from smaller ones.   56

anaerobic (an-a″er-o′bik) The phase of cellular respiration that occurs in the absence of oxygen; lacking oxygen.   66

analogous (a-nal′a-ges) Structures that have similar functions in two organisms but have not evolved from a common ancestral form.   6

anaphase (an′ah-fōaz) The stage in mitosis and meiosis, following metaphase, in which the centromeres divide and the chromatids, lined up on the mitotic spindle, begin to move apart toward the poles of the spindle to form the daughter chromosomes.   86

anatomy (ah-nat′o-me) The study of the structure of an organism and its parts.   16

androgen (an′dro-jen) Any substance that contributes to masculinization, such as the hormone testosterone.   676

aneuploidy (an′u-ploid′e) An addition or deletion of one or more chromosomes. Aneuploidy may be represented by 2n + 1, 2n − 1, etc.   112

animal behavior Activities animals perform during their lifetime.   182

Animalia (an′i-mal′eah) The kingdom of organisms whose members are multicellular, eukaryotic, and heterotrophic. The animals.   231

animal pole The region of a fertilized egg where meiosis is completed. It contains less yolk and is more metabolically active than the opposite vegetal pole.   137

Annelida (ah-nel′i-dah) The phylum of triploblastic, coelomate animals whose members are metameric (segmented) and wormlike. Annelids have a complete digestive tract and a ventral nerve cord.   331

annuli (an′u-li) Secondary divisions of each body segment of a leech (phylum Annelida, class Hirudinea).   353

antennal gland (an-ten′al) The excretory organ in some crustaceans (crayfish). Called antennal glands because of their location near the base of each second antenna and their green color; also called **green glands.**   657

anterior The head end; usually the end of a bilateral animal that meets its environment.   238

Anthozoa (an′tho-zo″ah) The class of cnidarians whose members are solitary or colonial polyps. Medusae absent; gametes originate in the gastrodermis; mesenteries divide the gastrovascular cavity. Sea anemones and corals.   270

anthropomorphism (an″thro-po-mor′fizm) The attribution of human characteristics to nonhuman beings and objects.   182

antibody A specific substance produced by cells in response to the presence of an antigen; it reacts with the antigen; also known as an immunoglobulin (Ig).   609

anticodon (an′ti-ko″don) A sequence of three bases on transfer RNA that pairs with codons of messenger RNA to position amino acids during protein synthesis.   122

antigen (an′ti-jen) A foreign (nonself) substance (such as a protein, nucleoprotein, polysaccharide, and some glycolipids) to which lymphocytes respond; also known as an immunogen because it induces the immune response.   609

antiparallel (an′ti-par″ah-lel′) Refers to opposing strands of DNA that are oriented in opposite directions.   119

Apicomplexa (a′pi-kom-plex′ah) The protozoan phylum characterized by members having an apical complex used for penetrating host cells; cilia and flagella lacking, except in certain reproductive stages. Examples include the gregarines (*Monocystis*), coccidians (*Eimeria, Isospora, Sarcocystis, Toxoplasma*), *Pneumocystis, and Plasmodium.* 250

Aplacophora (a′pla-kof″o-rah) The class of molluscs whose members lack a shell, mantle, and foot. Wormlike, burrowing animals with head poorly developed. Some authors divide this group into two classes: Caudofoveata and Solengasters. 329

aposematic coloration (ah′pos-mat′ik) Sharply contrasting colors of an animal that warn other animals of unpleasant or dangerous effects. 204

appendicular skeleton (ap″en-dik′u-lar) The bones of the upper and lower extremities; includes the shoulder and pelvic girdles. 537

appendix (a-pen′diks) Refers to the appendix vermiformis of the colon. 643

Arachnida (ah-rak′ni-dah) The class of chelicerate arthropods whose members are mostly terrestrial, possess book lungs, or tracheae, and usually have four pairs of walking legs as adults. Spiders, scorpions, ticks, mites, and harvestmen. 354

arachnoid (ah-rak′noid) The weblike middle covering (meninge) of the central nervous system. 555

archenteron (ar-ken″te-ron′) The embryonic digestive tract that is formed during gastrulation. 138

Aristotle's lantern The series of ossicles making up the jawlike structure of echinoid echinoderms. 410

arteriole (ar-te′re-ōl) A minute arterial branch, especially just proximal to a capillary. 603

artery A vessel that transports blood away from the heart. 603

Arthropoda (ar-thra-po′dah) The phylum of animals whose members possess metamerism with tagmatization, a jointed exoskeleton, and a ventral nervous system. Insects, crustaceans, spiders, and related animals. 349

artificially acquired active immunity The type of immunity that results from immunizing an animal with a vaccine. 608

artificially acquired passive immunity The type of immunity that results from introducing antibodies that have been produced either in another animal or by specific in vitro methods into an animal. 608

aschelminth (ask′hel-minth) Any animal in the phyla Gastrotricha, Rotifera, Kinorhyncha, Nematoda, Nematomorpha, Acanthocephala, Loricitera, Priapulida, or Entoprocta. 304

Ascidiacea (as-id′e as″e-ah) A class of urochordates whose members are sessile as adults, and solitary or colonial. 405

ascon (as′kon) The simplest of the three sponge body forms. Asconoid sponges are vaselike, with choanocytes directly lining the spongocoel. 267

asexual reproduction Having no sex; not sexual; not pertaining to sex. Reproduction of an organism without fusion of gametes. 670

aster The star-shaped structure seen in a cell during the prophase of mitosis; composed of a system of microtubules arranged in astral rays around the centrosome; may emanate from a centrosome or from a pole of a mitotic spindle. 86

Asteroidea (as′te-roi″de-ah) The class of echinoderms whose members have rays that are not sharply set off from the central disk; ambulacral grooves with tube feet; and suction disks on tube feet. Sea stars. 390

asymmetry (a-sim′i-tre) Without a balanced arrangement of similar parts on either side of a point or axis. 237

asynchronous flight *See* **indirect flight.**

atom Smallest particle of an element that has the same properties. The basic unit of an element that can enter into chemical combinations. 16

atomic mass A mass unit determined by arbitrarily assigning the carbon-12 isotope a mass of 12 atomic mass units. 16

atomic number A value equal to the number of protons in the nucleus of an atom. 16

auricle (aw′re-kl) The portion of the external ear not connected within the head. Also used to designate an atrium of a heart. In the class Turbellaria, the sensory lobes that project from the side of the head. 291

autosomes (au′te-sōmz′) Chromosomes other than sex chromosomes. 106

autotomy (au-tot′o-me) The self amputation of an appendage. For example, the casting off of a section of a lizard's tail caught in the grasp of a predator. The autotomized appendage is usually regenerated. 475

autotroph (aw′to-trōf) An organism that uses carbon dioxide as its sole or principal source of carbon and makes its organic nutrients from inorganic raw materials. 622

autotrophic (au′to-trōf″ic) Having the ability to synthesize food from inorganic compounds. 194

Aves (a′vez) A class of vertebrates whose members are characterized by scales modified into feathers for flight, endothermy, and amniotic eggs. The birds. 463

axial skeleton (ak′se-al) Portion of the skeleton that supports and protects the organs of the head, neck, and trunk. 537

axon (ak′son) A fiber that conducts a nerve impulse away from a neuron cell body. 548

axoneme (ak′so-nēm) The axial thread of the chromosome in which is located the axial combination of genes. The central core of a cilium or flagellum, consisting of a central pair of filaments surrounded by nine other pairs; also called axial filament. 46

axopodium (ak′se-pōd-eum) Fine, needlelike pseudopodium that contains a central bundle of microtubules. Also called axopod. Found in certain sarcodine protozoa. 251

B

B cell A type of lymphocyte derived from bone marrow stem cells that matures into an immunologically competent cell under the influence of the bursa of Fabricius in the chicken, and the bone marrow in nonavian species; following interaction with antigen, it becomes a plasma cell, which synthesizes and secretes antibody molecules involved in humoral immunity; B lymphocyte. 602

balanced polymorphism (pol′e-morf-ism) Occurs when different phenotypic expressions are maintained at a relatively stable frequency in a population. 172

baleen plate (bā-lēn) A keratined growth in toothless whales. 532

bare sensory nerve endings Nerve endings that are sensitive to pain. 572

baroreceptor (bar″o-re-sep′tor) A specialized nerve ending that is stimulated by changes in pressure. 562

Barr body A heterochromatic X chromosome usually found in the nucleus of female mammals. 111

basal body A centriole that has given rise to the microtubular system of a cilium or flagellum, and is located just beneath the plasma membrane. Serves as a nucleation site for the growth of the axoneme. 46

base A substance that ionizes in water to release hydroxyl ions (OH⁻) or other ions that combine with hydrogen ions.   20

basophil (ba′so-fil) White blood cell characterized by the presence of cytoplasmic granules that become stained by a basophilic dye.   601

Batesian mimicry (bats′e-an mim′ik-re) Occurs when one species, called the mimic, resembles a second species, the model, that is protected by aposematic coloration.   204

Bdelloidea (del-oid′e-a) A class of rotifers containing members where there are no males; anterior end retractile and bearing two disks; mastax adapted for grinding; paired ovaries; cylindrical body. Example: *Rotaria*.   300

behavioral ecology The scientific study of all aspects of animal behavior as related to the environment.   182

benthic animals (ben′thik) Refers to animals living in or on the bottom substrate of an ocean, lake, stream, or other body of water.   221

bilateral symmetry (bi-lat′er-al sim′i-tre) A form of symmetry in which only the midsagittal plane will divide an organism into mirror images; bilateral symmetry is characteristic of actively moving organisms that have definite anterior (head) and posterior (tail) ends.   238

bile A fluid secreted by the liver and poured into the small intestine via the bile duct; emulsifies fats.   636

bimodal breathing The ability of an organism to exchange respiratory gases simultaneously with both air and water; usually using gills for water breathing and lungs for air breathing.   613

binary fission (bi′ne-re fish′en) Asexual reproduction in protists in which mitosis is followed by cytoplasmic division, producing two new organisms.   245

binomial nomenclature (bi-no″me-al no″men-kla′cher) A system for naming in which each kind of organism (a species) has a name of two parts, the genus and the species epithet.   11

biochemistry The chemistry of living organisms and of vital processes; also known as physiological or biological chemistry. The study of the molecular basis of life.   16

biodiversity The variety of organisms in an ecosystem.   224

biogeochemical cycles The cycling of elements between reservoirs of inorganic compounds and living matter in an ecosystem.   214

biogeography The study of the distribution of life on earth.   5

biological magnification The concentration of substances in animal tissues as the substances are passed through ecosystem food webs.   224

biology The study of life.   4

biomass The part of an ecosystem consisting of living matter.   209

biomes (bi′ōmz) Distinctive associations of plant and animal populations; characterized by certain geographical boundaries and specific climatic and geographical features.   217

biotic potential (bi-ot′ik) or **intrinsic rate of growth** The capacity of a population to increase maximally.   198

biramous appendages (bi-ra′mus ah-pen′dij-ez) Appendages having two distal processes connected to the body by a single proximal process.   365

Bivalvia (bi″val′ve-ah) The class of molluscs whose members are enclosed in a shell consisting of two dorsally hinged valves, lack a radula, and possess a wedge-shaped foot. Clams, mussels, oysters.   329

bladder worm The unilocular hydatid cyst of a tapeworm. *See* **cysticercus.**   299

blastocoel (blas′to-sel) The fluid-filled cavity of the blastula.   138

blastocyst (blas′to-sist) An early stage of embryonic development consisting of a hollow ball of cells.   682

blastoderm (blas′to-derm) A small disk of cells at the animal end of the embryo of a reptile or bird that results from early cleavages.   144

blastomeres (blas′to-merz) Any of the cells produced by cleavage of a zygote.   137

blastopore (blas′to-por) The point at which cells on the surface of the blastula move to the interior of the embryo during gastrulation.   138

blastula (blas′tu-lah) An early stage in the development of an embryo; it consists of a sphere of cells enclosing a fluid-filled cavity (blastocoel).   138

blood A type of connective tissue with a fluid matrix called plasma in which blood cells are suspended. The fluid that circulates through the heart, arteries, capillaries, and veins.   48

blood pressure The force (energy) with which blood is pushed against the walls of blood vessels and circulated throughout the body when the heart contracts.   606

blubber The fat found between the skin and muscle of whales and other cetaceans, from which oil is made.   653

bone cells The hard, rigid form of connective tissue constituting most of the skeleton of vertebrates; composed chiefly of calcium salts. Also called bone (osseous) tissue.   48, 535

book gill Modifications of a horseshoe crab's exoskeleton into a series of leaflike plates that serve as a surface for gas exchange between the arthropod and the water (phylum Arthropoda, class Merostomata).   367

book lung Modification of the arthropod exoskeleton into a series of internal plates that provide surfaces for exchange of gases between the blood and air.   368, 612

bothria (both-re-ah) Dorsal or ventral grooves, which may be variously modified, on the scolex of a cestode.   299

bottleneck effect Changes in gene frequency that result when numbers in a population are drastically reduced, and genetic variability is reduced as a result of the population being built up again from relatively few surviving individuals.   170

Brachiopoda (bra-ke-op′o-dah) A phylum of marine animals whose members possess a bivalved calcareous and/or chitinous shell that is secreted by a mantle and encloses nearly all of the body. Unlike the molluscs, the valves are dorsal and ventral. Possess a lophophore. Lampshells.   415

broadcast spawning The release of gametes into the water, allowing external fertilization to occur.   672

brood patch The patch of feathers used by birds to incubate eggs; also known as incubation patch.   589

brown fat Mitochondria-rich, heat-generating adipose tissue of endothermic invertebrates.   653

buccal pump (buk′el) The mechanism by which lung ventilation occurs in amphibians; muscles of the mouth and pharynx create positive pressure to force air into the lungs.   459

buccopharyngeal respiration (buk′o-fah-rin′je-al res′pah-ra′shun) The diffusion of gases across moist linings of the mouth and pharynx of amphibians.   459

budding The process of forming new individuals asexually in many different invertebrates.   245, 670

buffer A substance that can react with a strong acid or base, to form a weaker acid or base and thus resist a change in pH.   20

bulb of Krause A sensory receptor in the skin believed to be the sensor for touch-pressure; also called bulbous corpuscle. 572

bulbourethral gland (bul″bo-u-re′thral gland) Gland that secretes a viscous fluid into the male urethra during sexual excitement. 675

bursa (bur′sah) A membranous sac that invaginates from the oral surface of ophiuroid echinoderms. Functions in diffusion of gases and waste material. 408

bursa of Fabricius (bur′sah of fah-bris′e-us) The lymphoid organ of birds that, like the thymus, develops as an outpouching of the gut near the cloaca rather than the foregut. 591

C

Calcarea (kal-kar′ea) The class of sponges whose members are small and possess monaxon, triaxon, or tetraaxon calcium carbonate spicules. 267

calcitonin (kal″si-to′nin) A thyroid hormone that lowers calcium and phosphate levels in the blood; also called thyrocalcitonin. 591

calorie A unit used in the measurement of heat energy and the energy value of foods. The amount of heat energy required to raise the temperature of 1g of water 1° C. 56, 622

Calorie Amount of heat energy required to raise the temperature of 1,000 g of water 1° C. 622

calyx (ka′liks) 1. A boat-shaped or cuplike central body of an entoproct or crinoid. The body and tentacles of an entoproct. 2. A cuplike set of ossicles that support the crown of a sea lily or feather star (class Crinoidea, phylum Echinodermata). 318, 412

capillary A small blood vessel that connects an arteriole and a venule; the functional unit of the circulatory system. 603

carapace (kar′ah-pās) The dorsal portion of the shell of a turtle. Formed from a fusion of vertebrae, ribs, and dermal bone. 471

carbaminohemoglobin (kar″bah-me′no he″mo-glo′bin) Compound formed by the union of carbon dioxide and hemoglobin. 601

carbohydrate An organic compound that contains carbon, hydrogen, and oxygen. Carbohydrates consist of simple single-monomer sugars (monosaccharides), disaccharides, or other multi-unit sugars (polysaccharides). 22

cardiac muscle Specialized type of muscle tissue found only in the heart. 539

cardiovascular system *See* **circulatory system.**

carnivore (kar′ne-vor) One of the flesh-eating animals of the order Carnivora; also, any organism that eats flesh. 622

carrying capacity The maximum population size that an environment can support. 198

cartilage (kar′ti-lij) Type of connective tissue in which cells are located within lacunae and are separated by a semisolid matrix. Provides a site for muscle attachment, aids in movement of joints, and provides support. 48, 535

caste (kast) One of the distinct kinds of individuals in a colony of social insects (e.g., queens, drones, and workers in a honeybee colony). 394

catabolism (kat″ah-bol′ism) Metabolic process by which large molecules are broken down into smaller ones; catabolic metabolism. Intermediates in these reactions are called catabolites. 56

catalysis (kah-tal′i-sis) An increase in the velocity of a chemical reaction or process produced by the presence of a substance that is not consumed in the net chemical reaction or process. 58

catalyst (kat-ah-list) A substance that increases the rate of a chemical reaction, but is not permanently altered by the reaction. Enzymes are protein catalysts. 58

caudal (kaw′dal) Having to do with, or toward, the tail of an animal. 238

Caudofoveata (kaw′do-fo′ve-at-ah) The class of molluscs characterized by a wormlike shell-less body and scalelike calcareous spicules; lack eyes, tentacles, statocysts, crystalline style, foot, and nephridia. Deep-water marine burrowers. *Chaetoderma.* 338

cecum (se′kum) 1. Each arm of the blind-ending Y-shaped digestive tract of trematodes (phylum Platyhelminthes). 2. A region of the vertebrate digestive tract where fermentation can occur. It is located at the proximal end of the large intestine. 511, 643

cell body Portion of a nerve cell that includes a cytoplasmic mass and a nucleolus, and from which the nerve fibers extend. 548

cell cycle The regular sequence of events during which a cell grows, prepares for division, duplicates its contents, and divides to form two daughter cells. 82

cell-mediated immunity Immunity resulting from T cells coming into close physical contact with foreign cells or infected cells to destroy them; it can be transferred to a nonimmune individual by the transfer of cells. 608

cellular respiration Process by which energy is released from organic compounds within cells. The aerobic process that involves glycolysis, the Krebs cycle, the electron transport chain, and chemiosmosis. 63

central dogma The relationship among the steps from DNA to the production of a protein. The synthesis of messenger RNA from DNA, and the movement mRNA out of the nucleus (transcription). Carries the genetic code into the cytoplasm. Within the cytoplasm, ribosomes and transfer RNA convert this genetic code in messenger RNA into a protein (translation). 120

central nervous system The brain and spinal cord. 555

centriole (sen′tre-ol) A cellular organelle that functions in the organization of the mitotic spindle during mitosis. A pair of centrioles is usually found in the center of a centrosome in animal cells. 46

centromere (sen′tro-mer) Constricted region of a mitotic chromosome that holds sister chromatids together; also the site on the DNA where the kinetochore forms and then captures microtubules from the mitotic spindle. 83

centrosome (sen′tro-sōm) The cell center; the centrosphere together with the two centrioles. 46

Cephalaspidomorphi (sef′a-las′pe-do-morf′e) The class of vertebrates characterized by the absence of paired appendages and the presence of sucking mouthparts with teeth and a rasping tongue. Lampreys. 422

cephalic (se-fal′ik) Having to do with, or toward, the head of an animal. 238

cephalization (sef′al-iz-a″shun) The development of a head with an accumulation of nervous tissue into a brain. 238

Cephalochordata (sef′a-lo-kor-dat′ah) The subphylum of chordates whose members possess a laterally compressed, transparent body. They are fishlike and possess all four chordate characteristics throughout life. Amphioxus. 427

cephalothorax (sef′al-o-thor″aks) The fused head and thoracic regions of crustaceans and some arachnids. 366

cercaria (ser-kar-e-a) Juvenile digenetic trematode, produced by asexual reproduction within a sporocyst or redia. Cercaria are freeswimming and have a digestive tract, suckers, and a tail. They develop into a metacercaria. 295

cerebellum (ser″e-bel′um) Portion of the brain that coordinates skeletal muscle movement. Part of the metencephalon, it consists of two hemispheres and a central vermis.   555

cerebrum (ser′e-brum) The main portion of the brain, occupying the upper part of the cranial cavity; its two hemispheres are united by the corpus callosum; forms the largest part of the central nervous system in mammals.   557

Cestoidea (ses-toid′e-ah) The class of platyhelminthes that has members that are all parasitic with no digestive tract; have great reproductive potentials. Tapeworms.   298

chaparral (shap′a-ral′) A relatively dry biome that occurs in the southwestern United States. Plants are low and shrubby and have tough, waxy leaves. Animals include insects, rodents, rabbits, lizards, snakes, and mule deer.   219

chelicerae (ke-lis′er-ae) One of the two pairs of anterior appendages of arachnids, may be pincerlike or modified for piercing and sucking or other functions.   366

Chelicerata (ke-lis″e-ra′tah) The subphylum of arthropods whose members have a body that is divided into prosoma and opisthoma. The first pair of appendages are feeding appendages called chelicerae. Spiders, scorpions, mites, and ticks.   366

chemical synapse (sin-apse) A synapse at which neurotransmitters released by one neuron diffuse across an extracellular gap to influence a second neuron's activity.   551

chemiosmosis (kem″e-os-mo′sis) The process whereby a proton gradient and an electrochemical gradient are generated by electron transport and then used to drive ATP synthesis by oxidative phosphorylation.   62

chemistry The science dealing with the elements and atomic relations of matter, and various elemental compounds. The study of the properties of substances and how substances react with one another.   16

chemolithoautotroph (kem′o-lith-o-au′te-trof) An organism that synthesizes organic matter by oxidizing inorganic compounds.   210

chemoreceptor (ke″mo-re-sep′tor) A receptor that is stimulated by the presence of certain chemical substances.   563

chiasma (ki-as′mah) A decussation or X-shaped crossing; the places where pairs of homologous chromatids remain in contact during late prophase to anaphase of the first meiotic division. The chiasma indicates where an exchange of homologous segments has taken place between nonsister chromatids by crossing over.   88

chief cell Cell of a gastric gland that secretes various digestive enzymes, including pepsinogen.   640

Chilopoda (ki′le-pod′ah) The class of uniramous arthropods whose members have one pair of legs per segment and whose body is oval in cross section. Centipedes.   383

chitin (ki′tin) The polysaccharide found in the exoskeleton of arthropods.   363

chloragogen tissue (klor′ah-gog′en tish′u) Cells covering the dorsal blood vessel and digestive tract of annelids; function in glycogen and fat synthesis and urea formation.   352

chlorocruorin (klo″ro-kroo′e-ren) The greenish iron-containing respiratory pigment dissolved in the blood plasma of certain marine polychaetes.   619

choanocytes (ko-an′o-sitz) Cells of sponges that create water currents and filter food.   265

Chondrichthyes (kon-drik′thi-es) The class of vertebrates whose members are fishlike, possess paired appendages and a cartilaginous skeleton, and lack a swim bladder. Skates, rays, and sharks.   422

chordamesoderm (kor′dah-mez″o-derm) Tissue in the amphibian gastrula that forms between ectoderm and endoderm in the dorsal lip region of the blastopore; develops into the mesoderm and notochord.   141

Chordata (kor-dat′ah) A phylum of animals whose members are characterized by a notochord, pharyngeal gill slits, a dorsal tubular nerve cord, and a postanal tail.   423

chorion (kor′e-on) The outermost extraembryonic membrane of the embryo of an amniote; becomes highly vascular and aids in gas exchange.   146

chromaffin tissue (kro-maf′in) Specialized endocrine cells located near the kidneys.   587

chromatid (kro′mah-tid) One copy of a chromosome formed by DNA replication.   83

chromatin (kro-mah-tin) Nuclear material that gives rise to chromosomes during mitosis; complex of DNA, histones, and nonhistone proteins.   47

chromatophores (kro-mah-tah-forz) Cells containing pigment that, through contraction and expansion, produce temporary color changes.   336

chromosome (kro″mo-sōm) Rodlike structure that appears in the nucleus of a cell during mitosis; contains the genes responsible for heredity. Structure composed of a very long DNA molecule and associated proteins that carries part (or all) of the hereditary information of an organism.   47

chrysalis (kris′ah-lis) The pupal case of a butterfly that forms from the exoskeleton of the last larval instar.   393

chylomicron (ki″lo-mi′kron) A particle of the class of lipoproteins responsible for the transport of cholesterol and triglycerides from the small intestine to tissues after meals.   643

chyme (kīm) Semifluid mass of food materials that pass from the stomach to the small intestine.   640

cilia (sil′e-ah) Microscopic, hairlike processes on the exposed surfaces of certain eukaryotic cells. Cilia contain a core bundle of microtubules and are capable of performing repeated beating movements. They are also responsible for the swimming of many single-celled organisms.   46, 538

ciliary creeping The principal means of nemertine locomotion.   538

Ciliophora (sil-o-of′or-ah) The protozoan phylum characterized by members with simple or compound cilia at some stage in their life history; heterotrophs with a well-developed cytostome and feeding organelles; at least one macronucleus and micronucleus present. Examples: *Paramecium*, *Stentor*, *Vorticella*, *Balantidium*.   256

circadian rhythms (sur′ka-de′an rith′emz) Daily cycles of activity. Circadian rhythms are usually based upon photoperiods.   196

circulatory system (ser′ku-lah-to″re) Pertaining to the circulation. Also **cardiovascular system.**   598

circumcision (ser′kum-sizh′un) The removal of all or part of the prepuce or foreskin.   676

cirri (ser′i) Any of various slender or filamentous, usually flexible appendages, such as one of the compound organelles composed of groups of fused cilia seen in certain peritrichous ciliate protozoa that are used for locomotion; an eversible penis in flatworms; a fingerlike projection of a polychete parapodium.   256

Cirripedia (sir′i-ped′eah) The class of crustaceans whose members are sessile and highly modified as adults. Enclosed by calcium carbonate valves. Barnacles.   378

citric acid cycle (sit-rik as'id si'kl) A series of chemical reactions in the mitochondrion by which various molecules are oxidized and energy is released from them; Krebs cycle, TCA or tricarboxylic acid cycle. 68

cladistics (klad-is-tiks) *See* **phylogenetic systematics.** 233

cladograms (klad'o-gramz) Diagrams depicting the evolutionary history of taxa, which are derived from phylogenetic systematics (cladistics). 234

class A level of classification between phylum and order. 230

classical conditioning A type of learning in which positive or negative reinforcement influences later responses of an animal to a stimulus. 184

claw The sharp, usually curved, nail on the foot of an animal or insect. The pincerlike extremity of specific limbs of certain arthropods (e.g., lobster claws). 532

cleavage (kle'vij) The early mitotic and cytoplasmic divisions of an embryo. 137

climax community A final, relatively stable stage in an ecological succession. 209

clitellum (klit'el-um) The region of an annelid responsible for secreting mucus around two worms in copula and for secreting a cocoon to protect developmental stages. 350

cloaca (klo-a-kah) A common opening for excretory, digestive, and reproductive systems. 447

closed circulatory system A circulatory system in an animal in which blood is confined to vessels throughout its circuit. 335, 598

clouds of electrons The distribution of electrons in space around the atomic nucleus. 17

Cnidaria (ni-dar'e-ah) The phylum of animals whose members are characterized by radial or biradial symmetry, diploblastic organization, a gastrovascular cavity, and nematocysts. Jellyfish, sea anemones, and their relatives. 270

cnidocytes (ni-do-sītz) The cell that produces and discharges the stinging organelles (nematocysts) in members of the phylum Cnidaria. 270

cocoon The protective covering of a resting or developmental stage; sometimes refers to both the covering and the contents. 292, 393

codominance (ko-dom'ah-nens) An interaction of two alleles such that both alleles are expressed in a phenotype. 102

codon (ko'don) A sequence of three bases on messenger RNA that specifies the position of an amino acid in a protein. 121

coelom (se'lom) A fluid-filled body cavity lined by mesoderm. 239

coelomic fluid (se'lom-ic flu'id) The fluid found within the body cavity of triploblastic animals. 598

coenzyme (ko-en'zīm) An organic nonprotein molecule, frequently a phosphorylated derivative of a water-soluble vitamin, that binds with the protein molecule (apoenzyme) to form the active enzyme (holoenzyme). Examples include biotin, NAD^+, and coenzyme A. 60

coevolution (ko-ev'ah-loo"shun) The evolution of ecologically related species such that each species exerts a strong selective influence on the other. 200

cofactor (ko'fak-tor) A metal ion or inorganic ion with which an enzyme must unite in order to function. 60

colloblasts (kol'ah-blasts) Adhesive cells on the tentacles of ctenophorans used to capture prey. 281

colonial hypothesis A hypothesis formulated to explain the origin of multicellularity from protist ancestors; animals may have been derived when protists associated together and cells became specialized and interdependent. 262

colony An aggregation of organisms; usually a group of closely associated individuals of one species. 670

colostrum (ko-los'trum) The first secretion of the mammary glands following the birth of an infant. 687

comb rows Rows of cilia that serve as the locomotor organs of ctenophorans. 281

commensalism (kah-men'sal-izm) Living within or on an individual of another species without harm. 202

communication Act on the part of one organism (or cell) that alters the probability of patterns of behavior in another organism (or cell) in an adaptive fashion. 187

community The different kinds of organisms living in an area. 208

community diversity The number of different kinds of organisms living in an area. 208

comparative anatomy The study of animal structure in an attempt to deduce evolutionary pathways in particular animal groups. 5

comparative embryology (em'bre-ol"o-je) The study of animal development in an attempt to deduce evolutionary pathways in particular animal groups. 322

comparative psychologist An ethologist who studies the genetic, neural, and hormonal bases of animal behavior. 182

competitive exclusion principle The idea that two species with identical niches cannot coexist. 200

complete linkage Two genes positioned so close to one another on the same chromosome that recombination between them does not occur. 109

complex camera eye The type of image-forming eye found in squids and octopuses. 565

compound A substance composed of atoms of two or more elements joined by chemical bonds and chemically united in fixed proportions. 18

compound eye An eye consisting of many individual lens systems (ommatidia). Present in many members of the phylum Arthropoda. 389, 564

Concentricycloidea (kon-sen'tri-si-kloi"de-ah) The class of echinoderms whose members are characterized by two concentric water-vascular rings encircling a disklike body; no digestive system; and internal brood pouches. Sea daisies. 413

conduction The conveyance of energy, such as heat, sound, or electricity. The direct transfer of thermal motion (heat) between molecules of the environment and those on the body surface of an animal. 648

cone cell A color-sensitive photoreceptor cell concentrated in the retina. 575

conjugation (kon'ju-ga"shun) A form of sexual union used by ciliates involving a mutual exchange of haploid micronuclei. 258

connective tissue A basic type of tissue that includes bone, cartilage, and various fibrous tissues. Connective tissue serves to support and bind tissues together. 48

continental drift The breakup and movement of land masses of the earth. The earth had a single landmass about 250 million years ago. This mass broke apart into continents, which have moved slowly to their present positions. 162

continuous feeder Usually slow-moving sessile animals that feed all of the time. 626

contour feathers Feathers that cover the body, wings, and tail of a bird. Contour feathers provide flight surfaces and are responsible for plumage colors. 487

contractile vacuole (kon-trak'til vak"u-ōl') An organelle that collects and discharges water in protists and a few lower metazoa. It takes up and releases water in a cyclical manner in order to accomplish osmoregulation and some excretion. 245, 656

control group In a scientific experiment, a control group is treated the same as the experimental group except that the variable being tested is omitted. A control group serves as a basis for comparing the data derived from the experiment. 13

convection The act of conveying or transmission. The movement of air (or a liquid) over the surface of a body and contributes to heat loss (if the air is cooler than the body) or heat gain (if air is warmer than the body). 648

convergent evolution Evolutionary changes that result in members of one species resembling members of a second unrelated (or distantly related) species. 5

coracidium (kor"ah-sid'e-um) Larva with a ciliated epithelium hatching from the egg of certain cestodes; a ciliated free-swimming oncosphere. 300

coralline algae (kor'ah-lin al'je) Any red alga that is impregnated with calcium carbonate. Coralline algae often contribute to coral reefs. 279

coral reefs Associations of stony coral organisms and algae that form one of the most highly productive ecosystems in the world. 223

corona (ko-ro'nah) A crown; an encircling structure. The ciliated organ at the anterior end of rotifers used for swimming or feeding. 306

cortisol (kor'ti-sol) A glucocorticoid secreted by the adrenal cortex. 593

counteracting osmolyte strategy (os-mo-lyt) An osmolyte (ion) that counteracts another ion. 660

countercurrent exchange mechanism The passive exchange of something between fluids moving in opposite directions past each other. 443

countershading Contrasting coloration that helps conceal the animal (e.g., the darkly pigmented top and lightly pigmented bottom of frog embryos). 203

covalent bond (ko'va-lent) Chemical bond created by the sharing of two electrons between two atoms. 18

coxal glands (koks'el) An organ of excretion found in some arthropods. 368, 658

Crinoidea (kri-noi'de-ah) The class of echinoderms whose members are attached by a stalk of ossicles or are free living. Possess a reduced central disk. Sea lilies and feather stars. 411

crossing-over The exchange of material between homologous chromosomes, during the first meiotic division, resulting in a new combination of genes. 88

Crustacea (krus-tas'eah) The subphylum of mandibulate arthropods whose members are characterized by having two pairs of antennae, one pair of mandibles, two pairs of maxillae, and biramous appendages. Crabs, crayfish, lobsters. 373

cryptic coloration (kript'ik) Occurs when an animal takes on color patterns of its environment. 203

crystalline style A proteinaceous, rodlike structure in the digestive tract of a bivalve (Mollusca) that rotates against a gastric shield and releases digestive enzymes. 331

Ctenophora (te-nof'er-ah) The phylum of animals whose members are characterized by biradial symmetry, diploblastic organization, colloblasts, and meridionally arranged comb rows. Comb jellies. 280

Cubozoa (ku'bo-zo"ah) The class of cnidarians whose members have prominent cuboidal medusae with tentacles that hang from the corner of the medusa. Small polyp, gametes gastrodermal in origin. *Chironex*. 276

cutaneous respiration (kyoo-ta'ne-us res'pah-ra'shun) Exchange of gases across thin, moist surfaces of the skin. Also cutaneous exchange or integumentary exchange. 459, 613

cuticle (ku-tikel) A noncellular, protective, organic layer secreted by the external epithelium (hypodermis) of many invertebrates; refers to the epidermis or skin in higher animals. 305, 345, 363, 528

cystacanth (sis"ta-kanth) Juvenile acanthocephalan that is infective to its definitive host. 316

cysticercosis (sis"ti-ser-ko'sis) Infection with the larval forms (*Cysticercus cellulosae*) of *Taenia solium*. 299

cysticercus (sis"ti-ser'kus) Metacestode developing from the oncosphere in most Cyclophyllidea; usually has a tail and a well-formed scolex and characterized by a fluid-filled oval body with an invaginated scolex; cysticercoid. 299

cytokinesis (si'ta-kin-e'sis) The division of the cytoplasm of a cell into two parts, as distinct from the division of the nucleus (which is mitosis). 82

cytopharynx (si'to-far'inks) A region of the plasma membrane and cytoplasm of some ciliated and flagellated protists specialized for endocytosis. A permanent oral canal. 245

cytoplasm (si'to-plazm) The contents of a cell surrounding the nucleus; consists of a semifluid medium and organelles. 32

cytoplasmic inclusion (si'to-plaz'mic in-kloo'zhun) The basic food material or stored product of a cell's metabolic activities. 47

cytopyge (si'to-pij) A region of the plasma membrane and cytoplasm of some ciliated protists specialized for exocytosis of undigested wastes. 245

cytoskeleton (si"to-skel'e-ton) In the cytoplasm of eukaryotic cells, an internal framework of microtubules, microfilaments, and intermediate filaments by which organelles and other structures are anchored, organized, and moved about. 45

cytosol (si'to-sol) Contents of the main compartment of the cytoplasm, excluding membrane-bound organelles. 42

D

daily torpor (tor'por) Daily sluggishness that some animals experience. A period of inactivity that is normally induced by cold; observed in numerous ectotherms and also endotherms; often used to describe the specific physiological state of endotherms with a circadian cycle of lowered body temperature and depressed metabolic rate. 650

daughter sporocysts In digenetic trematodes the embryonic cells that develop from sporocysts and give rise to rediae. 295

deamination reaction (de-am"i-na'shun re-ak'shun) A reaction in which an amino group, —NH_2, is enzymatically removed from a compound. 72

decomposer Mostly heterotrophic bacteria and fungi that obtain organic nutrients by breaking down the remains or products of other organic compounds; their activities help cycle the simple compounds back to the autotrophs. 56

definitive host The host in the life cycle of a parasite that harbors the adult stage or sexual stage of the parasite. 247

degeneracy (de-jen'er-ah-sē) The genetic code is said to be degenerate because more than one three-base sequence in DNA can code for one amino acid. 121

delayed fertilization Occurs when fertilization of an egg does not occur immediately following coitus, but may be delayed for weeks or months. 517

deletions The loss of a portion of a chromosome. 115

deme (deem) A small, local subpopulation. Isolated subpopulations sometimes display genetic changes that may contribute to evolutionary change in the subpopulation. 174

Demospongiae (de-mo-spun′je-e) The class of poriferans whose members have monaxon or tetraaxon siliceous spicules or spongin. Leuconoid body forms are present and vary in size from a few centimeters to 1 m in height. 267

denaturation (de-na″chur-a′shun) Disruption of bonds holding a protein in its three-dimensional form, such that its polypeptide chain(s) unfolds partially or completely. Denaturation can be caused by changes in pH, salt concentration, or environmental temperature. 60

dendrite Nerve fiber that transmits impulses toward a neuron cell body. 548

dental formula A notation that indicates the number of incisors, canines, premolars, and molars in the upper and lower jaw of a mammal. 508

denticle (den′ti-kl) A small toothlike process. 529

deoxyribonucleic acid (de′oks-e-ri′bo-nuk″la-ik as′id) A polymer of deoxyribonucleotides that is in the form of a double helix; DNA is the genetic molecule of life in that it codes for the sequence of amino acids in proteins; contains nucleotide monomers with deoxyribose sugar and nitrogenous bases adenine (A), cytosine (C), guanine (G), and thymine (T). *See* **gene.** 27

depolarization (de-po″lar-i-za′shun) The loss of an electrical charge on the surface of a membrane. 550

deposit feeding The type of feeding whereby an animal obtains its nutrients from the sediments of soft-bottom habitats (mud or sands) or terrestrial soils. 626

dermal branchiae (der′mal branch′e-ae) Thin folds of the body wall of a sea star that extend between ossicles and function in gas exchange and other exchange processes. 404

dermis The layer of the skin deep to the epidermis, consisting of a dense bed of vascular connective tissue. 528

desert The biome characterized by less than 25 cm of rainfall per year. Deserts are characterized by cacti and desert shrubs or sagebrush. Animals include birds, rodents, reptiles, and numerous species of arthropods. 219

deuterostomes (du′te-ro-stōms″) Animals in which the anus forms from, or in the region of, the blastopore; often characterized by enterocoelous coelom formation, radial cleavage, and the presence of a dipleurulalike larval stage. 322

diabetes (di″ah-be′tez) Condition characterized by a high blood glucose level and the appearance of glucose in the urine due to a deficiency of insulin or the inability of body cells to respond to insulin; diabetes mellitus. 595

diaphragm (di″ah-fram′) The domed respiratory muscle between thoracic and abdominal compartments of mammals. 512

diastole (di-as′to-le) Phase of the cardiac cycle during which a heart chamber wall is relaxed; also diastolic pressure. 606

diastolic pressure The blood pressure measurement during the interval between heartbeats; it is the second number shown in a blood pressure reading. 606

differentiation (dif′ah-ren′she-a′shun) The development of embryonic structures from a nondescript form in the early embryo to their form in the adult. 138

diffusion (di-fu′zhun) The random movement of molecules from one location to another because of random thermal molecular motion; net diffusion always occurs from a region of higher concentration to a region of lower concentration. 611

digestion (di-jest′yun) The process by which larger molecules of food substances are broken down into smaller molecules that can be taken up by the digestive system; hydrolysis. 622

dihybrid cross (di-hi′brid) A mating between individuals heterozygous for two traits. 99

dioecious (di-es′eus) Having separate (male and female) sexes. 249

diploblastic (dip″lo-blas′tik) Animals whose body parts are organized into layers that are derived embryologically from two tissue layers: ectoderm and endoderm. Animals in the phyla Cnidaria and Ctenophora are diploblastic. 239

diploid (dip′loid) Having two sets of chromosomes. 108

Diplopoda (dip′le-pod′ah) The class of arthropods whose members are characterized by having two pairs of legs per apparent segment and a body that is round in cross section. Millipedes. 383

direct flight Insect flight that is accomplished by flight muscles acting on wing bases and in which a single nerve impulse results in a single wing cycle; also called synchronous flight. *See* **indirect (asynchronous) flight.** 386

directional selection Natural selection that occurs when individuals at one phenotypic extreme have an advantage over individuals with more common phenotypes. 170

disaccharide (di-sak′ah-rīd) A sugar produced by the union of two monosaccharide molecules as a result of a dehydration synthesis. 22

discontinuous feeder An animal that does not feed all the time; instead it generally eats large meals sporadically and does not spend time in the continuous pursuit of prey. 626

disruptive selection Natural selection that occurs when individuals of the most common phenotypes are at a disadvantage; produces contrasting subpopulations. 171

distal Away from the point of attachment of a structure on the body (e.g., the toes are distal to the knee). 238

diving reflex The reflex certain animals have to stay underwater for prolonged periods of time. 619

dominance hierarchy (dom′i-nans hi′e-rar′ke) The physical domination of some members of a group by other members, in relatively orderly and long-lasting patterns. 191

dominant (dom′ah-nent) A gene that masks one or more of its alleles. *See* **recessive.** 98

dominant species (dom′ah-nent spe′shēz) A species that exerts an overriding influence in determining the characteristics of a community. 208

dorsal (dor′sal) The back of an animal; usually the upper surface; synonymous with posterior for animals that walk upright. 238

down feathers Feathers that provide insulation for adult and immature birds. 487

duplications (doo′ple-ka″shuns) The presence of two copies of one or more loci in a chromosome. 115

dura mater (du′rah mā′ter) The outermost meninx. 555

dyad (di′ad) A double chromosome resulting from the halving of a tetrad in the first meiotic division. 90

E

ecdysis (ek-dis′is) (1) The shedding of the arthropod exoskeleton to accommodate increased body size or a change in morphology (as may occur in molting from immature to adult); to molt; may also refer to the shedding of the outer epidermis of the skin of reptiles. (2) The shedding of the cuticle in aschelminths in order to grow. Also called **molting.** 305, 364

Echinodermata (i-ki'na-dur"ma-tah) The phylum of coelomate animals whose members are pentaradially symmetrical as adults and possess an endoskeleton covered by epithelium and a water-vascular system. Sea stars, sea urchins, sea cucumbers, sea lilies. 402

Echinoidea (ek'i-noi"de-ah) The class of echinoderms whose members are globular or disk shaped, possess moveable spines, and a skeleton of closely fitting plates. Sea urchins and sand dollars. 409

Echiura (ek-ee-yur'iah) A phylum of protostomate, marine animals whose members burrow in mud or sand or live in rock crevices. They possess a spatula-shaped proboscis and are 15 to 50 cm in length. Spoon worms. 359

echolocation (ek'o-lo-ka'shun) A method of locating objects by determining the time it takes for an echo to return and the direction from which it returns. As in bat echolocation. 390, 515

ecological niche (ek'o-loj'i-kal nich) The role of an organism in a community. 208

ecosystems (ek-o-sis'temz) All of the populations of organisms living in a certain area plus their physical environment. 208

ectoderm (ek'ta-durm") The outer embryological tissue layer; gives rise to skin epidermis and glands, also hair and nervous tissues in some animals. 138

ectoplasm (ek'to-plaz-em) The outer, viscous cytoplasm of a protist; contrasts with **endoplasm.** 245

Ectoprocta (ek-to-prok'tah) A phylum of animals whose members are colonial and fresh water or marine. Anus ends outside a ring of tentacles. Lophophore used in feeding. Moss animals or bryozoans. 415

ectotherm (ek'to-therm) Having a variable body temperature derived from heat acquired from the environment; contrasts with **endotherm.** 649

egestion vacuole (e-jes'chen vak'u-ol) A membrane-bound vesicle within the cytoplasm of a protist that functions in expelling wastes. 245

electrical synapse (sin-apse) A synapse at which local currents resulting from electrical activity flow between the two neurons through gap junctions joining them. 551

electrolyte (e-lek'tro-līt) A substance that dissociates into ions when fused or in solution and thus becomes capable of conducting electricity; an ionic solute. 20

electron A small, negatively charged particle that revolves around the nucleus of an atom. It has a very low mass. 16

electron transport chain In a cell membrane, electron carriers and enzymes positioned in an organized array that enhance oxidation-reduction reactions; such systems function in the release of energy that is used in ATP formation and other reactions. 69

electroreception (i-lek'tro-re-sep'shun) The ability to detect weak electrical fields in the environment. 445

electroreceptor (i-lek'tro-re-sep'tor) A receptor that senses changes in an electrical current usually in the surrounding water; also called an ampullary organ. 567

element A basic chemical substance. A substance that cannot be separated into simpler substances by chemical means. 16

elephantiasis (el"e-fan-ti'ah-sis) A chronic filarial disease most commonly occurring in the tropics due to infection of the lymphatic vessels with the nematode *Wuchereria* spp. 315

embryology (em'bre-ol'a-je) The study of development from the egg to the point that all major organ systems have formed. 134

embryonic diapause (em'bre-on'ik di'ah-pauz') The arresting of early development to allow young to hatch, or be born, when environmental conditions favor survival. 517

end bulb A tiny swelling on the terminal end of telodendria at the distal end of an axon; also called the synaptic bouton. 551

endergonic (end"er-gon-ik) Characterized by the absorption of energy; said of chemical reactions that require energy in order to proceed. 57

endocrine gland (en'do-krin) Ductless, hormone-producing gland that is part of the endocrine system. 585

endocrinology (en"do-kri-nol'o-je) The study of the endocrine system and its role in the physiology of an animal. 581

endocytosis (en"do-si-to'sis) Physiological process by which substances may move through a plasma membrane into the cell via membranous vesicles or vacuoles. 40

endoderm (en"do-durm') The innermost embryological tissue layer; gives rise to the inner lining of the gut tract. 138

endoplasm (en'do-plaz-em) The inner, fluid cytoplasm of a protist; contrasts with **ectoplasm.** 245

endoplasmic reticulum (en-do-plaz'mic re-tik'u-lum) Cytoplasmic organelle composed of a system of interconnected membranous tubules and vesicles; ER; rough ER has ribosomes attached to the side of the membrane facing the cytoplasm and smooth ER does not. Rough ER functions in protein synthesis while smooth ER functions in lipid synthesis. 42

endopodite (end-op'o-dīt) The medial ramus of the biramous appendage of crustaceans and trilobites (phylum Arthropoda). 373

endoskeleton (end'o-skel"e-ton) A skeleton that lies beneath the surface of the body (e.g., the bony skeleton of vertebrates and the calcium carbonate skeleton of echinoderms). 535

endostyle (en"do-stīl') A ciliated tract within the pharynx of some chordates that is used in forming mucus for filter feeding. 426

endosymbiont hypothesis (en'do-sim'bi-ont hi-poth'e-sis) The idea whereby the evolution of the eukaryotic cell might have occurred when a large anaerobic amoeboid prokaryote ingested small aerobic bacteria and stabilized them instead of digesting them. 31

endotherm (en'do-therm) Having a body temperature determined by heat derived from the animal's own metabolism; contrasts with **ectotherm.** 650

end-product (feedback) inhibition The inhibition of the first enzyme in a pathway by the end product of that pathway. 73

energy An ability to cause matter to move, and thus, to do work. 56

energy budget An accounting of the way in which energy coming into an ecosystem from the sun is lost or processed by organisms of the ecosystem. 194

energy-level shell The distribution of electrons around the nucleus of an atom. 17

Enteropneusta (ent'er-op-nus"tah) A class of hemichordates whose members live in burrows in shallow marine water. Their bodies are divided into three regions: proboscis, collar, and trunk. Acorn worms. 420

Entoprocta (en'to-procta) A phylum of aschelminths commonly called entoprocts. 318

entropy (en'tro-pe) A measure of the degree of disorganization of a system; how much energy in a system has become so dispersed (usually as heat) so that it is no longer available to do work. The higher the entropy, the more the disorder. 56

environmental resistance The constraints placed on a population by climate, food, space, and other environmental factors. 198

enzyme (en'zīm) A protein that is synthesized by a cell and acts as a catalyst in a specific cellular reaction. 58

enzyme-substrate complex (en′zīm sub-strāt com-plex) The binding of a substrate molecule to the active site of an enzyme. 59

eosinophil (e″o-sīn′o-fil) White blood cells characterized by the presence of cytoplasmic granules that become stained by an acid dye. 601

ephyra (e-fi′rah) Miniature medusae produced by asexual budding of a scyphistoma (class Scyphoza, phylum Cnidaria). Ephyrae mature into sexually mature medusae. 276

epiblast (ep′i-blast) An outer layer of cells in the embryo of an amniote that forms from the proliferation and movement of cells of the blastoderm. 144

epiboly (ep-ib′ol-e) A spreading and thinning of ectoderm from the animal pole of an amphibian gastrula toward the vegetal pole. 141

epidermis (ep′i-durm′is) A sheet of cells covering the surface of an animal's body. In invertebrates, a single layer of ectodermal epithelium. 270, 528

epigenesis (ep′i-jen′i-sis) The mistaken belief that the egg contains all the materials from which the embryo is constructed. 134

epithelial tissue (ep″i-the′le-al) The cellular covering of internal and external surfaces of the body; consists of cells joined by small amounts of cementing substances. Epithelium is classified into types based on the number of layers deep and the shape of the superficial cells. 48

epitoky (ep′i-to′ke) The formation of a reproductive individual (epitoke) that differs from the nonreproductive (atoke) form of that species. 349

esophagus (e-sof′ah-gus) The passage extending from the pharynx to the stomach. 640

estrus (es′trus) The recurrent, restricted period of sexual receptivity in female mammals (other than primates) marked by intense sexual urges. 673

estrus cycle (es′trus si′kel) A recurrent series of changes in the reproductive physiology of female mammals other than primates; females are receptive, physiologically and behaviorally, to the male only at certain times in this cycle. 517

estuaries (es′choo-er-ēz) Bodies of water where fresh water meets seawater. Estuaries are very productive ecosystems because streams carry nutrients into the estuary and tidal currents bring nutrients from the ocean. 221

ethologist (e-thol′o-jist) A person who studies the whole patterns of animal behavior in natural environments, stressing the analysis of adaptation and the evolution of the patterns. 182

ethology (e-thol′o-je) The study of whole patterns of animal behavior in natural environments, stressing the analysis of adaptation and the evolution of the patterns. 182

euchromatic regions (u′kro-mat′-ik) Less densely staining regions of chromosomes that contain active genes. 106

eukaryote (u-kar′e-ōt) Having a true nucleus; a cell that has membranous organelles, most notably the nucleus. 30

eutely (u′te-le) Condition where the body is composed of a constant number of cells or nuclei in all adult members of a species (e.g., rotifers, some nematodes, and acanthocephalans). 305

eutrophication (u-trof′i-ka′shun) Succession in a lake. The gradual accumulation of nutrients and plant and animal growth that eventually transforms a lake into a marsh and then a forest. The death of a lake. 221

evaporation The act or process of evaporating. Heat loss from a surface occurs as water molecules escape in the form of a gas. 649

evolution Change over time. Organic or biological evolution is a series of changes in the genetic composition of a population over time. *See also* **natural selection** and **punctuated equilibrium model.** 154

evolutionary systematics The study of the classification of, and evolutionary relationships among, animals; evolutionary systematists attempt to reconstruct evolutionary pathways based on resemblances between animals that result from common ancestry. 231

excretion (eks-kre′shun) The act, process, or function of excreting. The elimination of metabolic waste products from an animal's body. 655

exergonic (ek″ser-gon′ik) Characterized or accompanied by the release of energy; said of chemical reactions that release energy, so that the products have a lower free energy than the reactants. 57

exocrine gland (ek′so-krin) A gland that secretes its product to an epithelial surface, directly or through ducts. 585

exocytosis (eks′o-si-to′sis) The process by which substances are moved out of a cell; the substances are transported in the cytoplasmic vesicles, the surrounding membrane of which merges with the plasma membrane in such a way that the substances are dumped outside. 42

exopodite (eks-op′o-dīt) The lateral ramus of the biramous appendages of a crustacean or trilobite (phylum Arthropoda). 373

exoskeleton (eks′o-skel″e-ton) A skeleton that forms on the outside of the body (e.g., the exoskeleton of an arthropod). 363, 534

exponential growth (ek′spo-nen″shal) Population growth in which the number of individuals doubles in each generation. 197

extracellular digestion Digestion that occurs outside the cell. 625

F

facilitated diffusion (fah-sil′i-tāt″id di-fu′zhun) Diffusion in which substances are moved through membranes from a region of higher concentration to a region of lower concentration by protein carrier molecules. 36

fallopian tube (fal-lo′pe-an) *See* **uterine tube.**

family The level of classification between order and genus. 230

fermentation (fer″men-ta′shun) Degradative pathway that begins with glycolysis and ends with the electrons being transferred back to one of the breakdown products or intermediates; does not require molecular oxygen. 68

fertilization membrane A membrane that raises off the surface of an egg after sperm penetration; prevents multiple fertilization. 135

fibrillar flight muscle (fi′bra-lar) Insect flight muscle responsible for indirect flight. A single nerve impulse results in many cycles of flight muscle contraction and relaxation. 387

fibrocartilage (fi″bro-kar′ti-lij) The type of cartilage made up of parallel, thick, compact bundles, separated by narrow clefts containing typical cartilage cells (chondrocytes). 50

fibrous connective tissue (fi′brus) The tissue that is made up of fibers that are very densely packed (e.g., tendons and ligaments). 48

filoplume feather (fil′o-ploom) A small thin feather that probably has sensory functions in birds (pinfeather). 487

filopodium (fi′li-po-de-um) Pseudopodeum that is slender, clear, and sometimes branched. 251

filtration Movement of material through a membrane as a result of hydrostatic pressure. 40

first law of thermodynamics (thur′mo-di-nam-iks) The total amount of energy in the universe remains constant; more energy cannot be created and existing energy cannot be destroyed; energy can only undergo conversion from one form to another.   56

fission (fish′un) Asexual reproduction in which the cell divides into two (binary fission) or more (multiple fission) daughter parts, each of which becomes an individual organism.   670

flagella (flah-jel′ah) Relatively long motile processes that extend out from the surface of a cell. Eukaryotic flagella are longer versions of cilia. Flagellar undulations drive a cell through a fluid medium.   46, 538

flame cell Specialized, hollow excretory or osmoregulatory structure consisting of one to several cells containing a tuft of cilia (the "flame") and located at the end of a minute tubule; flame bulb.   291, 656

flavin adenine dinucleotide (fla′vin ad′e-nēn di″nuc′leo-tīd) A coenzyme that is a condensation product of riboflavin phosphate and adenylic acid; it forms the prosthetic group of certain enzymes; FAD.   68

fluid feeding The process by which an animal feeds on fluid.   627

fluke (flook) Any trematode worm; a member of the class Trematoda or class Monogenea.   293

food chain A linear sequence of organisms through which energy is transferred in an ecosystem from producers through several levels of consumers.   56

food vacuole (food vak′yoo-ol) An organelle in the cell that functions in intracellular digestion.   245

food web A sequence of organisms through which energy is transferred in an ecosystem; rather than being a linear series, a food web has highly branched energy pathways.   209

foraging behavior (for′ij-ing) The process animals use in locating food resources.   189

forebrain The forebrain consists of the diencephalon and telencephalon.   557

formed-element fraction The cellular component of vertebrate blood.   600

fossil Any remains, impressions, or traces of organisms of a former geological age.   5

founder effect Changes in gene frequency that occur when a few individuals from a parental population colonize new habitats; the change is a result of founding individuals not having a representative sample of the parental population's genes.   168

fragmentation (frag″men-ta′shun) Division into smaller units. A type of asexual reproduction whereby a body part is lost and then regenerates into a new organism.   670

Fungi (fun′ji) The kingdom of life whose members are characterized by being eukaryotic, multicellular, and saprophytic (mushrooms, molds).   231

G

Galápagos Islands (gah-lah″pe-gos′) An archipelago on the equator in the Pacific Ocean about 1,000 km west of Ecuador. Charles Darwin's observations of the plant and animal life of these islands were important in the formulation of the theory of evolution by natural selection.   156

gallbladder (gawl′blad-der) The pear-shaped reservoir for bile.   644

gamete (gam′ēt) Mature haploid cell (sperm or egg) that functions in sexual reproduction.   88

gametogenesis (gam″e-to-jen′e-sis) The formation of gametes by way of meiosis.   91

gametogony (ga′mēt-o-gony) Multiple fission that forms gametes that fuse to form a zygote. Also called gamogony. Occurs in the class Sporozoea.   254

ganglion (gang′gle-on) A group of nerve cell bodies located outside the central nervous system.   553, 555

gastric shield A chitinized plate in the stomach of a bivalve (phylum Mollusca) on which the crystalline style is rotated.   331

gastrodermis (gas-tro-derm′is) The endodermally derived lining of the gastrovascular cavity of Cnidaria.   270

Gastropoda (gas-trop′o-dah) The class of molluscs characterized by torsion. A shell, when present, is usually coiled. Snails.   326

Gastrotricha (gas-tro-tri′ka) A small phylum of marine and freshwater species of gastrotrichs that inhabit the spaces between bottom sediments.   306

gastrovascular cavity (gas′tro-vas′ku-lar kav′i-te) The large central cavity of cnidarians and flatworms that serves as a chamber for receiving and digesting food.   271, 598, 629

gastrozooid (gas′tro-zo′oid) A feeding polyp in a colonial hydrozoan (phylum Cnidaria).   273

gastrulation (gast′ru-la″shun) The embryological process that results in the formation of the gastrula; results in the formation of the embryonic gut, ectoderm, and endoderm.   138

gemmule (jem′yool) Resistant, overwintering capsule formed by freshwater, and some marine, sponges that contains masses of mesenchyme cells; amoeboid mesenchyme cells are released and organize themselves into a sponge.   268

gene A heritable unit in a chromosome; a series of nucleotide bases on the DNA molecule that codes for a single polypeptide.   97

gene flow Changes in gene frequency in a population that result from emigration or immigration.   170

gene insertion The process by which one or more genes from one organism are incorporated into the genetic makeup of a second organism.   127

gene pool The sum of all genes in a population.   166

generalists Animals that are capable of eating a variety of foods or living in a variety of places.   190

generator potential A graded potential that travels only a short distance along the plasma membrane of a sensory cell.   562

genetic drift (je-net′ik) Occurs when chance events influence evolution; also called **neutral selection.**   168

genetic recombination (je-net′ik re-kom-be-na′shun) Crossing-over; a major source of genetic variation in a population or a given species.   88

genetics (je-net′iks) The study of the mechanisms of transmission of genes from parents to offspring.   96

genotype (je′no-tīp) The specific gene combinations that characterize a cell or an individual.   98

genotypic ratio (je′no-tip-ik) The relative numbers of progeny in each genotypic category produced by a genetic cross.   99

genus (je′nus) The level of classification between species and family.   230

georeceptor (je′o-re-cep′tor) A specialized nerve ending that responds to the force of gravity.   563

gerontology (jer″on-tol′o-je) The scientific problems of aging in all their aspects, including clinical, biological, and sociological.   305

gestation (jes-ta′shun) Period of development of the young in viviparous animals, from the time of fertilization of the ovum until birth.   673

gestation period (jes-ta'shun) The time between fertilization and birth in viviparous animals. 517

giardiasis (je"ar-di'ah-sis) A common infection of the lumen of the small intestine with the flagellated protozoan *Giardia lamblia,* and spread via contaminated food and water and by direct person-to-person contact. 250

gill An aquatic respiratory organ for obtaining oxygen and getting rid of carbon dioxide. 611, 613

gill arches Bony or cartilaginous gill supports of some vertebrates; also called **visceral arches.** 443

gill filaments A thin-walled, fleshy extension of a gill arch that contains vessels carrying blood to and from gas exchange surfaces. 443

gill lamellae (la-mel'a) Thin plates of tissue on gill filaments that contain the capillary beds across which gases are exchanged. 443

gill slit One of several openings in the pharyngeal region of chordates. Gill slits allow water to pass from the pharynx to the outside of the body. In the process, water passes over gills or suspended food is removed in a filter-feeding mechanism. 424

glochidium (glo-kid'e-um) A larval stage of freshwater bivalves in the family Unionidae; it lives as a parasite on the gills or fins of fishes. 332

glomerulus (glo-mer'u-lus) A capillary tuft located within the capsule (Bowman's) of a nephron. 447, 663

gluon (gloo-on) Subatomic particle that binds quarks together in the nucleus of an atom. 16

glycocalyx (gli"ko-kal'iks) The glycoprotein and polysaccharide covering that surrounds many eukaryotic cells. 36

glycolysis (gli-kol'i-sis) The conversion of glucose to pyruvic acid (pyruvate) with the release of some energy in the form of ATP. Occurs in the cytosol; literally "sugar splitting." 66

Gnathostomata (na'tho-sto'ma-tah) A superclass of vertebrates whose members possess hinged jaws and paired appendages. Notochord may be replaced by the vertebral column. 436

Golgi apparatus (gol'je ap"ah-ra'tus) A cytoplasmic organelle that is membrane-bounded and is where the proteins and lipids made in the endoplasmic reticulum are modified and stored. 44

gonad (go'nad) A gamete-producing gland; an ovary or testis. 594

gonadotropin (go-nad"o-trop'in) A hormone that stimulates activity in the gonads. 676

gonozooid (gon'o-zo"id) A polyp of a hydrozoan cnidarian that produces medusae. 273

Gordian worm *See* **horsehair worms.**

grasslands A biome characterized by grasses and a few scattered trees. Grassland animals include numerous insects and other herbivores such as bison. 218

gray crescent A dark arching band that forms on the surface of the amphibian zygote opposite the point of sperm penetration; forms in the region where gastrulation will occur. 136

green gland *See* **antennal gland.**

greenhouse effect The warming of a global climate due to the accumulation of carbon dioxide in the atmosphere. Carbon dioxide accumulates as a result of burning fossil fuels. 224

gross primary production The total energy fixed by autotrophs in an ecosystem. 210

gular flutter (gu-lar flut'er) The type of breathing experienced by some birds. Rapid movement of the throat region promotes evaporative water loss. 652

gustation (gus-ta'shun) The act of tasting or the sense of taste. 574

H

habitat The native environment of an organism. 194

habitat selection The choice of an animal's place to live. Habitat selection involves the interaction of physiological and psychological factors. 189

habituation (hab-bich"u-a'shun) The gradual adaptation to a stimulus or to the environment. 184

hair A long slender filament. Applied especially to such filamentous appendages of the skin. 532

haploid (hap'loid) Having one member of each pair of homologous chromosomes; haploid cells are the product of meiosis and are often gametes. 108

Hardy-Weinberg equilibrium (har'de win'berg e'kwe-lib're-em) The condition in which the frequency of genes in a population does not change from one generation to another; the conditions defined by Hardy-Weinberg equilibrium define the conditions under which evolution does not occur. 167

head-foot The body region of a mollusc that contains the head and is responsible for locomotion as well as retracting the visceral mass into the shell. 325

heartworm disease A parasitic infection in dogs caused by the nematode *Dirofilaria immitis.* 315

hectocotylus (hek'to-kot'i-lus) A modified arm of some male cephalopods that is used in sperm transfer. 336

hemal system (he'mal sis'tem) Strands of tissue found in echinoderms. The hemal system is of uncertain function. It may aid in the transport of large molecules or coelomocytes, which engulf and transport waste particles within the body. 404

hematopoiesis (hem"ah-to-poi-e'sis) The formation and development of blood cells. 601

hemerythrin (hem"e-rith'rin) The red iron-containing respiratory pigment found in the blood plasma of some polychaetes, sipunculids, priapulids, and brachiopods. 619

Hemichordata (hem'i-kor-da'tah) The phylum of marine, wormlike animals whose members have an epidermal nervous system and pharyngeal gill slits. Acorn worms and pterobranchs. 420

hemimetabolous metamorphosis (hem'i-met-ab"ol-us met-ah-morf'a-sis) A type of insect metamorphosis in which immature insects are different in form and habitats from the adult. It is different from holometabolous metamorphosis in that there is a gradual series of changes in form during the transition from immature to adult. 393

hemizygous (hem"e-zi'gus) An individual having one member of a pair of genes. 109

hemocoel (hem'o-sel) Large tissue spaces within arthropods that contain blood; derived from the blastocoel of the embryo. 368

hemocyanin (he"mo-si'ah-nin) A nonheme, blue respiratory pigment that is found in the plasma of many molluscs and arthropods and is composed of monomers, each of which contains two atoms of copper and can bind one molecule of oxygen. 618

hemocyte (he'mo-sit) Any blood corpuscle or formed element of the blood. 598

hemoglobin (he"mo-glo'bin) An iron-containing respiratory pigment of red blood cells responsible for the transport of oxygen and carbon dioxide; occurs in vertebrate red blood cells and in the plasma of many invertebrates. 601, 618

hemolymph (he'ma-limf) The fluid in the coelom or hemocoel of some invertebrates that represents the blood and lymph of higher animals. 598

herbivore (her'bi-vor) A plant-eating animal; any organism that subsists on plants. 622

herbivory (her'bi-vor-e) The process of existing by eating macroscopic plants. 627

hermaphroditism (her-maf'ro-di-tizm) A state characterized by the presence of both male and female reproductive organs in the same animal. 672

heterochromatic regions (het'er-o-chrom"a-tik) Having inactive genes. Inactive regions of chromosomes are said to be heterochromatic. 106

heterodont (het'e-ro-dont) Having a series of teeth specialized for different functions. 507

heterotherm (het'e-ro-therm) An animal whose body temperature fluctuates markedly; "cold-blooded." 650

heterotrophic (het"er-o-trofic) The type of nutrition in which organisms derive energy from the oxidation of organic compounds either by consumption of or absorption of other organisms. 194

heterotrophs (het'er-o-trofs) Organisms that obtain both inorganic and organic raw materials from the environment in order to live; animals, fungi, many protists, and most bacteria are heterotrophs. 622

heterozygous (het'er-o-zi"ges) Having different expressions of a gene on homologous chromosomes. 98

Hexactinellida (hex-act'in-el'id-ah) The class of sponges whose members are characterized by triaxon siliceous spicules, which are sometimes formed into an intricate lattice. Cup or vase shaped. Scyconoid body form. Glass sponges. 267

Hexapoda (hex'sah-pod'ah) The class of mandibulate arthropods whose members are characterized by having three pairs of legs. Commonly called insects. Hexapods often have wings and a body divided into head, thorax, and abdomen. Insecta has been used as an alternate class name. 386

hibernation Condition of mammals that involves passing the winter in a torpid state in which the body temperature drops to nearly freezing and the metabolism drops close to zero. 195, 514, 654

hindbrain Includes the medulla oblongata, cerebellum, and pons. 555

Hirudinea (hi'roo-din"eah) The class of annelids whose members are characterized by bodies with 34 segments, each of which is subdivided into annuli. Anterior and posterior suckers present. Leeches. 353

holoblastic (hol'o-blas"tik) Division of a zygote that results in separate blastomeres. 137

holometabolous metamorphosis (hol'o-met-ab"ol-us met-ah-morf'a-sis) A type of insect metamorphosis in which immatures, called larvae, are different in form and habitats from the adult; the last larval molt results in the formation of a pupa; radical cellular changes in the pupal stage end in adult emergence. 393

Holothuroidea (hol'o-thu-roi"de-ah) The class of echinoderms whose members are elongate along the oral-aboral axis, have microscopic ossicles embedded in a muscular body wall, and have circumoral tentacles. Lack rays. Sea cucumbers. 410

homeostasis (ho"me-o-sta'sis) A state of equilibrium in which the internal environment of the body of an animal remains relatively constant. 36

homeotherm (ho'me-o-therm) Having nearly uniform body temperature, regulated independently of the environmental temperature; "warm-blooded." 650

homodont (ho'mo-dont) Having a series of similar, unspecialized teeth. 507

homologous (ho-mol'o-ges) Structures that have a common evolutionary origin; the wing of a bat and the arm of a human are homologous; each can be traced back to a common ancestral appendage. 5

homologous chromosomes (ho-mol'o-ges kro'mo-somz) Chromosomes that carry genes for the same traits. One of two copies of a particular chromosome in a diploid cell, each copy being derived from a different parent. 88

homozygous (ho"mo-zi'ges) Having the same expression of a gene on homologous chromosomes. 98

hormone A chemical secreted by an endocrine gland that is transmitted by the bloodstream or body fluids. 187, 581

horn The paired growths on the head of certain ungulate animals; the median growth of hair on the snout of the rhinoceros. 532

horsehair worms Pseudocoelomate animals that belong to the phylum Nematomorpha. Also known as Gordian worms or hairworms (*Gordius* is the name for an ancient king who tied an intricate knot). 315

host An animal or protist that harbors or nourishes another organism (parasite). 246

humoral immunity (hu'mor-al i-mu'ni-te) The type of immunity that results from the presence of antibodies that are soluble in blood and lymph. 608

hyaline cartilage (hi'ah-lin kar'ti-lij) The type of cartilage with a glassy, translucent appearance. 50

hydraulic skeleton (hi-dro'lik) The use of body fluids in open circulatory systems to give support and facilitate movement; muscles contracting in one part of the body force body fluids into some distant tissue space, thus causing a part of the body to extend or become turgid. *See* **hydrostatic skeleton.** 328

hydrocarbon (hi"dro-kar'bon) An organic molecule that contains only carbon and hydrogen and has its carbons bonded in a linear fashion. 21

hydrogen bond (hi'dro-jen bond) A weak to moderate attractive force between a hydrogen atom bonded to an electronegative atom and one pair of electrons of another electronegative atom. 19

hydrological cycle (hi'dro-loj'i-kal) The cycling of water between reservoirs in oceans, lakes, and groundwater, and the atmosphere. 216

hydrostatic skeleton (hi'dro-stat'ik) The use of body cavity fluids, confined by the body wall, to give support (e.g., the hydrostatic skeleton of nematodes and annelids). Also called hydroskeleton. 272, 533

hydrothermal vents (hi'dro-thur-mal) Deep, oceanic regions where the tectonic plates of the earth's crust are moving apart. They are characterized by occasional lava flows and hot water springs. These vents support a rich community by chemolithotrophy. 212

Hydrozoa (hi'dro-zo-ah) The class of cnidarians whose members have epidermally derived gametes, mesoglea without wandering amoeboid cells, and gastrodermis without nematocysts. Medusae, when present, with a velum. *Hydra, Obelia, Physalia.* 273

hygroreceptor (hi-gro're-sep'tor) A receptor found in insects that detects the water content of air. 563

hypertonic (hi"per-ton'ik) A solution having a greater number of solute particles than another solution to which it is compared. 38

hypoblast (hi'po-blast) An inner layer of cells that results from the proliferation and movement of cells in the blastoderm of an avian or reptilian embryo. 144

hypodermis (hi"po-der'mis) The layer of integument below the cuticle. The outer cellular layer of the body of invertebrates which secretes the cuticular exoskeleton. 528

hypothalamus ((hi"po-thal'ah-mus) A structure within the diencephalon and below the thalamus, which functions as an autonomic center and regulates the pituitary gland. 557

hypothesis (hi-poth′e-sis) A tentative explanation of a question; an explanation based on careful observations. 12

hypotonic (hi″po-ton′ik) A solution having a lesser number of solute particles than another solution to which it is compared. 38

I

immunity (i-myu′ni-te) The state of being immune from or not susceptible to a particular disease. 607

immunization (im′ye-ni-za-shun) The process of making one immune. The induction of protective immunity by administration of either (1) a vaccine or toxoid (active immunization) or (2) preformed antibodies (passive immunization). 608

immunology (im′u-nol′o-je) The study of the immune system. This study reveals the many phenomena that are responsible for both acquired and innate immunity. It also includes the use of antibody-antigen reactions in other laboratory work (serology and immunochemistry). 607

imprinting (im′print-ing) The development of an attachment toward an animal or object by a young animal. 183

incomplete dominance An interaction between alleles in which both alleles are expressed more or less equally, and the phenotype of the heterozygote is different from either homozygote. 102

incomplete linkage Two genes that are carried on the same chromosome but are far enough apart that crossing-over between them occurs. 109

indirect flight Insect flight accomplished by flight muscles acting on the body wall. Changes in shape of the thorax cause wing movements. A single nerve impulse results in many cycles of the wings; also called asynchronous flight. *See* **direct (synchronous) flight.** 386

induced fit The precise fit between an enzyme and its substrate. 59

inferior Below a point of reference (e.g., the mouth is inferior to the nose in humans). 238

inorganic molecules (compounds) Pertaining to compounds that are not hydrocarbons or their derivatives. Compounds other than organic compounds. 21

Insecta (in-sekt′ah) *See* **Hexapoda.**

insectivore (in-sek′te-vor) An insectivorous animal or plant. Any mammal of the order Insectivora, comprising the moles, shrews, and Old World hedgehogs. 622

insight learning The use of cognitive or mental processes to associate experiences and solve problems. 185

instrumental conditioning (in′stre-men′tal kon-dish′en-ing) Trial-and-error learning. The reinforcement of certain behaviors in animals leads to an animal repeating the behavior. 184

integument (in-teg′u-ment) A covering (e.g., the skin). 528

integumentary exchange The exchange of gases through the integument. Also cutaneous exchange. 611, 613

intercalated disk (in-ter″kah-lat′ed disk) Membranous boundary between adjacent cardiac muscle cells. 52

intermediate filament (in″ter-me′de-at fil′ah-ment) The chemically heterogeneous group of protein fibers, the specific proteins of which can vary with cell type. One of the three most prominent types of cytoskeletal filaments. 46

intermediate host (in′ter-me″de-it host) The organism in the life cycle of a parasite that harbors an immature stage of the parasite and where asexual reproduction usually occurs. 247

intermediate lobe The area in the pituitary gland between the anterior and posterior lobes. 591

interneuron (in′ter-nu′ron) A neuron located between a sensory neuron and a motor neuron. Interneurons function as integrating centers. 548

interphase (in′ter-fāz) Period between two cell divisions when a cell is carrying on its normal functions. Long period of the cell cycle between one mitosis and the next. Includes G_1 phase, S phase, and G_2 phase. The replication of DNA occurs during interphase. 82

intertidal (littoral) zone (in-ter-ti′del li′ter-al) The marine ecosystem that extends from the splash zone of ocean waves to the low tide marks. 222

intracellular digestion Digestion that occurs inside a cell. 624

intrinsic rate of growth *See* **biotic potential.**

introvert (in′tro-vert) The anterior narrow portion that can be withdrawn (introverted) into the trunk of a sipunculid worm. A loriciferan, or a bryozoan. 317

inversion (in-ver′zhen) A rearrangement in the structure of a chromosome in which two breaks occur and a segment of the chromosome is flip-flopped; genes in that segment occur in a reverse order. 115

involuntary (visceral or **autonomic) nervous system** Stimulates smooth and cardiac muscle and glands of the body. 555

involution (in′vo-lu″shun) The rolling of superficial cells over the dorsal lip of the blastopore during gastrulation of amphibian embryos. 141

ion (i′on) An atom or group of atoms with an electrical charge. The charged particle formed when a neutral atom or group of atoms gain or lose one or more electrons. 19

ionic bond (i-on′ik bond) An association between ions of opposite charges. The electrostatic force that holds ions together in an ionic compound. 19

isomer (i′so-mer) Organic compounds with the same molecular formula but different structures, functions, and properties. 22

isotonic (i′so-ton′ik) In a comparison of two solutions, both have equal concentrations of solutes. 37

isotope (i′se-tōp) Any of two or more forms of a chemical element having the same number of protons in the nucleus or the same atomic number, but having different numbers of neutrons in the nucleus, or different atomic weights. Isotopes of a single element possess almost identical chemical properties. 17

J

Jacobson's (vomeronasal) organ Olfactory receptor present in most reptiles; blind-ending sacs that open through the secondary palate into the mouth cavity; they are used to sample airborne chemicals. 479, 573

Johnston's organ Mechanoreceptor (auditory receptor) found at the base of the antennae of male mosquitoes and midges. 389

K

karyotyping (kar″i-o-tīp′ing) The determination of the number and structure of chromosomes in an individual. 112

keratin (ker′a-tin) A tough, water-resistant protein found in the epidermal layers of the skin. Found in hair, feathers, hoofs, nails, claws, bills, etc. 470

keystone species A species upon which several other species depend. Removal of the keystone species leads to the death or disappearance of the dependent species. 208

kilocalorie (kil′o-kal″o-re) A unit of heat equal to 1,000 calories. 56, 622

kinetic energy (ki-net′ik en′er-je) The energy associated with a body by virtue of its motion; the energy of a mass of matter that is moving. 56

kinetochore (ki-ne′to-kor) A centromere; serves as an attachment site for the microtubules of the mitotic apparatus and plays an active part in the movement of chromosomes to the pole. The kinetochore forms on the part of the chromosome known as the centromere. 83

kingdom The highest level of classification of life; the most widely accepted classification system includes five kingdoms: Monera, Protista, Fungi, Plantae, and Animalia. 230

Kinorhyncha (kin′o-rink-ah) The phylum of aschelminths that contains members called kinorhynchs; small elongate worms found exclusively in marine environments where they live in mud and sand. 308

kin selection The idea that natural selection acting on related animals can affect the fitness of an individual. When genes are common to related animals, an individual's fitness is based upon the genes the individual passes on and those common genes passed on by relatives. Kin selection is thought to explain how altruism could evolve in a population. *See* **altruism.** 191

Krebs cycle *See* **citric acid cycle.**

krill (kril) Any of the small, pelagic, shrimplike crustaceans. Krill are an important source of energy in antarctic food webs. 633

K-selected (ka si-lekt′ed) Organisms whose populations are maintained near the carrying capacity of the environment. 199

L

labial palp (la′be-al palp) 1. Chemosensory appendage found on the labium of insects (Arthropoda). 2. Flaplike lobe surrounding the mouth of bivalve molluscs that directs food toward the mouth. 330

labium (la′be-um) The posterior mouthpart of insects. It is often referred to as the "lower lip," is chemosensory, and was derived evolutionarily from paired head appendages (Hexapoda, Arthropoda). 387

lactation (lak-ta′shun) The production of milk by the mammary glands. 685

large intestine That part of the digestive system between the ileocecal valve of the small intestine and the anus; removes salt and water from undigested food and releases feces through the anus. 643

larva (lar′vah) 1. The immature, feeding stage of an insect that undergoes holometabolous metamorphosis. 2. The immature stage of any animal species in which adults and immatures are different in body form and habitat. 268

Larvacea (lar-vas′e-ah) The class of urochordates whose members are planktonic and whose adults retain a tail and notochord. With a gelatinous covering of the body. 422

larval instars (lar′ val′ in′starz) Any of the different immature feeding stages of an insect that undergoes holometabolous metamorphosis. 392

latent learning (lat′ent) Exploratory learning. Latent learning occurs when an animal makes associations without immediate reinforcement or reward. 185

lateral (lat′er-al) Away from the plane that divides a bilateral animal into mirror images. 238

lateral-line system 1. A line of sensory receptors along the side of some fishes and amphibians used to detect water movement (phylum Chordata). 2. The external manifestation of a lateral excretory canal of nematodes (phylum Nematoda). 445, 567

learning Changes in the behavior of an individual due to experience. 184

lentic ecosystem (len′tik ek-o-sis′tem) A freshwater ecosystem that has standing water (e.g., lakes or ponds). 221

leucon (lu′kon) The sponge body form that has an extensively branched canal system; the canals lead to chambers lined by choanocytes. 267

light microscope The type of microscope in which the specimen is viewed under ordinary illumination. 34

limiting factor A nutrient or other component of an organism's environment that is in relatively short supply and, therefore, restricts the organism's ability to reproduce successfully. 194

linkage group (link′kij) Genes linked to the same chromosome that tend to be inherited together. 109

linked gene Gene located on the same chromosome as another gene. 109

lipid (lip′id) A fat, oil, or fatlike compound that usually has fatty acids in its molecular structure. An organic compound consisting mainly of carbon and hydrogen atoms linked by nonpolar covalent bonds. Examples include fats, waxes, phospholipids, and steroids that are insoluble in water. 23

liver A large gland of a dark-red color. It carries out many vital functions such as the formation of urea, manufacture of plasma proteins, synthesis of amino acids, synthesis and storage of glycogen, and many others. 643

lobopodium (lo′bo-po-de-um) A blunt, lobelike pseudopodium that is commonly tubular, and is composed of both ectoplasm and endoplasm. 251

local chemical messenger A chemical that acts on nearby cells. 580

locus (lo′kus) The position of a gene in a chromosome. 101

looping movement The type of locomotion exhibited by leeches and some insect larvae whereby they alternate temporary points of attachment to move forward. 540

loose connective tissue The type of tissue in which the matrix contains strong, flexible fibers of the protein collagen that are interwoven with fine, elastic, and reticular fibers. 48

lophophore (lof′a-for) Tentacle-bearing ridge or arm within which is an extension of the coelomic cavity in lophophorate animals (e.g., brachiopods, ectoprocts, phoronids). 415

lorica (lo′re-ka) The protective external case found in rotifers and some protozoa. It is formed by a thickened cuticle. 307

Loricifera (lor′a-sif-er-a) A phylum of aschelminths. The most recent animal phylum to be described; members are commonly called loriciferans. 317

lotic ecosystems (lo′tik ek-o-sis′temz) Flowing water ecosystems. They include brooks, streams, and rivers. 220

lung An organ of the respiratory system in which gas exchange occurs between body fluids (e.g., blood) and air. 614

lymph (limf) Fluid transported by the lymphatic vessels. 606

lymphatic (lim-fat′ik) **system** The one-way system of lymphatic vessels. 606

lymphocyte (lim′fo-sīt) A type of white blood cell that functions to provide protection to an animal. 602

lysosome (li′so-sōm) Cytoplasmic, membrane-bounded organelle that contains digestive and hydrolytic enzymes, which are typically most active at the acid pH found in the lumen of lysosomes. 44

M

macronucleus (mak'ro-nuk"le-us) A large nucleus found within the Ciliata (Protista) that regulates cellular metabolism. Directly responsible for the phenotype of the cell. 257

macronutrient (mak"ro-noo'tre-ent) An essential nutrient for which an animal has a large minimal daily requirement (greater than 100 mg) (e.g., calcium, phosphorus, magnesium, potassium, sodium, and chloride along with carbohydrates, lipids, and proteins). 622

Malacostraca (mal-ah-kos'trah-kah) The class of crustaceans whose members are characterized by having appendages modified for crawling along the substrate, as in lobsters, crayfish, and crabs. Alternatively, the abdomen and body appendages may be used in swimming, as in shrimp. 373

malpighian tubules (mal-pig'e-an tu'bulz) The blind-ending excretory tubules that join the midgut of insects and some other arthropods. 368, 658

Mammalia (ma-may'le-ah) The class of vertebrates whose members are at least partially covered by hair, have specialized teeth, and are endothermic. Young are nursed from mammary glands. The mammals. 422

mammary gland (mam'ar-e) The breast. In female mammals, the mammary glands produce and secrete milk to nourish developing young. 506, 680

mandible (man'dib-el) 1. The lower jaw of vertebrates. 2. The paired, grinding and tearing mouthparts of arthropods, which were derived from anterior head appendages. 374

mantle (man'tel) The outer fleshy tissue of molluscs that secretes the shell. The mantle of cephalopods may be modified for locomotion. 325

mantle cavity (man'tel kav'i-te) The space between the mantle and the visceral mass of molluscs. 325

manubrium (me-nub're-um) A structure that hangs from the oral surface of a cnidarian medusa and surrounds the mouth. 273

mass A measure of the quantity of matter contained in an object. 16

mastax (mas'tax) The pharyngeal apparatus of rotifers used for grinding ingested food. 308

Mastigophora (mas-ti-gof'o-rah) The protozoan subphylum where members possess one or more flagella that are used for locomotion; autotrophic, heterotrophic, or saprozoic. 247

matter Anything that has mass and occupies space. 16

maturation (mach'oo-ra'shun) To complete the natural development of an animal system. Improvement in the performance of behavior occurs as parts of the nervous system and other structures complete development. 182

maxilla (maks'il-ah) One member of a pair of mouthparts located just posterior to the mandibles of many arthropods. 374

maxillary gland (mak'si-ler"e) In malacostracan crustaceans, the excretory organs are located near the maxillary segments and are termed maxillary glands. 657

mechanoreceptor (mek"ah-no-re-sep'tor) A sensory receptor that is sensitive to mechanical stimulation, such as changes in pressure or tension. 568

meconium (me-ko'ne-um) A dark green mucilaginous material in the intestine of the full-term fetus, being a mixture of the secretions of the intestinal glands and some amniotic fluid. 687

medial (me'de-al) On or near the plane that divides a bilateral animal into mirror images. Also median. 238

median (parietal) eye (me'de-an) A photoreceptor located middorsally on the head of some vertebrates; it is associated with the vertebrate epithalamus. 479, 575

medulla oblongata (me-dul'ah ob"lon-gah'tah) Portion of the brain stem located between the pons and the spinal cord. 555

medusa (me-du'sah) Usually, the sexual stage in the life cycle of cnidarians; the jellyfish body form. 271

meiosis (mi-o'sis) Process of cell division by which egg and sperm cells are formed, involving a diminution in the amount of genetic material. Comprises two successive nuclear divisions with only one round of DNA replication, which produces four haploid daughter cells from an initial diploid cell. 88

melatonin (mel"ah-to'nin) A hormone secreted by the pineal gland. Functions in regulating photoperiodicity. 586

memory cell A lymphocyte capable of initiating the antibody- mediated immune response on detection of a specific antigen molecule for

which it is genetically programmed. It circulates freely in the blood and lymph, and may live for years. 610

meninges (me-nin'jez) A group of three membranes that covers the brain and spinal cord. 555

menopause (men'o-pawz) Termination of the menstrual cycle. 681

menstrual cycle (men'stroo-al) The period of the regularly recurring physiologic changes in the endometrium that culminates in its shedding (menstruation). 680

menstruation (men"stroo-a'shun) Loss of blood and tissue from the uterus at the end of a female primate's reproductive cycle. 681

meroblastic (mer'ah-blas"tik) The division of a zygote in which cleavages do not completely divide the embryo. 137

Merostomata (mer'o-sto'mah-tah) The class of arthropods whose members are aquatic and possess book gills on the opisthosoma. Eurypterids (extinct) and horseshoe crabs. 366

mesenchyme (mez'en-kīm) Undifferentiated mesoderm. It will eventually develop into muscle, blood vessels, skeletal elements, and (other) connective tissues. 138

mesoderm (mez'ah-durm) The embryonic tissue that gives rise to tissues located between the ectoderm and endoderm (e.g., muscle, skeletal tissues, and excretory structures). 138

mesoglea (mez-o-gle'ah) A gel-like matrix found between the epidermis and gastrodermis of cnidarians. 270

mesohyl (mez-o-hīl') A jellylike layer between the outer (pinacocyte) and inner (choanocyte) layers of a sponge. Contains wandering amoeboid cells. 265

mesonephros (me-zo nef'ros) The middle of three pairs of embryonic renal organs in vertebrates. The functional kidney of fishes and amphibians; its collecting duct is a wolffian duct. 659

mesothorax (mes'o-thor"aks) The middle of the three thoracic segments of an insect; usually contains the second pair of legs and the first pair of wings. 386

Mesozoa (mes'o-zo"ah) A phylum of animals whose members are parasites of marine invertebrates. With a two-layered body organization. Dioecious, complex life histories. Orthonectids and dicyemids. 285

messenger RNA (mes′en-jer r-n-a) A single-stranded polyribonucleotide; formed in the nucleus from a DNA template and carries the transcribed genetic code to the ribosome where the genetic code is translated into protein.   121

metabolism (me-tab′o-lizm) All of the chemical changes and processes that occur within cells.   56

metacercaria (me′ta-ser-ka′re-ah) Stage between the cercaria and adult in the life cycle of most digenetic trematodes; usually encysted and quiescent.   295

metamerism (met-tam″a-riz′em) A segmental organization of body parts. Metamerism occurs in the Annelida, Arthropoda, and other smaller phyla.   343

metamorphosis (met″ah-mor′fo-sis) Change of shape or structure, particularly a transition from one developmental stage to another as from larva to adult form.   365

metanephridium (met′ah-ne-frid′e-um) An excretory organ found in many invertebrates; it consists of a tubule that has one end opening at the body wall and the opposite end in the form of a funnel-like structure that opens to the body cavity.   348, 656

metanephros (me′ta-ne′fros) The embryonic renal organs of vertebrates arising behind the mesonephros; the functional kidney of reptiles, birds, and mammals. It is drained by a ureter.   659

metaphase (met-ah-fāz) Stage in mitosis when chromosomes become aligned in the middle of the cell and firmly attached to the mitotic spindle but have not yet segregated toward opposite poles.   86

metathorax (met′ah-thor″aks) The posterior of the three segments of an insect thorax; it usually contains the third pair of walking legs and the second pair of wings (Arthropoda).   386

micelle (mi-sel) Lipid aggregates with a surface coat of bile salts. A stage in the digestion of lipids in the small intestine.   644

microfilaria (mi″kro-fi-lar′e-ah) The prelarval stage of filarial worms. Found in the blood of humans and the tissues of the vector.   315

microfilament (mi′kro′fil-ament) Component of the cytoskeleton; involved in cell shape, motion, and growth. Helical protein filament formed by the polymerization of globular actin molecules.   46

micronucleus (mi′kro-nuk″le-us) A small body of DNA that contains the hereditary information of ciliates (Protista); exchanged between protists during conjugation. It undergoes meiosis before functioning in sexual reproduction.   257

micronutrient (mi″kro-nu′tre-ent) A dietary element essential in only small quantities (e.g., iron, chlorine, copper, and vitamins).   622

microscopy (mi-kros′ko-pe) Examination with a microscope.   34

Microspora (mi-cro-spor′ah) The protozoan phylum characterized by members having unicellular spores; intracellular parasites in nearly all major animal groups. Examples: microsporeans (*Nosema*).   255

microtubule (mi″kro-tu′bul) A hollow cylinder of tubulin subunits; involved in cell shape, motion, and growth; functional unit of cilia and flagella. It is one of three major classes of filaments of the cytoskeleton.   45

mictic eggs (mik′tik) Pertaining to the haploid eggs of rotifers. If it isn't fertilized, the egg develops parthenogenetically into a male; if fertilized, mictic eggs secrete a heavy shell and become dormant, hatching in the spring into amictic females.   308

midbrain The portion of the brain between the pons and forebrain.   557

migration Periodic round trips of animals between breeding and nonbreeding areas or to and from feeding areas.   498

mimicry (mim′ik-re) When one species resembles one or more other species; often protection is afforded the mimic species.   204

miracidium (mi-rah-sid′e-um) The ciliated, free-swimming first stage larva of a digenean trematode that undergoes further development in the body of a snail.   294

mitochondrion (mi″to-kon′dre-on) Membrane-bounded organelle that specializes in aerobic respiration (oxidative phosphorylation) and produces most of the ATP in eukaryotic cells.   45

mitosis (mi-to′sis) Nuclear division in which the parental number of chromosomes is maintained from one cell generation to the next. Basis of reproduction of single-cell eukaryotes; basis of physical growth (through cell divisions) in multicellular eukaryotes.   82

mitotic apparatus (mi-to′tic ap′a-rat′es) Collectively, the asters, spindle, centrioles, and microtubules of a dividing cell.   86

modern synthesis The combination of principles of population genetics and Darwinian evolutionary theory.   161

molecular biology The study of the biochemical structure and function of organisms.   6

molecular genetics The study of the biochemical structure and function of DNA.   118

molecule A particle composed of two or more atoms bonded together. An aggregate of at least two atoms in a definite arrangement held together by special forces.   18

Mollusca (mol-lus′kah) The phylum of coelomate animals whose members possess a head-foot, visceral mass, mantle, and mantle cavity. Most molluscs also possess a radula and a shell. The molluscs. Bivalves, snails, octopuses, and related animals.   322

molting *See* ecdysis.

Monera (mon′er-ah) The kingdom of life whose members are characterized by having cells that lack a membrane-bound nucleus, as well as other internal, membrane-bound organelles (they are prokaryotic); bacteria.   231

monocyte (mon′o-sīt) A type of white blood cell that functions as a phagocyte.   602

monoecious (mon-es′e-es) An organism in which both male and female sex organs occur in the same individual.   249, 672

monogamous (mah-nog′ah-mus) Having one mate at a time.   495

Monogenea (mon′oh-gen′ee-uh) The class of Platyhelminthes that has members that are called monogenetic flukes; most ectoparasites on vertebrates (usually on fishes, occasionally on turtles, frogs, copepods, squids); one life-cycle form in only one host; bear an opisthaptor. Examples: *Disocotyle*, *Gyrodactylus*, *Polystoma*.   293

Monogononta (mon′o-go-non′ta) A class of rotifers containing members that possess one ovary; mastax not designed for grinding; produce mictic and amictic eggs. Example: *Notommata*.   307

monohybrid cross (mono-hi′brid) A mating between two individuals heterozygous for one particular trait.   98

monophyletic group (mon′o-fi-let′ik) A group of organisms descended from a single ancestor.   231

Monoplacophora (mon′o-pla-kof″o-rah) The class of molluscs whose members have a single, arched shell; a broad, flat foot; and certain serially repeated structures. *Neopilina*.   337

monosaccharide (mon″o-sak′ah-rīd) A simple sugar, such as glucose or fructose, that represents the structural unit of a carbohydrate. Monosaccharides are building blocks of more complex sugars (disaccharides) and polysaccharides. 22

morphogenesis (mor″fo-gen′e-sis) The evolution and development of form, as the development of the shape of a particular organ or part of the body. 138

morula (mor′u-lah) A stage in the embryonic development of some animals that consists of a solid ball of cells. 138, 682

mosaic evolution (mo-za-ik ev′ah-loo″shun) A change in a portion of an organism (e.g., a bird wing) while the basic form of the organism is retained. 176

motor (efferent) neuron or **nerve** A neuron or nerve that transmits impulses from the central nervous system to an effector such as a muscle or gland. 548

motor unit A motor neuron and the muscle fibers associated with it. 544

mucous cell A glandular cell that secretes mucus. 640

Müllerian mimicry (mul′er-e-an mim′ik-re) Occurs when two similar species are both distasteful to predators. 204

Muller's larva A free-swimming ciliated larva that resembles a modified ctenophore, characteristic of many marine polyclad turbellarians. 293

multiple alleles (mul′te-pel al-els′) The presence of more than two alleles in a population. 101

multiple fission (mul′te-pel fish′on) Asexual reproduction by the splitting of a cell or organism into many cells or organisms. *See* **schizogony.** 245

muscle fiber The contractile unit of a muscle. 539

muscle tissue The type of tissue that allows movement. The three kinds are skeletal, smooth, and cardiac. Tissue made of bundles of long cells called muscle fibers. 48

musk gland *See* **scent gland.**

mutation pressure (myoo-ta′shun presh′er) A measure of the tendency for gene frequencies to change through mutation. 170

mutualism (myoo′choo-ah-liz-em) A relationship between two species in which both members of the relationship benefit. 202

myelin (mi′e-lin) Fatty material that forms a sheathlike covering around some nerve fibers. 548

myofibril (mi″o-fi′bril) Contractile fibers found within muscle cells. 543

myoglobin (mi″o-glo′bin) The oxygen-transporting pigment of muscle tissue. 619

myomere (mi′o-mer) The muscle plate or portion of a somite that develops into voluntary muscle. 542

myosin (mi′o-sin) A protein that, together with actin, is responsible for muscular contraction and relaxation. 543

myriapods (mir′e-a-podz) Members of the four noninsect classes of the subphylum Uniramia. Includes centipedes, millipedes, pauropods, and symphylans. 383

Myxini (mik-sy-ny) The class of vertebrates whose members are fishlike, jawless, without paired appendages, and possess four pairs of tentacles around the mouth. Hagfishes. 422

Myxozoa (myx-o-zo-a) The protozoan phylum characterized by members having spores of multicellular origin; the myxozoans. 255

N

naiad (na′ad) The aquatic immature stage of any hemimetabolous insect. 393

nail The horny cutaneous plate of the dorsal surface of the distal end of a finger or toe. 532

natural killer (NK) cell A lymphocyte present in nonimmunized individuals that exhibits independent cytolytic activity against tumor cells; also called cytotoxic T cells. 609

natural selection A theory, conceived by Charles Darwin and Alfred Wallace of how some evolutionary changes occur. 159

naturally acquired active immunity The type of immunity that develops when an individual's immunologic system comes into contact with an appropriate antigenic stimulus during the course of normal activities; it usually arises as the result of recovering from an infection. 608

naturally acquired passive immunity The type of immunity that involves the transfer of antibodies from one individual to another. 608

nematocyst (ni-mat′ah-sist) An organelle characteristic of the Cnidaria that is used in defense, food gathering, and attachment. 271

Nematoda (nem-a-to-dah) The phylum of aschelminths that contains members commonly called either roundworms or nematodes. Triploblastic, bilateral, vermiform, unsegmented, and pseudocoelomate. 310

Nematomorpha (nem′a-to-mor-pha) The phylum of aschelminths commonly called horsehair worms. 315

Nemertea (nem-er′te-a) The phylum that has members commonly called the proboscis worms; elongate, flattened worms found in marine mud and sand; triploblastic; complete digestive tract with anus; closed circulatory system. 300

neo-Darwinism (ne′o-dar′wi-niz′um) *See* **modern synthesis.**

nephridiopore (ne-frid-i-o′por) The opening to the outside of a nephridium. 291

nephridium (ne-frid′e-um) The excretory organ of the embryo; the embryonic tube from which the kidney develops. Functions in excretion, osmoregulation, or both. 656

nephron (nef′ron) The functional unit of a kidney, consisting of a renal corpuscle and a renal tubule. 447, 663

neritic ecosystems (ne-rit′ik ek-o-sis′temz) The marine ecosystem that consists of relatively shallow water extending from the littoral zone to the edge of the continental shelves. 222

nerve A bundle of neurons or nerve cells outside the central nervous system. 555

nerve net A diffuse, two-dimensional plexus of bi- or multipolar neurons; found in cnidarians. 552

nervous tissue The type of tissue composed of individual cells called neurons and supporting neuroglial cells. 48

net primary production The total energy converted into biomass by autotrophs. Net primary production is equal to gross primary production less energy lost in maintenance functions of autotrophs. 210

neuroendocrine system (nu″ro-en′do-krin sys′tem) The combination of the nervous and endocrine systems. 581

neurofibril node (nu″ro-fi′bril nōd) Regular gaps in a myelin sheath around a nerve fiber; formerly called **node of Ranvier.** 549

neurohormone (nu″ro-hor′mōn) A chemical transmitter produced by nervous tissue. Uses the bloodstream or other body fluids for distribution to its target site. 581

neurolemmocyte (nu-ro-lem-o-sīt) The cell that surrounds a fiber of a peripheral nerve and forms the neurolemmal sheath and myelin; formerly called Schwann cell. 548

neuromast (nu-ro′mast) The hair-cell mechanoreceptor located within pits of the lateral-line system. Used to detect water currents and the movements of other animals. 568

neuromuscular junction (nu″ro-mus′ku-lar jungk′shun) The junction between nerve and muscle; myoneural junction or neuromuscular cleft.   544

neuron (nu′ron) A nerve cell that consists of a cell body and its processes.   548

neuropeptide (nu″ro-pep-tīd) A hormone produced by secretory nervous tissue.   581

neurotoxin (nu″ro-tok′sin) A toxin that is poisonous to or destroys nerve tissue.   553

neurotransmitter (nu″ro-trans-mit′er) Chemical substance secreted by the terminal end of an axon that stimulates a muscle fiber contraction or an impulse in another neuron.   551, 580

neurulation (noor′yah-la′shun) External changes along the upper surface of a chordate embryo that result in the formation of the neural tube.   141

neutral selection *See* **genetic drift.**

neutron (nu′tron) A neutral particle with a mass approximately the same as a proton that exists in atomic nuclei.   16

neutrophil (nu′tro-fil) A type of phagocytic white blood cell.   601

nicotine adenine dinucleotide (nik″o-tēn ad′e-nēn di-nu′kle-o-tīd) A local electron carrier that transfers hydrogen atoms and electrons within metabolic pathways; a free-moving carrier, not membrane bound in a transport system; NAD⁺.   60

nictitating membrane (nik′ti-tat-ing mem-brān) The thin, transparent lower eyelid of amphibians and reptiles.   461, 575

nociceptor (no″se-sep′tor) A sensory receptor responding to potentially harmful stimuli; produces a sensation of pain.   572

node of Ranvier (nōd ov Ran-ve-a) A constriction of mylelinated nerve fibers at regular intervals at which the myelin sheath is absent and the axon is enclosed only by sheath cell processes; also known as a **neurofibril node.**   549

nomenclature (no′men-kla-cher) The study of the naming of organisms in the fashion that reflects their evolutionary relationships.   230

nonamniote lineage (non-am′ne-ōt lin′e-ij) The vertebrate lineage leading to modern amphibians.   452

nondisjunction (non′dis-junk″shun) The failure of homologous chromosomes to separate during meiosis.   112

nonpolar covalent bond (non-po-lar co-va′lent bond) The type of bond that is formed when electrons spend as much time orbiting one nucleus as the other; thus, the distribution of charges is symmetrical.   19

nonshivering thermogenesis (non-shiv′er-ing ther-mo-gen′esis) The hormonal triggering of heat production.   653

norepinephrine (nor″ep-i-nef′rin) A neurotransmitter released from the axon ends of some nerve fibers; noradrenaline.   551

northern coniferous forest (nor′thern ko-nif′er-us) The biome characterized by cool summers, cold winters, and short growing seasons. Characteristic animals include insects, snowshoe hares, lynx, wolves, caribou, and moose.   217

notochord (no″ta-kord′) A rodlike, supportive structure that runs along the dorsal midline of all larval chordates and many adult chordates.   424, 554

nuclear envelope Double membrane forming the surface boundary of a eukaryotic nucleus; consists of outer and inner membranes perforated by nuclear pores.   47

nucleic acid (nu-kle-ik) A substance composed of nucleotides bonded together; RNA, DNA.   27

nucleolus (nu-kle′o-lus) A small structure that occurs within the nucleus of a cell and is where ribosomal RNA is transcribed and ribosomal subunits are assembled.   47

nucleon (nuk′le-on) The nucleus of an atom is built up of protons and neutrons, collectively called a nucleon.   16

nucleosome (noo-kle′ah-sōm) An association of DNA and histone proteins that makes up chromatin.   106

nucleotide (nu′kle-o-tīd) A component of a nucleic acid molecule consisting of a sugar, a nitrogenous base, and a phosphate group. Nucleotides are the building blocks of nucleic acids.   26

nucleus (nu′kle-us) Cell nucleus; a spheroid body within a cell, contained in a double membrane, the nuclear envelope, and containing chromosomes and one or more nucleoli. The genetic control center of a eukaryotic cell. The cell bodies of nerves within the central nervous system.   32

Nuda (nuda) The class of ctenophorans whose members lack tentacles and have a flattened body with a highly branched gastrovascular cavity.   281

numerical taxonomy (noo′mer′i-kal tak-son′ah-me) A system of classification in which there is no attempt to distinguish true and false similarities.   233

nutrition The study of the sources, actions, and interactions of nutrients.   622

nymph (nimf) The immature stage of a paurometabolous insect; resembles the adult but is sexually immature and lacks wings (Arthropoda).   393

O

oceanic ecosystems (o′she-an′ik ek-o-sis′temz) The marine ecosystem that extends from the continental shelves into the unproductive open ocean.   223

ocellus (o-sel-as) A simple eye or eyespot in many invertebrates; a small cluster of photoreceptors.   291, 564

odontophore (o-dont″o-for′) The cartilaginous structure that supports the radula of molluscs.   326

olfaction (ol-fak′shun) The act of smelling; the sense of smell.   572

Oligochaeta (ol″i-go-ket′ah) The class of annelids whose members are characterized by having few setae and no parapodia. Monoecious with direct development. The earthworm (*Lumbricus*) and *Tubifex*.   350

ommatidia (om′ah-tid″e-ah) The sensory units of the arthropod compound eye.   389, 564

omnivore (om-niv′or) Subsisting upon both plants and animals; an animal that obtains its nutrients by consuming plants and other animals.   622

onchosphere (ong′ko-sfer) The larva of the tapeworm contained within the external embryonic envelope and armed with six hooks and cilia. Typically referred to as a coracidium when released into the water.   299

oncomiracidium (on′ko-mir-a-sid′e-um) Ciliated larva of a monogenetic trematode.   293

one-gene–one-polypeptide theory The concept that one gene in DNA codes for a sequence of amino acids in a specific polypeptide.   120

Onychophora (on-y-kof′o-rah) A phylum of terrestrial animals with 14 to 43 pairs of unjointed legs, oral papillae, and two large antennae. Onycophorans live in humid tropical areas of the world. Their ancestors may have been an evolutionary transition between annelids and arthropods. Velvet worms or walking worms.   399

oogenesis (o″o-jen′e-sis) The process by which an egg cell forms from an oocyte.   91

Opalinata (op'ah-li-not'ah) The protozoan subphylum where members are cylindrical; covered with cilia. Examples: *Opalina, Zelleriella.* 247

open circulatory system A circulatory system in which blood is not confined to vessels in a part of its circuit within an animal; blood bathes tissues in blood sinuses. 328, 598

operculum (o-per'ku-lum) A cover. 1. The cover of a gill chamber of a bony fish (Chordata). 2. The cover of the genital pores of a horseshoe crab (Meristomata, Arthropoda). 3. The cover of the aperature of a snail shell (Gastropoda, Mollusca). 294, 327, 438

Ophiuroidea (o-fe-u-roi''de-ah) The class of echinoderms whose members have arms sharply set off from the central disk. Tube feet without suction disks. Brittle stars. 407

opisthaptor (a'pis-thap'ter) Posterior attachment organ of a mongenetic trematode. 294

opisthosoma (a'pis-tho-so''mah) The portion of the body of a chelicerate arthropod that contains digestive, reproductive, excretory, and respiratory organs. 366

oral Having to do with the mouth. The end of an animal containing the mouth. 238

oral cavity The cavity within the mouth. 638

oral sucker The sucker on the anterior end of a tapeworm, fluke, or leech. 294

order The level of classification between class and family. 230

organ A structure consisting of a group of specialized tissues that performs a specialized function. 52

organelle (or''gah-nel) A part of a cell that performs a specific function. 30

organic evolution The change in an organism over time; a change in the sum of all genes in a population. 154

organic molecule A molecule that contains one or more carbon atoms. 21

organizational effects of hormones Changes resulting from the presence of hormones at critical time periods such that specific developmental pathways for specific brain regions and developing gonadal tissues are influenced to become either female or malelike. 187

organ of Ruffini Sensory receptor in the skin believed to be a sensor for touch-pressure, position sense of a body part, and movement. Also known as corpuscle of Ruffini. 572

organ system A set of interconnected or interdependent parts that function together in a common purpose or produce results that cannot be achieved by one of them acting alone. 52

osmoconformer (oz-mo'con-form-er) An organism whose body fluids have the same or very similar osmotic pressure as that of its aquatic environment; a marine organism that does not utilize energy in osmoregulation. 655

osmoregulation (oz''mo-reg''u-la'shun) The maintenance of osmolarity by an organism or body cell with respect to the surrounding medium. 655

osmoregulator (oz-mo'reg-u'lat-er) An organism that regulates its internal osmotic pressure. 656

osmosis (oz-mo'sis) The movement of water through a selectively permeable membrane due to the existence of a concentration gradient. 37

Osteichthyes (os'te-ik'thee-ez) The class of fishes whose members are characterized by the presence of a bony skeleton, a swim bladder, and an operculum. Bony fishes. 422

ovarian cycle (o-va're-an) The cycle in the ovary during which the oocyte matures and ovulation occurs. 680

ovary (o'var-e) The primary reproductive organ of a female; where eggs (ova) are produced. 678

oviparous (o-vip'er-us) Organisms that lay eggs that develop outside the body of the female. 370, 674

ovipositor (ov-i-poz'it-or) A modification of the abdominal appendages of some female insects that is used for depositing eggs in or on some substrate (Arthropoda, Hexapoda). 392

ovoviviparous (o'vo-vi-vip'er-us) Organisms with eggs that develop within the reproductive tract of the female and are nourished by food stored in the egg. 370, 674

ovulation (o''vu-la'shun) The release of an egg from a mature ovarian follicle. 678

oxidation (ok''si-da'shun) The loss of electrons from a compound. 68

oxygen debt The amount of oxygen that must be supplied following physical exercise to convert accumulated lactic acid (lactate) to glucose. 619

oxyhemoglobin (ok''si-he''mo-glo'bin) Compound formed when oxygen combines with hemoglobin. 601

P

Pacinian corpuscle (Pa-cin-ian kor'pus'l) A sensory receptor in skin, muscles, body joints, body organs, and tendons that is involved with the vibratory sense and firm pressure on the skin; also called a lamellated corpuscle. 572

pain receptor A modified nerve ending that, when stimulated, gives rise to the sense of pain. 572

paedomorphosis (pe'dah-mor'fo-sis) The development of sexual maturity in the larval body form. 288

paleontology (pa'le-on-tol'o-je) The study of early life-forms on earth. 5

pancreas (pan'kre-as) Glandular organ in the abdominal cavity that secretes hormones and digestive enzymes. 594, 643

pancreatic islet (pan''kre-at'ic i'let) An island of special tissue in the pancreas. 594

parabronchi (par'ah-brong''ke) The tiny air tubes within the lung of a bird across which gas exchange occurs. 492

parapatric speciation (par'ah-pat'rik spe'she-a'shun) Speciation that occurs in small, local populations, called **demes.** 174

parapodia (par'ah-pod''e-ah) Paired lateral extensions on each segment of polychaetes (Annelida); may be used in swimming, crawling, and burrowing. 345

parasitism (par'ah-si'tiz-em) A relationship between two species in which one member lives at the expense of the second. 202

parasitoid (par'ah-si'toid) Animal that deposits eggs or other developmental stages on another animal; immatures feed on host tissues and eventually kill the host. 202

parasympathetic nervous system (par'ah-sim''pah-thet'ik ner-vus sis-tem) Portion of the autonomic nervous system that arises from the brain and sacral region of the spinal cord. 558

parathyroid gland (par''ah-thi'roid gland) One of the small glands located within a lobe of the thyroid gland. 593

parenchyma (pa''ren'ka-ma) A spongy mass of mesenchyme cells filling spaces around viscera, muscles, or epithelia in acoelomate animals. Depending on the species, parenchyma may function in providing skeletal support, nutrient storage, motility, reserves of regenerative cells, transport of materials, structural interactions with other tissues, modifiable tissue for morphogenesis, oxygen storage, and perhaps other functions that have yet to be determined. 289

parietal cell (pah-ri′e-tal) Cell of a gastric gland that secretes hydrochloric acid and intrinsic factor. 640

parietal eye (pah-ri′e-tal) *See* **median eye.**

parthenogenesis (par′the-no-jen′e-sis) A modified form of sexual reproduction by the development of a gamete without fertilization, as occurs in some bees, wasps, and certain lizards. 670

parturition (par″tu-rish′un) The process of childbirth. 685

paurometabolous metamorphosis (por′o-me-tab′a-lus met′ah-morf′a-sis) A form of insect development in which immatures resemble parents, and molting is restricted to the immature stages. 393

Pauropoda (por′e-pod′ah) A class of arthropods whose bodies are small, soft, 11 segmented, and have 9 pairs of legs. 385

pebrine (pa-brēn) An infectious disease of silkworms caused by the protozoan *Nosema bombicis.* 255

pedal locomotion The type of locomotion exhibited by flatworms, some cnidarians, and the gastropod molluscs. This locomotion involves waves of activity in the muscular system, which is applied to the substratum. 539

pedicellariae (ped′e-sel-ar″i-ae) Pincerlike structures found on the body wall of many echinoderms. They are used in cleaning and defense. 404

pedipalps (ped′e-palps) The second pair of appendages of chelicerate arthropods. These appendages are sensory in function. 366

pellicle (pel-ik-el) A thin, frequently noncellular covering of an animal (e.g., the protective and supportive pellicle of protists occurs just below the plasma membrane); may be composed of a cell membrane, cytoskeleton, and other organelles. 245, 528

pentaradial symmetry (pen′tah-ra′de-al sim′i-tre) A form of radial symmetry found in the echinoderms in which body parts are arranged in fives around an oral-aboral axis. 402

Pentastomida (pent-ta-stom′id-ah) A phylum of worms that are all endoparasites in the lungs or nasal passageways of carnivorous vertebrates. Tongue worms. 400

peptide bond The covalent bond that joins individual amino acids together; formed by dehydration synthesis. 25

peripheral nervous system (pe-rif′er-al) The nerves and ganglia of the nervous system that lie outside of the brain and spinal cord. 555

peristalsis (per″i-stal′sis) Rhythmic waves of muscular contraction that occur in the walls of various tubular organs. 638

peristomium (per″i-stom′e-um) The segment of the body of an annelid that surrounds the mouth. 345

phagocytosis (fag″o-si-to′sis) Process by which a cell engulfs bacteria, foreign proteins, macromolecules, and other cells and digests their substances; cellular eating. 40

phagolysosome (fag″o-li′so-sōm) The organelle that is formed when a lysosome combines with a vesicle. 41

pharyngeal gill slits (far-in′je-al) *See* **gill slit.**

pharynx (far′inks) The passageway posterior to the mouth that is common to respiratory and digestive systems. 639

phasmid (faz-mid) Sensory pit on each side near the end of the tail of nematodes of the class Phasmidea. 310

phenotype (fe′no-tīp) The expression that results from an interaction of one or more gene pairs and the environment. 98

phenotypic ratio (fe′no-tip-ik) The relative numbers of progeny in each phenotypic category produced by a genetic cross. 99

pheromone (fer′o-mōn) A chemical secreted to the outside of the body by an organism and perceived (as by smell) by a second organism of the same species, releasing a specific behavior in the recipient. 188, 581

phonoreceptor (fo″no-re-sep′tor) A specialized nerve ending that responds to sound. 564

Phoronida (fo-ron-i-dah) A phylum of marine animals whose members live in permanent chitinous tubes in muddy, sandy, or solid substrates. Feed via an anterior lophophore with two parallel rings of long tentacles. 417

photoautotroph (fo′to-au′te-trōf) Organism that synthesizes organic matter using the energy of light. 210

photoreceptor (fo″to-re-sep′tor) A nerve ending that is sensitive to light energy. 564

pH scale The numerical scale that measures acidity and alkalinity, ranging from 0 (most acidic) to 14 (most basic); pH stands for potential hydrogen and refers to the concentration of hydrogen ions (H^+). 20

phyletic gradualism (fi-let′ik graj′oo-el-izm) The idea that evolutionary change occurs at a slow, constant pace over millions of years. 174

phylogenetic systematics (fi-lo-je-net′ik sis-tem′at-iks) The study of the phylogenetic relationships among organisms in which true and false similarities are differentiated; cladistics. 233

phylum (fi′lum) The level of classification between kingdom and class; members are considered a monophyletic assemblage derived from a single ancestor. 230

physiology The branch of science that deals with the function of living organisms. 16

Phytomastigophorea (fi′to-mas-ti-go-for′ah) The protozoan class where members usually have chloroplasts; mainly autotrophic, some heterotrophic. Examples: *Euglena, Volvox, Chlamydomonas.* 248

pia mater (pi′ah mā′ter) The innermost meninx that is in direct contact with the brain and spinal cord. 555

pilidium larva (pi-lid-e-um lar′va) Free-swimming, hat-shaped larva of nemertean worms characterized by an apical tuft of cilia. 301

pinacocyte (pin′ah-ko′sīt) Thin, flat cell covering the outer surface, and some of the inner surface, of poriferans. 265

pineal gland (pin′e-al) A small gland in the midbrain that converts a signal from the nervous system into an endocrine signal; also called the pineal body. 586, 592

pinfeather *See* **filoplume feather.**

pinocytosis (pin″o-si-to′sis) Cell-drinking; the engulfment into the cell of liquid and of dissolved solutes by way of small membranous vesicles. 40

pioneer community The first community to become established in an area. 208

pit organ Receptor of infrared radiation (heat) on the head of some snakes (pit vipers). 479, 572

pituitary gland (pi-tu′i-tar″e) Endocrine gland that is attached to the base of the brain and consists of anterior and posterior lobes; hypophysis. 586

placenta (plah-sen′tah) Structure by which an unborn child or animal is attached to its mother's uterine wall and through which it is nourished. 503, 685

placid (plac-id) Plates on Kinorhyncha. 309

Placozoa (plak′o-zo″ah) A phylum of small, flattened, marine animals that feed by forming a temporary digestive cavity. *Tricoplax adherans.* 285

planktonic (plangk′ton-ik) Small organisms that passively float or drift in a body of water. 221

Plantae (plant′a) One of the five kingdoms of life; characterized by being eukaryotic and multicellular, and having rigid cell walls and chloroplasts. 231

planula (plan′u-lah) A ciliated, free-swimming larva of most cnidarians. The planula develops following sexual reproduction and metamorphoses into a polyp. 273

plasma The fluid or liquid portion of circulating blood. 600

plasma cell A mature, differentiated B lymphocyte chiefly occupied with antibody synthesis and secretion; a plasma cell lives for only five to seven days. 602

plasma membrane Outermost membrane of a cell; its surface has molecular regions that detect changes in external conditions and act as a selective barrier to the passage of ions and molecules between the cell and its environment. The external covering of a protozoan. 30, 528

plastron (plas′tron) The ventral portion of the shell of a turtle. Formed from bones of the pectoral girdle and dermal bone. 471

plate tectonics (tek-ton′iks) The study of the movement of the earth's crustal plates. These movements are called continental drift. 162

platelet Cytoplasmic fragment formed in the bone marrow that functions in blood coagulation; **thrombocyte.** 602

Platyhelminthes (plat″e-hel-min′thez) The phylum of flatworms; bilateral acoelomates. 289

plerocercoid larva (ple″ro-ser′koid) Metacestode that develops from a procercoid larva; it usually shows little differentiation. 300

pneumatic sacs (noo-mat′ik saks) Gas-filled sacs that arise from the esophagus, or another part of the digestive tract, of fishes. Pneumatic sacs are used in buoyancy regulation (swim bladders) or gas exchange (lungs). 443

pneumostome (nu″mo′stōm) The outside opening of the gas exchange structure (lung) in land snails and slugs (Pulmonata). 612

Pogonophora (po′go-nof′e-rah) A phylum of protostomate, marine animals that are distributed throughout the world's oceans. Live in secreted, chitinous tubes in cold water at depths exceeding 100 m. Lack a mouth and digestive tract. Nutrients absorbed across the body wall and from endosymbiotic bacteria that they harbor. Beard worms. 360

point mutations A change in the structure of a gene that usually arises from the addition, deletion, or substitution of one or more nitrogenous bases. 125

polar covalent bond (po′-lar co-va′lent bond) The type of bond that is formed by asymmetrical moving electrons. 19

polyandrous (pol″e-an′drous) Having more than one male mate. Polyandry is advantageous when food is plentiful but, because of predation or other factors, the chances of successfully rearing young are low. 496

Polychaeta (pol″e-kēt′ah) The class of annelids whose members are mostly marine and are characterized by a head with eyes and tentacles and a body with parapodia. Parapodia bear numerous setae. Examples: *Nereis, Arenicola.* 345

polygenes (pol′e-gēnz) Genes at multiple loci that influence a trait in a quantitative fashion. 103

polygynous (pa-lij′a-nus) Having more than one female mate. Polygyny tends to occur in species whose young are relatively independent at birth or hatching. 496

polyp (pol′ip) The attached, usually asexual, stage of a cnidarian. 271

polyphyletic group (pol′e-fi-let′ik) An assemblage of organisms that includes multiple evolutionary lineages. Polyphyletic assemblages usually reflect insufficient knowledge regarding the phylogeny of a group of organisms. 231

Polyplacophora (pol′e-pla-kof′o-rah) The class of molluscs whose members are elongate, dorsoventrally flattened, and have a shell consisting of eight dorsal plates. 336

polyploidy (pol′e-ploi-de) Having more than two sets of chromosomes. 108

polysaccharide (pol″e-sak′ah-rid) A carbohydrate composed of many monosaccharide molecules joined together by dehydration synthesis reactions. 23

pons (ponz) A portion of the brain stem above the medulla oblongata and below the midbrain. 557

population A group of individuals of the same species that occupy a given area at the same time and share a unique set of genes. 166

population genetics The study of events occurring in gene pools. 166

Porifera (po-rif′er-ah) The animal phylum whose members are sessile and either asymmetrical or radially symmetrical. Body organized around a system of water canals and chambers. Cells are not organized into tissues or organs. Sponges. 264

porocytes (por′o-sītz) Tubular cells found in a sponge body wall that create a water channel to an interior chamber. 265

postanal tail (post-an′al) A tail that extends posterior to the anus; one of the four unique characteristics of chordates. 424

postmating isolation (post-mat′ing i′sah-la′shun) Isolation that occurs when fertilization is prevented even though mating has occurred. 173

potential energy The energy matter has, by virtue of its position; stored energy. 56

preadaptation (pre-a-dap-ta′shun) Occurs when a structure or a process present in members of a species proves useful in promoting reproductive success when an individual encounters new environmental situations. 368

precocial (pre-ko′shel) Having developed to a high degree of independence at the time of hatching or birth. 496

predation (pre-da′shun) The derivation of an organism of elements essential for its existence from organisms of other species that it consumes and destroys. The ingestion of prey by a predator for energy and nutrients. 627

preformation (pre-for-ma′shun) The erroneous idea that gametes contain miniaturized versions of all of the elements present in an adult. 134

premating isolation (pre-mat′ing i′sah-la′shun) When behaviors or other factors prevent animals from mating. 173

preoptic nuclei Neurons in the hypothalamus that produce various neuropeptides. 586

Priapulida (pri′a-pyu-lida) A phylum of aschelminths commonly called priapulids. 318

primary consumer A plant-eating animal (an herbivore) that obtains organic molecules by eating producers or their products. 56

primary germ layers Blocks or layers of embryonic cells that give rise to tissues and organs of animals. *See* **ectoderm, mesoderm,** and **endoderm.** 137

primary immune response The initial immune response following antigen exposure. 610

primary producer An autotrophic organism; able to build its own complex organic molecules from simple inorganic substances in the environment. 56

Primates The order of mammals whose members include humans, monkeys, apes, lemurs, and tarsiers. 504

primitive streak A medial thickening along the dorsal margin of an amniote embryo that forms during the migration of endodermal and mesodermal cells into the interior of the embryo. 144

principle of independent assortment One of Mendel's observations on the behavior of hereditary units during gamete formation. A modern interpretation of this principle is that genes carried in one chromosome are distributed to gametes without regard to the distribution of genes in nonhomologous chromosomes. 99

principle of segregation One of Mendel's observations on the behavior of hereditary units during gamete formation. A modern interpretation of the principle of segregation is that genes exist in pairs, and during gamete formation, members of a pair of genes are distributed into separate gametes. 97

procercoid larva (pro-ser'koid lar'va) Cestode developing from a coracidium in some orders; it usually has a posterior cercomer. Developmental stage between oncosphere and plerocercoid. 300

proglottid (pro-glot'id) One set of reproductive organs in a tapeworm strobila; usually corresponds to a segment. One of the linearly arranged segmentlike sections that make up the strobila of a tapeworm. 298

prokaryote (pro-kar'e-ōt) Single-celled organism that has no membrane-bound nucleus or other membrane-enclosed organelles (e.g., bacteria). 30

pronephros (pro-nef'res) Most anterior of three pairs of embryonic renal organs of vertebrates; functional only in larval amphibians and fishes, and in adult hagfishes; vestigial in mammalian embryos. 659

prophase (pro'fāz) The stage of mitosis during which the chromosomes become visible under a light microscope. The first stage of mitosis during which the chromosomes are condensed but not yet attached to a mitotic spindle. 84

proprioceptor (pro″pre-o-sep'tor) A sensory nerve terminal that gives information concerning movements and positions of the body; they occur chiefly in the muscles, tendons, and the labyrinth of the ear. 566

prosoma (pro'soma) A sensory, feeding, and locomotor tagma of chelicerate arthropods. 366

prostate gland (pros″tāt gland) Gland located around the male urethra below the urinary bladder that adds its secretions to seminal fluid during ejaculation. 675

prostomium (pro-stōm'e-um) A lobe lying in front of the mouth, as found in the Annelida. 345

protandrous (pro-tan'drus) *See* **protandry.**

protandry (pro-tan'dre) The condition in a monoecious organism in which male gonads mature before female gametes; prevents self-fertilization. 279

protein Nitrogen-containing organic compound composed of amino acid molecules joined together. 25

prothorax (pro'thor'aks) The first of the three thoracic segments of an insect; usually contains the first pair of walking appendages. 386

Protista (pro-tist'ah) The kingdom whose members are characterized by being eukaryotic and unicellular or colonial. 231

protogynous (pro-toj'i-nus) Hermaphroditism in which the female gonads mature before the male gonads. 672

proton (pro'ton) A positively charged particle found in the atomic nucleus. The mass of a proton is about 1840 times that of an electron. 16

protonephridium (pro'to-ne-frid'e-um) Primitive osmoregulatory or excretory organ composed of a tubule terminating internally with a flame bulb or solenocyte; the unit of a flame bulb system. Protonephridia are specialized for ultrafiltration. 291, 656

protopodite (pro'to-po'dīt) The basal segment of a biramous appendage of a crustacean. 373

protostome (pro'to-stōm″) Animal in which the embryonic blastopore becomes the mouth; often possesses a trochophore larva, schizocoelous coelom formation, and spiral embryonic cleavage. 322

protostyle (pro'to-stīl″) A rotating mucoid mass into which food is incorporated in the gut of a gastropod (phylum Mollusca). 328

protozoa (pro″to-zo'ah) A subkingdom (formerly a phylum) comprising the simplest organisms called protista; divided into seven phyla. 245

protozoologist (pro'to-zo'ol-o-jist) A person who studies protozoa. 247

proximal (proks'em-al) Toward the point of attachment of a structure on an animal (e.g., the hip is proximal to the knee). 238

pseudocoelom (soo″do-se'lom) A body cavity between the mesoderm and endoderm; a persistent blastocoele that is not lined with peritoneum. Also pseudocoel. 239

pseudocoelomate (soo″do-sēl'o-māt) Animals having a pseudocoelom, as the aschelminths. 305

pseudopodia (soo'dah-po'de-ah) Temporary cytoplasmic extensions of amoebas that are used in feeding and locomotion. 251, 538

Pterobranchia (ter'o-brang″ke-ah) The class of hemichordates whose members lack gill slits and have two or more arms. Colonial, living in externally secreted encasements. 423

pulmonary circuit (pul'mo-ner″e) The system of blood vessels from the right ventricle of the heart to the lungs, transporting deoxygenated blood and returning oxygenated blood from the lungs to the left atrium of the heart. 604

pulmonate lung The gas exchange structure in the Pulmonata—the land snails and slugs. 612

punctuated equilibrium model (pungk'choo-at'ed e'kwe-lib'riam mod'el) The idea that evolutionary change can occur rapidly over periods of thousands of years and that these periods of rapid change are interrupted by periods of constancy (stasis). 174

Punnett square A tool used by geneticists to help predict the results of a genetic cross. Different kinds of gametes produced by each parent are placed on each axis of the square. Combining gametes in the interior of the square gives the results of random fertilization. 98

pupa (pu'pa) A nonfeeding immature stage in the life cycle of holometabolous insects. It is a time of radical cellular changes that result in a change from the larval to the adult body form. 393

puparium (pu-par'e-um) A pupal case formed from the last larval exoskeleton. *See* **pupa.** 393

purine (pyoor'ēn) A nitrogen-containing organic compound that contributes to the structure of a DNA or RNA nucleotide; uric acid is also derived from purines. 118

Pycnogonida (pik'no-gon″i-dah) The class of chelicerate arthropods whose members have a reduced abdomen and four to six pairs of walking legs. Without special respiratory or excretory structures. Sea spiders. 372

pygostyle (pig'o-stīl) The fused posterior caudal vertebrae of a bird; helps support tail feathers that are important in steering. 488

pyramid of biomass A representation showing the total mass of living matter in each trophic level of an ecosystem. 213

pyramid of energy A representation showing the total energy in each trophic level of an ecosystem. 213

pyramid of numbers A representation showing the number of individuals in each trophic level of an ecosystem. 213

pyrenoid (pi′re-noid) Part of the chloroplast that synthesizes and stores polysaccharides. 248

pyrimidine (pi-rim′i-dēn) A nitrogen-containing organic compound that is a component of the nucleotides making up DNA and RNA. 118

Q

quantitative trait A genetic trait that is determined by multiple interacting loci, and for which there is a range of phenotypes between phenotypic extremes. 103

quark (qu-ark) A subatomic particle found in the nucleus of the atom. 16

R

radial symmetry A form of symmetry in which any plane passing through the oral-aboral axis divides an organism into mirror images. 237

radiation A form of energy that includes visible light, ultraviolet light, and X rays; means by which body heat is lost in the form of infrared rays. 649

radioisotope (ra″de-o-i′so-tōp) An isotope that is radioactive, i.e., one having an unstable nucleus, which gives it the property of decay by one or more of several processes. Also called a radioactive isotope. 17

radula (raj′oo-lah) The rasping, tonguelike structure of most molluscs that is used for scraping food; composed of minute chitinous teeth that move over a cartilaginous odontophore. 325

ram ventilation The movement of water across gills as a fish swims through the water with its mouth open. 443

range of optimum The range of values for a condition in the environment that is best able to support survival and reproduction of an organism. 194

receptor-mediated endocytosis (re-cep′tor me′de-at-ed en″do-si-to′sis) The type of endocytosis that involves a specific receptor on the plasma membrane that recognizes an extracellular molecule and binds with it. 41

recessive A gene whose expression is masked when it is present in combination with a dominant allele. 98

recombinant DNA (re′kom-be-nant d-n-a) The incorporation of DNA from one organism into that of another organism (usually a bacteria) so that the second organism produces a desired protein. 126

rectal gland The excretory organ of elasmobranchs and the coelacanth located near the rectum; it excretes a hyperosmotic salt solution. 660

red blood cell (erythrocyte) The type of blood cell that contains hemoglobin and no nucleus. During their formation in mammals, erythrocytes lose their nuclei; those of other vertebrates retain the nuclei. 601

redia (re′de-ah) A larval, digenetic trematode produced by asexual reproduction within a miracidium, sporocyst, or mother redia. 295

reduction The gain of electrons by a compound. 68

refractory period Time period following stimulation during which a neuron or muscle fiber will not respond to a stimulus. 550

regulator genes Genes that control the activity of other genes that code for enzymes or structural proteins. 125

releaser gland A gland in turbellarians that secretes a chemical that dissolves the attachment of the organism from a substrate. 289

Remipedia (re-mi-pe′de-ah) A class of crustaceans whose members possess about 30 body segments and uniform, biramous appendages. This class contains a single species of cave-dwelling crustaceans from the Bahamas. 364

renette (re′net) An excretory structure found in some worms. 312

repolarized The reestablishment of polarity, especially the return of plasma membrane potential to resting potential after depolarization. 550

reproductive isolation Occurs when individuals are prevented from mating, even though they may occupy overlapping ranges. *See* **premating** and **postmating isolation.** 173

Reptilia (rep-til′e-ah) The class of vertebrates whose members have dry skin with epidermal scales and amniotic eggs that develop in terrestrial environments. Snakes, lizards, and alligators. 422

resilin (rez′i lin) The elastic protein found in some arthropod joints that stores energy and functions in jumping. 534

respiratory pigment Organic compounds that have either metallic copper or iron with which oxygen combines. 618

respiratory tree A pair of tubules attached to the rectum of a sea cucumber that branch through the body cavity and function in gas exchange. 411

resting membrane potential The potential difference that results from the separation of charges along the plasma membrane of a neuron. 549

rete mirabile (re′te ma-rab′a-le) A network of small blood vessels arranged so that the incoming blood runs countercurrent to the outgoing blood and, thus, makes possible efficient exchange of heat or gases between the two bloodstreams. 651

reticulopodium (re-tik′u-lo-po′de-um) A pseudopodium that forms a threadlike branched mesh and contains axial microtubules. 251

rhabdite (rab′dīt) A rodlike structure in the cells of the epidermis or underlying parenchyma in certain tubellarians that are discharged in mucous secretions. 289

rhodopsin (ro-dop′sin) Light-sensitive substance that occurs in the rods of the retina; visual purple. 576

rhopalium (ro-pal′e-um) A sensory structure at the margin of the scyphozoan medusa. It consists of a statocyst and a photoreceptor (phylum Cnidaria). 276

rhynchocoel (ring′ko-sēl) In nemerteans, the fluid-filled coelomic cavity that contains the inverted proboscis. 301

ribonucleic acid (ri′bo-nuk″la-ik as′id) A single-stranded polymer of ribonucleotides; RNA is formed from DNA in the nucleus and carries a code for proteins to ribosomes where the proteins are synthesized; RNA. Contains the nitrogenous bases adenine (A), cytosine (C), guanine (G), and uracil (U). 27

ribosomal RNA (ri′bo-sōm″al r-n-a) A form of ribonucleic acid that makes up a portion of ribosomes. 121

ribosome (ri-bo-sōm) Cytoplasmic organelle that consists of protein and RNA, and functions in protein synthesis. 42

rod cell A type of light receptor that is responsible for color vision. 575

Rotifera (ro-tif′era) The phylum of aschelminths that has members with a ciliated corona surrounding a mouth; muscular pharynx (mastax) present with jawlike features; nonchitinous cuticle; parthenogenesis common; both freshwater and marine species. 306

r-selected Populations that are maintained below the carrying capacity of the environment. 199

S

saliva (sah-li'vah) The enzyme-containing secretion of the salivary glands. 638

saltatory conduction (sal'tah-tor-e kon-duk'shun) A type of nerve impulse conduction in which the impulse seems to jump from one neurofibril node to the next. 550

salt gland An orbital gland of many reptiles and birds that secretes a hyperosmotic NaCl or KCl solution an important osmoregulatory organ, especially for marine species. 663

Sarcodina (sar'ko-din'ah) The protozoan subphylum where members have pseudopodia for movement and food gathering; naked or with shell or test; mostly free living. 251

sarcolemma (sar'ko-lem'ah) The plasma membrane of a muscle fiber. 544

Sarcomastigophora (sar'ko-mas-ti-gof'o-rah) The protozoan phylum where members possess flagella, pseudopodia, or both for locomotion and feeding; single type of nucleus. 247

sarcomere (sar'ko-mer) The contractile unit of a myofibril. The repeating units, delimited by the Z bands along the length of the myofibril. 543

scale A thin, compacted, flaky fragment. 529

scalid (sca-lid) A set of complex spines found on the kinorhynchs, loriciferans, priapulans, and larval nematomorphs, with sensory, locomotor, food capture, or penetrant function. 309

scanning electron microscope The type of microscope in which an electron beam, instead of light, forms a three-dimensional image for viewing, allowing much greater magnification and resolution. 34

scanning tunneling microscope The type of microscope that uses a needle probe and electrons to determine the surface features of specimens. 34

Scaphopoda (ska-fop'o-dah) A class of molluscs whose members have a tubular shell that is open at both ends. Possess tentacles but no head. *Dentalium*. 337

scent gland A gland located around the feet, face, or anus of many mammals; secretes pheromones, which may be involved with defense, species and sex recognition, and territorial behavior. Musk gland. 506

schizogony (skiz-og'on-e) A form of fission involving multiple nuclear divisions and the

formation of many individuals from the parental organism. *See* **multiple fission.** 245

Schwann cell *See* **neurolemmocyte.**

scientific method A system of thought and procedure that reflects how a scientist goes about defining and studying a problem. 12

scolex (sko'leks) The attachment or holdfast organ of a tapeworm, generally considered the anterior end; it is used to adhere to the host. 298

scrotum (skro'tum) A pouch of skin that encloses the testes. 675

scyphistoma (si-fis'to-mah) The polyp stage of a scyphozoan (phylum Cnidaria); develops from a planula and produces ephyrae by budding. 276

Scyphozoa (si'fo-zo''ah) A class of cnidarians whose members have prominent medusae. Gametes are gastrodermal in origin and are released to the gastrovascular cavity. Nematocysts are present in the gastrodermis. Polyps are small. *Aurelia*. 275

sebaceous (oil) gland (se-ba'shus) Gland of the skin that secretes sebum; oil gland. 506, 531

sebum (se'bum) Oily secretion from the sebaceous gland. 531

Secernentea (ses-er-nen'te-a) The class of nematodes formerly called Phasmidea. Examples: *Ascaris, Enterobius, Necator, Wuchereria*. 310

secondary consumer An animal that preys on and eats a primary consumer. 56

secondary immune response The immune response that follows a second exposure to a specific antigen. 610

secondary palate A plate of bone that separates the nasal and oral cavities of mammals and some reptiles. 475

second law of thermodynamics Physical and chemical processes proceed in such a way that the entropy of the universe (the system and its surroundings) increases to the maximum possible. 56

segmentation (seg''men-ta'shun) (1) In many animal species, a series of body units that may be externally similar to, or quite different from, one another. (2) The oscillating back-and-forth movement in the small intestine that mixes food with digestive secretions and increases the efficiency of absorption. 638

Seisonidea (sy'son-id'ea) A class of rotifers containing members that are commensals of crustaceans; large and elongate body with rounded corona. Example: *Seison*. 307

selection pressure The tendency for natural selection to occur; natural selection occurs whenever some genotypes are more fit than other genotypes. 170

selective permeability (si-lek'tiv per''me-ah-bil'i-te) The ability of the plasma membrane to let some substances in and keep others out. 36

semen (se'men) The thick, whitish secretion of the reproductive organs in the male; composed of sperm and secretions from the prostate, seminal vesicles, and various other glands and ducts. 675

seminal receptacle (sem'i-nal ri-sep'tah-kel) A structure in the female reproductive system that stores sperm received during copulation (e.g., many insects and annelids). 352

seminal vesicle (sem'i-nal ves'i-kel) 1. One of the paired accessory glands of the reproductive tract of male mammals. It secretes the fluid medium for sperm ejaculation (phylum Chordata). 2. A structure associated with the male reproductive tract that stores sperm prior to its release (e.g., earthworms—phylum Annelida). 352, 675

seminiferous tubule (se''mi-nif'er-us tu'bul) The male duct that conveys semen. 675

sensilla (sen-cil'ah) Modifications of the exoskeleton of an arthropod that, along with nerve cells, form sensory receptors. 368, 563

sensory (afferent) neuron or **nerve** A neuron or nerve that conducts an impulse from a receptor organ to the central nervous system. 555

sequential hermaphroditism (si-kwen'shal her-maf'ro-di-tizm) The type of hermaphroditism that occurs when an animal is one sex during one phase of its life cycle and an opposite sex during another phase. 672

seral stage (ser'al) A successional stage in an ecosystem. 209

sere (ser) An entire successional sequence in an ecosystem (e.g., the sequence of stages in the succession of a lake to a climax forest). 209

serially homologous (ser'e-al-e ho-mol'o-ges) Metameric structures that have evolved from a common form; the biramous appendages of crustaceans are serially homologous. 374

serum (se'rum) The fluid portion of coagulated blood; the protein component of plasma. 600

seta (se′tah) Hairlike modifications of an arthropod's exoskeleton that may be set into a membranous socket. Displacement of a seta initiates a nerve impulse in an associated cell. 345

sex chromosome A chromosome that carries genes determining the genetic sex of an individual. 106

sex-influenced traits Traits that behave as if they are dominant in one sex but recessive in the other sex. 111

sexual reproduction The generation of a new cell or organism by the fusion of two haploid cells so that genes are inherited from each parent. 672

shell The calcium carbonate outer layer of cnidarians, molluscs, and other animals. Produced by mucous glands. 528

shivering thermogenesis (shiv-er-ing ther″mo-jen′e-sis) The generation of heat by shivering, especially within the animal body. 653

Simphyla (sim-fi′lah) A class of arthropods whose members are characterized by having long antennae, 10 to 12 pairs of legs, and centipedelike bodies. Occupy soil and leaf mold. 384

simple diffusion The process of molecules spreading out randomly from where they are more concentrated to where they are less concentrated until they are evenly distributed. 36

siphon (si′fon) A tubular structure through which fluid flows; siphons of some molluscs allow water to enter and leave the mantle cavity. 328

Sipuncula (sigh-pun′kyu-lah) A phylum of protostomate worms whose members burrow in soft marine substrates throughout the world's oceans. Range in length from 2 mm to 75 cm. Peanut worms. 360

sister chromatid (kro′mah-tid) One of the two identical parts of a duplicated chromosome in a eukaryotic cell. Sister chromatids consist of exact copies of a long coiled DNA molecule with associated proteins. Sister chromatids are joined at the centromere of a duplicated chromosome. 83

skeletal muscle Type of muscle tissue found in muscles attached to skeletal parts. 539

skin The outer integument or covering of an animal body, consisting of the dermis and the epidermis and resting on the subcutaneous tissues. 528

small intestine The part of the digestive system consisting of the duodenum, jejunum, and ileum. 640

smooth muscle Type of muscle tissue found in the walls of the hollow organs; visceral muscle. 539

society A stable group of individuals of the same species that maintains a cooperative social relationship. 190

sociobiology (so′se-o-bi-ol′o-je) The study of the evolution of social behavior. 182

sodium-potassium ATPase pump The active transport mechanism that functions to concentrate sodium ions on the outside of a plasma membrane and potassium ions on the inside of the membrane. 549

somatic cell (so-mat′ik) Ordinary body cell; pertaining to or characteristic of a body cell. Any cell other than a germ cell or germ-cell precursor. 88

somites (so′mītz) Segmental thickenings along the side of a vertebrate embryo that result from the development of mesoderm. 141

sonar (so′nar) or **biosonar** A system that uses sound at sonic or ultrasonic frequencies to detect and locate objects. 572

specialists Animals that are very efficient at utilizing a particular resource. 189

speciation (spe′she-a′shun) The process by which two or more species are formed from a single ancestral stock. 173

species A group of populations in which genes are actually, or potentially, exchanged through multiple generations; numerous problems with this definition make it difficult to apply in all circumstances. 172

species diversity *See* **community diversity.**

spermatogenesis (sper″mah-to-jen′e-sis) The production of sperm cells. 91

spermatophores (sper-mat″ah-fors) Encapsulated sperm that can be deposited on a substrate by a male and picked up by a female, or transferred directly to a female by a male. 336

sphincter (sfingk′ter) A ringlike band of muscle fibers that constricts a passage or closes a natural orifice. 638

spicules (spik′ulz) Skeletal elements secreted by some mesenchyme cells of a sponge body wall; may be made of calcium carbonate or silica. 267

spiracle (spi′rah-kel) An opening for ventilation. The opening(s) of the tracheal system of an arthropod or an opening posterior to the eye of a shark, skate, or ray. 368

spongin (spun′jin) A fibrous protein that makes up the supportive framework of some sponges. 267

sporocyst (spor′oo-sist) (1) Stage of development of a sporozoan protozoan, usually with an enclosing membrane, the oocyst. (2) An asexual stage of development in some digenean trematodes that arises from a miracidium and gives rise to rediae. 295

sporogony (spor-og-a-ne) Multiple fission that produces sporozoites after zygote formation. Occurs in the class Sporozoea. 254

stabilizing selection Natural selection that results in the decline of both extremes in a phenotypic range; results in a narrowing of the phenotypic range. 172

statocyst (stat″o-sist) An organ of equilibrium and balance found in many invertebrates. Statocysts usually consist of a fluid-filled cavity containing sensory hairs and a mineral mass called a statolith. The statolith stimulates the sensory hairs, which helps orient the animal with regard to the pull of gravity. 273, 563

statolith *See* **statocyst.**

steroid (ste′roid) An organic substance whose molecules include four complex rings of carbon and hydrogen atoms. Examples are estrogen, cholesterol, and testosterone. 25

stigma (stig′ma) The mass of bright red photoreceptor granules found in certain flagellated protozoa (Euglena) that serves as a shield for the photoreceptor. Also the spiracle of certain terrestrial arthropods. 248, 564

stimulus Any form of energy an animal is able to detect with its receptors. 562

stimulus filter (stim′ye-lus fil′ter) The ability of the nervous system to block incoming stimuli that are unimportant for the animal. 186

stomach The expansion of the alimentary canal between the esophagus and duodenum. 640

strobila (stro-bi′lah) The chain of proglottids constituting the bulk of the body of adult tapeworms. 298

structural genes Genes that code for enzymes or structural proteins rather than proteins that control the function of other genes. 125

substrate The substance or molecule upon which an enzyme acts. 58

substrate-level phosphorylation (sub′strāt level fos″for-i-la′shun) The generation of ATP by coupling strongly exergonic reactions with the synthesis of ATP from ADP and phosphate. 62

succession A sequence of community types that occurs during the maturation of an ecosystem. 208

sudoriferous gland (su″do-rif′er-us) A sweat gland. 506, 531

superior Above a point of reference (e.g., the neck is superior to the chest of humans). 238

suspension feeder The type of feeding whereby an animal obtains its nutrients by the removal of suspended food particles from the surrounding water by some sort of capturing, trapping, or filtering structure. 626

swim bladder A gas-filled sac, which is usually located along the dorsal body wall of bony fishes; it is an outgrowth of the digestive tract and regulates buoyancy of a fish. 426

sycon (si′kon) A sponge body form characterized by choanocytes lining radial canals. 267

symbiosis (sim″bi-o′sis) The biological association of two individuals or populations of different species, classified as mutualism, commensalism, or parasitism, depending on the advantage or disadvantage derived from the relationship. 202

symmetry (sim′i-tre) A balanced arrangement of similar parts on either side of a common point or axis. 237

sympathetic nervous system Portion of the autonomic nervous system that arises from the thoracic and lumbar regions of the spinal cord; also called thoracolumbar division. 558

sympatric speciation (sim′pat′rik spe′she-a′shun) Speciation that occurs in populations that have overlapping ranges. 174

symplesiomorphies (sim-ples′e-o-mor′fēz) Taxonomic characters that are common to all members of a group of organisms. These characters indicate common ancestry but cannot be used to describe relationships within the group. 234

synapomorphies (sin-ap′o-mor′fēz) Characters that have arisen within a group since it diverged from a common ancestor. Synapomorphies are used to indicate degrees of relatedness within a group. Also called shared, derived characters. 234

synapse (sin-aps) The junction between the axon end of one neuron and the dendrite or cell body of another neuron. 551

synapsis (si-nap′sis) The time in reduction division when the pairs of homologous chromosomes lie alongside each other in the first meiotic division. 88

synaptic cleft (si-nap′tik kleft) The narrow space between the terminal ending of a neuron and the receptor site of the postsynaptic cell. 551

synchronous flight *See* **direct flight.**

syncytial hypothesis (sin-sit′e-al hi-poth′e-sis) The idea that multicellular organisms could have arisen by the formation of cell boundaries within a large multinucleate protist. 262

syngamy (sin′ga-me) The fertilization of one gamete with another individual gamete to form a zygote; found in most animals that have sexual reproduction. 88

synsacrum (sin-sak′rum) The fused posterior thoracic vertebrae, all lumbar and sacral vertebrae, and anterior caudal vertebrae of a bird; helps maintain proper flight posture. 488

systematics The study of the classification and phylogeny of organisms. *See* **taxonomy.** 230

systemic circuit (sis-tem′ik) The portion of the circulatory system concerned with blood flow from the left ventricle of the heart to the entire body and back to the heart via the right atrium. 604

systole (sis′to-le) Phase of the cardiac cycle during which a heart chamber wall is contracted; also systolic pressure. 606

systolic pressure The portion of blood pressure measurement that represents the highest pressure reached during ventricular ejection; it is the first number shown in a blood pressure reading. 606

T

T cell A type of lymphocyte derived from bone marrow stem cells that matures into an immunologically competent cell under the influence of the thymus. T cells are involved in a variety of cell-mediated immune reactions; also known as a T lymphocyte. 602

tactile (touch) receptor (tak′til ri-sep′ter) A sensory receptor in the skin that detects light pressure; formerly called Meissner's corpuscle. 566, 572

tagmatization (tag′mah-ti-za″shun) The specialization of body regions of a metameric animal for specific functions. The head of an arthropod is specialized for feeding and sensory functions, the thorax is specialized for locomotion, and the abdomen is specialized for visceral functions. 344

Tardigrada (tar-di-gray′dah) A phylum of animals whose members live in marine and freshwater sediments and in water films on terrestrial lichens and mosses. Possess four pairs of unsegmented legs and a proteinaceous cuticle. Water bears. 400

target cell The cell influenced by a specific hormone. 581

taste bud The receptor organs located in the tongue that are stimulated and give rise to the sense of taste. 574

taxis (tak′sis) The movement of an organism in a particular direction in response to an environmental stimulus. 194

taxon (tak′son) A group of organisms that are genetically (evolutionarily) related. 230

taxonomy (tak′son′ah-me) The description of species and the classification of organisms into groups that reflect evolutionary relationships. *See* **phylogenetic systematics, evolutionary systematics,** and **numerical taxonomy.** Also **systematics.** 230

tegument (teg′u-ment) The external epithelial covering in cestodes, trematodes, and acanthocephalans; once called a cuticle. 294, 528

telophase (tel′o-fāz) Stage in mitosis during which daughter cells become separate structures; the two sets of separated chromosomes decondense, and become enclosed by nuclear envelopes. 86

temperate deciduous forest (tem′per-it di-sij′oo-es) An ecosystem that occurs in regions with moderate climate and well-defined seasons; deciduous trees predominate; animals include insects, white-tailed deer, and wolves. 218

tendon A cord or bandlike mass of white fibrous connective tissue that connects a muscle to a bone. 542

Tentaculata (ten-tak′u-lata) The class of ctenophorans with tentacles that may or may not be associated with sheaths into which tentacles can be retracted. *Pleurobranchia.* 281

territory An area defended by an animal. Territories are established to provide food, shelter, or reproductive space. 191

testcross A cross between an individual of an unknown genotype and an individual that is homozygous recessive for the trait in question in order to determine the unknown genotype. 99

test A shell or hardened outer covering, typically covered externally by cytoplasm or living tissue. 251

testis (tes′tis) Primary reproductive organ of a male; a sperm-cell producing organ. 675

testosterone (tes-tos′te-rōn) Male sex hormone secreted by the interstitial cells of the testes. 676

tetrad (tet′rad) A pair of homologous chromosomes during synapsis (prophase I of meiosis). A tetrad consists of four chromatids. 88

tetrapods (te′trah-podz) A nontaxonomic designation used to refer to amphibians, reptiles, birds, and mammals. 452

Thaliacea (tal′e-as″e-ah) A class of urochordates whose members are planktonic. Adults are tailless and barrel shaped. Oral and atrial openings are at opposite ends of the tunicate. Water currents are produced by muscular contractions of the body wall and result in a weak form of jet propulsion. 422

thalamus (thal′ah-mus) An oval mass of gray matter within the diencephalon that serves as a sensory relay area. 557

theory A generalized statement that accounts for a body of facts. 13

theory of evolution by natural selection A theory conceived by Charles Darwin and Alfred Russell Wallace on how some evolutionary changes occur. 154

theory of inheritance of acquired characteristics The mistaken idea that organisms develop new organs, or modify existing organs as environmental problems present themselves, and that these traits are passed on to offspring. 154

thermoconformer (ther″mo-con′form-er) To conform to the temperature of one's external environment. 650

thermodynamics (ther″mo-di-nam′iks) The branch of science that deals with heat, energy, and the interconversion of these; the study of energy transformations. 56

thermogenesis (ther′mo-jen′a-sis) The generation of heat by muscle contraction. 653

thermoreceptor (ther″mo-re-sep′tor) A sensory receptor that is sensitive to changes in temperature; a heat receptor. 566

thermoregulation (ther″mo-reg″u-la′shun) Heat regulation. 648

thrombocyte See **platelet**. 602

thymus gland (thi-mus) A ductless mass of flattened lymphoid tissue situated behind the top of the sternum; it forms antibodies in the newborn and is involved in the development of the immune system. 595

thyroid gland (thi′roid) An endocrine gland located in the neck and involved with the metabolic functions of the body. 593

tissue (tish′u) A group of similar cells that performs a specialized function. 48

tolerance range The range of variation in an environmental parameter that is compatible with the life of an organism. 194

tonicity (to-nis′i-te) The state of tissue tone or tension; in body fluid physiology, the effective osmotic pressure equivalent. 37

tornaria (tor-nar′iah) The ciliated larval stage of an acorn worm (class Enteropneusta, phylum Hemichordata). 422

torpor A time of decreased metabolism and lowered body temperature that occurs in daily activity cycles. 195

torsion (tor′shun) A developmental twisting of the visceral mass of a gastropod mollusc that results in an anterior opening of the mantle cavity and a twisting of nerve cords and the digestive tract. 326

tracheae (tra′che-e) The small tubes that carry air from spiracles through the body cavity of an arthropod; arthropod tracheae are modifications of the exoskeleton. 368

tracheal system See **tracheae**.

tract A bundle of nerve fibers within the central nervous system. 555

transcription (tran-skrip′shun) The formation of a messenger RNA molecule that carries the genetic code from the nucleus to the cytoplasm of a cell. 121

transducer A receptor that converts one form of energy into another. 562

transfer RNA (trans′fer r-n-a) A single-stranded polyribonucleotide that carries amino acids to a ribosome and positions those amino acids by matching the tRNA anticodon with the messenger RNA codon. 121

transgenic (tranz-gen′ik) An animal that develops from a cell that received a foreign gene. 129

translation (trans-la′shun) The production of a protein based on the code in messenger RNA. 121

translocation (trans-lo-ka′shun) The movement of a segment of one chromosome to a nonhomologous chromosome. 115

transmission electron microscope The type of microscope that produces highly magnified images of ultrathin tissue sections or other specimens. 34

Trematoda (trem′a-to′da) The class of platyhelminthes that has members that are all parasitic; several holdfast devices present; have complicated life cycles involving both sexual and asexual reproduction. 293

trichinosis (trik″i-no′sis) A disease resulting from infection by *Trichinella spiralis* (Nematoda) larvae by eating undercooked meat; characterized by muscular pain, fever, edema, and other symptoms. 315

trichocysts (trik′o-sists) An anchoring structure present in the ectoplasm of some ciliates. A bottle-shaped extrusible organelle of the ciliate pellicle. 256

Trilobitamorpha (tri″lo-bit′a-mor′fah) The subphylum of arthropods whose members had bodies divided into three longitudinal lobes. Head, thorax, and abdomen present. One pair of antennae and biramous appendages. Entirely extinct. 365

triploblastic (trip′lo-blas″tik) Animals whose body parts are organized into layers that are derived embryologically from three tissue layers: ectoderm, mesoderm, and endoderm. Platyhelminthes and all coelomate animals are triploblastic. 239

trochophore larva (trok″o-for lar′va) A larval stage characteristic of many molluscs, annelids, and some other protostomate animals. 322

trophic levels (trōf′ik lev′elz) The feeding level of an organism in an ecosystem; green plants and other autotrophs function at producer trophic levels; animals function at the consumer trophic levels. 209

tropical rain forest An ecosystem characterized by very high rainfall and temperatures between 20 and 25° C; very diverse life-forms; broad-leaved, nondeciduous trees; highly stratified forest. 220

tube feet Muscular projections from the water-vascular system of echinoderms that are used in locomotion, gas exchange, feeding, and attachment. 403

tubular nerve cord A hollow nerve cord that runs middorsally along the back of chordates; one of four unique chordate characteristics; also called the neural tube and, in vertebrates, the spinal cord. 424

tundra An ecosystem that exists in far northern reaches of North America or at high altitudes; mosses, lichens, grasses, and shrubs predominate; rodents, musk-oxen, caribou, owls, foxes, and weasels are common. 217

Turbellaria (tur'bel-lar'e-a) The class of Platyhelminthes that has members that are mostly free living and aquatic; external surface usually ciliated; predaceous; possess rhabdites; protrusable proboscis; mostly hermaphroditic. Examples: *Convoluta, Notoplana, Dugesia.* 289

tympanal (tympanic) organs (tim-pan'al) Auditory receptors present on the abdomen or legs of some insects. 389, 564

U

ultimobranchial gland (ul-ti'mo-bronk-e-el) In jawed fishes, primitive tetrapods, and birds, the small gland(s) that forms ventral to the esophagus; produces the hormone calcitonin that helps regulate calcium concentrations. 587

umbilical cord (um-bil'i-kal) Cordlike structure that connects the fetus to the placenta. 685

umbo (um'bo) The rounded prominence at the anterior margin of the hinge of a bivalve (Mollusca) shell; it is the oldest part of the shell. 329

unicellular (cytoplasmic) organization The life-form in which all functions are carried out within the confines of a single plasma membrane; members of the kingdom Protista display unicellular organization; also called **cytoplasmic organization.** 238

uniformitarianism (yoo'nah-for'mi-tar'e-an-ism) The idea that today the earth is shaped by forces of wind, rain, rivers, volcanoes, and geological uplift, just as it was formed in the past. 157

Uniramia (yoo'ne-ram'eah) The subphylum of arthropods whose members are characterized by a head with one pair of antennae and one pair of mandibles. All appendages are uniramous. 382

ureotelic excretion (u"re-o-tel'ik) Having urea as the chief excretory product of nitrogen metabolism; occurs in mammals. 660

ureter (u-re'ter) The tube which conveys urine from the kidney to the bladder. 667

urethra (u-re'thrah) The tube which conveys urine from the bladder to the exterior of the body. 667

uricotelic excretion (u"ri-ko-tel'ik) Having uric acid as the chief excretory product of nitrogen metabolism; occurs in reptiles and birds. 660

urinary bladder (u'ri-ner"e) The storage organ for urine. 667

Urochordata (u'ro-kor-dat'ah) The subphylum of chordates whose members have all four chordate characteristics as larvae. Adults are sessile or planktonic and enclosed in tunic that usually contains cellulose. Sea squirts or tunicates. 424

urophysis (u"ro-phy-sis) A discrete structure in the spinal cord of the fish tail that produces neuropeptides that help control water and ion balance, blood pressure, and smooth muscle contractions. 586

uterine tube (u'ter-in) The tube that leads from the ovary to the uterus; also called **fallopian tube.** 678

uterus (u'ter-us) The hollow muscular organ in female mammals in which the fertilized ovum normally becomes embedded and in which the developing embryo and fetus is nourished. 680

V

vaccine A preparation of either killed microorganisms; living, weakened (attenuated) microorganisms; or inactivated bacterial toxins (toxoids); administered to induce development of the immune response and protect the individual against a pathogen or toxin. 608

vagina (vah-ji'nah) Tubular organ that leads from the uterus to the vestibule of the female reproductive tract. 680

valves 1. Devices that permit a one-way flow of fluids through a vessel or chamber. 2. The halves of a bivalve (Mollusca) shell. 329

vegetal pole The lower pole of an egg; usually more dense than the animal pole because it contains more yolk. 137

vein A vessel that carries blood toward the heart. 603

veliger larva (vel'i-jer lar'va) The second free-swimming larval stage of many molluscs; develops from the trochophore and forms rudiments of the shell, visceral mass, and head-foot before settling to the substrate and undergoing metamorphosis. 329

ventral The belly of an animal; usually the lower surface; synonymous with anterior for animals that walk upright. 238

venule (ven'ul) A small blood vessel that collects blood from a capillary bed and joins a vein. 603

Vertebrata (ver'te-bra'tah) The subphylum of chordates whose members are characterized by cartilaginous or bony vertebrae surrounding a nerve cord. The skeleton is modified anteriorly into a skull for protection of the brain. 422

vestigial structures (ve-stij'e-al) Visible evidence of a structure that was present in an earlier stage in the evolution of an organism. One of the sources of evidence for evolution. 6

vibrissa (vi-bris'ah) A long coarse hair, such as those occurring about the nose (muzzle) of an animal such as a dog or cat. 572

villus (vil'us) Tiny, fingerlike projection that extends outward from the inner lining of the small intestine. 640

visceral arches *See* **gill arches.**

visceral mass (vis'er-al mas) The region of a mollusc's body that contains visceral organs. 325

vitamin An organic substance other than a carbohydrate, lipid, or protein that is needed for normal metabolism but cannot be synthesized in adequate amounts by the body. 624

viviparous (vi-vip'er-us) Having eggs that develop within the female reproductive tract and are nourished by the female. 370

voluntary (somatic) nervous system That part of the nervous system that relays commands to skeletal muscles. 555

vomeronasal organ *See* **Jacobson's organ.**

vulva (vul'vah) The external genital organs in the female. 680

W

water-vascular system (wah'ter vas'ku-lar) A series of water-filled canals and muscular tube feet present in echinoderms; provides the basis for locomotion, food gathering, and attachment. 403, 540

white blood cell (leukocyte) A type of blood cell involved with body defenses. 601

winter sleep A period of inactivity in which a mammal's body temperature remains near normal and the mammal is easily aroused. 196, 514

work The exertion or effort that is needed to accomplish something. 56

Y

yolk plug The large yolk-filled cells that protrude from beneath the ectoderm at the blastopore of the amphibian gastrula. 141

yolk sac The stored food reserve (yolk) and its surrounding membranes, which is found in embryonic reptiles, birds, and mammals. 144

Z

zonite (zo-nīt) The individual body unit of a member of the phylum Kinorhyncha. 309

zooid (zo-oid) An individual member of a colony of animals, such as colonial cnidarians and ectoprocts, produced by incomplete budding. 292

zoology (zo-ol′-o-je) The study of animals. 4

Zoomastigophorea (zo′o-mas-ti-go-for′ah) The protozoan class where members lack chloroplasts; heterotrophic or saprozoic. Examples: *Trypanosoma, Trichonympha, Trichomonas, Giardia.* 249

zooxanthellae (zo′o-zan-thel″e) A group of dinoflagellates that live in mutualistic relationships with some cnidarians. They promote high rates of calcium carbonate deposition in coral reefs. 279

zygote (zi′gōt) Diploid cell produced by the fusion of an egg and sperm; fertilized egg cell. 88

PHOTOS

Part Openers

1 Main: © Gregory G. Dimijian/Photo Researchers, Inc.; **1 Inset:** Photo Courtesy of Digital Stock Images, Undersea Life CD; **2 Main:** © K.G. Murti/Visuals Unlimited; **2 Inset:** Photo Courtesy of Digital Stock Images, Animals CD; **3 Main:** © K.H. Switak/Photo Researchers, Inc.; **3 Inset:** Photo Courtesy of Digital Stock Images, Undersea Life CD; **4 Main:** © Rod Planck/Tom Stack & Associates; **4 Inset:** Photo Courtesy of Digital Stock Images, Animals CD; **5 Main:** © Dave B. Fleetham/Tom Stack & Associates; **5 Inset:** Photo Courtesy of Digital Stock Images, Undersea Life CD; **6 Main:** © Kevin Schaefer/Martha Hill/Tom Stack & Associates; **6 Inset:** Photo Courtesy of Digital Stock Images, Animals CD

Chapter 1

Opener: Photo Courtesy of Digital Stock Images, Undersea Life CD; **1.1:** © Ron Austing/Photo Researchers, Inc.; **1.3a:** © Renee Lynn/Photo Researchers, Inc.; **1.3b:** © Gerald and Buff Corsi/Tom Stack & Associates; **1.5:** © Sinclair Stammers/SPL/Photo Researchers, Inc.; **1.8 a,b:** © Stephen Dalton/Animals Animals/Earth Scenes; **1.9a:** © Doug Wechsler/Animals Animals/Earth Scenes; **1.9b:** © Dr. Nigel Smith/Animals Animals/Earth Scenes

Chapter 2

Opener: Photo Courtesy of Digital Stock Images, Undersea Life CD; **2.16c:** © Ken Edward/Science Source/Photo Researchers, Inc.

Chapter 3

Opener: Photo courtesy of Digital Stock Images, Undersea Life CD; **Box 3.2e:** © Ed Reschke/Peter Arnold, Inc.; **Box 3.2f, Box 3.2g, 3.11 a-c:** © David M. Phillips/Visuals Unlimited; **3.18a:** Dr. Keith Porter; **3.24 a,b:** © Ed Reschke; **3.23:** © K. G. Murti/Visuals Unlimited; **3.24c:** © Manfred Kage/Peter Arnold, Inc.; **3.24d:** © Ed Reschke; **3.24e:** © Fred Hossler/Visuals Unlimited; **3.24 f-k:** © John D. Cunningham/Visuals Unlimited; **3.24l:** © Victor B. Eichler, Ph.D.; **3.24m:** © Ed Reschke; **3.24n:** © Manfred Kage/Peter Arnold, Inc.; **3.24o, 3.24p:** © Ed Reschke; **3.24q:** © Manfred Kage/Peter Arnold, Inc.

Chapter 4

Opener: Photo Courtesy of Digital Stock Images, Undersea Life CD

Chapter 5

Opener: Photo Courtesy of Digital Stock Images, Undersea Life CD

Chapter 6

Opener: Photo Courtesy of Digital Stock Images, Animals CD; **6.5 a,b:** © John D. Cunningham/Visuals Unlimited; **6.5 c,d:** © John D. Cunningham/Visuals Unlimited; **6.9a:** Courtesy of Dr. James Kezer

Chapter 7

Opener: Photo Courtesy of Digital Stock Images, Animals CD; **7.1:** © William E. Ferguson

Chapter 8

Opener: Photo Courtesy of Digital Stock Images, Animals CD; **8.1a:** From D. Olins, A. Olins, "Nucleosomes: The Structural Quantum in Chromosomes," *American Scientist*, 66: Nov. 1978.; **8.5a:** © Hans Reinhard/OKAPIA/Photo Researchers, Inc.; **8.5b (both):** From Wilson and Foster, *Williams Textbook of Endocrinology* 7th ed. © W.B. Saunders 1985; **8.7b:** © CNRI/SPL/Photo Researchers, Inc.

Chapter 9

Opener: Photo Courtesy of Digital Stock Images, Animals CD; **9.10a:** © Visuals Unlimited; **9.10 b-e:** © Dan McCoy/Rainbow; **9.11 a-c:** © David Dressler, Huntington Potter/Life Magazine, Time Warner Inc.

Chapter 10

Opener: Photo Courtesy of Digital Stock Images, Animals CD; **10.2a:** Courtesy Dr. E. William Byrd; **10.2b:** Courtesy Dr. Gerlad Schatten; **10.2c:** From M.J. Tegner, "Sea Urchin Sperm: Eggs Instruction Studied with The Scanning Electron Microscope," *Science* 179:685, Feb. 1973. © 1973 by the AAAS.; **10.2d:** From M.J. Tegner, "Sea Urchin Sperm: Eggs Instruction Studied with The Scanning Electron Microscope," *Science* 179:685, Feb. 1973. © 1973 by the AAAS.; **10.6 a-h:** © Carolina Biological/Visuals Unlimited; **10.6i:** © David M. Phillips/Visuals Unlimited; **10.8a:** © Bill Beatty/Visuals Unlimited; **10.8b:** © Carolina Biological/Visuals Unlimited; **10.9 a-d:** © Carolina Biological/Visuals Unlimited; **10.9e:** © Nathan Cohen/Visuals Unlimited; **10.9f:** © Joe McDonald/Visuals Unlimited

Chapter 11

Opener: Photo Courtesy of Digital Stock Images, Undersea Life CD; **11.2a:** © Walt Anderson/Visuals Unlimited; **11.2b:** © Joe McDonald/Visuals Unlimited; **11.4a:** © Alan L. Deitrick/Photo Researchers, Inc.; **11.4b:** © Walt Anderson/Visuals Unlimited

Chapter 12

Opener: Photo Courtesy of Digital Stock Images, Undersea Life CD; **12.2a:** © Don W. Fawcett/Visuals Unlimited; **12.3:** © Kevin Schafer/Tom Stack & Associates; **12.5 a,b:** © Michael Tweedie/Photo Researchers, Inc.

Chapter 13

Opener: Photo Courtesy of Digital Stock Images, Animals CD; **13.1 a-d:** Courtesy of Prof. Dr. Eibl-Eibesfeldt; **13.2c:** © Nina Leen, Life Magazine/Time Inc.; **13.4:** © Richard Wood/The Picture Cube; **13.5b:** © Tom McHugh/Photo Researchers, Inc.; **13.6:** © C.P. Hickman/Visuals Unlimited; **13.7:** © Mitch Reardon/Photo Researchers, Inc.; **13.8:** © Dwight Kuhn; **13.10:** © Gerard Lacz/Peter Arnold, Inc.

Chapter 14

Opener: Photo Courtesy of Digital Stock Images, Animals CD; **14.8a:** © Robert C. Simpson/Tom Stack & Associates; **14.8b:** © S. Maslowski/Visuals Unlimited; **14.8c:** © Ron Austing/Photo Researchers, Inc.; **14.8d:** © Johann Schumacher/Peter Arnold, Inc.; **14.8e:** © S. Maslowski/Visuals Unlimited; **14.9:** © Anthony Mercieca/ Photo Researchers, Inc.; **14.10a:** © Daniel W. Gotshall/Visuals Unlimited; **14.10b:** © Marty Snyderman/Visuals Unlimited; **14.11:** © E.R. Degginer/Color-Pic, Inc.; **14.12:** © Paul Oppler/Visuals Unlimited

Chapter 15

Opener: Photo Courtesy of Digital Stock Images, Animals CD; **15.2a:** © Richard Thom/Visuals Unlimited; **15.2b:** © Tom Ulrich/Visuals Unlimited; **15.2c:** © Joe McDonald/Visuals Unlimited; **Box 15.1b:** © Science VU/WHOI, J. Edward/Visuals Unlimited; **15.9, 15.10:** © Steve McCutcheon/Visuals Unlimited; **15.11:** © Tom Edwards/Visuals Unlimited; **15.12:** © Richard Thom/Visuals Unlimited; **15.13:** © Ron Spomer/Visuals Unlimited; **15.14:** © Glenn M. Oliver/Visuals Unlimited; **15.15:** © Kjell Sandved; **15.16, 15.18:** © Dwight Kuhn; **15.20:** © Walt Anderson/Visuals Unlimited

Chapter 16

Opener: Photo Courtesy of Digital Stock Images, Undersea Life CD; **16.1:** © Kevin Schafer/Martha Hill/Tom Stack & Associates; **16.6:** © Daniel W. Gotshall/Visuals Unlimited; **16.7:** © Dave B. Fleetham/Visuals Unlimited

Chapter 17

Opener: Photo Courtesy of Digital Stock Images, Undersea Life CD; **17.1:** © David John/Visuals Unlimited; **17.5 a-d:** © Dennis Diener/Visuals Unlimited; **17.6:** © Terry Hazen/Visuals Unlimited; **17.8a:** © James W. Richards/Visuals Unlimited; **Box 17.1:** Courtesy of Dr. Stanley Erlandsen; **17.9b:** © John D. Cunningham/Visuals Unlimited; **17.11a:** © M. Abbey/Visuals Unlimited; **17.13:** © A.M. Siegelman/Visuals Unlimited; **17.14a:** © M. Schliwa/Visuals Unlimited; **17.14b:** © G. Shih - R. Kessel/Visuals Unlimited; **17.17a:** © Karl Auffderheide/Visuals Unlimited; **17.18:** © M. Abbey/Visuals Unlimited; **17.19:** © Biophoto Associates/Photo Researchers, Inc.; **17.20:** © D.J. Patterson/OSF/Animals Animals/Earth Scenes

Chapter 18

Opener: Photo Courtesy of Digital Stock Images, Undersea Life CD; **18.1:** © John D. Cunningham/Visuals Unlimited; **18.4a:** © Nancy Sefton/Photo Researchers, Inc.; **18.4b:** © Daniel W. Gotshall/Visuals Unlimited; **Box 18.1:** Field Museum of Natural History Neg. #80872, Chicago; **18.6, 18.13a:** © Carolina Biological/Visuals Unlimited; **18.14a:** © Edward Hodgson/Visuals Unlimited; **18.14b:** © N. G. Daniel/Tom Stack & Associates; **18.17:** © Neville Coleman/Visuals Unlimited; **18.18a:** © Daniel W. Gotshall/Visuals Unlimited; **18.18b:** © Milton H. Tierney, Jr./Visuals Unlimited; **18.21a:** © Daniel W. Gotshall/Visuals Unlimited; **18.21b:** © Marty Snyderman/Visuals Unlimited; **Box 18.2:** © Edward Hodgson/Visuals Unlimited; **18.22a:** © R. De Goursey/Visuals Unlimited

Endpaper 1

1: © Tom J. Ulrich/Visuals Unlimited

Chapter 19

Opener: Photo Courtesy of Digital Stock Images, Undersea Life CD; **19.1:** © Gary R. Robinson/Visuals Unlimited; **19.17b:** © Drs. Kessel & Shih/Peter Arnold, Inc.

Chapter 20

Opener: Photo Courtesy of Digital Stock Images, Undersea Life CD; **20.1:** © Lauritz Jensen/Visuals Unlimited; **20.4a:** © Peter Parks/OSF/Animals Animals/Earth Scenes; **20.5a:** © Cabisco/Visuals Unlimited; **20.14b:** Steve Miller (author); **20.15:** © Science VU-AFIP/Visuals Unlimited; **20.17:** © R. Calentine/Visuals Unlimited; **20.18b:** © Lauritz Jensen/Visuals Unlimited

Chapter 21

Opener: Photo Courtesy of Digital Stock Images, Undersea Life CD; **21.1:** © Gary Miburn/Tom Stack & Associates; **21.6b:** © Science VU-Polaroid/Visuals Unlimited; **21.8a:** © William J. Weber/Visuals Unlimited; **21.9a:** © OSF/Animals Animals/Earth Scenes; **21.9b:** © Daniel W. Gotshall/Visuals Unlimited; **Box 21.1:** © Scott Camazine/Photo Researchers, Inc.; **21.15c:** © Ed Reschke; **21.17a:** © William E. Ferguson; **21.17b:** © Michael Di Spezio; **21.21a:** © Robert A. Ross; **21.22:** © Kjell B. Sandved/Photo Researchers, Inc.; **21.24:** © James Culter/Visuals Unlimited

Chapter 22

Opener: Photo Courtesy of Digital Stock Images, Undersea Life CD; **22.1:** © Marty Snyderman/Visuals Unlimited; **22.5:** © R. DeGoursey/Visuals Unlimited; **Box 22.1:** © C. P. Hickman/Visuals Unlimited

Endpaper 2

2: © WHOI/D. Foster/Visuals Unlimited

Chapter 23

Opener: Photo Courtesy of Digital Stock Images, Undersea Life CD; **23.1:** © Roger Klocek/Visuals Unlimited; **23.6:** © John Cancalosi/Tom Stack & Associates; **23.8a:** © Francois Gohier/Photo Researchers, Inc.; **23.11a:** © Tom McHugh/Photo Researchers, Inc.; **23.13:** © Ken Highfill/Photo Researchers, Inc.; **23.14:** © David Scharf/Peter Arnold, Inc.; **Box 23.1a:** © S. Masiowski/Visuals Unlimited; **Box 23.1b:** © Richard Walters/Visuals Unlimited; **23.15a:** © R. Calentine/Visuals Unlimited; **23.15b:** © Scott Camazine/Photo Researchers, Inc.; **23.16:** © Frank T.Awbrey/Visuals Unlimited; **23.18:** © Andrew J. Martinez/Photo Researchers, Inc.; **23.21a:** © John D. Cunningham/Visuals Unlimited; **23.21b:** © Biophoto Assoc./Photo Researchers, Inc.; **23.22a:** © David M. Dennis/Tom Stack & Associates; **23.22b:** © Alan Desbonnet/Visuals Unlimited; **23.23:** © James Bell/Photo Researchers, Inc.; **23.24b:** © Tom Stack/Tom Stack & Associates

Chapter 24

Opener: Photo Courtesy of Digital Stock Images, Undersea Life CD; **24.1:** © Patti Murray/Animals Animals/Earth Scenes; **24.3a:** © Bill Beatty/Visuals Unlimited; **24.3b:** © Glenn M. Oliver/Visuals Unlimited; **24.10a:** © S.L. Flegler/Visuals Unlimited; **24.14a:** © Treat Davidson/Photo Researchers, Inc.

Endpaper 3

1: © Tom J. Ulrich/Visuals Unlimited; **2:** Photomicrograph by John Ubelaker; **3:** Courtesy Diane R. Nelson, Ph.D.

Chapter 25

Opener: Photo Courtesy of Digital Stock Images, Undersea Life CD; **25.1:** © Carl Roessler/Tom Stack & Associates; **25.3a:** © Michael DiSpezio; **Box 25.1:** © Daniel W. Gotshall/Visuals Unlimited; **25.8a:** © Robert L. Dunne/Photo Researchers, Inc.; **25.8b:** © Harold W. Pratt/Biological Photo Service; **25.10a:** © C. McDaniel/Visuals Unlimited; **25.10b:** © Bruce Iverson/Visuals Unlimited; **25.12:** © Daniel W. Gotshall/Visuals Unlimited; **25.16:** Courtesy of the Museum of New Zealand Te Papa Tongarewa, Alan N. Baker, photographer

Endpaper 4

2: © John D. Cunningham/Visuals Unlimited; **3:** © Daniel W. Gotshall/Visuals Unlimited

Chapter 26

Opener: Photo Courtesy of Digital Stock Images, Undersea Life CD; **26.1:** © Michael DiSpezio; **Box 26.1:** © Gary R.Robinson/Visuals Unlimited; **26.6a:** © William C. Jorgenson/Visuals Unlimited; **26.6b:** © Daniel W. Gotshall/Visuals Unlimited

Chapter 27

Opener: Photo Courtesy of Digital Stock Images, Undersea Life CD; **27.1:** © Albert Copley/Visuals Unlimited; **27.5:** © Russ Kinne/Photo Researchers, Inc.; **27.8a:** © Ed Robinson/Tom Stack & Associated; **27.8 b,c:** © Daniel W. Gotshall/Visuals Unlimited; **27.9a:** © Science VU/NOAA/Visuals Unlimited; **Box 27.1:** © Roger Klocek/Visuals Unlimited; **27.10:** © John D. Cunningham/Visuals Unlimited; **27.11:** © Tom Stack/Tom Stack & Associates; **27.12 a,b:** © Patrice Ceisel/Visuals Unlimited; **27.13a:** © R. DeGoursey/Visuals Unlimited; **27.13b:** © Fred Rohde/Visuals Unlimited; **27.13c:** © Patrice Ceisel/Visuals Unlimited; **27.15b:** © Fred Hossler/Visuals Unlimited; **27.17b:** © Tom McHugh/Photo Researchers, Inc.; **27.18, 27.20:** © Daniel W. Gotshall/Visuals Unlimited

Chapter 28

Opener: Photo Courtesy of Digital Stock Images, Undersea Life CD; **28.1:** © Joe McDonald/Visuals Unlimited; **28.4:** © John D. Cunningham/Visuals Unlimited; **28.5 a,b:** © Dwight Kuhn; **28.5c:** © Joel Arrington/Visuals Unlimited; **28.6:** © Tom McHugh/Photo Researchers, Inc.; **28.7:** © John Serrao/Visuals Unlimited; **Box 28.1:** © Dennis Paulson/Visuals Unlimited; **28.15a:** © Nada Pecnik/Visuals Unlimited; **28.15b:** © Edward S. Ross; **28.16b:** © Dan Kline/Visuals Unlimited; **28.17:** © M.J. Tyler, The University of Adelaide, South Australia; **28.18 a-d:** © Jane Burton/Bruce Coleman, Inc.

Chapter 29

Opener: Photo Courtesy of Digital Stock Images, Undersea Life CD; **29.1:** © E.R. Degginger/Photo Researchers, Inc.; **29.5:** © Valorie Hodgson/Visuals Unlimited; **29.6:** © Nathan W. Cohen/Visuals Unlimited; **29.7:** © Joe McDonald/Visuals Unlimited; **29.8:** © Thomas Gula/Visuals Unlimited; **29.9:** © John D. Cunningham/Visuals Unlimited; **29.11:** © Stephen Dalton/Animals Animals/Earth Scenes; **29.12a:** © Joe McDonald/Visuals Unlimited; **29.14:** © Carolina Biological/Visuals Unlimited; **29.15:** © Robert Hermes/Photo Researchers, Inc.

Chapter 7

Chapter 8

Chapter 9

Chapter 10

Chapter 11

Chapter 12

Chapter 13

Chapter 15

Chapter 16

Chapter 17

Chapter 18

Endpaper 1

Chapter 19

Chapter 22

Chapter 24

Chapter 27

Chapter 29

Chapter 32

ILLUSTRATORS

Gwen Afton: 10.1, 10.5, 10.7, 10.10, 33.11
M. Albury-Noyes: 37.14B
Laurel Antler: 39.13
Brian Evans: 5.6
Beck: 39.15
Todd Buck: 33.1, 32.12A, 33.12
Chris Creek: 32.9, 34.14, 38.23
Diphrent Strokes: 1.3C, 3.24M-1, 3.24N-1, 3.24O-1, 3.24P-1, 3.24Q-1, 9.1A-B, 9.2A-B, 9.5, 9.6, 9.11, 9.12, 10.3, BOX 11.2, 12.1, 12.4, 13.9, 14.1, 14.2, 14.3, 14.4, 14.8A-E, 15.1, 15.5, 15.17, 15.19, 16.4, 16.5, 16.8, 17.4, 17.8B, 17.9A, 17.12, 17.22, 18.8, 18.9, 18.13B, 18.15A-B, 18.20, 18.22B-C, 18.23, 19.4, 19.5, 19.6, 19.7, 19.8, 19.9, 19.17A, 19.21, 20.3, 20.4B, 20.19, 20.21, 21.5, 21.11, 21.12, 21.13, 21.14, 21.15A-B, 21.18, 21.19, 21.20, 21.25, 22.8, 22.14, 22.16, 22.18, 23.3, 23.5, 23.7, 23.8B, 23.9, 23.10, 23.11B, 23.12, 23.17, 23.19, 23.20, 23.24A, 24.4, 24.5, 24.6, 24.7, 24.8, 24.9, 24.10B-C, 24.11, 24.14D, 24.15A-B, 25.5, 25.6, 25.7, 25.9, 25.17, 26.3, 26.4, 26.5, 26.7, 26.8, 26.9, 26.10, 27.2, 27.15ACD, 27.16, 28.2, 28.3, 28.8, 28.10, 28.11, 28.13, 28.16A, BOX 29.1B-C, 29.2, 29.3, 29.10, 29.12B-C, 30.1B, 30.3, 30.4, 30.6A-D, 30.10A-B, 30.12, 30.13, 31.3, 31.7, 31.8, 31.13, 32.2, 32.3, 32.5, 32.6, 32.7, 32.8, 32.11B, 32.14, 32.15, 32.17, 32.18, 32.19, 32.20, 32.21, 32.23, 32.24A, 32.26, 32.28, 33.7A-E, 33.9, 33.10, 34.1, 34.3, 34.4, 34.5, 34.9, 34.16, 35.7, 35.11, 35.15, 36.8, 36.9, 36.10, 36.15, 36.16, 36.17, 36.18, 36.21, 36.22, 36.23, 36.24, 36.25, 36.26, 36.27, 36.28, BOX 37.1A-D, 37.3, 37.8, 37.9, 37.10, 37.12, 38.1, 38.7, 38.10, 38.11, 38.13, 38.22, 39.8, E2.1, E2.3, E3.1B, E4.1, E4.2B, E4.3B, E4.4
Felicia Paras: 37.13A
Fineline: 3.12
Peg Gerrity: 36.6
Rob Gordon: 39.10
Marcia Hartsock/Kessler Hartsock Associates: 27.3, 27.4, 27.6, 27.7, 27.9B, 27.14A-B, 27.17A, 27.19A-B, 28.9, 28.12, 28.14, BOX 29.1A, 29.4, 29.13, 30.5, 30.9
Marlene Hill-Werner: 25.4, 25.11, 25.13, 25.14, 25.15, 38.17, 38.18, 38.21
Hans & Cassady: 8.6
Illustrious, Inc.: 1.2, 1.11, 4.5, 4.9, 5.1, 6.2, 39.4B
Carlyn Iverson: 17.17B, 35.8, 35.10, 35.12, 35.13, 38.3, 38.4, 38.15
Keith Kasnot: 34.11
Ruth Krabach: 19.3
Laurie O'Keefe: 3.18B, 13.5A-B, 15.3, 15.6, 15.7, 16.2, 37.7, 37.14A
Marjorie Leggitt: 11.5
Loechel: 35.16, 35.18, 37.15, 37.16A-B, 37.16C, 38.19, 38.20, 39.5
Nancy Marshburn: 3.4, 33.6
Iris Nichols: 31.9, 31.10, 31.12, 31.14, 31.15B
Rictor Lew: 37.13B, 39.16
Rolin Graphics: 1.4, 1.6, 1.10, 2.1, 2.2, 2.3A, 2.3B, 2.4, 2.5, 2.6, 2.7A-B, 2.8, 2.9, 2.10, 2.11, 2.12, 2.13, 2.14, 2.15, 2.16A-B, 3.1, BOX 3.1, BOX 3.2A-D, 3.3, 3.5, 3.6, 3.7, 3.10, 3.17, 3.20, 4.1, 4.2, 4.3, 4.4, 4.6, 4.7, 4.8, 4.10, 4.11, 5.2, 5.3, 5.4, 5.5, 5.8, 5.9, 6.1, 6.3, 6.4, 6.5A-1, 6.6, 6.7, 6.8, 6.9B-C, 6.10, 6.11, 7.2, 7.3, 7.4, 7.5, 7.6, 7.7, 8.1B-C, 8.2, 8.3, 8.4, 8.7A, 8.8, 8.9, BOX 9.1, 9.3, 9.4, 9.7, 9.8, 9.9, 10.4, 10.11, 10.12, 10.13, 11.1, BOX 12.1, 12.2B, 12.6, 12.7, 14.5, 14.6, 14.7, BOX 15.1A, 15.4, 15.8, 16.3, 17.2, 17.11B, 17.16, 18.2, 19.2, 19.10, 19.11, 19.13, 19.14, 20.2, 20.5B, 20.6, 20.7, 20.8, 20.9, 20.10, 21.2, 22.2, 22.9, 23.2, 23.4, 24.2, 24.12, 24.13, 25.2, 25.3B, 26.2, 31.2, 32.1, 32.4, 32.10C, 32.24B, 33.2, 33.3, 33.4, 33.5, 33.8, 34.2, 34.7, 34.8, 34.12, 34.19, 35.2, 35.3, 35.5, 35.6, 36.1, 36.2, 36.3, 36.7, 36.11, 36.12, 36.14, 36.19, 37.1, 37.2, 37.4, 37.5, 38.5B, 38.8, 38.14, 39.2, 39.6, 39.11
Nadine Sokol: 1.1, 1.2, 3.2, 3.8, 3.9, 3.13, 3.14, 3.15, 3.16, 3.19, 3.21, 3.22, 5.7, 16.9, 16.10, 17.3, 17.7, 17.10, 17.15, 17.21, 18.3, 18.5, 18.7, 18.10, 18.11, 18.12, 18.16, 18.19, 19.12, 19.15, 19.16, 19.18, 19.19, 20.11, 20.12, 20.13, 20.14A, 20.16, 20.18A, 20.20, 35.1, 35.14, 35.17
Kevin Somerville: 21.3, 21.4, 21.6A, 21.7, 21.8B, 21.10, 21.16, 21.21B-C, 21.23, 22.3, 22.4, 22.6, 22.7, 22.10, 22.11, 22.12, 22.13, 22.15, 22.17
Tom Waldrop: 39.7, 39.12